ENGAGING VIDEOS

Active learning opportunities in the form of short, interactive pieces or videos within an assignment pique your interest and motivate you to learn more about the concept. Aplia™ integrates your textbook, art, and media to give you a comprehensive, visual, and interactive experience.

> Multimedia material reinforces key concepts and ties the homework to the textbook, helping you visualize dynamic biological processes.

> Sequential parts of a question provide incremental explanations for complex concepts.

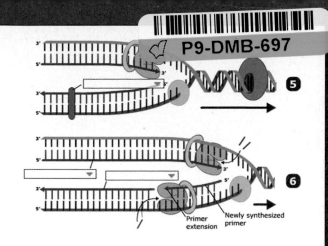

Determine whether the following statements about DNA replication are true or false.

RNA primers are left intact in the DNA and are not replaced until after DNA replication.	▼
DNA polymerases attach free nucleotides to the 3' end of a growing strand.	▼
Nucleotides are added according to complementary base-pairing rules.	▼
DNA polymerases can only add DNA nucleotides to the end of an existing DNA chain.	▼

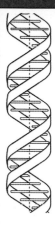

We wish to put forward a radically different structure for the salt of deoxyribose nucleic acid. This structure has two helical chains each coiled round the same axis (see diagram). We have made the usual chemical assumptions, namely, that each chain consists of phosphate diester groups joining deoxyribose residues with β-linkages.[1] Both chains follow right-handed helices, but the sequences of the atoms in the two chains run in _____.[2] Each chain loosely resembles Furberg's model No. 1; that is, the _____ are on the inside of the helix and the _____ on the outside. ...

[1] [This sentence] describes the sugar–phosphate backbone.

[2] [This sentence] describes the _____ ▼

[Clear this section's highlighting]

The novel feature of the structure is the manner in which the two chains are held together by the purine and pyrimidine bases. The planes of the bases are perpendicular to the fibre axis. They are joined together in pairs, a single base from one chain being _____ to a single base from the other chain, so that the two lie side by side.[3] ... One of the pair must be a purine and the other a pyrimidine for bonding to occur. ...

It is found that only specific pairs of bases can bond together.

[3] [This sentence] describes the _____ ▼

EMPIRICAL RESEARCH

Aplia's text-specific problems offer a variety of question types and styles and encourage you to think critically.

> Aplia™ helps you analyze primary research data with questions that are varied to accommodate different learning styles.

> Graph-based questions test your qualitative understanding.

KEY CONCEPTS

Interactive assignments and tools ensure that you grasp and can apply fundamental course concepts.

◄ The optional highlighting tool makes it easy to interact with the text on the screen the way you would on a page.

Greenish warblers live throughout Asia, as shown on the distribution map on the left. Although they share a broad range in central Siberia, the eastern Siberian greenish warblers (range represented in red) and western Siberian greenish warblers (range represented in purple) do not interbreed.

Source: D. E. Irwin, S. Bensch, J. H. Irwin, and T. D. Price, "Speciation by distance in a ring species," Science 307, no. 5708 (January 2005): 414-416. Copyright © 2005 by the American Association for the Advancement of Science. Reprinted by permission.

On the map, a graduated transition in color from one geographic region to another represents gene flow between adjacent populations. Notice that, despite the physical distance between them, the eastern Siberian population does exchange genes with the populations to the south. Based on the information provided, the greenish warblers consist of _____.

In 2000, Dr. Darren E. Irwin traveled all over Asia and collected data about local green warbler populations. The symbols on the map above refer to locations he visited. These locations are represented on the graphs below by a two-letter designation (for example, MN, which stands for Mongolia). At each site, he quantified characteristics of the local greenish warbler song and properties of the local environment that would have a strong influence on bird song. For example, the density of the forest has direct effects on the acoustics of bird song, or how it is heard.

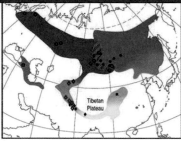

Source: Darren E. Irwin, "Song variation in an avian ring species," Science 54, no. 3 (2000): 998-1010, Figure 5. Copyright © 2000. Reprinted by permission of John Wiley & Sons, Inc.

As he moved farther north (increase in latitude), what observations did he make about how the environment changed?

○ The habitat becomes less open.
○ The habitat becomes more open.

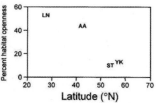

As he moved farther north (increase in latitude), what observations did he make about how song behavior changed?

○ The warblers repeat themselves more.
○ The warblers repeat themselves less.

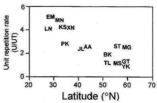

P9-DMB-697

BIOLOGY

Exploring the Diversity of Life

Second Canadian Edition

Volume One

Peter J. Russell

Paul E. Hertz

Beverly McMillan

M. Brock Fenton
University of Western Ontario

Heather Addy
University of Calgary

Denis Maxwell
University of Western Ontario

Tom Haffie
University of Western Ontario

Bill Milsom
University of British Columbia

NELSON EDUCATION

NELSON / EDUCATION

Biology: Exploring the Diversity of Life, Second Canadian Edition, Volume One

by Peter J. Russell, Paul E. Hertz, Beverly McMillan, Brock Fenton, Heather Addy, Denis Maxwell, Tom Haffie, Bill Milsom

Vice President, Editorial Higher Education:
Anne Williams

Publisher:
Paul Fam

Executive Marketing Manager:
Sean Chamberland

Senior Developmental Editor:
Mark Grzeskowiak

Photo Researcher:
Kristiina Paul

Permissions Coordinator:
Kristiina Paul

Content Production Manager:
Christine Gilbert

Production Service:
Integra Software Services Pvt. Ltd.

Copy Editor:
Julia Cochrane

Proofreader:
Integra Software Services Pvt. Ltd.

Indexer:
Jin Tan

Production Coordinator:
Ferial Suleman

Design Director:
Ken Phipps

Managing Designer:
Franca Amore

Interior Design:
Dianna Little

Cover Design:
Jennifer Stimson

Cover Image:
Sea slug: Dr. Mary Tyler & Dr. Mary Rumpho, University of Maine, (2008). "Horizontal gene transfer of the algal nuclear gene psbO to the photosynthetic sea slug Elysia chlorotica," *PNAS*, 105 (46), 17868, Copyright 2008 National Academy of Sciences, U.S.A. Generic DNA code: kentoh/Shutterstock

Compositor:
Integra Software Services Pvt. Ltd.

Printer:
RR Donnelley

COPYRIGHT © 2013, 2010 by Nelson Education Ltd.

Adapted from Biology: The Dynamic Science, Second Edition, by Peter J. Russell, Paul E. Hertz, and Beverly McMillan, published by Brooks/Cole, Cengage Learning. Copyright ©2011 Brooks/Cole, Cengage Learning.

Printed and bound in the United States of America
2 3 4 15 14 13 12

For more information contact Nelson Education Ltd., 1120 Birchmount Road, Toronto, Ontario, M1K 5G4. Or you can visit our Internet site at http://www.nelson.com

Statistics Canada information is used with the permission of Statistics Canada. Users are forbidden to copy this material and/or redisseminate the data, in an original or modified form, for commercial purposes, without the expressed permissions of Statistics Canada. Information on the availability of the wide range of data from Statistics Canada can be obtained from Statistics Canada's Regional Offices, its World Wide Web site at <http://www.statcan.gc.ca>, and its toll-free access number 1-800-263-1136.

ALL RIGHTS RESERVED. No part of this work covered by the copyright herein may be reproduced, transcribed, or used in any form or by any means—graphic, electronic, or mechanical, including photocopying, recording, taping, Web distribution, or information storage and retrieval systems—without the written permission of the publisher.

For permission to use material from this text or product, submit all requests online at www.cengage.com/permissions. Further questions about permissions can be emailed to permissionrequest@cengage.com

Every effort has been made to trace ownership of all copyrighted material and to secure permission from copyright holders. In the event of any question arising as to the use of any material, we will be pleased to make the necessary corrections in future printings.

Interior Images: Closeup of girl looking into a microscope: Yuri Arcurs/Shutterstock; Pickleweed Growing from Cracked Landscape: © DLILLC/Corbis

ISBN-13: 978-0-17-665131-2
ISBN-10: 0-17-665131-4

For, and because of, our generations
of students.

About the Canadian Authors

M.B. (BROCK) FENTON received his Ph.D. from the University of Toronto in 1969. Since then, he has been a faculty member in biology at Carleton University, then at York University, and then at the University of Western Ontario.

In addition to teaching parts of first-year biology, he has also taught vertebrate biology, animal biology, and conservation biology, as well as field courses in the biology and behaviour of bats. He has received awards for his teaching (Carleton University Faculty of Science Teaching Award; Ontario Confederation of University Faculty Associations Teaching Award; and a 3M Teaching Fellowship, Society for Teaching and Learning in Higher Education) in addition to recognition of his work on public awareness of science (Gordin Kaplan Award from the Canadian Federation of Biological Societies; Honourary Life Membership, Science North, Sudbury, Ontario; Canadian Council of University Biology Chairs Distinguished Canadian Biologist Award; The McNeil Medal for the Public Awareness of Science of the Royal Society of Canada; and the Sir Sanford Fleming Medal for public awareness of Science, the Royal Canadian Institute). He also received the C. Hart Merriam Award from the American Society of Mammalogists for excellence in scientific research. Bats and their biology, behaviour, evolution, and echolocation are the topics of his research, which has been funded by the Natural Sciences and Engineering Research Council of Canada (NSERC).

HEATHER ADDY is a graduate of the University of Alberta and received her Ph.D. in plant–soil relationships from the University of Guelph in 1995. During this training and in a subsequent post-doctoral fellowship focusing on mycorrhizas and other plant–fungus symbioses at the University of Alberta, she discovered a love of teaching. In 1998, she joined the Department of Biological Sciences at the University of Calgary in a faculty position that emphasizes teaching and teaching-related scholarship. In addition to teaching introductory biology classes and an upper-level mycology class, she has developed investigative labs for introductory biology courses and introduced peer-assisted learning groups in large biology and chemistry classes. She received the Faculty of Science Award for Excellence in Teaching in 2005 and an Honourable Mention for the Students' Union Teaching Excellence Award in 2008.

DENIS MAXWELL received his Ph.D. from the University of Western Ontario in 1995. His thesis, under the supervision of Norm Hüner, focused on the role of the redox state of photosynthetic electron transport in photoacclimation in green algae. Following his doctorate, he was awarded an NSERC post-doctoral fellowship. He undertook post-doctoral training at the Department of Energy Plant Research Laboratory at Michigan State University, where he studied the function of the mitochondrial alternative oxidase. After taking up a faculty position at the University of New Brunswick in 2000, he moved in 2003 to the Department of Biology at the University of Western Ontario. His research program, which is supported by NSERC, is focused on understanding the role of the mitochondrion in intracellular stress sensing and signalling. In addition to research, he is passionate about teaching biology and science to first-year university students.

TOM HAFFIE is a graduate of the University of Guelph and the University of Saskatchewan in the area of microbial genetics. Tom has devoted his 20-year career at the University of Western Ontario to teaching large biology classes in lecture, laboratory, and tutorial settings. He led the development of the innovative core laboratory course in the biology program; was an early adopter of computer animation in lectures; and, most recently, has coordinated the implementation of personal response technology across campus. He holds a UWO Pleva Award for Excellence in Teaching, a UWO Fellowship in Teaching Innovation, a Province of Ontario Award for Leadership in Faculty Teaching (LIFT), and a national 3M Fellowship for Excellence in Teaching.

Bill Milsom

BILL MILSOM (Ph.D., University of British Columbia) is currently the Head of the Department of Zoology at the University of British Columbia, where he has taught a variety of courses, including first-year biology, for over 30 years. His research interests include the evolutionary origins of respiratory processes and the adaptive changes in these processes that allow animals to exploit diverse environments. He examines respiratory and cardiovascular adaptations in vertebrate animals in rest, sleep, exercise, altitude, dormancy, hibernation, diving, and so on. This research contributes to our understanding of the mechanistic basis of biodiversity and the physiological costs of habitat selection. His research has been funded by NSERC, and he has received several academic awards and distinctions, including the Fry Medal of the Canadian Society of Zoologists, the August Krogh Award of the American Physiological Society, and the Izaak Walton Killam Award for Excellence in Mentoring. He has served as the President of the Canadian Society of Zoologists and as President of the International Congress of Comparative Physiology and Biochemistry.

About the U.S. Authors

PETER J. RUSSELL received a B.Sc. in Biology from the University of Sussex, England, in 1968 and a Ph.D. in Genetics from Cornell University in 1972. He has been a member of the biology faculty of Reed College since 1972; he is currently a Professor of Biology. He teaches a section of the introductory biology course, a genetics course, an advanced molecular genetics course, and a research literature course on molecular virology. In 1987, he received the Burlington Northern Faculty Achievement Award from Reed College in recognition of his excellence in teaching. Since 1986, he has been the author of a successful genetics textbook; current editions are *iGenetics: A Mendelian Approach, iGenetics: A Molecular Approach, and Essential iGenetics*. He wrote nine of the BioCoach Activities for The Biology Place. Russell's research is in the area of molecular genetics, with a specific interest in characterizing the role of host genes in pathogenic RNA plant virus gene expression; yeast is used as the model host. His research has been funded by agencies including the National Institutes of Health, the National Science Foundation (NSF), and the American Cancer Society. He has published his research results in a variety of journals, including *Genetics, Journal of Bacteriology, Molecular and General Genetics, Nucleic Acids Research, Plasmid,* and *Molecular and Cellular Biology*. He has a long history of encouraging faculty research involving undergraduates, including cofounding the biology division of the Council on Undergraduate Research (CUR) in 1985. He was Principal Investigator/Program Director of an NSF Award for the Integration of Research and Education (AIRE) to Reed College, 1998–2002.

PAUL E. HERTZ was born and raised in New York City. He received a bachelor's degree in Biology at Stanford University in 1972, a master's degree in Biology at Harvard University in 1973, and a doctorate in Biology at Harvard University in 1977. While completing field research for the doctorate, he served on the biology faculty of the University of Puerto Rico at Rio Piedras. After spending two years as an Izaac Walton Killam Postdoctoral Fellow at Dalhousie University, Hertz accepted a teaching position at Barnard College, where he has taught since 1979. He was named Ann Whitney Olin Professor of Biology in 2000, and he received The Barnard Award for Excellence in Teaching in 2007. In addition to his service on numerous college committees, Hertz was Chair of Barnard's Biology Department for eight years. He has also been the Program Director of the Hughes Science Pipeline Project at Barnard, an undergraduate curriculum and research program funded by the Howard Hughes Medical Institute, since its inception in 1992. The Pipeline Project includes the Intercollegiate Partnership, a program for local community college students that facilitates their transfer to four-year colleges and universities. He teaches one semester of the introductory sequence for biology majors and preprofessional students as well as lecture and laboratory courses in vertebrate zoology and ecology. Hertz is an animal physiological ecologist with a specific research interest in the thermal biology of lizards. He has conducted fieldwork in the West Indies since the mid-1970s, most recently focusing on the lizards of Cuba. His work has been funded by the National Science Foundation (NSF), and he has published his research in such prestigious journals as *The American Naturalist, Ecology, Nature, Oecologia,* and *Proceedings of the Royal Society*. In 2010, he received funding from NSF for a project designed to detect the effects of global climate warming on the biology of Anolis lizards in Puerto Rico.

BEVERLY McMILLAN has been a science writer for more than 20 years and is coauthor of a college text in human biology, now in its seventh edition. She has worked extensively in educational and commercial publishing, including eight years in editorial management positions in the college divisions of Random House and McGraw-Hill. In a multifaceted freelance career, McMillan has also written or coauthored six trade books and numerous magazine and newspaper articles, as well as story panels for exhibitions at the Science Museum of Virginia and the San Francisco Exploratorium. She has worked as a radio producer and speechwriter for the University of California system and as a media relations advisor for the College of William and Mary. She holds undergraduate and graduate degrees from the University of California, Berkeley.

Brief Contents

UNIT ONE SETTING THE STAGE 1

1   Light and Life   1
2   The Cell: An Overview   25
3   Defining Life and Its Origins   50

UNIT TWO ENERGY: PROCESS AND FACILITATION 71

4   Energy and Enzymes   71
5   Cell Membranes and Signalling   92
6   Cellular Respiration   115
7   Photosynthesis   139

UNIT THREE GENES 161

8   Cell Cycles   161
9   Genetic Recombination   181
10   Mendel, Genes, and Inheritance   211
11   Genes, Chromosomes, and Human Genetics   234

UNIT FOUR DNA AND GENE EXPRESSION 257

12   DNA Structure, Replication, and Organization   257
13   Gene Structure and Expression   283
14   Control of Gene Expression   308
15   DNA Technologies and Genomics   332

The Chemical, Physical, and Environmental Foundations of Biology   F-2

Glossary   G-1
Appendix A: Answers to Self-Test Questions   A-1
Index   I-1

Contents

About the Canadian Authors vi

About the U.S. Authors viii

Brief Contents ix

Preface xiii

New to This Edition xv

The Big Picture xviii

Think Like a Scientist xx

Visual Learning xxii

Review xxiii

Ancillaries xxiv

Prospering in Biology xxvii

Acknowledgements xxix

Unit One Setting the Stage 1

1 Light and Life 1

1.1 The Physical Nature of Light 2

1.2 Light as a Source of Energy 4

1.3 Light as a Source of Information 6

People behind Biology
Isaac Newton 7

1.4 The Uniqueness of Light 10

1.5 Light Can Damage Biological Molecules 12

1.6 Using Light to Tell Time 14

1.7 The Role of Light in Behaviour and Ecology 17

1.8 Life in the Dark 20

1.9 Organisms Making Their Own Light: Bioluminescence 21

2 The Cell: An Overview 25

2.1 Basic Features of Cell Structure and Function 26

2.2 Prokaryotic Cells 30

2.3 Eukaryotic Cells 31

2.4 Specialized Structures of Plant Cells 43

2.5 The Animal Cell Surface 45

3 Defining Life and Its Origins 50

3.1 What Is Life? 51

3.2 The Chemical Origins of Life 52

3.3 From Macromolecules to Life 57

Molecule behind Biology
L1 Ligase Ribozyme 60

3.4 The Earliest Forms of Life 60

People behind Biology
Lyle Whyte, Astrobiologist—McGill University 63

3.5 The Eukaryotic Cell and the Rise of Multicellularity 64

3.6 The Search for Extraterrestrial Life 68

Unit Two Energy: Process and Facilitation 71

4 Energy and Enzymes 71

4.1 Energy and the Laws of Thermodynamics 72

4.2 Free Energy and Spontaneous Reactions 75

4.3 Adenosine Triphosphate Is the Energy Currency of the Cell 79

4.4 The Role of Enzymes in Biological Reactions 81

PEOPLE BEHIND BIOLOGY
Maud Menten (1879–1960) 83

4.5 Conditions and Factors That Affect Enzyme Activity 85

MOLECULE BEHIND BIOLOGY
Penicillin: A Competitive Inhibitor of Enzyme Action 87

5 Cell Membranes and Signalling 92

5.1 An Overview of the Structure of Membranes 93

5.2 The Lipid Fabric of a Membrane 94

5.3 Membrane Proteins 97

MOLECULE BEHIND BIOLOGY
Trans Fats 98

5.4 Passive Membrane Transport 100

5.5 Active Membrane Transport 104

5.6 Exocytosis and Endocytosis 107

5.7 Role of Membranes in Cell Signalling 109

PEOPLE BEHIND BIOLOGY
Lap-Chee Tsui, University of Hong Kong 112

6 Cellular Respiration 115

6.1 The Chemical Basis of Cellular Respiration 116

6.2 Cellular Respiration: An Overview 118

6.3 Glycolysis: The Splitting of Glucose 120

6.4 Pyruvate Oxidation and the Citric Acid Cycle 122

6.5 Oxidative Phosphorylation: Electron Transport and Chemiosmosis 123

PEOPLE BEHIND BIOLOGY
Peter Mitchell (1920–1992) 128

6.6 The Efficiency and Regulation of Cellular Respiration 129

6.7 Oxygen and Cellular Respiration 132

MOLECULE BEHIND BIOLOGY
Cyanide 135

7 Photosynthesis 139

7.1 Photosynthesis: An Overview 140

7.2 The Photosynthetic Apparatus 142

MOLECULE BEHIND BIOLOGY
The D1 Protein Keeps Photosystem II Operating 146

7.3 The Light Reactions 146

7.4 The Calvin Cycle 149

PEOPLE BEHIND BIOLOGY
Norm Hüner, University of Western Ontario 150

7.5 Photorespiration and CO_2-Concentrating Mechanisms 152

7.6 Photosynthesis and Cellular Respiration Compared 157

UNIT THREE GENES 161

8 Cell Cycles 161

8.1 The Cycle of Cell Growth and Division: An Overview 162

8.2 The Cell Cycle in Prokaryotic Organisms 163

8.3 Mitosis and the Eukaryotic Cell Cycle 164

8.4 Formation and Action of the Mitotic Spindle 171

8.5 Cell Cycle Regulation 174

MOLECULE BEHIND BIOLOGY
Roscovitine 177

PEOPLE BEHIND BIOLOGY
Dr. John Dick, University of Toronto 178

9 Genetic Recombination 181

9.1 Mechanism of Genetic Recombination 182

9.2 Genetic Recombination in Bacteria 183

9.3 Genetic Recombination in Eukaryotes: Meiosis 191

MOLECULE BEHIND BIOLOGY
Bisphenol A and the Grandmother Effect 198

PEOPLE BEHIND BIOLOGY
Dr. Aurora Nedelcu, University of New Brunswick 199

9.4 Mobile Elements 201

10 Mendel, Genes, and Inheritance 211

10.1 The Beginnings of Genetics: Mendel's Garden Peas 212

10.2 Later Modifications and Additions to Mendel's Hypotheses 223

MOLECULE BEHIND BIOLOGY
Phenylthiocarbamide (PTC) 226

PEOPLE BEHIND BIOLOGY
Dr. Charles Scriver, Professor Emeritus, McGill University 231

11 Genes, Chromosomes, and Human Genetics 234

11.1 Genetic Linkage and Recombination 235

11.2 Sex-Linked Genes 240

MOLECULE BEHIND BIOLOGY
Drosopterin 241

11.3 Chromosomal Alterations That Affect Inheritance 245

PEOPLE BEHIND BIOLOGY
Dr. Irene Ayako Uchida, Professor Emeritus, McMaster University 249

11.4 Human Genetics and Genetic Counselling 249

11.5 Nontraditional Patterns of Inheritance 253

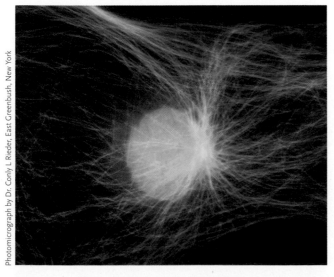

Photomicrograph by Dr. Conly L Rieder, East Greenbush, New York

UNIT FOUR DNA AND GENE EXPRESSION 257

12 DNA Structure, Replication, and Organization 257

12.1 Establishing DNA as the Hereditary Molecule 258

12.2 DNA Structure 261

12.3 DNA Replication 264

MOLECULE BEHIND BIOLOGY
Acyclic Nucleoside Phosphonates as Antiviral Drugs 271

12.4 Mechanisms That Correct Replication Errors 276

12.5 DNA Organization in Eukaryotic versus Prokaryotic Cells 277

PEOPLE BEHIND BIOLOGY
Dr. Robert (Bob) Haynes, York University, Toronto 278

13 Gene Structure and Expression 283

13.1 The Connection between DNA, RNA, and Protein 284

13.2 Transcription: DNA-Directed RNA Synthesis 289

13.3 Processing of mRNAs in Eukaryotes 291

13.4 Translation: mRNA-Directed Polypeptide Synthesis 294

PEOPLE BEHIND BIOLOGY
Dr. Steve Zimmerly, University of Calgary 295

MOLECULE BEHIND BIOLOGY
Amanitin 301

14 Control of Gene Expression 308

14.1 Regulation of Gene Expression in Prokaryotic Cells 309

MOLECULE BEHIND BIOLOGY
AI-2 315

14.2 Regulation of Transcription in Eukaryotes 315

PEOPLE BEHIND BIOLOGY
Dr. Shirley Tilghman, Princeton University 321

14.3 Posttranscriptional, Translational, and Posttranslational Regulation 322

14.4 The Loss of Regulatory Controls in Cancer 326

15 DNA Technologies and Genomics 332

15.1 DNA Cloning 333

15.2 Applications of DNA Technologies 341

MOLECULE BEHIND BIOLOGY
Ethidium Bromide 342

PEOPLE BEHIND BIOLOGY
Dr. Michael Smith, University of British Columbia 353

15.3 Genome Analysis 353

The Chemical, Physical, and Environmental Foundations of Biology F-2

The Scientific Basis of Biology F-2

Measurement and Scale F-6

The Organization of Matter F-8

Chemical Bonds F-11

Water F-15

Carbon Compounds F-20

Carbohydrates F-24

Proteins F-28

Nucleic Acids F-37

Lipids F-40

The Biosphere F-44

History of the Earth F-50

Model Research Organisms F-52

Glossary G-1

Appendix A: Answers to Self-Test Questions A-1

Index I-1

electerra/Shutterstock

Preface

Welcome to an exploration of the diversity of life. The main goal of this text is to guide you on a journey of discovery about life's diversity across levels ranging from molecules to genes, cells to organs, and species to ecosystems. Along the way, we will explore many questions about the mechanisms underlying diversity as well as the consequences of diversity for our own species and for others.

At first glance, the riot of life that animates the biosphere overwhelms the minds of many who try to understand it. One way to begin to make sense of this diversity is to divide it into manageable sections on the basis of differences. In this book, we highlight the divisions between plants and animals, prokaryotic organisms and eukaryotes, protostomes and deuterostomes, but we also consider features found in all life forms. We examine how different organisms solve the common problems of finding nutrients, energy, and mates on the third rock from our Sun. What basic evolutionary principles inform the relationships among life forms regardless of their different body plans, habitats, or life histories? Unlike many other first-year biology texts, this book has chapters integrating basic concepts such as the effects of genetic recombination, light, nutrition, and domestication across the breadth of life from microbes to mistletoe to moose. As you read this book, you will be referred frequently to other chapters for linked information that expands the ideas further.

Evolution provides a powerful conceptual lens for viewing and understanding the roots and history of diversity. We will demonstrate how knowledge of evolution helps us appreciate the changes we observe in organisms. Whether the focus is the conversion of free-living prokaryotic organisms into mitochondria and chloroplasts or the steps involved in the domestication of rice, selection for particular traits over time can explain the current condition.

We hope that Canadian students will find the subject of biology as it is presented here accessible and engaging because it is presented in familiar contexts. We have highlighted the work of Canadian scientists, used examples of Canadian species, referred to Canadian regulations and institutions, and highlighted discoveries made by Canadians.

Although many textbooks use the first few chapters to introduce and/or review background information, we have used the first chapters to convey the excitement and interest of biology itself. Within the centre of the book, we have placed important background information about biology and chemistry in the reference section entitled *The Chemical, Physical, and Environmental Foundations of Biology*. With their purple borders, these pages are distinct and easy to find and have become affectionately known as *The Purple Pages*. These pages enable information to be readily identifiable and accessible to students as they move through the textbook rather than being tied to a particular chapter. This section keeps background information out of the mainstream of the text, allowing you to focus on the bigger picture.

In addition to presenting material about biology, this book also makes a point of highlighting particular people, important molecules, interesting contexts, and examples of life in extreme conditions. Science that appears in textbooks is the product of people who have made careful and systematic observations that led them to formulate hypotheses about these observations and, where appropriate, design and execute experiments to test these hypotheses. We illustrate this in each chapter with boxed stories about how particular people have used their ingenuity and creativity to expand our knowledge of biology. We have endeavoured to show not just the science itself but also the process behind the science.

Although biology is not simply chemistry, specific chemicals and their interactions can have dramatic effects on biological systems. From water to progesterone, amanitin, and DDT, each chapter features the activity of a relevant chemical.

To help frame the material with an engaging context, we begin each chapter with a section called "Why It Matters." In addition, several chapters include boxed accounts of organisms thriving "on the edge" at unusual temperatures, pressures, radiation dosages, salt concentrations, and so on. These brief articles explain how our understanding of "normal" can be increased through study of the "extreme."

Examining how biological systems work is another theme pervading this text and underlying the idea of diversity. We have intentionally tried to include examples that will tax your imagination, from sea slugs that steal chloroplasts for use as solar panels, to hummingbirds fuelling their hovering flight, to adaptive radiation of viruses. In each situation, we examine how biologists have explored and assessed the inner workings of organisms from gene regulation to the challenges of digesting cellulose.

Solving problems is another theme that runs throughout the book. Whether the topic is gene therapy to treat a disease in people, increasing crop production, or conserving endangered species, both the problem and the solution lie in biology. We will explore large problems facing planet Earth and the social implications that arise from them.

Science is by its nature a progressive enterprise in which answers to questions open new questions for consideration. Each chapter presents questions for discussion to emphasize that biologists still have a lot to learn—topics for you to tackle should you decide to pursue a career in research.

Study Breaks occur after most sections in the chapters. They contain questions written by students to identify some of the important features of the section. At the end of each chapter is a group of multiple-choice self-test questions, the answers to which can be found at the end of the book. Questions for Discussion at the end of each chapter challenge you to think more broadly about biology. You are encouraged to use these in discussions with other students and to explore potential answers by using the resources of the electronic or physical library.

To maximize the chances of producing a useful text that draws in students (and instructors), we sought the advice of colleagues who teach biology (members of the Editorial Advisory Board). We also asked students (members of the Student Advisory Boards) for their advice and comments. Both groups read draft chapters and provided valuable feedback, but any mistakes are ours. The members of the Student Advisory Boards also wrote the Study Break questions found throughout the text.

We hope that you are as captivated by the biological world as we are and are drawn from one chapter to another. But don't stop there—use electronic and other resources to broaden your search for understanding.

M. Brock Fenton
Heather Addy
Denis Maxwell
Tom Haffie
Bill Milsom

London, Calgary, and Vancouver
November 2011

New to This Edition

This section highlights the changes we made to enhance the effectiveness of *Biology: Exploring the Diversity of Life,* Second Canadian Edition. Every chapter has been updated to ensure currency of information. We made organizational changes to more closely link related topics and reflect preferred teaching sequences. New features in the text have been developed to help students actively engage in their study of biology. Enriched media offerings provide students with a broad spectrum of learning opportunities.

Organizational Changes

We divided "Origins of Life and Cells" into two chapters: "The Cell: An Overview" with expanded coverage of cell biology and the emergent properties of life, and "Defining Life and Its Origins," which builds on the content from the First Canadian Edition with more in-depth coverage of multicellularity, key experiments into the origins of life, and a discussion on the probability of extraterrestrial life.

In response to reviewers' comments, we integrated the topics from Chapter 3 Selection, Biodiversity, and Biosphere from the First Canadian Edition into other chapters to strengthen those sections and enhance the flow of topics in the first section of the textbook.

The chapter sequence in Unit 5 Evolution and Classification from the First Canadian Edition was rearranged to improve the flow of topics and include the section on evolution of humans, which was in Chapter 27 Deuterostomes: Vertebrates and Their Closest Relatives in the First Canadian Edition.

New Features

A priority for the Second Canadian Edition was improved illustrations throughout the book; many figures have been redrawn in response to feedback from reviewers, colleagues, and students, and new photographs have been added, such as the photomicrographs provided by Dr. E.C. Yeung, a plant anatomist at the University of Calgary. Another priority was to reorganize some animal biology chapters and to integrate new material (e.g., the discovery of a new species of *Australopithecus* and the presence of photoreceptors in the tube feet of echinoderms).

Our new Concept Fixes **CONCEPT FIX** draw on the extensive research literature dealing with misconceptions commonly held by biology students. Strategically placed throughout the text, these short segments help students identify—and correct—a wide range of misunderstandings. ⬡

Major revisions to selected chapters are listed below:

Chapter 2 The Cell: An Overview
- Combination of the fundamentals of eukaryotic and prokaryotic cell structure and function into a single chapter
- Addition of a detailed figure describing the major types of light and electron microscopy

Chapter 3 Defining Life and Its Origins
- New dedicated chapter addressing fundamental questions such as: What is life? How did life arise? What drove the evolution of the eukaryotic cell and multicellularity?
- Addition of a section on astrobiology and the search for extraterrestrial life

Chapter 4 Energy and Enzymes
- Clarification of the role of ATP breakdown as distinct from ATP hydrolysis in biochemical reactions

Chapter 5 Cell Membranes and Signalling
- Integration of membrane structure and function along with fundamentals of signal transduction into one chapter

Chapter 6 Cellular Respiration
- Improved figures illustrating electron transport

Chapter 7 Photosynthesis
- Improved figures illustrating light absorption and photosynthetic electron transport

Chapter 8 Cell Cycles
- New information and figure about prokaryotic cell cycle
- Modernized immunofluorescence photomicrographs illustrating stages of mitosis
- Clarification of cell cycle controls

Chapter 12 DNA Structure, Replication, and Organization
- Clarification of enzymology of DNA replication, particularly the action of telomerase

Chapter 13 Gene Structure and Expression
- Addition of a figure to illustrate charging of tRNA molecules with amino acids

Chapter 14 Control of Gene Expression
- Addition of figures to illustrate DNA-binding motifs and breast cancer genes

Chapter 15 DNA Technologies and Genomics

- Expanded treatment of comparative genomics and microarrays

Chapter 18 Classification, Evolution, and Phylogeny

- New information about phylogenetic analysis
- Expanded section on human evolution, including latest (2011) findings

Chapter 19 Species

- New information about variation in giraffes, connection appearance, and genetic distinctiveness
- New information about speciation via hybridization

Chapter 20 Bacteria and Archaea

- Title change from "Prokaryotes" to better reflect the content, and updated terminology throughout this chapter and the rest of the book
- Rewrite of section on metabolic diversity for greater clarity
- Redrawn figures comparing cell wall structure of Gram-positive and Gram-negative bacteria

Chapter 22 Protists

- Some figures and photographs replaced or revised to increase clarity, for example, figure showing life cycle of organism that causes malaria
- Rewrite of section on primary and secondary endosymbiosis for greater clarity

Chapter 24 Plants

- Updates to numerous figures
- Revision of material relating to comparisons of bryophytes and vascular plants to clarify the key differences and similarities

Chapter 26 Diversity of Animals 2: Deuterostomes: Vertebrates and Their Closest Relatives

- Streamlined
- Human evolution moved to chapter on evolution and phylogeny

Chapter 27 The Plant Body

- Update of numerous figures
- New photomicrographs from Dr. E.C. Yeung, a plant anatomist at the University of Calgary, for many figures
- Descriptions of structures and processes rewritten to help students understand the most important general principles without overwhelming them with too much terminology and too many details

Chapter 28 Transport in Plants

- Several sections rewritten to provide better clarity on key concepts (e.g., water potential)
- Topics related to the Canadian forest industry and to forestry research in Canada added to the chapter

Chapter 31 Introduction to Animal Organization and Physiology

- Revised section on homeostasis

Chapter 33 Reproduction in Animals

- More emphasis on energy partitioning as a function of reproductive strategy

Chapter 34 Animal Development

- Discussion of epigenetics

Chapter 36 Control of Animal Processes: Neural Control and Chapter 37 Control of Animal Processes: Neural Integration

- New Chapter 36 covering the basics of the nervous system (including afferent sensory neurons) and new Chapter 37 covering neural integration, both at the level of the sensory receptors and within the central nervous system

Chapter 38 Muscles, Skeletons, and Body Movements

- Serious errors in crossbridge cycling during muscle contraction corrected

Chapter 39 Animal Behaviour

- New information about migration, including flight paths of Arctic Terns

Chapter 44 Population Ecology

- New section on challenges to population biologists

Chapter 46 Ecosystems

- New information about nitrogen fixation
- New information about impact of salmon on riparian forests

Chapter 48 Putting Selection to Work

- Added information about human evolution and domestication of other species

Enhanced Art Program

Helping today's students understand biological processes requires effective visual learning support. In preparation for this edition, we undertook a rigorous review of all of the art in the text.

The effective integration of text and illustration has also been a top priority for the development of the art.

Enriched Media

New to the second Canadian edition is Aplia™ for *Biology*, an automatically graded homework management system tailored to this edition. Aplia™ courses are customized to fit with each instructor's syllabus and provide automatically graded homework with detailed, immediate feedback on every question. Aplia's interactive tools serve to increase student engagement and understanding. New interactive 3-D animations have been developed that help students visualize processes in a more dynamic way. These animations promote in-depth understanding of key biological topics, including cellular respiration, photosynthesis, DNA replication, and evolutionary processes. Embedded assessments in the animations ensure that students have the necessary foundation for understanding these important concepts. Also new to the second Canadian edition are clips from the BBC Motion Gallery. This diverse and robust library of high-quality videos features clips from well-respected scientists and naturalists, including Sir David Attenborough. The clips can be used in conjunction with the text to spark discussion and help students connect the material to their lives outside the classroom.

We now invite you and your students to preview the many exciting features that will help them think and engage like scientists.

THE BIG PICTURE

Each chapter of *Biology: Exploring the Diversity of Life,* Second Canadian Edition, is carefully organized and presented in digestible chunks so you can stay focused on the most important concepts. Easy-to-use learning tools point out the topics covered in each chapter, show why they are important, and help you learn the material.

Study Plan The Study Plan provides a list of the sections and subsections in the chapter. Each section breaks the material into a manageable amount of information, building on knowledge and understanding as you acquire it.

Why It Matters For each chapter we provide a brief overview, outlining the main points that follow.

Study Breaks The Study Breaks encourage you to pause and think about the key concepts you have just encountered before moving to the next section. The Study Break questions are written by Canadian students for their peers across the country and are intended to identify some of the important features of the section.

a.

b.

Paintings by Claude Monet (1840–1926). Compared to his early works, including "The Water-Lily Pond" **(a)**, his later paintings, including "The Japanese Footbridge" **(b)**, bordered on the abstract with almost complete loss of light blue. Monet suffered from vision degenerative disease cataracts, diagnosed in 1912.

STUDY PLAN

1.1 The Physical Nature of Light
1.1a What Is Light?
1.1b Light Interacts with Matter

1.2 Light as a Source of Energy

1.3 Light as a Source of Information
1.3a Rhodopsin, the Universal Photoreceptor
1.3b Sensing Light without Eyes
1.3c The Eye
1.3d Darwin and the Evolution of the Eye

1.4 The Uniqueness of Light

1.5 Light Can Damage Biological Molecules
1.5a Damage Is an Unavoidable Consequence of Absorption
1.5b Ultraviolet Light Is Particularly Harmful
1.5c Melanin, Suntanning, and Vitamin D

1.6 Using Light to Tell Time
1.6a Circadian Rhythms Are Controlled by a Biological Clock
1.6b Biological Clocks Track the Changing Seasons
1.6c Jet Lag and the Need to Reset Biological Clocks

1.7 The Role of Light in Behaviour and Ecology
1.7a Using Colour as a Signal: Animals
1.7b Using Colour as a Signal: Plants
1.7c Camouflage
1.7d Ecological Light Pollution

1.8 Life in the Dark

1.9 Organisms Making Their Own Light: Bioluminescence

1 Light and Life

WHY IT MATTERS

Claude Monet (1840–1926), a French painter, is considered by many to be the master of the impressionist form that rose to prominence in the late nineteenth century. Other well-known impressionists include Edgar Degas and Paul Cézanne. Impressionism as an art movement was characterized by the use of small visible brush strokes that emphasized light and colour, rather than lines, to define an object. The artists used pure, unmixed colour, not smoothly blended, as was the custom at the time. For example, instead of physically mixing yellow and blue paint, they placed unmixed yellow paint on the canvas next to unmixed blue paint so that the colours would mingle in the eye of the viewer to create the impression of green. The impressionists found that they could capture the momentary and transient effects of sunlight and the changing colour of a scene by painting *en plein air,* in the open air, outside the studio, where they could more accurately paint the reflected light of an immediate scene.

Interestingly, compared with his early works, which included "The Water-Lily Pond" (1899), Monet's later paintings verge on the abstract, with colours bleeding into each other and a lack of rational

STUDY BREAK

1. Define light.
2. What structural feature is common to all pigments?

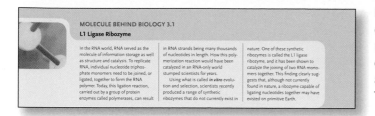

MOLECULE BEHIND BIOLOGY 3.1
L1 Ligase Ribozyme

In the RNA world, RNA served as the molecule of information storage as well as structure and catalysis. To replicate RNA, individual nucleotide triphosphate monomers need to be joined, or ligated, together to form the RNA polymer. Today, this ligation reaction, carried out by a group of protein enzymes called polymerases, can result

in RNA strands being many thousands of nucleotides in length. How this polymerization reaction would have been catalyzed in an RNA-only world stumped scientists for years.

Using what is called *in vitro* evolution and selection, scientists recently produced a range of synthetic ribozymes that do not currently exist in

nature. One of these synthetic ribozymes is called the L1 ligase ribozyme, and it has been shown to catalyze the joining of two RNA monomers together. This finding clearly suggests that, although not currently found in nature, a ribozyme capable of ligating nucleotides together may have existed on primitive Earth.

Molecule behind Biology "Molecule behind Biology" boxes give students a sense of the exciting impact of molecular research. From water to progesterone, amanitin, and DDT, each chapter features the activity of a relevant chemical.

People behind Biology "People behind Biology" boxes in each chapter contain boxed stories about how particular people have used their ingenuity and creativity to expand our knowledge of biology. The purpose of these boxes is to recognize that advances in biology are accomplished by people.

PEOPLE BEHIND BIOLOGY 3.2
Lyle Whyte, Astrobiologist—McGill University

The heightened research interest into extremophiles coupled with technological advances that are driving the robotic exploration of Mars and other planets has spurred the development of the multidisciplinary science of astrobiology. Broadly defined, astrobiology is the study of the origin, evolution, distribution, and future of life in the universe. The field encompasses the search for habitable environments within and outside our solar system and the search for evidence of prebiotic chemistry and life on Mars and elsewhere. As well, astrobiology includes laboratory and field research into the origins and early evolution of life on Earth and studies of the potential for life to adapt to challenges on Earth and in space.

Canada is at the forefront of astrobiology research, as the government has recently established the Canadian Astrobiology Training Program. The program will create the first cross-disciplinary, multi-institutional undergraduate, graduate, and postdoctoral training program in astrobiology. This initiative brings together researchers at five institutions (McGill University, McMaster University, University of Western Ontario, University of Winnipeg, and University of Toronto) with expertise in fields as diverse as geology, chemistry, physics, astronomy, microbiology, and robotics.

The head of the Canadian Astrobiology Training Program is Lyle Whyte of McGill University. Whyte is a

Canada Research Chair in Environmental Microbiology. His research examines microbial biodiversity and ecology in unique Canadian high-Arctic ecosystems and is contributing significantly to the knowledge of the diversity, abundance, and critical roles played by microorganisms in polar regions. His research is providing new insights into microbial life at subzero temperatures and their role in global biogeochemical cycling. Whyte and his colleagues do considerable field research in the Canadian Arctic, which is considered by NASA and the Canadian Space Agency to be one of the best sites around the globe to mimic conditions on Mars.

LIFE ON THE EDGE 23.3
Cryptoendolithic Lichens

We tend to think of Antarctica as completely covered in ice, but some valleys of this continent are completely lacking in ice **(Figure 1a)**. These dry valleys may look barren, but they are home to many endoliths—organisms that live in a narrow band under the surface of porous rocks. Predominant among these endoliths are cryptoendo-

lithic lichens ("crypto" = hidden; "endo" = inside; "lith" = rock) **(Figure 1b)**. These lichens lack the stratified layers typical of most other lichens; instead, hyphae and clusters of photobiont cells grow around and between the rock crystals, and the lichen that forms is embedded inside the rock. Enough light penetrates the

translucent surface layer of rock to allow photosynthesis. Studying endolithic organisms not only helps us understand the diversity of life on Earth but may also be a model for life on other planets. If some organisms can live in such extreme conditions here on Earth, could similar kinds of organisms also exist elsewhere in the universe?

FIGURE 1
(a) Antarctic dry valley. **(b)** Cryptoendolithic lichen.

Life on the Edge "Life on the Edge" boxes provide accounts of organisms thriving "on the edge" at unusual temperatures, pressures, radiation dosages, salt concentrations, and so on. These boxes explain how our understanding of "normal" can be increased through study of the "extreme."

Chemical, Physical, and Environmental Foundations of Biology

While many textbooks use the first few chapters to introduce and/or review, we believe that the first chapters should convey the excitement and interest of biology itself. We therefore placed important background information about biology and chemistry in the reference section entitled Chemical, Physical, and Environmental Foundations of Biology, in the centre of the book. With their purple borders, these pages are distinct and easy to find and have become affectionately known as *The Purple Pages*. *The Purple Pages* enable information to be readily identifiable and accessible to students as they move through the textbook, rather than tied to one particular chapter. *The Purple Pages* keep background information out of the main text, allowing you to focus on the bigger picture.

CONCEPT FIX **Concept Fix Icons** Concept Fixes draw on the extensive research literature dealing with misconceptions commonly held by biology students. Strategically placed throughout the text, these short segments help students identify—and correct—a wide range of misunderstandings. ⬢

PURPLE PAGES

The Chemical, Physical, and Environmental Foundations of Biology

The Scientific Basis of Biology

The information contained in this textbook represents the culmination of hundreds of years of research involving a huge number of experiments carried out by countless scientists. The entire content of this book—every observation, experimental result, and generality—

is the product of **biological research**, the collective effort of individuals who have worked to understand every aspect of the living world. This section describes how biologists working today pose and find answers to questions.

The Scientific Method

Beginning about 500 years ago in Europe, inquisitive people began to understand that direct observation is the most reliable and productive way to study natural phenomena. By the nineteenth century, researchers were using the **scientific method**—an investigative approach to acquiring knowledge in which scientists make observations about the natural world, develop working explanations about what they observe, and then test those explanations by collecting more information.

Application of the scientific method requires both curiosity and skepticism: successful scientists question the current state of our knowledge and challenge old concepts with new ideas and new observations. Explanations of natural phenomena must be backed up by objective evidence rooted in observation and measurement. Most importantly, scientists share their ideas and results by publishing their work.

Testing a Hypothesis Is Central to the Scientific Method

A **hypothesis** can be defined as a tentative explanation for an observation, phenomenon, or scientific problem that can be tested by further investigation. Scientific hypotheses have two fundamental elements. First a hypothesis must be *testable*. That is, there must be some set of observations or experiments that can be undertaken to support the hypothesis. For example, you may be studying a gene in yeast that you find is activated when cells are placed under conditions of heat stress. You may hypothesize that the protein encoded by this gene is essential for the yeast to survive short-term exposure to high temperature. Using modern molecular techniques, you can test this hypothesis by inactivating the gene in a population of yeast cells and observing if there is a change in heat tolerance. Today, this hypothesis is easily testable. A scientist may have had a similar idea 30 years ago, but given the lack of molecular techniques, the hypothesis would not have been testable at that time.

The second key to a scientific hypothesis is that it must be *falsifiable*. That is, through observation or experimentation you must be able to show that the original hypothesis may not be correct. Getting back to our yeast analogy, it is very possible that through analysis you would find that inactivation of the gene does not change the ability of yeast cells to survive high temperatures.

Scientists test the predictions that come from hypotheses with experimental or observational tests that generate relevant data. And if data from just one study refute a scientific hypothesis (that is, demonstrate that its predictions are incorrect), the scientist must modify the hypothesis and test it again or abandon it altogether. However, no amount of data can prove beyond a doubt that a hypothesis is correct; there may always be a contradictory example somewhere on Earth, and it is impossible to test every imaginable example. That is why scientists say that positive results are consistent with, support, or confirm a hypothesis.

F-2   THE CHEMICAL, PHYSICAL, AND ENVIRONMENTAL FOUNDATIONS OF BIOLOGY   NEL

THINK LIKE A SCIENTIST

Your study of biology focuses not only on *what* scientists now know about the living world but also on *how* they know it. Use these unique features to learn through example how scientists ask scientific questions and pose and test hypotheses.

Throughout the book, we identify recent discoveries made possible by the development of new techniques and new knowledge. In "Using the Genome as an Investigative Tool," Box 37.2, page 916, for example, learn how the photoreceptors of sea urchins were found in their tube feet.

USING THE GENOME AS AN INVESTIGATIVE TOOL 37.2
Seeing with Your Feet

It is one thing to demonstrate that an animal responds behaviourally to external stimuli, but it may be more challenging to determine how the stimuli were detected. For example, there is evidence of animals such as garden toads (*Bufo bufo*) changing their behaviour in advance of an earthquake, but we do not know what cues trigger the response.

For some time, it has been clear that echinoderms such as sea urchins respond to changing light conditions, but nobody had found photoreceptors in these animals (see Chapter 1 for a discussion of the significance of light and light sensing). The publication of

the genome of purple urchins (*Strongylocentrotus purpuratus*) **(Figure 1)** provided biologists with a means of investigating photoreception in these animals.

Specifically, data in the genome showed that sea urchins possess several genes that code for a widely occurring eye protein, opsin. Discovering this, the researchers designed antibodies against different opsin proteins and performed *in situ* hybridization (see Chapter 15 for a discussion of DNA technologies and genomics). They found that the urchins possess *Sp-opsin4* and *Sp-pax6*, two proteins that regulate

phototaxis. This approach also allowed them to visualize where the photoreceptor cells were located—in the urchin's tube feet. The sea urchin photoreceptive cells are microvillar r-opsin, previously known only from protostomes. Since tube feet are found all over the body of the sea urchin, it appears that the entire adult sea urchin acts as a huge compound eye!

There are many other mysteries about the sensory world of animals. We know that many animals show a magnetic sense, but in most cases we do not know the details of the receptor.

FIGURE 1
(a) The purple sea urchin Strongylocentrotus purpuratus. *(b) Close-up showing the tube feet between the spines. The photoreceptors are located at the tips of the tube feet.*

of light that enters. In dim light, radial muscles contract and enlarge the pupil, increasing the amount of light that enters the eye. Muscles move the lens forward and back with respect to the retina to focus the image. This is an example of **accommodation**, a process by which the lens changes to enable the eye to focus on objects at different distances. A neural network lies under the retina, meaning that light rays do not have to pass through the neurons to reach the photoreceptors. The vertebrate eye has the opposite arrangement. This and other differences in structure and function indicate that cephalopod and vertebrate eyes evolved independently.

37.4c Vertebrate Eyes Have a Complex Structure

The human eye **(Figure 37.15)** has similar structures— cornea, iris, pupil, lens, and retina—to those of the cephalopod eye just described. Light entering the eye

through the cornea passes through the iris and then the lens. The lens focuses an image on the retina, and the axons of afferent neurons originating in the retina converge to form the optic nerve leading from the eye to the brain. A clear fluid called the **aqueous humour** fills the space between the cornea and the lens. This fluid carries nutrients to the lens and cornea, which do not contain any blood vessels. The main chamber of the eye, located between the lens and the retina, is filled with the jellylike **vitreous humour** (*vitrum* = glass). The outer wall of the eye contains a tough layer of connective tissue (the *sclera*). Inside it is a darkly pigmented layer (the *choroid*) that prevents light from entering except through the pupil. It also contains the blood vessels nourishing the retina.

Two types of photoreceptors, rods and cones, occur in the retina along with layers of neurons that carry out an initial integration of visual information before it is

---

H_3N^+ — Phe | Val | Asn | Gln | His | Leu | Cys | Gly | Ser | His | Leu | Val | Glu | Ala | Leu | Tyr | Leu | Val | Cys | Gly | Glu | Arg | Gly | Phe | Phe | Tyr | Thr | Pro | Lys | Ala — COO^-

Ball-and-stick model of α helix

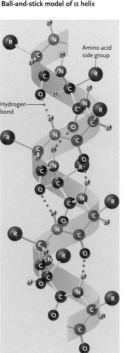

Amino acid side group

Hydrogen bond

Cylinder representation of α helix

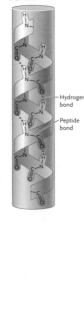

Hydrogen bond

Peptide bond

Hydrogen bond

The Chemical, Physical, and Environmental Foundations of Biology. Also known as *The Purple Pages,* these distinct and easy-to-find pages contain readily identifiable and accessible information in one place, rather than tied to a particular chapter, allowing you to focus on the bigger picture.

Special boxes in most chapters present research topics in more depth.

Molecule Behind Biology boxes give students a sense of the exciting impact of molecular research.

People Behind Biology boxes profile Canadian and international researchers and discoveries, and their impact on research in biology.

Life on the Edge boxes explain how our understanding of "normal" can be increased through study of the "extreme" through accounts of organisms thriving "on the edge" at unusual temperatures, pressures, radiation dosages, salt concentrations, and so on.

Research Figures throughout the book contain information about how biologists formulate and test specific hypotheses by gathering and interpreting data.

Research Method

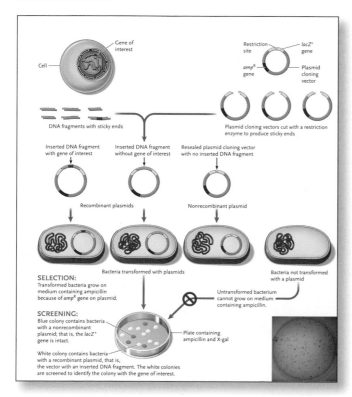

Observational Research

a. *Eurytoma gigantea*, a parasitic wasp

b. *Picoides pubescens*, a predatory bird

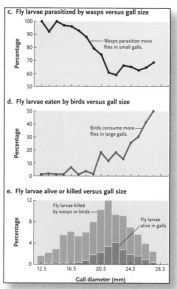

Experimental Research

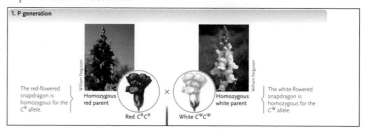

THINK LIKE A SCIENTIST |

VISUAL LEARNING

Spectacular illustrations—developed with great care—help you visualize biological processes, relationships, and structures.

Illustrations of complex biological processes are annotated with numbered step-by-step explanations that lead you through all the major points. Orientation diagrams are inset on figures and help you identify the specific biological process being depicted and where the process takes place.

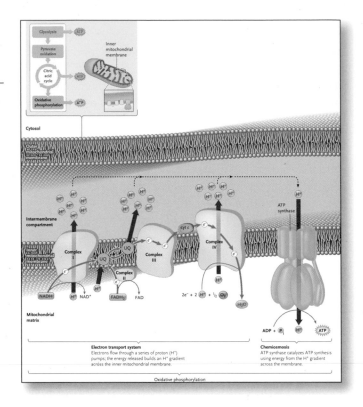

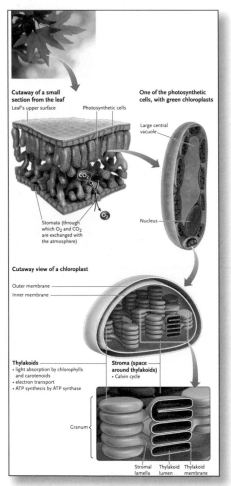

From Macro to Micro: Multiple views help you visualize the levels of organization of biological structures and how systems function as a whole.

Electron micrographs are keyed to selected illustrations to help clarify biological structures.

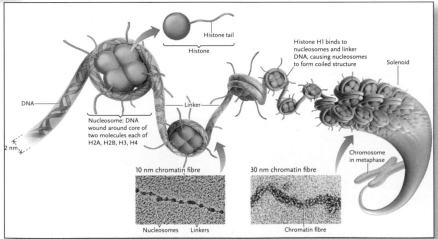

End-of-chapter material encourages you to review the content, assess your understanding, think analytically, and apply what you have learned to novel situations.

Review Key Concepts This brief review often references figures and tables in the chapter and provides a summary of important ideas developed in the chapter.

Review

CourseMate Access an interactive eBook, chapter-specific interactive learning tools, including flashcards, quizzes, videos, and more in your Biology **CourseMate**, accessed through NelsonBrain.com **Aplia™** is an online interactive learning solution that helps you improve comprehension—and your grade—by integrating a variety of mediums and tools such as videos, tutorials, practice tests, and an interactive eBook.

12.1 Establishing DNA as the Hereditary Molecule

- Griffith found that a substance derived from killed virulent *Streptococcus pneumoniae* bacteria could transform nonvirulent living *S. pneumoniae* bacteria to the virulent type (Figure 12.2).
- Avery and his coworkers showed that DNA, and not protein or RNA, was the molecule responsible for transforming *S. pneumoniae* bacteria into the virulent form.
- Hershey and Chase showed that the DNA of a phage, not the protein, enters bacterial cells to direct the life cycle of the virus. Taken together, the experiments of Griffith, Avery and his coworkers, and Hershey and Chase established that DNA is the hereditary molecule (Figure 12.3).

The short lengths produced by this discontinuous replication are then linked into a continuous strand (Figures 12.14 and 12.15).

- DNA synthesis begins at sites that act as replication origins and proceeds from the origins as two replication forks moving in opposite directions (Figures 12.16 and 12.17).
- The ends of eukaryotic chromosomes consist of telomeres: short sequences repeated hundreds to thousands of times. These repeats provide a buffer against chromosome shortening during replication. Although most somatic cells show this chromosome shortening, some cell types do not because they have a telomerase enzyme that adds telomere repeats to the chromosome ends (Figure 12.18).

12.4 Mechanisms That Correct Replication Errors

- In proofreading, the DNA polymerase reverses and removes the most recently added base if it is mispaired as a result of a replication error. The enzyme then resumes DNA synthesis in the forward direction (Figure 12.19).
- In DNA mismatch repair, enzymes recognize distorted regions caused by mispaired base pairs and remove a section of DNA that includes the mispaired base from the newly synthesized nucleotide chain. A DNA polymerase then resynthesizes the section correctly, using the original template chain as a guide (Figure 12.20).

12.5 DNA Organization in Eukaryotes and Prokaryotes

- Eukaryotic chromosomes consist of DNA complexed with histone and nonhistone proteins.
- In eukaryotic chromosomes, DNA is wrapped around a core consisting of two molecules each of histones H2A, H2B, H3, and H4 to produce a nucleosome. Linker DNA connects adjacent nucleosomes. The chromosome structure in this form is the 10 nm chromatin fibre. The binding of histone H1 causes the nucleosomes to package into a coiled structure called the 30 nm chromatin fibre (Figure 12.21).
- Chromatin is distributed between euchromatin, a loosely packed region in which genes are active in RNA transcription, and heterochromatin, densely packed masses in which genes, if present, are inactive. Chromatin also folds and packs to form thick, rodlike chromosomes during nuclear division.
- Nonhistone proteins help control the expression of individual genes.
- The bacterial chromosome is a closed, circular double helix of DNA; it is packed into the nucleoid region of the cell. Replication begins from a single origin and proceeds in both directions. Many bacteria also contain plasmids, which replicate independently of the host chromosome (Figure 12.22).
- Bacterial DNA is organized into loops through interaction with proteins. Other proteins similar to eukaryotic nonhistones regulate gene activity in prokaryotic organisms.

Questions

Self-Test Questions

1. Working on the Amazon River, a biologist isolated DNA from two unknown organisms, P and Q. He discovered that the adenine content of P was 15% and the cytosine content of Q was 42%. Which of the following conclusions can be drawn?
   a. The amount of adenine in Q is 42%.
   b. The amount of guanine in P is 15%.
   c. The amount of guanine and cytosine combined in P is 70%.
   d. The amount of thymine in Q is 21%.

2. The Hershey and Chase experiment involved infecting bacterial cells with radioactively labelled viruses. What did this experiment show?
   a. ^{35}S-labelled DNA ended up inside the virus progeny.
   b. ^{32}P-labelled DNA entered bacterial cells.
   c. ^{35}S-labelled protein was incorporated into bacterial cells.
   d. ^{32}P-labelled protein was incorporated into virus coats.

3. Which of the following would appear on a list of pyrimidines?
   a. cytosine and thymine
   b. cytosine and guanine
   c. adenine and thymine
   d. adenine and guanine

4. Which of the following statements about DNA replication is TRUE?
   a. DNA polymerase III extends an RNA primer.
   b. Some DNA polymerases can add new bases to the 5′ end of a growing strand.
   c. Each eukaryotic chromosome has a single origin of replication.
   d. Okazaki fragments are made only of RNA.

5. Which of the following statements about DNA structure is TRUE?
   a. Each DNA strand has a 3′ OH on one end and a 5′ OH on the other end.
   b. Each strand of the double helix runs parallel to the other.
   c. The binding of adenine to thymine is through three hydrogen bonds.
   d. Bonds between components of the backbone (i.e., sugar–phosphate) are stronger than those between one strand and the other.

6. In the Meselson and Stahl experiment, the DNA in the parental generation was all ^{15}N^{15}N, and after one round of replication, the DNA was all ^{15}N^{14}N. What ratio of DNA would be seen after three rounds of replication?
   a. one ^{15}N^{14}N : one ^{14}N^{14}N
   b. one ^{15}N^{14}N : two ^{14}N^{14}N
   c. one ^{15}N^{14}N : three ^{14}N^{14}N
   d. one ^{15}N^{14}N : four ^{14}N^{14}N

7. Since DNA is synthesized in the 5′ → 3′ direction, which of the following must be true?
   a. The template must be read in the 5′ → 3′ direction.
   b. Polymerase must add successive nucleotides to the 3′ –OH end of the newly forming chain.
   c. Ligase must unwind the two DNA strands in opposite directions.
   d. Primase must add RNA nucleotides to the growing 5′ end.

8. Which of the following is a characteristic of telomerase?
   a. It is active in cancer cells.
   b. It is more active in adult than in embryonic cells.
   c. It has telomeres made of RNA.
   d. It shortens the ends of chromosomes.

9. What does the process of mismatch repair accomplish?
   a. It seals Okazaki fragments with ligase into a continual DNA strand.
   b. It removes RNA primers and replaces them with the correct DNA.
   c. It restores DNA sequence that is lost during the replication of the ends of chromosomes.
   d. It replaces incorrect bases that escape proofreading by DNA polymerase.

10. The DNA of prokaryotic organisms differs from that of eukaryotes. In what way?
   a. Prokaryotic DNA is surrounded by densely packed histones; eukaryotic DNA is not.
   b. Prokaryotic DNA has many sites for the initiation of DNA replication; eukaryotic DNA does not.
   c. Prokaryotic DNA is typically single stranded; eukaryotic DNA is typically double stranded.
   d. Prokaryotic DNA is rarely packaged in linear chromosomes, eukaryotic DNA is commonly packaged in linear chromosomes.

Questions for Discussion

1. Chargaff's data suggested that adenine pairs with thymine and guanine pairs with cytosine. What other data available to Watson and Crick suggested that adenine–guanine and cytosine–thymine pairs normally do not form?

2. Exposing cells to radioactive thymidine can label eukaryotic chromosomes during the S phase of interphase. If cells are exposed to radioactive thymidine during the S phase, would you expect both or only one of the sister chromatids of a duplicated chromosome to be labelled at metaphase of the following mitosis (see Section 8.3)?

3. If the cells in question 2 finish division and then enter another round of DNA replication in a medium that has been washed free of radioactive label, would you expect both or only one of the sister chromatids of a duplicated chromosome to be labelled at metaphase of the following mitosis?

4. During replication, an error uncorrected by proofreading or mismatch repair produces a DNA molecule with a base mismatch at the indicated position:

   AATTCCGACTCCTATGG
   TTAAGGTTGAGGATACC
   　　　　　　　↑

   This DNA molecule is received by one of the two daughter cells produced by mitosis. In the next round of replication and division, the mutation appears in only one of the two daughter cells. Develop a hypothesis to explain this observation.

5. Strains of bacteria that are resistant to an antibiotic sometimes appear spontaneously among other bacteria of the same type that are killed by the antibiotic. In view of the information in this chapter about DNA replication, what might account for the appearance of this resistance?

Questions (description callout)

Self-Test Questions These end-of-chapter questions focus on factual content in the chapter while encouraging you to apply what you have learned. These questions have been revised as per Nelson Education's NETA program, as described in detail in the Ancillaries section on page xxviii.

Questions for Discussion

1. Chargaff's data suggested that adenine pairs with thymine and guanine pairs with cytosine. What other data available to Watson and Crick suggested that adenine–guanine and cytosine–thymine pairs normally do not form?

2. Exposing cells to radioactive thymidine can label eukaryotic chromosomes during the S phase of interphase. If cells are exposed to radioactive thymidine during the S phase, would you expect both or only one of the sister chromatids of a

Questions for Discussion These questions enable you to participate in discussions on key questions to build your knowledge and learn from others.

ANCILLARIES

An extensive array of supplemental materials is available to accompany *Biology: Exploring the Diversity of Life,* Second Canadian Edition. These supplements are designed to make teaching and learning more effective. For more information on any of these resources, please contact your local Nelson Education sales representative or call Nelson Education Limited Customer Support at 1-800-268-2222.

Instructor Ancillaries

The **Nelson Education Teaching Advantage (NETA)** program delivers research-based instructor resources that promote student engagement and higher-order thinking to enable the success of Canadian students and educators.

Instructors today face many challenges. Resources are limited, time is scarce, and a new kind of student has emerged: one who is juggling school with work, has gaps in his or her basic knowledge, and is immersed in technology in a way that has led to a completely new style of learning. In response, Nelson Education has gathered a group of dedicated instructors to advise on the creation of richer and more flexible ancillaries that respond to the needs of today's teaching environments.

The members of our editorial advisory board, listed below, have experience across a variety of disciplines and are recognized for their commitment to teaching:

> **Norman Althouse**, Haskayne School of Business, University of Calgary
> **Brenda Chant-Smith**, Department of Psychology, Trent University
> **Scott Follows**, Manning School of Business Administration, Acadia University
> **Jon Houseman**, Department of Biology, University of Ottawa
> **Glen Loppnow**, Department of Chemistry, University of Alberta
> **Tanya Noel,** Department of Biology, York University
> **Gary Poole**, Director, Centre for Teaching and Academic Growth and School of Population and Public Health, University of British Columbia
> **Dan Pratt**, Department of Educational Studies, University of British Columbia
> **Mercedes Rowinsky-Geurts**, Department of Languages and Literatures, Wilfrid Laurier University
> **David DiBattista**, Department of Psychology, Brock University
> **Dr. Roger Fisher**, Ph.D.

In consultation with the editorial advisory board, Nelson Education has completely rethought the structure, approaches, and formats of our key textbook ancillaries. We've also increased our investment in editorial support for our ancillary authors. The result is the Nelson Education Teaching Advantage (NETA) and its key components: *NETA Engagement, NETA Assessment,* and *NETA Presentation.* Each component includes one or more ancillaries prepared according to our best practices and a document explaining the theory behind the practices.

NETA Engagement presents materials that help instructors deliver engaging content and activities to their classes. Instead of Instructor's Manuals that regurgitate chapter outlines and key terms from the text, NETA Enriched Instructor's Manuals (EIMs) provide genuine assistance to teachers. The EIMs answer questions such as *What should students learn? Why should students care?* and *What are some common student misconceptions and stumbling blocks?* EIMs not only identify the topics that cause students the most difficulty but also describe techniques and resources to help students master these concepts. Dr. Roger Fisher's *Instructor's Guide to Classroom Engagement (IGCE)* accompanies every EIM. (Information about the NETA EIM prepared for *Biology: Exploring the Diversity of Life,* Second Canadian Edition, is included in the description of the Instructor's Resource DVD (IRDVD) below.)

NETA Assessment relates to testing materials: not just Nelson's Test Banks and Computerized Test Banks, but also in-text self-tests, Study Guides, and web quizzes, and homework programs like CNOW. Under *NETA Assessment,* Nelson's authors create multiple-choice questions that reflect research-based best practices for constructing effective questions and testing not just recall but also higher-order thinking. Our guidelines were developed by David DiBattista, a 3M National Teaching Fellow whose recent research as a professor of psychology at Brock University has focused on multiple-choice testing. All Test Bank authors receive training at workshops conducted by DiBattista, as do the copy editors assigned to each Test Bank. A copy of *Multiple Choice Tests: Getting beyond Remembering,* DiBattista's guide to writing effective tests, is included with every Nelson Test Bank/Computerized Test Bank package. (Information about the NETA Test Bank prepared for *Biology: Exploring the Diversity of Life,* Second Canadian Edition, is included in the description of the IRDVD on the next page.)

NETA Presentation has been developed to help instructors make the best use of PowerPoint in their classrooms. With a clean and uncluttered design developed by Maureen Stone of StoneSoup Consulting, *NETA Presentation* features slides with improved readability, more multimedia and graphic materials, activities to use in class, and tips for instructors on the Notes page. A copy of *NETA Guidelines for Classroom Presentations* by Maureen Stone is included with each set of PowerPoint slides. (Information about the NETA PowerPoint prepared for *Biology: Exploring the Diversity of Life,* Second Canadian Edition, is included in the description of the IRDVD below.)

Instructor's Resource DVD (IRDVD)

Key instructor ancillaries are provided on the *Instructor's Resource DVD (IRDVD)* (ISBN 0-17-661837-6), giving instructors the ultimate tool for customizing lectures and presentations. (Downloadable web versions are also available at **http://biologyedl2e.nelson.com**.) The IRD includes the following components:

- **NETA Engagement:** The Enriched Instructor's Manual was written by Tanya Noel and Tamara Kelly from York University. It is organized according to the textbook chapters and addresses eight key educational concerns, such as typical stumbling blocks students face and how to address them. Other features include tips on teaching using cases as well as suggestions on how to present material and use technology and other resources effectively, integrating the other supplements available to both students and instructors. This manual doesn't simply reinvent what's currently in the text; it helps the instructor make the material relevant and engaging to students.

- **NETA Assessment:** The Test Bank was written by Ivona Mladenovic of Simon Fraser University and Ian Dawe of Selkirk College. It includes over 2500 multiple-choice questions written according to NETA guidelines for effective construction and development of higher-order questions. Also included are true/false, essay, short answer, matching, and completion questions. Test Bank files are provided in Word format for easy editing and in PDF format for convenient printing, whatever your system.

    The ExamView Computerized Test Bank includes all the questions from the Test Bank. The easy-to-use ExamView software is compatible with Microsoft Windows and Mac. Create tests by selecting questions from the question bank, modifying these questions as desired, and adding new questions you write yourself. You can administer quizzes online and export tests to WebCT, Blackboard, and other formats.

- **NETA Presentation:** Microsoft PowerPoint lecture slides for every chapter have been created by Dr. Jane P. Young, University of Northern British Columbia. There is an average of 80 slides per chapter, many featuring key figures, tables, and photographs from *Biology: Exploring the Diversity of Life, Second Canadian Edition.* NETA principles of clear design and engaging content have been incorporated throughout.

- **Image Library:** This resource consists of digital copies of figures, short tables, and photographs used in the book. Instructors may use these JPEGs to create their own PowerPoint presentations.

- **DayOne:** DayOne—ProfInClass is a PowerPoint presentation that you can customize to orient your students to the class and their text at the beginning of the course.

- **TurningPoint:** Another valuable resource for instructors is **TurningPoint classroom response software** customized for *Biology: Exploring the Diversity of Life,* Second Canadian Edition by Dr. Jane P. Young, University of Northern British Columbia. Now you can author, deliver, show, access, and grade, all in PowerPoint, with no toggling back and forth between screens! JoinIn on TurningPoint is the only classroom response software tool that gives you true PowerPoint integration. With JoinIn, you are no longer tied to your computer. You can walk about your classroom as you lecture, showing slides and collecting and displaying responses with ease. There is simply no easier or more effective way to turn your lecture hall into a personal, fully interactive experience for your students. If you can use PowerPoint, you can use JoinIn on Turning-Point! (Contact your Nelson publishing representative for details.) These have been adapted by Dr. Jane P. Young, University of Northern British Columbia, and contain poll slides and pre- and post-test slides for each chapter in the text.

Student Ancillaries

CourseMate The more you study, the better the results. Make the most of your study time by accessing everything you need to succeed in one place. Your Biology CourseMate includes the following components:

- An interactive eBook with highlighting, note taking, and an interactive glossary
- Interactive learning tools, including:
  - Quizzes
  - Design an Experiment, Interpret the Data, and Apply Evolutionary Concepts exercises
  - Flashcards
  - Videos
  - BioExperience 3D Animations

The CourseMate for *Biology: Exploring the Diversity of Life,* Second Canadian Edition, was prepared by Dora Cavallo-Medved, University of Windsor and Reehan Mirza, Nipissing University.

 Founded in 2000 by economist and Stanford professor Paul Romer, Aplia™ is an educational technology company dedicated to improving learning by increasing student effort and engagement. Currently, Aplia™ products have been used by more than 650 000 students at over 750 institutions.

For students, Aplia™ offers a way to stay on top of coursework with regularly scheduled homework assignments. Interactive tools and additional content are provided to further increase engagement and understanding.

For instructors, Aplia™ offers high-quality, auto-graded assignments that ensure students put forth effort on a regular basis throughout the term. These assignments have been developed for a range of textbooks and are easily customized for individual teaching schedules. The Aplia course for *Biology: Exploring the Diversity of Life,* Second Canadian Edition, was prepared by Anna Hicks, Memorial University, and Todd Nickle and Alexandria Farmer, Mount Royal University.

Study Guide

The Study Guide (ISBN: 0-17-663368-5) from the First Canadian Edition has been adapted for the Second Canadian Edition by Colin Montpetit of the University of Ottawa, Julie Smit of the University of Windsor, and Wendy J. Keenleyside of the University of Guelph. The Study Guide contains unique case studies to integrate the concepts within the text, study strategies, interactive exercises, self-test questions, and more.

Students and Instructors

Visit the website accompanying *Biology: Exploring the Diversity of Life,* Second Canadian Edition, at **http://biologyedl2e.nelson.com.** This website contains flashcards, weblinks, and much more.

Prospering in Biology

Using This Book

The following are things you will need to know in order to use this text and prosper in biology.

Names

What's in a name? People are very attached to names—their own names, the names of other people, the names of flowers and food and cars and so on. It is not surprising that biologists would also be concerned about names. Take, for example, our use of scientific names. Scientific names are always italicized and Latinized.

Castor canadensis Kuhl is the scientific name of the Canadian beaver. *Castor* is the genus name; *canadensis* is the specific epithet. Together they make up the name of the species, which was first described by a person called Kuhl. "Beaver" by itself is not enough because there is a European beaver, *Castor fiber,* and an extinct giant beaver, *Castoides ohioensis.* Furthermore, common names can vary from place to place (*Myotis lucifugus* is sometimes known as the "little brown bat" or the "little brown myotis").

Biologists prefer scientific names because the name (Latinized) tells you about the organism. There are strict rules about the derivation and use of scientific names. Common names are not so restricted, so they are not precise. For example, in *Myotis lucifugus, Myotis* means "mouse-eared" and *lucifugus* means "flees the light"; hence, this species is a mouse-eared bat that flees the light.

Birds can be an exception. There are accepted "standard" common names for birds. The American Robin is *Turdus migratorius.* The common names for birds are usually capitalized because of the standardization. However, the common names of mammals are not capitalized, except for geographic names or patronyms (*geographic* = named after a country, e.g., Canadian beaver; *patronym* = named after someone, e.g., Ord's kangaroo rat).

Although a few plants that have very broad distributions may have accepted standard common names (e.g., white spruce, *Picea glauca*), most plants have many common names. Furthermore, the same common name is often used for more than one species. Several species in the genus *Taraxacum* are referred to as "dandelion." It is important to use the scientific names of plants to be sure that it is clear exactly which plant we mean. The scientific names of plants also tell us something about the plant. The scientific name for the weed quack grass, *Elymus repens,* tells us that this is a type of wild rye (*Elymus*) and that this particular species spreads or creeps (*repens* = creeping). Anyone who has tried to eliminate this plant from their garden or yard knows how it creeps! Unlike for animals, plant-naming rules forbid the use of the same word for both genus and species names for a plant; thus, although *Bison bison* is an acceptable scientific name for buffalo, such a name would never be accepted for a plant.

In this book, we present the scientific names of organisms when we mention them. We follow standard abbreviations; for example, although the full name of an organism is used the first time it is mentioned (e.g., *Castor canadensis*), subsequent references to that same organism abbreviate the genus name and provide the full species name (e.g., *C. canadensis*).

In some areas of biology, the standard representation is of the genus, for example, *Chlamydomonas.* In other cases, names are so commonly used that only the abbreviation may be used (e.g., *E. coli* for *Escherichia coli*).

Units

The units of measure used by biologists are standardized (metric or SI) units, used throughout the world in science.

Definitions

The science of biology is replete with specialized terms (sometimes referred to as "jargon") used to communicate specific information. It follows that, as with scientific names, specialized terms increase the precision with which biologists communicate among themselves and with others. Be cautious about the use of terms because jargon can obscure precision. When we encounter a "slippery" term (such as species or gene), we explain why one definition for all situations is not feasible.

Time

In this book, we use CE (Common Era) to refer to the years since year 1 and BCE (Before the Common Era) to refer to years before that.

Geologists think of time over very long periods. A geological time scale (see *The Purple Pages,* pp. F-50–F-51) shows that the age of Earth could be measured in years, but it's challenging to think of billions of years expressed in days (or hours, etc.). With the advent of using the decay rates of radioisotopes to measure the age of rocks, geologists adopted 1950 as the baseline, the "Present," and the past is referred to as BP ("Before Present"). A notation of 30 000 years BP (^{14}C) indicates 30 000 years before 1950 using the ^{14}C method of dating.

Other dating systems are also used. Some archaeologists use PPNA (PrePottery Neolithic A, where A is the horizon or stratum). In deposits along the Euphrates River, 11 000 PPNA appears to be the same as 11 000 BP. In this book, we use BCE or BP as the time units, except when referring to events or species from more than 100 000 years ago. For those dates, we refer you to the geological time scale (see *The Purple Pages,* pp. F-50–F-51).

Sources

Where does the information presented in a text or in class come from? What is the difference between what you read in a textbook or an encyclopedia and the material you see in a newspaper or tabloid? When the topic relates to science, the information should be based on material that has been published in a scholarly journal. In this context, "scholarly" refers to the process of review. Scholars submit their manuscripts reporting their research findings to the editor (or editorial board) of a journal. The editor, in turn, sends the manuscript out for comment and review by recognized authorities in the field. The process is designed to ensure that what is published is as accurate and appropriate as possible. The review process sets the scholarly journal apart from the tabloid.

There are literally thousands of scholarly journals, which, together, publish millions of articles each year. Some journals are more influential than others, for example, *Science* and *Nature.* These two journals are published weekly and invariably contain new information of interest to biologists.

To collect information for this text, we have drawn on published works that have gone through the process of scholarly review. Specific references (citations) are provided, usually in the electronic resources designed to complement the book.

A citation is intended to make the information accessible. Although there are many different formats for citations, the important elements include (in some order) the name(s) of the author(s), the date of publication, the title, and the publisher. When the source is published in a scholarly journal, the journal name, its volume number, and the pages are also provided. With the citation information, you can visit a library and locate the original source. This is true for both electronic (virtual) and real libraries.

Students of biology benefit by making it a habit to look at the most recent issues of their favourite scholarly journals and use them to keep abreast of new developments.

M. Brock Fenton
Heather Addy
Denis Maxwell
Tom Haffie
Bill Milsom

London, Calgary, and Vancouver
November 2011

Acknowledgements

We thank the many people who have worked with us on the production of this text, particularly Paul Fam, Publisher, whose foresight brought the idea to us and whose persistence saw the project through. Thanks go to those who reviewed the First Canadian Edition text to provide us with feedback for the Second Canadian Edition, including Dora Cavallo-Medved, University of Windsor; Anna Hicks, Memorial University; Heather Roffey, McGill University; and Todd Nickle, Mount Royal University. We are also grateful to the members of the Editorial Advisory Board and the Student Advisory Boards, who provided us with valuable feedback and alternative perspectives (special acknowledgements to these individuals are listed below). We also thank Richard Walker at the University of Calgary and Ken Davey at York University, who began this journey with us but were unable to continue. We thank Carl Lowenberger for contributing Chapter 43 Defences against Disease. We are especially grateful to Mark Grzeskowiak, Senior Developmental Editor, who kept us moving through the chapters at an efficient pace, along with Sreejith Govindan, Project Manager, and Christine Gilbert, Content Production Manager. We thank Kristiina Paul, our photo researcher, for her hard work with the numerous photos in the book, Julia Cochrane for her careful and thoughtful copy editing, and Sandra Peters, who did a cold read as a further check on our presentation. Finally, we thank Sean Chamberland, Executive Marketing Manager, for making us look good.

Brock Fenton would like to thank Allan Noon, who offered much advice about taking pictures; Laura Barclay, Jeremy McNeil, Tony Percival-Smith, C.S. (Rufus) Churcher, and David and Meg Cumming for the use of their images; and Karen Campbell for providing a critical read on Chapter 48 Putting Selection to Work.

Heather Addy would like to thank Ed Yeung for generously providing many images and assistance with revision of figures, and Cindy Graham, David Bird, Fengshan Ma, and William Huddleston for providing feedback and valuable suggestions for improving several chapters.

Tom Haffie would like to acknowledge the cheerful and insightful editorial work of Jennifer Waugh on Chapter 16. The authors are all indebted to Johnston Miller whose extensive background research anchored our Concept Fixes in the education literature.

It is never easy to be in the family of an academic scientist. We are especially grateful to our families for their sustained support over the course of our careers, particularly during those times when our attentions were fully captivated by bacteria, algae, fungi, parasites, snakes, geese, or bats. Saying "yes" to a textbook project means saying "no" to a variety of other pursuits. We appreciate the patience and understanding of those closest to us that enabled the temporary reallocation of considerable time from other endeavours and relationships.

Many of our colleagues have contributed to our development as teachers and scholars by acting as mentors, collaborators, and, on occasion, "worthy opponents." Like all teachers, we owe particular gratitude to our students. They have gathered with us around the discipline of biology, sharing their potent blend of enthusiasm and curiosity and leaving us energized and optimistic for the future.

Editorial and Student Advisory Boards

We were very fortunate to have the assistance of some extraordinary students and instructors of biology across Canada who provided us with feedback that helped shape this textbook into what you see before you. As such, we would like to say a very special thank you to the following people:

Editorial Advisory Board

Declan Ali, University of Alberta
David Creasey, University of Victoria
Ken Davey, York University
Mark Fitzpatrick, University of Toronto Scarborough
Wendy Keenleyside, University of Guelph
Tamara Kelly, York University
Paul Marino, Memorial University
Yves Maufette, Université du Québec à Montréal
Iain McKinnell, Carleton University
Todd Nickle, Mount Royal University
Carol Pollock, University of British Columbia
Ken Wilson, University of Saskatchewan

Depicted above are the author team, Nelson Education representatives, and the members of the Student and Editorial Advisory Boards at the Royal Ontario Museum on January 20, 2011. Top row (l-r): Brock Fenton, Tamara Kelly, Todd Nickle, Ken Wilson, Mark Fitzpatrick, Wendy Keenleyside, Yves Maufette, Paul Fam, Mark Grzeskowiak. Bottom row [l-r]: Bill Milsom, Heather Addy, Tom Haffie, Denis Maxwell, Ken Davey, Laura Anne Aubrey, and Leah Blain.

Student Advisory Boards

University of Calgary
Jason Abboud
Jessica Hann
Carolyn Gratton
Jennifer Mikhayel
Emily Mitic
Simon Sun
Bhavisha Thankey
Anita Tieu
Sahar Zaidi

Depicted above are members of the Student Advisory Board at Mount Royal University. Top row (l-r): Todd Nickle; Sean Davis; Nathan Scherger; Matthew Bell; Annabelle Stratton. Bottom row (l-r): Bayli Law; Samantha Mann; Jennifer Corbin; Erin Froome; Kristina Lindsay. Not shown: Christina Bruce, Danielle Gronnestad, Melodie Lough, Brittney Morgan

Depicted above are members of the University of Calgary Student Advisory Board. Top row (l to r): Jason Abboud, Simon Sun, Jessica Hann, Carolyn Gratton. Bottom row (l to r): Sahar Zaidi, Jennifer Mikhayel, Emily Mitic, Bhavisha Thankey

University of Western Ontario
Alexandra Katz
Chanelle Ramsubick
Laura Anne Aubrey
Anam Islam
Elissa Pendergast
Samira Khajehi
Samuel Joshua Rothman
Eden Amber
Iva Lucic

Mount Royal University
Todd Nickle
Sean Davis
Nathan Scherger
Matthew Bell
Annabelle Stratton
Bayli Law
Samantha Mann
Jennifer Corbin
Erin Froome
Kristina Lindsay
Christina Bruce
Danielle Gronnestad
Melodie Lough
Brittney Morgan

Depicted above are members of the Student Advisory Board at the University of Western Ontario. (l-r) Samuel Joshua Rothman, SAB member, Chanelle Ramsubick, Laura Anne Aubrey, Alexandra Katz, SAB member. Not shown: Anam Islam, Elissa Pendergast, Samira Khajehi, Eden Amber, Iva Lucic.

Carleton University
Andres Acero
Shawna Reddie
Jaime Graham

a.

b.

Paintings by Claude Monet (1840–1926). Compared to his early works, including "The Water-Lily Pond" **(a),** his later paintings, including "The Japanese Footbridge" **(b),** bordered on the abstract with almost complete loss of light blue. Monet suffered from vision degenerative disease cataracts, diagnosed in 1912.

STUDY PLAN

1.1   The Physical Nature of Light
1.1a What Is Light?
1.1b Light Interacts with Matter

1.2   Light as a Source of Energy

1.3   Light as a Source of Information
1.3a Rhodopsin, the Universal Photoreceptor
1.3b Sensing Light without Eyes
1.3c The Eye
1.3d Darwin and the Evolution of the Eye

1.4   The Uniqueness of Light

1.5   Light Can Damage Biological Molecules
1.5a Damage Is an Unavoidable Consequence of Absorption
1.5b Ultraviolet Light Is Particularly Harmful
1.5c Melanin, Suntanning, and Vitamin D

1.6   Using Light to Tell Time
1.6a Circadian Rhythms Are Controlled by a Biological Clock
1.6b Biological Clocks Track the Changing Seasons
1.6c Jet Lag and the Need to Reset Biological Clocks

1.7   The Role of Light in Behaviour and Ecology
1.7a Using Colour as a Signal: Animals
1.7b Using Colour as a Signal: Plants
1.7c Camouflage
1.7d Ecological Light Pollution

1.8   Life in the Dark

1.9   Organisms Making Their Own Light: Bioluminescence

1   Light and Life

WHY IT MATTERS

Claude Monet (1840–1926), a French painter, is considered by many to be the master of the impressionist form that rose to prominence in the late nineteenth century. Other well-known impressionists include Edgar Degas and Paul Cézanne. Impressionism as an art movement was characterized by the use of small visible brush strokes that emphasized light and colour, rather than lines, to define an object. The artists used pure, unmixed colour, not smoothly blended, as was the custom at the time. For example, instead of physically mixing yellow and blue paint, they placed unmixed yellow paint on the canvas next to unmixed blue paint so that the colours would mingle in the eye of the viewer to create the impression of green. The impressionists found that they could capture the momentary and transient effects of sunlight and the changing colour of a scene by painting *en plein air*, in the open air, outside the studio, where they could more accurately paint the reflected light of an immediate scene.

Interestingly, compared with his early works, which included "The Water-Lily Pond" (1899), Monet's later paintings verge on the abstract, with colours bleeding into each other and a lack of rational shape and perspective. For example, "The Japanese Footbridge" is an explosion of orange, yellow, and red hues, with heavy, broad brush strokes, leaving the viewer barely able to discern the vague shape of the arched bridge. In many of Monet's later works, the colours in his paintings became more muted, far less vibrant and bright, with a pronounced colour shift from blue green to red yellow and an almost total absence of light blues. The sense of atmosphere and light that he was famous for in his earlier works disappeared.

Although the change in Monet's paintings could easily be explained by an intentional change in style or perhaps an age-related change in manual dexterity, Monet himself realized that it was not his style or dexterity that had changed but, rather, his ability to see. Monet suffered from cataracts, a vision-deteriorating disease diagnosed in both eyes by a Parisian ophthalmologist in 1912 when Monet was 72. A cataract is a change in the lens of the eye, making it more opaque. The underlying cause is a progressive denaturation of one of the proteins that make up the lens. The increased opaqueness of the lens absorbs certain wavelengths of light, decreasing the transmittance of blue light. Thus, to a cataract sufferer such as Monet, the world appears more yellow.

In this, the first of the 48 chapters that make up the textbook, we introduce you to the science of biology by using light as a central connecting theme. Light is arguably the most fundamental of natural phenomena, and foundational experiments into the nature of light were a key part of the scientific revolution that took place in the sixteenth and seventeenth centuries. Beyond formally defining light and discussing its properties, in this chapter we explore the huge diversity of areas of biology that light influences, from the molecular to the ecological. This introductory tour is not intended to be complete or exhaustive but to simply set the stage for the topics that come in subsequent chapters.

1.1 The Physical Nature of Light

Light serves two important functions for life on Earth. First, it is a source of energy that directly or indirectly sustains virtually all organisms. Second, light provides organisms with information about the physical world that surrounds them. An excellent example of an organism that uses light for both energy and information is the green alga *Chlamydomonas reinhardtii* (**Figure 1.1**). *C. reinhardtii* is a single-celled photo-

synthetic eukaryote that is commonly found in ponds and lakes. Each cell contains a single large chloroplast that harvests light energy and uses it to make energy-rich molecules through the process of photosynthesis. In addition, each cell contains a light sensor called an eyespot that allows individual cells to gather information about the location and intensity of a light source. Regardless of whether the light is used as a source of energy or as a source of information about the environment, both uses rely on the same fundamental properties of light and require the light energy to be captured by the organism.

1.1a What Is Light?

The reason there is life on Earth and, as far as we know, nowhere else in our solar system has to do with distance—specifically, the distance of 150 million kilometres separating Earth from the Sun (**Figure 1.2**). By converting hydrogen into helium at the staggering rate of some 3.4×10^{38} hydrogen nuclei per second, the Sun converts over 4 million tonnes of matter into energy every second. This energy is given off as *electromagnetic radiation,* which travels in the form of a wave at a speed of 1 079 252 848 km/h (the speed of light) and reaches Earth in just over 8 minutes. Scientists often distinguish different types of electromagnetic radiation by their wavelength, the distance between two successive peaks (**Figure 1.3**). The wavelength of electromagnetic radiation ranges from less than one picometre (10^{-12} m) for cosmic rays to more than a kilometre (10^{6} m) for radio waves.

So what is light? **Light** is most commonly defined as the portion of the electromagnetic spectrum that

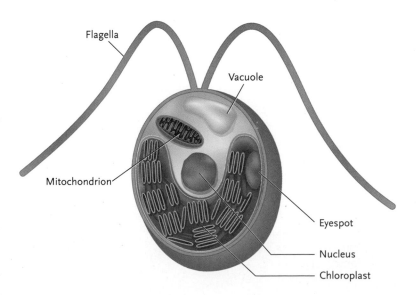

Flagella

Vacuole

Mitochondrion

Eyespot

Nucleus

Chloroplast

Figure 1.1

Chlamydomonas reinhardtii. Each cell contains a single chloroplast used for photosynthesis as well as an eyespot for sensing light in the environment.

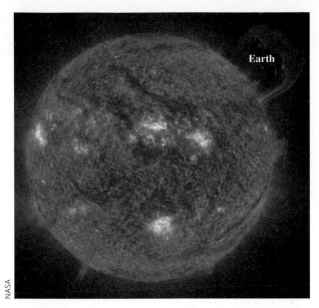

Figure 1.2

The Sun. Like most stars, the Sun generates electromagnetic radiation as a result of the nuclear fusion of hydrogen nuclei into helium. Note the superimposed image of Earth used to illustrate the relative sizes.

humans can detect with their eyes. This is a very narrow portion of the total electromagnetic spectrum, only spanning the wavelengths from about 400 to 700 nm (see Figure 1.3). In the field of physics, the definition of light often includes other regions of the electromagnetic spectrum, and thus terms such as *visible light, ultraviolet light,* and *infrared light* are commonly used.

The physical nature of light has been the focus of scientific inquiry for hundreds of years, but it is still not simple to grasp. Unlike the atoms that make up matter, light has no mass. As well, although the results of some experiments suggest that light behaves as a wave as it travels through space, the results of other experiments are best explained by light being composed of a stream of energy particles called **photons.** That light has properties of both a wave and a stream of photons is often referred to as the particle-wave duality. And so we are left with a compromise description—light is best understood as a wave of photons. The relationship between the wavelength of light and the energy of the photons it carries is an inverse one: the longer the wavelength, the lower the energy of the photons it contains. Looking at Figure 1.3, this means that shorter-wavelength blue light consists of photons of higher energy than red light, which has a longer wavelength and photons of lower energy.

1.1b Light Interacts with Matter

Although light has no mass, it is still able to interact with matter and cause change. This change is what allows the energy of light to be used by living things. When a photon of light hits an object, the photon has three possible fates: it can be reflected off the object; transmitted through the object; or, it can be absorbed by the object. To be used as a source of energy or information by an organism, it is absorption that must take place. The absorption of light occurs when

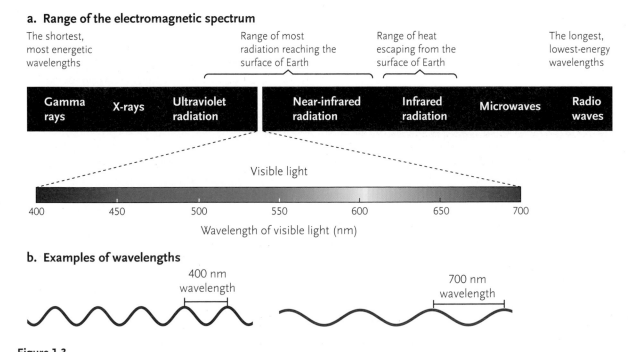

a. Range of the electromagnetic spectrum

The shortest, most energetic wavelengths

Range of most radiation reaching the surface of Earth

Range of heat escaping from the surface of Earth

The longest, lowest-energy wavelengths

| Gamma rays | X-rays | Ultraviolet radiation | Near-infrared radiation | Infrared radiation | Microwaves | Radio waves |

Visible light

400   450   500   550   600   650   700

Wavelength of visible light (nm)

b. Examples of wavelengths

400 nm wavelength

700 nm wavelength

Figure 1.3

The electromagnetic spectrum. (a) The electromagnetic spectrum ranges from gamma rays to radio waves; visible light and the wavelengths used for photosynthesis occupy only a narrow band of the spectrum. **(b)** Examples of wavelengths, showing the difference between the longest and shortest wavelengths of visible light.

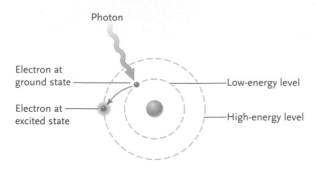

Figure 1.4

The absorption of a photon by a molecule results in the energy being transferred to an electron. This results in the electron being raised to a higher energy, excited state.

the energy of the photon is transferred to an electron within a molecule. This excites the electron, moving it from its ground state to a higher-energy level that is referred to as an excited state **(Figure 1.4)**. An important fact to remember is that a photon can be absorbed by an electron of a molecule only if the photon energy equals the energy difference between the electron's ground state and an excited state. If the energies don't match, then the photon is transmitted through the molecule or reflected. It is the excited-state electron that represents the source of energy required for processes such as photosynthesis and vision.

A major class of molecules that are very efficient at absorbing photons are called **pigments (Figure 1.5)**. There is a large diversity of pigments, including chlorophyll *a*, which is involved in photosynthesis; retinal, which is involved in vision; and indigo, which is used to dye jeans their distinctive blue colour.

An important question we can ask is: what is it about pigments that enable them to capture light? At first glance, the molecules shown in Figure 1.5 seem to be structurally very different from each other. However, they all share a common feature critical to light absorption: a region where carbon atoms are covalently bonded to each other with alternating single and double bonds. This bonding arrangement is called a *conjugated system,* and it results in the delocalization of electrons. None of these electrons are closely associated with a particular atom or involved in bonding and thus are available to interact with a photon of light.

Most pigments absorb light at distinctly different wavelengths. This is because they differ in the number of excited states available to the excitable electrons. While some pigments can absorb, for example, only blue photons because they have only one high-energy excited state, others can absorb two or more different

wavelengths because they have two or more excited states. Photon absorption is intimately related to the concept of colour. A pigment's colour is the result of photons of light that it *does not* absorb. Instead of being absorbed, these photons are reflected off the pigment or transmitted through the pigment to reach your eyes **(Figure 1.6)**.

STUDY BREAK

1. Define light.
2. What structural feature is common to all pigments?

1.2 Light as a Source of Energy

Energy from the Sun enters the biosphere through photosynthesis – the process whereby light energy is used by plants and related organisms to convert carbon dioxide into sugars (carbohydrates). We discuss this photosynthesis in detail in Chapter 7. Following light absorption, the potential energy of excited electrons within pigment molecules such as chlorophyll is used in photosynthetic electron transport to synthesize the energy-rich compounds NADPH (nicotinamide adenine dinucleotide phosphate) and ATP (adenosine triphosphate). These molecules are in turn consumed in the Calvin cycle of photosynthesis to convert carbon dioxide into carbohydrates **(Figure 1.7, p. 6)**. Although the energy of one photon is very small, the photosynthetic apparatus within the chloroplast of a single *C. reinhardtii* cell absorbs millions of photons each second. And a single cell within a typical plant leaf contains hundreds of chloroplasts!

While photosynthesis converts carbon dioxide into carbohydrates, it is the process of cellular respiration that breaks down carbohydrates and other molecules, trapping the released energy as ATP (see Figure 1.7). This in turn is used in the energy-requiring metabolic and biosynthetic processes that are fundamental to life.

Not all organisms that use light as a source of energy are classified as photosynthetic. That is, some organisms do not use the light energy to convert carbon dioxide into carbohydrates. A good example is a genus of organisms within the Archaea called *Halobacterium*. These remarkable microbes thrive in habitats that contain salt levels that are lethal to most other forms of life **(Figure 1.8, p. 6)**. Species of *Halobacterium* contain a pigment–protein complex called bacteriorhodopsin, which functions as a light-driven proton pump. The pigment component of bacteriorhodopsin captures photons of light that provide the energy supply needed to pump protons out of the cell. The resulting difference in H^+ concentration across the plasma membrane represents a source of potential

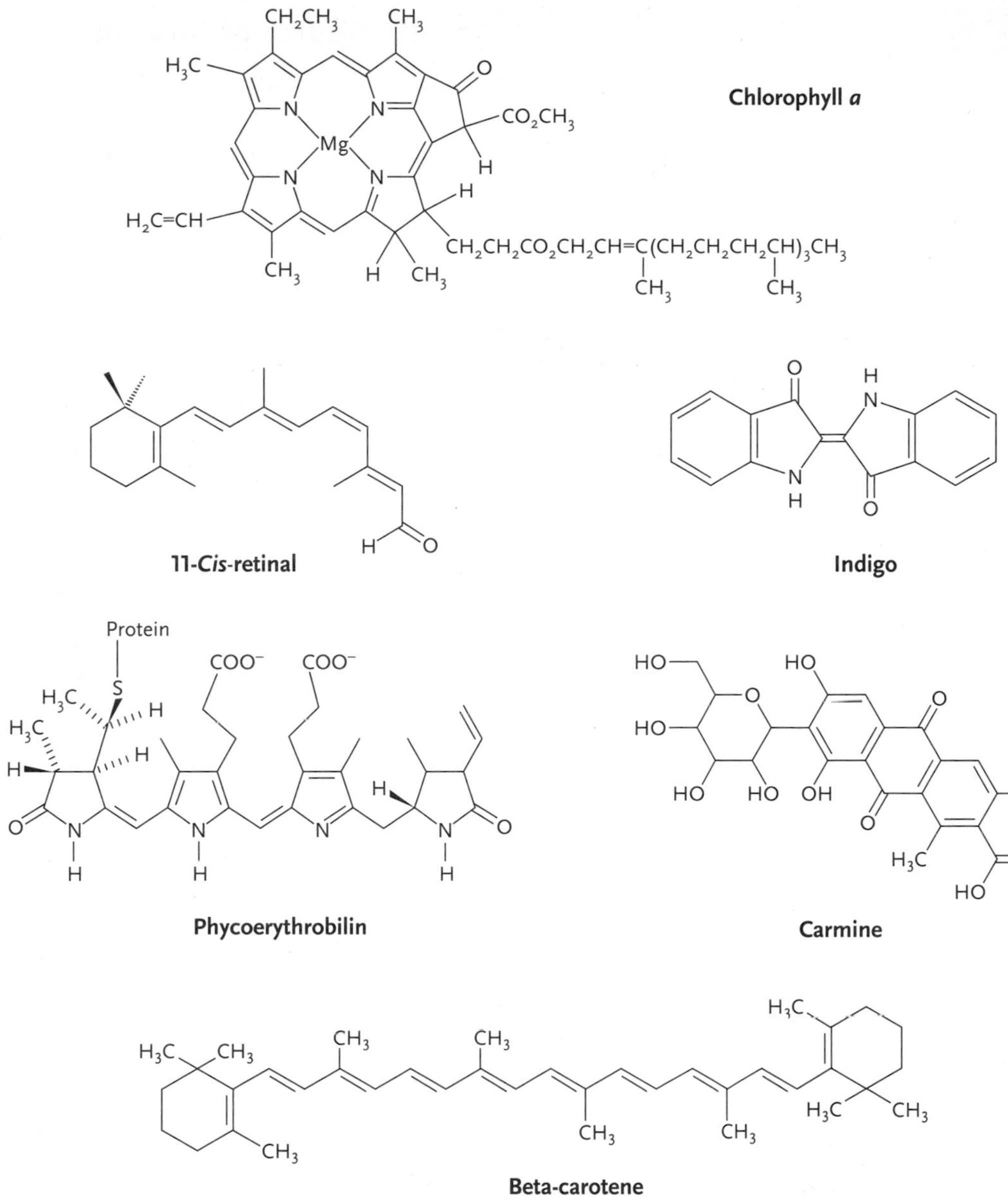

Chlorophyll *a*

11-*Cis*-retinal

Indigo

Phycoerythrobilin

Protein

Carmine

Beta-carotene

Figure 1.5
Structure of some common pigments. Chlorophyll *a*, photosynthesis. 11-*Cis*-retinal, vision. Indigo, dye. Phycoerythrobilin, red photosynthetic pigment found in red algae. Carmine, scale pigment found in some insects. Beta-carotene, an orange accessory photosynthetic pigment. A common feature of all these pigments that is critical for light absorption is the presence of a conjugated system of double/single carbon bonds (shown in red for beta-carotene).

energy that is used by the enzyme ATP synthase to generate ATP from ADP (adenosine diphosphate) and inorganic phosphate (P_i) (see Figure 1.8, p. 6). We will discuss the mode of ATP generation in detail in Chapters 6 and 7. In Halobacteria the ATP synthesized through bacteriorhodopsin is used for a range of energy-requiring reactions – but not for the synthesis of carbohydrates from carbon dioxide.

STUDY BREAK

1. Why is the pigment indigo blue in colour?
2. How is light absorption linked to ATP synthesis in *Halobacteria*?

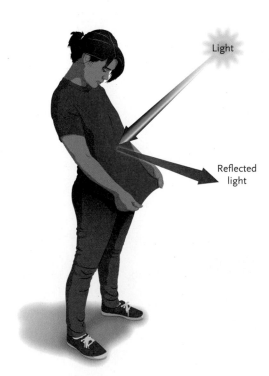

Light

Reflected light

Figure 1.6
Why the t-shirt is red. Pigment molecules bound to the fabric of the shirt absorb blue, green, and yellow photons of light. Red photons are not absorbed and are instead transmitted through the shirt or reflected. Because they are not absorbed, it is the red wavelength of light that we detect with our eyes.

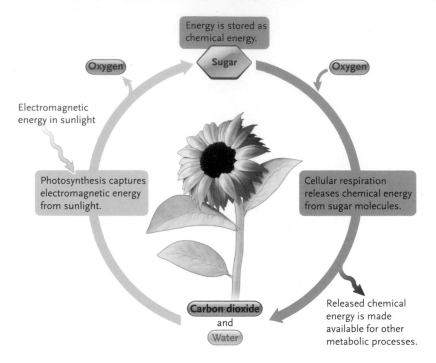

Energy is stored as chemical energy.

Sugar

Oxygen

Oxygen

Electromagnetic energy in sunlight

Photosynthesis captures electromagnetic energy from sunlight.

Cellular respiration releases chemical energy from sugar molecules.

Carbon dioxide and Water

Released chemical energy is made available for other metabolic processes.

Figure 1.7
Photosynthesis converts light into a usable form of energy. Photosynthesis uses the energy in sunlight to build sugar molecules from carbon dioxide and water, releasing oxygen as a by-product. In many organisms, the process of cellular respiration breaks down the products of photosynthesis and releases usable energy.

1.3 Light as a Source of Information

As mentioned in "Why It Matters," the deterioration of Monet's eyesight changed the way he saw the world, and thus changed the way he painted. This reminds us that many organisms use light to sense their environment—to provide them with crucial information about what is around them. The experience of trying to perform even the simplest of tasks in a dark room makes one quickly realize how important the ability to sense light has become for many forms of life. The change in Monet's eyesight during his later life also suggests that not every person, and certainly not every species, sees the world in the same way.

1.3a Rhodopsin, the Universal Photoreceptor

The basic light-sensing system is termed the photoreceptor. And the most common photoreceptor in nature is rhodopsin **(Figure 1.9, p. 8)**, which is the basis of vision in animals but is also very common in other organisms, including *C. reinhardtii,* where it serves as the light-sensing unit of the eyespot. Each rhodopsin molecule consists of a protein called

a. *Halobacerium salinarum*

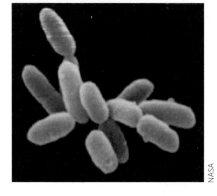

NASA

b. Hutt Lagoon, Western Australia

© J Marshall - Tribaleye Images/Alamy

Figure 1.8
Halobacterium are a genus of Archaea that have a light-driven proton pump.
(a) Electron micrograph of a colony of *Halobacterium salinarum*
(b) Species of *Halobacterium* thrive in hypersaline environments such as Hutt Lagoon in Australia. The pink colour of the water is due to the presence of bacteriorhodopsin within individual cells.
(c) A model of bacteriorhodopsin shows the pigment retinal bound to a protein.
(d) Bacteriorhodopsin functions as a light-driven proton pump, the proton gradient being used to synthesize ATP.

c. A model of bacteriorhodopsin

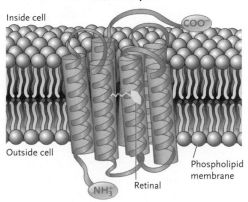

Inside cell

COO⁻

Outside cell

Phospholipid membrane

NH₃⁺

Retinal

d. Bacteriorhodopsin-driven ATP formation

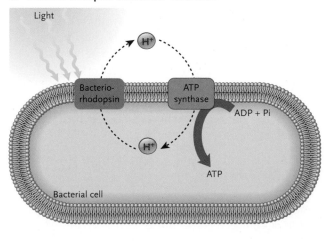

Light

H⁺

Bacteriorhodopsin

ATP synthase

ADP + Pi

H⁺

ATP

Bacterial cell

Sir Isaac Newton (1643–1727) was an English mathematician, physicist, and astronomer and is generally regarded as one of the greatest scientists and mathematicians in history. Newton wrote the *Philosophiae Naturalis Principia Mathematica,* in which he described universal gravitation and the three laws of motion, laying the groundwork for classical mechanics. He was the first to show that the motion of objects on Earth and elsewhere in the solar system is governed by the same set of natural laws. Newton also undertook key experiments about the nature of light. In Newton's time it was thought that light from the Sun was colourless and that the colours seen in a rainbow during a rain shower, for example, were somehow made by the rain droplets. In the same way, it was thought that colours produced when light passed through a glass prism were somehow made by the prism itself. It was Newton who laid the groundwork for fundamental breakthroughs in the nature of light by demonstrating through a series of experiments that these assumptions were false.

Using light entering his room through a slit in his curtains, Newton undertook a series of remarkably simple experiments that profoundly changed science. In one experiment, he passed the red light from one prism through a second prism and found the colour unchanged. From this Newton concluded that the prism does not make colour, but rather the colour is already present in the incoming light.

In Newton's "Experimentum Crucis" (shown here), he was able to use a combination of three prisms and one lens, enabling him to (from right to left) split white light into the spectrum, which was then passed through a convex lens that focused the light onto a second prism, and then reconstitute the spectrum into a single beam of white light and then split it again into the spectrum after passage through a third prism. An interesting property of light that is illustrated by a prism is that as light passes from one medium into another (e.g., air to glass), it changes speed, which causes the light to refract or bend. Light of shorter wavelength (blue) refracts to a greater degree than light of longer wavelength (red).

Newton's experiments were simple yet wonderfully elegant, leading to tremendous insight into the workings of the natural world. His experiments are classic examples of the approach to discovery that was introduced during what is called the Scientific Revolution, which swept Europe during the sixteenth and seventeenth centuries. This was a period in science when religion, superstition, and fear were replaced by reason and knowledge based on the observation, explanation, and prediction of real-world phenomena through experimentation (see *The Purple Pages* for more on the scientific method). Besides Newton, other key figures during this period were Francis Bacon, Johannes Kepler, Nicolaus Copernicus, René Descartes, Antonie van Leeuwenhoek, and William Harvey.

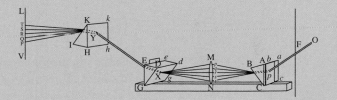

opsin that binds a single pigment molecule called retinal. Opsins are membrane proteins that span a membrane multiple times and form a complex with the retinal molecule at the centre (see Figure 1.9, p. 8). As the name suggests, rhodopsin is structurally similar, and evolutionarily related, to the bacteriorhodopsin found in *Halobacterium*.

As shown in Figure 1.9, absorption of a photon of light causes the retinal pigment molecule to change shape. This change triggers alterations to the opsin protein, which, in turn, trigger downstream events, including alterations in intracellular ion concentrations and electrical signals. As we will see in Chapter 37, in the case of vision, these electrical signals are sent to the visual centres of the brain. In humans, light captured by the eye involves the approximately 125 million photoreceptor cells (rods and cones) that line the retina. Each photoreceptor cell contains thousands of individual rhodopsin molecules.

Rhodopsin is the most common photoreceptor found in nature, but it is not the only one. Both plants and animals have a range of other photoreceptors that absorb light of particular wavelengths. However, it remains a mystery why rhodopsin became the most common photoreceptor. Perhaps its widespread occurrence is because it developed very early during the evolution of life. Interestingly, whereas vision and smell are different senses, proteins very similar to opsins are used in olfaction, suggesting that specific aspects of opsin proteins are particularly useful for sensory perception.

1.3b Sensing Light without Eyes

When we think about sensing light, we automatically think about our ability to see with our eyes. However, many organisms can sense the light in their surroundings even though they lack organs that we would

How rhodopsin functions

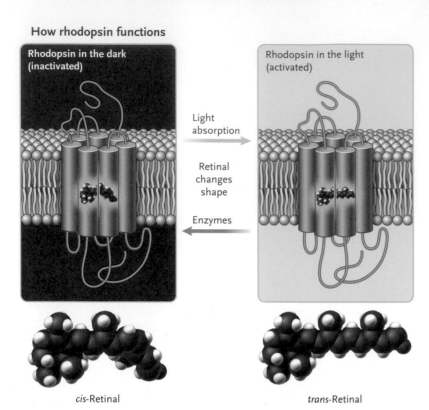

Figure 1.9
Model of the photoreceptor rhodopsin. Rhodopsin consists of a protein (opsin) that binds a pigment molecule (retinal). Upon absorption of a photon of light, retinal changes shape, which triggers changes to the opsin molecule. These changes trigger signalling events, which allow the organism to respond to the light.

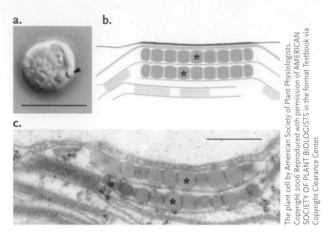

The plant cell by American Society of Plant Physiologists. Copyright 2006 Reproduced with permission of AMERICAN SOCIETY OF PLANT BIOLOGISTS in the format Textbook via Copyright Clearance Center.

Figure 1.10
The eyespot of *Chlamydomonas*. (a) Light microscope image of one *Chlamydomonas* cell. Arrowhead points to the eyespot. Bar = 10 µM. **(b)** Drawing of the eyespot apparatus with the asterisks indicating the orange pigment-rich globule layers that are found inside the chloroplast outer membrane. **(c)** Transmission electron micrograph of the same area. Bar = 300 nM.

consider to be eyes. These organisms include plants, algae, invertebrates, and even some prokaryotes. As an example, let's take a closer look at the eyespot of *C. reinhardtii*. The eyespot is a light-sensitive structure that is approximately 1 µm in diameter and is found within the chloroplast of the cell, in a region closely associated with the cell membrane **(Figure 1.10).** The eyespot is composed of two layers of carotenoid-rich lipid globules that seem to play a role in focusing and directing incoming light toward the photoreceptors. Recent research has shown that about 200 different proteins are assembled to produce the eyespot apparatus, including specific opsin proteins that are the basis of the rhodopsin-based photoreceptors. Although it is in the chloroplast, the eyespot does not play a role in photosynthesis. Instead the photoreceptors of the eyespot allow the cell to sense light direction and intensity. Using a pair of flagella, *C. reinhardtii* cells can respond to light by swimming toward or away from the light source in a process called *phototaxis.* This allows the cell to stay in the optimum light environment to maximize light capture for photosynthesis. Light absorption by the eyespot is linked to the swimming response by a signal transduction pathway; light absorption triggers rapid changes in the concentrations of ions, including potassium and calcium, which

generate a cascade of electrical events. These, in turn, change the beating pattern of the flagella used for locomotion.

In plants, a photoreceptor called phytochrome senses the light environment and is critical for *photomorphogenesis,* the normal developmental process activated when seedlings are exposed to light **(Figure 1.11).** Phytochrome is present in the cytosol of all plant cells, and when a seedling is exposed to wavelengths of red light, phytochrome becomes active and initiates a signal transduction pathway that reaches

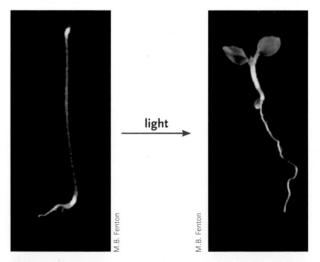

light

M.B. Fenton

M.B. Fenton

Figure 1.11
Photomorphogenesis. Shifting a seedling from darkness to light triggers a developmental program within the plant called photomorphogenesis. Light sensed by the photoreceptor phytochrome initiates the program that involves the activation of hundreds of genes.

the nucleus. In the nucleus, these signals activate hundreds of genes, many of which code for proteins involved in photosynthesis and leaf development. Plant development is the topic of discussion in Chapters 29 and 30.

1.3c The Eye

The **eye** can be defined as the organ animals use to sense light. It is described in detail in Chapter 37. What distinguishes the eye of an invertebrate, for example, from the eyespot of *C. reinhardtii* is vision. The process of vision requires not only an eye to focus and absorb incoming light but also a brain or at least a simple nervous system that interprets signals sent from the eye. The eye and brain are thought to have co-evolved because detailed visual processing occurs in the brain rather than in the eye. Essentially, we see not with our eyes but, rather, with our brain.

The simplest eye is the *ocellus* (plural, *ocelli*), which consists of a cup or pit lined with up to 100 photoreceptor cells. Found in all forms of true eyes, the photoreceptor cell is actually a modified nerve cell that contains thousands of individual photoreceptor molecules. A common group of organisms that contain ocelli are flatworms of the genus *Planaria* **(Figure 1.12)**. Information sent to the cerebral ganglion from individual eyes enables the worms to orient themselves so that the amount of light falling on the two ocelli remains equal and diminishes as they swim.

This reaction carries them directly away from the source of the light and toward darker areas, where the risk of predation is smaller. Ocelli occur in a variety of animals, including a number of insects, arthropods, and molluscs.

In many ways, the eye of a *Planaria* (plural, *Planarians*) is not much more advanced than the eyespot of *C. reinhardtii*. In both cases, the organ is used to sense light intensity and direction to a light source, but little else. The greatest advance in eye development came with the greater sophistication that produced an actual image of the lighted environment, which allowed objects and shapes to be discerned. These image-forming eyes are found in two distinctly different types: compound eyes and single-lens eyes. *Compound eyes,* which are common in arthropods such as insects and crustaceans, are built of hundreds of individual units called ommatidia (*omma* = eye) fitted closely together **(Figure 1.13)**. Each ommatidium samples only a small part of the visual field with incoming light being focused onto a bundle of photoreceptor cells. From these signals, the brain receives a mosaic image of the world.

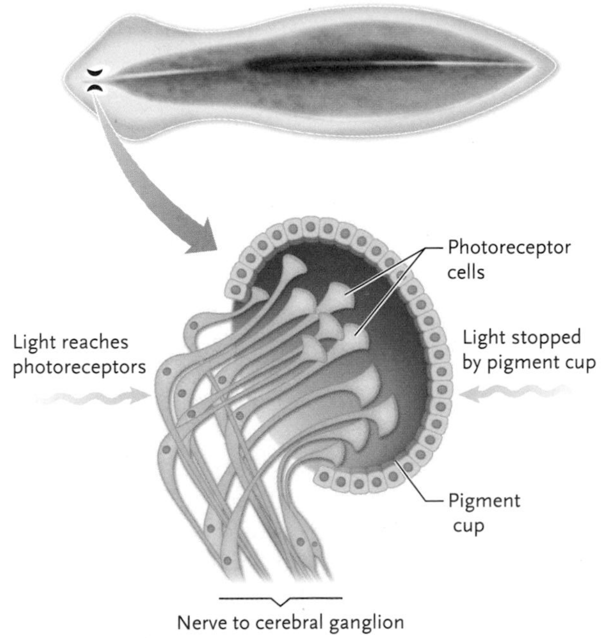

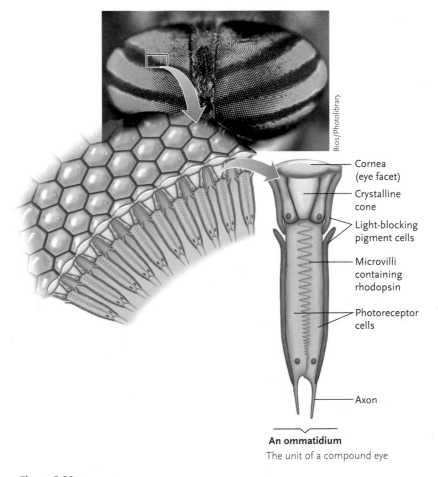

Cornea
(eye facet)

Crystalline cone

Light-blocking pigment cells

Microvilli containing rhodopsin

Photoreceptor cells

Axon

An ommatidium
The unit of a compound eye

Figure 1.13
The compound eye of a deer fly. Each ommatidium has a cornea that directs light into the crystalline cone; in turn, the cone focuses light on the photoreceptor cells. A light-blocking pigment layer at the sides of the ommatidium prevents light from scattering laterally in the compound eye.

Photoreceptor cells

Light reaches photoreceptors

Light stopped by pigment cup

Pigment cup

Nerve to cerebral ganglion

Figure 1.12
The ocellus of *Planaria*, a flatworm, and the arrangement of photoreceptor cells that allows worms to orient themselves in response to light.

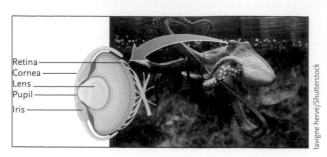

Figure 1.14
The single-lens eye of a cephalopod mollusc (an octopus).

Retina
Cornea
Lens
Pupil
Iris

lavigne herve/Shutterstock

Because even the slightest motion is detected simultaneously by many ommatidia, organisms with compound eyes are extraordinarily good at detecting movement, a lesson soon learned by fly-swatting humans.

The other major type of eye is called the single-lens eye **(Figure 1.14)** or camera-like eye and is found in some invertebrates and most vertebrates, including humans. Unlike compound eyes, in a single-lens eye, as light enters through the transparent cornea, a lens concentrates the light and focuses it onto a layer of photoreceptor cells at the back of the eye, the retina. The photoreceptor cells of the retina send information to the brain through the optic nerve.

1.3d Darwin and the Evolution of the Eye

When Charles Darwin presented his theory of evolution by natural selection in *On the Origin of Species by Means of Natural Selection* (1859), he recognized that what he called "organs of extreme perfection," such as the eye, would present a problem. He wrote:

> To suppose that the eye, with all its inimitable contrivances for adjusting the focus to different distances, for admitting different amounts of light, and for the correction of spherical and chromatic aberration, could have been formed by natural selection, seems, I freely confess, absurd in the highest possible degree. Yet reason tells me, that if numerous gradations from a perfect and complex eye to one very imperfect and simple, each grade being useful to its possessor, can be shown to exist; if further, the eye does vary ever so slightly, and the variations be inherited, which is certainly the case; and if any variation or modification in the organ be ever useful to an animal under changing conditions of life, then the difficulty of believing that a perfect and complex eye could be formed by natural selection, though insuperable by our imagination, can hardly be considered real.

Darwin found a way out of this dilemma by proposing that the eye as it exists in humans and other animals did not appear suddenly but evolved over

time from a simple, primitive eye. It now seems Darwin was very astute. Starting with a patch of light-sensitive cells on the skin, a recent study concluded that about 2000 small improvements over time would gradually yield a single-lens eye in less than 500 thousand years **(Figure 1.15)**. Considering that animals with primitive eyes appeared in the fossil record about 500 million years ago, the single-lens eye found in humans could have evolved more than 1000 times. This kind of timing supports fossil evidence that indicates that the eye has evolved independently at least 40 times in different animal lineages before converging into a handful of fundamental designs found today.

It is somewhat surprising that something so complex as the eye could evolve 40 or more different times. However, recently it has been shown that most eyes have fundamental similarities in their underlying developmental program. For example, a diversity of organisms have recruited a similar set of highly conserved genes to orchestrate eye development. This includes a gene called *Pax6* that has been identified as a master control gene that is almost universally employed for eye formation in animals. And let's not forget that what drove eye evolution in many different animal phyla is the huge advantage eyesight, and then improved eyesight, would have to an animal. The development of heightened visual ability in a predator, as an example, would force comparable eye improvements in both prey and potentially other predators. Rapid improvements in eye development over time would therefore be critical to survival.

STUDY BREAK

1. What is a photoreceptor?
2. How was Darwin able to rationalize the evolution of something so complex as the eye?

1.4 The Uniqueness of Light

Although visible light is a very small portion of the total electromagnetic spectrum, it is essential to life on Earth. In fact, it is this narrow band of energy, from a wavelength of about 400 to 700 nm, that is used for photosynthesis, vision, phototaxis, navigation, and other light-driven processes. Is it just a coincidence that all of these processes depend on such a narrow band of the electromagnetic spectrum? According to the Harvard physiologist and Nobel laureate George Wald (1906–1997), it is not a coincidence at all. Wald reasoned that visible light is used by organisms because it is the most dominant form of electromagnetic radiation reaching Earth's

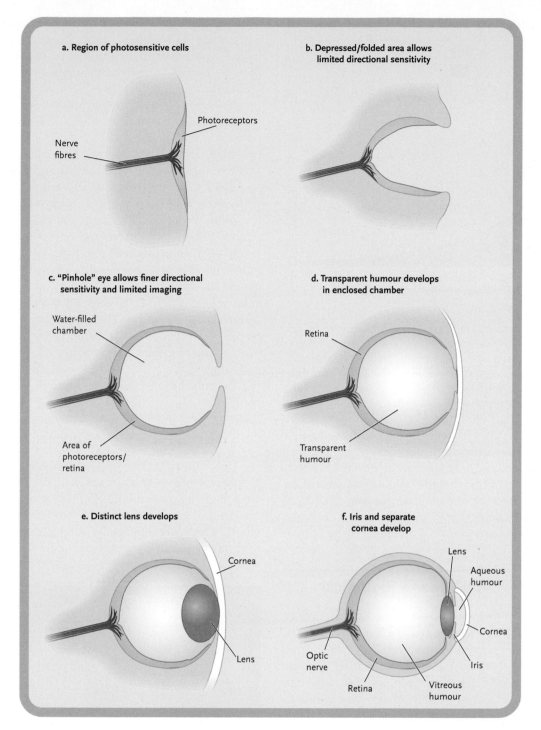

a. Region of photosensitive cells

Photoreceptors

Nerve fibres

b. Depressed/folded area allows limited directional sensitivity

c. "Pinhole" eye allows finer directional sensitivity and limited imaging

Water-filled chamber

Area of photoreceptors/ retina

d. Transparent humour develops in enclosed chamber

Retina

Transparent humour

e. Distinct lens develops

Cornea

Lens

f. Iris and separate cornea develop

Lens

Aqueous humour

Cornea

Iris

Optic nerve

Retina

Vitreous humour

Figure 1.15

The evolution of the eye. Starting with a layer of light-sensitive cells, recent research suggests that a camera-like eye could evolve in less than 500 000 years. The evolution of a more sophisticated eye can be explained by the huge advantage improved eyesight would give an organism.

surface **(Figure 1.16, p. 12)**. Shorter wavelengths of electromagnetic radiation are absorbed by the ozone layer high in the atmosphere, whereas wavelengths longer than those in the visible spectrum are absorbed by water vapour and carbon dioxide in the atmosphere.

Another reason life uses light over other wavelengths of electromagnetic radiation has to do with the energy it contains. Remember that living things are made up of molecules held together by chemical bonds (for a refresher see *The Purple Pages*). Radiation of shorter wavelengths than light contains enough energy to destroy these bonds. Alternatively, electromagnetic radiation of wavelengths longer than light are energetically relatively weak and would not supply enough energy to move an electron from a ground state to a higher, excited state. Furthermore, longer wavelengths are readily absorbed by water, which is the bulk of all

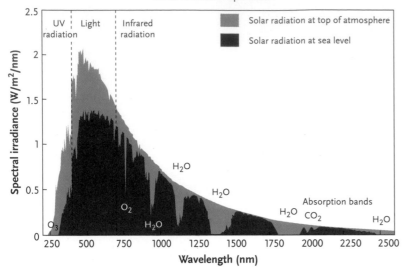

Figure 1.16

Electromagnetic radiation reaching the top of Earth's atmosphere (orange) and at sea level (red). As the energy passes through the atmosphere, short-wavelength radiation (250–300 nm) gets absorbed by ozone (O_3). Other wavelengths get partially absorbed by other gases, including O_2, H_2O, and CO_2. Compared to the electromagnetic radiation that reaches the outer atmosphere, the radiation reaching Earth's surface is reduced in both short wavelengths and long wavelengths.

living things. Given these fundamental aspects of photon energy and light absorption, it would not be at all surprising to find that life on other planets within our galaxy relied on the same narrow wavelengths of the electromagnetic spectrum for a source of energy and information.

1.5 Light Can Damage Biological Molecules

Like many forms of energy, photons of light can damage biological molecules. Recall that to be used for a source of either energy or information, photons of light must be absorbed by molecules. However, absorption of excessive light energy can result in damage that in some cases may be permanent. Of particular concern is higher-energy ultraviolet radiation, which, along with visible light, reaches Earth's surface.

1.5a Damage Is an Unavoidable Consequence of Light Absorption

The photoreceptor cells that line the human retina can be damaged by exposure to bright light. The high-energy environment associated with pigment molecules and excited electrons can result in what is referred to as photo-oxidative damage. The absorption of excess light energy can result in excited electrons reacting with O_2, producing what are called reactive oxygen species. These forms of oxygen,

which include the molecule hydrogen peroxide, are particularly damaging to proteins and other biological molecules, often resulting in a loss of function. Excessive damage to photoreceptor cells can lead to the death of the cell.

Unlike eyes, the photosynthetic apparatus of plants and algae is often exposed to full sunlight for hours and thus is particularly susceptible to photo-oxidative damage. A typical chloroplast contains hundreds of photosystems, each one trapping the energy of thousands of photons each second, converting the light into chemical energy. Compared to the photoreceptor cells of the retina, damage to photosystems can be repaired by a very efficient mechanism that involves removing damaged proteins and replacing them with newly synthesized copies. In fact, under normal light conditions, a single photosystem II (**Figure 1.17**) complex needs to be repaired about every 20 minutes. Because damage to the photosynthetic apparatus is unavoidable, a mechanism of efficient repair must have developed early during the evolution of life so that photosynthesis could be maintained even under high light conditions.

1.5b Ultraviolet Light Is Particularly Harmful

Ultraviolet light is electromagnetic radiation that has a wavelength between blue light (400 nm) and X-rays (200 nm). Because it consists of wavelengths that are shorter than visible light, the energy of the photons of ultraviolet light is greater and more damaging to

Courtesy of Curtis Neveu

Figure 1.17

Molecular model of the structure of photosystem II. The coloured ribbons and rods represent proteins to which pigments and other cofactors are precisely bound. Light absorption results in unavoidable damage to proteins. An efficient repair system maintains photosystem function even under high light conditions.

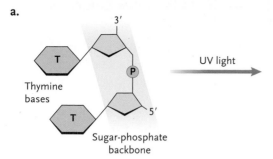
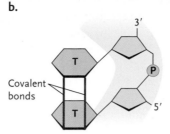

biological molecules. Life on Earth is protected from the shortest-wavelength and most damaging form of ultraviolet light by the atmosphere's ozone layer. Ozone, O_3, is produced when photons of ultraviolet light interact with molecular oxygen, O_2. While short wavelengths of ultraviolet light are absorbed by ozone, longer wavelengths of ultraviolet light reach Earth's surface.

Along with shorter-wavelength X-rays and gamma rays, ultraviolet light is classified as a form of *ionizing radiation*. The photons at these wavelengths are energetic enough to remove an electron from an atom, resulting in the formation of *ions*—atoms where the total number of protons and electrons are not equal. Ultraviolet light can be destructive to a range of biological molecules; however, it is the structure of DNA that is particularly susceptible to damage **(Figure 1.18)**. The interaction of ultraviolet light with nucleotide bases that make up DNA can result in the formation of a dimer—when two neighbouring bases become covalently linked together. Dimers change the shape of the double-helix structure of DNA and prevent its replication, as well as hindering gene transcription. These process are discussed in detail in Chapter 13. Nucleotide dimers are detected and repaired by a specific enzyme. Even so, the formation of nucleotide dimers can give rise to genetic mutation and has been linked to skin cancer.

For most organisms, exposure to ultraviolet light is unavoidable. Because of this, organisms use a range of behavioural, structural, and biochemical mechanisms to protect themselves from its damaging effects. For example, many animals are protected by the presence of fur or feathers covering their skin. Organisms with naked skin, such as humans and whales, are less protected and more susceptible to sunburn due to ultraviolet light exposure.

1.5c Melanin, Suntanning, and Vitamin D

To protect cells from the harmful effects of ultraviolet light, many organisms synthesize melanin, a pigment that strongly absorbs ultraviolet light. Melanin is a remarkable pigment found in all branches of the tree of life. Along with playing a key role in ultraviolet light protection in organisms as diverse as microbes

and humans, it is also the major component of the ink released by cephalopods such as squid.

Melanin is very efficient at absorbing ultraviolet light and yet it dissipates over 99% of this energy harmlessly as heat. The specific wavelength of radiation that a pigment such as melanin can absorb can be determined using an instrument called a spectrophotometer. By passing light of varying wavelengths through a solution of pure pigment, the spectrophotometer detects which wavelengths of light are transmitted through the sample and thus determines which wavelengths are absorbed by the pigment. The data from the spectrophotometer can be used to produce an *absorption spectrum,* a plot of absorbance in relation to the wavelength of light **(Figure 1.19)**.

Humans synthesize melanin in specialized skin cells called melanocytes, and melanin synthesis increases upon sun exposure, which results in the brown colour of a suntan. In general, people from countries receiving a lot of sunlight, including countries of Africa, have more melanin in their skin

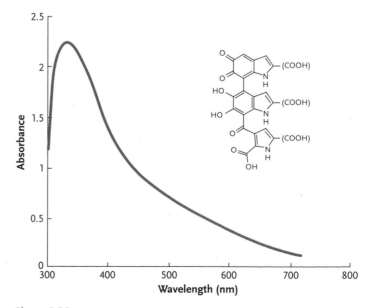

Figure 1.19
Absorption spectrum of melanin. A pure solution of melanin absorbs strongly in the ultraviolet region (300–400 nm) of the spectrum. Also shown is a portion of the chemical structure of melanin.

Figure 1.20

People differ in the amount of melanin in their skin cells.

than people from regions receiving less direct sunlight, such as Scandinavian countries **(Figure 1.20)**. Since melanin protects us from ultraviolet light, why don't all humans have high melanin levels? Although melanin filters out damaging ultraviolet wavelengths, humans require some ultraviolet radiation to synthesize vitamin D, which is critical for normal bone development. People with high melanin levels who live in regions that do not receive abundant sunlight are susceptible to vitamin D deficiency. This could occur, for example, for someone of African descent living in Winnipeg. However, in much of the developed world, vitamin D deficiency is rare because many foods, such as milk, yogurt, and grain products, are fortified with this essential nutrient.

STUDY BREAK

1. What biological molecule is particularly susceptible to damage by ultraviolet radiation?
2. What wavelengths of electromagnetic radiation does melanin absorb?

1.6 Using Light to Tell Time

As it revolves around the Sun once a year, Earth rotates on its axis once every 24 hours. These two motions give rise to very predictable changes to the light and temperature at Earth's surface. The two motions give rise to the seasons and day/night, respectively, and have been an almost inescapable influence on the evolution of all forms of life. The rhythmic and predictable nature of light and darkness during the 24 hour day has led to many physiological and behavioural phenomena that also display diurnal (*daily*) and seasonal rhythmicity.

1.6a Circadian Rhythms Are Controlled by a Biological Clock

The daily cycling of some biological phenomena is due simply to an organism responding to changes in sunlight. For example, photosynthesis and vision occur during the day and not in darkness because they both require photons of light. However, the diurnal cycling of other phenomena called **circadian** (*circa* = "around"; *diem* = "day") **rhythms** are quite different **(Figure 1.21)**. Circadian rhythms are not driven by an organism constantly detecting changes in daylight but rather are governed by an internal *biological clock* (also known as the circadian clock). Phenomena that are classified as circadian rhythms and thus are controlled by a biological clock include sleep-wake cycles, body temperature, metabolic processes, cell division, and the behaviours associated with foraging for food and mating.

A key attribute of all biological clocks is that while they are set by the external light environment, they can run along time independently of external conditions—a phenomenon called *free-running*. This is analogous to winding an old-fashioned wrist watch. Once it is wound it can function for a long time without being rewound. The free-running nature of circadian rhythms was first described in 1729 by the French astronomer Jean-Jacques d'Ortous de Mairan. He found that the daily rhythmic movements of certain plant leaves continued when he placed the plants in complete darkness. In humans, the free-running nature of circadian rhythms is shown by the fact that daily fluctuations in body temperature and hormone levels, for example, will occur even if an individual is subjected to conditions of constant light or darkness.

A key question we can ask at this stage is: what is the physical basis of a biological clock? A requirement

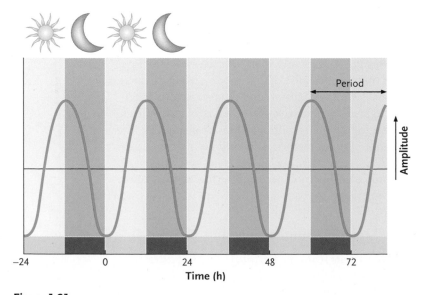

Figure 1.21

Circadian rhythms are oscillations in behaviour and physiology that have a period of approximately 24 hours. These rhythms are set by the external light environment but can run for some time (free-running) under constant conditions.

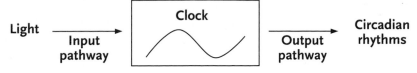

Figure 1.22
Model showing the components of circadian timekeeping. The clock is composed of a set of genes and proteins that oscillate in a very regular manner. Through an output pathway, the clock influences a wide range of behavioural and physiological phenomena. An input pathway ensures that the clock can be reset by changes to the external light environment.

of anything that keeps time is the presence of something that oscillates. In the case of a traditional clock or watch it's often a crystal, or pendulum (tick, tock, tick, tock…). By comparison, a biological clock is built around a small set of so-called clock genes and clock proteins. The expression of these genes and proteins is autoregulatory; that is, they control their own abundance, and this causes them to oscillate in activity in a very regular way—rising and falling over the course of the 24-hour day **(Figure 1.22)**. The oscillating nature of the clock is what in turn influences factors that control the circadian nature of various behaviours and physiological processes (Figure 1.22).

Circadian rhythms have been found in all organisms in which they have been searched for, including species from a diverse array of phyla such as bacteria, fungi, animals, and plants. The widespread occurrence of circadian rhythms suggests that there is a selective advantage to being able to tell time. So why are circadian rhythms and the use of an underlying biological clock an advantage? The presence of biological clocks enhances an organism's ability to survive under ever-changing environments by giving them the ability to anticipate or predict when a change will occur. This ability to predict change is seen as advantageous and increases survivability because it enables organisms to restrict their activities to specific, most beneficial, times of the day. Such activities include foraging for food, finding a mate, and avoiding predators, just to name a few. Let's work

through some specific examples. In insects, emergence as adults from the pupal case is under circadian control and occurs close to dawn. This time of the day is when the humidity in the air is highest, which is thought to prevent desiccation (drying out) of the insects, which in turn enhances their survival. In many organisms, proteins required for DNA replication are controlled by a biological clock and are synthesized at dusk. This allows for DNA replication to occur at night, which protects replicating DNA from damaging ultraviolet radiation during the day.

1.6b Biological Clocks Track the Changing Seasons

Not only are biological clocks central to diurnal behaviour and physiology, but they have also been shown to be critical to an organism's ability to keep track of the time of year. Organisms keep track of the changing seasons in part by being able to measure day length or *photoperiod*. Changes in day length and thus seasons occur because Earth is tilted on its axis as it orbits the Sun (see *The Purple Pages*). In Canada, the longest and shortest days of the year are June 21 and December 21, respectively.

Being able to determine the time of year assures that for both plants and animals certain phenomena occur under the most appropriate environmental conditions. This means that the onset of flowering occurs in the spring or summer for most angiosperm plant species, and that leaf drop followed by entrance into dormancy occurs in the autumn for trees. In animals, a huge range of phenomena are linked to being able to sense the time of year. Changes in photoperiod have been shown to provoke changes in colour of fur and feathers, and trigger migration, entry into hibernation, and changes in sexual behaviour **(Figure 1.23)**.

Figure 1.23
Changes in photoperiod trigger behavioural and developmental changes. Biological clocks keep track of day length, which is critical for organisms to ensure that specific events occur only at certain times of the year. Examples of photoperiod-dependent phenomena include leaf-drop in trees and colour change in the coat of the Arctic fox (*Vulpes lagopus*).

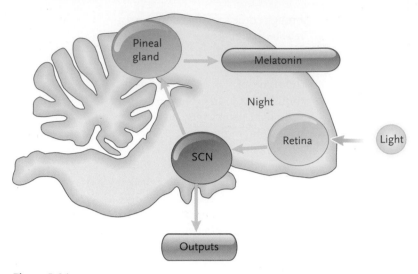

Figure 1.24
In humans the central timekeeping is found in the brain. The suprachiasmatic nucleus (SCN) within the brain is the central biological clock in humans. It is set by direct light input from the eye. It controls circadian rhythms directly through an output pathway or through the synthesis of the hormone melatonin by the pineal gland.

1.6c Jet Lag and the Need to Reset Biological Clocks

In animals, cells in a range of different tissues contain clock components that regulate localized circadian-controlled processes. However, most of these so-called peripheral clocks are set by a central biological clock that is found in a very small part of the brain, the suprachiasmatic nucleus (SCN) **(Figure 1.24)**. This central clock can receive direct light inputs through the optic nerve of the eye so that it can be reset periodically. The suprachiasmatic nucleus regulates the timing of clocks in peripheral tissues in part through the release during the night of the hormone melatonin from the pineal gland.

Several conditions can interfere with normal circadian cycling. Probably the best example is jet lag, which occurs when you travel rapidly east or west across many time zones, putting your circadian cycling out of synchronization with the external light environment. As an example, let's say you take an 8-hour flight from Paris to Toronto starting at 2 p.m. **(Figure 1.25)**. When you arrive in Toronto, your body feels like it is 10 p.m. and expects it to be dark. But because of the 6-hour time zone change, when you step off the plane it is only 4 p.m. and still daylight. The external light environment is out of synchronization with your internal biological clock. It is this confusion that results in the symptoms of jet lag, which can include lack of appetite, fatigue, insomnia, and mild depression. The clearly defined health effects of jet lag indicate that a range of behavioural and physiological processes are intimately linked to circadian timekeeping. It also shows that biological clocks cannot be automatically reset to new light conditions, but instead it often takes a few days to adjust. Poor synchronization between circadian clocks and the external light environment is a particular problem for shift workers (e.g., nurses, police officers, fire fighters), who usually alternate working a few weeks during the day followed by shifts at night. While there is growing evidence that this lack of synchronization is unhealthy, low-dosage melatonin treatment seems to help.

STUDY BREAK

1. What is the advantage in having biological clocks?
2. What is the cause of jet lag?

Figure 1.25
Jet lag. Flights over many time zones result in your biological clock becoming out of synchronization with the external light environment. This results in a number of unpleasant responses that are collectively referred to as jet lag. The effects subside as the clock within the suprachiasmatic nucleus is reset to the new light environment.

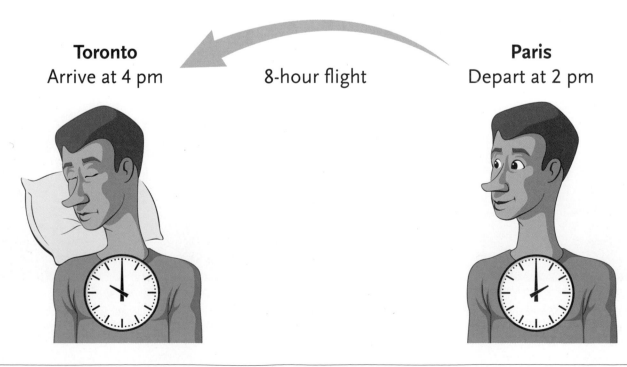

Toronto
Arrive at 4 pm

8-hour flight

Paris
Depart at 2 pm

1.7 The Role of Light in Behaviour and Ecology

Nature provides a great range of light environments, ranging from the total darkness of caves and the deep ocean to the stark brightness of deserts and polar regions. Differences in the intensity and spectral composition of the light coincide with an organism's adaptations to the specific light environment of a particular habitat. For many animals, it leads to unique colourations that may serve to attract members of the same species while making them potentially less visible to potential predators.

1.7a Using Colour as a Signal: Animals

In animals, bright colouration is thought to serve a valuable role in communication. Research suggests that what is most often communicated by the colouring is an individual's worth as a rival or as a mate. What remains unclear, and is currently being extensively studied, is what type of information is being conveyed and for which individuals the information is intended. A range of particularly colourful fish and bird species have become model systems used by ecologists investigating the role of colour in communication, while biochemists are interested in the chemistry of the actual pigments and how they are synthesized.

In the Eclectus parrot (*Eclectus roratus*), the female is more brightly coloured than the male **(Figure 1.26).** This is an exception to the general rule that the male of a species is usually more brightly coloured and therefore more conspicuous than the female. It has been shown in a number of species, including the European barn swallow (*Hirundo rustica rustica*), that more colourful males are more likely to find a mate. An interesting finding shown for penguins has been that for both males and females, individuals with brighter yellow colouring around the eye and upper chest were found to be older and healthier and able to raise more chicks in a given year than mating pairs that were less brightly coloured (Figure 1.26).

Not only does being brightly coloured make an animal more visible, research including the study on penguins indicates that it is also a sign of being in good health. In part, this finding is based on an understanding of the pigments used for ornamentation. Many of these belong to the carotenoid family—the structure of beta-carotene is shown in Figure 1.5, p. 5. Unlike in plants, where carotenoids are synthesized in plant cells from precursor molecules, the carotenoids used for colouring in birds are obtained from what they eat and circulate in the blood stream before being deposited in feathers. Biochemical studies have shown that carotenoids play an important role in breaking

Figure 1.26
Coloured plumage of four avian species often used in studies of the role of colour in behaviour. Clockwise from top left: Eclectus parrot (*Eclectus rotatus*) showing a green male and red female, European barn swallow (*Hirundo rustica rustica*), Red-winged blackbird (*Agelaius phoeniceus*), and King penguin (*Aptenodytes patagonicus*).

down potentially harmful reactive oxygen species. Thus, more brightly coloured individuals suggest a good diet rich in molecules that maintain good health. Besides carotenoids, different types of melanin-based pigments are also found in darker and brown colourations in birds. Finally, the dominant pigment class found in parrots, psittacofulvins, is found nowhere else in nature.

1.7b Using Colour as a Signal: Plants

Although humans marvel at the diversity of colours and patterns of flowers, botanists correctly concluded centuries ago that such displays were not designed to please humans but rather to attract pollinators. Pollination involves the movement of pollen from the anthers (male parts) of one flower to the stigma (female parts) of the same or other flowers to effect fertilization and production of fruit and seeds. Plant reproduction, including pollination, is discussed in more detail in Chapter 29. The goal of an insect or bird visiting a flower is not to effect pollination, it is to obtain food. This reward may be the protein-rich pollen itself, the sugar-rich nectar, or the waxes or resins found in the flower.

Plants that use animals as pollinators must attract the correct candidates to ensure efficient pollination, in part because the excess pollen, nectar, or can be energetically costly for the plant to produce. The

Figure 1.27
Flowering plants and their animal pollinators.

more attractive to specific groups of potential pollinators **(Figure 1.27)**. For example, the food reward of the flower has become an important part of the pollinator's diet, and the colour and shape of the flower coincide with the visual preferences and shape of the animal pollinator, respectively. As well, co-evolution has resulted in the breeding time of the animal often matching the flowering time of the plant.

The visual systems of pollinators differ considerably among broad groupings such as bees, bats, and birds. Thus, co-evolution has led to flower colour as a key factor that attracts specific groups of pollinators. For example, whereas hummingbirds can perceive colour across a broad range of wavelengths, bees are unable to see red. This explains why hummingbirds dominate the pollination of red-coloured flowers, whereas bees are attracted primarily to blue and yellow flowers. In addition, bees and some other insects can also see in the ultraviolet region of the electromagnetic spectrum and are particularly attracted to flowers that strongly reflect ultraviolet radiation. The role of ultraviolet light in flower–pollinator interactions is widely studied and has been aided by the development of photographic approaches that readily capture the ultraviolet radiation reflected off flowers. It is striking how different flowers look that were photographed using this technique compared to flowers photographed using visible wavelengths. The organization of distinct ultraviolet-reflecting pigments reveals patterning that is undetectable to humans. In general, it is shown that the region around the anthers and stigma is darker and thus more easily detected by the pollinating insects **(Figure 1.28)**.

dependence of a specific plant species on certain animals to act as pollinators, and the reliance of certain animals on particular flowers as a food source, has led to the co-evolution of flower–pollinator associations. Mentioned in the 1877 publication *Fertilisation of Orchids* by Charles Darwin, co-evolution refers to the fact that over evolutionary time, a change in one species triggers changes in the other. The result is that specifics of flower shape, colour, and smell make them

Figure 1.28
Two species of flowering plants (angiosperms) that are pollinated by bees. *Oenothera biennis* (top) and *Ranunculus ficaria* (bottom). Photographs capturing visible light are shown on the left, while photographs capturing only ultraviolet light are on the right.

a.

b.

c.

M.B. Fenton

Figure 1.29
From a distance, **(a)** it is easy to overlook the duck (*Anas* spp.) sitting on her nest in an urban graveyard. Up close **(b),** the pattern on her feathers breaks up her body outline, making her difficult to see, particularly when she does not move. As usual, looking for eyes can be a good way to see animals you otherwise might have overlooked, such as the Scops owl **(c)** (*Otus scops*).

1.7c Camouflage

Camouflage is a way of hiding that, in the natural world, usually involves an organism having a similar appearance to its environment. The reason for camouflage is concealment from either predators or prey. Besides simple colour, pattern and behaviour play central roles in camouflage **(Figure 1.29)**.

An excellent example of the development of camouflage is demonstrated by the peppered moth, *Biston betularia*. Before the Industrial Revolution in England, light-coloured peppered moths were far more common than the dark-coloured individuals that were prized by moth collectors. Light colour made the moths inconspicuous when resting on lichen-covered tree trunks during the day **(Figure 1.30, p. 20)**. The situation changed after the Industrial Revolution, when many tree trunks became dark-coloured from deposits of soot and air pollution killed the lichens. In this setting, light-coloured moths were easily detected by hunting birds, and dark-coloured individuals quickly became the most common form (Figure 1.30, p. 20). Today, as a result of clean-air legislation and reduced air pollution, the ratio of light- to dark-coloured moths has returned to the pre-Industrial Revolution norm in some areas.

The case of the peppered moth has become an often-cited example of evolution by natural selection, which is discussed further in Chapter 17.

1.7d Ecological Light Pollution

The electric light bulb is considered one of the greatest inventions because it allowed people to carry on pursuits at night that otherwise would not have been possible. However, the rapid proliferation of artificial lighting that illuminates public buildings, streets, and signs has resulted in light pollution, which has transformed the night-time environment over significant portions of Earth's surface **(Figure 1.31, p. 20)**. For example, in the United States, only about 40% of people live in an area that truly gets dark at night.

Ecologists have begun to study the sometimes devastating consequences of light pollution on natural populations. The presence of artificial light disrupts orientation in nocturnal animals otherwise accustomed to operating in the dark. For example, newly hatched sea turtles emerge from nests on sandy beaches and orient themselves and move toward the ocean because it is brighter than the silhouette of dark dunes. However, with increased beachfront lighting,

Figure 1.30
An example of camouflage in the peppered moth, *Biston betularia*. The moth is found in one of two forms: light-coloured and dark-coloured. During the industrial revolution, pollution darkened the bark of the trees **(a)** that were part of the moth's habitat. This resulted in increased predation of the light-coloured moth. Following antipollution measures, trees returned to being light-coloured **(b)**, which resulted in an increase in the numbers of the moths that are similarly coloured.

Figure 1.31
An example of light pollution.

hatchlings become disoriented, head inland, and die. The nocturnal lives of other animals, including many species of frogs and salamanders, have been disrupted by light pollution. As well, artificial lighting has a negative effect on migrating birds as hundreds of thousands of migrating birds are killed each year when they collide with lighted buildings and towers. Other animals, such as bats and geckos, benefit from night lights that attract insects, effectively concentrating their prey.

STUDY BREAK

1. What is a potential advantage for a parrot in being brightly coloured?
2. Explain the environmental events that drove the colour change in the peppered moth.

1.8 Life in the Dark

Humans see very well during the day, but our visual acuity quickly falters when night approaches. With decreasing light levels, we first lose our ability to see colour, followed by our ability to distinguish shapes. This is because rod photoreceptors, which do not perceive different colours, are about 100 times as sensitive to light as cone photoreceptors (see Chapter 37 for more on this topic).

Animals that are nocturnal (active at night), or live in low-light conditions, often display improved visual acuity under low-light conditions compared to animals that are active during the day. A good example of a nocturnal animal is the Philippine tarsier (*Tarsius syrichta*), one of the smallest primates **(Figure 1.32)**.

Figure 1.32
Philippine tarsier (*Tarsius syrichta*).

Improved vision is often a consequence of simply having large eyes and thus being able to collect more photons, which is certainly the case for the tarsier as well as the giant squid (genus *Architeuthis*), which has eyes that measure over 30 cm in diameter! Deep-water crustaceans as well as nocturnal insects have specially designed compound eyes that enhance their light-gathering ability.

In some environments, such as caves and ocean depths, animals live in complete darkness. In fact over 90% of the ocean is at a depth where no light penetrates. Many of the animals that have become adapted to these environments cannot see even though their ancestors may have had functional eyes. A great example of this is the blind mole rat (genus *Spalax*), which spends all of its life in underground darkness, only rarely venturing above ground **(Figure 1.33)**. Twenty-five million years of adaptation to life in the dark has resulted in the natural degeneration of the *Spalax* visual system to the point that it is effectively blind. Their eyes are not only small (less than 1 mm in diameter), but they are also covered by several layers of tissue. Behavioural and physiological studies have shown that the photoreceptors of the eye remain functional even though the image-forming part of the brain is dramatically reduced. So what purpose do these functional photoreceptors have? Since individual mole rats are exposed to brief periods of natural light, it is thought that the maintenance of functional photoreceptors allows for the proper setting of biological clocks necessary for the regulation of circadian rhythms. This is supported by the finding that while the image-forming portion of the brain is small, the suprachiasmatic nucleus (see Section 1.6) is well developed.

Another good example of the degeneration of the eye over time is found in the Mexican cavefish, which occurs as two morphological types: a surface-water form that has eyes and skin pigment and a cave-dwelling form that lacks eyes and pigment **(Figure 1.34)**. The ancestors of the cavefish lived on the surface, and both eyes and pigment have been lost over approximately 10 000 years.

a.

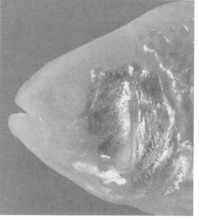

b.

Figure 1.34

An example of eye degeneration in the Mexican cave fish, *Astyanax mexicanus*. The single species exists as a surface-dwelling form **(a)** and a blind cave-dwelling form **(b)**.

Reprinted by permission from Macmillan Publishers Ltd: NATURE, Yoshiyuki Yamamoto, David W. Stock and William R. Jeffery, "Hedgehog signalling controls eye cegeneration in blind cavefish," vol. 431, 844–847, copyright 2004.

STUDY BREAK

1. Why do you think that the blind mole rat is still able to detect light?

1.9 Organisms Making Their Own Light: Bioluminescence

Many organisms, including certain bacteria, algae, fungi, insects, squid, and fish, are able to make their own light, a process called bioluminescence **(Figure 1.35, p. 22)**. Recall from Section 1.1 that in the process of light absorption by a pigment, the energy of a photon is transferred to an electron, raising it from the ground state to an excited state. Bioluminescence is essentially the same process in reverse (see Figure 1.35, p. 22). Chemical energy in the form of ATP is used to excite an electron in a substrate molecule from the ground state to a higher excited state, and when the electron returns to the ground state, the energy is released as a photon of light. The conversion of the chemical energy in ATP into light is very efficient. Considering that up to 95% of the

Hoberman Collection UK/Photolibrary

Figure 1.33

The blind mole rat (*Spalax* sp.) is subterranean and rarely ventures above ground. It is functionally blind.

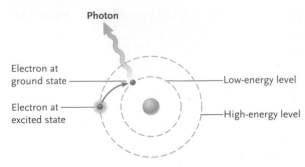

Figure 1.35

Bioluminescence. Chemical energy is used to excite an electron in a molecule. A photon of light is released when the electron decays back down to the ground state.

energy of a light bulb is lost as heat, it is remarkable that less than 5% of the energy in ATP is lost as heat during the process of bioluminescent light production. This extraordinary efficiency is essential because high heat production would be incompatible with life.

Bioluminescent organisms generate light for a range of uses. These include attracting a mate or prey, camouflage, and communication. For example, dinoflagellates, which are unicellular algae, use bioluminescence as an alarm mechanism to scare off potential predators. In these tiny organisms, bioluminescence is triggered simply by a disturbance of the water surrounding them. When a predator such as a small fish swims close to a dinoflagellate at night, the resulting burst of light produced by all the dinoflagellates in the vicinity lights up the water around the fish. This defensive behaviour makes the fish clearly visible to its own predators.

Some marine bacteria use bioluminescence in a type of communication called *quorum*

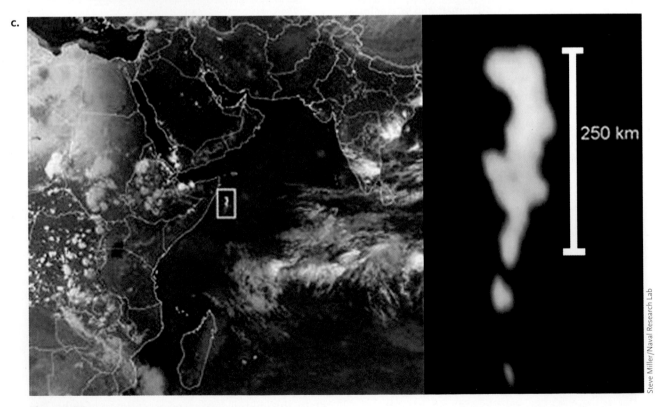

Figure 1.36

Examples of bioluminescence. **(a)** Bioluminescent insect. **(b)** Bioluminescent squid. **(c)** Satellite image of a "milky sea," a bloom of bioluminescent bacteria off the east coast of Africa.

sensing. Individual bacteria often release compounds into their environment at concentrations too low to elicit a response from their neighbours. However, as a bacterial population grows, its size reaches a threshold, a quorum, whereby the concentration of compounds is high enough to elicit a physiological response in all members of the population. The response results in the activation of certain genes, including those that encode for proteins required for bioluminescence. Quorum sensing is now believed to be the basis for what are termed "milky seas" (see **Figure 1.36**). This strange phenomenon of light on the surface of the ocean has been reported many times over the past several hundred years by sailors and is mentioned in Jules Verne's classic book *Twenty Thousand Leagues under the Sea.*

Many bioluminescent organisms are marine and are most abundant below 800 m, a depth to which sunlight does not penetrate. Bioluminescence has not been reported in land plants or higher vertebrates. Why is bioluminescence absent in these organisms? We do not yet have the answers to this or other questions about bioluminescence,

reminding us how much there is still to discover about life on Earth.

In closing, this introductory chapter discussed one phenomenon, light, and how it affects the biology of Earth. From absorption of a single photon by a pigment molecule in a single cell to affecting the composition of entire ecosystems, the influence of light spans all levels of biological organization. This chapter touched on many topics, from physics and chemistry, photosynthesis, genes and proteins, evolution and natural selection to ecology and behaviour. As you work through the remaining chapters of this textbook, you will learn much more about these topics.

STUDY BREAK

1. Compare and contrast bioluminescence with photon absorption.
2. Given that bioluminescence takes energy on the part of the organism, what are some roles that it may serve?

Review

  Access an interactive eBook, chapter-specific interactive learning tools, including flashcards, quizzes, videos, and more in your Biology CourseMate, accessed through NelsonBrain.com **Aplia™** is an online interactive learning solution that helps you improve comprehension—and your grade—by integrating a variety of mediums and tools such as videos, tutorials, practice tests, and an interactive eBook.

1.1 The Physical Nature of Light

- For organisms, light serves as a source of energy and as a source of information.
- Light can be defined as electromagnetic radiation that humans can detect with their eyes.
- Light can be thought of as a wave of discrete particles called photons.
- To be used, light energy must be absorbed by molecules called pigments.
- The colour of a pigment includes all wavelengths of light that are not absorbed.

1.2 Light as a Source of Energy

- The absorption of light by a pigment results in electrons becoming excited. This represents a source of potential energy.
- Photosynthesis is the dominant process on Earth that uses pigments to capture light energy and uses it to convert carbon dioxide into energy-rich carbohydrates.
- *Halobacteria* use the bacteriorhodopsin to harvest light energy and for the generation of ATP.

1.3 Light as a Source of Information

- A photoreceptor (e.g., rhodopsin) consists of a pigment molecule (retinal) bound to a protein (opsin).

- The *C. reinhardtii* eyespot allows the organism to sense both light direction and intensity and respond by swimming toward or away from the light (phototaxis).
- The eye can be defined as the organ animals use to sense light. Vision requires a brain to interpret signals sent from the eye.
- The simplest eye is the ocellus found in planarians. It enables the sensing of light direction and intensity.
- Image-forming eyes include compound eyes found in arthropods and single-lens eyes found in some invertebrates and most vertebrates, including humans.
- Because the eye was thought to be an organ of "extreme perfection," Darwin initially had a difficult time explaining how it could have arisen by evolution.
- The relatively rapid evolution of the eye is explained by the huge advantage an improved eye would give an organism.

1.4 The Uniqueness of Light

- Photosynthesis, vision, and most other light-driven processes use only a narrow band of the electromagnetic spectrum. This may be because shorter wavelengths are more harmful (higher energy) and longer wavelengths tend not to reach Earth's surface.

1.5 Light Can Damage Biological Molecules

- Light is a form of energy; thus the absorption of too much light can damage biological molecules.
- The photosynthetic apparatus is constantly being damaged by light and the damage repaired.
- Ultraviolet radiation, because of its high energy, is particularly harmful to biological molecules, particularly DNA.

- Human skin cells are protected by the pigment melanin that absorbs ultraviolet radiation.

1.6 Using Light to Tell Time

- Many physiological and behavioural responses are geared to the daily changes in light and darkness and are called circadian rhythms.
- Circadian rhythms are found in all forms of life and evolved to enable organisms to anticipate changes in the light environment.
- Jet lag is caused when your biological clock is out of synchronization with the external light environment.

1.7 The Role of Light in Ecology and Behaviour

- Many organisms use colour to attract, warn, or hide from other organisms.
- Bright colouration is thought to convey good health.

- The widespread use of artificial lighting has been shown to disrupt numerous biological phenomena, including bird migration and the orientation of nocturnal animals.

1.8 Life in the Dark

- Unlike humans, many nocturnal animals (moths, fish, bats, frogs) see very well under dim light conditions.
- Some animals, such as the blind mole rat, are functionally blind yet are descended from ancestors that had functional eyes.

1.9 Organisms Making Their Own Light: Bioluminescence

- A range of organisms can use chemical energy to make light— this is called bioluminescence.
- Bioluminescent organisms use light to attract a mate, for camouflage, to attract prey, or to communicate.

Questions

Self-Test Questions

1. Which of the following statements about light is correct?
   a. Like sound, light is a form of electromagnetic radiation.
   b. Light of a longer wavelength contains more energy.
   c. Visible light is more energetic than radio waves.
   d. A photon of red light contains more energy than a photon of blue light.

2. For a photon of light to be used by an organism what must occur?
   a. The photon must be absorbed.
   b. The photon must be reflected off a substance.
   c. The photon must interact with a protein in the plasma membrane.
   d. The photon must have sufficient energy to oxidize a molecule.

3. What are the components of a photoreceptor?
   a. a pigment molecule bound to a protein
   b. a protein that is involved in photosynthesis
   c. a group of many pigment molecules
   d. a molecule of chlorophyll

4. Which of the following is true for an eye, but NOT about the eyespot of *Chlamydomonas reinhardtii*?
   a. It can generate a image.
   b. It is composed of photoreceptors.
   c. It can detect changes in light intensity.
   d. It can activate a signal transduction pathway when it absorbs light.

5. Which of the following statements regarding the harmful effects of light is correct?
   a. Visible light is more harmful than ultraviolet light.
   b. Damage to the photosynthetic apparatus caused by excess light cannot be repaired.
   c. Melanin protects skins cells because it specifically absorbs ultraviolet light.
   d. Ultraviolet light specifically damages proteins.

6. Light represents only a very narrow region of the electromagnetic spectrum. However, why is it the dominant form of electromagnetic radiation that is used in biology?
   a. light contains the most energy per photon.
   b. light can excite electrons within molecules without destroying them.

   c. light is the only form of electromagnetic radiation to reach Earth's surface.
   d. All other wavelengths of electromagnetic radiation are too destructive to biological molecules.

7. Which of the following statements is correct about a biological process that is under circadian control?
   a. A mutation to a single gene could never destroy the circadian cycling of a biological process.
   b. The amplitude of the biological process oscillates with a period of approximately 12 hours.
   c. Circadian cycling of biological processes rarely follows the actual cycling of day and night.
   d. The oscillating nature of the phenomenon continues if the organism is placed in complete darkness.

8. Which of the following statements about jet lag is correct?
   a. Someone who is blind because of non-functioning optic nerves would still experience jetlag.
   b. Jetlag occurs even when the external environment and the SCN are synchronized.
   c. Taking melatonin pills would have no effect on experiencing jetlag.
   d. Jetlag is more severe after traveling by airplane from Toronto to Hawaii than from Toronto to Lima Peru.

9. Which of the following is illustrated by the Mexican cavefish?
   a. You don't need eyes for vision.
   b. Animals can still see in complete darkness.
   c. Eyes can still function without photoreceptors.
   d. Organs that are no longer of use can degenerate over time.

10. Which of the following is correct about bioluminescence?
    a. It requires ATP.
    b. It cannot occur in complete darkness.
    c. It is found only in bacteria and archaea.
    d. Like vision, it requires the absorption of a photon of light.

Questions for Discussion

1. Nothing can ruin a nice coloured shirt more than accidently adding bleach when washing it. What do you think bleach does?

2. In writing this chapter, the authors found it difficult to define the "eye." Why do you think this was difficult?

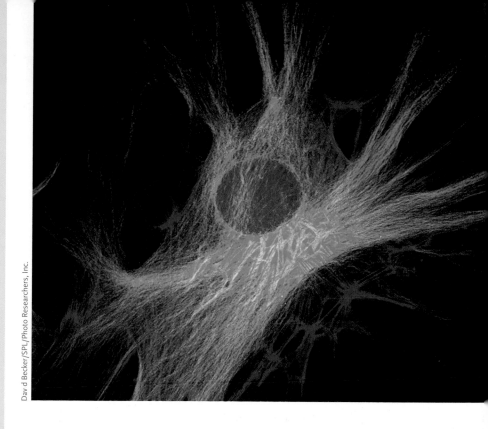

Cells fluorescently labelled to visualize their internal structure (confocal light micrograph). Cell nuclei are shown in blue and parts of the cytoskeleton in red and green.

David Becker/SPL/Photo Researchers, Inc.

STUDY PLAN

2.1   Basic Features of Cell Structure and Function

2.1a   Cells Are Small and Are Visualized Using a Microscope

2.1b   Cells Have a DNA-Containing Central Region That Is Surrounded by Cytoplasm

2.1c   Cells Occur in Prokaryotic and Eukaryotic Forms, Each with Distinctive Structures and Organization

2.2   Prokaryotic Cells

2.3   Eukaryotic Cells

2.3a   Eukaryotic Cells Have a True Nucleus and Cytoplasmic Organelles Enclosed within a Plasma Membrane

2.3b   The Eukaryotic Nucleus Contains Much More DNA Than the Prokaryotic Nucleoid

2.3c   Eukaryotic Ribosomes Are Either Free in the Cytosol or Attached to Membranes

2.3d   An Endomembrane System Divides the Cytoplasm into Functional and Structural Compartments

2.3e   Mitochondria Are the Organelles in Which Cellular Respiration Occurs

2.3f   The Cytoskeleton Supports and Moves Cell Structures

2.3g   Flagella Propel Cells, and Cilia Move Materials over the Cell Surface

2.4   Specialized Structures of Plant Cells

2.4a   Chloroplasts Are Biochemical Factories Powered by Sunlight

2.4b   Central Vacuoles Have Diverse Roles in Storage, Structural Support, and Cell Growth

2.4c   Cell Walls Support and Protect Plant Cells

2.5   The Animal Cell Surface

2.5a   Cell Adhesion Molecules Organize Animal Cells into Tissues and Organs

2.5b   Cell Junctions Reinforce Cell Adhesions and Provide Avenues of Communication

2.5c   The Extracellular Matrix Organizes the Cell Exterior

2   The Cell: An Overview

WHY IT MATTERS

In the mid-1600s, Robert Hooke, Curator of Instruments for the Royal Society of England, was at the forefront of studies applying the newly invented light microscopes to biological materials. When Hooke looked at thinly sliced cork from a mature tree through a microscope, he observed tiny compartments **(Figure 2.1a, p. 26)**. He gave them the Latin name *cellulae,* meaning "small rooms"—hence the origin of the biological term *cell.* Hooke was actually looking at the walls of dead cells, which is what cork consists of.

Reports of cells also came from other sources. By the late 1600s, Anton van Leeuwenhoek **(Figure 2.1b, p. 26),** a Dutch shopkeeper, observed "many very little animalcules, very prettily a-moving" using a single-lens microscope of his own construction. Leeuwenhoek discovered and described diverse protists, sperm cells, and even bacteria, organisms so small that they would not be seen by others for another two centuries.

In the 1820s, improvements in microscopes brought cells into sharper focus. Robert Brown, an English botanist, noticed a discrete, spherical body inside some cells; he called it a *nucleus.* In 1838, a German botanist, Matthias Schleiden, speculated that the nucleus

a. Hooke's microscope   **b. Leeuwenhoek and microscope**

Figure 2.1

Investigations leading to the first descriptions of cells. **(a)** The cork cells drawn by Robert Hooke and the compound microscope he used to examine them. **(b)** Anton van Leeuwenhoek holding his microscope, which consisted of a single, small sphere of glass fixed in a holder. He viewed objects by holding them close to one side of the glass sphere and looking at them through the other side.

had something to do with the development of a cell. The following year, the zoologist Theodor Schwann of Germany expanded Schleiden's idea to propose that all animals and plants consist of cells that contain a nucleus. He also proposed that even when a cell forms part of a larger organism, it has an individual life of its own. However, an important question remained: Where do cells come from? A decade later, the German physiologist Rudolf Virchow answered this question. From his studies of cell growth and reproduction, Virchow proposed that cells arise only from pre-existing cells by a process of division.

Thus, by the middle of the nineteenth century, microscopic observations had yielded three profound generalizations, which together constitute what is now known as the **cell theory**:

1. All organisms are composed of one or more cells.
2. The cell is the basic structural and functional unit of all living organisms.
3. Cells arise only from the division of pre-existing cells.

These tenets were fundamental to the development of biological science.

This chapter provides an overview of our current understanding of the structure and functions of cells, emphasizing both the similarities among all cells and some of the most basic differences among cells of various organisms. The variations in cells that help make particular groups of organisms distinctive are

discussed in later chapters. This chapter also introduces some of the modern microscopes that enable us to learn more about cell structure.

2.1 Basic Features of Cell Structure and Function

As the basic structural and functional units of all living organisms, cells carry out the essential processes of life. They contain highly organized systems of molecules, including the nucleic acids DNA and RNA, which carry hereditary information and direct the manufacture of cellular molecules. Cells use chemical molecules or light as energy sources for their activities. Cells also respond to changes in their external environment by altering their internal reactions. Further, cells duplicate and pass on their hereditary information as part of cellular reproduction. All of these activities occur in cells that, in most cases, are invisible to the naked eye.

Some types of organisms, including almost all bacteria and archaea; some protists, such as amoebas; and some fungi, such as yeasts, are unicellular. Each of these cells is a functionally independent organism capable of carrying out all activities necessary for its life. In more complex multicellular organisms, including plants and animals, the activities of life are divided among varying numbers of specialized cells. However, individual cells of multicellular organisms are potentially capable of surviving by themselves if placed in a chemical medium that can sustain them. If cells are broken open, the property of life is lost: they are unable to grow, reproduce, or respond to outside stimuli in a coordinated, potentially independent fashion. This fact confirms the second tenet of the cell theory: Life as we know it does not exist in units simpler than individual cells.

2.1a Cells Are Small and Are Visualized Using a Microscope

As discussed in more detail in Chapter 3 and subsequent chapters, all forms of life are grouped into one of three domains: the Bacteria, the Archaea, and the Eukarya. Until very recently, bacteria and archaea were grouped into a single domain: the Prokaryota (prokaryotes); however, this domain is no longer considered to be accurate as recent research has shown that bacteria and archaea are not evolutionarily related.

As shown in **Figure 2.2**, cells representing all three domains of life assume a wide variety of forms. Individual cells range in size from tiny bacteria to an egg yolk, a single cell that can be several centimetres in diameter. Yet, all cells are organized according to the same basic plan, and all have structures that perform similar activities.

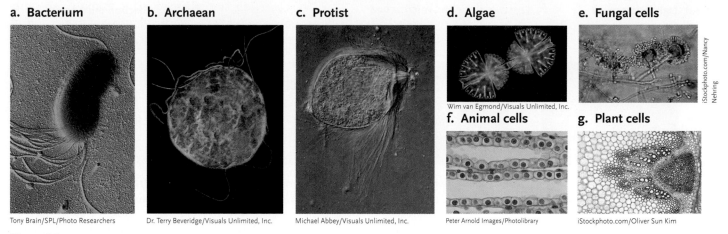

a. Bacterium **b. Archaean** **c. Protist** **d. Algae** **e. Fungal cells**

f. Animal cells **g. Plant cells**

Wim van Egmond/Visuals Unlimited, Inc.

iStockphoto.com/Nancy Nehring

Tony Brain/SPL/Photo Researchers   Dr. Terry Beveridge/Visuals Unlimited, Inc.   Michael Abbey/Visuals Unlimited, Inc.   Peter Arnold Images/Photolibrary   iStockphoto.com/Oliver Sun Kim

Figure 2.2

Examples of the various kinds of cells. **(a)** A bacterial cell with flagella, *Pseudomonas fluorescens*. **(b)** An archaean, the extremophile *Sulfolobus acidocaldarius*. **(c)** *Trichonympha*, a protist that lives in a termite's gut. **(d)** Two cells of *Micrasterias*, an algal protist. **(e)** Fungal cells of the bread mould *Aspergillus*. **(f)** Cells of a surface layer in the human kidney. **(g)** Cells in the stem of a sunflower, *Helianthus annuus*.

Most cells are too small to be seen by the unaided eye: Humans cannot see objects smaller than about 0.1 mm in diameter. The smallest bacteria have diameters of about 0.5 µm (a micrometre is one thousandth of a millimetre). The cells of multicellular animals range from about 5 to 30 µm in diameter. Your red blood cells are 7 to 8 µm across—a string of 2500 of these cells is needed to span the width of your thumbnail. Plant cells range from about 10 µm to a few hundred micrometres in diameter. (**Figure 2.3** explains the units of measurement used in biology to study molecules and cells.)

To see cells and the structures within them we use **microscopy**, a technique for producing visible images of objects, biological or otherwise, that are too small to be seen by the human eye (**Figure 2.4, p. 28**). The instrument of microscopy is the **microscope**. The two common types of microscopes are **light microscopes**, which use light to illuminate the specimen (the object being viewed), and **electron microscopes**, which use electrons to illuminate the specimen. Different types of microscopes give different magnification and resolution of the specimen. Just as for a camera or a pair of binoculars, **magnification** is the ratio of the object as viewed to its real size, usually given as something like 1200:3. Resolution is the minimum distance by which two points in the specimen can be separated and still be seen as two points. Resolution depends primarily on the wavelength of light or electrons used to illuminate the specimen: the shorter the wavelength, the better the resolution. Hence, electron microscopes have higher resolution than light microscopes. Biologists choose the type of microscopy technique based on what they need to see in the specimen; selected examples are shown in Figure 2.4.

Why are most cells so small? The answer depends partly on the change in the surface area-to-volume ratio of an object as its size increases (**Figure 2.5, p. 29**). For example, doubling the diameter of a cell multiplies its volume by eight but multiplies its surface area by only four. The significance of this relationship is that the

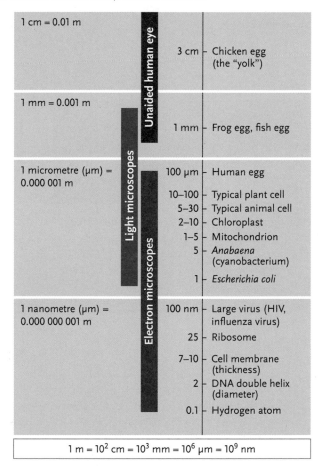

1 cm = 0.01 m

Unaided human eye

3 cm — Chicken egg (the "yolk")

1 mm = 0.001 m

1 mm — Frog egg, fish egg

1 micrometre (µm) = 0.000 001 m

Light microscopes

100 µm — Human egg
10–100 — Typical plant cell
5–30 — Typical animal cell
2–10 — Chloroplast
1–5 — Mitochondrion
5 — *Anabaena* (cyanobacterium)
1 — *Escherichia coli*

1 nanometre (µm) = 0.000 000 001 m

Electron microscopes

100 nm — Large virus (HIV, influenza virus)
25 — Ribosome
7–10 — Cell membrane (thickness)
2 — DNA double helix (diameter)
0.1 — Hydrogen atom

$1 \text{ m} = 10^2 \text{ cm} = 10^3 \text{ mm} = 10^6 \text{ µm} = 10^9 \text{ nm}$

Figure 2.3

Units of measure and the ranges in which they are used in the study of molecules and cells. The vertical scale in each box is logarithmic.

volume of a cell determines the amount of chemical activity that can take place within it, whereas the surface area determines the amount of substances that can be exchanged between the inside of the cell and the outside environment. Nutrients must constantly enter cells, and wastes must constantly leave; however, past a certain point, increasing the diameter of a cell gives a surface area that is insufficient to maintain an adequate nutrient–waste exchange for its entire volume.

Some cells increase their ability to exchange materials with their surroundings by flattening or by

Light microscopy

Micrographs are of the protist *Paramecium*.

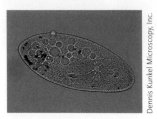

Bright field microscopy:
Light passes directly through the specimen. Many cell structures have insufficient contrast to be discerned. Staining with a dye is used to enhance contrast in a specimen, as shown here, but this treatment usually fixes and kills the cells.

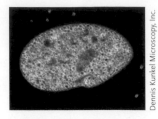

Dark field microscopy:
Light illuminates the specimen at an angle, and only light scattered by the specimen reaches the viewing lens of the microscope. This gives a bright image of the cell against a black background.

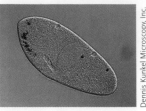

Phase-contrast microscopy:
Differences in refraction (the way light is bent) caused by variations in the density of the specimen are visualized as differences in contrast. Otherwise invisible structures are revealed with this technique, and living cells in action can be photographed or filmed.

Transmission electron microscopy (TEM): A beam of electrons is focused on a thin section of a specimen in a vacuum. Electrons that pass through form the image; structures that scatter electrons appear dark. TEM is used primarily to examine structures within cells. Various staining and fixing methods are used to highlight structures of interest.

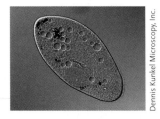

Nomarski (differential interference contrast):
Similar to phase-contrast microscopy, special lenses enhance differences in density, giving a cell a 3D appearance.

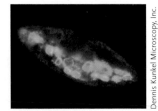

Fluorescence microscopy:
Different structures or molecules in cells are stained with specific fluorescent dyes. The stained structures or molecules fluoresce when the microscope illuminates them with ultraviolet light, and their locations are seen by viewing the emitted visible light.

Confocal laser scanning microscopy: Lasers scan across a fluorescently stained specimen, and a computer focuses the light to show a single plane through the cell. This provides a sharper 3D image than other light microscopy techniques.

Scanning electron microscopy (SEM): A beam of electrons is scanned across a whole cell or organism, and the electrons excited on the specimen surface are converted to a 3D-appearing image.

Figure 2.4
Different techniques of light and electron microscopy. Each technique produces images that reveal different structures or functions of the specimen. A micrograph is a photograph of an image formed by a microscope.

developing surface folds or extensions that increase their surface area. For example, human intestinal cells have closely packed, fingerlike extensions that increase their surface area, which greatly enhances their ability to absorb digested food molecules.

2.1b Cells Have a DNA-Containing Central Region That Is Surrounded by Cytoplasm

All cells are bounded by the **plasma membrane**, a bilayer made of lipids with embedded protein molecules **(Figure 2.6)**. The lipid bilayer is a hydrophobic barrier to the passage of water-soluble substances, but selected water-soluble substances can penetrate cell membranes through transport protein channels. The selective movement of ions and water-soluble molecules through the transport proteins maintains the specialized internal ionic and molecular environments required for cellular life. (Membrane structure and functions are discussed further in Chapter 5.)

The central region of all cells contains DNA molecules, which store hereditary information. The hereditary information is organized in the form of *genes*—segments of DNA that code for individual

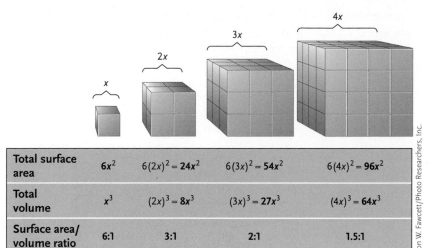

	x	$2x$	$3x$	$4x$
Total surface area	$6x^2$	$6(2x)^2 = \mathbf{24}x^2$	$6(3x)^2 = \mathbf{54}x^2$	$6(4x)^2 = \mathbf{96}x^2$
Total volume	x^3	$(2x)^3 = \mathbf{8}x^3$	$(3x)^3 = \mathbf{27}x^3$	$(4x)^3 = \mathbf{64}x^3$
Surface area/volume ratio	6:1	3:1	2:1	1.5:1

Don W. Fawcett/Photo Researchers, Inc.

Figure 2.5

Relationship between surface area and volume. The surface area of an object increases as the square of the linear dimension, whereas the volume increases as the cube of that dimension.

proteins. The central region also contains proteins that help maintain the DNA structure and enzymes that duplicate DNA and copy its information into RNA.

All parts of the cell between the plasma membrane and the central region make up the **cytoplasm**. The cytoplasm contains the *organelles,* the *cytosol,* and the *cytoskeleton.* The **organelles** ("little organs") are small, organized structures important for cell function. The **cytosol** is an aqueous (water) solution containing ions and various organic molecules. The **cytoskeleton** is a protein-based framework of filamentous structures that, among other things, helps maintain proper cell shape and plays key roles in cell division and chromosome segregation from cell generation to cell generation. The cytoskeleton was once thought to be specific to eukaryotes, but recent research has shown that all major eukaryotic cytoskeletal proteins have functional equivalents in prokaryotes.

Many of the cell's vital activities occur in the cytoplasm, including the synthesis and assembly of most of the molecules required for growth and reproduction (except those made in the central region) and the conversion of chemical and light energy into forms that can be used by cells. The cytoplasm also conducts stimulatory signals from the outside into the cell interior and carries out chemical reactions that respond to these signals.

2.1c Cells Occur in Prokaryotic and Eukaryotic Forms, Each with Distinctive Structures and Organization

There are two fundamentally different types of cells: prokaryotic (*pro* = before; *karyon* = nucleus) and eukaryotic. As we discussed earlier in this chapter, the term *prokaryote* to describe a unique group of evolutionarily related organisms has fallen out of use by microbiologists as bacteria and archaea are seen as evolutionarily distinct. However, the term *prokaryotic cell* is still used as it refers not to a single group of organisms but rather to a particular cell architecture, that is, one lacking a nucleus. Within the prokaryotic cell that is a characteristic of both bacteria and archaea, the DNA-containing central region of the cell, the **nucleoid**, has no boundary membrane separating it from the cytoplasm. Many species of archaea and bacteria contain few if any internal membranes, but a number of other species of both groups contain extensive internal membranes.

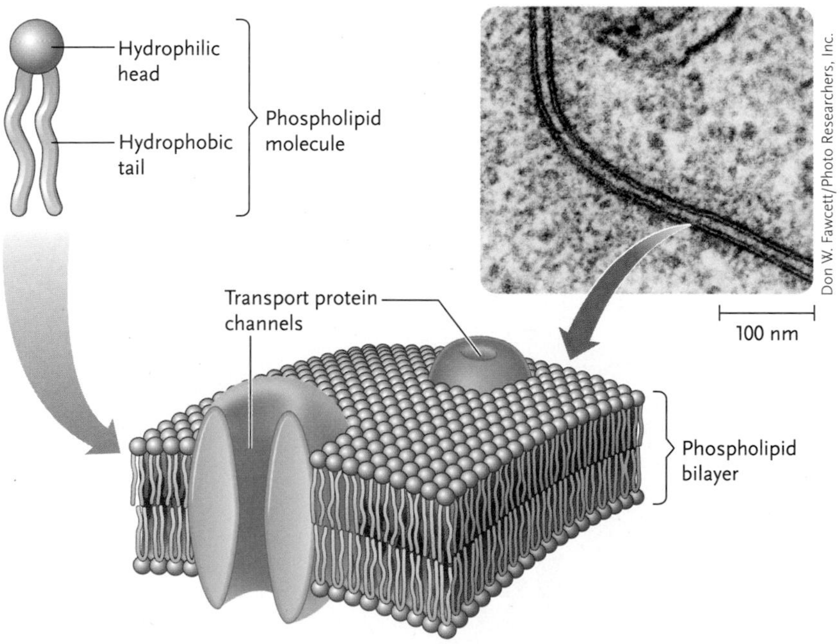

Hydrophilic head

Hydrophobic tail

Phospholipid molecule

Transport protein channels

Don W. Fawcett/Photo Researchers, Inc.

100 nm

Phospholipid bilayer

Figure 2.6

The plasma membrane consists of a phospholipid bilayer, an arrangement of phospholipids two molecules thick, which provides the framework for all biological membranes. Water-soluble substances cannot pass through the phospholipid part of the membrane. Instead, they pass through protein channels in the membrane; two proteins that transport substances across the membrane are shown. Other types of proteins are also associated with the plasma membrane. (*Inset*) Electron micrograph showing the plasma membranes of two adjacent animal cells.

The **eukaryotes** (*eu* = true) make up the domain Eukarya and are defined by having cells where DNA is contained within a membrane-bound compartment called the **nucleus**. The cytoplasm of eukaryotic cells typically contains extensive membrane systems that form organelles with their own distinct environments and specialized functions. As in archaea and bacteria, a plasma membrane surrounds eukaryotic cells as the outer limit of the cytoplasm.

The remainder of this chapter surveys the components of prokaryotic and eukaryotic cells in more detail.

STUDY BREAK

What is the plasma membrane, and what are its main functions?

2.2 Prokaryotic Cells

Most prokaryotic cells are relatively small, usually not much more than a few micrometres in length and a micrometre or less in diameter. A typical human cell has about 10 times the diameter and over 8000 times the volume of an average prokaryotic cell.

The three shapes most common among prokaryotes are spherical, rodlike, and spiral. *Escherichia coli* (*E. coli*), a normal inhabitant of the mammalian intestine that has been studied extensively as a model organism in genetics, molecular biology, and genomics research, is rod-like in shape. **Figure 2.7** shows an electron micrograph and a diagram of *E. coli* to illustrate the basic features of prokaryotic cell structure. More detail about prokaryotic cell structure and function, as well as about the diversity of prokaryotic organisms, is presented in Chapter 20.

The genetic material of archaea and bacteria is located in the nucleoid; in an electron microscope, that region of the cell is seen to contain a highly folded mass of DNA (see Figure 2.7). For most species, the DNA is a single, circular molecule that unfolds when released from the cell. This DNA molecule is the **prokaryotic chromosome**, the organization and regulation of which are detailed in Chapters 13 and 14.

Individual genes in the DNA molecule encode the information required to make proteins. This information is copied into a type of RNA molecule called *messenger RNA* (mRNA). Small, roughly spherical particles in the cytoplasm, the **ribosomes**, use the information in the mRNA to assemble amino acids into proteins. A prokaryotic ribosome consists of a large and a small subunit, each formed from a combination of *ribosomal RNA* (rRNA) and protein molecules. Each prokaryotic ribosome contains three types of rRNA molecules, which are also copied from the DNA, and more than 50 proteins.

In almost all prokaryotic cells, the plasma membrane is surrounded by a rigid external layer of material, the cell wall, which ranges in thickness from 15 to 100 nm or more (a nanometre is one-billionth of a metre). The **cell wall** provides rigidity to prokaryotic cells and, with the capsule, protects the cell from physical damage. In many prokaryotic cells, the wall is coated with an external layer of polysaccharides called

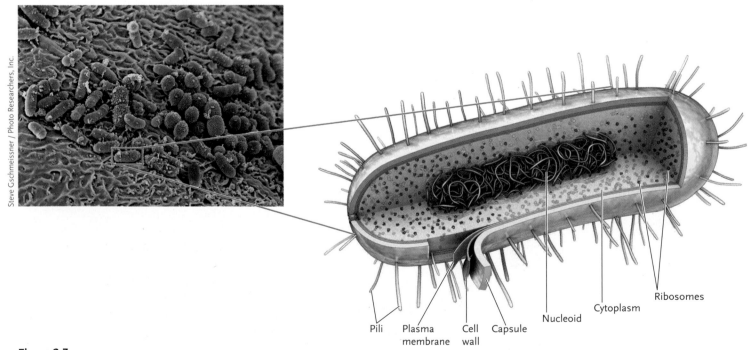

Steve Gschmeissner / Photo Researchers, Inc.

Pili Plasma membrane Cell wall Capsule Nucleoid Cytoplasm Ribosomes

Figure 2.7

Prokaryotic cell structure. An electron micrograph (left) and a diagram (right) of the bacterium *Escherichia coli*. The pili extending from the cell wall attach bacterial cells to other cells of the same species or to eukaryotic cells as a part of infection. A typical *E. coli* has four flagella.

the **glycocalyx** (a "sugar coating" from *glykys* = sweet; *calyx* = cup or vessel). When the glycocalyx is diffuse and loosely associated with the cells, it is a **slime layer**; when it is gelatinous and more firmly attached to cells, it is a **capsule**. The glycocalyx helps protect prokaryotic cells from physical damage and desiccation and may enable a cell to attach to a surface, such as other prokaryotic cells (as in forming a colony), eukaryotic cells (as in *Streptococcus pneumoniae* attaching to lung cells), or nonliving substrate (such as a rock).

The plasma membrane itself performs several vital functions in both bacteria and archaea. Besides transporting materials into and out of the cells, it contains most of the molecular systems that metabolize food molecules into the chemical energy of ATP. In photosynthetic bacteria, the molecules that absorb light energy and convert it to the chemical energy of ATP are also associated with the plasma membrane or with internal, saclike membranes derived from the plasma membrane.

Many prokaryotic species contain few if any internal membranes; in such cells, most cellular functions occur either on the plasma membrane or in the cytoplasm. But some archaea and bacteria have more extensive internal membrane structures. For example, photosynthetic bacteria have complex layers of intracellular membranes formed by invaginations of the plasma membrane on which photosynthesis takes place.

As mentioned earlier, prokaryotic cells have filamentous cytoskeletal structures with functions similar to those in eukaryotes. Prokaryotic cytoskeletons play important roles in creating and maintaining the proper shape of cells, in cell division and, for certain bacteria, in determining the polarity of the cells.

Many bacteria and archaeans can move through liquids and across wet surfaces. Most commonly they do so using long, threadlike protein fibres called **flagella** (singular, *flagellum* = whip), which extend from the cell surface (see Figure 2.2a, p. 27). The **bacterial flagellum**, which is helically shaped, rotates in a socket in the plasma membrane and cell wall to push the cell through a liquid medium (see Chapter 20). In *E. coli,* for instance, rotating bundles of flagella propel the bacterium. Archaeal flagella function similarly to bacterial flagella, but the two types differ significantly in their structures and mechanisms of action. Both types of prokaryotic flagella are also fundamentally different from the much larger and more complex flagella of eukaryotic cells, which are described in Section 2.3.

Some bacteria and archaea have hairlike shafts of protein called **pili** (singular, *pilus*) extending from their cell walls. The main function of pili is attaching the cell to surfaces or other cells. A special type of pilus, the *sex pilus,* attaches one bacterium to another during mating (see Chapter 9).

STUDY BREAK

Where in a prokaryotic cell is DNA found? How is that DNA organized?

2.3 Eukaryotic Cells

The domain of the eukaryotes, Eukarya, is divided into four major groups: protists, fungi, animals, and plants. The rest of the chapter focuses on the cell components that are common to all large groups of eukaryotic organisms.

2.3a Eukaryotic Cells Have a True Nucleus and Cytoplasmic Organelles Enclosed within a Plasma Membrane

The cells of all eukaryotes have a true nucleus enclosed by membranes. The cytoplasm surrounding the nucleus contains a remarkable system of membranous organelles, each specialized to carry out one or more major functions of energy metabolism and molecular synthesis, storage, and transport. The cytosol, the cytoplasmic solution surrounding the organelles, participates in energy metabolism and molecular synthesis and performs specialized functions in support and motility.

The eukaryotic plasma membrane carries out various functions through several types of embedded proteins. Some of these proteins form channels through the plasma membrane that transport substances into and out of the cell. Other proteins in the plasma membrane act as receptors; they recognize and bind specific signal molecules in the cellular environment and trigger internal responses. In some eukaryotes, particularly animals, plasma membrane proteins recognize and adhere to molecules on the surfaces of other cells. Yet other plasma membrane proteins are important markers in the immune system, labelling cells as "self," that is, belonging to the organism. Therefore, the immune system can identify cells without those markers as being foreign, most likely *pathogens* (disease-causing organisms or viruses).

A supportive cell wall surrounds the plasma membrane of fungal, plant, and many protist cells. Because the cell wall lies outside the plasma membrane, it is an *extracellular* structure (*extra* = outside). Although animal cells do not have cell walls, they also form extracellular material with supportive and other functions.

Figure 2.8, p. 32, presents a diagram of a representative animal cell and **Figure 2.9, p. 32,** presents a diagram of a representative plant cell to show where the nucleus, cytoplasmic organelles, and other structures are located. The following sections discuss the structure and function of eukaryotic cell parts in more detail, beginning with the nucleus.

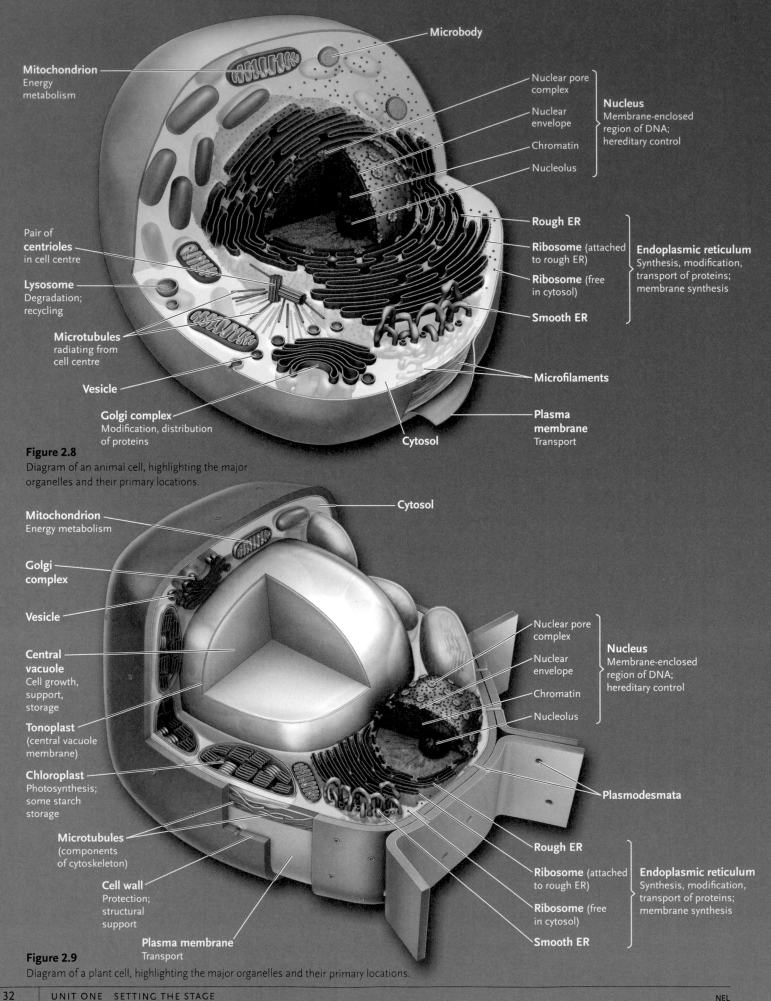

Mitochondrion
Energy
metabolism

Microbody

Nuclear pore
complex

Nuclear
envelope

Chromatin

Nucleolus

Nucleus
Membrane-enclosed
region of DNA;
hereditary control

Rough ER

Ribosome (attached
to rough ER)

Ribosome (free
in cytosol)

Endoplasmic reticulum
Synthesis, modification,
transport of proteins;
membrane synthesis

Smooth ER

Pair of
centrioles
in cell centre

Lysosome
Degradation;
recycling

Microtubules
radiating from
cell centre

Vesicle

Golgi complex
Modification, distribution
of proteins

Cytosol

Microfilaments

**Plasma
membrane**
Transport

Figure 2.8
Diagram of an animal cell, highlighting the major
organelles and their primary locations.

Mitochondrion
Energy metabolism

Cytosol

**Golgi
complex**

Vesicle

**Central
vacuole**
Cell growth,
support,
storage

Tonoplast
(central vacuole
membrane)

Chloroplast
Photosynthesis;
some starch
storage

Microtubules
(components
of cytoskeleton)

Cell wall
Protection;
structural
support

Plasma membrane
Transport

Nuclear pore
complex

Nuclear
envelope

Chromatin

Nucleolus

Nucleus
Membrane-enclosed
region of DNA;
hereditary control

Plasmodesmata

Rough ER

Ribosome (attached
to rough ER)

Ribosome (free
in cytosol)

Endoplasmic reticulum
Synthesis, modification,
transport of proteins;
membrane synthesis

Smooth ER

Figure 2.9
Diagram of a plant cell, highlighting the major organelles and their primary locations.

2.3b The Eukaryotic Nucleus Contains Much More DNA Than the Prokaryotic Nucleoid

The nucleus (see Figures 2.8 and 2.9) is separated from the cytoplasm by the **nuclear envelope**, which consists of two membranes, one layered just inside the other and separated by a narrow space **(Figure 2.10)**. A network of protein filaments called *lamins* lines and reinforces the inner surface of the nuclear envelope in animal cells. Lamins are a type of intermediate filament (see later in this section). Unrelated proteins line the inner surface of the nuclear envelope in protists, fungi, and plants.

Embedded in the nuclear envelope are many hundreds of nuclear pore complexes. A **nuclear pore complex** is a large, octagonally symmetrical, cylindrical structure formed of many types of proteins, called the *nucleoporins*. Probably the largest protein complex in the cell, it exchanges components between the nucleus and cytoplasm and prevents the transport of material not meant to cross the nuclear membrane. A channel through the nuclear pore complex—a nuclear pore—is the path for the assisted exchange of large molecules such as proteins and RNA molecules with the cytoplasm, whereas small molecules simply pass through unassisted. A protein or RNA molecule (called the *cargo*) associates with a transport protein acting as a chaperone to shuttle the cargo through the pore.

Some proteins—for instance, the enzymes for replicating and repairing DNA—must be imported into the nucleus to carry out their functions. Proteins to be imported into the nucleus are distinguished from those that function in the cytosol by the presence of a special, short amino acid sequence called a nuclear localization signal. A specific protein in the cytosol recognizes and binds to the signal and moves the protein containing it to the nuclear pore complex, where it is transported through the pore into the nucleus.

The liquid or semi-liquid substance within the nucleus is called the **nucleoplasm**. Most of the space inside the nucleus is filled with **chromatin**, a combination of DNA and proteins. By contrast with most bacteria and archaea, most of the hereditary information of a eukaryote is distributed among several to many linear DNA molecules in the nucleus. Each individual DNA molecule with its associated proteins is a **eukaryotic chromosome**. The terms *chromatin* and *chromosome* are similar but have distinct meanings. *Chromatin* refers to any collection of eukaryotic DNA molecules with their associated proteins. *Chromosome* refers to one complete DNA molecule with its associated proteins.

Eukaryotic nuclei contain much more DNA than do prokaryotic nucleoids. For example, the entire

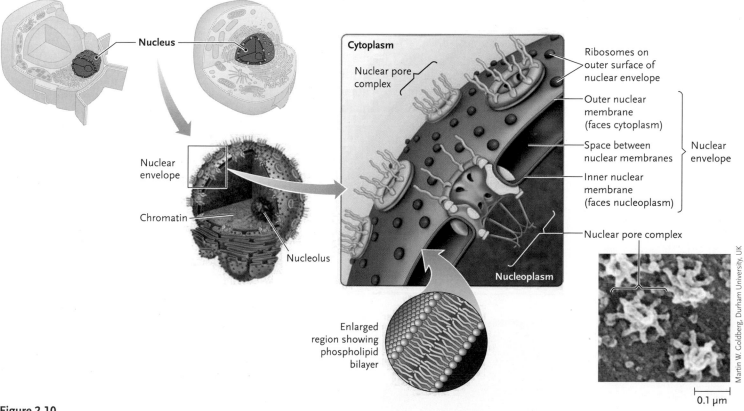

Figure 2.10

The nuclear envelope, which consists of a system of two concentric membranes with nuclear pore complexes embedded. Nuclear pore complexes are octagonally symmetrical protein structures with a channel—the nuclear pore—through the centre. They control the transport of molecules between the nucleus and cytoplasm.

complement of 46 chromosomes in the nucleus of a human cell has a total DNA length of about 2 m, compared with about 1.5 m in prokaryotic cells with the most DNA. Some eukaryotic cells contain even more DNA; for example, a single frog or salamander nucleus, although of microscopic diameter, is packed with about 10 m of DNA!

A eukaryotic nucleus also contains one or more **nucleoli** (singular, *nucleolus*), which look like irregular masses of small fibres and granules (see Figures 2.9, p. 32, and 2.10, p. 33). These structures form around the genes coding for the rRNA molecules of ribosomes. Within the nucleolus, the information in rRNA genes is copied into rRNA molecules, which combine with proteins to form ribosomal subunits. The ribosomal subunits then leave the nucleoli and exit the nucleus through the nuclear pore complexes to enter the cytoplasm, where they join on mRNAs to form complete ribosomes.

The genes for most of the proteins that the organism can make are found within the chromatin, as are the genes for specialized RNA molecules such as rRNA molecules. Expression of these genes is carefully controlled as required for the function of each cell. (The other proteins in the cell are specified by DNA in the mitochondria and chloroplasts.)

2.3c Eukaryotic Ribosomes Are Either Free in the Cytosol or Attached to Membranes

Like prokaryotic ribosomes, a eukaryotic ribosome consists of a large and a small subunit **(Figure 2.11)**. However, the structures of bacterial, archaeal, and eukaryotic ribosomes, although similar, are not identical. In general, eukaryotic ribosomes are larger than either bacterial or archaeal ribosomes; they contain 4 types of rRNA molecules and more than 80 proteins. Their function is identical to that of prokaryotic ribosomes: they use the information in mRNA to assemble amino acids into proteins.

Some eukaryotic ribosomes are freely suspended in the cytosol; others are attached to membranes. Proteins made on free ribosomes in the cytosol may remain in the cytosol; pass through the nuclear pores into the nucleus; or become parts of mitochondria, chloroplasts, the cytoskeleton, or other cytoplasmic structures. Proteins that enter the nucleus become part of chromatin, line the nuclear envelope (the lamins), or remain in solution in the nucleoplasm.

Many ribosomes are attached to membranes. Some ribosomes are attached to the nuclear envelope, but most are attached to a network of membranes in the cytosol called the *endoplasmic reticulum* (ER) (described in more detail next). The proteins made on ribosomes attached to the ER follow a special path to other organelles within the cell.

2.3d An Endomembrane System Divides the Cytoplasm into Functional and Structural Compartments

Eukaryotic cells are characterized by an **endomembrane system** (*endo* = within), a collection of interrelated internal membranous sacs that divide the cell into functional and structural compartments. The endomembrane system has a number of functions, including the synthesis and modification of proteins and their transport into membranes and organelles or to the outside of the cell, the synthesis of lipids, and the detoxification of some toxins. The membranes of the system are connected either directly in the physical sense or indirectly by **vesicles**, which are small membrane-bound compartments that transfer substances between parts of the system.

The components of the endomembrane system include the nuclear envelope, endoplasmic reticulum, Golgi complex, lysosomes, vesicles, and plasma membrane. The plasma membrane and the nuclear envelope were discussed earlier in this chapter. The functions of the other organelles are described in the following sections.

Endoplasmic Reticulum. The **endoplasmic reticulum** (ER) is an extensive interconnected network (*reticulum* = little net) of membranous channels and vesicles called cisternae (singular, *cisterna*). Each cisterna is formed by a single membrane that surrounds an enclosed space called the **ER lumen (Figure 2.12).** The ER occurs in two forms: rough ER and smooth ER, each with specialized structure and function.

The **rough ER** (see Figure 2.12a) gets its name from the many ribosomes that stud its outer surface.

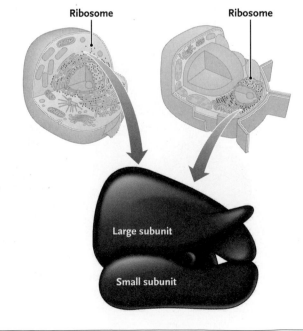

Figure 2.11
A ribosome. The diagram shows the structures of the two ribosomal subunits of mammalian ribosomes and how they come together to form the whole ribosome.

Ribosome

Ribosome

Large subunit

Small subunit

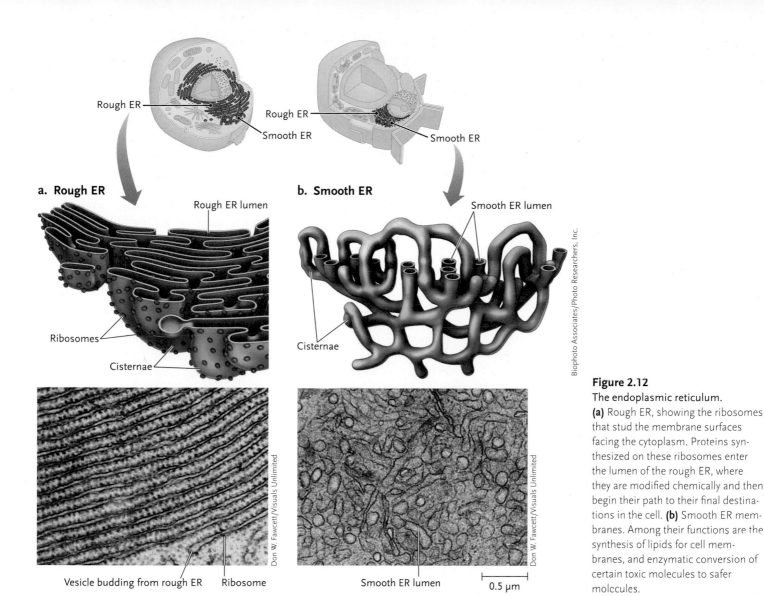

a. **Rough ER**

Rough ER lumen

Ribosomes

Cisternae

b. **Smooth ER**

Smooth ER lumen

Cisternae

Biophoto Associates/Photo Researchers, Inc.

Vesicle budding from rough ER   Ribosome

Don W. Fawcett/Visuals Unlimited

Smooth ER lumen   0.5 μm

Don W. Fawcett/Visuals Unlimited

Figure 2.12
The endoplasmic reticulum.
(a) Rough ER, showing the ribosomes that stud the membrane surfaces facing the cytoplasm. Proteins synthesized on these ribosomes enter the lumen of the rough ER, where they are modified chemically and then begin their path to their final destinations in the cell. **(b)** Smooth ER membranes. Among their functions are the synthesis of lipids for cell membranes, and enzymatic conversion of certain toxic molecules to safer molecules.

The proteins made on ribosomes attached to the ER enter the ER lumen, where they fold into their final form. Chemical modifications of these proteins, such as addition of carbohydrate groups to produce glycoproteins, occur in the lumen. The proteins are then delivered to other regions of the cell within small vesicles that pinch off from the ER, travel through the cytosol, and join with the organelle that performs the next steps in their modification and distribution. For most of the proteins made on the rough ER, the next destination is the Golgi complex, which packages and sorts them for delivery to their final destinations.

The outer membrane of the nuclear envelope is closely related in structure and function to the rough ER, to which it is connected. This membrane is also a rough membrane, studded with ribosomes attached to the surface facing the cytoplasm. The proteins made on these ribosomes enter the space between the two nuclear envelope membranes. From there, the proteins can move into the ER and on to other cellular locations.

The **smooth ER** (see Figure 2.12b) is so called because its membranes have no ribosomes attached to

their surfaces. The smooth ER has various functions in the cytoplasm, including synthesis of lipids that become part of cell membranes. In some cells, such as those of the liver, smooth ER membranes contain enzymes that convert drugs, poisons, and toxic byproducts of cellular metabolism into substances that can be tolerated or more easily removed from the body.

The rough and smooth ER membranes are often connected, making the entire ER system a continuous network of interconnected channels in the cytoplasm. The relative proportions of rough and smooth ER reflect cellular activities in protein and lipid synthesis. Cells that are highly active in making proteins to be released outside the cell, such as pancreatic cells that make digestive enzymes, are packed with rough ER but have relatively little smooth ER. By contrast, cells that primarily synthesize lipids or break down toxic substances are packed with smooth ER but contain little rough ER.

Golgi Complex. Camillo Golgi, a late-nineteenth-century Italian neuroscientist and Nobel laureate, discovered the **Golgi complex**. The Golgi complex consists of a stack of flattened, membranous sacs (without attached ribosomes) known as cisternae **(Figure 2.13)**. In most cells, the complex looks like a stack of cupped pancakes, and like pancakes, they are separate sacs, not interconnected as the ER cisternae are. Typically there are between three and eight cisternae, but some organisms have Golgi complexes with several tens of cisternae. The number and size of Golgi complexes can vary with cell type and the metabolic activity of the cell. Some cells have a single complex, whereas cells highly active in secreting proteins from the cell can have

hundreds of complexes. Golgi complexes are usually located near concentrations of rough ER membranes, between the ER and the plasma membrane.

The Golgi complex receives proteins that were made in the ER and transported to the complex in vesicles. When the vesicles contact the *cis* face of the complex (which faces the nucleus), they fuse with the Golgi membrane and release their contents directly into the cisternal (see Figure 2.13). Within the Golgi complex, the proteins are chemically modified, for example, by removing segments of the amino acid chain, adding small functional groups, or adding lipid or carbohydrate units. The modified proteins are transported within the Golgi to the *trans* face of the complex (which faces the plasma membrane), where they are sorted into vesicles that bud off from the margins of the Golgi (see Figure 2.13). The content of a vesicle is kept separate from the cytosol by the vesicle membrane. Three quite different models have been proposed for how proteins move through the Golgi complex. The mechanism is a subject of active current research.

The Golgi complex regulates the movement of several types of proteins. Some are secreted from the cell, others become embedded in the plasma membrane as integral membrane proteins, and yet others are placed in lysosomes. The modifications of the proteins within the Golgi complex include adding "postal codes" to the proteins, which tags them for sorting to their final destinations. For instance, proteins secreted from the cell are transported to the plasma membrane in **secretory vesicles**, which release their contents to the exterior by **exocytosis (Figure 2.14a)**. In this process, a secretory vesicle fuses with the plasma membrane and spills the vesicle contents to the outside. The contents of secretory vesicles vary, including signalling molecules such as hormones and neurotransmitters (see Chapter 5), waste products or toxic substances, and enzymes (such as from cells lining the intestine). The membrane of a vesicle that fuses with the plasma membrane becomes part of the plasma membrane. In fact, this process is used to expand the surface of the cell during cell growth.

Vesicles may also form by the reverse process, called endocytosis, which brings molecules into the cell from the exterior **(Figure 2.14b)**. In this process, the plasma membrane forms a pocket, which bulges inward and pinches off into the cytoplasm as an **endocytic vesicle**. Once in the cytoplasm, endocytic vesicles, which contain segments of the plasma membrane as well as proteins and other molecules, are carried to the Golgi complex or to other destinations such as lysosomes in animal cells. The substances carried to the Golgi complex are sorted and placed into vesicles for routing to other locations, which may include lysosomes. Those routed to lysosomes are digested into molecular subunits that may be recycled as building blocks for the biological molecules of the cell. Exocytosis and endocytosis are discussed in more detail in Chapters 35 and 36.

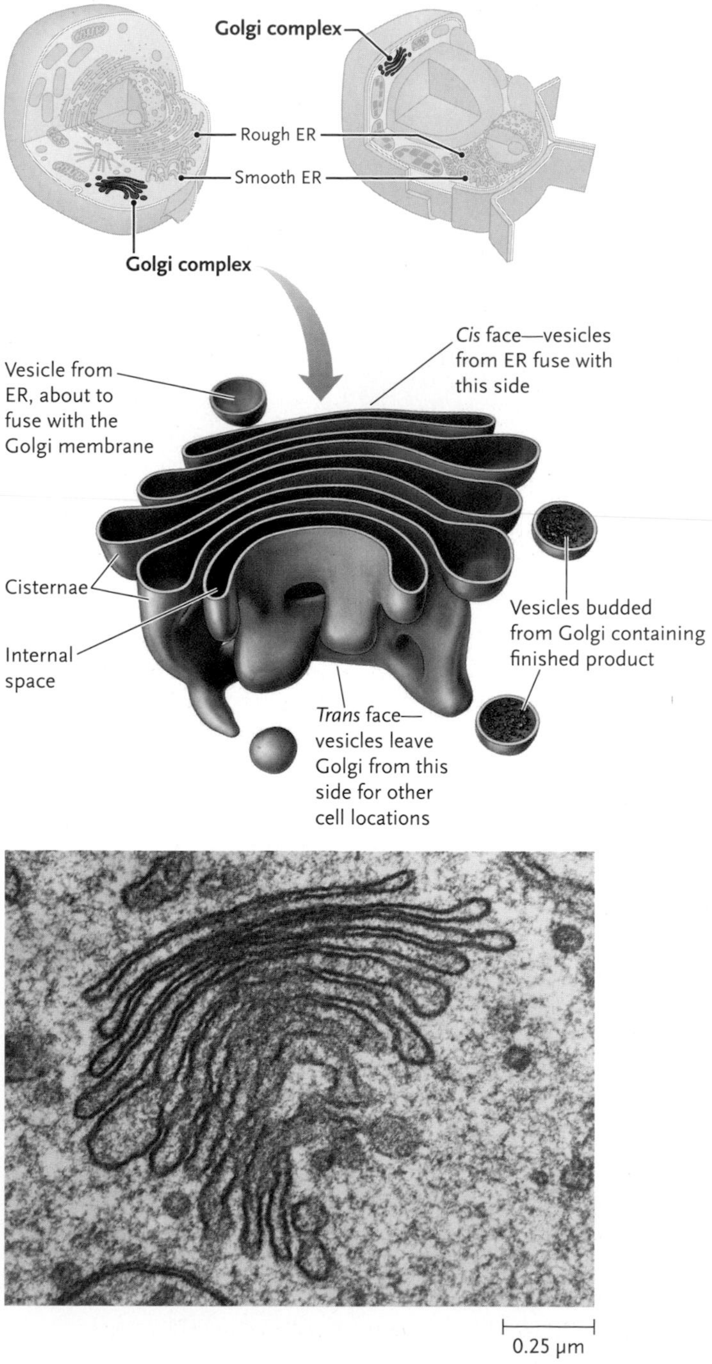

Figure 2.13
The Golgi complex.

a. Exocytosis: A secretory vesicle fuses with the plasma membrane, releasing the vesicle contents to the cell exterior. The vesicle membrane becomes part of the plasma membrane.

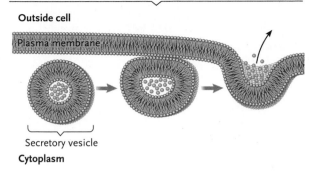

Outside cell

Plasma membrane

Secretory vesicle

Cytoplasm

b. Endocytosis: Materials from the cell exterior are enclosed in a segment of the plasma membrane that pockets inward and pinches off as an endocytic vesicle.

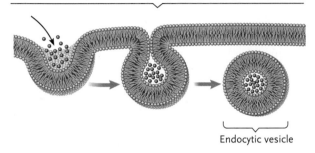

Endocytic vesicle

Figure 2.14
Exocytosis and endocytosis.

Lysosomes. Lysosomes (*lys* = breakdown; *some* = body) are small, membrane-bound vesicles that contain more than 30 hydrolytic enzymes for the digestion of many complex molecules, including proteins, lipids, nucleic acids, and polysaccharides **(Figure 2.15)**. The cell recycles the subunits of these molecules. Lysosomes are found in animals but not in plants. The functions of lysosomes in plants are carried out by the central vacuole (see Section 2.4). Depending on the contents they are digesting, lysosomes assume a variety of sizes and shapes instead of a uniform structure as is characteristic of other organelles. Most commonly, lysosomes are small (0.1–0.5 μm in diameter) oval or spherical bodies. A human cell contains about 300 lysosomes.

Lysosomes are formed by budding from the Golgi complex. Their hydrolytic enzymes are synthesized in the rough ER, modified in the lumen of the ER to identify them as being bound for a lysosome, transported to the Golgi complex in a vesicle, and then packaged in the budding lysosome.

The pH within lysosomes is acidic (pH = 5) and is significantly lower than the pH of the cytosol (pH = 7.2). The hydrolytic enzymes in the lysosomes function optimally at the acidic pH within the organelle, but they do not function well at the pH of the cytosol; this difference reduces the risk to the viability of the cell should the enzymes be released from the vesicle.

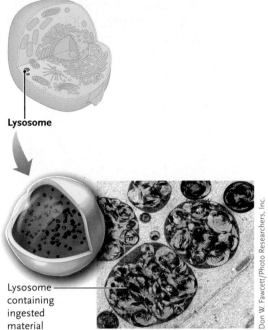

Lysosome

Lysosome containing ingested material

Figure 2.15
A lysosome.

Don W. Fawcett/Photo Researchers, Inc.

Lysosomal enzymes can digest several types of materials. They digest food molecules entering the cell by endocytosis when an endocytic vesicle fuses with a lysosome. In a process called *autophagy,* they digest organelles that are not functioning correctly. A membrane surrounds the defective organelle, forming a large vesicle that fuses with one or more lysosomes; the organelle is then degraded by the hydrolytic enzymes. They also play a role in **phagocytosis**, a process in which some types of cells engulf bacteria or other cellular debris to break them down. These cells include the white blood cells known as *phagocytes,* which play an important role in the immune system (see Chapter 5). Phagocytosis produces a large vesicle that contains the engulfed materials until lysosomes fuse with the vesicle and release the hydrolytic enzymes necessary for degrading them.

In certain human genetic diseases known as *lysosomal storage diseases,* one of the hydrolytic enzymes normally found in the lysosome is absent. As a result, the substrate of that enzyme accumulates in the lysosomes, and this accumulation eventually interferes with normal cellular activities. An example is Tay–Sachs disease, which is a fatal disease of the central nervous system caused by the failure to synthesize the enzyme needed for hydrolysis of fatty acid derivatives found in brain and nerve cells.

Summary. In summary, the endomembrane system is a major traffic network for proteins and other substances within the cell. The Golgi complex in particular is a key distribution station for membranes and proteins **(Figure 2.16, p. 38).** From the Golgi complex, lipids and proteins may move to storage or secretory vesicles, and from the secretory vesicles, they may move to the

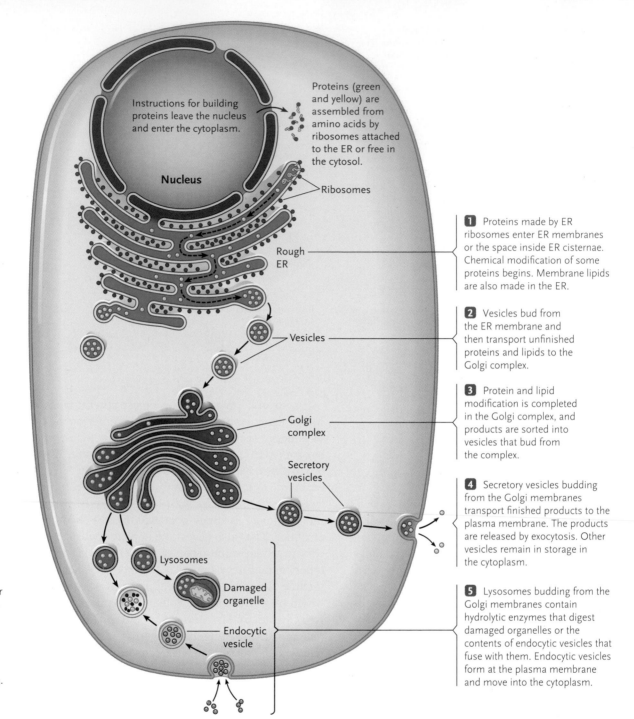

Instructions for building proteins leave the nucleus and enter the cytoplasm.

Proteins (green and yellow) are assembled from amino acids by ribosomes attached to the ER or free in the cytosol.

Nucleus

Ribosomes

Rough ER

1 Proteins made by ER ribosomes enter ER membranes or the space inside ER cisternae. Chemical modification of some proteins begins. Membrane lipids are also made in the ER.

Vesicles

2 Vesicles bud from the ER membrane and then transport unfinished proteins and lipids to the Golgi complex.

Golgi complex

3 Protein and lipid modification is completed in the Golgi complex, and products are sorted into vesicles that bud from the complex.

Secretory vesicles

4 Secretory vesicles budding from the Golgi membranes transport finished products to the plasma membrane. The products are released by exocytosis. Other vesicles remain in storage in the cytoplasm.

Lysosomes

Damaged organelle

Endocytic vesicle

5 Lysosomes budding from the Golgi membranes contain hydrolytic enzymes that digest damaged organelles or the contents of endocytic vesicles that fuse with them. Endocytic vesicles form at the plasma membrane and move into the cytoplasm.

Figure 2.16
Vesicle traffic in the cytoplasm.
The ER and Golgi complex are part of the endomembrane system, which releases proteins and other substances to the cell exterior and gathers materials from outside the cell.

Eldon Newcomb, University of Wisconsin

Keith R. Porter

cell exterior by exocytosis. Membranes and proteins may also move between the nuclear envelope and the endomembrane system. Proteins and other materials that enter cells by endocytosis also enter the endomembrane system to travel to the Golgi complex for sorting and distribution to other locations.

2.3e Mitochondria Are the Organelles in Which Cellular Respiration Occurs

Mitochondria (singular, *mitochondrion*) are the membrane-bound organelles in which cellular respiration occurs. *Cellular respiration* is the process by which energy-rich molecules such as sugars, fats, and other

fuels are broken down to water and carbon dioxide by mitochondrial reactions, with the release of energy. Much of the energy released by the breakdown is captured in ATP. In fact, mitochondria generate most of the ATP of the cell. Mitochondria require oxygen for cellular respiration—when you breathe, you are taking in oxygen primarily for your mitochondrial reactions (see Chapter 6).

Mitochondria are enclosed by two membranes **(Figure 2.17)**. The **outer mitochondrial membrane** is smooth and covers the outside of the organelle. The surface area of the **inner mitochondrial membrane** is expanded by folds called **cristae** (singular, *crista*). Both membranes surround the innermost compartment of

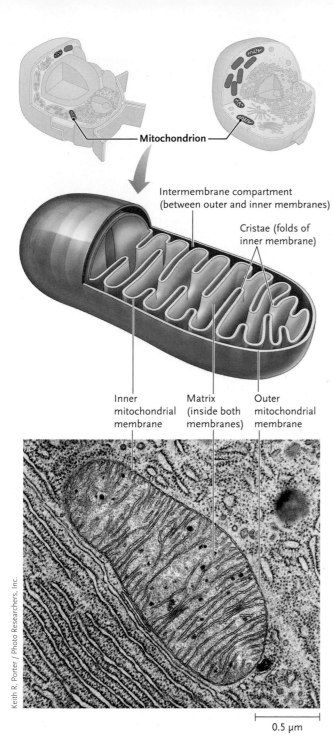

Mitochondrion

Intermembrane compartment
(between outer and inner membranes)

Cristae (folds of
inner membrane)

Inner
mitochondrial
membrane

Matrix
(inside both
membranes)

Outer
mitochondrial
membrane

Keith R. Porter / Photo Researchers, Inc.

0.5 μm

Figure 2.17

Mitochondria. The electron micrograph shows a mitochondrion from a bat pancreas, surrounded by cytoplasm containing rough ER. Cristae extend into the interior of the mitochondrion as folds from the inner mitochondrial membrane. The darkly stained granules inside the mitochondrion are probably lipid deposits.

the mitochondrion, called the **mitochondrial matrix**. The ATP-generating reactions of mitochondria occur in the cristae and matrix.

The mitochondrial matrix also contains DNA and ribosomes that resemble the equivalent structures in bacteria. These and other similarities suggest that mitochondria originated from ancient bacteria that became permanent residents of the cytoplasm during

the evolution of eukaryotic cells. This is discussed in more detail in Chapter 3.

2.3f The Cytoskeleton Supports and Moves Cell Structures

The characteristic shape and internal organization of each type of cell is maintained in part by its cytoskeleton, the interconnected system of protein fibres and tubes that extends throughout the cytoplasm. The cytoskeleton also reinforces the plasma membrane and functions in movement, both of structures within the cell and of the cell as a whole. It is most highly developed in animal cells, in which it fills and supports the cytoplasm from the plasma membrane to the nuclear envelope **(Figure 2.18, p. 40).** Although cytoskeletal structures are also present in plant cells, the fibres and tubes of the system are less prominent; much of cellular support in plants is provided by the cell wall and a large central vacuole (described in Section 2.4).

The cytoskeleton of animal cells contains structural elements of three major types: *microtubules, intermediate filaments,* and *microfilaments.* Plant cytoskeletons likewise contain the same three structural elements. Microtubules are the largest cytoskeletal elements, and microfilaments are the smallest. Each cytoskeletal element is assembled from proteins— microtubules from *tubulins,* intermediate filaments from a large and varied group of *intermediate filament proteins,* and microfilaments from *actins* **(Figure 2.19, p. 40).** The keratins of animal hair, nails, and claws contain a common form of intermediate filament proteins known as *cytokeratins.* For example, human hair consists of thick bundles of cytokeratin fibres extruded from hair follicle cells. The lamins that line the inner surface of the nuclear envelope in animal cells are also assembled from intermediate filament proteins.

Microtubules (Figure 2.19a) are microscopic tubes with an outer diameter of about 25 nm and an inner diameter of about 15 nm; they function much like the tubes used by human engineers to construct supportive structures. Microtubules vary widely in length from less than 200 nm to several micrometres. The wall of the microtubule consists of 13 protein filaments arranged side by side. A filament is a linear polymer of tubulin dimers, each dimer consisting of one α-tubulin and one β-tubulin subunit bound noncovalently together. The dimers are organized head-to-tail in each filament, giving the microtubule a polarity, meaning that the two ends are different. One end, called the 1 (plus) end, has α-tubulin subunits at the ends of the filaments; the other end, called the 2 (minus) end, has β-tubulin subunits at the ends of the filaments. Microtubules are dynamic structures, changing their lengths as required by their functions. This is seen readily in animal cells that are changing shape. Microtubules change length by the addition or removal of tubulin

a. Microtubules

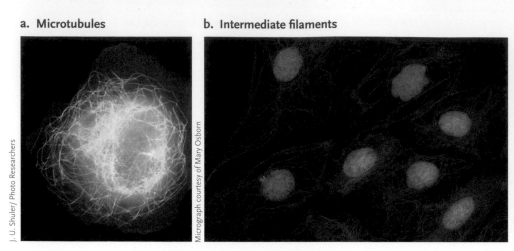

J. U. Shuler / Photo Researchers

Micrograph courtesy of Mary Osborn

b. Intermediate filaments

c. Microfilaments

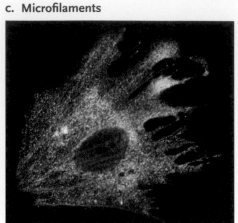

Courtesy of Dr. Vincenzo Cirulli; Diabetes and Obesity Center of Excellence, University of Washington, Department of Medicine, Institute for Stem Cells and Regenerative Medicine

Figure 2.18

Cytoskeletons of eukaryotic cells, as seen in cells stained for light microscopy. **(a)** Microtubules (yellow) and microfilaments (red) in a pancreatic cell. **(b)** keratin intermediate filaments viewed by immunofluorescence microscopy in the rat kangaroo cell line PtK2. The nucleus is stained blue in these cells. **(c)** Microfilaments (red) in a migrating mammalian cell.

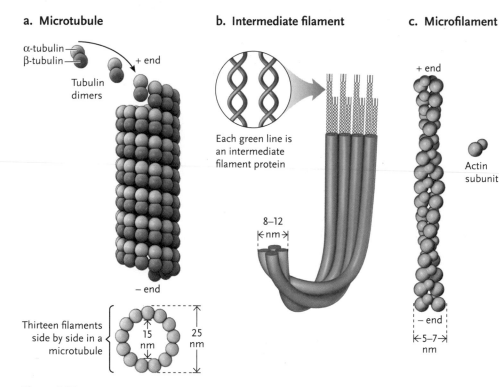

a. Microtubule

α-tubulin
β-tubulin
Tubulin dimers
+ end
− end

Thirteen filaments side by side in a microtubule
15 nm
25 nm

b. Intermediate filament

Each green line is an intermediate filament protein

8–12 nm

c. Microfilament

+ end
Actin subunit
− end
5–7 nm

Figure 2.19

The major components of the cytoskeleton. **(a)** A microtubule, assembled from dimers of α- and β-tubulin proteins. **(b)** An intermediate filament. Eight protein chains wind together to form each subunit, shown as a green cylinder. **(c)** A microfilament, assembled from two linear polymers of actin proteins wound around each other into a helical spiral.

dimers; this occurs asymmetrically, with dimers adding or detaching more rapidly at the 1 end than at the 2 end. The lengths of microtubules are tightly regulated in the cell.

Many of the cytoskeletal microtubules in animal cells are formed and radiate outward from a site near the nucleus termed the **cell centre** or **centrosome** (see Figure 2.8). At its midpoint are two short, barrel-shaped structures also formed from microtubules called the **centrioles** (see Figure 2.23). Often, intermediate filaments also extend from the cell centre, apparently held in the same radiating pattern by linkage to microtubules. Microtubules that radiate from the cell centre anchor the ER, Golgi complex, lysosomes, secretory vesicles, and at least some mitochondria in position. The microtubules also provide tracks along which vesicles move from the cell interior to the plasma membrane and in the reverse direction. The intermediate filaments probably add support to the microtubule arrays.

Microtubules play other key roles, for instance, in separating and moving chromosomes during cell division, determining the orientation for growth of the new cell wall during plant cell division, maintaining the shape of animal cells, and moving animal cells themselves. Animal cell movements are generated by "motor" proteins that push or pull against microtubules or microfilaments, much as our muscles produce body movements by acting on bones of the skeleton. One end of a motor protein is firmly fixed to a cell structure such as a vesicle or to a microtubule or microfilament. The other end has reactive groups that "walk" along another microtubule or microfilament by making an attachment, forcefully swivelling a short distance, and then releasing **(Figure 2.20)**. ATP supplies the energy for the walking movements. The motor proteins that walk along microfilaments are called *myosins,* and the ones that walk along microtubules are called *dyneins* and *kinesins.* Some cell movements, such as the whipping motions of sperm tails, depend entirely on microtubules and their motor proteins.

a. "Walking" end of a kinesin molecule

Connects to cell structure
such as a vesicle

One "foot" of
motor protein

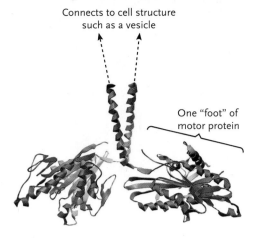

b. How a kinesin molecule "walks"

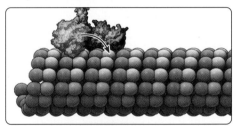

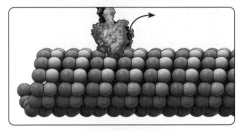

Figure 2.20

The microtubule motor protein kinesin. **(a)** Structure of the end of a kinesin molecule that "walks" along a microtubule, with α-helical segments shown as spirals and β strands as flat ribbons. **(b)** How a kinesin molecule walks along the surface of a molecule by alternately attaching and releasing its "feet."

Intermediate filaments (Figure 2.19b) are fibres with diameters of about 8 to 12 nm. ("Intermediate" signifies, in fact, that these filaments are intermediate in size between microtubules and microfilaments.) These fibres occur singly, in parallel bundles, and in interlinked networks, either alone or in combination with microtubules, microfilaments, or both. Intermediate filaments are only found in multicellular organisms. Moreover, whereas microtubules and microfilaments are the same in all tissues, intermediate filaments are tissue specific in their protein composition. Despite the molecular diversity of intermediate filaments, however, they all play similar roles in the cell, providing structural support in many cells and tissues. For example, the nucleus in epithelial cells is held within the cell by a basketlike network of intermediate filaments made of keratins.

Microfilaments (Figure 2.19c) are thin protein fibres 5 to 7 nm in diameter that consist of two polymers of actin subunits wound around each other in a long helical spiral. The actin subunits are asymmetrical in shape, and they are all oriented in the same way in the polymer chains of a microfilament. Thus, as for microtubules, microfilaments have a polarity: the two ends are designated 1 (plus) and 2 (minus). And, as for microtubules, growth and disassembly occur more rapidly at the 1 end than at the 2 end.

Microfilaments occur in almost all eukaryotic cells and are involved in many processes, including a number of structural and locomotor functions. Microfilaments are best known as one of the two components of the contractile elements in muscle fibres of vertebrates (the roles of myosin and microfilaments in muscle contraction are discussed in Chapter 38). Microfilaments are involved in the actively flowing motion of cytoplasm called *cytoplasmic streaming*, which can transport nutrients, proteins, and organelles in both animal and plant cells, and which is responsible for amoeboid movement. When animal cells divide, microfilaments are responsible for dividing the cytoplasm (see Chapter 9 for further discussion).

2.3g Flagella Propel Cells, and Cilia Move Materials over the Cell Surface

Flagella and cilia (singular, *cilium*) are elongated, slender, motile structures that extend from the cell surface. They are identical in structure except that cilia are usually shorter than flagella and occur on cells in greater numbers. The whiplike or oarlike movements of a flagellum propel a cell through a watery medium, and cilia move fluids over the cell surface.

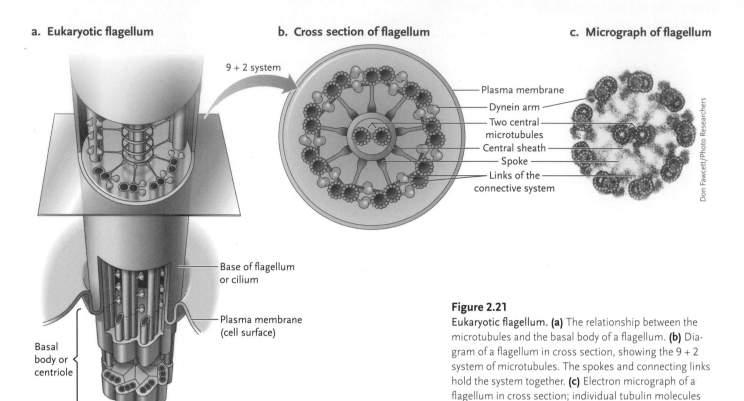

a. Eukaryotic flagellum

9 + 2 system

Base of flagellum
or cilium

Plasma membrane
(cell surface)

Basal
body or
centriole

b. Cross section of flagellum

Plasma membrane
Dynein arm
Two central
microtubules
Central sheath
Spoke
Links of the
connective system

c. Micrograph of flagellum

Don Fawcett/Photo Researchers

Figure 2.21

Eukaryotic flagellum. **(a)** The relationship between the microtubules and the basal body of a flagellum. **(b)** Diagram of a flagellum in cross section, showing the 9 + 2 system of microtubules. The spokes and connecting links hold the system together. **(c)** Electron micrograph of a flagellum in cross section; individual tubulin molecules are visible in the microtubule walls.

A bundle of microtubules extends from the base to the tip of a flagellum or cilium **(Figure 2.21)**. In the bundle, a circle of nine double microtubules surrounds a central pair of single microtubules, forming what is known as the 9 + 2 complex. Dynein motor proteins slide the microtubules of the 9 + 2 complex over each other to produce the movements of a flagellum or cilium **(Figure 2.22)**.

Flagella and cilia arise from the centrioles. These barrel-shaped structures contain a bundle of microtubules similar to the 9 + 2 complex, except that the central pair of microtubules is missing and the outer

circle is formed from a ring of nine triple rather than double microtubules (compare Figure 2.21 and **Figure 2.23**).

During the formation of a flagellum or cilium, a centriole moves to a position just under the plasma membrane. Then two of the three microtubules of each triplet grow outward from one end of the centriole to form the ring of nine double microtubules. The two central microtubules of the 9 + 2 complex also grow from the end of the centriole, but without direct connection to any centriole microtubules. The centriole remains at the innermost end of a flagellum or cilium

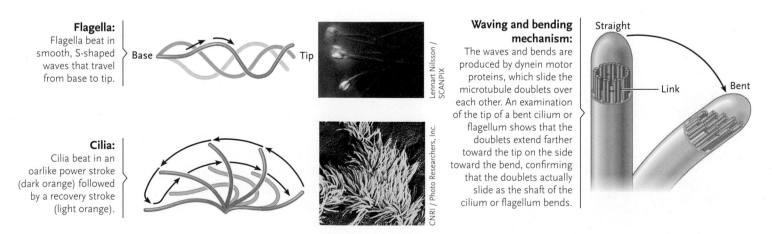

Flagella:
Flagella beat in smooth, S-shaped waves that travel from base to tip.

Base

Tip

Lennart Nilsson / SCANPIX

Cilia:
Cilia beat in an oarlike power stroke (dark orange) followed by a recovery stroke (light orange).

CNRI / Photo Researchers, Inc.

Waving and bending mechanism:
The waves and bends are produced by dynein motor proteins, which slide the microtubule doublets over each other. An examination of the tip of a bent cilium or flagellum shows that the doublets extend farther toward the tip on the side toward the bend, confirming that the doublets actually slide as the shaft of the cilium or flagellum bends.

Straight

Link

Bent

Figure 2.22

Flagellar and ciliary beating patterns. The micrographs show a few human sperm, each with a flagellum (top), and cilia from the lining of an airway in the lungs (bottom).

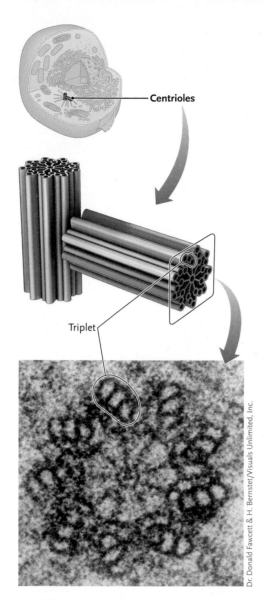

Centrioles

Triplet

Dr. Donald Fawcett & H. Bernstet/Visuals Unlimited, Inc.

Figure 2.23

Centrioles. The two centrioles of the pair at the cell centre usually lie at right angles to each other as shown. The electron micrograph shows a centriole from a mouse cell in cross section. A centriole gives rise to the 9 + 2 system of a flagellum and persists as the basal body at the inner end of the flagellum.

when its development is complete as the **basal body** of the structure (see Figure 2.21).

Cilia and flagella are found in protozoa and algae, and many types of animal cells have flagella—the tail of a sperm cell is a flagellum—as do the reproductive cells of some plants. In humans, cilia cover the surfaces of cells lining cavities or tubes in some parts of the body. For example, cilia on cells lining the ventricles (cavities) of the brain circulate fluid through the brain, and cilia in the oviducts conduct eggs from the ovaries to the uterus. Cilia covering cells that line the air passages of the lungs sweep out mucus containing bacteria, dust particles, and other contaminants.

Although the purpose of the eukaryotic flagellum is the same as that of prokaryotic flagella, the genes that encode the components of the flagellar apparatus of cells of Bacteria, Archaea, and Eukarya are different in each case. Thus, as mentioned earlier in the chapter, the three types of flagella are analogous, not homologous, structures, and they must have evolved independently.

With a few exceptions, the cell structures described so far in this chapter occur in all eukaryotic cells. The major exception is lysosomes, which appear to be restricted to animal cells. The next section describes three additional structures that are characteristic of plant cells.

STUDY BREAK

1. Where in a eukaryotic cell is DNA found? How is that DNA organized?
2. What is the nucleolus, and what is its function?
3. Explain the structure and function of the endomembrane system.
4. What is the structure and function of a mitochondrion?
5. What is the structure and function of the cytoskeleton?

2.4 Specialized Structures of Plant Cells

Chloroplasts, large and highly specialized central vacuoles, and cell walls give plant cells their distinctive characteristics, but these structures also occur in some other eukaryotes—for example, chloroplasts in algal protists and cell walls in algal protists and fungi.

2.4a Chloroplasts Are Biochemical Factories Powered by Sunlight

Chloroplasts (*chloro* = yellow-green), the sites of photosynthesis in plant cells, are members of a family of plant organelles known collectively as **plastids**. Other members of the family include amyloplasts and chromoplasts. **Amyloplasts** (*amylo* = starch) are colourless plastids that store starch, a product of photosynthesis. They occur in great numbers in the roots or tubers of some plants, such as the potato. **Chromoplasts** (*chromo* = colour) contain red and yellow pigments and are responsible for the colours of ripening fruits or autumn leaves. All plastids contain DNA genomes and molecular machinery for gene expression and the synthesis of proteins on ribosomes. Some of the proteins within plastids are encoded by their genomes; others are encoded by nuclear genes and are imported into the organelles.

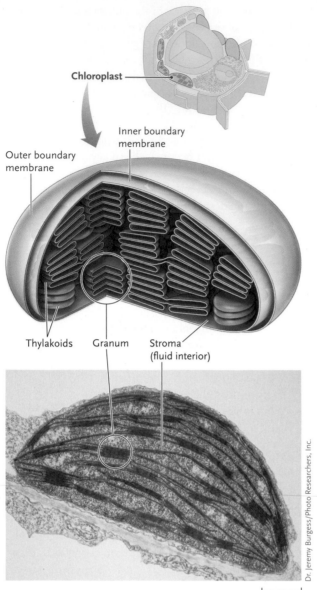

Figure 2.24
Chloroplast structure. The electron micrograph shows a maize (corn) chloroplast.

Chloroplast

Inner boundary membrane

Outer boundary membrane

Thylakoids   Granum   Stroma (fluid interior)

Dr. Jeremy Burgess/Photo Researchers, Inc.

1.0 μm

Chloroplasts, like mitochondria, are usually lens or disc shaped and are surrounded by a smooth **outer boundary membrane** and an **inner boundary membrane**, which lies just inside the outer membrane **(Figure 2.24).** These two boundary membranes completely enclose an inner compartment, the stroma. Within the stroma is a third membrane system that consists of flattened, closed sacs called thylakoids. In higher plants, the thylakoids are stacked, one on top of another, forming structures called **grana** (singular, *granum*).

The thylakoid membranes contain molecules that absorb light energy and convert it to chemical energy in photosynthesis. The primary molecule absorbing light is *chlorophyll,* a green pigment that is present in all chloroplasts. The chemical energy is used by enzymes in the stroma to make carbohydrates and other complex organic molecules from water, carbon

dioxide, and other simple inorganic precursors. The organic molecules produced in chloroplasts, or from biochemical building blocks made in chloroplasts, are the ultimate food source for most organisms. (The physical and biochemical reactions of chloroplasts are described in Chapter 7.)

The chloroplast stroma contains DNA and ribosomes that resemble those of certain photosynthetic bacteria. Because of these similarities, chloroplasts, like mitochondria, are believed to have originated from ancient bacteria that became permanent residents of the eukaryotic cells ancestral to the plant lineage (see Chapter 3 for further discussion).

2.4b Central Vacuoles Have Diverse Roles in Storage, Structural Support, and Cell Growth

Central vacuoles (see Figure 2.9, p. 32) are large vesicles identified as distinct organelles of plant cells because they perform specialized functions unique to plants. In a mature plant cell, 90% or more of the cell's volume may be occupied by one or more large central vacuoles. The remainder of the cytoplasm and the nucleus of these cells is restricted to a narrow zone between the central vacuole and the plasma membrane. The pressure within the central vacuole supports the cells.

The membrane that surrounds the central vacuole, the **tonoplast**, contains transport proteins that move substances into and out of the central vacuole. As plant cells mature, they grow primarily by increases in the pressure and volume of the central vacuole.

Central vacuoles conduct other vital functions. They store salts, organic acids, sugars, storage proteins, pigments, and, in some cells, waste products. Pigments concentrated in the vacuoles produce the colours of many flowers. Enzymes capable of breaking down biological molecules are present in some central vacuoles, giving them some of the properties of lysosomes. Molecules that provide chemical defences against pathogenic organisms also occur in the central vacuoles of some plants.

2.4c Cell Walls Support and Protect Plant Cells

The cell walls of plants are extracellular structures because they are located outside the plasma membrane **(Figure 2.25).** Cell walls provide support to individual cells, contain the pressure produced in the central vacuole, and protect cells against invading bacteria and fungi. Cell walls consist of cellulose fibres, which give tensile strength to the walls, embedded in a network of highly branched carbohydrates. Cell walls are perforated by minute channels, the plasmodesmata

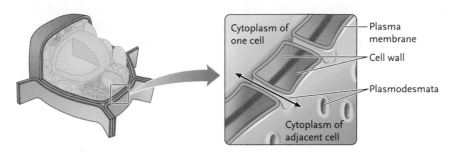

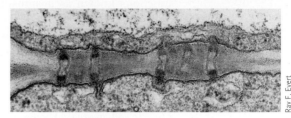

Section through five plasmodesmata that bridge the middle lamella and primary walls of two plant cells.

Figure 2.25

Cell wall structure in plants. The right diagram and electron micrograph show plasmodesmata, which form openings in the cell wall that directly connect the cytoplasm of adjacent cells.

(singular, *plasmodesma;* see Figure 2.25). A typical plant cell has between 1000 and 100 000 plasmodesmata connecting it to abutting cells. These cytosol-filled channels are lined by plasma membranes, so that connected cells essentially all have one continuous surface membrane. Most plasmodesmata also contain a narrow tubelike structure derived from the smooth endoplasmic reticulum of the connected cells. Plasmodesmata allow ions and small molecules to move directly from one cell to another through the connecting cytosol, without having to penetrate the plasma membranes or cell walls. Proteins and nucleic acids move through some plasmodesmata using energy-dependent processes.

Cell walls also surround the cells of fungi and algal protists. Carbohydrate molecules form the major framework of cell walls in most of these organisms, as they do in plants. In some, the wall fibres contain chitin instead of cellulose. Details of cell wall structure in the algal protists and fungi, as well as in different subgroups of the plants, are presented in later chapters devoted to these organisms. As noted earlier, animal cells do not form rigid, external, layered structures equivalent to the walls of plant cells. However, most animal cells secrete extracellular material and have other structures at the cell surface that play vital roles in the support and organization of animal body structures. The next section describes these and other surface structures of animal cells.

2.5 The Animal Cell Surface

Animal cells have specialized structures that help hold cells together, produce avenues of communication between cells, and organize body structures. Molecular systems that perform these functions are organized at three levels: individual **cell adhesion molecules** bind cells together, more complex **cell junctions** seal the spaces between cells and provide direct communication between cells, and the **extracellular matrix** (ECM)

supports and protects cells and provides mechanical linkages, such as those between muscles and bone.

2.5a Cell Adhesion Molecules Organize Animal Cells into Tissues and Organs

Cell adhesion molecules are glycoproteins embedded in the plasma membrane. They help maintain body form and structure in animals ranging from sponges to the most complex invertebrates and vertebrates. Rather than acting as a generalized intercellular glue, cell adhesion molecules bind to specific molecules on other cells. Most cells in solid body tissues are held together by many different cell adhesion molecules.

Cell adhesion molecules make initial connections between cells early in embryonic development, but then attachments are broken and remade, as individual cells or tissues change position in the developing embryo. As an embryo develops into an adult, the connections become permanent and are reinforced by cell junctions. Cancer cells typically lose these adhesions, allowing them to break loose from their original locations, migrate to new locations, and form additional tumours.

Some bacteria and viruses—such as the virus that causes the common cold—target cell adhesion molecules as attachment sites during infection. Cell adhesion molecules are also partially responsible for the ability of cells to recognize one another as being part of the same individual or foreign to that individual. For example, rejection of organ transplants in mammals results from an immune response triggered by the foreign cell-surface molecules.

2.5b Cell Junctions Reinforce Cell Adhesions and Provide Avenues of Communication

Three types of cell junctions are common in animal tissues **(Figure 2.26, p. 46)**. **Anchoring junctions** form buttonlike spots, or belts, that run entirely around cells, "welding" adjacent cells together. For some anchoring junctions known as **desmosomes**, intermediate filaments anchor the junction in the underlying cytoplasm; in other anchoring junctions known as **adherens junctions**, microfilaments are the anchoring cytoskeletal component. Anchoring junctions are most common in tissues that are subject to stretching, shear, or other mechanical forces—for example, heart muscle, skin, and the cell layers that cover organs or line body cavities and ducts.

Tight junctions, as the name indicates, are regions of tight connections between membranes of adjacent cells (see Figure 2.26). The connection is so tight that it can keep particles as small as ions from moving between the cells in the layers.

Tight junctions seal the spaces between cells in the cell layers that cover internal organs and the outer surface of the body, or the layers that line internal cavities and ducts. For example, tight junctions between cells that line the stomach, intestine, and bladder keep the contents of these body cavities from leaking into surrounding tissues.

A tight junction is formed by direct fusion of proteins on the outer surfaces of the two plasma membranes of adjacent cells. Strands of the tight junction proteins form a complex network that gives the appearance of stitch work holding the cells together. Within a tight junction, the plasma membrane is not joined continuously; instead, there are regions of intercellular space. Nonetheless, the network of junction proteins is sufficient to make the tight cell connections characteristic of these junctions.

Gap junctions open direct channels that allow ions and small molecules to pass directly from one cell to another (see Figure 2.26). Hollow protein cylinders embedded in the plasma membranes of adjacent cells line up and form a sort of pipeline that connects the cytoplasm of one cell with the cytoplasm of the next. The flow of ions and small molecules through the channels provides almost instantaneous communication between animal cells, similar to the communication that plasmodesmata provide between plant cells.

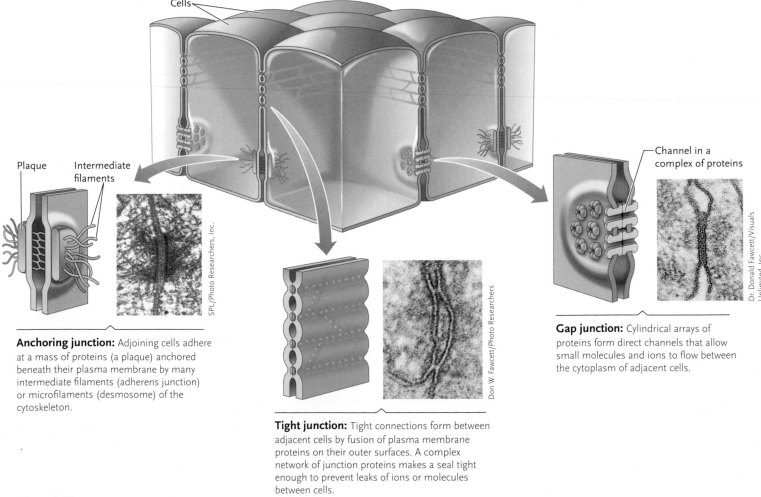

Anchoring junction: Adjoining cells adhere at a mass of proteins (a plaque) anchored beneath their plasma membrane by many intermediate filaments (adherens junction) or microfilaments (desmosome) of the cytoskeleton.

Tight junction: Tight connections form between adjacent cells by fusion of plasma membrane proteins on their outer surfaces. A complex network of junction proteins makes a seal tight enough to prevent leaks of ions or molecules between cells.

Gap junction: Cylindrical arrays of proteins form direct channels that allow small molecules and ions to flow between the cytoplasm of adjacent cells.

Figure 2.26
Anchoring junctions, tight junctions, and gap junctions, which connect cells in animal tissues. Anchoring junctions reinforce the cell-to-cell connections made by cell adhesion molecules, tight junctions seal the spaces between cells, and gap junctions create direct channels of communication between animal cells.

In vertebrates, gap junctions occur between cells within almost all body tissues, but not between cells of different tissues. These junctions are particularly important in heart muscle tissues and in the smooth muscle tissues that form the uterus, where their pathways of communication allow the cells of the organ to operate as a coordinated unit. Although most nerve tissues do not have gap junctions, nerve cells in dental pulp are connected by gap junctions; they are responsible for the discomfort you feel if your teeth are disturbed or damaged, or when a dentist pokes a probe into a cavity.

2.5c The Extracellular Matrix Organizes the Cell Exterior

Many types of animal cells are embedded in an ECM that consists of proteins and polysaccharides secreted by the cells themselves **(Figure 2.27)**. The primary function of the ECM is protection and support. The ECM forms the mass of skin, bones, and tendons; it also forms many highly specialized extracellular structures such as the cornea of the eye and filtering networks in the kidney. The ECM also affects cell division, adhesion, motility, and embryonic development, and it takes part in reactions to wounds and disease.

Glycoproteins are the main component of the ECM. In most animals, the most abundant ECM glycoprotein is *collagen,* which forms fibres with great tensile strength and elasticity. In vertebrates, the collagens of tendons, cartilage, and bone are the most abundant proteins of the body, making up about half of the total body protein by weight. (Collagens and their roles in body structures are described in further detail in Chapter 31.)

The consistency of the matrix, which may range from soft and jellylike to hard and elastic, depends on a network of proteoglycans that surrounds the collagen fibres. *Proteoglycans* are glycoproteins that consist of small proteins noncovalently attached to long polysaccharide molecules. Matrix consistency depends on the number of interlinks in this network, which determines how much water can be trapped in it. For example, cartilage, which contains a high proportion of interlinked glycoproteins, is relatively soft. Tendons, which are almost pure collagen, are tough and elastic. In bone, the glycoprotein network that surrounds collagen fibres is impregnated with mineral crystals, producing a dense and hard—but still elastic—structure that is about as strong as fibreglass or reinforced concrete.

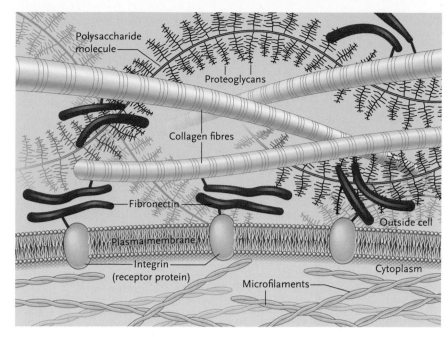

Figure 2.27
Components of the extracellular matrix in an animal cell.

Yet another class of glycoproteins is *fibronectins,* which aid in organizing the ECM and help cells attach to it. Fibronectins bind to receptor proteins called *integrins* that span the plasma membrane. On the cytoplasmic side of the plasma membrane, the integrins bind to microfilaments of the cytoskeleton. Integrins integrate changes outside and inside the cell by communicating changes in the ECM to the cytoskeleton.

Having laid the groundwork for cell structure and function in this chapter, we next take up further details of individual cell structures, beginning with the roles of cell membranes in transport in the next chapter.

STUDY BREAK

1. Distinguish between anchoring junctions, tight junctions, and gap junctions.
2. What is the structure and function of the extracellular matrix?

Review

CourseMate Access an interactive eBook, chapter-specific interactive learning tools, including flashcards, quizzes, videos, and more in your Biology **CourseMate**, accessed through NelsonBrain.com

Aplia™ is an online interactive learning solution that helps you improve comprehension—and your grade—by integrating a variety of mediums and tools such as videos, tutorials, practice tests, and an interactive eBook.

2.1 Basic Features of Cell Structure and Function

- According to the cell theory, (1) all living organisms are composed of cells, (2) cells are the structural and functional units of life, and (3) cells arise only from the division of pre-existing cells.

- Cells of all kinds are divided internally into a central region containing the genetic material and the cytoplasm, which consists of the cytosol, the cytoskeleton, and organelles and is bounded by the plasma membrane.

- The plasma membrane is a lipid bilayer in which transport proteins are embedded (Figure 2.6).

- In the cytoplasm, proteins are made, most of the other molecules required for growth and reproduction are assembled, and energy absorbed from the surroundings is converted into energy usable by the cell.

2.2 Prokaryotic Cells

- Prokaryotic cells are surrounded by a plasma membrane and, in most groups, are enclosed by a cell wall. The genetic material, typically a single, circular DNA molecule, is located in the nucleoid. The cytoplasm contains masses of ribosomes (Figure 2.7).

2.3 Eukaryotic Cells

- Eukaryotic cells have a true nucleus, which is separated from the cytoplasm by the nuclear envelope perforated by nuclear pores. A plasma membrane forms the outer boundary of the cell. Other membrane systems enclose specialized compartments as organelles in the cytoplasm (Figures 2.8 and 2.9).

- The eukaryotic nucleus contains chromatin, a combination of DNA and proteins. A specialized segment of the chromatin forms the nucleolus, where ribosomal RNA molecules are made and combined with ribosomal proteins to make ribosomes. The nuclear envelope contains nuclear pore complexes with pores that allow passive or assisted transport of molecules between the nucleus and the cytoplasm (Figure 2.10).

- Eukaryotic cytoplasm contains ribosomes (Figure 2.11), an endomembrane system, mitochondria, microbodies, the cytoskeleton, and some organelles specific to certain organisms. The endomembrane system includes the nuclear envelope, the endoplasmic reticulum (ER), the Golgi complex, lysosomes, vesicles, and the plasma membrane.

- The endoplasmic reticulum (ER) occurs in two forms: rough and smooth ER. The ribosome-studded rough ER makes proteins that become part of cell membranes or are released from the cell. Smooth ER synthesizes lipids and breaks down toxic substances (Figure 2.12).

- The Golgi complex chemically modifies proteins made in the rough ER and sorts finished proteins to be secreted from the cell, embedded in the plasma membrane, or included in lysosomes (Figure 2.13).

- Lysosomes, specialized vesicles that contain hydrolytic enzymes, digest complex molecules such as food molecules that enter the cell by endocytosis, cellular organelles that are no longer functioning correctly, and engulfed bacteria and cell debris (Figure 2.15).

- Mitochondria carry out cellular respiration, the conversion of fuel molecules into the energy of ATP (Figure 2.17).

- The cytoskeleton is a supportive structure built from microtubules, intermediate filaments, and microfilaments. Motor proteins walking along microtubules and microfilaments produce most movements of animal cells (Figures 2.18–2.20).

- Motor protein–controlled sliding of microtubules generates the movements of flagella and cilia. Flagella and cilia arise from centrioles (Figures 2.21–2.23).

2.4 Specialized Structures of Plant Cells

- Plant cells contain all the eukaryotic structures found in animal cells except for lysosomes. They also contain three structures not found in animal cells: chloroplasts, a central vacuole, and a cell wall (Figure 2.9).

- Chloroplasts contain pigments and molecular systems that absorb light energy and convert it to chemical energy. The chemical energy is used inside the chloroplasts to assemble carbohydrates and other organic molecules from simple inorganic raw materials (Figure 2.24).

- The large central vacuole, which consists of a tonoplast enclosing an inner space, develops pressure that supports plant cells, accounts for much of cellular growth by enlarging as cells mature, and serves as a storage site for substances including waste materials (Figure 2.9).

- A cellulose cell wall surrounds plant cells, providing support and protection. Plant cell walls are perforated by plasmodesmata, channels that provide direct pathways of communication between the cytoplasm of adjacent cells (Figure 2.25).

2.5 The Animal Cell Surface

- Animal cells have specialized surface molecules and structures that function in cell adhesion, communication, and support.

- Cell adhesion molecules bind to specific molecules on other cells. The adhesions organize and hold together cells of the same type in body tissues.

- Cell adhesions are reinforced by various junctions. Anchoring junctions hold cells together. Tight junctions seal together the plasma membranes of adjacent cells, preventing ions and molecules from moving between the cells. Gap junctions open direct channels between the cytoplasm of adjacent cells (Figure 2.26).

- The extracellular matrix (ECM), formed from collagen proteins embedded in a matrix of branched glycoproteins, functions primarily in cell and body protection and support but also affects cell division, motility, embryonic development, and wound healing (Figure 2.27).

Questions

Self-Test Questions

1. Suppose you are examining a cell from a crime scene using an electron microscope, and you find it contains ribosomes, DNA, a plasma membrane, a cell wall, and mitochondria. What type of cell is it?
   a. a lung cell
   b. a plant cell
   c. a prokaryotic cell
   d. a cell from the surface of a human fingernail
   e. a sperm cell

2. A bacterium converts food energy into the chemical energy of ATP using proteins that are found on what part of the cell?
   a. Golgi complex.
   b. flagellum
   c. ribosome
   d. cell wall.
   e. plasma membrane.

3. Which of the following is present in members of the domain Archaea?
   a. Nuclear envelope
   b. Chloroplast
   c. Microtubules
   d. Ribosomes
   e. Plasmodesmata

4. Which statement about cell size is correct?
   a. As cell size increases its surface area/volume ratio increases
   b. A typical animal cell is about 1000 times the size of a bacterium.
   c. The surface area of a cell increases as the cube of the linear dimension.
   d. Increasing membrane surface area allows for a cell to maintain a larger volume.

5. How does a large nuclear-localized protein such as a transcription factor get into the nucleus?
   a. It diffuse across the lipid bilayer of the nuclear envelope.
   b. It is translated on ribosomes that are already within the nucleus.
   c. It contains a nuclear localization signal that is recognized by the nuclear pore complex.
   d. It is synthesized is the cytosol as a set of small polypeptides that diffuse into the nuceus prior to assembly.

6. Which structure is *not* used in eukaryotic protein manufacture and secretion?
   a. ribosome
   b. lysosome
   c. rough ER
   d. secretory vesicle
   e. Golgi complex

7. Suppose an electron micrograph shows that a cell has extensive amounts of smooth ER throughout. What can you deduce about the cell?
   a. that the cell is synthesizing ATP.
   b. that the cell is metabolically inactive.
   c. that the cell is synthesizing and secreting proteins.
   d. that the cell is synthesizing and metabolizing lipids.

8. Which of the following contributes to sealing the lining of digestive track so that it can retain food?
   a. tight junctions formed by direct fusion of proteins
   b. plasmodesmata that help cells communicate their activities
   c. desmosomes forming buttonlike spots or a belt to keep cells joined together
   d. gap junctions that communicate between cells of the stomach lining and its muscular wall

9. Which of the following statements about proteins is correct?
   a. Proteins are transported to the rough ER for use within the cell.
   b. Lipids and carbohydrates are added to proteins by the Golgi complex.
   c. Proteins are transported directly into the cytosol for secretion from the cell.
   d. Proteins that are to be stored by the cell are moved to the rough ER.
   e. Proteins are synthesized in vesicles.

10. Which of the following is NOT a component of the cytoskeleton?
    a. cilia
    b. actins
    c. microfilaments
    d. microtubules
    e. cytokeratins

Questions for Discussion

1. Many compound microscopes have a filter that eliminates all wavelengths except that of blue light, thereby allowing only blue light to pass through the microscope. Use the spectrum of visible light (see Figure 7.4 in Chapter 7) to explain why the filter improves the resolution of light microscopes.

2. Explain why aliens invading Earth are not likely to be giant cells the size of humans.

3. An electron micrograph of a cell shows the cytoplasm packed with rough ER membranes, a Golgi complex, and mitochondria. What activities might this cell concentrate on? Why would large numbers of mitochondria be required for these activities?

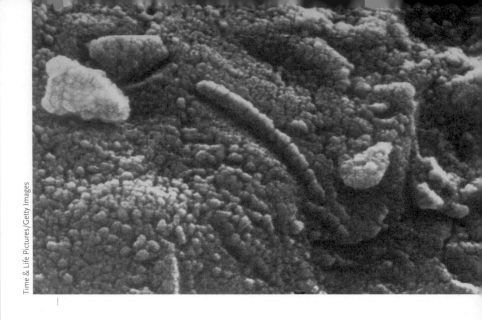

Scanning electron microscope image of a portion of the meteorite ALH84001. The elongate structure may represent a fossilized microorganism.

Time & Life Pictures/Getty Images

STUDY PLAN

3.1   What Is Life?

3.1a   Seven Characteristics Shared by All Life-Forms

3.1b   The Characteristics of Life Are Emergent

3.2   The Chemical Origins of Life

3.2a   Earth Is 4.6 Billion Years Old

3.2b   Earth Lies within the Habitable Zone around the Sun

3.2c   Biologically Important Molecules Can Be Synthesized Outside of Living Cells

3.2d   Life Requires the Synthesis of Polymers

3.3   From Macromolecules to Life

3.3a   Lipid Spheres May Have Led to the Development of Cells

3.3b   RNA Can Carry Information and Catalyze Reactions

3.3c   RNA Is Replaced by DNA for Information Storage and Proteins for Catalysis

3.3d   Simple Oxidation–Reduction Reactions Probably Preceded Metabolism

3.4   The Earliest Forms of Life

3.4a   The Earliest Evidence of Life Is Found in Fossils

3.4b   The First Cells Relied on Anaerobic Metabolism

3.4c   Oxygenic Photosynthesis Led to the Rise in Oxygen in the Atmosphere

3.4d   Could Life Have Come to Earth from Space?

3.4e   All Present-Day Organisms Are Descended from a Common Ancestor

3.5   The Eukaryotic Cell and the Rise of Multicellularity

3.5a   The Theory of Endosymbiosis Suggests That Mitochondria and Chloroplasts Evolved from Ingested Prokaryotes

3.5b   Several Lines of Evidence Support the Theory of Endosymbiosis

3.5c   Horizontal Gene Transfer Followed Endosymbiosis

3.5d   The Endomembrane System May Be Derived from the Plasma Membrane

3.5e   Solving an Energy Crisis Led to Eukaryotes

3.5f   The Evolution of Multicellular Eukaryotes Led to Increased Specialization

3.6   The Search for Extraterrestrial Life

3   Defining Life and Its Origins

WHY IT MATTERS

In 1984, a group of scientists in the Antarctic discovered a 1.9 kg meteorite that they catalogued as ALH84001. Initial studies of the meteorite showed that it was about 4.5 billion years old, which is about the same age as the solar system. Its chemical composition indicated that it had originated from Mars and had impacted Earth approximately 13 000 years ago. The meteorite garnered headlines around the world in 1996 when an article was published in the prestigious journal *Science* with evidence that ALH84001 contained distinct evidence that life had at one time existed on Mars.

Chemical analysis showed that, when on Mars, ALH84001 had at one time been fractured and subsequently infiltrated by liquid water. Using scanning electron microscopy, the coauthors of the article observed very small, elliptical, ropelike, and tubular structures in the fractured surfaces of ALH84001 that look very similar to fossilized prokaryotic cells. Furthermore, the scientists found microscopic mineral "globules," which bear strong resemblance to mineral alterations caused by primitive cells on Earth.

The analysis of meteorites for microfossils continues and remains controversial. In 2011, an article published in the *Journal of*

Cosmology provided additional evidence of bacteria-like fossils within meteorites. Using sophisticated electron microscopy techniques and chemical analysis on three freshly fractured carbonaceous meteorites, data are presented in the article that show the presence of filaments that are strikingly similar in shape to cyanobacteria, a dominant form of photosynthetic bacteria on Earth. The difficulty of unequivocally assigning these structures as remnants of ancient life will continue to make the conclusions of such analyses controversial.

In this chapter, we explore two of the most basic of biological questions: What is life, and how did life evolve? After introducing the fundamental characteristics that all organisms share, we work through a discussion of the origins of life. Starting with how biologically important molecules could have been synthesized in the absence of life, we move through hypotheses regarding the first cells, to evolution of various macromolecules (DNA, RNA, proteins), and finally to what drove the evolution of the eukaryotic cell. The chapter closes where it begins in "Why It Matters," with a discussion on the possibility of life existing elsewhere in the galaxy.

3.1 What Is Life?

As we saw in the last chapter, all life is composed of cells—the fundamental unit of all life. But what is life? How can we define it? Picture a frog sitting on a rock, slowly shifting its head to follow the movements of insects flying nearby **(Figure 3.1).** You know instinctively that the frog is alive and the rock is not. But if you examine both at the atomic level, you will find that the difference between them is lost. The types of elements and atoms found in living things are also found in nonliving forms of matter. As well, living cells obey the same fundamental laws of physics and chemistry as the abiotic (nonliving) world. For example, the biochemical reactions that take place within living cells, although remarkable, are only modifications of chemical reactions that occur outside cells.

3.1a Seven Characteristics Shared by All Life-Forms

Although life seems relatively easy to recognize, it is not easy to define using a single sentence or even two. Life is defined most effectively by a list of attributes that all forms of life possess. As detailed in **Figure 3.2, p. 52,** all life displays order, harnesses and utilizes energy, reproduces, responds to stimuli, exhibits homeostasis, grows and develops, and evolves.

There are a small number of biological systems that straddle the line between the biotic and abiotic worlds. The best example of this is a virus **(Figure 3.3, p. 52).**

Figure 3.1
Red-eyed tree frog on a rock.

Sascha Burkard/Shutterstock

Viruses are very small infectious agents that you will learn more about in Chapter 21. They display many of the properties of life, including the ability to reproduce and evolve over time. However, the characteristics of life that a virus has are based on its ability to infect cells. For example, although viruses contain nucleic acids (DNA and RNA), they lack the cellular machinery and metabolism to use that genetic information to synthesize their own proteins. To make proteins, they have to infect living cells and essentially hijack their translational machinery and metabolism in order to reproduce. For this reason, most scientists do not consider viruses to be alive.

3.1b The Characteristics of Life Are Emergent

Each of the characteristics of life depicted in Figure 3.2, p. 52, reflects a remarkable complexity resulting from a hierarchy of interactions that begins with atoms and progresses through molecules to macromolecules and cells. Depending upon the organism, this hierarchy may continue upward in complexity and include organelles, tissues, and organs. The seven properties of life shown in Figure 3.2, p. 52, are called emergent because they come about, or emerge, from many simpler interactions that, in themselves, do not have the properties found at the higher levels. For example, the ability to harness and utilize energy is not a property of molecules or proteins or biological membranes in isolation; rather the ability emerges from the interactions of all three of these as part of a metabolic process. In this way, not only is the structural or functional complexity of living systems more than the sum of the parts, but it is fundamentally different.

A classic example that illustrates the concept of emergence is a type of termite nest called a cathedral **(Figure 3.4, p. 53).** These elegantly complex structures,

a. Display order: All forms of life including this flower are arranged in a highly ordered manner, with the cell being the fundamental unit of life.

harmeet/StockXchng

b. Harness and utilize energy: Like this hummingbird, all forms of life acquire energy from the environment and use it to maintain their highly ordered state.

Steve Byland/Shutterstock

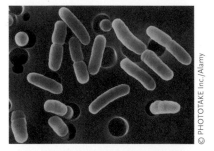

c. Reproduce: All organisms have the ability to make more of their own kind. Here, some of the bacteria have just divided into two daughter cells.

© PHOTOTAKE Inc./Alamy

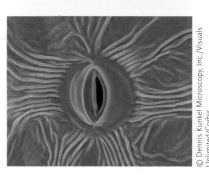

d. Respond to stimuli: Organisms can make adjustments to their structure, function, and behaviour in response to changes to the external environment. A plant can adjust the size of the pores (stomata) on the surface of its leaves to regulate gas exchange.

© Dennis Kunkel Microscopy, Inc./Visuals Unlimited/Corbis

e. Exhibit homeostasis: Organisms are able to regulate their internal environment such that conditions remain relatively constant. Sweating is one way in which the body attempts to remove heat and thereby maintain a constant temperature.

© Tim Pannell/CORBIS

f. Growth and development: All organisms increase their size by increasing the size and/or number of cells. Many organisms also change over time.

© Karin Duthie/Alamy

g. Evolve: Populations of living organisms change over the course of generations to become better adapted to their environment. The snowy owl illustrates this perfectly.

Art Wolfe/Stone/Getty Images

Figure 3.2
The seven characteristics of life.

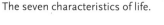

STUDY BREAK

1. List the seven fundamental characteristics common to all life.
2. What does it mean that life displays emergent properties?

Figure 3.3
Bacteriophage infecting a bacterium. Notice bacteriophage on the cell surface as well as inside the bacterium. A bacteriophage is a type of virus. Viruses are generally not considered to be alive.

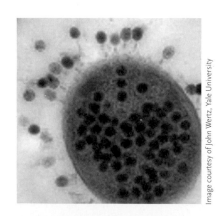

Image courtesy of John Wertz, Yale University

most common in Australia, can grow to over 3 m tall and are the product of the activities of thousands of termites. Remarkably, there is no master plan that is followed or "queen" that gives instructions. Termites build up the mound cell by cell, based on local conditions, totally unaware of the overall structure that emerges.

3.2 The Chemical Origins of Life

Recall from Chapter 2 that one of the tenets of the cell theory states that cells arise only from the growth and division of pre-existing cells. This tenet has probably been true for hundreds of millions of years, yet there must have been a time when this was not the case. There must have been a time when no cells existed, when there was no life. It is thought that over the course of hundreds of millions of years, cells with the characteristics of life arose out of a mixture of molecules that existed on primordial Earth. In this section we discuss the formation of the solar system and present hypotheses for how biologically important molecules could have been synthesized on early Earth in the absence of life.

Figure 3.4
A **termite cathedral.** The sophisticated structure of a termite nest emerges from the simple work of thousands of individual termites. In a similar way, the complex properties of life emerge from much simpler molecular interactions.

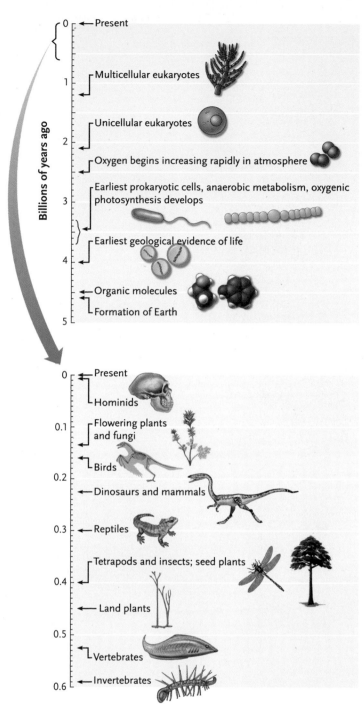

Figure 3.5
A timeline for the evolution of major forms of life. The dates presented are derived mostly from geological evidence.

3.2a The Earth Is 4.6 Billion Years Old

Before we discuss the origins of life, we present in **Figure 3.5** a timeline of the evolution of major present-day organisms. Each date is still the subject of some debate within the scientific community and is based primarily on radiometric dating methods (see *The Purple Pages, P-XX*). A more complete presentation of the timeline for the evolution of organismal life is found in *The Purple Pages, P-XX*. An overview of the fossil record from which the dating and thus ordering of the major events is obtained is presented in Chapter 17. This is followed in later chapters by in-depth discussions of the evolution of the major groups of organisms, including, for example, land plants (Chapter 24), birds (Chapter 26), and mammals (Chapter 26)

Earth was formed approximately 4.6 billion years ago. To give us some sense of just how long 4.6 billion years is, as well as the relative timing of some major events in the history of life on Earth, **Figure 3.6, p. 54,** condenses the entire history of Earth into a unit of time that we are more familiar with—one year. With 4.6 billion years condensed into a single year, each day represents an interval of 12.6 million years!

Using our condensed version of the history of Earth, we set the date of the formation of Earth as January 1 at 12:00 a.m. Based on chemical evidence, life may have started as early as 4.0 billion years ago. This translates to mid-March in our one-year calendar. The first clear fossil evidence of prokaryotic cells occurs in late March or about 3.5 billion years ago. Fossil evidence of eukaryotes has been dated to about 2 billion years ago, which is not until early July using our one-year analogy. Perhaps surprisingly, animals do not make an appearance until mid-October (about 525

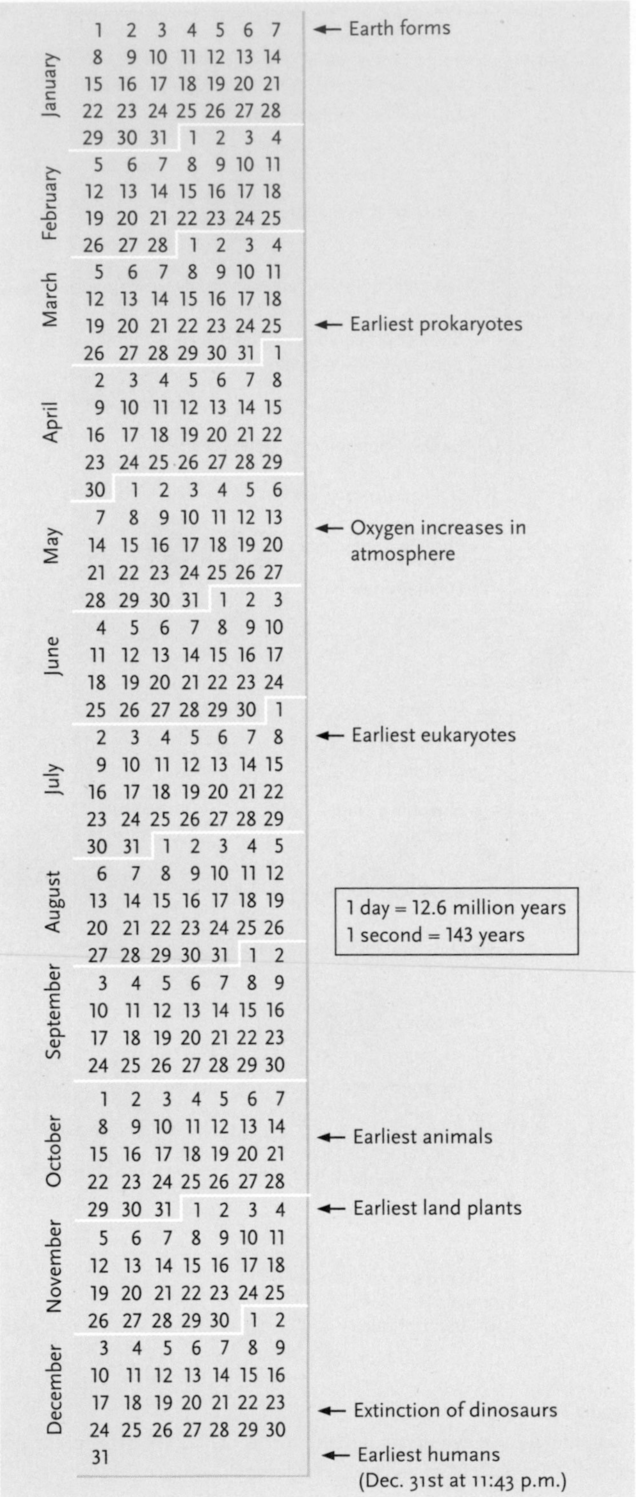

January: 1 2 3 4 5 6 7 / 8 9 10 11 12 13 14 / 15 16 17 18 19 20 21 / 22 23 24 25 26 27 28 / 29 30 31 ← Earth forms

February: 1 2 3 4 / 5 6 7 8 9 10 11 / 12 13 14 15 16 17 18 / 19 20 21 22 23 24 25 / 26 27 28

March: 1 2 3 4 / 5 6 7 8 9 10 11 / 12 13 14 15 16 17 18 / 19 20 21 22 23 24 25 ← Earliest prokaryotes / 26 27 28 29 30 31 1

April: 2 3 4 5 6 7 8 / 9 10 11 12 13 14 15 / 16 17 18 19 20 21 22 / 23 24 25 26 27 28 29 / 30

May: 1 2 3 4 5 6 / 7 8 9 10 11 12 13 / 14 15 16 17 18 19 20 ← Oxygen increases in atmosphere / 21 22 23 24 25 26 27 / 28 29 30 31 1 2 3

June: 4 5 6 7 8 9 10 / 11 12 13 14 15 16 17 / 18 19 20 21 22 23 24 / 25 26 27 28 29 30 1

July: 2 3 4 5 6 7 8 ← Earliest eukaryotes / 9 10 11 12 13 14 15 / 16 17 18 19 20 21 22 / 23 24 25 26 27 28 29 / 30 31 1 2 3 4 5

August: 6 7 8 9 10 11 12 / 13 14 15 16 17 18 19 / 20 21 22 23 24 25 26 / 27 28 29 30 31 1 2

September: 3 4 5 6 7 8 9 / 10 11 12 13 14 15 16 / 17 18 19 20 21 22 23 / 24 25 26 27 28 29 30

October: 1 2 3 4 5 6 7 / 8 9 10 11 12 13 14 / 15 16 17 18 19 20 21 ← Earliest animals / 22 23 24 25 26 27 28 / 29 30 31 1 2 3 4 ← Earliest land plants

November: 5 6 7 8 9 10 11 / 12 13 14 15 16 17 18 / 19 20 21 22 23 24 25 / 26 27 28 29 30 1 2

December: 3 4 5 6 7 8 9 / 10 11 12 13 14 15 16 / 17 18 19 20 21 22 23 ← Extinction of dinosaurs / 24 25 26 27 28 29 30 / 31 ← Earliest humans (Dec. 31st at 11:43 p.m.)

1 day = 12.6 million years
1 second = 143 years

Figure 3.6
The history of Earth condensed into one year.

3.2b Earth Lies within the Habitable Zone around the Sun

According to the most widely accepted hypothesis, all components of the solar system were formed at the same time by the gravitational condensation of matter present in an interstellar cloud, which initially consisted mostly of hydrogen. Intense heat and pressure generated in the central region of the cloud formed the Sun, whereas the remainder of the spiralling dust and gas condensed into the planets. Astronomers agree that this series of events is probably typical for the vast majority of the stars and planetary systems in our galaxy, the Milky Way.

Once Earth was formed, its early history was marked by bombardment of rock from the still-forming solar system and extensive volcanic and seismic activity **(Figure 3.7).** Over time, Earth radiated away some of its heat, and surface layers cooled and solidified into the rocks of the crust. Because of its size, Earth's gravitational pull was strong enough to hold an atmosphere around the planet. The atmosphere was derived partly from the original dust cloud and partly from gases released from Earth's interior as it cooled. It is estimated that it took approximately 500 million years for Earth to cool to temperatures that could nurture the development of life.

Within the Solar System, there is currently no conclusive evidence that a planet other than Earth harbours life. The primary reason for this is that, unlike the other planets, Earth is situated at a position where heat from the Sun allows for surface temperatures to be within a range that allows water to exist in a liquid state. Interestingly, recent data from NASA's Mars Reconnaissance Orbiter suggest that some liquid water may exist on Mars as well. It is the presence of liquid water that is seen as a fundamental prerequisite for the development of life (see *The Purple Pages* for more on the structure and unique properties of water). Because of the importance of water for the development of life, the region of space around a star where temperatures would allow for liquid water is termed the *habitable zone* **(Figure 3.8).** As you would expect, the precise distance from the star that defines the habitable zone will vary depending upon the type of star and how much energy it emits.

3.2c Biologically Important Molecules Can Be Synthesized Outside of Living Cells

All forms of life are composed of the major macromolecules nucleic acids, proteins, lipids, and carbohydrates (see *The Purple Pages* for an overview of these molecules). With the exception of lipids, these macromolecules are derived from simpler molecules such as nucleotides, amino acids, and sugars, that in modern-day cells, are the products of complex metabolic pathways. But how were these molecules formed in the absence of life? There are three major hypotheses.

Hypothesis 1: Reducing Atmosphere. The atmosphere of 4 billion years ago was vastly different from the one

million years ago) and land plants until the following month. The extinction of dinosaurs, which was completed by about 65 million years ago, does not occur until late December. What about humans? We may think humans, *Homo sapiens,* have been around a long time, but relative to other forms of life, the roughly 150 000 years that modern humans have existed is a very short period of time—a blip on our time-scale. Using our year analogy, modern humans have existed only since December 31—more precisely, December 31 at 11:42 p.m.!

Reproduced courtesy of Bonestell LLC

Figure 3.7
An artist's depiction of the primordial Earth.

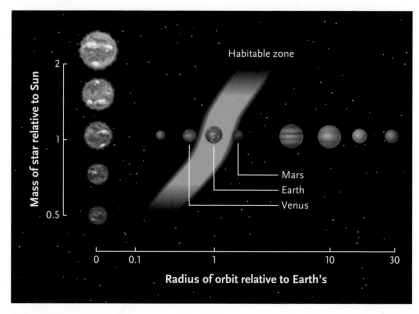

Figure 3.8
The habitable zone. The region around a star where water would exist in a liquid state and thus be conducive to the development of life is termed the habitable zone (shown in blue). The distance from the star where the zone occurs varies depending upon the energy output of the parent star. The Sun, which is considered an average star, is shown as 1 on the scale at the left.

reactions with one another that would have yielded larger and more complex organic molecules.

In comparison to the proposed reducing atmosphere of primordial Earth, today's atmosphere is classified as an *oxidizing atmosphere*. The presence of high levels of oxygen prevents complex, electron-rich molecules from being formed because oxygen is a particularly strong oxidizing molecule and would itself accept the electrons from organic molecules and be reduced to water. Besides allowing for the build up of electron-rich molecules, the lack of oxygen in the primordial atmosphere also meant that there was no ozone (O_3) layer, which only developed after oxygen levels in the atmosphere began to increase. Both Oparin and Haldane hypothesized that without the ozone layer, energetic ultraviolet light was able to reach the lower atmosphere, and along with abundant lightning, provided the energy needed to drive the formation of biologically important molecules.

Experimental evidence in support of the Oparin–Haldane hypothesis came in 1953 when Stanley Miller, a graduate student of Harold Urey at the University of Chicago, created a laboratory simulation of the reducing atmosphere believed to have existed on early Earth. Miller placed components of a reducing atmosphere—hydrogen, methane, ammonia, and water vapour—in a closed apparatus and exposed the gases to an energy source in the form of continuously sparking electrodes **(Figure 3.9, p. 56)**. Water vapour was added to the "atmosphere" in one part of the apparatus and subsequently condensed back into water by cooling in another part. After running the experiment for one week, Miller found a large assortment of organic compounds including urea; amino acids; and lactic, formic, and acetic acids after condensing the atmosphere into a liquid. In fact, as much as 15% of the carbon that was originally in the methane at the start of the experiment ended up in molecules that are common in living organisms.

Other chemicals have been tested in the Miller–Urey apparatus, including hydrogen cyanide (HCN) and formaldehyde (CH_2O), which are considered to have been among the substances formed in the primitive atmosphere. When cyanide and formaldehyde were added to the simulated primitive atmosphere

today. The primordial atmosphere probably contained an abundance of water vapour from the evaporation of water at the surface, as well as large quantities of hydrogen (H_2), carbon dioxide (CO_2), ammonia (NH_3), and methane (CH_4). There was an almost complete absence of oxygen (O_2). In the 1920s, two scientists, Aleksander Oparin and John Haldane, independently proposed that organic molecules, essential to the formation of life could have formed in the atmosphere of primordial Earth. A critical aspect of what is known as the Oparin–Haldane hypothesis is that the early atmosphere was a *reducing atmosphere* because of the presence of large concentrations of molecules such as hydrogen, methane, and ammonia. These molecules contain an abundance of electrons and hydrogen and would have entered into

Figure 3.9
The Miller–Urey experiment. Using this apparatus, Stanley Miller, a graduate student, demonstrated that organic molecules can be synthesized under conditions simulating primordial Earth.

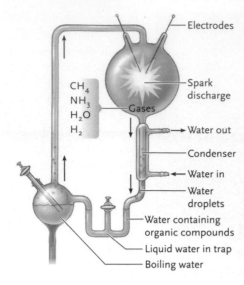

Electrodes

Spark discharge

Gases

CH₄
NH₃
H₂O
H₂

Water out

Condenser

Water in

Water droplets

Water containing organic compounds

Liquid water in trap

Boiling water

Figure 3.10
Deep-sea vent. Researchers from the Woods Hole Oceanographic Institute watch from inside the submersible Alvin as a "black smoker" chimney erupts from a seafloor vent. The regions surrounding these vents have been found to be teeming with a diversity of life.

in Miller's apparatus, all the building blocks of complex biological molecules were produced—amino acids; fatty acids; the purine and pyrimidine components of nucleic acids; sugars such as glyceraldehyde, ribose, glucose, and fructose; and phospholipids, which form the lipid bilayers of biological membranes.

Over the years since the Miller–Urey experiment was first conducted, considerable debate has developed in the scientific community as to whether the atmosphere of primitive Earth contained enough methane and ammonia to be considered reducing. Some geologists have suggested that based on the analysis of volcanic activity, primitive Earth was probably somewhat less reactive—neither reducing nor oxidizing—with molecules including nitrogen gases (N_2), carbon monoxide (CO), and carbon dioxide (CO_2) the most dominant. Even with this composition, scientists have been able to successfully synthesize the same crucial building blocks of life in the laboratory. Regardless of the actual composition of the atmosphere on primordial Earth, the significance of the Miller–Urey experiment cannot be overstated. It was the first experiment to demonstrate the abiotic formation of molecules critical to life, such as amino acids, nucleotides, and simple sugars, and it showed that they could be produced relatively easily. At the time, this remarkable finding laid the groundwork for further research into the origins of life.

Hypothesis 2: Deep-Sea Vents. Besides the atmosphere, an alternative hypothesis maintains that the complex organic molecules necessary for life could have originated on the ocean floor at the site of deep-sea (hydrothermal) vents. These cracks are found around the globe near sites of volcanic or tectonic activity and release superheated nutrient-rich water at temperatures in excess of 300°C, as well as reduced molecules including methane, ammonia, and hydrogen sulfide (H_2S) **(Figure 3.10)**. Today, the areas around these vents support a remarkable diversity of life. Many of these life forms are of tremendous scientific interest because of

their ability to thrive in an environment that is characterized by extreme pressure and the total absence of light.

Hypothesis 3: Extraterrestrial Origins. It is entirely possible that the key organic molecules required for life to begin came from space. Each year more than 500 meteorites impact the Earth, many of which belong to the class called carbonaceous chondrites, which are particularly rich in organic molecules. One of the most famous is the Murchison meteorite that landed in Murchison, Victoria, Australia, in 1969 **(Figure 3.11)**. Analysis of the Murchison meteorite showed that it contains an assortment of biologically important molecules including a range of amino acids such as glycine, glutamic acid, and alanine, as well as purines and pyrimidines.

3.2d Life Requires the Synthesis of Polymers

Primordial Earth contained very little oxygen, and because of this, complex organic molecules could have existed for much longer than would be possible in today's oxygen-rich world. Even if they did accumulate on early Earth, molecules such as amino acids and nucleotides are monomers, which are simpler and easier to synthesize than the key chemical components of life, such as nucleic acids and proteins, which are **polymers**—macromolecules formed from the bonding together of individual monomers. Nucleic acids are polymers of nucleotides, proteins are polymers of amino acids, and many carbohydrates are polymers of simple sugars. Polymers are synthesized by dehydration synthesis, which is discussed in *The Purple Pages*.

Today, the synthesis of proteins and nucleic acids requires protein-based catalysts called enzymes and results in macromolecules that often consist of hundreds to many thousands of monomers linked together. So how do you make the polymers that are required for life

© Woods Hole Oceanographic Institution

Figure 3.11

The Murchison meteorite. Many meteorites have been shown to contain a range of biologically important molecules, including a number of amino acids.

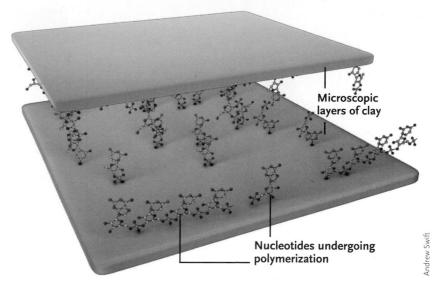

Microscopic layers of clay

Nucleotides undergoing polymerization

Figure 3.12

Clay surfaces catalyze polymerization. The charged microscopic layered structure of clay allows for the formation of relatively short polymers of proteins and nucleic acids (shown).

without sophisticated enzymes? The basis of a working hypothesis to address this question must be built from the supposition that the very earliest forms of life must have been very simple—far simpler than a modern bacterium, for example. Scientists hypothesize that a polymer that consists of even 10–50 monomers may have been of sufficient length to impart a specific function (like a protein) or store sufficient information (like a nucleic acid) to make their formation advantageous to an organism. It is, however, doubtful that polymerization could have occurred in the aqueous environment of early Earth, as it would be very rare for monomers to interact precisely enough with one another to polymerize. It is more likely that solid surfaces, especially clays, could have provided the type of environment necessary for polymerization to occur **(Figure 3.12)**. Clays consist of very thin layers of minerals separated by layers of water only a few nanometres thick. The layered structure of clay is also charged, allowing for molecular adhesion forces to bring monomers together in precise orientations that could more readily lead to polymer formation. Clays can also store the potential energy that may have been used for energy-requiring polymerization reactions. This *clay hypothesis* is supported by laboratory experiments that demonstrate the formation of short nucleic acid chains and polypeptides can be synthesized on a clay surface.

STUDY BREAK

1. For the understanding of the origins of life, what was the significance of the Miller–Urey experiment?
2. What is the difference between a reducing atmosphere and an oxidizing atmosphere?

3.3 From Macromolecules to Life

In the previous section, we discussed how processes present on early Earth could have generated macromolecules crucial to the development of life. However, if we are to develop a comprehensive model for the origin of life, we need to explain the evolution of three key attributes of a modern cell: (1) a membrane-defined compartment—the cell, (2) a system to store genetic information and use it to guide the synthesis of specific proteins, and (3) energy-transforming pathways to bring in energy from the surroundings and harness it to sustain life. In this section, we discuss possible scenarios for the evolution of these key attributes and consider a number of hypotheses, some of which are supported by laboratory experiments.

3.3a Lipid Spheres May Have Led to the Development of Cells

A critical step along the path to life is the formation of a membrane-defined compartment. Such a compartment would allow for primitive metabolic reactions to take place in an environment that is distinctly different than the external surroundings; the concentration of key molecules could be higher, and greater complexity could be maintained in a closed space. **Protobiont** is the term given to a group of abiotically produced organic molecules that are surrounded by a membrane or membranelike structure. Laboratory experiments have shown that protobionts could have formed spontaneously, that is, without any input of energy, given the conditions on primordial Earth. An early type of protobiont could have been similar to a liposome, which is a lipid vesicle in which the lipid molecules form a bilayer very similar to a cell membrane **(Figure 3.13, p. 58)**. Liposomes can easily be made in the laboratory and are selectively permeable,

Figure 3.13

Liposome. **(a)** An artist's rendition of a liposome, which is composed of a lipid bilayer. Liposomes can assemble spontaneously under simulated primordial conditions. **(b)** Phase micrograph of lipid vesicles assembled from phospholipids in the laboratory.

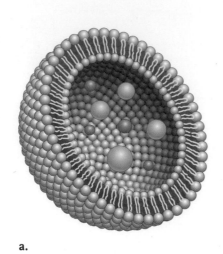

a.

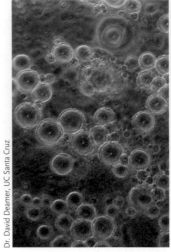

b.

Dr. David Deamer, UC Santa Cruz

allowing only some molecules to move in and out. As well, liposomes can swell and contract depending on the osmotic conditions of their environment.

Recent research from the laboratory of Jack Szostak at Harvard University has shown that the presence of clay not only catalyzes the polymerization of nucleic acids (see Section 3.2) but also accelerates the formation of lipid vesicles. As well, clay particles often become encapsulated in these vesicles, which would provide catalytically active surfaces within membrane vesicles upon which key reactions could take place. Researchers continue to experiment with producing different types of protobionts in the laboratory as a step toward understanding the origins of the first living cell. Present-day thinking is that a lipid membrane system must have evolved simultaneously with a genetic information system (see below).

referred to as the central dogma **(Figure 3.14)**. Each step of the information flow requires the involvement of a group of proteins called enzymes, which catalyze the transcription of DNA into RNA and the translation of the RNA into protein. Enzymes are discussed in detail in Chapter 4.

A fundamental question about the flow of information from DNA to RNA to protein is: how did such a system evolve when the products of the process, proteins, are required to catalyze each step of the process? A breakthrough in our understanding of how such a system may have evolved came in 1979 when Thomas Cech discovered a group of RNA molecules that could themselves act as catalysts. This group of RNA catalysts, called **ribozymes**, can catalyze reactions on the precursor RNA molecules that lead to their own synthesis, as well as on unrelated RNA molecules **(Figure 3.15)**. Ribozymes have catalytic properties because these single-stranded molecules can fold into very specific shapes based on intramolecular hydrogen bonding or base pairing. The fact that specificity in folding imparts specificity in function is very common to proteins, especially enzymes where precise three-dimensional shape is critical for reacting with substrate molecules. Protein folding is discussed in more detail in *The Purple Pages*.

The discovery of ribozymes revolutionized thinking about the origin of life. Instead of the contemporary system that requires all three molecules—DNA, RNA, and protein—early life may have existed in an "RNA

3.3b RNA Can Carry Information and Catalyze Reactions

As discussed in Chapter 2, DNA is the molecule that provides every cell with the genetic instructions necessary to function. Recall as well that the information in DNA is copied into RNA, which directs protein synthesis on ribosomes. Even the simplest prokaryotic cell contains thousands of proteins, each coded by a unique DNA sequence, a gene. The flow of information from DNA to RNA to protein is common to all forms of life and is

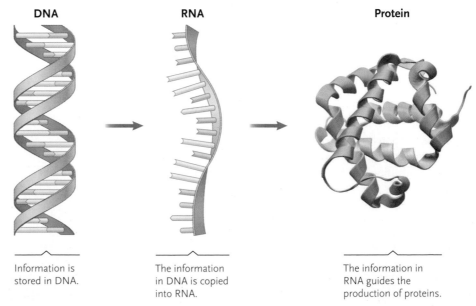

DNA   **RNA**   **Protein**

Information is stored in DNA.

The information in DNA is copied into RNA.

The information in RNA guides the production of proteins.

Figure 3.14

The central dogma. Information in DNA is used to synthesize proteins through an RNA intermediate. How did such a system evolve when the product, proteins, is required in modern-day cells to catalyze each step?

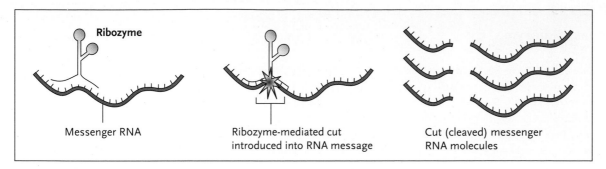

Figure 3.15

Ribozyme. An example of a ribozyme binding to an RNA molecule and catalyzing its breakage. Within a modern-day cell, such reactions may help control gene expression by altering the abundance of functional messenger RNA (mRNA) molecules.

world," where a single type of molecule, RNA, could serve as a carrier of information (due to its nucleotide sequence) and a structural/functional molecule similar to a protein (due to its ability to form unique three-dimensional shapes). Before the discovery of ribozymes, enzymes were the only known biological catalysts. For his remarkable discovery, Thomas Cech was awarded the Nobel Prize in Chemistry in 1989.

3.3c RNA Is Replaced by DNA for Information Storage and Proteins for Catalysis

If life developed in an RNA world, where RNA served as both an information carrier and a catalyst, why is it that in all contemporary organisms genetic information is stored in DNA, and why do enzymes (proteins) catalyze the vast majority of biological reactions? The simple answer is that they do the respective jobs of information storage (DNA) and catalysis (protein) far better than RNA does by itself; thus, the evolution of these molecules would have given organisms that had them a distinct advantage over others that relied solely on RNA.

A possible scenario for the development of today's system of information transfer is shown in **Figure 3.16**. The first cells may have contained only RNA, which was self-replicating and could catalyze a small number of reactions critical for survival. It is hypothesized that a small population of RNA molecules then evolved that could catalyze the formation of very short proteins before the development of ribosomes. Recall from Chapter 2 that the ribosome is the organelle in contemporary organisms required for protein synthesis. It is interesting to note that the ribosome, which plays a key role as an intermediate between RNA and protein, is composed of about two-thirds RNA and one-third protein. In fact, it is the RNA component of the ribosome, not the protein, that actually catalyzes the incorporation of amino acids onto a growing peptide chain. Thus, the ribosome can be considered a type of ribozyme.

Cells that evolved the ability to use the information present in RNA to direct the synthesis of even small proteins would be at a tremendous advantage because

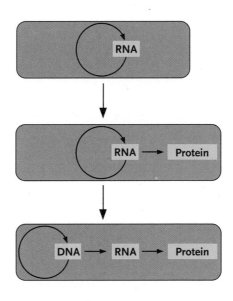

Figure 3.16

Possible scenario for the evolution of the flow of information from DNA to RNA to protein.

proteins are far more versatile than RNA molecules—for three reasons. First, the catalytic power of most enzymes is much greater than that of a ribozyme. A typical enzyme can catalyze the same reaction using a pool of substrate molecules many thousands of times a second. By comparison, the rate of catalysis of most ribozymes is one-tenth to one-hundredth that of enzymes. Second, while the number of ribozymes is very small, a typical cell synthesizes a huge array of different proteins. Twenty different kinds of amino acids, in different arrangements, can be incorporated into a protein, whereas an RNA molecule is composed of different combinations of only four nucleotides. Third, amino acids can interact chemically with each other in bonding arrangements not possible between nucleotides. For these reasons, proteins are the dominant structural and functional molecule of a modern cell.

Continuing with the possible scenario shown in Figure 3.16, the evolution of DNA would have followed that of proteins. Compared with RNA, molecules of DNA are more structurally complex. Not only is DNA double stranded, but it also contains the sugar deoxyribose, which is more difficult to synthesize than the ribose found in molecules of RNA. A possible sequence begins with DNA nucleotides being produced by random removal of an oxygen atom from the ribose

MOLECULE BEHIND BIOLOGY 3.1

L1 Ligase Ribozyme

In the RNA world, RNA served as the molecule of information storage as well as structure and catalysis. To replicate RNA, individual nucleotide triphosphate monomers need to be joined, or ligated, together to form the RNA polymer. Today, this ligation reaction, carried out by a group of protein enzymes called polymerases, can result in RNA strands being many thousands of nucleotides in length. How this polymerization reaction would have been catalyzed in an RNA-only world stumped scientists for years.

Using what is called *in vitro* evolution and selection, scientists recently produced a range of synthetic ribozymes that do not currently exist in nature. One of these synthetic ribozymes is called the L1 ligase ribozyme, and it has been shown to catalyze the joining of two RNA monomers together. This finding clearly suggests that, although not currently found in nature, a ribozyme capable of ligating nucleotides together may have existed on primitive Earth.

subunits of RNA nucleotides. At some point, the DNA nucleotides paired with the RNA informational molecules and were assembled into complementary copies of the RNA sequences. Some modern-day viruses carry out this RNA-to-DNA reaction using the enzyme reverse transcriptase (see Chapter 21). Once the DNA copies were made, selection may have favoured DNA, as it is a much better way to store information than RNA, for three main reasons:

- Each strand of DNA is chemically more stable, and less likely to degrade, than a strand of RNA.
- The base uracil found in RNA is not found in DNA; it has been replaced by thymine. This may be because the conversion of cytosine to uracil is a common mutation in DNA. By utilizing thymine in DNA, any uracil is easily recognized as a damaged cytosine that needs to be repaired.
- DNA is double stranded, so in the case of a mutation to one of the stands, the information contained on the complementary strand can be used to correctly repair the damaged strand.

The stability of DNA is illustrated by the fact that intact DNA can be successfully extracted from tissues that are many thousands of years old. The well-known novel and movie *Jurassic Park* are based on this demonstrated ability. By comparison, RNA needs to be quickly isolated, even from freshly isolated cells, using a strict protocol to prevent its degradation.

3.3d Simple Oxidation–Reduction Reactions Probably Preceded Metabolism

Hypotheses concerning the evolution of energy transduction and metabolism have been particularly difficult to test. Oxidation–reduction reactions were probably among the first energy-releasing reactions of the primitive cells. In our cells, we *oxidize* food molecules (e.g., sugars) and use some of the liberated energy (in the form of electrons) to *reduce* other molecules. In primitive cells, the electrons removed in an oxidation reaction would have been transferred in a one-step process to the substances being reduced. This, however, is not very efficient and leads to a lot of wasted energy. Over time, multi-step processes would have evolved, whereby the energy from oxidation is slowly released. A good example of the slow release of energy is cellular respiration, which is discussed in Chapter 6. The greater efficiency of stepwise energy release would have favoured development of intermediate carriers and opened the way for primitive electron transport chains.

As part of the energy-harnessing reactions, adenosine triphosphate (ATP) became established as the coupling agent that links energy-releasing reactions to those requiring energy. ATP may have first entered early cells as one of many organic molecules absorbed from the primitive environment. Initially, it was probably simply hydrolyzed into adenosine diphosphate (ADP) and inorganic phosphate, resulting in the release of energy. Later, as early cells evolved, some of the energy released during electron transfer was probably used to synthesize ATP directly from ADP and inorganic phosphate. Because of the efficiency and versatility of energy transfer by ATP, it gradually became the primary substance connecting energy-releasing and energy-requiring reactions in early cells.

STUDY BREAK

1. What are ribozymes, and what is their significance in our understanding of the origins of life?
2. In what ways is DNA better than RNA for storing genetic information?

3.4 The Earliest Forms of Life

Given hypotheses proposed for how they may have developed, what do we actually know about the earliest forms of life? In this section, we look at geological and fossil records for the earliest evidence of life. As

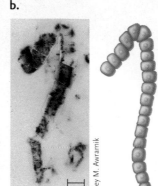

Bill Bachmann, Photo Researchers, Inc.

Stanley M. Awramik

5 μm

Figure 3.17
Early fossil evidence of life.
(a) Stromatolites exposed at low tide in Western Australia's Shark Bay. These mounds, which consist of mineral deposits made by photosynthetic cyanobacteria, are about 2000 years old; they are highly similar in structure to fossil stromatolites that formed more than 3 billion years ago. **(b)** Structures that are believed to be a strand of fossil prokaryote cells in a rock sample that is 3.5 billion years old.

discussed in Chapter 2, because the architecture of prokaryotic cells is the simplest known, they were most probably the first types of cells to evolve.

3.4a The Earliest Evidence of Life Is Found in Fossils

The earliest conclusive evidence of life is found in the fossilized remains of structures called stromatolites, the oldest being formed about 3.5 billion years ago. **Stromatolites** are a type of layered rock that is formed when microorganisms bind particles of sediment together, forming thin sheets **(Figure 3.17)**. Stromatolites are found in habitats characterized by warm shallow water and are most common in Australia. Modern-day stromatolites are formed by the action of a specific group of photosynthetic bacteria called cyanobacteria. Because they possess a sophisticated metabolism (discussed below), cyanobacteria do not represent the earliest forms of life but rather were preceded by much simpler organisms.

Indirect (nonfossil) evidence of life existing before 3.5 billion years ago comes from research looking at the carbon composition of ancient rocks. Early photosynthetic organisms would have had the ability to take CO_2 from the atmosphere and use it to synthesize various organic molecules (sugars, amino acids, etc.). During this process, organisms would have preferentially incorporated the carbon-12 isotope (^{12}C) over other isotopes such as carbon-13 (^{13}C) (see *The Purple Pages*, for a discussion of isotopes). Researchers have discovered sedimentary rocks originating from the ocean floor that contain deposits that have lower levels of the ^{13}C isotope than expected. The most likely explanation is that the deposits are actually the remains of ancient microbes. These sediments have been dated to approximately 3.9 billion years ago. If correct, this would push the origins of life to perhaps as early as 4 billion years ago- approximately 600 million years after the formation of the planet.

3.4b The First Cells Relied on Anaerobic Metabolism

The earliest forms of life were most likely **heterotrophs**, which are organisms that obtain carbon from organic molecules. Modern animals including humans are examples of heterotrophs, we extract energy from organic molecules such as sugars, proteins and fats. Since the early atmosphere contained only trace amounts of oxygen, the earliest heterotrophs must have relied on anaerobic (without oxygen) forms of respiration and fermentative pathways to extract energy from organic molecules (these forms of metabolism are discussed in Chapter 6).

Compared to heterotrophs, **autotrophs** obtain carbon from the environment in an inorganic form, most often carbon dioxide. Plants and other photosynthetic organisms are the dominant autotrophs today. The earliest type of photosynthesis, which probably developed soon after heterotrophy, was *anoxygenic photosynthesis*. Today this form of autotrophy is found only in some groups of bacteria. In anoxygenic photosynthesis, compounds such as hydrogen sulfide and ferrous iron (Fe^{2+}) are used as electron donors for the light reactions of photosynthesis. As we will discuss in detail in Chapter 7, the products of the light reactions, ATP and NADPH, are used to synthesize organic molecules from CO_2.

3.4c Oxygenic Photosynthesis Led to the Rise in Oxygen in the Atmosphere

Starting about 2.5 billion years ago, oxygen (O_2) levels in the atmosphere began increasing. Evidence for this comes from dating a type of sedimentary rock called banded iron **(Figure 3.18, p. 62)**. Geologists believe that these distinctive striped rocks were formed in the sediments of lakes and oceans when dissolved oxygen reacted with the iron in the water, forming a red-coloured precipitate, iron oxide (rust), which ended up being incorporated into the resulting sedimentary rock formations (see Figure 3.18, p. 62).

© Commonwealth of Australia

Figure 3.18
Banded iron. The rust layers in banded iron formations provide evidence for the rise of atmospheric oxygen.

An obvious question to ask is: where did the oxygen come from? Recall from the last section that ancient stromatolites were most probably formed by the action of a group of bacteria called cyanobacteria. Unlike other autotrophs that used hydrogen sulfide or Fe^{2+} as an electron donor for photosynthesis, cyanobacteria had the remarkable ability to use an electron donor that was far more common—water **(Figure 3.19).** The oxidation of water releases not only electrons, which can be used for photosynthetic electron transport, but also molecular oxygen. It is thought that initially the free oxygen was incorporated into mineral deposits including iron. It was only after these reservoirs became full that the oxygen started to accumulate in the atmosphere. Because it releases oxygen, photosynthesis that relies on the oxidation of water as the source of electrons is termed *oxygenic photosynthesis.*

Unlike organisms that use hydrogen sulfide or Fe^{2+}, the ability to oxidize water meant that cyanobacteria could thrive almost anywhere on the planet where there was sunlight. After all, when was the last time you crossed campus and stepped in a puddle of hydrogen sulfide? As a result of the huge ecological advantage that came with being able to oxidize water, the abundance of cyanobacteria on the planet exploded and they quickly became a dominant form of life. Astonishingly, although it evolved perhaps as early as 3.5 billion years ago, oxygenic photosynthesis remains the dominant form of photosynthesis and is used by all plants and algae, as well as present-day cyanobacteria.

Figure 3.19
Cyanobacteria.
(a) Micrograph of a filamentous cyanobacterium of the genus *Nostoc.* **(b)** Ancient cyanobacteria, like modern photosynthetic organisms, were able to use water as an electron donor for photosynthesis. A consequence was the formation of oxygen (O_2), which accumulated in the atmosphere.

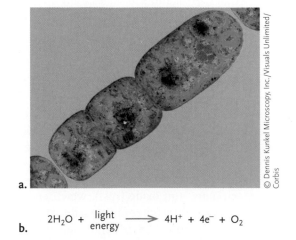

© Dennis Kunkel Microscopy, Inc./Visuals Unlimited/Corbis

a.

b. $\quad 2H_2O + \overset{\text{light}}{\underset{\text{energy}}{}} \longrightarrow 4H^+ + 4e^- + O_2$

3.4d Could Life Have Come to Earth from Space?

Some scientists believe that instead of the evolution of life through processes mentioned above, life on Earth had an extraterrestrial origin. **Panspermia** is the name given to the hypothesis that very simple forms of life are present in outer space and that these may have "seeded" early Earth. As scientists have never found any life existing outside of Earth, there is no evidence to directly support this hypothesis. However, two points of discussion lend support to the idea of an extraterrestrial origin of life on Earth:

First, although life seems very complex, it arose relatively quickly after the formation of Earth. Earth formed 4.6 billion years ago, and we have clear fossil evidence of life dated to about 3.5 billion years ago and chemical evidence to about 3.9 billion years ago. Given that primordial Earth had to cool after being formed before life could develop, some scientists argue that this represents too short a period of time for life to develop solely by abiotic processes occurring on the cooling planet.

Second, research in the past few decades has shown that life is far more resilient than previously thought and could possibly survive for millennia in space. An *extremophile* is the general term given to an organism that is found growing in environments that are lethal to most other organisms. Most extremophiles—mostly bacteria and archaea—can thrive under conditions such as extreme temperature, high pressure, high salinity, and high radiation levels. Research on extremophiles in recent years has shown that life is far more resilient than previously thought and thus it is quite possible that organisms may be able to survive in a dormant state in interstellar space. Prolonged dormancy is a property of reproductive structures called spores, which are produced by a number of bacteria and simple eukaryotes. Bacterial spores, in particular, are highly resistant to changes in the external environment and can be restored to active growth after exposure to water and moderate temperatures. Extremophiles have become a major area of research and have led, in part, to the development of the science of astrobiology (see "People behind Biology").

3.4e All Present-Day Organisms Are Descended from a Common Ancestor

Based on comparing the sequence of ribosomal RNA, all present-day organisms can be categorized into one of three *domains:* Archaea, Bacteria, and Eukarya **(Figure 3.20).** A detailed discussion on the use of nucleic acid sequence information to infer evolutionary relationships is presented in Chapter 18. Because both archaea and bacteria share a similar cell architecture (see Chapter 2), including the lack of a nucleus, they are often referred to as prokaryotes. But as discussed in

Lyle Whyte, Astrobiologist—McGill University

The heightened research interest into extremophiles coupled with technological advances that are driving the robotic exploration of Mars and other planets has spurred the development of the multidisciplinary science of astrobiology. Broadly defined, astrobiology is the study of the origin, evolution, distribution, and future of life in the universe. The field encompasses the search for habitable environments within and outside our solar system and the search for evidence of prebiotic chemistry and life on Mars and elsewhere. As well, astrobiology includes laboratory and field research into the origins and early evolution of life on Earth and studies of the potential for life to adapt to challenges on Earth and in space.

Canada is at the forefront of astrobiology research, as the government has recently established the Canadian Astrobiology Training Program. The program will create the first cross-disciplinary, multi-institutional undergraduate, graduate, and postdoctoral training program in astrobiology. This initiative brings together researchers at five institutions (McGill University, McMaster University, University of Western Ontario, University of Winnipeg, and University of Toronto) with expertise in fields as diverse as geology, chemistry, physics, astronomy, microbiology, and robotics.

The head of the Canadian Astrobiology Training Program is Lyle Whyte of McGill University. Whyte is a Canada Research Chair in Environmental Microbiology. His research examines microbial biodiversity and ecology in unique Canadian high-Arctic ecosystems and is contributing significantly to the knowledge of the diversity, abundance, and critical roles played by microorganisms in polar regions. His research is providing new insights into microbial life at subzero temperatures and their role in global biogeochemical cycling. Whyte and his colleagues do considerable field research in the Canadian Arctic, which is considered by NASA and the Canadian Space Agency to be one of the best sites around the globe to mimic conditions on Mars.

detail in Chapter 20, archaea and bacteria are quite distinct, and evidence indicates that they do not share a close evolutionary origin. In fact, molecular evidence indicates that archaea are more closely related to eukaryotes (the Eukarya) than to bacteria (see Figure 3.20).

As will be discussed in detail in subsequent chapters, there are clear distinctions in structure and function among archaea, bacteria, and eukaryotes. This said, all life-forms currently on Earth share a remarkable set of common attributes. Perhaps the most fundamental of these are the following: (1) cells made of lipid molecules brought together forming a bilayer; (2) a genetic system based on DNA; (3) a system of information transfer—DNA to RNA to protein;

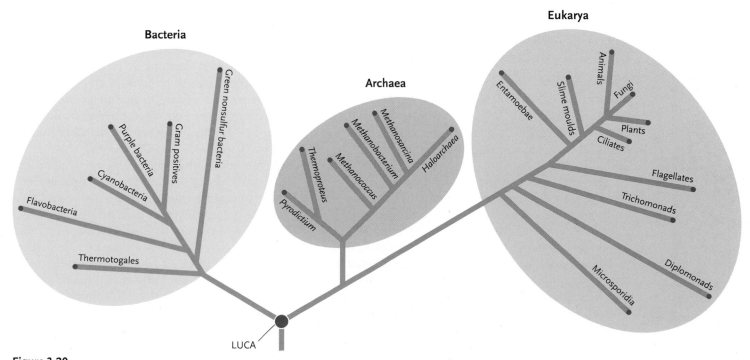

Figure 3.20

The three domains of life: Bacteria, Archaea, and Eukarya. This evolutionary tree is based on the sequencing of ribosomal RNA. All present-day organisms are thought to be descended from a common ancestor—the last universal common ancestor or LUCA.

(4) a system of protein assembly from a pool of amino acids by translation using messenger RNA (mRNA) and transfer RNA (tRNA) using ribosomes; (5) reliance on proteins as the major structural and catalytic molecule; (6) use of ATP as the molecule of chemical energy; and (7) the breakdown of glucose by the metabolic pathway of glycolysis to generate ATP.

The fact that these seven attributes are shared by all life on Earth suggests that all present-day organisms descended from a common ancestor (Figure 3.20, p. 63) that had all of these attributes. This is not to say that life evolved only once. It is quite possible that life arose many times on early Earth, each form perhaps having some of the attributes listed above. The similarities across all domains of life present today indicate, however, that only one of these primitive life-forms has descendants that survive today. We call the original life-form from which all archaea, bacteria, and eukaryotes are descended **LUCA** for last universal common ancestor (see Figure 3.20, p. 63). Recent sequence analysis of certain proteins that have representatives in all three domains of life has given strong quantitative support to the common-ancestry hypothesis.

STUDY BREAK

1. Compared to anoxygenic photosynthesis, what is the ecological advantage to an organism of oxygenic photosynthesis?
2. What is meant by the term *last universal common ancestor (LUCA)*?

3.5 The Eukaryotic Cell and the Rise of Multicellularity

There is general agreement within the scientific community that the oldest fossils of eukaryotes are about 2.1 billion years old. Understandably, the very first eukaryotes may have appeared earlier. In fact, there is chemical evidence of eukaryotes existing as early as 2.5 billion years ago.

Present-day eukaryotic cells have two major characteristics that distinguish them from either the archaea or bacteria: (1) the separation of DNA and cytoplasm by a nuclear envelope and (2) the presence in the cytoplasm of membrane-bound compartments with specialized metabolic and synthetic functions—mitochondria, chloroplasts, the endoplasmic reticulum (ER), and the Golgi complex, among others. Hypotheses for how various eukaryotic structures and functions arose abound, some with very strong scientific evidence, others backed mostly with conjecture. In this section, we discuss how eukaryotes most probably evolved from associations of prokaryotic cells, ending with a discussion of the rise of multicellular eukaryotes.

3.5a The Theory of Endosymbiosis Suggests That Mitochondria and Chloroplasts Evolved from Ingested Prokaryotes

One feature that is found in virtually all eukaryotic cells is energy-transforming organelles: mitochondria and chloroplasts. A large amount of evidence indicates that mitochondria and chloroplasts are actually descended from free-living prokaryotic cells **(Figure 3.21)**: mitochondria are descended from aerobic (with oxygen) bacteria, while chloroplasts are descended from cyanobacteria. The established model of **endosymbiosis** states that the prokaryotic ancestors of modern mitochondria and chloroplasts were engulfed by larger prokaryotic cells, forming a mutually advantageous relationship called a symbiosis. Slowly, over time, the host cell and the endosymbionts became inseparable parts of the same organism.

3.5b Several Lines of Evidence Support the Theory of Endosymbiosis

If the theory of endosymbiosis is correct and both mitochondria and chloroplasts are indeed descendants of prokaryotic cells, then these organelles should share some clear structural and biochemical features with prokaryotic cells. Six lines of evidence suggest that these energy-transducing organelles do have distinctly prokaryotic characteristics that are not found in other eukaryotic organelles:

1. **Morphology.** The form or shape of both mitochondria and chloroplasts is similar to that of bacteria and archaea.
2. **Reproduction.** A cell cannot synthesize a mitochondrion or a chloroplast. Just like free-living prokaryotic cells, mitochondria and chloroplasts are derived only from pre-existing mitochondria and chloroplasts. Both chloroplasts and mitochondria divide by binary fission, which is how bacteria and archaea divide (see Chapter 20).
3. **Genetic information.** If the ancestors of mitochondria and chloroplasts were free-living cells, then these organelles should contain their own DNA. This is indeed the case. Both mitochondria and chloroplasts contain their own DNA, which contains protein-coding genes that are essential for organelle function. As with bacteria and archaea, the DNA molecule in mitochondria and chloroplasts is circular, while the DNA molecules in the nucleus are linear.
4. **Transcription and translation.** Both chloroplasts and mitochondria contain a complete transcription and translational machinery: genes encoded by the organelle genomes are translated into mRNA and translated on the ribosomes, messenger RNA

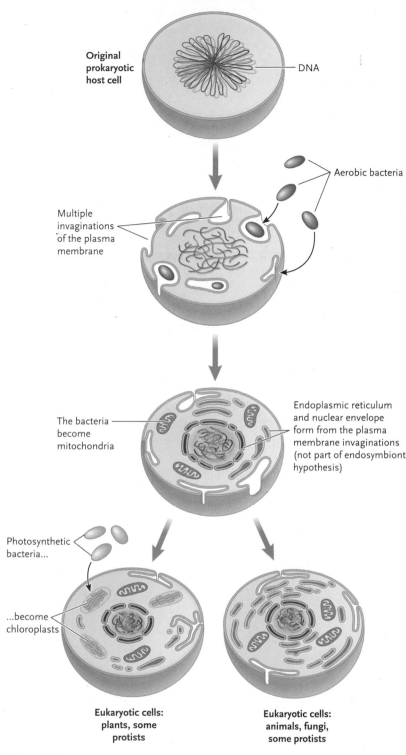

Original prokaryotic host cell

DNA

Aerobic bacteria

Multiple invaginations of the plasma membrane

The bacteria become mitochondria

Endoplasmic reticulum and nuclear envelope form from the plasma membrane invaginations (not part of endosymbiont hypothesis)

Photosynthetic bacteria...

...become chloroplasts

Eukaryotic cells: plants, some protists

Eukaryotic cells: animals, fungi, some protists

Figure 3.21
The theory of endosymbiosis. The mitochondrion is thought to have originated from an aerobic prokaryote that lived as an endosymbiont within an anaerobic prokaryote. The chloroplast is thought to have originated from a photosynthetic prokaryote that became an endosymbiont within an aerobic cell that had mitochondria.

(mRNA), and transfer RNA (tRNA) necessary to synthesize the proteins encoded by their DNA. The ribosomes of mitochondria and chloroplasts are very similar to the type found in bacteria (see point 6 on this page).

5. **Electron transport.** Similar to free-living prokaryotic cells, both mitochondria and chloroplasts have electron transport chains (ETCs) used to generate chemical energy. The ETCs of bacteria and archaea are found in the plasma membrane, and for such cells, swallowed up by endosymbiosis, this membrane would be found inside the membrane of the endocytic vesicle. Indeed, both mitochondria and chloroplasts have double membranes and it is the inner membrane that contains the ETC.

6. **Sequence analysis.** Sequencing of the RNA that makes up the ribosomes of chloroplasts and mitochondria firmly establishes that they belong on the bacterial branch of the tree of life (see Figure 3.20, p. 63). Chloroplast ribosomal RNA is most similar to that of cyanobacteria, while mitochondrial ribosomal RNA is most similar to that of proteobacteria.

Whereas virtually all eukaryotic cells contain mitochondria, only plants and algae contain both mitochondria and chloroplasts. This fact indicates that endosymbiosis occurred in stages (see Figure 3.21), with the event leading to the evolution of mitochondria occurring first. Once eukaryotic cells with the ability for aerobic respiration developed, some of these became photosynthetic after taking up cyanobacteria, evolving into the plants and algae of today.

3.5c Horizontal Gene Transfer Followed Endosymbiosis

The term **genome** is defined as the complete complement of an organism's genetic material. For eukaryotes, it is common to distinguish between the DNA found in the nucleus (the nuclear genome) and the DNA that resides in either the mitochondrion (mitochondrial genome) or the chloroplast (chloroplast genome).

A typical bacterium has a genome that contains about 3000 protein-coding genes. If both mitochondria and chloroplasts had once been free-living prokaryotic cells, then their genomes should have roughly the same number of genes—interestingly, they don't. The human mitochondrial genome comprises only 37 genes, and the chloroplast genome of the green alga, *Chlamydomonas reinhardtii* has 99 genes. What happened to all those other genes?

Following endosymbiosis, the early eukaryotic cell would have contained at least two (nucleus and protomitochondria) and perhaps three (nucleus, protomitochondria, and protochloroplast) compartments—each with its own complete genome. These compartments and genomes would have functioned independently, each coding for proteins required for their own structure and function, just like free-living organisms. This view contrasts strongly with a modern eukaryotic cell, where the function of the cell is highly integrated—mitochondrial function, for example, is strongly linked to the overall metabolism of the cell. Two major processes led to this integration. First, some of the genes that were within the protomitochondrion or protochloroplast were lost. Many of these genes would have been redundant, as the nucleus would already have genes that encode proteins with the same function. Second, many of the genes within the protomitochondria and protochloroplast were relocated to the nucleus. This process, called horizontal gene transfer (HGT), is thought to have occurred because of the evolutionary advantage that the early eukaryotic cell would gain by centralizing crucial genetic information in one place, the nucleus. It's important to realize that the outcome of HGT was not a change in gene function, only a change in the location of the gene—the nucleus as opposed to the mitochondrion or chloroplast **(Figure 3.22)**. As a side note,

HGT doesn't pertain only to endosymbiotic gene transfer but to any movement of genes between organisms other than to offspring. HGT is seen as a major mechanism of diversification of genomes and thus evolution, especially in archaea and bacteria.

In a typical eukaryotic cell today, over 90% of the proteins required for mitochondrial or chloroplast function are encoded by genes that are found in the nucleus. To go along with this change of location, a large protein trafficking and sorting machinery had to evolve (Figure 3.22). Following transcription in the nucleus and translation on cytosolic ribosomes, proteins destined for the chloroplast or mitochondrion need to be correctly sorted and imported into these energy-transducing organelles, where they are trafficked to the correct location.

A major unanswered question that is being actively studied is: why do both mitochondrion and chloroplasts still retain a genome—why haven't all genes moved to the nucleus? One possibility is that perhaps gene transfer is not yet complete. This seems to be the case for many chloroplast genomes. Related plant species can differ with regard to the location of a particular gene. It is not uncommon for one species to have it in the nucleus and a related species to have the same gene localized to the chloroplast. Another hypothesis is that since most of the genes that are retained by the mitochondrion or chloroplast code for proteins involved in electron transport, the tight regulation of these genes, which is difficult to do if the genes are in the nucleus, is essential to maintain optimal rates of energy transformation.

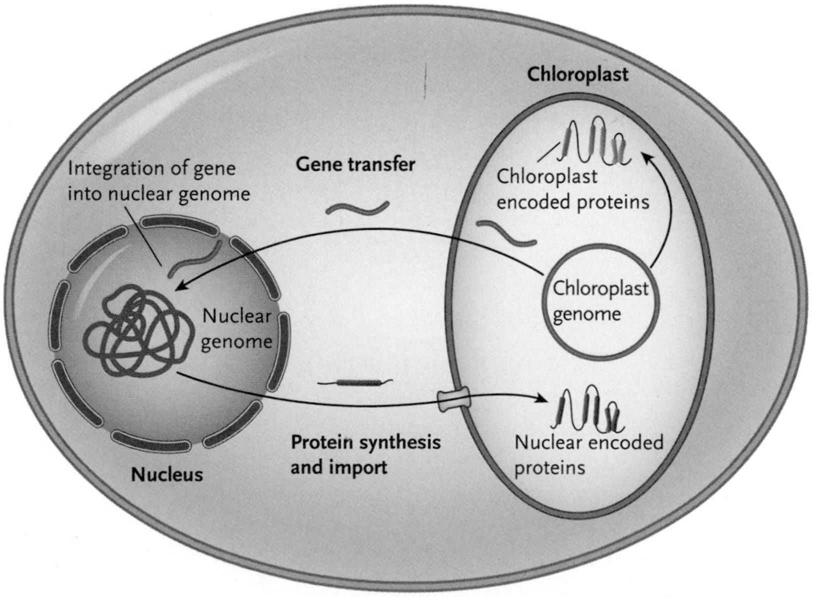

3.5d The Endomembrane System May Be Derived from the Plasma Membrane

Recall from Chapter 2 that in addition to energy-transforming organelles (mitochondria and chloroplasts), eukaryotic cells are characterized by an **endomembrane system**—a collection of internal membranes that divide the cell into structural and functional regions. These include the nuclear envelope, the endoplasmic reticulum, and the Golgi complex. As we have just seen, there is very strong evidence in support of the endosymbiotic origin of chloroplasts and mitochondria; however, the origin of the endomembrane system remains unclear. The most widely held hypothesis is that it is derived from the infolding of the plasma membrane **(Figure 3.23)**. Researchers hypothesize that, in cell lines leading from prokaryotic cells to eukaryotes, pockets of the plasma membrane may have extended inward and surrounded the nuclear region. Some of these membranes fused around the DNA, forming the nuclear envelope, which defines the nucleus. The remaining membranes formed vesicles in the cytoplasm that gave rise to the endoplasmic reticulum and the Golgi complex.

Figure 3.22

Horizontal gene transfer. Over evolutionary time, genes that were once part of the chloroplast or mitochondrial genome have been relocated to the nuclear genome. Following transcription, translation occurs in the cytosol before protein import into the organelle (mitochondrion or chloroplast).

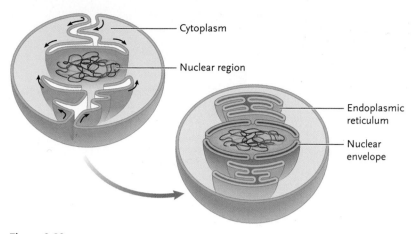

Figure 3.23

A hypothetical route for formation of the nuclear envelope and endoplasmic reticulum, through segments of the plasma membrane that were brought into the cytoplasm by endocytosis.

Labels in figure: Cytoplasm, Nuclear region, Endoplasmic reticulum, Nuclear envelope

3.5e Solving an Energy Crisis May Have Led to Eukaryotes

Bacteria and archaea outnumber eukaryotes on the planet by a huge margin. Compared to eukaryotes, archaea and bacteria show remarkable biochemical flexibility, being able to use an assortment of molecules as sources of energy and carbon and thrive in harsh environments uninhabitable to eukaryotes. That said, prokaryotic cells are simple—they lack the complexity of eukaryotes, which evolved into a tremendous diversity of forms, including plants, fungi, and animals. Within each of these groups are cells with remarkable specialization in form and function. Contrast this to archaea and bacteria, which have remained remarkably simple even though they evolved as early as 4 billion years ago.

The reason that bacteria and archaea have remained very simple is that increased complexity requires increased energy, and while eukaryotic cells can generate huge amounts of it, prokaryotic cells cannot. Mitochondria, like their aerobic progenitor bacteria, undergo aerobic respiration, which generates much greater amounts of ATP from the breakdown of organic molecules than pathways of anaerobic metabolism (this is discussed further in Chapter 6). As well, while a typical aerobic bacterium relies on its plasma membrane for many functions, including nutrient and waste transport and energy production, a typical eukaryotic cell contains hundreds of mitochondria, each having a huge internal membrane surface area dedicated to generating ATP.

The ability of early eukaryotes to generate more ATP led to remarkable changes. Cells could become larger, as now there was enough energy to support a greater volume. And cells could become more complex. This complexity comes about by being able to support a larger genome that codes for a greater number of proteins. By overcoming the energy barrier, eukaryotes had the energy to support a wider variety of genes that led to what we know today to be eukaryotic-specific traits such as the cell cycle, sexual reproduction, phagocytosis, endomembrane trafficking, the nucleus, and multicellularity.

3.5f The Evolution of Multicellular Eukaryotes Led to Increased Specialization

One of the most profound transitions in the history of life was the evolution of multicellular eukaryotes. Clear evidence of multicellular eukaryotes, primarily small algae, appears in the fossil record starting about 1.2 billion years ago. It is easy to see how multicellularity could have developed. Perhaps a group of individual cells of a species came together to form a colony, or a single cell divided and the resulting two cells remained together. In the most simplest of multicellular organisms, all cells are structurally and functionally autonomous (independent). This gave way to a key trait of more advanced multicellular organisms: division of labour. That is, the cells were not functionally identical and thus usually not structurally similar. Some cells may specialize in harvesting energy, for example, whereas others may serve a specific role in the motility of the organism. In a multicellular system, the cells cooperate with one another for the benefit of the entire organism. Over evolutionary time, this specialization of cell function led to the development of the specialized tissues and organs that are so clearly evident in larger eukaryotes.

Like the earliest forms of life, there is little, if any, evidence in the fossil record of the earliest multicellular organisms. How they arose and developed is still an area of intense research. It is thought, however, that multicellularity arose more than once, most probably independently along the lineages leading to fungi, plants, and animals. A very useful model for the study of multicellularity is found in a group of green algae called the volvocine. All of the members of this group are evolutionarily closely related and span the full range of size and complexity, from the unicellular *Chlamydomonas*, through various colonial genera, to the multicellular *Volvox* **(Figure 3.24, p. 68)**. Unlike a true multicellular organism, a cell colony is a group of cells that are all of one type; there is no specialization in cell structure or function. *Volvox* consists of a sphere of two to three thousand small, flagellated, *Chlamydomonas*-like cells that provide the individual *Volvox* with the ability to move. In addition, within the sphere lie about 16 large nonmotile cells that serve a specialized role in reproduction.

Figure 3.24
Differences in degree of multicellularity among volvocine algae.

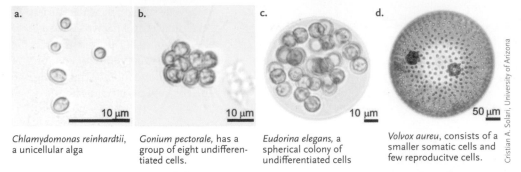

a. *Chlamydomonas reinhardtii*, a unicellular alga

b. *Gonium pectorale*, has a group of eight undifferentiated cells.

c. *Eudorina elegans*, a spherical colony of undifferentiated cells

d. *Volvox aureu*, consists of a smaller somatic cells and few reproducitve cells.

Cristian A. Solari, University of Arizona

3.6 The Search for Extraterrestrial Life

Overall, the events outlined in this chapter may seem highly improbable: the formation of a habitable planet, followed by the abiotic synthesis of organic molecules, the development of the first cells, the development of DNA, RNA, proteins, and pathways of energy acquisition- all the way to the development of multicellular eukaryotes. Improbable? Perhaps. But we must keep in mind that these events took place over an almost unimaginable length of time—4.6 billion years! And as scientist and author George Wald of Harvard University put it, given so much time "the impossible becomes possible, the possible probable, and the probable virtually certain."

Most scientists maintain that the evolution of life on Earth was an inevitable outcome of the initial physical and chemical conditions on primordial Earth, brought about by its position relative to the Sun. If that is the case—that all you need is a planet in the habitable zone, then what is the probability of life existing elsewhere in our galaxy? Let's do a little arithmetic: the Milky Way galaxy contains an estimated 100 billion stars. Because the formation of planetary systems is thought to be a normal consequence of star formation, lets conservatively estimate that 50% of stars in the galaxy have planets. That would give us about 50 billion planetary systems. Given that perhaps two planets around each star would fall within the habitable zone, this would put the total number of planets able to support life within our galaxy at 100 billion! Now of course the number of those planets that actually go on to develop life would be much less and the proportion that develop intelligent life and

communicating civilizations would reduce the number even further. But even still, it is distinctly possible that the galaxy is teeming with many advanced civilizations. Now how about finding them.

The search for extraterrestrial life is hampered by the incredible vastness of space. The closest star outside our solar system is some 40 trillion kilometres away, and using the fastest spacecraft humankind currently has, it would take a staggering 150 000 years to get there! For this reason, the search for extraterrestrial life, which started about 50 years ago, has primarily

a.

NASA

b.

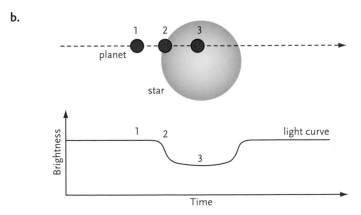

Figure 3.25

Search for Earth-like planets. **(a)** Artist's depiction of the Kepler spacecraft, which is equipped with a photometer to detect Earth-like planets. **(b)** The transit method relies on measuring the very small but regular changes in the brightness of a star caused by an orbiting (transiting) planet.

been focused on listening for the distinct signals of a communicating civilization using the science of radio astronomy. This type of detection has a huge advantage over spaceflight because radio waves travel at the speed of light. While using radio astronomy to detect signals from extraterrestrial civilizations continues, more recent initiatives are centred on the detection of Earth-like planets orbiting other stars. One method for this has been employed in the NASA Kepler Mission that was launched in 2009 **(Figure 3.25)**. This project, named after the German astronomer Johannes Kepler, is a space observatory designed to continuously monitor the brightness of over 145 000 stars. Armed with a powerful photometer, the observatory can detect the very faint but regular fluctuations in the brightness of stars. In what is termed the *transit method*, the photometer detects the slight but very regular changes

in brightness of a star that are caused by a planet moving in front of and then behind the star relative to the position of the detector. Even before the Kepler Mission started, Earthbound observatories had identified over 400 extrasolar planets (planets outside our solar system). As of 2011, the Kepler mission had identified over 1200 planets, 408 of which are part of systems containing multiple planets.

STUDY BREAK

1. What is the evidence in support of endosymbiosis?
2. What are the key traits of a multicellular organism?

Review

Access an interactive eBook, chapter-specific interactive learning tools, including flashcards, quizzes, videos, and more in your Biology **CourseMate**, accessed through NelsonBrain.com **Aplia™** is an online interactive learning solution that helps you improve comprehension—and your grade—by integrating a variety of mediums and tools such as videos, tutorials, practice tests, and an interactive eBook.

3.1 What Is Life?

- All forms of life share seven characteristics: order, energy utilization, homeostasis, response to stimuli, growth, reproduction, and evolution.

- While a virus has some of the characteristics of life, these require it to infect living cells. Because of this it is not considered a form of life.

- The characteristics of life are referred to as emergent because they come about, or emerge, from many simpler interactions that, in themselves, do not have the properties found at the higher levels.

3.2 The Chemical Origins of Life

- Earth and the rest of the solar system were formed about 4.6 billion years ago.

- Life evolved on Earth in part because the planet is situated at a distance from the Sun so that water can exist in a liquid state. Earth is within the habitable zone of the solar system.

- The Oparin–Haldane hypothesis maintains that the organic molecules that formed the building blocks of life, such as amino acids, could have been formed given the conditions that prevailed on primitive Earth, including a reducing atmosphere that lacked oxygen.

- The Miller–Urey experiment demonstrated that abiotic synthesis of biologically important molecules is possible.

- The key macromolecules of life, such as proteins and nucleic acids, are polymers that were not formed by the Miller–Urey experiment. Instead, it is thought that polymerization reactions could have occurred on solid surfaces, such as clay.

3.3 From Macromolecules to Life

- The spontaneous formation of lipid vesicles (liposomes) may have served as the first membrane-bound compartments that developed into the first cells.

- Ribozymes are a group of RNA molecules that can catalyze specific reactions. Because they can store information and drive catalysis, it is thought that RNA was the first molecule.

- Because of their greater diversity and much higher rate of catalysis, proteins became the dominant structural and functional macromolecule of all cells

- DNA is more stable than RNA and thus evolved as a better repository of genetic information.

- Early metabolism was probably based on simple oxidation–reduction reactions.

3.4 The Earliest Forms of Life

- Stromatolites dated to as early as 3.5 billion years ago represent the earliest fossil evidence of life. Chemical evidence suggest life may have originated 3.9 billion years ago.

- Panspermia is the hypothesis that very simple forms of life are present in space and seeded Earth soon after it cooled.

- Some early cells developed the capacity to carry out photosynthesis using water as an electron donor; the oxygen produced as a by-product accumulated, and the oxidizing character of Earth's atmosphere increased. From this time on, organic molecules produced in the environment were quickly broken down by oxidation, and life could arise only from pre-existing life, as in today's world.

3.5 The Eukaryotic Cell and the Rise of Multicellularity

- The energy-transducing organelles—the chloroplasts and the mitochondria—are thought to have been derived from free-living prokaryotic cells.

- According to the theory of endosymbiosis, mitochondria developed from ingested aerobic bacteria; chloroplasts developed from ingested cyanobacteria.
- Following endosymbiosis, genes residing in the mitochondria and chloroplasts moved to the nucleus. This is a type of horizontal gene transfer (HGT).
- Eukaryotic cells possess an endomembrane system that probably evolved from infolding of the plasma membrane. The endomembrane system consists of the nuclear envelope, the endoplasmic reticulum, and the Golgi complex.
- Eukaryotic cells are more complex than bacteria or archaea because mitochondria provide them with more energy.
- Multicellular eukaryotes probably evolved by differentiation of cells of the same species that had congregated into colonies. Multicellularity evolved several times, producing lineages of several algae and ancestors of fungi, plants, and animals.

3.6 The Search for Extraterrestrial Life

- The Milky Way galaxy contains about 100 billion stars. If 50% of those had planetary systems, and in each system 2 planets were within the habitable zone, that's potentially 100 billion planets able to sustain life.
- Interstellar distances are too great to use spacecraft to search for extraterrestrial life. Instead radio astronomy is used to listen for signals of intelligent civilization.
- Using powerful photometers, observatories in space and on the ground search for extrasolar planets by detecting the small but very regular changes in the brightness of a star caused by a transiting planet.

Questions

Self-Test Questions

1. Why are viruses not considered a form of life?
   a. They don't have a nucleus.
   b. They are not made of protein.
   c. They lack ribosomes.
   d. They cannot evolve.
   e. Thy lack nucleic acid.

2. According to the Oparin–Haldane hypothesis, what was composition of the primordial atmosphere?
   a. water, molecular nitrogen (N_2), and carbon dioxide
   b. molecular hydrogen (H_2), water, ammonia, and methane
   c. water, molecular oxygen (O_2), and ammonia
   d. water, argon, and neon.

3. Clay may have played an important role in what aspect of the development of life?
   a. formation of monomers such as amino acids.
   b. formation of polymers such as short proteins or nucleic acids.
   c. formation of membrane-bound compartments such as liposomes.
   d. formation of multicellular organisms.
   e. Both a and c are correct.

4. The Miller–Urey experiment was a huge breakthrough in our understanding of the origins of life. What was its major conclusion?
   a. That abiotic synthesis of molecules requires oxygen (O_2)
   b. That biological molecules could be formed without energy.
   c. That proteins could be synthesized without ribosomes.
   d. That abiotic synthesis of amino acids was possible.

5. Which of the following list of events is in the correct order of first appearance?
   a. O_2 in the atmosphere, anoxygenic photosynthesis, aerobic respiration, oxygenic photosynthesis.
   b. oxygenic photosynthesis, anoxygenic photosynthesis, aerobic respiration, O_2 in the atmosphere.
   c. anoxygenic photosynthesis, oxygenic photosynthesis, O_2 in the atmosphere, aerobic respiration.
   d. aerobic respiration, O_2 in the atmosphere, Oxygenic photosynthesis, anoxygenic photosynthesis.

6. Which of the following statements about ribozymes is correct?
   a. The are composed of only RNA.
   b. They are able to catalyze reactions faster than enzymes.
   c. They were present only in ancient cells.
   d. Like proteins they are polymers of amino acids.

7. Why did DNA replace RNA as the means to store genetic information?
   a. The sugar ribose, present in DNA but not RNA, is less prone to breakdown.
   b. DNA contains uracil which is more stable than the thymine present in RNA.
   c. Unlike RNA, DNA can exist in very complex three-dimensional shapes, which are very stable.
   d. The presence of complementary strands in DNA means that single base mutations can be easily repaired.

8. As part of the evolution of eukaryotic cells, infolding of the plasma membrane is thought to have led to the formation of which of the following?
   a. ribosomes
   b. microtubules
   c. mitochondria
   d. chromosomes
   e. endoplasmic reticulum

9. Which of the following statements supports the theory of endosymbiosis?
   a. Mitochondria contain proteins.
   b. Both mitochondria and chloroplasts possess their own genomes.
   c. Both mitochondria and chloroplasts are surrounded by a membrane.
   d. The nuclear envelope is derived from infolding of the plasma membrane.

10. What was an outcome of horizontal gene transfer (HGT)?
    a. Import of proteins into mitochondria.
    b. Increase in size of the chloroplast genome.
    c. Proteins once localized to the mitochondria were relocated to the nucleus.
    d. Decrease in the number of proteins in the chloroplast

Questions for Discussion

1. What evidence supports the idea that life originated through abiotic chemical processes?

2. Most scientists agree that life on Earth can arise only from preexisting life, but also that life could have originated spontaneously on primordial Earth. Can you reconcile these seemingly contradictory statements?

3. What conditions would likely be necessary for a planet located elsewhere in the universe to evolve life similar to that on Earth?

4. What drove the evolution of the eukaryotic cell?

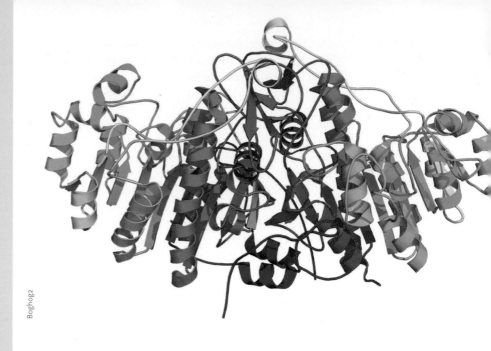
Model of the enzyme alkaline phosphatase

Boghog2

STUDY PLAN

4.1 Energy and the Laws of Thermodynamics

4.1a Energy Exists in Different Forms and States

4.4b The Laws of Thermodynamics Describe Energy and Its Transformation

4.1c The First Law of Thermodynamics: Energy Can be Transformed but Not Created or Destroyed

4.1d The Second Law of Thermodynamics: Energy Transformations Increase Disorder

4.1e Life Obeys the Second Law of Thermodynamics

4.2 Free Energy and Spontaneous Reactions

4.2a Energy Content and Entropy Contribute to Making a Reaction Spontaneous

4.2b The Change in Free Energy Indicates Whether a Reaction Is Spontaneous

4.2c Exergonic Reactions Reach Equilibrium Rather than Going to Completion

4.2d Metabolic Pathways Consist of Exergonic and Endergonic Reactions

4.3 Adenosine Triphosphate Is the Energy Currency of the Cell

4.3a ATP Breakdown Releases Free Energy

4.3b Energy Coupling Links the Energy of ATP to Other Molecules

4.3c Cells Also Couple Reactions to Regenerate ATP

4.4 The Role of Enzymes in Biological Reactions

4.4a The Activation Energy of a Reaction Represents a Kinetic Barrier

4.4b Enzymes Accelerate Reactions by Reducing the Activation Energy

4.4c Enzymes Combine with Reactants and Are Released Unchanged

4.4d Enzymes Reduce the Activation Energy by Inducing the Transition State

4.5 Conditions and Factors That Affect Enzyme Activity

4.5a Enzyme and Substrate Concentrations Can Change the Rate of Catalysis

4.5b Enzyme Inhibitors Have Characteristic Effects on Enzyme Activity

4.5c Cells Adjust Enzyme Activity to Meet the Needs for Reaction Products

4.5d Temperature and pH Are Key Factors Affecting Enzyme Activity

4 Energy and Enzymes

WHY IT MATTERS

Earth is a cold place—at least when it comes to chemical reactions. Life cannot survive at the high temperatures routinely used in most laboratories and industrial plants to synthesize chemicals. Instead, life relies on a group of catalysts called enzymes that speed up the rates of reaction without the need for an increase in temperature.

Until recently, however, just how good enzymes are at increasing the rate of a reaction was not fully appreciated. Richard Wolfenden, professor of Chemistry, Biochemistry, and Biophysics at the University of North Carolina, and his colleagues estimated the rate of the uncatalyzed versus the enzyme-catalyzed reaction for a range of biologically relevant reactions. The prize for the greatest difference between the uncatalyzed rate and the enzyme-catalyzed rate goes to a reaction that simply removes a phosphate group. In the cell, a group of enzymes called phosphatases catalyze the removal of phosphate groups from a range of molecules, including proteins. The rapid reversible phosphorylation of particular proteins is a central mechanism of signal transduction in almost all cells.

The dephosphorylation reaction within a cell using a phosphatase enzyme is completed in approximately 10 milliseconds. Wolfenden's group calculated that in an aqueous environment such as a cell, without an enzyme, the dephosphorylation reaction would take over 1 trillion years to occur. This exceeds the current estimate for the age of the universe! The difference between the enzyme-catalyzed and uncatalyzed rate is 21 orders of magnitude (10^{21}). For most reactions, the rate difference between the uncatalyzed rate and the catalyzed rate is on the order of a million fold (10^6).

Enzymes are key players in the metabolic pathways, made of hundreds of individual biochemical reactions, that collectively accomplish the activities we associate with life, such as growth, reproduction, movement, and the ability to respond to stimuli. Central to these processes is the ability of organisms to harness and utilize energy from the surroundings, and thus this chapter starts with an overview of the principles of energy flow as governed by the laws of thermodynamics. This is followed by a focused discussion on the factors that govern chemical reactions and the central role played by free energy. We finish with an in-depth discussion of enzymes, the fundamental biological catalysts, which enable life to exist on this cold planet.

4.1 Energy and the Laws of Thermodynamics

Life, like many chemical and physical activities, is an energy-driven process. Yet, energy cannot be measured or weighed directly. We can detect it only through its ability to do *work:* to move objects against opposing forces, such as friction, gravity, or pressure, or to push chemical reactions toward completion. Therefore, **energy** is most conveniently defined as the capacity to do work. It takes energy to move a car on a highway, and it takes energy to climb a mountain. It also takes energy to build a protein from a group of amino acids or pump sucrose across a cell membrane.

4.1a Energy Exists in Different Forms and States

Energy can exist in many different forms, including heat, chemical, electrical, and mechanical forms. Electromagnetic radiation, including visible, infrared, and ultraviolet light, is also a type of energy. Although the forms of energy are different, they can be converted or transformed readily from one form to another. For example, the chemical energy present in a flashlight battery is converted into electrical energy that passes through the flashlight bulb, where it is transformed into light and heat. Through the process of photosynthesis, the energy of light is converted into chemical energy in the form of complex sugars and other organic molecules.

All forms of energy can be grouped into one of two different types. **Kinetic energy** is the energy possessed by an object because it is in motion. Obvious examples of objects that possess kinetic energy are waves in the ocean, a falling rock, or a kicked football. A less obvious example is the kinetic energy of electricity, which is a flow of electrons. Photons of light are also a form of kinetic energy. The movement present in kinetic energy is of use because it can perform work by making other objects move. **Potential energy** is stored energy—the energy an object has because of its location or chemical structure. A boulder at the top of a cliff has potential energy because of its position in the gravitational field of Earth. The arrangement of atoms in a molecule of glucose or gasoline has potential energy stored in the specific arrangement of atoms. This type of energy is often called *chemical potential energy* and is discussed further in reference to cellular respiration, which is the topic of Chapter 6.

4.1b The Laws of Thermodynamics Describe Energy and Its Transformation

The study of energy and its transformations is called **thermodynamics.** When discussing thermodynamics, scientists refer to something called the *system,* which is the object being studied. A system can be anything—a single molecule, one cell, or a planet. Everything outside the system is called the *surroundings.* The *universe,* in this context, is the total of the system and the surroundings. It is important that we distinguish between three different types of systems: isolated, open, and closed. As shown in **Figure 4.1,** an isolated system is one that does not exchange matter or energy with its surroundings. A good example of this is a perfectly insulated Thermos bottle. A *closed system* can exchange energy, but not matter, with its surroundings. A greenhouse is a good example of a closed system. Earth can also be considered a closed system—it takes in an enormous amount of energy generated by the Sun and releases heat, but no matter is exchanged between Earth and the rest of the universe. Each year a few meteorites hit Earth, but essentially we can consider it a closed system. In an *open system,* both energy and matter can move freely between the system and the surroundings. The ocean is a good example of an open system—it absorbs and releases energy, and, as a component of the hydrological cycle, water is constantly being lost and gained by the ocean through evaporation and precipitation.

4.1c The First Law of Thermodynamics: Energy Can Be Transformed but Not Created or Destroyed

Research by physicists and chemists in the nineteenth century concerning energy flow between systems and the surroundings led to the formulation of two

a. Isolated system   **b.** Closed system   **c.** Open system

Figure 4.1
Isolated, closed, and open systems in thermodynamics.

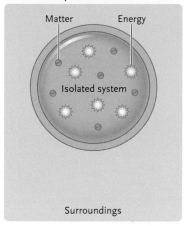

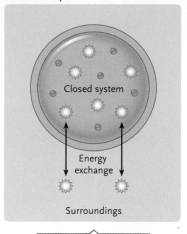

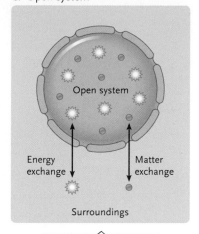

An isolated system does not exchange matter or energy with its surroundings.

A closed system exchanges energy with its surroundings.

An open system exchanges both energy and matter with its surroundings.

fundamental laws of thermodynamics that apply equally to living cells as to inanimate objects like a car. According to the **first law of thermodynamics,** *energy can be transformed from one form into another or transferred from one place to another, but it cannot be created or destroyed.* This law is also called the principle of the conservation of energy. The first law of thermodynamics is illustrated nicely by Niagara Falls **(Figure 4.2a),** which borders Canada and the United States. Water at the top of the falls has high potential energy because of its location within Earth's gravitational field. As the water moves over the waterfall, its potential energy is converted into kinetic energy. The higher the waterfall, the more kinetic energy the water will possess. When it reaches the bottom of the waterfall, the kinetic energy of the water is transformed into other types of energy, including heat, sound, and mechanical energy (causing weathering of the rocks). For thousands of years, the kinetic energy of waterfalls has been harnessed by people to do work. At Niagara Falls today, some of the kinetic energy present in the moving water is converted into electricity through the use of hydroelectric turbines **(Figure 4.2b)** and is used to supply electricity to thousands of homes and businesses.

4.1d The Second Law of Thermodynamics: Energy Transformations Increase Disorder

Another important principle of thermodynamics is that each time energy is transformed from one form into another, some of the energy is lost and unavailable to do work. You can think of this as the reason why machines are never 100% efficient. For example, the engine of a car converts only about 25% of the potential energy in gasoline into the kinetic energy that makes the car move **(Figure 4.3a, p. 74).** Likewise, only a portion of the energy in a notebook computer battery is

a.

© Corel

b.

Figure 4.2
Niagara Falls, which borders New York, U.S.A., and Ontario, Canada. **(a)** The potential energy of the water is converted into kinetic energy as it moves over the falls. **(b)** A small portion of this kinetic energy is used to turn hydroelectric turbines, converting the gravitational energy into electrical energy. In accordance with the first law of thermodynamics, energy hasn't been gained or lost but has changed form. Niagara Falls generates approximately 4.4 gigawatts of power each year—enough to power thousands of homes and businesses.

a.

CP Images/© Lehtikuva [2005] all rights reserved

b.

© Wally McNamee/CORBIS

Figure 4.3
Two examples of thermodynamic systems that display the second law of thermodynamics.
(a) A car engine converts only about 25% of the available energy in gasoline into mechanical energy. **(b)** A runner converts only about 40% of the energy in glucose into ATP, which powers his muscles. In both cases, a significant portion of the energy is unused and is given off as heat, which increases the disorder, or entropy, of the surroundings.

used to run the computer. If you touch a car engine that has just been turned off or put a notebook computer on your lap for an extended period of time, it is obvious where a lot of the energy is going. It is being lost to the surroundings as *heat,* which is the energy associated with random molecular motion. This concept of energy efficiency also applies to living cells. As we will see in Chapter 6, through the process of cellular respiration, cells are able to convert only about 40% of the potential energy in glucose into a form usable for metabolism **(Figure 4.3b)**. In most cases, including living cells, heat cannot be harnessed to do work; instead, it is simply lost to the environment.

Whether in a car engine or a living cell, the unusable energy that is produced during energy transformations results in an increase in the disorder or randomness of the universe. In thermodynamics, this randomness or disorder is a quantity called **entropy.** This measure of disorder forms the basis of the **second law of thermodynamics,** which can be stated as follows: *the total disorder of a system and its surroundings always increases.* There is no single inclusive way to think of entropy, and that is part of what makes it difficult for first-year biology students to grasp. So let's work through some examples: A cup of hot coffee gets cold. A new car doesn't stay new; first, it loses its new car smell, and soon you need new brakes and a tune-up, until, eventually, the passenger door falls off! These situations are inevitable and will occur given enough time. The physical disintegration of an organized system is the second law

of thermodynamics in action. Systems will move spontaneously toward arrangements with greater disorder—greater entropy. Thus, to maintain order (i.e., to keep your car from falling apart) requires work on the part of a mechanic. It takes energy to maintain low entropy!

4.1e Life Obeys the Second Law of Thermodynamics

But what about life: does it obey the second law of thermodynamics? Recall from Chapter 3 that one of the defining characteristics of life is that it displays order. That is, the molecules and structures that define life are very precisely arranged in a nonrandom manner. Living cells have the ability to create ordered structures out of less ordered starting materials. A molecule of DNA, a protein, and a ribosome are all very ordered structures that living things make out of much simpler building blocks. There is nothing random or disordered about a brain or a flower or photosystem II. These examples suggest that life goes against the second law of thermodynamics: things don't become more random in a living cell; they become more ordered. How is this possible? The answer lies in understanding what was discussed at the end of the last section—it takes energy to maintain low entropy.

Living cells are not isolated but rather are thermodynamically open systems, exchanging energy and matter with their surroundings. The energy and matter

Figure 4.4
Why do we need to eat? The average person needs to ingest about 1500 kcal per day. A significant amount of this energy is needed to maintain order within our cells. We eat food to maintain low entropy.

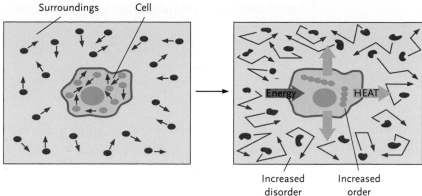

Figure 4.5
A simple thermodynamic example of a living cell. In the diagram on the left, molecules of both the cell and the surroundings are in a relatively disordered state. In the diagram on the right, the cell has taken in energy from the surroundings and used it to perform the work required to make molecules more ordered. This energy transformation releases heat, which increases the disorder (or entropy) of the surroundings.

that is brought into a living system may take the form of a falafel sandwich and a milkshake for you and me or photons of light and carbon dioxide for a cyanobacterium. Living things bring in energy and matter and use them to generate order out of disorder. It is understandable why elite athletes need to eat a lot of food, but people who don't exercise at all also need to ingest well over a thousand kilocalories every day. Although some of this food supplies us with the energy to use our muscles, much of the food energy we ingest is used simply to maintain our cells in their highly ordered state **(Figure 4.4).** According to the second law of thermodynamics, things are constantly breaking down. For living organisms this means that cellular components (proteins, organelles, etc.) become damaged and need to be constantly repaired or replaced. New cells need to be made and old ones maintained by the synthesis of a huge array of proteins, carbohydrates, and lipid molecules. In other words, we eat food to maintain low entropy!

But according to the second law of thermodynamics, the entropy of a system and the surroundings is always supposed to increase. Is this true of living cells as well? Absolutely—in the course of the thousands of chemical reactions that take place to generate order, living things give off heat and byproducts of metabolism such as carbon dioxide that are much less ordered and increase the disorder, or entropy, of the surroundings **(Figure 4.5).** The entropy of a system such as an organism is allowed to decrease as long as the entropy of the universe as a

whole increases. Because of this, living organisms can be thought of as islands of low entropy in a sea (the surroundings) that is constantly becoming more disordered.

STUDY BREAK

1. Distinguish between kinetic and potential energy.
2. Define entropy.
3. From the perspective of thermodynamics, why do we need to eat?

4.2 Free Energy and Spontaneous Reactions

Applying the first and second laws of thermodynamics together allows us to predict whether any particular chemical or physical reaction will occur without an input of energy—what in thermodynamics are called **spontaneous reactions.** In the language of science, the word *spontaneous* has a very particular definition: it means that a reaction will occur. That's it. It does not tell us anything about the actual rate of a reaction. Spontaneous reactions may proceed very slowly, such as the formation of rust on a car, or very quickly, such as a match bursting into flame. We will expand on this point later in the chapter.

4.2a Energy Content and Entropy Contribute to Making a Reaction Spontaneous

Two factors related to the first and second laws of thermodynamics need to be taken into account for us to determine whether a reaction is spontaneous: (1) the change in energy content of a system and (2) its change in entropy:

1. *Reactions tend to be spontaneous if the products have less potential energy than the reactants.* The potential energy in a system is called its **enthalpy**, or *H*. Reactions that absorb energy from the surroundings are termed **endothermic**, which results in the products of a reaction having more potential energy than the reactants. By comparison, those processes that release energy are called **exothermic**, the products have less potential energy than the reactants. As an example, when natural gas burns, methane reacts spontaneously with oxygen to produce carbon dioxide and water:

$$CH_4 + 2O_2 \rightarrow CO_2 + 2H_2O$$

The reaction is exothermic, producing a large amount of heat. The heat energy comes from the high potential energy in methane, which is greater than the potential energy of the products (carbon dioxide and water). We discuss the chemical basis for why molecules such as methane have high potential energy in Chapter 6. As a second example, let's look at a glass of ice water **(Figure 4.6)**. Why does the ice spontaneously melt at 25°C? It is melting because the glass of ice water is absorbing energy from the surroundings. This results in the product of the reaction, the water, having greater potential energy than the reactant, the ice. The melting of ice is clearly an endothermic process and yet the process is spontaneous! Clearly, some other factor besides potential needs to be considered.

2. *Reactions tend to be spontaneous when the products are less ordered than the reactants.* Reactions tend to occur spontaneously if the entropy (abbreviated as S) of the products is greater than the entropy of the reactants, that is, if the products are more random than the reactants. In the glass of ice water (see Figure 4.6), it is an increase in entropy that makes the melting of the ice a spontaneous process at 25°C. Molecules of ice are far more

ordered (possess lower entropy) than molecules of water, which are moving around randomly. In general, phase changes from solid to liquid and liquid to gas result in an increase in entropy, and condensation from gas to a solid results in a decrease in entropy.

4.2b The Change in Free Energy Indicates Whether a Reaction Is Spontaneous

Recall from the second law of thermodynamics that energy transformations are not 100% efficient; some of the energy is lost as an increase in entropy. So how much energy is available? The portion of a system's energy that is available to do work is called **free energy**, which is abbreviated by the letter *G* in recognition of the physicist Josiah Willard Gibbs, who developed the concept. In living organisms, free energy accomplishes the chemical and physical work involved in activities such as the synthesis of molecules, movement, and reproduction. The change in free energy, ΔG ($\Delta G = G_{\text{final state}} - G_{\text{initial state}}$), can be calculated for any specific chemical reaction using the formula

$$\Delta G = \Delta H - T\Delta S$$

where ΔH is the change in the enthalpy and ΔS is the change in the entropy of the system over the course of the reaction. *T* is the absolute temperature in kelvins (K, where the temperature in kelvin = the temperature in degrees Celsius (°C) + 273.16). The equation says that *the free energy change as a system goes from the initial to the final state is the sum of the changes in energy content and entropy.*

For a reaction to be spontaneous, ΔG must be negative, the free energy of the products must be less than that of the reactants. As the above formula tells us, both the entropy and the enthalpy of a reaction can influence the overall ΔG of a reaction. That is, for all chemical and physical processes, there is an interplay of both entropy and enthalpy to determine whether a reaction will occur spontaneously. In some processes, such as the combustion of methane, the large loss of potential energy, negative enthalpy (ΔH), dominates in making a reaction spontaneous. In other reactions, a decrease in order (ΔS is positive) dominates, such as the melting of ice at 25°C.

Another way to think about free energy has to do with stability. Systems that have high free energy are less stable than systems that have less free energy. Furthermore, systems will spontaneously change into a more stable state but cannot spontaneously change into being less stable. For example, a molecule of glucose can be considered unstable and will spontaneously break down into molecules, including carbon dioxide, that have less free energy and are more stable. Likewise, a concentration gradient that exists across a membrane is less stable and contains more free energy

Figure 4.6

The melting of ice at room temperature. This is an example of a spontaneous reaction that is endothermic: the energy content of the product (water) is greater than that of the reactant (ice). The reaction is spontaneous because the entropy of the system increases.

© iStockphoto.com/Anna Lyubimtseva

than after diffusion, when the molecules are equally distributed on both sides of a membrane.

4.2c Exergonic Reactions Reach Equilibrium Rather Than Going to Completion

In the late nineteenth century, chemists were surprised to find that many chemical reactions never went to completion. The products were always "contaminated" with molecules of reactant. More shocking was the finding that regardless of the amount of reactants and products in the initial mixture, the system reached the same state, in which the proportion of products to reactants was a constant. As an example, consider a chemical reaction in which glucose 1-phosphate is converted into glucose 6-phosphate **(Figure 4.7)**. Starting with 0.02 M glucose 1-phosphate, the reaction will proceed spontaneously until there is 0.019 M of glucose 6-phosphate (product) and 0.001 M of glucose 1-phosphate (reactant) in the solution. In fact, regardless of the amounts of each you start with, the reaction will reach a point at which there is 95% glucose 6-phosphate and 5% glucose 1-phosphate! The point at which there is no longer any overall change in the concentration of products and reactants is called the point of **chemical equilibrium**. In this state, molecules do not stop reacting; rather the rate of the forward reaction equals the rate of the backward reaction. As a system moves toward equilibrium, the free energy of the system becomes progressively lower and reaches its lowest point when the system is at equilibrium. It is at this point that there is no tendency for spontaneous change in either the forward or the reverse direction.

The system reaches a state of maximum stability, it has no capacity to do work, and $\Delta G = 0$.

The point of equilibrium is related to the ΔG for the reaction, in that the more negative the ΔG, the farther toward completion the reaction will move before equilibrium is established. Many reactions have a ΔG that is near zero and are thus readily reversible by adjusting the concentrations of products and reactants slightly. A nagging question that may be on your mind is this: if the ΔG for a reaction is negative, why doesn't the reaction proceed to completion, with all the reactant molecules being converted into product? The answer is that the free energy of the system is actually lower when the products are contaminated (or diluted) by some molecules of reactant than when the system is made up of pure product. This is because the mixture is more disordered—it has higher entropy.

The chemical reaction shown in Figure 4.7 is an example of an isolated system, and a key characteristic of all isolated systems is that over time, equilibrium is reached, and the ΔG becomes zero. As we discuss in the next section, many individual reactions in living organisms never reach an equilibrium point because living systems are open; thus, the supply of reactants is constant and, as products are formed, they do not accumulate but are consumed as the reactants of another reaction.

4.2d Metabolic Pathways Consist of Exergonic and Endergonic Reactions

Metabolism can be defined as the sum of all of the chemical reactions that take place within an organism. Based on the free energy of reactants and products, every one of these reactions can be placed into one of two groups. An **exergonic reaction (Figure 4.8a, p. 78)** is one that releases free energy—the ΔG is negative. An **endergonic reaction (Figure 4.8b, p. 78)** consumes free energy—the ΔG is positive.

Each of the thousands of chemical reactions that are found within a cell is not an isolated reaction but is usually part of a metabolic pathway, which is a series of sequential reactions in which the products of one reaction are used immediately as the reactants for the next reaction in the series **(Figure 4.9, p. 78)**. In one type of metabolic pathway called a **catabolic pathway** (Figure 4.9a), energy is released by the breakdown of complex molecules to simpler compounds. An example of a catabolic pathway that we discuss in detail in Chapter 6 is cellular respiration, whereby energy is extracted from the breakdown of food such as glucose. In contrast, **anabolic pathways** (see Figure 4.9b, p. 78) consume energy to build complicated molecules from simpler ones; these are often called biosynthetic pathways. Examples of anabolic pathways include photosynthesis as well as the synthesis of macromolecules such as proteins and nucleic acids.

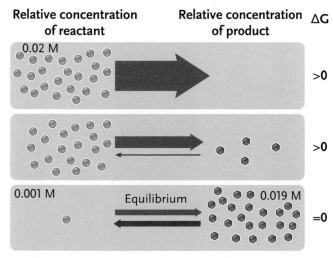

Relative concentration of reactant   **Relative concentration of product**   ΔG

0.02 M   >0

>0

0.001 M   Equilibrium   0.019 M   =0

Figure 4.7

Chemical reactions run to equilibrium. No matter what quantities of glucose 1-phosphate and glucose 6-phosphate are dissolved in water, when equilibrium is attained, there will always be 95% glucose 6-phosphate and 5% glucose 1-phosphate. At equilibrium, the number of reactant molecules being converted to products equals the number of product molecules being converted back to reactants.

a. Exergonic reaction

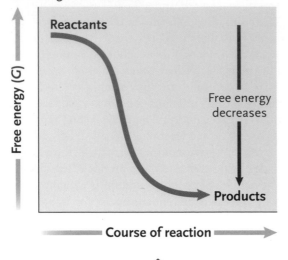

In an exergonic reaction, free energy is released. The products have less free energy than was present in the reactants, and the reaction proceeds spontaneously.

b. Endergonic reaction

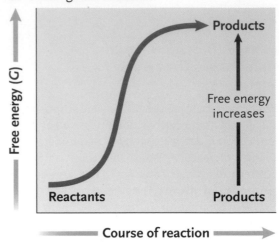

In an endergonic reaction, free energy is gained. The products have more free energy than was present in the reactants. An endergonic reaction is not spontaneous: it proceeds only if energy is supplied.

Figure 4.8
Metabolism consists of a combination of exergonic (a) and endergonic (b) reactions.

As shown in Figure 4.9, the overall ΔG of an anabolic pathway is positive, whereas the overall ΔG of a catabolic pathway is negative. However, both types of pathways can be made up of a mixture of both exergonic and endergonic reactions. For example, cellular respiration, is a metabolic pathway made up of many individual reactions, some of which release energy ($-\Delta G$), while others require energy ($+\Delta G$). However, when you sum the ΔG of all the reactions, the overall free energy is negative, and the pathway of cellular respiration is thus said to be catabolic (see Figure 4.9).

If we summed the free energy changes for each of the anabolic and catabolic processes that constitute the metabolism of a organism the overall ΔG would be negative. Recall that organisms extract energy from their surroundings and use that energy to maintain low entropy. However, because of the second law of thermodynamics, energy transformations are never 100% efficient, and thus organisms must bring in much more energy than they actually require. So living organisms are defined as having a $-\Delta G$ and reach equilibrium, $\Delta G = 0$, only when they die.

STUDY BREAK

1. What two factors need to be considered to determine if a reaction will proceed spontaneously?
2. Define and distinguish between exergonic and endergonic reactions and anabolic and catabolic pathways.

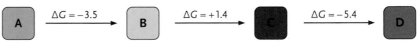

Catabolic pathway: Overall $\Delta G = -7.5$ kcal/mol

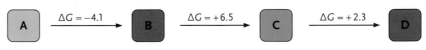

Anabolic pathway: Overall $\Delta G = +4.7$ kcal/mol

Figure 4.9
Hypothetical examples of the two major types of metabolic pathways. The starting molecule A is converted by a series of enzyme-catalyzed reactions to the product D. In catabolic pathways, the starting molecule A has high free energy, which is released as it gets converted into D. In anabolic pathways, energy must be provided to convert a molecule with low free energy (A) to one with higher free energy (D). Although each pathway will have either an overall negative or positive ΔG, individual reactions can have the opposite sign.

4.3 Adenosine Triphosphate Is the Energy Currency of the Cell

A huge number of the reactions that take place within cells are endergonic and are key reactions in anabolic pathways. The form of energy that is supplied to drive these endergonic reactions is almost always the nucleotide adenosine triphosphate (ATP). Like money to purchase goods, ATP is the currency of energy that is universally accepted for almost all reactions in all forms of life from bacteria to humans.

4.3a ATP Breakdown Releases Free Energy

As shown in **Figure 4.10a,** ATP consists of a five-carbon sugar, ribose, linked to the nitrogenous base adenine and a chain of three phosphate groups. Adenine is one of four bases that constitute the monomers of DNA and RNA (See the *Purple Pages*).

The breakdown of ATP in an aqueous environment is a *hydrolysis* reaction (**Figure 4.10b;** also see *The Purple Pages*) that liberates free energy and results in the formation of adenosine diphosphate (ADP) and the orthophosphate ion (HPO_4^{2-}), which is often abbreviated as P_i (inorganic phosphate):

$$ATP + H_2O \rightarrow ADP + P_i$$

$$\Delta G = -7.3 \text{ kcal/mol}$$

The high free energy of the hydrolysis of ATP is due to three major factors. First, both products of the hydrolysis reaction (ADP and P_i) carry a negative charge, and the repulsion between these ionic products favours hydrolysis. Second, release of the terminal phosphate allows greater opportunity for hydration (solvation), and this is an energetically favoured state. Third, the orthophosphate group can exist in a wide variety of resonance forms, not all of which are available when it is bonded. Thus release of the orthophosphate increases the disorder of the system. The commonly held notion that ATP has high free energy because of the energy held within the phosphate groups is misleading. The high free energy of hydrolysis is simply due to the large difference in the usable energy content of the reactants (high) as compared to the products (low).

4.3b Energy Coupling Links the Energy of ATP to Other Molecules

Although ATP releases a large amount of free energy upon hydrolysis, this does not mean that it is an especially reactive molecule. In fact, the hydrolysis of ATP in an aqueous environment such as the cytosol of a cell is kinetically slow—it's just that when it does occur free energy is released. If ATP were especially

a. Chemical structure of ATP

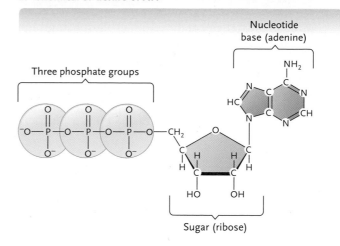

b. Hydrolysis reaction removing a phosphate group from ATP

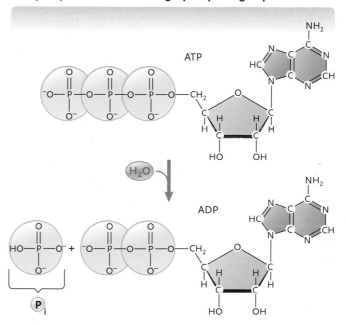

Figure 4.10

ATP, the primary molecule used to supply the energy for endergonic reactions. **(a)** Structure of one ATP molecule. **(b)** Reaction of ATP hydrolysis that releases energy.

reactive in an aqueous solution, it would be difficult to see how controlled metabolism involving ATP could ever occur. The rapid hydrolysis of ATP would simply release heat, which is a form of energy that is very difficult for the cell to trap and use to do work. In addition, the generation of high amounts of heat would kill the cell.

So how do cells harness the high free energy available in ATP to do cellular work? In a process called **energy coupling**, the exergonic release of energy when ATP is converted to ADP and P_i is used to drive an endergonic reaction. Energy coupling requires enzyme-based catalysis, which involves the enzyme bringing a molecule of ATP and a reactant molecule into close contact. During the reaction, the free energy of ATP is moved to the reactant molecule through the transfer of the terminal phosphate group, which results in the reactant molecule becoming more unstable and reactive. The reason that energy is not simply lost as heat when ATP is broken down is that ATP is not actually hydrolyzed during energy-coupling reactions. Hydrolysis is prevented because the site on the enzyme where the ATP and substrate react is not accessible to water. As well, P_i is not produced during energy coupling; rather the phosphate group is directly transferred from ATP to the reactant molecule.

An example of energy coupling that is very common in most cells is the reaction in which ammonia (NH_3) is added to glutamic acid, an amino acid with one amino group, to produce glutamine, an amino acid with two amino groups **(Figure 4.11a):**

$$\text{glutamic acid} + NH_3 \rightarrow \text{glutamine} + H_2O$$

$$\Delta G = +3.4 \text{ kcal/mol}$$

The glutamine is used in the assembly of proteins and is a donor of nitrogen for other reactions in the cell. The positive value for the ΔG shows that the reaction cannot proceed spontaneously.

How, then, do cells synthesize glutamine? As shown in **Figure 4.11b,** the reaction proceeds by harnessing the energy of ATP. As a first step, glutamic acid is *phosphorylated;* that is, the phosphate group removed

from ATP is transferred to glutamic acid, forming glutamyl phosphate:

$$\text{glutamic acid} + ATP \rightarrow \text{glutamyl phosphate} + ADP$$

The ΔG for this reaction is negative, making the reaction spontaneous. In the second step, glutamyl phosphate reacts with NH_3:

$$\text{glutamyl phosphate} + NH_3 \rightarrow \text{glutamine} + P_i$$

This second reaction also has a negative value for the ΔG and is spontaneous. Even though the reaction proceeds in two steps, it is usually written for convenience as one reaction, with a combined negative value for the ΔG:

$$\text{glutamic acid} + NH_3 + ATP \rightarrow \text{glutamine} + ADP + P_i$$

$$\Delta G = -3.9 \text{ kcal/mol}$$

Because the ΔG is negative, the coupled reaction is spontaneous and releases energy. The difference between −3.9 kcal/mol and the −7.3 kcal/mol released by the breakdown of ATP represents potential chemical energy transferred to the glutamine molecules produced by the reaction. In effect, the coupling system works by joining an exergonic reaction, the breakdown of ATP to ADP and phosphate, to the endergonic biosynthesis reaction, producing an overall reaction that is exergonic. All the endergonic reactions of living organisms, including those of growth, reproduction, movement, and response to stimuli, are made possible by coupling reactions in this way.

It is often mentioned in textbooks and lectures that energy-coupling reactions involve the hydrolysis of ATP. But as we have just discussed, this is not really accurate, even though the amounts of energy available from ATP for coupling and from hydrolysis are equivalent: 7.3 kcal/mol. That ATP hydrolysis does not occur during energy-coupling mechanisms is what explains the high efficiency of energy transfer between ATP and reactant molecules, with very little energy being lost as heat.

4.3c Cells Also Couple Reactions to Regenerate ATP

We have just seen how the breakdown of ATP is an exergonic reaction that can be harnessed to make otherwise endergonic reactions proceed spontaneously. These coupling reactions occur continuously in living cells, consuming a tremendous amount of ATP. The question we can now ask is how do cells generate ATP? ATP is a renewable resource that is made by recombining ADP and P_i. If ATP hydrolysis is an exergonic process, then ATP synthesis from ADP and P_i is an endergonic process. The energy for ATP synthesis comes from the exergonic breakdown of complex molecules that contain an abundance of free energy. For animals we are essentially referring to food—carbohydrates, fats, and proteins—all abundant sources of energy.

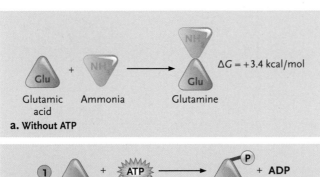

a. Without ATP

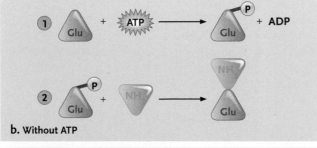

b. Without ATP

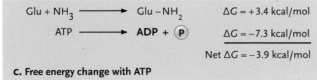

c. Free energy change with ATP

Figure 4.11
Energy coupling using ATP in the synthesis of glutamine from glutamic acid and ammonia.

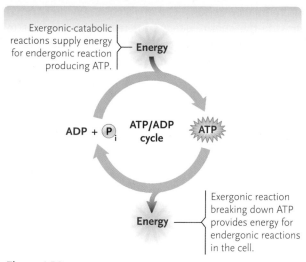

Figure 4.12
The ATP/ADP cycle that couples reactions releasing free energy and reactions requiring free energy.

The continued breakdown and resynthesis of ATP is called the **ATP cycle (Figure 4.12).** Approximately 10 million ATP molecules are broken down and resynthesized each second in a typical cell, illustrating that this cycle operates at an astonishing rate. In fact, if ATP were not regenerated from ADP and P_i, it is estimated that the average human would use an estimated 75 kg of ATP per day. It makes sense that cells should never be limited in their availability of ATP. In fact, a typical cell maintains an ATP concentration that is about 1000 times that of ADP—very far from equilibrium.

STUDY BREAK

1. Explain, given the structure of ATP, why its hydrolysis releases free energy.
2. What is meant by the term *energy coupling*?

4.4 The Role of Enzymes in Biological Reactions

Recall from the introduction to Section 4.2 that the laws of thermodynamics are useful because they can tell us if a process will occur without an input of energy or, said another way, if the process is spontaneous. However, the laws of thermodynamics do not tell us anything about the speed of a reaction. For example, even though the breakdown of the disaccharide sucrose into the monosaccharides glucose and fructose is a spontaneous process, a solution of sucrose can sit for years without any detectable fructose or glucose being formed. At this point we can make the distinction between thermodynamic instability and kinetic instability. A reaction is *thermodynamically unstable* if the free energy change of the reaction (ΔG) is negative.

In a *kinetically unstable* reaction, the reactants will rapidly be converted into products.

CONCEPT FIX That a reaction is spontaneous does not convey anything about how rapidly the reaction will occur. ◉

In the next few sections, we discuss how the speed of a reaction can be altered through the use of a special group of proteins called enzymes.

4.4a The Activation Energy of a Reaction Represents a Kinetic Barrier

What is it that prevents sucrose from being rapidly converted into glucose and fructose or ATP being rapidly hydrolyzed into ADP and P_i? For chemical reactions to occur, established bonds need to be broken and new bonds need to be formed. For bonds to be broken, they must first be strained or otherwise made less stable so that bond breakage can actually occur. To get reacting molecules into a more unstable state requires a small input of energy **(Figure 4.13a).** This initial energy investment required to start a reaction is called the **activation energy** (E_a). Molecules that gain the necessary activation energy occupy what is called the **transition state**, where bonds are unstable and are ready to be broken.

A rock resting in a depression at the top of a hill provides a physical example of activation energy **(Figure 4.13b).** The rock will not roll downhill spontaneously, even though its position represents considerable

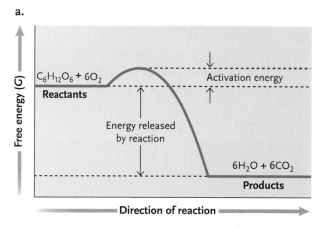

Figure 4.13
The concept of activation energy (E_a).

potential energy and the total "reaction"—the downward movement of the rock—is spontaneous and releases free energy. In this example, the activation energy is the effort required to raise the rock over the rim of the depression and start its downhill roll.

What provides the activation energy for chemical reactions? The molecules taking part in chemical reactions are in constant motion (at temperatures above absolute zero), and, periodically, reacting molecules may gain enough energy to reach the transition state. For a solution of sucrose, the number of molecules that reach the transition state at any one time is very small. However, if a significant number of reactant molecules reach the transition state, then the free energy that is released may be enough to get the remaining reactants to the transition state. A good example of this is illustrated by a propane torch **(Figure 4.14)**. Propane is a molecule that contains an abundance of free energy and spontaneously decomposes into carbon dioxide and water. However, the reaction proceeds very slowly—the propane in a torch can sit for years and remain unchanged. This is because if left undisturbed, it is a rare event for molecules of propane to acquire the energy needed to reach the transition state. However, if you supply a stream of propane with a spark (see Figure 4.14), then you provide molecules of propane with the energy to reach the transition state, resulting in a tremendous release of free energy into the environment.

4.4b Enzymes Accelerate Reactions by Reducing the Activation Energy

If you walk through a typical undergraduate chemistry lab, you will find that the benches have Bunsen burners, which are used to provide the heat for a range of chemical reactions. Chemists routinely use heat to provide the energy needed for reactant molecules to get to the transition state and thus speed up the rate of a reaction. In biology, using heat to speed up a reaction is problematic for two reasons: First, high temperatures destroy the structural components of cells, particularly proteins, and can result in cell death. Second, an increase in temperature would speed up all possible chemical reactions in a cell, and thus the critical regulation of the activity of metabolic pathways would be lost. So how can you increase the rate of a reaction without raising the temperature? You can use a **catalyst**, which is a chemical agent that speeds up the rate of a reaction without itself taking part in the reaction. The most common biological catalyst is a group of proteins called **enzymes.**

Recall that the activation energy represents a hurdle that a reaction needs to get over in order to proceed spontaneously. This activation energy represents a real *kinetic* barrier that prevents spontaneous reactions from proceeding quickly. The greater the activation energy barrier, the more slowly the reaction will proceed. Enzymes increase the rate of a reaction by lowering this barrier—by lowering the activation energy of the reaction **(Figure 4.15)**. Since the rate of a reaction is proportional to the number of reactant molecules that can acquire the necessary energy to get to the transition state, enzymes make it possible for a greater proportion of reactant molecules to attain the activation energy.

An important point that is shown in Figure 4.15 is that although enzymes lower the activation energy of a reaction, they do not alter the change in free energy (ΔG) of the reaction. The free energy of the reactants and products is the same; the only difference is the path the reaction takes.

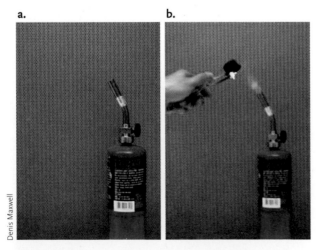

Figure 4.14

Combustion of propane. **(a)** The combustion of propane is a spontaneous reaction; however, the activation energy is a barrier that makes propane kinetically stable. **(b)** When a spark is provided, propane obtains the energy required to attain the transition state.

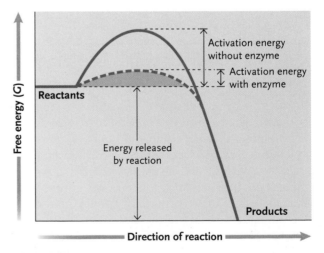

Figure 4.15

Enzymes lower the activation energy (E_a) of a reaction. The reduction allows biological reactions to proceed rapidly at the relatively low temperatures that can be tolerated by living organisms.

PEOPLE BEHIND BIOLOGY 4.1
Maud Menten (1879–1960)

A fundamental topic covered in almost all introductory biochemistry courses is the Michaelis–Menten equation. First stated in 1913, the equation provides a mathematical description of the kinetics of an enzyme-catalyzed reaction. The equation represents one of the fundamental concepts of biochemistry.

The Menten of the equation refers to Maud Menten, who was born on March 20, 1879, in Port Lambton, Ontario. After completing secondary school, Menten attended the University of Toronto and earned a bachelor of arts degree in 1904, followed by a master's degree in physiology in 1907. In the same year, Menten was appointed a fellow at the Rockefeller Institute for Medical Research in New York City, where she studied the effect of radium bromide on cancerous tumours in rats. Menten and two other scientists published the results of their experiment, producing the institute's first monograph. She returned to Canada and began studies at the

University of Toronto a year later. In 1911, she became one of the first Canadian women to receive a doctor of medicine degree.

In 1912, Menten travelled to Germany to work with Leonor Michaelis, a biochemist who shared her interest in understanding enzyme kinetics. After a year of research, the two scientists coauthored a paper that put forward a description of the basis of enzyme-catalyzed chemical kinetics. The paper introduced the Michaelis–Menten equation as a tool for measuring the rates of enzyme reactions. The formula gave scientists a way to record how enzymes worked and is the standard for most enzyme-kinetic measurements. Michaelis and Menten were able to demonstrate that each enzyme, given enough substrate, has its own rate of causing that substrate to undergo chemical change. The Michaelis–Menten equation profoundly changed the study of biochemistry and earned Menten and Michaelis worldwide recognition.

When Menten returned from Berlin, she enrolled at the University of Chicago, where she obtained a Ph.D. in biochemistry in 1916. Unable to find an academic position in her native Canada, in 1918 she joined the medical school faculty at the University of Pittsburgh. While maintaining an active research program, she was also known as an avid mountain climber who went on several expeditions to the Arctic. As well, she spoke numerous languages, loved to paint, and played the clarinet. Over the years, Menten authored more than 70 publications, including discoveries related to blood sugar, hemoglobin, and kidney functions. In so-called retirement, she returned to British Columbia to do research at the British Columbia Medical Research Institute, almost until her death. A plaque commemorating the life and work of Maud Menten is located in the Medical Sciences Building, University of Toronto, Queen's Park.

CONCEPT FIX By lowering the activation energy, enzymes increase the rate of spontaneous (exergonic) reactions. However, enzymes do not supply free energy to a reaction. Therefore, enzymes cannot make an endergonic reaction proceed spontaneously—they do not change the ΔG of a reaction.

4.4c Enzymes Combine with Reactants and Are Released Unchanged

In enzymatic reactions, an enzyme combines briefly with reacting molecules and is released unchanged when the reaction is complete. For example, the enzyme in **Figure 4.16,** hexokinase, catalyzes the following reaction:

$$glucose + ATP \longrightarrow glucose\ 6\text{-phosphate} + ADP$$

The reactant that an enzyme acts on is called the enzyme's substrate, or substrates if the enzyme binds two or more molecules. Each type of enzyme catalyzes the reaction of only a single type of molecule or a group of closely related molecules. This enzyme specificity explains why the metabolism of a typical cell is

represented by about 4000 different enzymes. Notice in Figure 4.16 that the enzyme is much larger than the substrate. As well, the substrate interacts with only a very small region of the enzyme. This region is called

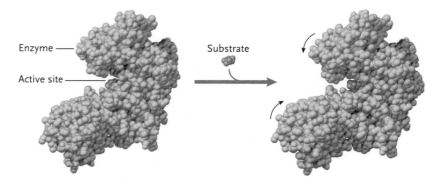

Figure 4.16

Space-filling models showing the combination of an enzyme, hexokinase (in blue), with its substrate, glucose (in orange). Hexokinase catalyzes the phosphorylation of glucose to form glucose 6-phosphate. The phosphate group that enters the reaction is not shown. Note how the enzyme undergoes a conformational change, closing the active site more tightly as it binds the substrate.

the **active site**—the specific site on an enzyme where catalysis takes place. The active site is usually a pocket or groove that is formed when the newly synthesized enzyme folds into its correct conformation.

In the early twentieth century, biochemists proposed the *lock-and-key hypothesis* to explain the specificity of the substrate–enzyme interaction. The analogy worked well to explain how even somewhat similar substrates (keys) were unable to bind to the same enzyme (lock) to cause catalysis (unlocking of the door). However, more recently, this hypothesis has been superseded by what has become known as the *induced-fit hypothesis*. Research has shown that unlike locks, enzymes are not rigid objects but instead are flexible. Just before substrate binding, the enzyme changes its shape (conformation) so that the active site becomes even more precise in its ability to bind substrate. This is shown in Figure 4.16, where the conformation of the enzyme changes slightly upon substrate binding.

As shown in **Figure 4.17,** the enzyme binds to the substrate, forming an enzyme–substrate complex. Catalysis occurs when the two are joined, with the action of the enzyme converting the substrate (or substrates) into one or more products. Because enzymes are released unchanged after a reaction, enzyme molecules can rapidly bind to other substrate molecules, catalyzing

the same reaction again, repeating what is called the enzyme cycle (see Figure 4.17). The rate at which enzymes catalyze reactions varies widely depending on the specifics of the enzyme and substrates involved, but typical rates vary from a low of about 100 reactions up to a high of 10 million reactions per second.

Many enzymes require a *cofactor,* a nonprotein group that binds very precisely to the enzyme. Cofactors are often metals, such as iron, copper, zinc, or manganese. Although most cells need very small amounts of these metals, they are absolutely essential for the catalytic activity of the enzyme to which they bind. Organic cofactors called *coenzymes* play similar roles and are often derived from vitamins.

4.4d Enzymes Reduce the Activation Energy by Inducing the Transition State

A central question of enzyme function is: how do they actually reduce the activation energy of a reaction? Recall that reactant molecules need to acquire the transition state for catalysis to occur. Enzymes increase the rate of a reaction by increasing the number of substrate molecules that attain the transition state conformation. Enzymes do this through three fundamental mechanisms **(Figure 4.18):**

1. *Bringing the reacting molecules together.* Reacting molecules can assume the transition state only when they collide; binding to an enzyme's active site brings the reactants together in the right orientation for catalysis to occur.

Bring reacting molecules close together

2. *Exposing the reactant molecule to altered charge environments that promote catalysis.* In some systems, the active site of the enzyme may contain ionic groups whose positive or negative charges alter the substrate in a way that favours catalysis.

Charge interactions

Figure 4.17
The catalytic cycle of an enzyme. Shown is the enzyme β-galactosidase, which cleaves the sugar lactose to produce glucose and galactose.

The disaccharide lactose

Glucose   Galactose

Active site

1 The substrate, lactose, binds to the enzyme β-galactosidase, forming an enzyme–substrate complex. Transition state is reached—tightest binding but least stable

β-galactosidase

Glucose   Galactose   H₂O

3 Enzyme can catalyze another reaction.

2 β-galactosidase catalyzes the breakage of the bond between the two sugars of lactose, and the products are released.

Figure 4.18
The binding of substrate(s) to an active site results in the substrate acquiring the transition state conformation.

(continued)

3. *Changing the shape of a substrate molecule.* The active site may strain or distort substrate molecules into a conformation that mimics the transition state.

Distort or strain substrate molecules

Regardless of the mechanism, the binding of the substrate to the active site results in the substrate attaining the transition state conformation. Although without the enzyme, substrate molecules do acquire the transition state, this may be a very rare event. The inclusion of an enzyme enables many more molecules to reach the transition state. This is fundamentally why enzymes increase the rate of a reaction.

STUDY BREAK

1. How do enzymes increase the rate of a chemical reaction?
2. Sketch out the catalytic cycle.

4.5 Conditions and Factors That Affect Enzyme Activity

Several conditions can alter the activity of an enzyme, including changes in the concentration of substrate and other molecules that bind to enzymes. In addition, a number of control mechanisms modify enzyme activity, thereby adjusting reaction rates to meet a cell's requirements for chemical products. As well, changes in temperature and pH can have a significant impact on enzyme activity.

4.5a Enzyme and Substrate Concentrations Can Change the Rate of Catalysis

Biochemists use a wide range of approaches to study an enzyme. These include molecular tools to study the structure and regulation of the gene that encodes the enzyme and sophisticated computer programs to model the three-dimensional structure of the enzyme itself. The most fundamental and central approach has been to determine the rate of an enzyme-catalyzed reaction and how it changes in response to altering certain experimental parameters. This usually requires isolating the enzyme from the remainder of the cell, incubating it in an appropriate buffered solution, and supplying the reaction mixture with substrate. With these constituents, one can then determine the rate of catalysis. This is most often done by measuring the rate at which the product is formed—so, for example, micromoles of product per second.

As shown in **Figure 4.19a, p. 86,** in the presence of excess substrate, the rate of catalysis is proportional to the amount of enzyme. That is, as enzyme concentration increases, the rate of product formation increases. In this system (see Figure 4.19a, p. 86), what is limiting the rate of the reaction (the rate-limiting component) is the amount of enzyme in the reaction mixture. Now what happens to the rate of the reaction if we keep the amount of enzyme constant at some intermediate concentration but change the substrate concentration from low to high? As shown in **Figure 4.19b, p. 86,** at very low concentrations, substrate molecules collide so infrequently with enzyme molecules that the reaction proceeds slowly. As the substrate concentration increases, the reaction rate initially increases as enzyme and substrate molecules collide more frequently. But as the enzyme molecules approach the maximum rate at which they can combine with reactants and release products, increasing the substrate concentration has a smaller and smaller effect, and the rate of reaction eventually levels off. When the catalytic cycle (see Figure 4.17) is turning as rapidly as possible, further increases in substrate concentration have no effect on the reaction rate. At this point, the enzyme is said to be saturated with substrate.

4.5b Enzyme Inhibitors Have Characteristic Effects on Enzyme Activity

The rate at which an enzyme can catalyze a reaction can be lowered by enzyme inhibitors, which are non-substrate molecules that bind to an enzyme and decrease its activity. Some inhibitors work by binding to the active site of an enzyme, whereas other inhibitors bind to critical sites located elsewhere in the structure of the enzyme.

Inhibitors that combine with the active site have shapes that resemble the normal substrate closely enough to fit into and occupy the active site, thereby blocking access for the normal substrate and slowing the reaction rate. If the concentration of the inhibitor is high enough, the reaction may stop completely. Inhibition of this type is called **competitive inhibition** because the inhibitor competes with the normal substrate for access to the active site of the enzyme **(Figure 4.20a, p. 86).** Competitive inhibitors are useful in enzyme research because their structure helps identify the specific part of a substrate molecule that binds the active site of an enzyme.

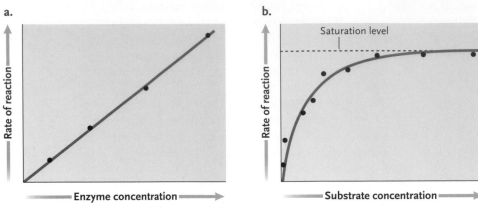

Figure 4.19

Effect of increasing enzyme concentration **(a)** or substrate concentration **(b)** on the rate of an enzyme-catalyzed reaction.

In **noncompetitive inhibition**, specific molecules inhibit enzyme activity, but rather than binding at the active site, they bind somewhere else on the enzyme. Because of this, a noncompetitive inhibitor does not compete with substrate molecules for access to the active site of the enzyme **(Figure 4.20b)**. A noncompetitive inhibitor decreases enzyme activity because upon binding it changes the conformation of the enzyme, which reduces the ability of the active site to efficiently bind substrate.

Inhibitors differ with respect to how strongly they bind to enzymes. In *reversible inhibition,* the binding of inhibitors to the enzyme is weak and readily reversible, with the enzyme activity returning to normal following inhibitor release. By contrast, some inhibitors bind so strongly to the enzyme through the formation of covalent bonds that the enzyme is completely disabled—this is *irreversible inhibition.* Not surprisingly, many irreversible inhibitors that act on critical enzymes are highly toxic to the cell. This includes a wide variety of drugs and pesticides. Cyanide is a potent poison because it binds strongly to and inhibits cytochrome oxidase, the enzyme that catalyzes the last step of respiratory electron transport (see Chapter 6). In addition, many antibiotics are toxins that inhibit enzyme activity in bacteria (see *Molecule behind Biology*). Irreversible inhibition can only be overcome by the cell synthesizing more of the particular enzyme.

4.5c Cells Adjust Enzyme Activity to Meet the Needs for Reaction Products

Metabolism consists of both anabolic and catabolic pathways, where each type of pathway is made of a series of enzyme-catalyzed reactions. The product of any one reaction often represents an intermediate of the pathway. It is not the end product of the pathway but rather the substrate to be used for the next reaction in the series. Because of this design it is important for metabolism to work efficiently that the activity of metabolic enzymes can be adjusted upward or downward so that the amount of product synthesized by any reaction matches the needs of the cell for the product. This important kind of metabolic regulation is often facilitated by various metabolites that act as reversible activators and inhibitors of enzyme activity. A typical cell contains thousands of enzymes, and for each enzyme that synthesizes a specific molecule, there is usually another enzyme that catalyzes the reverse reaction. If both enzymes were active in the same cell compartment at the same time, the two processes would run simultaneously in opposite directions and have no overall effect other than wasting energy. To prevent this futile cycling, the cell is able to regulate enzyme activity in such a way that not all enzymes are active at the same time. Two major mechanisms directly regulate enzyme activity: allosteric regulation and covalent modification.

Allosteric Regulation. In the mechanism of **allosteric regulation (Figure 4.21)**, enzyme activity is controlled by the reversible binding of a regulatory molecule to the **allosteric site**, a location on the enzyme outside the active site. The mechanism of control may either increase or decrease enzyme activity. Because these molecules alter enzyme activity by binding at sites separate from the active site, their action is noncompetitive.

Figure 4.20

How competitive **(a)** and noncompetitive **(b)** inhibitors reduce enzyme activity.

a. Competitive inhibition

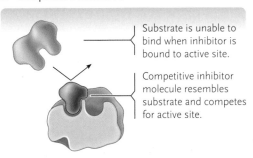

Substrate is unable to bind when inhibitor is bound to active site.

Competitive inhibitor molecule resembles substrate and competes for active site.

b. Noncompetitive inhibition

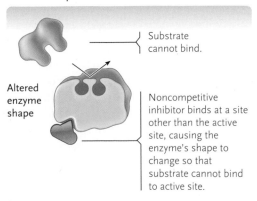

Substrate cannot bind.

Altered enzyme shape

Noncompetitive inhibitor binds at a site other than the active site, causing the enzyme's shape to change so that substrate cannot bind to active site.

MOLECULE BEHIND BIOLOGY 4.2

Penicillin: A Competitive Inhibitor of Enzyme Action

Penicillin is an antibiotic that is used in the treatment of bacterial infections. It was first discovered by Alexander Fleming, who isolated it from the mould *Penicillium* after he accidentally found that the presence of the mould inhibited the growth of bacteria on a Petri plate. Following the development of methods for its mass production, penicillin became a true wonder drug as it was effective at treating a wide range of bacterial infections that in the past often led to death.

Penicillin acts by inhibiting the synthesis of peptidoglycan, a key component of the bacterial cell wall. Peptidoglycan is a complex polymer consisting of sugars and amino acids that forms a meshlike structure outside the plasma membrane. As such, peptidoglycan provides structural strength and protects the bacterial cell from osmotic changes that would otherwise cause the cell to burst. If a bacterium is unable to synthesize components necessary for its cell wall, it is unable to grow and divide.

A key factor that is required for the synthesis of peptidoglycan is the enzyme transpeptidase, which catalyzes the formation of a peptide bond between two amino acids, effectively linking two portions of the peptidoglycan together. Penicillin inhibits peptidoglycan synthesis because it is a competitive inhibitor of transpeptidase activity. The structure of penicillin mimics that of the two amino acids, which are normally brought together by the active site. Penicillin binds irreversibly to the active site of transpeptidase, effectively destroying the molecule. Given the concentrations of penicillin usually administered to a patient, this leads to total inhibition of all transpeptidase activity.

Although penicillin was widely employed in the 1950s and 1960s, most infections today involve bacteria that have acquired resistance to the drug. New antibiotics are constantly being developed to try to stop the growing problem of antibiotic-resistant bacteria.

Allosteric activation

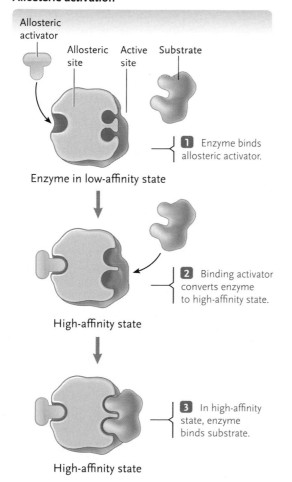

Allosteric activator

Allosteric site   Active site   Substrate

1 Enzyme binds allosteric activator.

Enzyme in low-affinity state

2 Binding activator converts enzyme to high-affinity state.

High-affinity state

3 In high-affinity state, enzyme binds substrate.

High-affinity state

Allosteric inhibition

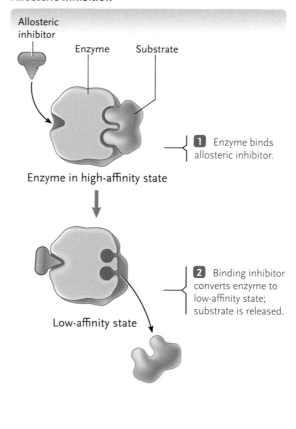

Allosteric inhibitor

Enzyme   Substrate

1 Enzyme binds allosteric inhibitor.

Enzyme in high-affinity state

2 Binding inhibitor converts enzyme to low-affinity state; substrate is released.

Low-affinity state

Figure 4.21
Allosteric regulation.

Enzymes controlled by allosteric regulation typically have two alternative conformations controlled from the allosteric site. In one conformation, called the *high-affinity state* (the active form), the enzyme binds strongly to its substrate; in the other conformation, the *low-affinity state* (the inactive form), the enzyme binds the substrate weakly or not at all. Binding with regulatory substances may induce either state: binding an **allosteric inhibitor** converts an allosteric enzyme from the high- to the low-affinity state, and binding an **allosteric activator** converts it from the low- to the high-affinity state (see Figure 4.21, p. 87).

Frequently, allosteric inhibitors are a product of the metabolic pathway that they regulate. If the product accumulates in excess, its effect as an inhibitor automatically slows or stops the enzymatic reaction producing it. If the product becomes too scarce, the inhibition is reduced, and the product begins to accumulate again. This type of metabolic regulation, in which the product of a reaction acts to inhibit its own synthesis, is termed **feedback inhibition.** In multireaction pathways, feedback inhibition usually involves the final product inhibiting the enzyme that catalyzes one of the early reactions in the pathway. In this way, cellular resources are not wasted in producing intermediates that are not needed.

The biochemical pathway that makes the amino acid isoleucine from threonine is an excellent example of feedback inhibition. The pathway proceeds in five steps, each catalyzed by an enzyme **(Figure 4.22).** The end product of the pathway, isoleucine, is an allosteric inhibitor of the first enzyme of the pathway, threonine deaminase. If the cell makes more isoleucine than it needs, isoleucine combines reversibly with threonine deaminase at the allosteric site, converting the enzyme to the low-affinity state and inhibiting its ability to combine with threonine, the substrate for the first reaction in the pathway. If isoleucine levels drop too low, the allosteric site of threonine deaminase is vacated, the enzyme is converted to the high-affinity state, and isoleucine production increases.

Covalent Modification. While allosteric regulation allows for very rapid changes in enzyme activity, some enzymes are often completely inactive and are activated only when their structure changes by covalent modification. The opposite situation also occurs—some enzymes are always active and are made inactive by covalent modification. For example, chemical modification by the addition or removal of phosphate groups is a major mechanism of enzyme regulation that is used by all organisms, from bacteria to humans. Typically, regulatory phosphate groups derived from ATP or other nucleotides are added to the regulated enzymes by other enzymes known as protein kinases. The addition of a phosphate group—*phosphorylation*—either increases or decreases enzyme activity or activates or deactivates

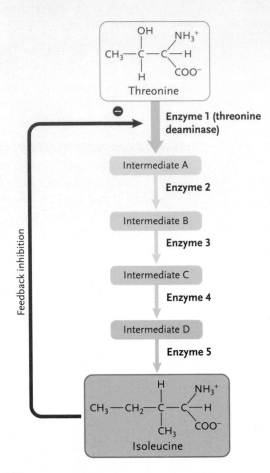

Figure 4.22
Feedback inhibition in the pathway that produces isoleucine from threonine. If the product of the pathway, isoleucine, accumulates in excess, it slows or stops the pathway by acting as an allosteric inhibitor of the enzyme that catalyzes the first step in the pathway.

the enzyme, depending on the particular enzyme and where the phosphate group is added to the enzyme. Removal of phosphate groups—*dephosphorylation*—reverses the effects of phosphorylation. Dephosphorylation is carried out by a different group of enzymes called protein phosphatases. The balance between phosphorylation and dephosphorylation of the enzymes modified by the protein kinases and protein phosphatases closely regulates cellular activity. Another important type of covalent modification that results in enzyme activation is *proteolytic cleavage*. Some enzymes are synthesized in catalytically inactive forms that are activated after the protein is shortened slightly by an enzyme called a protease. The best example of this occurs with the powerful digestive enzymes, including trypsin and chymotripsin. In response to hormone signals triggered by ingestion of food, these enzymes are synthesized in the pancreas as a slightly longer, inactive form that becomes active only in the small intestine by specific proteases. This modification prevents active digestive enzymes being present in the sensitive tissues of the pancreas.

4.5d Temperature and pH Are Key Factors Affecting Enzyme Activity

The activity of most enzymes is strongly altered by changes in pH and temperature. Characteristically, enzymes reach maximal activity within a narrow range of temperature or pH; at levels outside this range, enzyme activity drops off. These effects produce a typically peaked curve when enzyme activity is plotted, with the peak where temperature or pH produces maximal activity.

Effects of pH Changes. Typically, each enzyme has an optimal pH where it operates at peak efficiency in speeding the rate of its biochemical reaction **(Figure 4.23)**. On either side of this pH optimum, the rate of the catalyzed reaction decreases because of the resulting alterations in charged groups. The effects on the structure and function of the active site become more extreme at pH values farther from the optimum, until the rate drops to zero. Most enzymes have a pH optimum near the pH of the cellular contents, about pH 7. Enzymes that are secreted from cells may have pH optima farther from neutrality. An example is pepsin, an enzyme secreted into the stomach. This enzyme's pH optimum is 1.5, close to the acidity of stomach contents. Similarly, trypsin has a pH optimum at about pH 8, allowing it to function well in the somewhat alkaline contents of the intestine, where it is secreted.

Effects of Temperature Changes. The effects of temperature changes on enzyme activity reflect two distinct processes. First, temperature has a general effect on chemical reactions of all kinds. As the temperature rises, the rate of chemical reactions typically increases.

This effect reflects increases in the kinetic motion of all molecules, with more frequent and stronger collisions as the temperature rises. Second, temperature has a more specific effect on all proteins, including enzymes. As the temperature rises, the kinetic motions of the amino acid chains of an enzyme increase, along with the strength and frequency of collisions between enzymes and surrounding molecules. At some point, these disturbances become strong enough to denature the enzyme: the hydrogen bonds and other forces that maintain its three-dimensional structure break, making the enzyme unfold and lose its function (see *The Purple Pages* for a more detailed description of protein denaturation). The two effects of temperature act in opposition to each other to produce characteristic changes in the rate of enzymatic catalysis **(Figure 4.24)**. In the range of 0°C to about 40°C, the reaction rate doubles for every 10°C increase in temperature. Above 40°C, the increasing kinetic motion begins to denature the enzyme, reducing the rate of increase in enzyme activity. At some point, as the temperature rises, the denaturation of the enzyme causes the reaction rate to level off at a peak. Further increases cause such extensive unfolding that the reaction rate decreases rapidly to zero.

For most enzymes, the peak in activity lies between 40°C and 50°C; the drop-off becomes steep at 55°C and falls to zero at about 60°C. Thus, the rate of an enzyme-catalyzed reaction peaks at the temperature at which kinetic motion is greatest, but no significant unfolding of the enzyme has occurred. Although most enzymes have a temperature optimum between 40°C and 50°C, some have activity peaks below or above this range. For example, the enzymes of maize (corn) pollen function best near

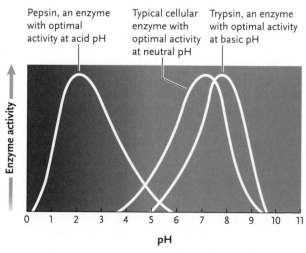

Figure 4.23
Effects of pH on enzyme activity. An enzyme typically has an optimal pH at which it is most active; at pH values above or below the optimum, the rate of enzyme activity drops off. At extreme pH values, the rate drops to zero.

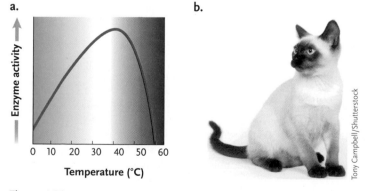

Figure 4.24
Effect of temperature on enzyme activity. **(a)** As the temperature rises, the rate of the catalyzed reaction increases proportionally until the temperature reaches the point at which the enzyme begins to denature. The rate drops off steeply as denaturation progresses and becomes complete. **(b)** Visible effects of environmental temperature on enzyme activity in Siamese cats. The fur on the extremities—ears, nose, paws, and tail—contains more dark brown pigment (melanin) than the rest of the body. A heat-sensitive enzyme controlling melanin production is denatured in warmer body regions, so dark pigment is not produced, but fur colour is.

30°C and undergo steep reductions in activity above 32°C. As a result, environmental temperatures above 32°C can seriously inhibit the growth of corn crops. Many animals living in frigid regions have enzymes with much lower temperature optima than average. For example, the enzymes of arctic snow fleas are most active at 10°C. At the other extreme are the enzymes of archaeans that live in hot springs, which are so resistant to denaturation that they remain active at temperatures of 85°C or more.

STUDY BREAK

1. Why do enzyme-catalyzed reactions reach a saturation level when substrate concentration is increased?
2. Distinguish between competitive and noncompetitive inhibition.
3. Explain why the activity of an enzyme will eventually decrease to zero as the temperature rises.

Review

  Access an interactive eBook, chapter-specific interactive learning tools, including flashcards, quizzes, videos, and more in your Biology **CourseMate**, accessed through NelsonBrain.com **Aplia™** is an online interactive learning solution that helps you improve comprehension—and your grade—by integrating a variety of mediums and tools such as videos, tutorials, practice tests, and an interactive eBook.

4.1 Energy and the Laws of Thermodynamics

- Energy is the capacity to do work. Kinetic energy is the energy of motion; potential energy is energy stored in an object because of its location or chemical structure. Energy may be readily converted between potential and kinetic states, but it cannot be created or destroyed.

- Thermodynamics is the study of energy flow between a system and its surroundings during chemical and physical reactions. A system that does not exchange energy or matter with its surroundings is an isolated system. A system that exchanges energy but not matter with its surroundings is a closed system. A system that exchanges both energy and matter with its surroundings is an open system (Figure 4.1).

- The first law of thermodynamics states that the total amount of energy in a system and its surroundings remains constant. The second law states that in any process involving a spontaneous (possible) change from an initial to a final state, the total entropy (disorder) of the system and its surroundings always increases.

- Life obeys the second law of thermodynamics. Life is maintained in a highly ordered state because it is an open system, bringing energy in from the surroundings and in turn increasing the disorder of the surroundings (Figure 4.5).

4.2 Free Energy and Spontaneous Reactions

- A spontaneous reaction is one that will occur without the input of energy from the surroundings. A spontaneous reaction releases free energy—energy that is available to do work.

- The free energy equation, $\Delta G = \Delta H - T\Delta S$, states that the free energy change, ΔG, is influenced by two factors: the change in enthalpy (potential energy in a system) and the change in entropy of the system as a reaction goes to completion.

- Factors that oppose the completion of spontaneous reactions, such as the relative concentrations of reactants and products, produce an equilibrium point at which reactants are converted to products and products are converted back to reactants, at equal rates (Figure 4.7). Organisms reach equilibrium ($\Delta G = 0$) only when they die.

- Reactions with a negative ΔG are spontaneous; they release free energy and are known as exergonic reactions. Reactions with a positive ΔG require free energy and are known as endergonic reactions (Figure 4.8).

- Metabolism is the biochemical modification and use of energy in the synthesis and breakdown of organic molecules. A catabolic pathway releases the potential energy of a molecule in breaking it down to a simpler molecule. An anabolic (biosynthetic) pathway uses energy to convert a simple molecule to a more complex molecule (ΔG is positive).

4.3 Adenosine Triphosphate Is the Energy Currency of the Cell

- The hydrolysis of ATP releases free energy that can be used as a source of energy for the cell (Figure 4.10).

- A cell can couple the exergonic reaction of ATP breakdown (not technically a hydrolysis reaction) to make an otherwise endergonic reaction proceed spontaneously. These coupling reactions require enzymes (Figure 4.11).

- The ATP used in coupling reactions is replenished by reactions that link ATP synthesis to catabolic reactions. ATP thus cycles between reactions that release free energy and reactions that require free energy (Figure 4.12).

4.4 The Role of Enzymes in Biological Reactions

- What prevents many exergonic reactions from proceeding rapidly is that they need to overcome an energy barrier (the activation energy, E_a) to get to the transition state (Figure 4.13).

- Enzymes are catalysts that greatly speed the rate at which spontaneous reactions occur because they lower the activation energy (Figure 4.15).

- Enzymes are usually specific: they catalyze reactions of only a single type of molecule or a group of closely related molecules (Figure 4.16).

- Catalysis occurs at the active site, which is the site where the enzyme binds to the substrate (reactant molecule). After combining briefly with the substrate, the enzyme is released unchanged when the reaction is complete (Figure 4.17).

- Enzymes reduce the activation energy by inducing the transition state of the reaction, from which the reaction can move easily in the direction of either products or reactants.

- Three major mechanisms contribute to enzymatic catalysis by reducing the activation energy: (1) enzymes bring reacting molecules together, (2) enzymes expose reactant molecules to altered charge environments that promote catalysis, and (3) enzymes change the shape of substrate molecules (Figure 4.18).

4.5 Conditions and Factors That Affect Enzyme Activity

- When substrate is abundant, the rate of a reaction is proportional to the amount of enzyme. At a fixed enzyme concentration, the rate of a reaction increases with substrate concentration until the enzyme becomes saturated with reactants. At that point, further increases in substrate concentration do not increase the rate of the reaction (Figure 4.19).

- Many cellular enzymes are regulated by nonsubstrate molecules called inhibitors. Competitive inhibitors interfere with reaction rates by combining with the active site of an enzyme; noncompetitive inhibitors combine with sites elsewhere on the enzyme (Figure 4.20).

- Allosteric regulation resembles noncompetitive inhibition except that regulatory molecules may either increase or decrease enzyme activity. Allosteric regulation often carries out feedback inhibition, in which a product of an enzyme-catalyzed pathway acts as an allosteric inhibitor of the first enzyme in the pathway (Figures 4.21 and 4.22).

- Many key enzymes are regulated by chemical modification by substances such as ions and certain functional groups. The modifications change enzyme conformation, resulting in increased or decreased activity.

- Typically, an enzyme has optimal activity at a certain pH and a certain temperature; at pH and temperature values above and below the optimum, the reaction rate falls off (Figures 4.23 and 4.24).

Questions

Self-Test Questions

1. Which of the following statements about energy and thermodynamics is correct?
   a. Earth is an isolated system.
   b. Living organisms are closed systems.
   c. Energy conversions can never be 100% efficient.
   d. The total amount of energy in the universe is always decreasing.

2. Which of the following statements about entropy is correct?
   a. We eat food to maintain high entropy.
   b. The entropy of any system always increases.
   c. It is a measure of the total energy content of a system.
   d. The entropy of water increases as it turns from a liquid into a gas.

3. For a reaction to be exergonic which of the following must occur?
   a. It must also be exothermic.
   b. There must be an input of energy to proceed.
   c. The products must have less enthalpy than the reactants.
   d. The products must have less free energy than the reactants.
   e. The entropy of the products must be greater than the entropy of the reactants.

4. Which of the following statements is correct?
   a. At equilibrium, the ΔG is negative.
   b. Living organisms are never at equilibrium.
   c. An isolated system will never reach equilibrium.
   d. Molecules that have high free energy are very stable.
   e. Most biochemical reactions have a ΔG far from zero.

5. Instructors often mention the "hydrolysis of ATP" as the source of energy for cellular reactions. But this statement is inaccurate. Why?
   a. A molecule can never be the source of energy.
   b. ATP actually contains very little free energy.
   c. The hydrolysis of GTP is more common than ATP in cellular reactions.
   d. Water does not enter the active site of enzymes linked to ATP breakdown.

6. Propane is thermodynamically unstable; why is it kinetically stable?
   a. It is highly electronegative.
   b. Its breakdown is exergonic ($-\Delta G$).
   c. It has a high activation energy (E_A).
   d. It contains an abundance of oxygen and little hydrogen.

7. Which of the following statements about an enzyme is correct?
   a. It decreases the ΔG of an endergonic reaction.
   b. It is a protein and therefore is encoded by a gene.
   c. It can make an endergonic reaction proceed spontaneously.
   d. One enzyme molecule can only bind a single substrate molecule at any one time.

8. Compared with competitive inhibition, which of the following statements is correct only for noncompetitive inhibition of an enzyme-catalyzed reaction?
   a. It changes the conformation of the enzyme.
   b. The inhibitory molecule is similar to the normal substrate.
   c. Inhibition decreases the rate at which the product is made.
   d. It results in the enzyme becoming permanently inactive.

9. Which of the following statements about allosteric enzymes is correct?
   a. An allosteric activator prevents binding at the active site.
   b. Their activity can be finely controlled by metabolites within the cell.
   c. The allosteric site of the enzyme binds additional substrate molecules.
   d. An enzyme that possesses allosteric sites does not possess an active site.

10. Which of the following explains the shape of a curve that plots enzyme activity as a function of temperature?
    a. As temperature increases, the rate of all reactions slows down.
    b. At high temperatures, the structural integrity of the enzyme breaks down.
    c. At high temperatures, the rate of catalysis stays high and constant—it saturates.
    d. At low but increasing temperatures, the rate of collisions between substrate and enzyme molecules decreases.

Questions for Discussion

1. Trees become more complex as they develop spontaneously from seeds to adults. Does this process violate the second law of thermodynamics? Why or why not?

2. Trace the flow of energy through your body. What products increase the entropy of you and your surroundings?

3. You have found a molecular substance that accelerates the rate of a particular reaction. What kind of information would you need to demonstrate that this molecular substance is an enzyme?

4. The addition or removal of phosphate groups from ATP is a fully reversible reaction. In what way does this reversibility facilitate the use of ATP as a coupling agent for cellular reactions?

The cystic fibrosis transmembrane conductance regulator (CFTR) is a chloride pump. Mutations to the CFTR gene result in the pump being defective, causing cystic fibrosis.

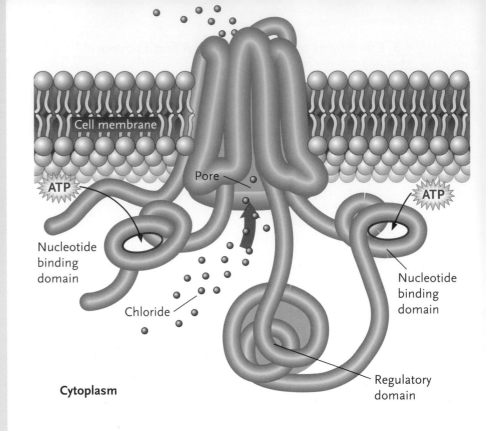

Cell membrane

Pore

ATP

ATP

Nucleotide binding domain

Nucleotide binding domain

Chloride

Regulatory domain

Cytoplasm

5 Cell Membranes and Signalling

STUDY PLAN

5.1 An Overview of the Structure of a Membrane

5.1a A Membrane Consists of Proteins in a Fluid of Lipid Molecules

5.1b Experimental Evidence Supports the Fluid Mosaic Model

5.2 The Lipid Fabric of a Membrane

5.2a Phospholipids Are the Dominant Lipids in Membranes

5.2b Fatty Acid Composition and Temperature Affect Membrane Fluidity

5.2c Organisms Can Adjust Fatty Acid Composition

5.3 Membrane Proteins

5.3a Membrane Proteins Serve a Diversity of Key Roles

5.3b Integral Membrane Proteins Interact with the Membrane Hydrophobic Core

5.3c Peripheral Membrane Proteins Interact with the Membrane Hydrophilic Surface

5.4 Passive Membrane Transport

5.4a Passive Transport Is Based on Diffusion

5.4b There Are Two Types of Passive Transport: Simple and Facilitated

5.4c Two Groups of Transport Proteins Carry Out Facilitated Diffusion

5.4d Osmosis Is the Passive Diffusion of Water

5.5 Active Membrane Transport

5.5a Active Transport Requires Energy

5.5b Primary Active Transport Moves Positively Charged Ions

5.5c Secondary Active Transport Moves Both Ions and Organic Molecules

5.6 Exocytosis and Endocytosis

5.6a Exocytosis Releases Molecules to the Outside by Means of Secretory Vesicles

5.6b Endocytosis Brings Materials into Cells in Endocytic Vesicles

5.7 Role of Membranes in Cell Signalling

5.7a Signal Transduction Links Signals with Downstream Cellular Responses

5.7b Membrane Surface Receptors Bind a Diversity of Molecules

5.7c Signal Reception Triggers Response Pathways within the Cells

WHY IT MATTERS

Cystic fibrosis (CF) is one of the most common genetic diseases. It affects approximately 1 in 3900 children born in Canada. People with CF suffer from a progressive impairment of lung and gastrointestinal function. Although the treatment of CF patients is slowly improving, their average life span remains under 40 years. CF is caused by mutation to a gene that codes for a protein called the cystic fibrosis transmembrane conductance regulator (CFTR). In normal cells, CFTR acts as a membrane transport protein that pumps chloride (Cl^-, negatively charged) out of the cells that line the lungs and intestinal tract into the covering mucus lining. This results in an electrical gradient across the membrane and leads to the movement of (positively charged) sodium ions in the same direction as the chloride. Because of the high ion concentration (Na^+ and Cl^-), water moves, by osmosis, out into the mucus lining, keeping it moist. Keeping the lining of the lungs and intestinal tract wet is critical to their proper functioning. In individuals with CF, the Cl^- channel CFTR does not function properly, which results in water being retained within cells, resulting in a buildup of thick mucus that cannot effectively be removed by coughing. Besides obstructing airways and preventing normal breathing, the buildup of mucus in the lungs makes CF patients very susceptible to bacterial infections.

Currently, there is no cure for CF, with lung transplantation being a common procedure as the disease progresses. Since CF is caused by a defect to a single gene, the greatest hope is in gene therapy (see Chapter 15) that would attempt to insert normal copies of the CFTR gene into affected cells. However, many technical hurdles need to be overcome before gene therapy becomes a viable treatment option.

The structure and function of biological membranes is the focus of this chapter. We first consider the structure of membranes and then examine how membranes selectively transport substances in and out of cells and organelles. We close the chapter with a discussion of the critical role membranes play in signal transduction through the binding of molecules and the subsequent activation of intracellular signalling pathways.

5.1 An Overview of the Structure of Membranes

One of the keys to the evolution of life was the development of the cell or **plasma membrane.** By acting as a selectively permeable barrier, the plasma membrane allow for the uptake of key nutrients and elimination of waste products while maintaining a protected environment for cellular processes to occur. The subsequent development of internal membranes allowed for compartmentalization of processes and increased complexity. A good example of this is the nuclear envelope, which defines the hallmark of the eukaryotic cell—the nucleus.

5.1a A Membrane Consists of Proteins in a Fluid of Lipid Molecules

Our current view of membrane structure is based on the **fluid mosaic model (Figure 5.1).** The model proposes that membranes are not rigid with molecules locked into place but rather consist of proteins within a mixture of lipid molecules the consistency of olive oil.

The lipid molecules of all biological membranes exist in a double layer called a bilayer that is less than 10 nm thick. By comparison, this page is approximately 100 000 nm thick. The lipid molecules of the bilayer vibrate, flex back and forth, spin around their long axis, move sideways, and exchange places within the same bilayer half. Only rarely does a lipid molecule flip-flop between the two layers. Exchanging places within a layer occurs millions of times a second, making the lipid molecules in the membrane highly dynamic. As we will discuss later, maintaining the membrane in a fluid state is critical to membrane function.

The mosaic aspect of the fluid mosaic model refers to the fact that most membranes contain an assortment of different types of proteins. This includes proteins involved in transport and attachment, signal

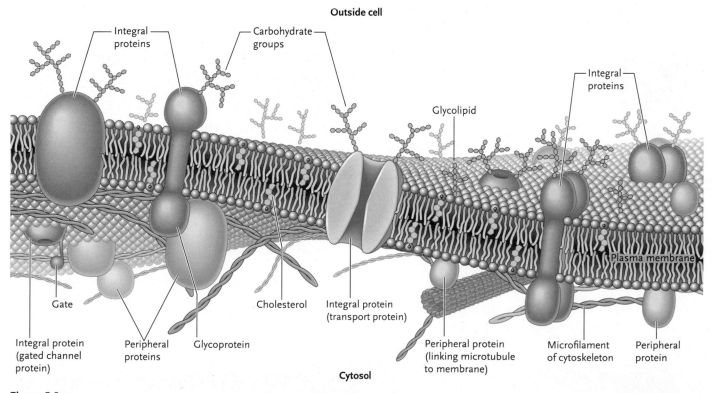

Figure 5.1

Membrane structure according to the fluid mosaic model. The model proposes that integral membrane proteins are suspended individually in a fluid lipid bilayer. Peripheral proteins are attached to integral proteins or membrane lipids mostly on the cytoplasmic side of the membrane (shown only on the inner surface in the figure). In the plasma membrane, carbohydrate groups of membrane glycoproteins and glycolipids face the cell exterior.

transduction, and processes such as electron transport. Because they are larger than lipid molecules, proteins move more slowly in the fluid environment of the membrane. As well, a small number of membrane proteins anchor cytoskeleton filaments to the membrane and do not move (Figure 5.1). As also shown in Figure 5.1, a number of the lipid and protein components of some membranes have carbohydrate groups linked to them, forming glycolipids and glycoproteins.

The relative proportions of lipid and protein within a membrane vary considerably depending on the type of membrane. For example, membranes that contain protein complexes involved in electron transport, such as the inner mitochondrial membrane, contain large amounts of protein (76% protein and only 24% lipid), whereas the plasma membrane contains nearly equal amounts of protein and lipid (49% and 51%, respectively). Myelin, which is a membrane that functions to insulate nerve fibres, is composed mostly of lipids (18% protein and 82% lipid).

An important characteristic of membranes, illustrated in Figure 5.1, is that the proteins and other components of one half of the lipid bilayer are different from those that make up the other half of the bilayer. This is referred to as membrane asymmetry, and it reflects differences in the functions performed by each side of the membrane. For example, a range of glycolipids and carbohydrate groups are attached to proteins on the external side of the plasma membrane, whereas components of the cytoskeleton bind to proteins on the internal side of the plasma membrane. In addition, hormones and growth factors bind to receptor proteins that are found only on the external surface of the plasma membrane.

5.1b Experimental Evidence in Support of the Fluid Mosaic Model

The fluid mosaic model of membrane structure is supported by two major pieces of experimental evidence.

Membranes Are Fluid. In a now classic study carried out in 1970, David Frye and Michael A. Edidin grew human cells and mouse cells separately in tissue culture. They were able to tag the human or mouse membrane proteins **(Figure 5.2)** with dye molecules: the human proteins were linked to red dye molecules and the mouse proteins were linked to green. Frye and Edidin then fused the human and mouse cells. Within minutes, they found that the two distinctly coloured

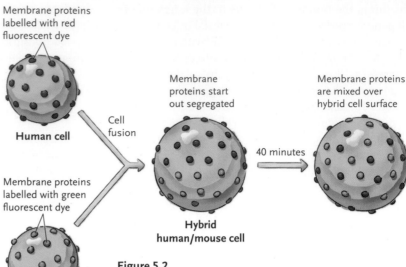

Figure 5.2
The Frye-Edidin experiment provided evidence that the membrane bilayer is fluid. In the experiment, membrane proteins were found to rapidly migrate over the surface of the hybrid cell.

proteins began to mix. In less than an hour, the two colours had completely intermixed on the fused cells, indicating that the mouse and human proteins had moved around in the fused membranes.

Based on the measured rates at which molecules mix in biological membranes, the membrane bilayer appears to be about as fluid as olive oil or light machine oil.

Membrane Asymmetry. One of the key experiments revealing membrane asymmetry utilizes the freeze-fracture technique in combination with electron microscopy **(Figure 5.3)**. In this technique, a block of cells is rapidly frozen by dipping it in liquid nitrogen ($-196°C$). Then the block is fractured by hitting it with a microscopically sharp knife edge. Often the fracture splits bilayers into inner and outer halves, exposing the membrane interior. Using electron microscopy, the split membranes appear as smooth layers in which individual particles the size of proteins are embedded (shown in Figure 5.3c). From these images, it is clear that the particles on either side of the membrane differ in size, number, and shape, providing evidence that the two sides are distinctly different.

STUDY BREAK

1. Describe the fluid mosaic model of membrane structure.
2. What is meant by the term *membrane asymmetry*?

5.2 The Lipid Fabric of a Membrane

The foundation or underlying fabric of all biological membranes are the lipid molecules. Collectively, the term *lipid* refers to a diverse group of water-insoluble

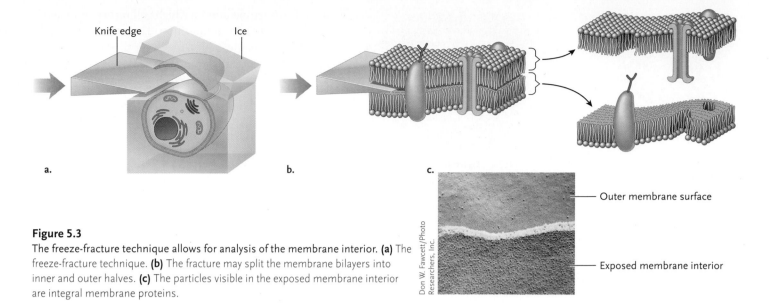

Figure 5.3

The freeze-fracture technique allows for analysis of the membrane interior. **(a)** The freeze-fracture technique. **(b)** The fracture may split the membrane bilayers into inner and outer halves. **(c)** The particles visible in the exposed membrane interior are integral membrane proteins.

Knife edge

Ice

a.

b.

c.

Outer membrane surface

Exposed membrane interior

Don W. Fawcett/Photo Researchers, Inc.

molecules that includes fats; phospholipids, which are the dominant lipids in membranes; and steroids. A structural overview of these molecules is found in *The Purple Pages*. As we discuss in this section, keeping membranes in a fluid state is important to membrane function. Many organisms can adjust the types of lipids in the membranes such that membranes do not become too stiff (viscous) or too fluid (liquid).

5.2a Phospholipids Are the Dominant Lipids in Membranes

The lipid bilayer, which represents the foundation of biological membranes, is formed of **phospholipids**. As shown in **Figure 5.4a,** each phospholipid consists of a head group attached to two long chains of carbon and hydrogen (a hydrocarbon) called a fatty acid. The head group consists of glycerol linked to one of several types of alcohols or amino acids by a phosphate group (see Figure 5.4a). A property that all phospholipids possess, which is critical to the structure and function of membranes, is they are amphipathic—the molecule contains a region that is *hydrophobic* (water fearing) and a region that is *hydrophilic* (water loving). Whereas the fatty acid chains of a lipid are nonpolar, the phosphate-containing head group is polar. Overall, polar molecules tend to be hydrophilic and nonpolar molecules hydrophobic. (For a review of molecular polarity, see *The Purple Pages*.) Laundry detergents are common amphipathic molecules—they are excellent at removing oil stains from clothing while also being soluble in water.

As illustrated in Figure 5.4a, phospholipids can differ in the degree of unsaturation of their fatty acids. Notice in Figure 5.4a that one of the fatty acids is fully saturated—all the carbons are bound to the maximum number of hydrogen atoms. The second fatty acid contains a carbon–carbon double bond (denoted by the arrow) and thus is unsaturated. As shown by the space-filling model, the presence of the C–C double

bond imparts a kink or bend to the fatty acid tail **(Figure 5.4b).**

When added to an aqueous solution, phospholipids self-assemble into one of three structures—a

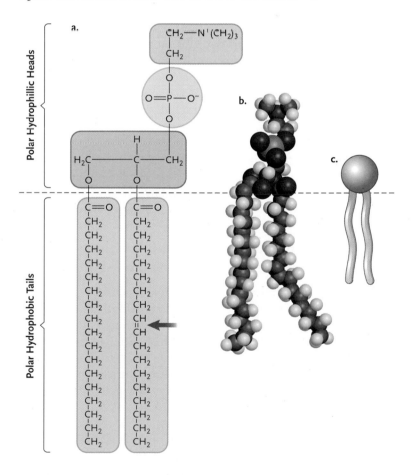

Figure 5.4

Phospholipid structure. **(a)** Chemical formula of phosphatidylcholine. The polar head group consists of glycerol (shown in pink) linked to the organic molecule choline (shown in green) by a phosphate group (shown in yellow). In addition, the glycerol is linked to two fatty acids, each 18 carbons long. The structure of phospholipids is also often represented as space-filling models **(b)** and as an icon **(c)**. As shown in the space-filling model, the presence of a carbon–carbon double bond (denoted by the arrow) imparts a bend to one of the fatty acids.

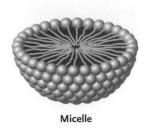

Micelle

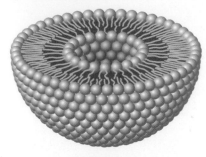

Liposome

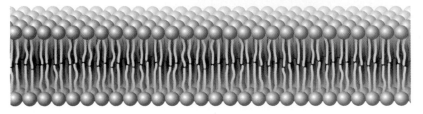

Phospholipid bilayer

Figure 5.5

In an aqueous environment, phospholipids self-assemble into micelles, liposomes, or bilayers.

micelle, a liposome, or a bilayer **(Figure 5.5)**. Which structure forms depends mostly on the phospholipid concentration. Phospholipids spontaneously form these structures in an aqueous environment because of the *hydrophobic effect*—the tendency of polar molecules like water to exclude hydrophobic molecules such as fatty acids. This results in the aggregation of lipid molecules in structures where the fatty acid tails interact with each other and the polar head groups associate with water. These arrangements are favoured because they represent the lowest energy state and are more likely to occur over any other arrangement.

5.2b Fatty Acid Composition and Temperature Affect Membrane Fluidity

The fluidity of the lipid bilayer is primarily influenced by two factors: the type of fatty acids that make up the lipid molecules and the temperature. Fully saturated fatty acids are linear, which allows lipid molecules to pack tightly together **(Figure 5.6a).** In contrast, lipid molecules with one or more unsaturated fatty acids are prevented from packing closely together because the presence of double bonds introduces kinks in the fatty acid backbone **(Figure 5.6b).** As a result, the more unsaturated the fatty acids of the lipid molecules, the more fluid the membrane.

Membranes remain in a fluid state over a relatively wide range of temperatures. But as the temperature drops and the random molecular motion of lipid molecules slows down, a point is reached where fluidity is lost and the phospholipid molecules form a semisolid gel. This is exactly what happens when melted butter cools—at a certain temperature it turns from a liquid into

a solid. The temperature at which gelling occurs depends upon the fatty acid composition. The more unsaturated a group of lipid molecules, the lower the temperature at which gelling occurs. For most membrane systems, the normal fluid state is achieved by a mixed population of saturated and unsaturated fatty acids.

5.2c Organisms Can Adjust Fatty Acid Composition

Keeping membranes in a fluid state is absolutely essential to cell function. Yet for many organisms that cannot regulate their temperature (these organisms are termed ectotherms; see Chapter 42), exposure to low temperatures may result in membrane gelling. This can have drastic consequences to membrane function from deleterious changes to membrane permeability to inhibiting the function of membrane-bound enzymes. Electron transport chains, for example, require molecules to migrate rapidly within the membrane bilayer. If the membrane solidifies, electron transport ceases to operate. Problems also arise at high temperature. Membranes may become too fluid due to the increase in molecular motion, which can result in membrane leakage. Ions such as K^+, Na^+, and Ca^{2+} begin to freely diffuse across the membrane, resulting in an irreversible disruption of cellular ion balance that can rapidly lead to cell death.

Most organisms can actively adjust the fatty acid composition of their membranes so that proper fluidity is maintained over a broad temperature range. For example, many bacteria, archaea, protists, and plants can thrive at temperatures that are far below the temperature at which a typical animal membrane would solidify. These ectotherms are able to survive at low temperatures, in part because they are able to increase the relative proportion of unsaturated fatty acids in their membranes.

Unsaturated fatty acids are produced during fatty acid biosynthesis through the action of a group of enzymes called desaturases **(Figure 5.7a)**. All fatty acids are initially synthesized as fully saturated molecules without any double bonds. Desaturases act on these

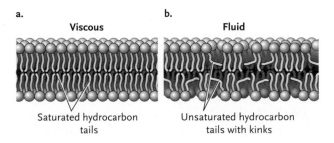

a.   **b.**

Viscous   **Fluid**

Saturated hydrocarbon tails   Unsaturated hydrocarbon tails with kinks

Figure 5.6

Lipid molecule composition affects how closely they interact. Lipid molecules that contain saturated hydrocarbon tails are closely packed **(a)**, whereas unsaturated hydrocarbon tails have kinks that prevent lipid molecules from packing closely together **(b)**.

a. Stearic acid, $CH_3(CH_2)_{16}COOH$

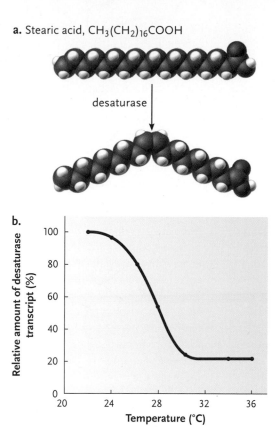

desaturase

b.

[Graph: y-axis: Relative amount of desaturase transcript (%), ranging 0 to 100; x-axis: Temperature (°C), ranging 20 to 36. The curve starts at 100% at low temperature and decreases to about 20% at higher temperatures.]

Figure 5.7
Organisms can regulate the degree of fatty acid unsaturation. **(a)** Desaturases are a class of enzymes that introduce double bonds into fatty acids, thereby altering the degree of unsaturation. **(b)** In organisms where body temperature changes with the environment, the abundance of specific desaturases can be adjusted so that proper membrane fluidity is maintained.

saturated fatty acids by catalyzing a reaction that removes two hydrogen atoms from neighbouring carbon atoms and introducing a double bond. There are many different desaturase enzymes, each one introducing a double bond at a specific point along the fatty acid chain. Whereas some unsaturated fatty acids contain only one carbon–carbon double bond, others may contain two or more, which indicates the action of more than one desaturase.

Like many proteins, desaturase abundance is regulated at the level of gene transcription, which results in changes to desaturase transcript (mRNA) abundance. **Figure 5.7b** shows how the abundance of a specific desaturase transcript changes with growth temperature in a cyanobacterium. As growth temperature decreases, desaturase transcript abundance goes up, which results in an increase in synthesis of the desaturase enzyme. Higher amounts of desaturases, in turn, result in an increase in the abundance of unsaturated fatty acids. By regulating desaturase abundance, many organisms can closely regulate the amount of unsaturated fatty acids that get incorporated into membranes and thereby maintain proper membrane fluidity.

Cholesterol

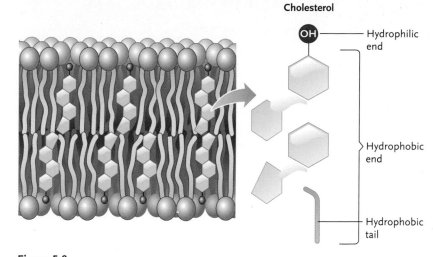

Hydrophilic end

Hydrophobic end

Hydrophobic tail

Figure 5.8
The position taken by cholesterol within a membrane. The hydrophilic –OH group at one end of the molecule extends into the hydrophilic region of the bilayer; the ring structure extends into the hydrophobic membrane interior.

Besides lipids, a group of compounds called sterols also influence membrane fluidity. The best example of a sterol is cholesterol **(Figure 5.8)**, which is found in the membranes of animal cells but not in those of plants or prokaryotes. Sterols act as membrane buffers: at high temperatures, they help restrain the movement of lipid molecules, thus reducing the fluidity of the membrane. However, at lower temperatures, sterols disrupt fatty acids from associating by occupying space between lipid molecules, thus slowing the transition to the nonfluid gel state.

STUDY BREAK

1. Why is maintaining proper membrane fluidity important for membrane function?
2. What is the relationship between temperature and desaturase expression?

5.3 Membrane Proteins

While the lipid molecules constitute the backbone of a membrane, the unique set of proteins that are associated with the membrane is what determines its function and makes each membrane unique. As we will discuss in this section, two major types of proteins are associated with membranes: integral and peripheral membrane proteins.

5.3a The Key Functions of Membrane Proteins

Membrane proteins can be separated into four major functional categories, as shown in **Figure 5.9, p. 99**. It should be noted that all of these functions may exist in

MOLECULE BEHIND BIOLOGY 5.1
Trans Fats

In the food industry, the use of fats containing saturated fatty acids is more desirable than the use of oils that contain unsaturated fatty acids. The lack of double bonds means that lipids containing saturated fatty acids are more stable and less prone to the oxidation that can decrease shelf life and affect the texture and taste of the final product. Moreover, hard fats have a higher melting temperature, which makes them useful in many applications, such as in baking and deep-frying.

Because animal-based saturated fats such as butter and lard are expensive and susceptible to spoilage, the food industry has, for many decades, used saturated fats produced through the industrial process of hydrogenation. This process removes *cis* double bonds from fatty acids by heating vegetable oil in the presence of hydrogen gas and a catalyst. In the food industry, partial hydrogenation is practised, which results in a product that is still malleable and not too hard. One of the unintended consequences of partial hydrogenation is that the *cis* double bonds that do not become hydrogen-ated tend to be reconfigured into the *trans* orientation. Although small amounts of *trans* fats are found naturally in the milk and meat of ruminant animals such as cows and sheep, through partial hydrogenation, human consumption of *trans* fats has increased tremendously over the last 70 years.

There is now clear medical evidence that the consumption of *trans* fats is unhealthy. A comprehensive review of research on *trans* fat consumption and health by the *New England Journal of Medicine* in 2006 clearly demonstrated the existence of a strong connection between *trans* fat consumption and elevated risk of coronary heart disease, a leading cause of death in North America. *Trans* fats have also been linked to increased incidence of other health problems as well. The physiological basis for the increased risk to health by increased *trans* fat consumption is not fully understood and remains a very active area of research. The increased risk may be due, in part, to the fact that a major group of enzymes called lipases, which aid in the breakdown of many types of lipids, including *cis* unsatur-ated fats, do not recognize the *trans* configuration. This leads to *trans* fats staying in the bloodstream longer, which may lead to increased incidence of arterial deposition, which may lead to coronary heart disease.

In response to the overwhelming medical evidence that *trans* fats are harmful, governments around the world are implementing restrictions on the amount of *trans* fats foods can contain. In Canada, the *trans* fat content of vegetable oils and soft margar-ines is now limited to 2% of the total fat content, whereas the *trans* fat content for all other foods is 5% of the total fat content, including ingredients sold to restaurants. Similar guidelines are in place in many European countries, as well as being implemented in the United States.

In response to these new guidelines, food manufacturers and restaurant chains have reformulated their products to be *trans* fat free. This has primarily been achieved by simply replacing hydrogenated fats with natur-ally saturated fats. Many nutritionists argue that these fully saturated alternatives may not offer any health benefit.

---

a single membrane and that one protein or protein complex may serve more than one of these functions:

1. **Transport.** Many substances cannot freely diffuse through the membrane. Instead, a protein may provide a hydrophilic channel that allows movement of a specific compound. Alternatively, a membrane protein may change its shape and in so doing shuttle specific molecules from one side of a membrane to the other.
2. **Enzymatic activity.** A number of enzymes are membrane proteins. The best example of this is the enzymes associated with the respiratory and photosynthetic electron transport chains.
3. **Signal transduction.** Membranes often contain receptor proteins on their outer surface that bind to specific chemicals such as hormones. On binding, these receptors trigger changes on the inside surface of the membrane that lead to trans-duction of the signal through the cell.
4. **Attachment/recognition.** Proteins exposed to both the internal bend external membrane surfaces act as attachment points for a range of cytoskeleton elements, as well as components involved in cell–cell recognition.

5.3b Integral Membrane Proteins Interact with the Membrane Hydrophobic Core

Proteins that are embedded in the phospholipid bilayer are called **integral membrane proteins.** A subset of integral membrane proteins that traverse the entire lipid bilayer are referred to as *transmembrane proteins.* Because they have to interact with both the aqueous environment on both sides of the membrane and the hydrophobic core, transmembrane proteins have distinct regions (called domains) that differ markedly in polarity. The domain that interacts with the lipid bilayer consists predominantly of nonpolar amino acids that collectively form a type of secondary structure termed an *alpha helix* (**Figure 5.10**) (see *The Purple Pages* for an overview of protein structure). By contrast, the portions of a transmembrane protein that are exposed on either side of the membrane are composed of primarily polar amino acids (The different classes of amino acids are presented in the Purple Pages).

a. Transport

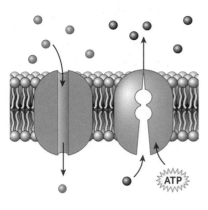

b. Enzymatic activity

Enzymes

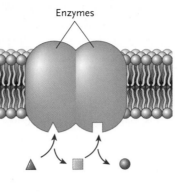

c. Signal transduction

Signal

Receptor

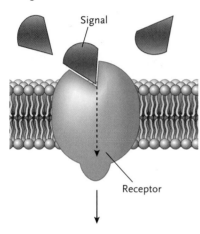

d. Attachment/recognition

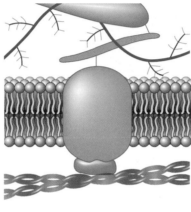

Figure 5.9
The major functions of membrane proteins.

Given the amino acid sequence (primary structure) of a protein, it is usually quite simple to determine if it is likely a transmembrane protein. What one looks for, usually with the aid of a computer program, are stretches of primarily nonpolar amino acids. These stretches are about 17 to 20 amino acids in length, which matches the peptide length needed to span the lipid bilayer **(Figure 5.11)**. Most transmembrane proteins span the membrane more than once. So, for example, if a protein has three membrane-spanning domains, the primary sequence would show three distinct regions of predominantly nonpolar amino acids linked by regions that are dominated by polar and charged amino acids. These polar amino acids are found in the portions of the protein that are exposed to the aqueous environment on either side of the membrane (see Figure 5.11).

5.3c Peripheral Membrane Proteins Interact with the Membrane Hydrophilic Surface

The second major group of membrane proteins are **peripheral membrane proteins**, so called because they are positioned on the surface of a membrane and do not interact with the hydrophobic core of the mem-

Outside cell

Channel

Alpha helix

NH₂

Membrane surface

Plasma membrane interior

Cytosol

COOH

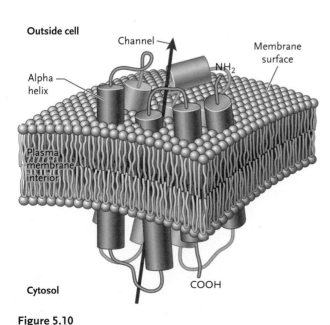

Figure 5.10
The structure of membrane proteins. A typical integral membrane protein showing the membrane-spanning alpha-helical segments (red cylinders), connected by flexible loops of the amino acid chain at the membrane surfaces.

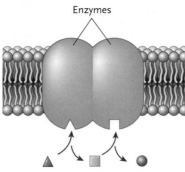

The polar and charged amino acids are hydrophilic

The nonpolar amino acids are hydrophobic

Figure 5.11
Transmembrane proteins can be identified by the presence of stretches of amino acids that are primarily nonpolar. These regions of the protein interact with the hydrophobic regions of the membrane. usually between 17 and 20 amino acids are needed to span the membrane once. For clarity this model shows only five nonpolar amino acids spanning the membrane.

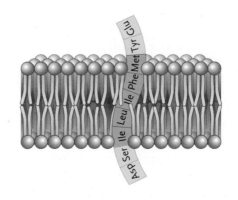

brane. Peripheral proteins are held to membrane surfaces by noncovalent bonds—hydrogen bonds and ionic bonds—usually by interacting with the exposed portions of integral proteins as well as directly with membrane lipid molecules. Many peripheral proteins are found on the cytoplasmic side of the plasma membrane and form part of the cytoskeleton (Look back at Figure 5.1). In addition, as we will see in later chapters, key enzymes involved in both respiratory and photosynthetic electron transport are peripheral membrane proteins. Because peripheral membrane proteins do not interact with the hydrophobic core of the membrane, they are made up of a mixture of polar and nonpolar amino acids.

STUDY BREAK

1. What roles are served by membrane proteins?
2. What are the two major classes of membrane proteins?

5.4 Passive Membrane Transport

The hydrophobic nature of membranes severely restricts the free movement of many molecules into and out of cells and from one compartment to another. Molecules such as O_2 diffuse very rapidly across membranes, which is important considering the vital role O_2 plays in cellular respiration. However, a range of other molecules, including ions, charged molecules, and macromolecules, do not readily move across membranes. In this section, we consider the diffusion of molecules from one compartment to the other and the factors that influence the rate of that diffusion.

5.4a Passive Transport Is Based on Diffusion

Passive transport is defined as the movement of a substance across a membrane without the need to expend chemical energy such as ATP. What drives passive transport is **diffusion**, the net movement of a substance from a region of higher concentration to a region of lower concentration. Above absolute zero (–273°C), molecules are in constant motion, which results in molecules becoming uniformly distributed in space. Diffusion is the primary mechanism of solute movement within a cell and between cellular compartments separated by a membrane.

The driving force behind diffusion is an increase in entropy. In the initial state, when molecules are more concentrated in one region of a solution or on one side of a membrane, the molecules are more ordered and in a state of lower entropy. As diffusion occurs, the entropy, or disorder, increases until, when the molecules are evenly distributed, entropy is highest

(Figure 5.12). As the distribution proceeds to the state of maximum disorder, the molecules release free energy, which can accomplish work (see Section 4.1 for a discussion of entropy and free energy).

The rate of diffusion depends on the concentration difference (concentration gradient) that exists between two areas or across a membrane. The larger the gradient, the faster the rate of diffusion. Similar to chemical equilibrium (see Chapter 4), when diffusing molecules reach equilibrium there is still movement of molecules from one space to another, but no net change in concentration (see Figure 5.12).

5.4b There Are Two Types of Passive Transport: Simple and Facilitated

There are two types of passive transport: simple diffusion and facilitated diffusion. **Simple diffusion** is the movement of molecules directly across a membrane without the involvement of a transporter. The rate of simple diffusion of a molecule depends upon two factors: molecular size and lipid solubility. As shown in **Figure 5.13,** some molecules diffuse very rapidly across the membrane, while other molecules are essentially unable to transit the membrane.

Small nonpolar molecules such as O_2 and CO_2 are readily soluble in the hydrophobic interior of a membrane and move very rapidly from one side to the other. As well, steroid hormones and many drugs that tend to be amphipathic can readily transit the lipid bilayer. Small uncharged molecules such as water or glycerol, even though they are polar, are still able to move quite rapidly across the membrane (see Figure 5.13). In contrast, the membrane is practically impermeable to charged molecules, including ions such as Cl^-, Na^+, and phosphate (PO_4^{3-}). Transport of small ions is about a billionth (10^{-9}) the rate of the transport of water. Their charge and associated hydration shell contribute to ions being prevented from entering the hydrophobic core of the membrane.

The diffusion of molecules across a membrane through the aid of a transporter is called **facilitated diffusion.** The diffusion of many polar and charged molecules, such as water, amino acids, sugars, and ions,

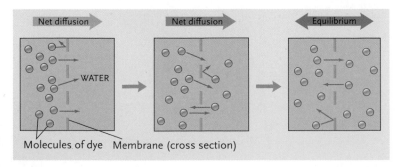

Figure 5.12

Diffusion is an entropy-driven process as molecules move from regions of high concentration to areas of low concentration. Entropy is at its maximum when equilibrium is reached.

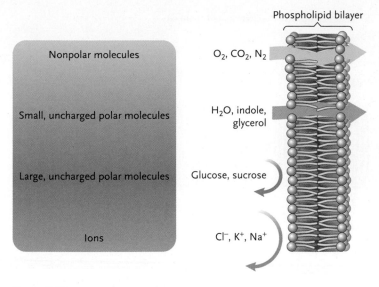

Figure 5.13

The size and charge of a molecule affect the rate of diffusion across a membrane.

relies on specific transport complexes for their rapid movement from one compartment to another. Although facilitated diffusion involves specific transporters, just like simple diffusion, transport depends upon a concentration gradient across the membrane—when the gradient falls to zero, diffusion stops.

5.4c Two Groups of Transport Proteins Carry Out Facilitated Diffusion

Facilitated diffusion is carried out by two types of transport proteins: channel proteins and carrier proteins, both of which are transmembrane proteins **(Figure 5.14, p. 102)**. **Channel proteins** form hydrophilic pathways in the membrane through which molecules can pass. The channel aids the diffusion of molecules by providing an avenue that is shielded from the hydrophobic core of the bilayer. Specific channel proteins are involved in the transport of certain ions and, most interestingly, the transport of water.

The diffusion of water is facilitated by water-specific transport proteins called aquaporins (Figure 5.14a, p. 102). Aquaporins have been found in organisms as diverse as bacteria, plants, and humans. The aquaporin channel is very narrow and allows for the single-file movement of about a billion water molecules every second. Remarkably, the channel is very specific for water and does not allow for the diffusion of ions including protons. The structural basis of this is explained by recent three-dimensional models of aquaporin-1, which show the presence of positive charges in the centre of the channel that are thought to specifically repel the transport of protons. For his discovery of aquaporins, Peter Agre at Johns Hopkins University received the Nobel Prize for chemistry in 2003.

Another type of channel protein that is found in all eukaryotes is the **gated channel** (Figure 5.14b, p. 102). These transporters can switch between open, closed, and intermediate states and are critical to the movement of most ions, for example, sodium (Na^+), potassium (K^+), calcium (Ca^{2+}), and chlorine (Cl^-). The gates may be opened or closed by changes in voltage across the membrane, for instance, or by binding signal molecules. The opening or closing involves changes in the protein's three-dimensional shape. In animals, voltage-gated ion channels are used in nerve conduction and the control of muscle contraction (see Chapters 36 and 38). As well, CFTR, the Cl^- channel that is defective in individuals with cystic fibrosis, is a gated channel (see "Why It Matters").

The second class of transport proteins that form passageways through the lipid bilayer are **carrier proteins** (Figure 5.14c, p. 102). Each carrier protein binds a single specific solute, such as a sugar molecule or an amino acid, and transports it across the lipid bilayer. Because a single solute is transferred in this carrier-mediated fashion, the transfer is called *uniport transport*. In performing the transport step, the carrier protein undergoes conformational changes that progressively move the solute binding site from one side of the membrane to the other, thereby transporting the solute. This property distinguishes carrier protein function from channel protein function.

Many transport proteins display a high degree of substrate specificity, in a way similar to an enzyme. For example, transporters that carry glucose are unable to transport fructose, which is structurally similar. This specificity allows various cells and cellular compartments to tightly control what gets in and out. The kinds of transport proteins present in the plasma membrane or, for example, on the inner membrane of the mitochondrion depend ultimately on the type of cell and growth conditions.

How can you experimentally determine if a molecule is transported by facilitated diffusion and not just simple diffusion? First, with facilitated diffusion, the rate of movement across the membrane is much faster than one would predict based just on the chemical structure of the molecule being transported **(Figure 5.15, p. 103)**. Second, facilitated diffusion can be saturated in the same way as an enzyme can be saturated, by substrate. A membrane has a limited number of transporters for a particular molecule. If you measure the rate of transport at increasing concentration differences across a membrane, the rate of transport of a particular molecule (the substrate) reaches a plateau that represents a state when essentially all of the transporters are occupied all the time by substrate. Increasing the

a. Channel protein (aquaporin)

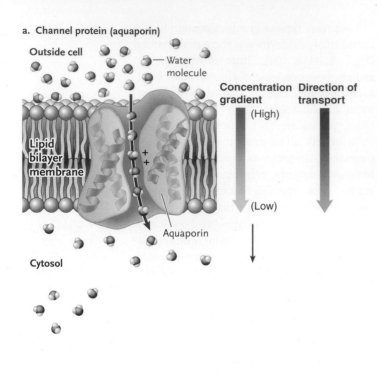

Outside cell

Water molecule

Lipid bilayer membrane

Aquaporin

Cytosol

Concentration gradient
(High)
(Low)

Direction of transport

b. Channel protein (K⁺ voltage-gated channel)

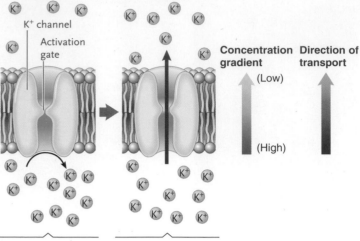

K^+ channel

Activation gate

Concentration gradient
(Low)
(High)

Direction of transport

With normal voltage across the membrane, the activation gate of the K^+ channel is closed and K^+ cannot move across the membrane.

In response to a voltage change across the membrane, the activation gate of the K^+ channel opens, and K^+ moves with its concentration gradient from the cytoplasm to outside the cell.

c. Carrier protein

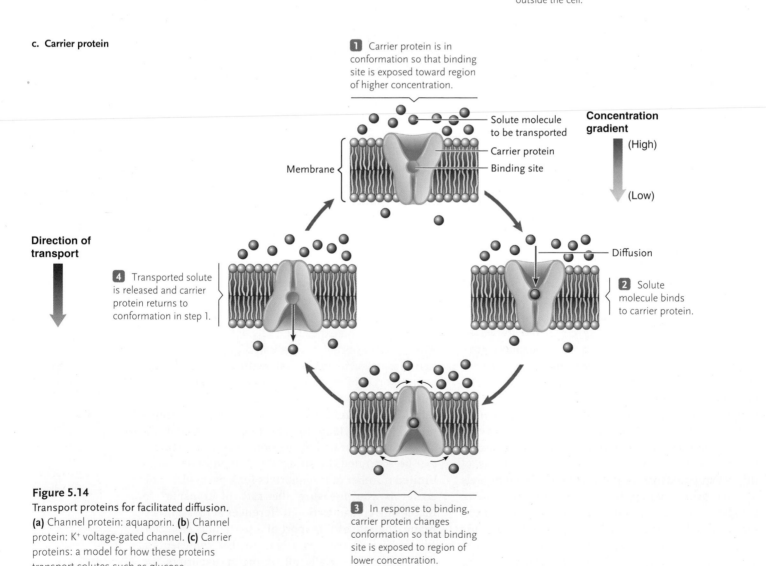

1 Carrier protein is in conformation so that binding site is exposed toward region of higher concentration.

Solute molecule to be transported

Carrier protein

Binding site

Membrane

Concentration gradient
(High)
(Low)

Diffusion

2 Solute molecule binds to carrier protein.

Direction of transport

4 Transported solute is released and carrier protein returns to conformation in step 1.

3 In response to binding, carrier protein changes conformation so that binding site is exposed to region of lower concentration.

Figure 5.14
Transport proteins for facilitated diffusion.
(a) Channel protein: aquaporin. **(b)** Channel protein: K⁺ voltage-gated channel. **(c)** Carrier proteins: a model for how these proteins transport solutes such as glucose.

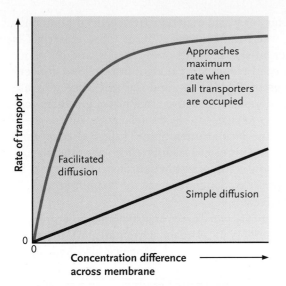

Figure 5.15
Simple diffusion and facilitated diffusion display different transport kinetics. Compared with simple diffusion, facilitated diffusion leads to higher rates of transport and displays saturation kinetics.

concentration further has no effect on the rate of transport (see Figure 5.15). By comparison, in simple diffusion, the whole membrane surface is effectively the transporter; thus, the rate of transport, although usually slower, never reaches a plateau but keeps increasing with increasing concentration gradient.

5.4d Osmosis Is the Passive Diffusion of Water

Like solutes, water can also move passively across membranes in a process called osmosis. The passive transport of water occurs constantly in living cells. Inward or outward movement of water by osmosis develops forces that can cause cells to swell or shrink. Formally, **osmosis** is defined as the diffusion of water molecules across a selectively permeable membrane from a solution of lesser solute concentration to a solution of greater solute concentration. For osmosis to take place, the selectively permeable membrane must allow water molecules to pass but not molecules of the solute. Osmosis occurs in cells because they contain a solution of proteins and other molecules that are retained in the cytoplasm by a membrane impermeable to them but freely permeable to water. Osmosis can occur by simple diffusion through the lipid bilayer or be facilitated by aquaporins (see Section 5.4c).

The movement of water by osmosis is dictated by solute concentration. If the solution surrounding a cell contains dissolved substances at lower concentrations than in the cell, the solution is said to be hypotonic to the cell (*hypo* = under or below; *tonos* = tension or tone). When a cell is in a hypotonic solution, water enters by osmosis, and the cell tends to swell **(Figure 5.16a)**.

Animal cells, such as red blood cells, in a hypotonic solution may actually swell to the point of bursting. This is in contrast to plant cells, where the presence of the cell wall prevents the cells from bursting in a hypotonic solution. Instead the cell pushes against the cell wall, resulting in what is called turgor pressure. This is discussed in more detail in Chapter 28.

If the solution that surrounds a cell contains solutes at higher concentrations than in the cell, then the outside solution is said to be hypertonic to the cell (*hyper* = over or above) **(Figure 5.16b)**. When a cell is in

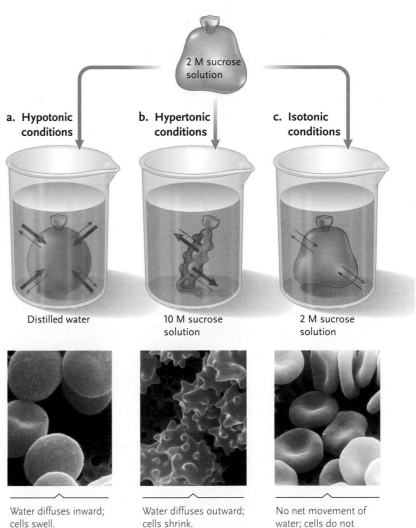

©The Rockefeller University Press.
The Journal of Cell Biology, 1976, 70:193-203, doi: 10.1083/jcb.70.1.193.

Figure 5.16
Tonicity and osmotic water movement. The diagrams show what happens when a cellophane bag filled with a 2 M sucrose solution is placed in **(a)** a hypotonic, **(b)** a hypertonic, or **(c)** an isotonic solution. The cellophane is permeable to water but not to sucrose molecules. The width of the arrows shows the amount of water movement. In the first beaker, the distilled water is hypotonic to the solution in the bag; net movement of water is into the bag. In the second beaker, the 10 M solution is hypertonic to the solution in the bag; net movement of water is out of the bag. In the third beaker, the solutions inside and outside the bag are isotonic; there is no net movement of water into or out of the bag. The animal cell micrographs show the corresponding effects on red blood cells placed in hypotonic, hypertonic, or isotonic solutions. (Micrographs, M. Sheetz, R. Painter, and S. Singer. *Journal of Cell Biology*, 70:493, 1976. By permission of Rockefeller University Press.)

a hypertonic solution, water leaves by osmosis. If the outward osmotic movement exceeds the capacity of cells to replace the lost water, both animal and plant cells will shrink (Figure 5.16b).

In animals, ions, proteins, and other molecules are concentrated in extracellular fluids, as well as inside cells so that the concentration of water inside and outside cells is usually equal or isotonic (*iso* = the same), as shown in **Figure 5.16c, p. 103.** However, this comes at an energetic cost of constantly having to pump ions from one side to the other. For example, the ATP-dependent transport of Na^+ from inside to outside the cell is essential, otherwise water would move inward by osmosis and cause the cells to burst. Osmotic movement in plant cells is discussed more in depth in Chapter 28, whereas the mechanisms by which animals balance their water content are discussed in Chapter 42.

STUDY BREAK

1. How do the size and charge of a molecule influence its transport across a membrane?
2. Explain how aquaporin functions to transport water.
3. What is the difference between passive transport and active transport?

5.5 Active Membrane Transport

As shown in Figure 5.15, compared to simple diffusion, facilitated diffusion increases the rate of movement of molecules across membranes. However, this type of transport is limited to movement down a concentration gradient. Many cellular processes require molecules to be maintained in various cell compartments at very high concentrations. This is achieved by energy-dependent transport that moves molecules against a concentration gradient—from a region of lower concentration to a region of higher concentration.

5.5a Active Transport Requires Energy

The transport of molecules across a membrane against a concentration gradient, that is, movement from low to high concentration, requires the expenditure of energy and is referred to as **active transport.** The energy is usually in the form of ATP, and it is estimated that about 25% of a cell's ATP requirements are for the active transport of molecules. Active transport concentrates molecules such as sugars and amino acids inside cells and pushes ions in or out of cells.

The three main functions of active transport in cells and organelles are (1) uptake of essential nutrients from the fluid surrounding cells even when their concentrations are lower than in cells, (2) removal of secretory or waste materials from cells or organelles even when the concentration of those materials is higher outside the cells or organelles, and (3) maintenance of essentially constant intracellular concentrations of H^+, Na^+, K^+, and Ca^{2+}. Because ions are charged molecules, active transport of ions may contribute to voltage—an electrical potential difference—across the plasma membrane, called a membrane potential. This electrical difference across the plasma membrane is important in neurons and muscle cells and is discussed in more detail in Chapters 36 and 38, respectively.

There are two classes of active transport: primary and secondary. In **primary active transport,** the same protein that transports a substance also hydrolyses ATP to power the transport directly. In **secondary active transport,** the transport is indirectly driven by ATP. That is, the transport proteins use a favourable concentration gradient of ions built up by primary active transport as their energy source to drive the transport of a different molecule.

Other features of active transport resemble facilitated diffusion (listed in **Table 5.1**). Both processes depend on membrane transport proteins, both are specific, and both can be saturated. The transport proteins are carrier proteins that change their conformation as they function.

5.5b Primary Active Transport Moves Positively Charged Ions

All primary active transport pumps move positively charged ions—H^+, Ca^{2+}, Na^+, and K^+—across membranes **(Figure 5.17).** The gradients of positive ions established by primary active transport pumps underlie functions that are absolutely essential for life. For example, the proton pumps (H^+ pumps) in plasma membranes push hydrogen ions from the cytoplasm to the cell exterior. These pumps (as in Figure 5.17) temporarily bind a phosphate group removed from ATP during the pumping cycle. Proton pumps have various functions. For example, in bacteria, archaea, and plants and fungi, proton pumps in the plasma membrane generate membrane potential. Proton pumps in lysosomes of animals and vacuoles of plants and fungi keep the pH within the organelle low, serving to activate the enzymes contained within them.

Another active transport system is the calcium pump (Ca^{2+} pump), which is widely distributed among eukaryotes. It pushes Ca^{2+} from the cytoplasm to the cell exterior and from the cytosol into the vesicles of the endoplasmic reticulum (ER). As a result, Ca^{2+} concentration is typically high outside cells and inside ER vesicles and low in the cytoplasmic solution. This Ca^{2+} gradient is used universally among eukaryotes as a regulatory control of cellular activities as diverse as

Table 5.1 | Characteristics of Transport Mechanisms

Characteristic	Passive Transport		Active Transport
	Simple Diffusion	Facilitated Diffusion	
Membrane component responsible for transport	Lipids	Proteins	Proteins
Binding of transported substance	No	Yes	Yes
Energy source	Concentration gradients	Concentration gradients	ATP hydrolysis or concentration gradients
Direction of transport	With gradient of transported substance	With gradient of transported substance	Against gradient of transported substance
Specificity for molecules or molecular classes	Nonspecific	Specific	Specific
Saturation at high concentrations of transported molecules	No	Yes	Yes

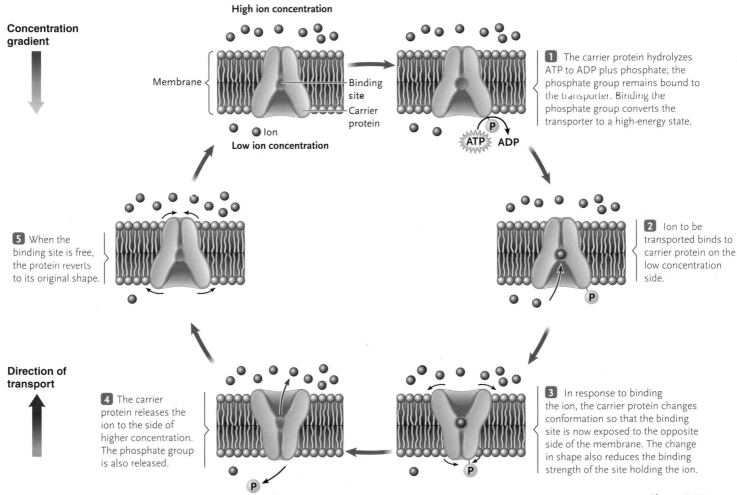

Concentration gradient

High ion concentration

Membrane { Binding site / Carrier protein

Ion
Low ion concentration

1 The carrier protein hydrolyzes ATP to ADP plus phosphate; the phosphate group remains bound to the transporter. Binding the phosphate group converts the transporter to a high-energy state.

ATP ADP

2 Ion to be transported binds to carrier protein on the low concentration side.

3 In response to binding the ion, the carrier protein changes conformation so that the binding site is now exposed to the opposite side of the membrane. The change in shape also reduces the binding strength of the site holding the ion.

4 The carrier protein releases the ion to the side of higher concentration. The phosphate group is also released.

5 When the binding site is free, the protein reverts to its original shape.

Direction of transport

Figure 5.17
Model for how a primary active transport pump operates.

secretion, microtubule assembly, and muscle contraction. The latter is discussed further in Chapter 38.

The **sodium–potassium pump** (or **Na⁺/K⁺ pump**), located in the plasma membrane of all animal cells, pushes 3 Na⁺ ions out of the cell and two K⁺ ions into the cell in the same pumping cycle (**Figure 5.18, p. 106**). As a result, positive charges accumulate in excess out-side the membrane, and the inside of the cell becomes negatively charged with respect to the outside. Voltage—an electrical potential difference—across the plasma membrane results from this difference in charge as well as from the unequal distribution of ions across the membrane created by passive transport. The voltage across a membrane, called a **membrane**

potential, measures from about −50 to −200 millivolts (mV), with the minus sign indicating that the charge inside the cell is negative versus the outside. In sum, we have both a concentration difference (of the ions) and an electrical charge difference on the two sides of the membrane, constituting what is called an **electrochemical gradient.** Electrochemical gradients store energy that is used for other transport mechanisms.

For instance, the electrochemical gradient across the membrane is involved with the movement of ions associated with nerve impulse transmission (described in Chapter 36). A membrane potential derived from a proton gradient across a membrane is the basis for ATP synthesis in mitochondria and chloroplasts, which will be discussed in Chapters 6 and 7, respectively.

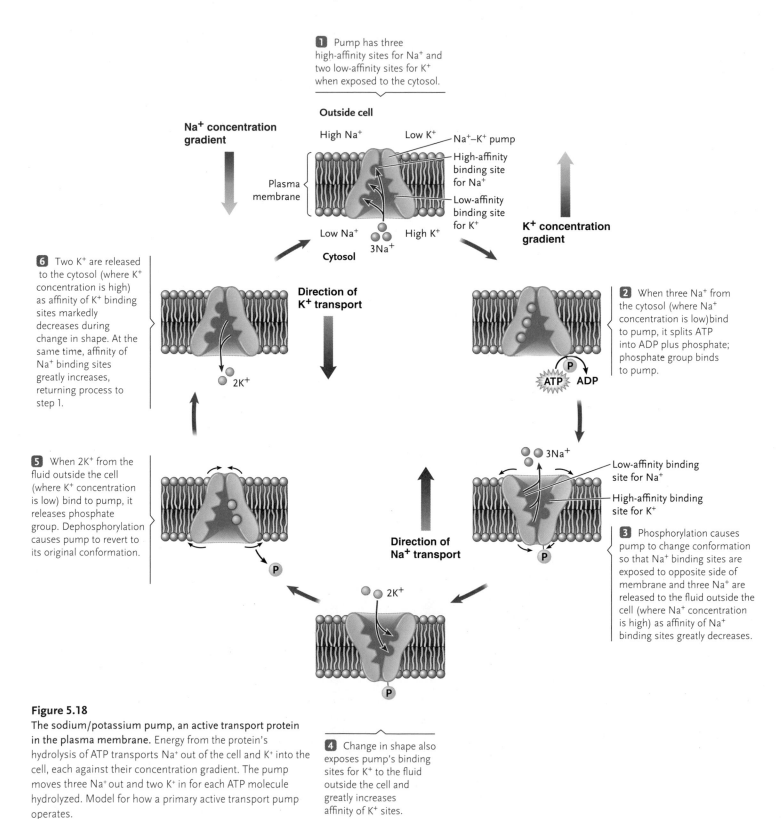

1 Pump has three high-affinity sites for Na⁺ and two low-affinity sites for K⁺ when exposed to the cytosol.

Na⁺ concentration gradient

Outside cell

High Na⁺   Low K⁺   Na⁺–K⁺ pump

Plasma membrane   High-affinity binding site for Na⁺

Low-affinity binding site for K⁺

Low Na⁺   High K⁺   **K⁺ concentration gradient**

3Na⁺

Cytosol

6 Two K⁺ are released to the cytosol (where K⁺ concentration is high) as affinity of K⁺ binding sites markedly decreases during change in shape. At the same time, affinity of Na⁺ binding sites greatly increases, returning process to step 1.

Direction of K⁺ transport

2K⁺

2 When three Na⁺ from the cytosol (where Na⁺ concentration is low) bind to pump, it splits ATP into ADP plus phosphate; phosphate group binds to pump.

ATP   ADP   P

5 When 2K⁺ from the fluid outside the cell (where K⁺ concentration is low) bind to pump, it releases phosphate group. Dephosphorylation causes pump to revert to its original conformation.

3Na⁺   Low-affinity binding site for Na⁺

High-affinity binding site for K⁺

Direction of Na⁺ transport

P

3 Phosphorylation causes pump to change conformation so that Na⁺ binding sites are exposed to opposite side of membrane and three Na⁺ are released to the fluid outside the cell (where Na⁺ concentration is high) as affinity of Na⁺ binding sites greatly decreases.

2K⁺

P

Figure 5.18

The sodium/potassium pump, an active transport protein in the plasma membrane. Energy from the protein's hydrolysis of ATP transports Na⁺ out of the cell and K⁺ into the cell, each against their concentration gradient. The pump moves three Na⁺ out and two K⁺ in for each ATP molecule hydrolyzed. Model for how a primary active transport pump operates.

4 Change in shape also exposes pump's binding sites for K⁺ to the fluid outside the cell and greatly increases affinity of K⁺ sites.

5.5c Secondary Active Transport Moves Both Ions and Organic Molecules

As already noted, secondary active transport pumps use the concentration gradient of an ion established by a primary pump as their energy source. For example, the driving force for most secondary active transport in animal cells is the high outside/low inside Na⁺ gradient set up by the sodium–potassium pump. In secondary active transport, the transfer of the solute across the membrane is always coupled with the transfer of the ion supplying the driving force.

Secondary active transport occurs by two mechanisms, known as *symport* and *antiport* **(Figure 5.19)**. In **symport**, the cotransported solute moves through the membrane channel in the same direction as the driving ion, a phenomenon known as **cotransport**. Sugars such as glucose and amino acids are examples of molecules actively transported into cells by symport. In **antiport**, the driving ion moves through the membrane channel in one direction, providing the energy for the active transport of another molecule in the opposite direction, a phenomenon known as **exchange diffusion**. In many cases, ions are exchanged by antiport. For example, antiport is the mechanism used in red blood cells for the coupled movement of chloride ions and bicarbonate ions through a membrane channel.

Active transport and passive transport move ions and smaller hydrophilic molecules across cellular membranes. Cells can also move much larger molecules or aggregates of molecules from inside to outside, or in the reverse direction, by including them in the cell's inward or outward vesicle traffic. The mechanisms carrying out this movement—exocytosis and endocytosis—are discussed in the next section.

STUDY BREAK

1. What is the difference between primary active transport and secondary active transport?
2. How is a membrane potential generated?

5.6 Exocytosis and Endocytosis

The largest molecules transported through cellular membranes by passive and active transport are about the size of amino acids or monosaccharides such as glucose. Eukaryotic cells import and export larger molecules by endocytosis and exocytosis. The export of materials by exocytosis primarily carries secretory proteins and some waste materials from the cytoplasm to the cell exterior. Import by endocytosis may carry proteins, larger aggregates of molecules, or even whole cells from the outside into the cytoplasm. Exocytosis and endocytosis also contribute to the back-and-forth flow of membranes between the endomembrane system and the plasma membrane. Both exocytosis and endocytosis require energy; thus, both processes stop if a cell's ability to make ATP is inhibited.

5.6a Exocytosis Releases Molecules to the Outside by Means of Secretory Vesicles

In exocytosis, secretory vesicles move through the cytoplasm and contact the plasma membrane **(Figure 5.20a, p. 108)**. The vesicle membrane fuses with the plasma membrane, releasing the vesicle's contents to the cell exterior.

All eukaryotic cells secrete materials to the outside through exocytosis. For example, in animals, glandular cells secrete peptide hormones or milk proteins, and cells lining the digestive tract secrete mucus and digestive enzymes. Plant cells secrete carbohydrates by exocytosis to build a strong cell wall.

5.6b Endocytosis Brings Materials into Cells in Endocytic Vesicles

In endocytosis, proteins and other substances are trapped in pitlike depressions that bulge inward from the plasma membrane. The depression then pinches off as an endocytic vesicle. Endocytosis takes place in most eukaryotic cells by one of two distinct but related pathways. In the simpler of these mechanisms, **bulk-phase endocytosis** (sometimes called **pinocytosis**, meaning "cell drinking"), extracellular water is taken in along

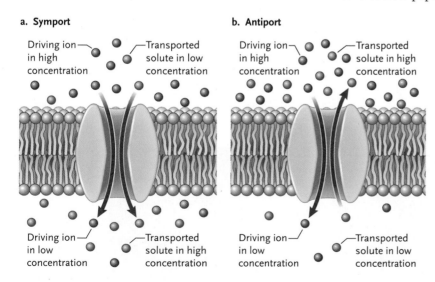

a. Symport

Driving ion in high concentration — Transported solute in low concentration

Driving ion in low concentration — Transported solute in high concentration

b. Antiport

Driving ion in high concentration — Transported solute in high concentration

Driving ion in low concentration — Transported solute in low concentration

Figure 5.19

Secondary active transport, in which a concentration gradient of an ion is used as the energy source for active transport of a solute. **(a)** In symport, the transported solute moves in the same direction as the gradient of the driving ion. **(b)** In antiport, the transported solute moves in the direction opposite to the gradient of the driving ion.

a. Exocytosis: vesicle joins plasma membrane, releases contents

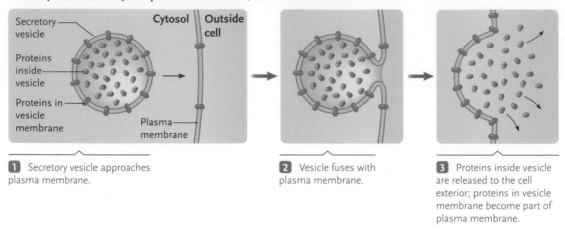

1 Secretory vesicle approaches plasma membrane.

2 Vesicle fuses with plasma membrane.

3 Proteins inside vesicle are released to the cell exterior; proteins in vesicle membrane become part of plasma membrane.

b. Bulk-phase endocytosis (pinocytosis): vesicle imports water and other substances from outside cell

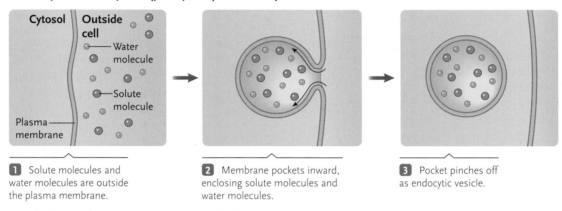

1 Solute molecules and water molecules are outside the plasma membrane.

2 Membrane pockets inward, enclosing solute molecules and water molecules.

3 Pocket pinches off as endocytic vesicle.

c. Receptor-mediated endocytosis: vesicle imports specific molecules

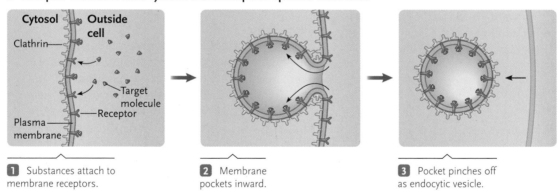

1 Substances attach to membrane receptors.

2 Membrane pockets inward.

3 Pocket pinches off as endocytic vesicle.

d. Micrographs of stages of receptor-mediated endocytosis shown in c

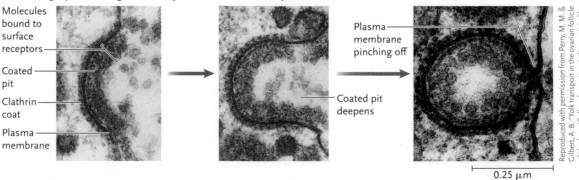

0.25 μm

Reproduced with permission from Perry, M. M. & Gilbert, A. B. "Yolk transport in the ovarian follicle of the hen (Gallus domesticus): lipoprotein-like particles at the periphery of the oocyte in the rapid growth phase." *J. Cell Sci.* 39, 257–272 (1979). Journal of Cell Science: jcs.biologists.org.

Figure 5.20
Exocytosis and endocytosis.

with any molecules that happen to be in solution in the water **(Figure 5.20b).** No binding by surface receptors takes place.

In the second endocytic pathway, **receptor-mediated endocytosis,** the molecules to be taken in are bound to the outer cell surface by receptor proteins **(Figure 5.20c).** The receptors, which are integral proteins of the plasma membrane, recognize and bind only certain molecules—primarily proteins, or other molecules carried by proteins—from the solution surrounding the cell. After binding their target molecules, the receptors collect into a depression in the plasma membrane called a **coated pit** because of the network of proteins (called **clathrin**) that coat and reinforce the cytoplasmic side. With the target molecules attached, the pits deepen and pinch free of the plasma membrane to form endocytic vesicles. Once in the cytoplasm, an endocytic vesicle rapidly loses its clathrin coat and may fuse with a lysosome. The enzymes within the lysosome then digest the contents of the vesicle, breaking them down into smaller molecules useful to the cell. These molecular products—for example, amino acids and monosaccharides—enter the cytoplasm by crossing the vesicle membrane via transport proteins. The membrane proteins are recycled to the plasma membrane.

Some cells, such as certain white blood cells (*phagocytes*) in the bloodstream or protists such as *Amoeba proteus,* can take in large aggregates of molecules, cell parts, or even whole cells by a process related to receptor-mediated endocytosis. The process, called **phagocytosis** (meaning "cell eating"), begins when surface receptors bind molecules on the substances to be taken in **(Figure 5.21).** Cytoplasmic lobes then extend, surround, and engulf the materials, forming a pit that pinches off and sinks into the cytoplasm as a large endocytic vesicle. The materials are then digested within the cell as in receptor-mediated endocytosis, and any remaining residues are sequestered permanently into storage vesicles or are expelled from cells as waste by exocytosis.

The combined workings of exocytosis and endocytosis constantly cycle membrane segments between the internal cytoplasm and the cell surface. The balance of the two mechanisms maintains the surface area of the plasma membrane at controlled levels.

STUDY BREAK

1. What is the mechanism of exocytosis?
2. What is the difference between bulk-phase endocytosis and receptor-mediated endocytosis?

5.7 Role of Membranes in Cell Signalling

Recall from Chapter 2 that one of the key attributes of all living things is the ability to sense and respond to changes to the environment. At the cellular level this is accomplished by the perception of signals. In multicellular organisms, signals may be derived from other cell types and tissues as well as factors external to the organism. These signals may be physical, such as changes in light and temperature, or they may be chemical, such as a hormone or growth regulator.

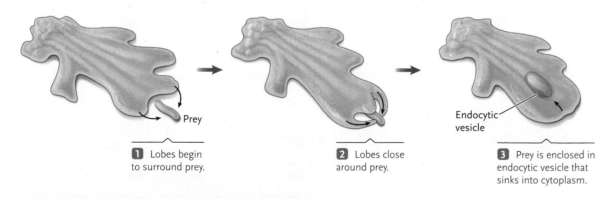

Prey

Endocytic vesicle

1 Lobes begin to surround prey.

2 Lobes close around prey.

3 Prey is enclosed in endocytic vesicle that sinks into cytoplasm.

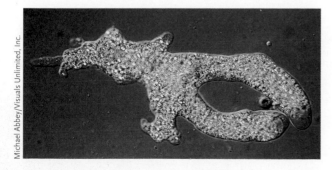

Michael Abbey/Visuals Unlimited, Inc.

Figure 5.21
Phagocytosis, in which lobes of the cytoplasm extend outward and surround a cell targeted as prey. The micrograph shows the protistan *Chaos carolinense* preparing to engulf a single-celled alga (*Pandorina*) by phagocytosis; white blood cells called phagocytes carry out a similar process in mammals.

In this section, we discuss the crucial role that membranes play in the perception of signals and the transduction of the signal to bring about changes in cell function. The ability of cells to sense and respond appropriately to changes in their growth environment is critical for the maintenance of organismal homeostasis, another hallmark of living systems.

5.7a Signal Transduction Links Signals with Downstream Cellular Responses

The steps that link the initial perception of a signal with its ultimate downstream effects is termed a signal transduction pathway or cascade. Most signal pathways involve the following three steps (Figure 5.22):

1. **Reception.** The binding of a signal molecule with a specific receptor of target cells is termed reception (see Figure 5.22). Target cells have receptors that are specific for the signal molecule, which distinguishes them from cells that do not respond to the signal molecule. Most receptors are found on the plasma membrane, but some are found on internal membranes such as the endoplasmic reticulum. In addition, other receptors are soluble proteins that are found in the cytoplasm.

2. **Transduction.** The process whereby signal reception triggers other changes within the cell necessary to cause the cellular response is transduction (see Figure 5.22). Transduction typically involves a cascade of reactions that include several different molecules, referred to as a *signalling cascade*.

3. **Response.** In the third and last stage, the transduced signal causes a specific cellular response (see Figure 5.22). Different signalling pathways lead to different downstream responses. For example, some signal transduction pathways lead to the direct activation of a specific enzyme, while others often trigger changes in gene expression.

5.7b Membrane Surface Receptors

The membrane receptors that recognize and bind signal molecules are integral membrane proteins that extend through the entire membrane (Figure 5.23a). Typically, the signal-binding site of the receptor is the part of the protein that extends from the outer membrane surface

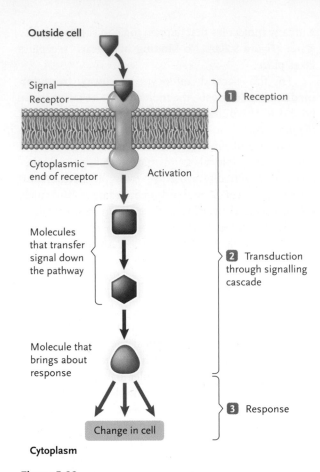

Figure 5.22
The three stages of signal transduction: reception, transduction, and response (shown for a system using a surface receptor).

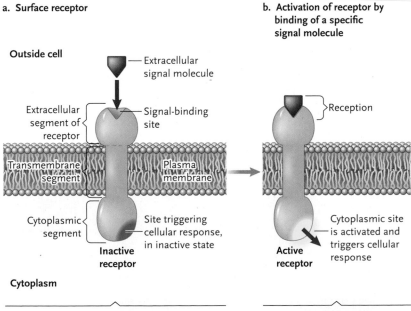

A surface receptor has an extracellular segment with a site that recognizes and binds a particular signal molecule.

When the signal molecule is bound, a conformational change is transmitted through the transmembrane segment that activates a site on the cytoplasmic segment of the receptor. The activation triggers a reaction pathway that results in the cellular response.

Figure 5.23
The mechanism by which a surface receptor responds when it binds a signal molecule.

and is folded in a way that closely fits the signal molecule. The fit, which is similar to an enzyme–substrate interaction, is specific so that a particular receptor binds only one type of signal. When a signal molecule binds, for example, to a surface receptor associated with the plasma membrane, the molecular structure of that receptor changes so that it transmits the signal through the plasma membrane, activating the cytoplasmic end of the receptor protein. The activated receptor then initiates the first step in a cascade of molecular events—the signalling cascade—that triggers the cellular response **(Figure 5.23b)**. The cells of most organisms typically have hundreds of membrane receptors that represent many receptor types. Receptors for a specific animal peptide hormone, for example, may number from 500 to as many as 100 000 or more per cell. Different cell types contain distinct combinations of receptors, allowing them to react individually to a diversity of signal molecules.

5.7c Signal Reception Triggers Response Pathways within the Cell

The binding of a signal molecule to a plasma membrane receptor, for example, is sufficient to trigger the activation of the signalling cascade. The signal molecule does not enter the cell. For example, experiments have shown that (1) a signal molecule produces no response if it is injected directly into the cytoplasm and (2) unrelated molecules that mimic the structure of the normal extracellular signal molecule can trigger or block a full cellular response as long as they can bind to the recognition site of the receptor. In fact, many medical conditions are treated with drugs that are signal molecule mimics.

A common characteristic of signalling mechanisms is that the signal is relayed inside the cell by **protein kinases**, enzymes that transfer a phosphate group from ATP to one or more sites on particular proteins. As shown in **Figure 5.24,** protein kinases often act in a chain, catalyzing a series of phosphorylation reactions called a *phosphorylation cascade,* to pass along a signal. The first kinase catalyzes phosphorylation of the second, which then becomes active and phosphorylates the third kinase, which then becomes active, and so on. The last protein in the cascade is the *target protein*. Phosphorylation of a target protein stimulates or inhibits its activity depending on the particular protein. This change in activity brings about the cellular response. For example, phosphorylating a target protein may alter the activity of a transcription factor that regulates the expression of a suite of genes.

The effects of protein kinases in the signal transduction pathways are balanced or reversed by another group of enzymes called **protein phosphatases,** which remove phosphate groups from target proteins. Unlike the protein kinases, which are active only when a surface receptor binds a signal molecule, most of the protein phosphatases are continuously active in cells. By

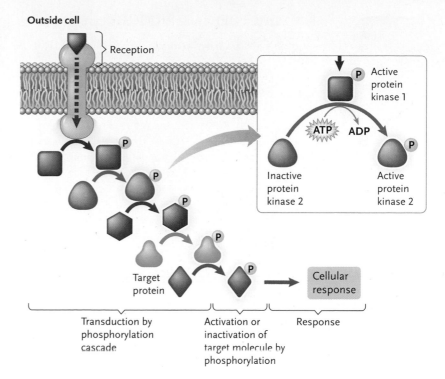

Figure 5.24
Phosphorylation, a key reaction in many signalling pathways.

continually removing phosphate groups from target proteins, the protein phosphatases quickly shut off a signal transduction pathway if its signal molecule is no longer bound at the cell surface.

Another characteristic of signal transduction pathways is **amplification**—an increase in the magnitude of each step as a signal transduction pathway proceeds **(Figure 5.25)**. Amplification occurs because many of the proteins that carry out individual steps in the pathways,

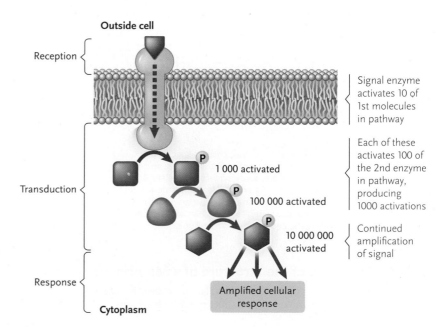

Figure 5.25
Amplification in signal transduction.

PEOPLE BEHIND BIOLOGY 5.2

Lap-Chee Tsui, University of Hong Kong

Identifying the gene that is defective in patients with cystic fibrosis (CF) (see "Why It Matters", p. 52) was a breakthrough in human genetics and was achieved by a research team headed by Lap-Chee Tsui (1950–) of the Department of Genetics at the Hospital for Sick Children in Toronto.

Born in Shanghai, Tsui studied biology at the Chinese University of Hong Kong and was awarded a bachelor of science degree in 1972, which was followed by a master of philosophy degree in 1974. He undertook doctoral research in the United States, completing his Ph.D. at the University of Pittsburgh in 1979. He followed this with postdoctoral training at Oak Ridge National Laboratory in Tennessee before moving in 1981 to the Department of Genetics at the Hospital for Sick Children, where soon after he became a staff member investigating the underlying genetic cause of CF.

Although today reports of gene discovery are commonplace, in the 1980s, the discovery of the gene that is mutated in patients with CF was particularly noteworthy for two major reasons. First, researchers relied on DNA isolated from people with CF to identify genetic markers of the disease. Using these, researchers used the novel method of positional cloning to identify the CF gene without any knowledge of the gene itself or what it did. Second, CF is the most common single-gene disease among Caucasians; thus, much anticipation awaited this particular discovery, with many research teams worldwide trying to be the first to identify the gene.

In 1985, Tsui and his team identified the first DNA marker linked to CF, on chromosome 7. Four years later, Tsui's team, along with collaborators at the University of Michigan, finally identified the defective gene responsible for CF, defining the principal mutation (Δ*F508). This mutation is the result of a three-nucleotide deletion that results in the loss of the amino acid phenylalanine (F) at the 508th position of the protein. As a result, the protein does not fold normally and is more quickly degraded.

The research was described in three seminal papers in the September 8, 1989, issue of *Science*. The gene was called the cystic fibrosis transmembrane regulator (CFTR). *Science* named Tsui's achievement "the most refreshing scientific development of 1989," and *Maclean's* Honour Roll hailed it as one of the "discoveries of hope at the heart of human life" in the same year.

Tsui has received many honours, including fellow of the Royal Society of Canada, several honorary doctoral degrees, and the Order of Canada. Tsui is currently the vice-chancellor of the University of Hong Kong, but he remains an active researcher and is still affiliated with the Hospital for Sick Children's Program in Genetics and Genomic Biology.

including the protein kinases, are enzymes. Once activated, each enzyme can activate hundreds of proteins, including other enzymes that enter the next step in the pathway. Generally, the more enzyme-catalyzed steps in a response pathway, the greater the amplification. As a result, just a few extracellular signal molecules binding to their receptors can produce a full internal response.

This chapter has introduced you to the fundamentals of membrane structure and the role membranes serve in an array of functions, from transport through cellular signalling. Membranes and the compartments they define play a fundamental role in energy metabolism, which is the central theme of the next two chapters on respiration and photosynthesis.

Review

Access an interactive eBook, chapter-specific interactive learning tools, including flashcards, quizzes, videos, and more in your Biology **CourseMate**, accessed through NelsonBrain.com **Aplia™** is an online interactive learning solution that helps you improve comprehension—and your grade—by integrating a variety of mediums and tools such as videos, tutorials, practice tests, and an interactive eBook.

5.1 An Overview of the Structure of a Membrane

- The fluid mosaic model proposes that the membrane consists of a fluid lipid bilayer in which proteins are embedded and float freely (Figure 5.1).
- Membranes are asymmetrical. The two halves of a membrane are not the same. The membrane proteins found on one half of

the bilayer are structurally and functionally distinct from those of the other half.

5.2 The Lipid Fabric of a Membrane

- The lipid bilayer forms the structural framework of membranes and serves as a barrier preventing the passage of most water-soluble molecules.
- The structural basis of a membrane is a fluid phospholipid bilayer in which the polar regions of phospholipid molecules lie at the surfaces of the bilayer and their nonpolar tails associate together in the interior (Figures 5.4 and 5.5).
- Saturated fatty acids contain the maximum number of hydrogen atoms and are linear molecules. Unsaturated fatty acids contain one or more double bonds, which cause the fatty acid to kink (Figure 5.6).

- Organisms can adjust the fatty acid composition of membrane lipids to maintain proper fluidity through the action of a group of enzymes called desaturases (Figure 5.7).

5.3 Membrane Proteins

- Proteins embedded in the phospholipid bilayer carry out most membrane functions, including transport of selected hydrophilic substances, enzymatic activity, recognition, and signal reception (Figure 5.9).
- Integral membrane proteins interact with the hydrophobic core of the membrane bilayer. Most integral membrane proteins, called transmembrane proteins, have domains that span the membrane numerous times. These domains are dominated by nonpolar amino acids (Figures 5.10 and 5.11).
- Peripheral membrane proteins associate with membrane surfaces.

5.4 Passive Membrane Transport

- Passive transport depends on diffusion, the net movement of molecules from a region of higher concentration to a region of lower concentration. Passive transport does not require cells to expend energy (Figure 5.12).
- Simple diffusion is the passive transport of substances across a membrane through the lipid molecules. Small uncharged molecules can move rapidly across membranes, whereas large or charged molecules may be strongly impeded from transiting a membrane (Figure 5.13).
- Facilitated diffusion is the diffusion of molecules across membranes by the use of specific membrane proteins—channel proteins and carrier proteins. Both channel proteins and carrier proteins are specific for certain substances. For many molecules, facilitated diffusion results in higher rates of transport compared to simple diffusion (Figures 5.14 and 5.15).
- Osmosis is the net diffusion of water molecules across a selectively permeable membrane in response to differences in the concentration of solute molecules.
- Water moves from hypotonic solutions (lower concentrations of solute molecules) to hypertonic solutions (higher concentrations of solute molecules). When the solutions on each side are isotonic, there is no osmotic movement of water in either direction (Figure 5.16).

5.5 Active Membrane Transport

- Active transport moves substances against their concentration gradients and requires cells to expend energy. Active transport depends on membrane proteins, is specific for certain substances, and becomes saturated at high concentrations of the transported substance.
- Active transport proteins are either primary transport pumps, which directly use ATP as their energy source, or secondary

transport pumps, which use favourable concentration gradients of positively charged ions, set up by primary transport pumps, as their energy source for transport (Figure 5.17).

- Secondary active transport may occur by symport, in which the transported substance moves in the same direction as the concentration gradient used as the energy source, or by antiport, in which the transported substance moves in the direction opposite to the concentration gradient used as the energy source (Figure 5.19).

5.6 Exocytosis and Endocytosis

- Large molecules and particles are moved out of and into cells by exocytosis and endocytosis. The mechanisms allow substances to leave and enter cells without directly passing through the plasma membrane (Figure 5.20).
- In exocytosis, a vesicle carrying secreted materials contacts and fuses with the plasma membrane on its cytoplasmic side. The fusion introduces the vesicle membrane into the plasma membrane and releases the vesicle contents to the cell exterior.
- In endocytosis, materials on the cell exterior are enclosed in a segment of the plasma membrane that pockets inward and pinches off on the cytoplasmic side as an endocytic vesicle. Endocytosis occurs in two overall forms, bulk-phase endocytosis (pinocytosis) and receptor-mediated endocytosis. Most of the materials entering cells are digested into molecular subunits small enough to be transported across the vesicle membranes (Figure 5.20b, c).

5.7 Role of Membranes in Cell Signalling

- Cell communication systems based on surface receptors have three components: (1) extracellular signal molecules, (2) surface receptors that receive the signals, and (3) internal response pathways triggered when receptors bind a signal (Figure 5.22).
- Surface receptors are integral membrane proteins that extend through the plasma membrane. Binding a signal molecule induces a molecular change in the receptor that activates its cytoplasmic end (Figure 5.23).
- Many cellular response pathways operate by activating protein kinases, which add phosphate groups that stimulate or inhibit the activities of the target proteins, bringing about the cellular response (Figure 5.24). Protein phosphatases that remove phosphate groups from target proteins reverse the response. In addition, receptors are removed by endocytosis when signal transduction has run its course.
- Each step of a response pathway catalyzed by an enzyme is amplified, because each enzyme can activate hundreds or thousands of proteins that enter the next step in the pathway. Through amplification, a few signal molecules can bring about a full cellular response (Figure 5.25).

Questions

Self-Test Questions

1. Which of the following statements about the fluid mosaic model is correct?
   a. The fluid refers to the phospholipid bilayer.
   b. Plasma membrane proteins orient their hydrophilic sides toward the internal bilayer.
   c. Phospholipids often flip-flop between the inner and outer layers.
   d. The mosaic refers to proteins attached to the underlying cytoskeleton.
   e. The mosaic refers to the symmetry of the internal membrane proteins and sterols.

2. What was demonstrated by the freeze-fracture technique?
   a. the plasma membrane is fluid.
   b. membranes remain fluid at freezing temperatures.
   c. the arrangement of membrane lipids and proteins is symmetric.
   d. the plasma membrane is a bilayer with individual proteins suspended in it.
   e. proteins are bound to the cytoplasmic side but not embedded in the lipid bilayer.

3. Which statement is correct regarding temperature and membrane fluidity?
   a. Membrane fluidity increases with decreasing temperature.
   b. Membrane fluidity remains constant over the temperature range of 0°C to 100°C.
   c. at any given temperature, membrane fluidity increases as desaturase activity increases.
   d. At any given temperature, membrane fluidity decreases as the abundance of unsaturated fatty acids increases.

4. The integral membrane protein rhodopsin, which is used in light perception, is a protein that spans the membrane seven times. Which statement about rhodopsin is correct?
   a. It contains seven hydrophobic amino acids.
   b. It is composed only of hydrophobic amino acids.
   c. It contains both hydrophobic and hydrophilic domains.
   d. It contains one long stretch of hydrophobic amino acids.
   e. It has a random assortment of both polar and nonpolar amino acids.

5. Which one of the following molecules shows the slowest rate of membrane diffusion and why?
   a. Na+, because it is small
   b. K+, because it is charged
   c. glucose, because it is large
   d. CO_2, because it contains three atoms
   e. H_2O, because water is the main component of the cytosol

6. Compared to simple diffusion, which of the following statements is correct for only facilitated diffusion?
   a. It can only transport hydrophobic molecules.
   b. It can be saturated by high substrate concentrations.
   c. It requires a source of chemical energy, such as ATP.
   d. It can transport molecules against a concentration gradient.

7. In the following diagram, assume that the setup was left unattended. Which statement is correct?

Selectively Permeable Membrane			
Inside a Cell		Extracellular Fluid	
Solvent	95%	Solvent	98%
Solute	5%	Solute	2%

a. The cell will soon shrink.
b. The net flow of solvent is into the cell.
c. The cell is in a hypertonic environment.
d. Diffusion can occur here but not osmosis.
e. The relation of the cell to its environment is isotonic.

8. An ion moving through a membrane channel in one direction gives energy to actively transport another molecule in the opposite direction. What process does this describe?
   a. cotransport
   b. symport transport
   c. exchange diffusion
   d. facilitated diffusion
   e. primary active transport pump

9. Phagocytosis illustrates?
   a. exocytosis.
   b. pinocytosis.
   c. cotransport.
   d. bulk-phase endocytosis.
   e. receptor-mediated endocytosis.

10. Many signal transduction pathways are initiated by a signal binding to a membrane receptor. Which statement about this type of signalling mechanism is correct?
   a. signal binding may activate a protein kinase.
   b. a signal molecule injected into the cytoplasm will activate the pathway.
   c. a mutation in a single gene can disrupt an entire signalling pathway.
   d. signal transduction pathways never include components within the nucleus.
   e. Both a and c are correct.

Questions for Discussion

1. In Chapter 4, we discussed thermodynamics. What role does thermodynamics play in membrane transport?

2. The bacterium *Vibrio cholerae* causes cholera, a disease characterized by severe diarrhea that may cause infected people to lose up to 20 L of fluid in a day. The bacterium enters the body when a person drinks contaminated water. It adheres to the intestinal lining, where it causes cells of the lining to release sodium and chloride ions. Explain how this release is related to the massive fluid loss.

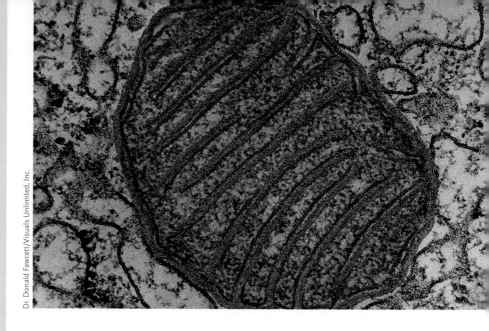

Scanning electron micrograph of a mitochondrion. Mitochondria are the sites of cellular respiration.

Dr. Donald Fawcett/Visuals Unlimited, Inc.

STUDY PLAN

6.1 The Chemical Basis of Cellular Respiration

6.1a Food Is Fuel

6.1b Coupled Oxidation–Reduction Reactions Are Central to Energy Metabolism

6.1c Cellular Respiration Is Controlled Combustion

6.2 Cellular Respiration: An Overview

6.2a Cellular Respiration Can Be Divided into Three Phases

6.2b The Mitochondrion Is the Site of Cellular Respiration in Eukaryotes

6.3 Glycolysis: The Splitting of Glucose

6.3a Glycolysis Is a Universal and Ancient Metabolic Process

6.3b Glycolysis Includes Energy-Requiring and Energy-Releasing Steps

6.4 Pyruvate Oxidation and the Citric Acid Cycle

6.4a Pyruvate Oxidation Links Glycolysis and the Citric Acid Cycle

6.4b The Citric Acid Cycle Oxidizes Acetyl Groups to Carbon Dioxide

6.5 Oxidative Phosphorylation: Electron Transport and Chemiosmosis

6.5a The Electron Transport Chain Converts the Potential Energy in NADH and $FADH_2$ into a Proton-Motive Force

6.5b Electrons Move Spontaneously along the Electron Transport Chain

6.5c Chemiosmosis Powers ATP Synthesis by a Proton Gradient

6.5d ATP Synthase Is a Molecular Motor

6.5e Electron Transport and Chemiosmosis Can Be Uncoupled

6.6 The Efficiency and Regulation of Cellular Respiration

6.6a What Are the ATP Yield and Efficiency of Cellular Respiration?

6.6b Fats, Proteins, and Carbohydrates Can Be Oxidized by Cellular Respiration

6.6c Respiratory Intermediates Are Utilized for Anabolic Reactions

6.6d Cellular Respiration Is Controlled by Supply and Demand

6.7 Oxygen and Cellular Respiration

6.7a In Eukaryotic Cells, Low Oxygen Levels Result in Fermentation

6.7b In Anaerobic Respiration, the Terminal Electron Acceptor Is Not Oxygen

6.7c Organisms Differ with Respect to Their Ability to Use Oxygen

6.7d The Paradox of Aerobic Life Is That Oxygen Is Both Essential and Toxic

6 Cellular Respiration

WHY IT MATTERS

In the early 1960s, Swedish physician Rolf Luft mulled over some odd symptoms of a patient. The young woman was hot all the time. Even on the coldest winter days, she never stopped perspiring and her skin was always flushed. She also felt weak and was thin, despite a huge appetite.

Luft inferred that his patient's symptoms pointed to a metabolic disorder. Her cells seemed to be active, but much of their activity was being dissipated as metabolic heat. He decided to order tests to measure her metabolic rates. The patient's oxygen consumption was the highest ever recorded!

Luft also examined a tissue sample from the patient's skeletal muscles. Using a microscope, he found that her muscle cells contained many more mitochondria—the adenosine triphosphate (ATP)–producing organelles of the cell—than normal; also, her mitochondria were abnormally shaped. Other studies showed that the mitochondria were engaged in cellular respiration—their prime function—but little ATP was being generated.

The disorder, now called *Luft syndrome,* was the first disorder to be linked directly to a defective cellular organelle. This syndrome is extremely rare and has now been shown to be due to a defect in one of the complexes of cellular respiration that links electron transport to proton pumping and subsequent ATP generation. With such a disorder, skeletal and heart muscles and the brain, the tissues with the highest energy demands, are affected the most. More than 100 mitochondrial disorders are now known. Defective mitochondria are now linked to a range of diseases and disorders including amyotrophic lateral sclerosis (ALS, also called Lou Gehrig's disease), as well as Parkinson's, Alzheimer's, and Huntington diseases.

Clearly, human health depends on mitochondria that are structurally sound and functioning properly. But of course there is nothing unique to humans here—every animal, plant, and fungus requires correctly functioning mitochondria in order to live. In eukaryotes, this organelle is the site of key reactions of cellular respiration—the process whereby the energy present in food molecules is extracted and converted into a form usable to the cell. In this chapter, we explore the fundamentals of cellular respiration, starting by addressing what makes a good fuel molecule.

6.1 The Chemical Basis of Cellular Respiration

We can define **cellular respiration** as the collection of metabolic reactions within cells that breaks down food molecules to produce ATP—the almost universal energy currency that fuels nearly all the reactions that keep cells, and organisms, metabolically active—a defining characteristic of life (see Chapter 2). The ultimate source of the complex organic molecules that are oxidized in cellular respiration is *photosynthesis,* which is the focus of the next chapter. In photosynthesis, light energy is used to extract electrons from water, which combine with hydrogen to reduce carbon dioxide into carbohydrates. A major by-product of photosynthesis is oxygen, a molecule needed for the most common type of cellular respiration. Thus, life

and its systems are driven by a cycle of electron flow that is powered by light in photosynthesis and oxidation in cellular respiration (**Figure 6.1**).

6.1a Food Is Fuel

Looking at **Figure 6.2,** we can ask the following question: what is it about glucose that makes it a source of chemical energy? We could ask the same question of gasoline - what makes it good at powering a car? Both glucose and gasoline are good fuel molecules because they contain an abundance of C—H bonds. The energetic nature of the C—H bond is explained in **Figure 6.3.** For any atom, an electron that is farther away from the nucleus contains more energy than an electron that is more closely held by the nucleus. And as an electron moves closer to the nucleus of an atom it loses energy; as it moves away it gains energy (Figure 6.3). The electrons that form the covalent C—H bond are equidistant from both atomic nuclei—not being strongly held by either. Because of this, the electrons can be easily removed and used to perform work. In contrast to glucose and gasoline, molecules that contain more oxygen, for example, carbon dioxide, contain less potential energy because oxygen is strongly electronegative. The more electronegative an atom, the greater the force that holds the electrons to that atom, and, therefore, the greater the energy required to remove the electrons. To review the basics of electronegativity, see *The Purple Pages.* In the case of a C—H bond, neither carbon nor hydrogen is strongly electronegative. This fundamental principle of chemistry has an everyday relevance: it explains why, for example, compared to proteins and carbohydrates, fats contain more calories (energy) per unit of weight. A fat is almost entirely C—H bonds, while both proteins and carbohydrates contain varying amounts of other atoms, including oxygen. (To review the structure of these molecules, see *The Purple Pages.*)

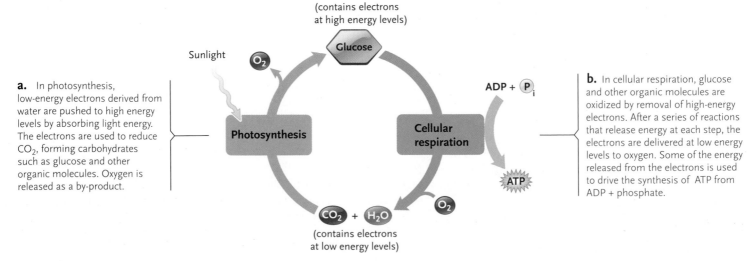

a. In photosynthesis, low-energy electrons derived from water are pushed to high energy levels by absorbing light energy. The electrons are used to reduce CO_2, forming carbohydrates such as glucose and other organic molecules. Oxygen is released as a by-product.

b. In cellular respiration, glucose and other organic molecules are oxidized by removal of high-energy electrons. After a series of reactions that release energy at each step, the electrons are delivered at low energy levels to oxygen. Some of the energy released from the electrons is used to drive the synthesis of ATP from ADP + phosphate.

Figure 6.1
Flow of energy linking photosynthesis and respiration. Photosynthesis uses light energy to convert carbon dioxide and water into energy-rich organic molecules such as glucose, which, in turn, are oxidized by cellular respiration.

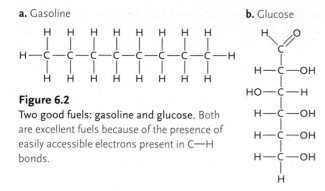

a. Gasoline   **b.** Glucose

Figure 6.2
Two good fuels: gasoline and glucose. Both are excellent fuels because of the presence of easily accessible electrons present in C—H bonds.

6.1b Coupled Oxidation–Reduction Reactions Are Central to Energy Metabolism

The potential energy contained in fuel molecules is released when the molecules lose electrons, becoming **oxidized.** The electrons released from a molecule that is oxidized are gained by another molecule that becomes **reduced.** Oxidation and reduction reactions are coupled processes—one cannot happen without the other. A simple mnemonic to remember the direction of electron transfer is OIL RIG—Oxidation Is Loss (of electrons), Reduction Is Gain (of electrons). For short, oxidation–reduction reactions are called redox reactions. A generalized redox reaction can be written like this:

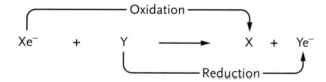

The redox reaction describing the respiratory breakdown of glucose is as follows:

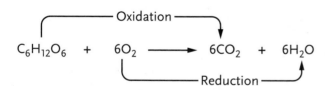

The term *oxidation* comes from that fact that many reactions in which electrons are removed from fuel molecules involve oxygen as the atom that accepts the electrons (or the molecule that gets reduced: the electron acceptor). The involvement of oxygen is essential for many common oxidation reactions: a car engine requires large amounts of air (21% oxygen) to be delivered to each piston for combustion to take place; an oil fire on a stove can be rapidly extinguished by putting a lid on the pot, restricting the air supply. As we will see later in this chapter, the high affinity of O_2 for electrons (its high electronegativity) makes it ideal as the terminal electron acceptor of cellular respiration.

The concept of redox is made a little more challenging to understand by two facts. First, although many oxidation reactions involve oxygen, others, including a number involved in cellular respiration, do not. Second,

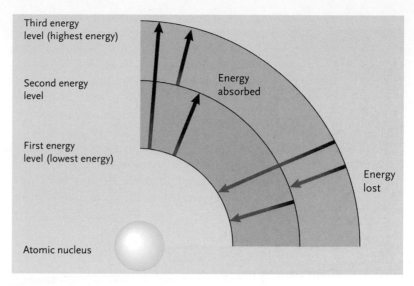

Figure 6.3
Energy levels of the electrons of an atom. Electrons can exist only in discrete energy states. Electrons that gain energy move to a higher energy level that is farther away from the nucleus. Electrons that lose energy move closer to the nucleus.

the gain or loss of an electron in a redox reaction is not always complete. That is, whereas in some redox reactions electrons are transferred completely from one atom to another, in other redox reactions, what changes is the degree to which electrons are shared between two atoms. The reaction between methane and oxygen (the burning of natural gas in air) illustrates a redox reaction in which only the degree of electron sharing changes **(Figure 6.4).** The blue dots (see Figure 6.4) indicate the positions of the electrons involved in the covalent bonds of the reactants and products. Compare the reactant methane with the product carbon dioxide—in methane, the electrons are shared equally between the carbon and hydrogen atoms. In the product, carbon dioxide, electrons are closer to the oxygen than to the carbon because oxygen atoms are more electronegative. Overall, this means that the carbon atom has partially lost its shared

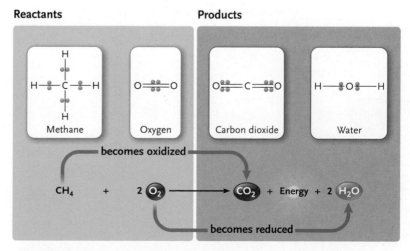

Figure 6.4
A redox reaction. The burning of methane in oxygen. Compare the positions of the electrons in the covalent bonds of reactants and products. In this redox reaction, methane is oxidized and oxygen is reduced.

electrons in the reaction: methane has been oxidized. Now compare the oxygen reactant with the product water. In the oxygen molecule, the two oxygen atoms share their electrons equally. The oxygen reacts with the hydrogen from methane, producing water, in which the electrons are closer to the oxygen atom than to the hydrogen atoms. This means that each oxygen atom has partially gained electrons: oxygen has been reduced. Because of this, the reaction between methane and oxygen releases heat. The energy is released as the electrons in the C—H bonds of methane move closer to the electronegative oxygen atoms that form carbon dioxide.

6.1c Cellular Respiration Is Controlled Combustion

Like gasoline or methane, glucose can also undergo combustion and burn. The combustion of glucose releases energy as electrons are transferred to oxygen, reducing it to water, and the carbon in glucose is converted to carbon dioxide.

Recall from Chapter 4 that for a spontaneous reaction to proceed, the substrate molecules need to reach the transition state, which requires an energy input referred to as the activation energy. To get glucose to ignite, we can use a flame to provide the high activation energy **(Figure 6.5a)**. In contrast, within a cell, the oxidation of glucose occurs through a series of enzyme-catalyzed reactions **(Figure 6.5b)**, each with a small activation energy. Thermodynamically, the two processes are identical: they are both exergonic, having the same change in free energy (ΔG) of -686 kcal/mol. The big difference is that if you simply burn glucose, the energy is released as heat and therefore not available to drive metabolic reactions. So a good way to think of the process of cellular respiration is controlled combustion—where the energy of the C—H bonds is not liberated suddenly, producing heat, but is slowly released in a stepwise fashion, with the energy being transferred to other molecules.

In cellular respiration, the oxidation of food molecules occurs in the presence of a group of enzymes called *dehydrogenases* that facilitate the transfer of electrons from food to a molecule that acts as an energy carrier or shuttle. The most common energy carrier is the coenzyme **nicotinamide adenine dinucleotide** (NAD^+, oxidized; NADH, reduced) **(Figure 6.6)**. During respiration, the dehydrogenases remove two hydrogen atoms from a substrate molecule and transfer the two electrons—but only one of the protons—to NAD^+, reducing it to NADH. The efficiency of the enzyme-catalyzed transfer of energy between food molecules and NAD^+ is very high. As we will see later in the chapter, the potential energy carried in NADH is used to synthesize ATP.

STUDY BREAK

1. What is it about the structure of gasoline and glucose that makes them both good fuels?
2. In the respiratory breakdown of glucose, what gets oxidized and what gets reduced?

6.2 Cellular Respiration: An Overview

At this point, let's step back and remind ourselves of the primary goal of cellular respiration: it is to transform the potential energy found in food molecules into a form that can be used for metabolic processes, ATP. We will see later in the chapter that both proteins and lipids can be oxidized by the respiratory pathway and their potential energy harnessed; however, because the oxidation of glucose utilizes the entire respiratory pathway, it is the main focus of our discussion.

6.2a Cellular Respiration Can Be Divided into Three Phases

Cellular respiration can be divided into three phases **(Figure 6.7)**:

1. *Glycolysis.* Enzymes break down a molecule of glucose into two molecules of pyruvate. Some ATP and NADH is synthesized.
2. *Pyruvate oxidation and the citric acid cycle.* Acetyl coenzyme A (acetyl-CoA), which is formed from the oxidation of pyruvate, enters a metabolic cycle, where it is completely oxidized to carbon dioxide. Some ATP and NADH is synthesized.
3. *Oxidative phosphorylation.* The NADH synthesized by both glycolysis and the citric acid cycle is oxidized, with the liberated electrons being passed along an electron transport chain until they are transferred to oxygen, producing water. The free energy released during electron transport is used to generate a proton gradient across a membrane, which, in turn, is used to synthesize ATP.

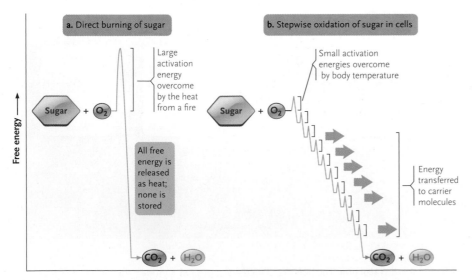

Figure 6.5

A comparison of the oxidation of glucose by combustion and cellular respiration.

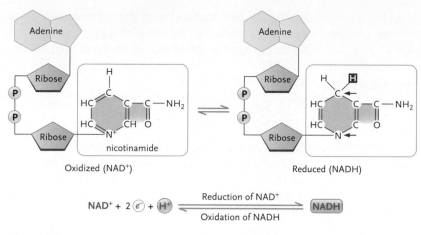

Figure 6.6

Electron carrier NAD⁺. As the carrier is reduced to NADH, an electron is added at each of the two positions marked by a red arrow; a proton is also added at the position boxed in red. The nitrogenous base (blue) that adds and releases electrons and protons is nicotinamide, which is derived from the vitamin niacin (nicotinic acid).

All three stages are required to extract the maximum amount of energy that is biologically possible from a molecule of glucose; however, not all organisms possess all three stages.

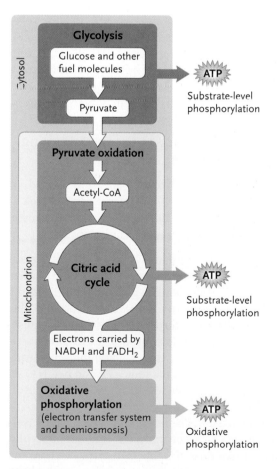

Figure 6.7

The three stages of cellular respiration: glycolysis, pyruvate oxidation and the citric acid cycle, and oxidative phosphorylation.

6.2b The Mitochondrion Is the Site of Cellular Respiration in Eukaryotes

In archaea and bacteria, glycolysis and the citric acid cycle occur in the cytosol, whereas oxidative phosphorylation occurs on internal membranes. By comparison, in eukaryotic cells, the citric acid cycle and oxidative phosphorylation occur in a specialized membrane-bound organelle called the mitochondrion (plural, *mitochondria*) **(Figure 6.8)**. This membrane-bound organelle is often referred to as the powerhouse of the cell because as the location of both the citric acid cycle and oxidative phosphorylation, it is the largest generator of ATP in the cell.

The mitochondrion is composed of two membranes, the outer membrane and the inner membrane, which together define two compartments (see Figure 6.8): the intermembrane space, which is found between the outer and inner membranes, and the matrix, which is the interior aqueous environment.

In the description of cellular respiration that follows, we often refer specifically to mitochondria and their various compartments, but it is important to remember that there is nothing uniquely eukaryotic about cellular respiration. Neither archaea nor bacteria have mitochondria, but many species of both possess the entire complement of reactions that make up cellular respiration—from glycolysis through oxidative phosphorylation.

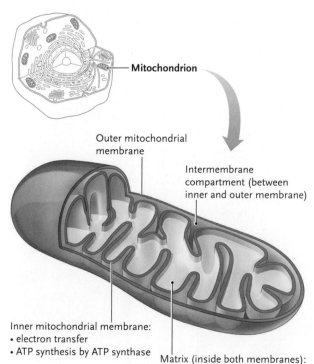

Figure 6.8

Membranes and compartments of mitochondria. Label lines that end in a dot indicate a compartment enclosed by the membranes.

Mitochondrion

Outer mitochondrial membrane

Intermembrane compartment (between inner and outer membrane)

Inner mitochondrial membrane:
• electron transfer
• ATP synthesis by ATP synthase

Matrix (inside both membranes):
• reactions removing electrons from fuel molecules (pyruvate oxidation, citric acid cycle)

6.3 Glycolysis: The Splitting of Glucose

Glycolysis (*glykys* = sweet; *lysis* = breakdown) consists of 10 sequential enzyme-catalyzed reactions that lead to the oxidation of the six-carbon sugar glucose,

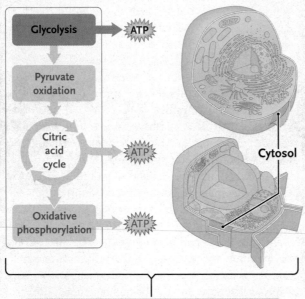

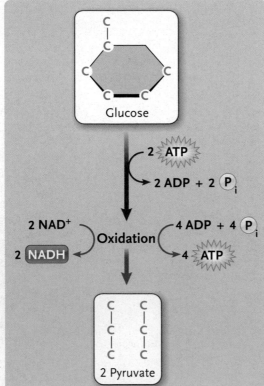

Figure 6.9
Overall reactions of glycolysis. Glycolysis splits glucose (six carbons) into pyruvate (three carbons) and yields ATP and NADH.

producing two molecules of the three-carbon compound pyruvate. The potential energy released in the oxidation leads to the overall synthesis of both NADH and ATP.

6.3a Glycolysis Is a Universal and Ancient Metabolic Process

Glycolysis was one of the first metabolic pathways studied and is one of the best understood in terms of the enzymes involved, their mechanisms of action, and how the pathway is regulated to meet the energy needs of the cell. The first experiments investigating glycolysis took place over 100 years ago and were some of the first to show, using the extracts from yeast cells, that one could study biological reactions in an isolated, cell-free system. These experiments became the foundation of modern biochemistry.

Glycolysis is the most fundamental and probably most ancient of all metabolic pathways. This is supported by the following facts:

1. Glycolysis is universal, being found in all three domains of life— Archaea, Bacteria, and Eukarya.
2. Glycolysis does not depend upon the presence of O_2, which became abundant in Earth's atmosphere only about 2.5 billion years ago—about 1.5 billion years after scientists think life first evolved (see Chapter 3).
3. Glycolysis occurs in the cytosol of all cells using soluble enzymes and therefore does not require more sophisticated electron transport chains and internal membrane systems in order to function.

6.3b Glycolysis Includes Energy-Requiring and Energy-Releasing Steps

The key features of glycolysis are summarized in **Figure 6.9,** while **Figure 6.10** provides a detailed look at each reaction of the glycolytic pathway. From both figures, there are three major concepts to come away with:

1. *Energy investment followed by payoff.* Glycolysis can be considered as consisting of two distinct phases: an initial five-step energy investment followed by a five-step energy payoff. Initially, two molecules of ATP are consumed as glucose and fructose-6-phosphate become phosphorylated. The investment of two ATP for each glucose molecule leads to an energy reward, as four ATP and two NADH molecules are produced during the energy payoff phase.
2. *No carbon is lost.* The reactions of glycolysis convert glucose (a six-carbon molecule) into two molecules of the three-carbon compound pyruvate. Thus, no carbon is lost. However, since glucose has been oxidized, the potential energy in two molecules of pyruvate is less than that of one molecule of glucose.

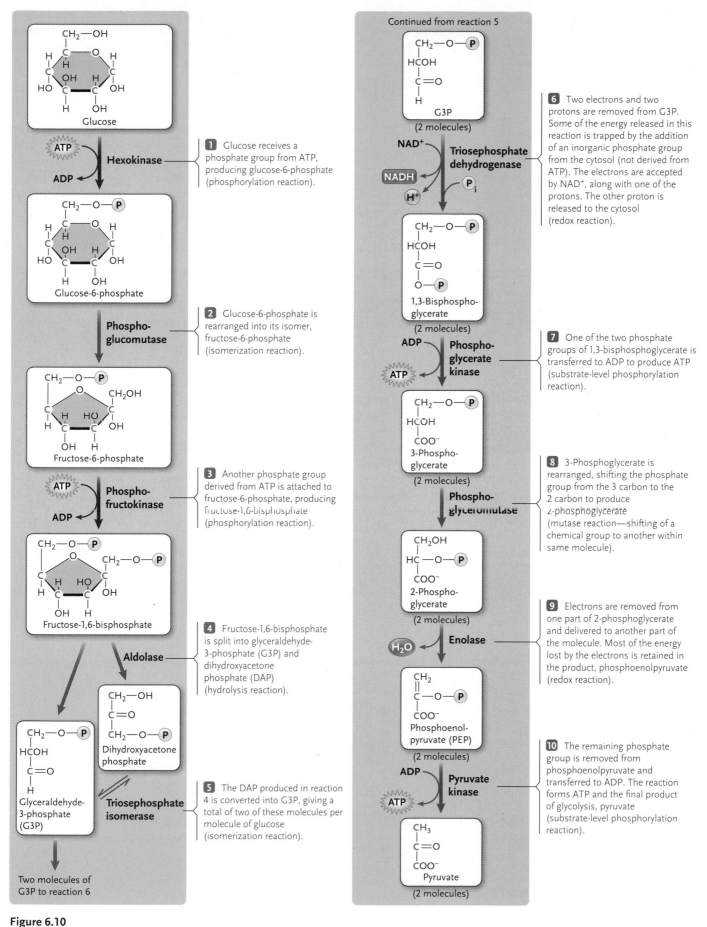

Figure 6.10

Reactions of glycolysis, which occur in the cytosol. Because two molecules of G3P are produced in reaction 5, all the reactions from 6 to 10 are doubled (not shown). The name of the enzyme that catalyzes each reaction is in red.

Figure 6.11
Mechanism that synthesizes ATP by substrate-level phosphorylation. A phosphate group is transferred from a high-energy donor directly to ADP, forming ATP.

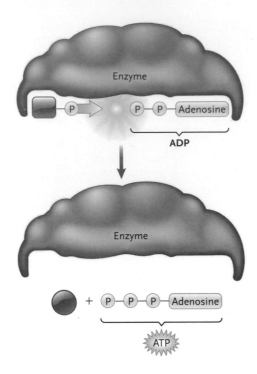

3. *ATP is generated by substrate-level phosphorylation.* During glycolysis, ATP is generated by the process of **substrate-level phosphorylation.** This mode of ATP synthesis, shown in **Figure 6.11,** involves the transfer of a phosphate group from a high-energy substrate molecule to adenosine diphosphate (ADP), producing ATP. Substrate-level phosphorylation, which is mediated by a specific enzyme, is also the mode of ATP synthesis used in the citric acid cycle.

STUDY BREAK

1. What evidence suggests that glycolysis is an ancient metabolic pathway?
2. What accounts for the fact that two molecules of pyruvate have less free energy than one molecule of glucose?

6.4 Pyruvate Oxidation and the Citric Acid Cycle

The two molecules of pyruvate synthesized by glycolysis still contain usable free energy. The extraction of the remaining free energy in pyruvate and the trapping of this energy in the form of ATP and electron carriers such as NADH are the overarching goals of the series of reactions described in this section.

6.4a Pyruvate Oxidation Links Glycolysis and the Citric Acid Cycle

Because the reactions of the citric acid cycle are localized to the mitochondrial matrix, the pyruvate synthesized during glycolysis must pass through both

the outer and inner mitochondrial membranes **(Figure 6.12).** Large pores in the outer membrane allow pyruvate to simply diffuse through, but crossing the inner membrane requires a pyruvate-specific membrane carrier.

Once it gets into the matrix, pyruvate is converted into acetyl-CoA through a multistep process that is referred to as *pyruvate oxidation* (see Figure 6.12). The conversion of pyruvate to acetyl-CoA starts with a decarboxylation reaction whereby the carboxyl ($-COO^-$) group of pyruvate is lost as carbon dioxide. This reaction is understandable given that the carboxyl

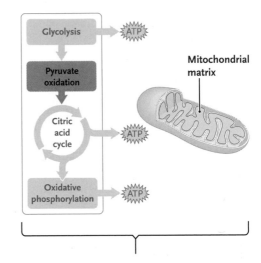

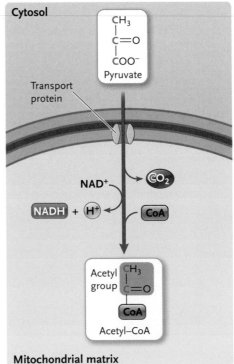

Figure 6.12
Reactions of pyruvate oxidation. Pyruvate (three carbons) is oxidized to an acetyl group (two carbons), which is carried to the citric acid cycle by CoA. The third carbon is released as CO_2. NAD^+ accepts two electrons and one proton removed in the oxidation. The acetyl group carried from the reaction by CoA is the fuel for the citric acid cycle.

group itself contains little potential energy. The decarboxylation reaction is followed by oxidation of the remaining two carbon molecules, producing acetate. This dehydrogenation reaction leads to the transfer of two electrons and a proton to NAD$^+$, forming NADH. Lastly, the acetyl group reacts with coenzyme A (CoA), forming the high-energy intermediate acetyl-CoA. Notice in Figure 6.12 that acetyl-CoA still contains three C—H bonds. Liberating the electrons in those bonds as a source of chemical energy is the goal of the reactions that make up the citric acid cycle.

6.4b The Citric Acid Cycle Oxidizes Acetyl Groups to Carbon Dioxide

The **citric acid cycle** consists of eight enzyme-catalyzed reactions: seven are soluble enzymes located in the mitochondrial matrix, and one enzyme is bound to the matrix side of the inner mitochondrial membrane. Combined, the reactions result in the oxidization of acetyl groups to carbon dioxide accompanied by the synthesis of ATP; NADH; and another nucleotide-based molecule, flavin adenine dinucleotide (FAD; the reduced form is FADH$_2$). A summary of the inputs and outputs of the citric acid cycle is shown in **Figure 6.13.** To put the cycle in context, the summary also includes the conversion of pyruvate to acetyl-CoA.

Looking at the stoichiometry (Figure 6.13), for one turn of the citric acid cycle, three NADH, one FADH$_2$, and a single molecule of ATP are synthesized. The energy for the synthesis of these molecules comes from the complete oxidation of one acetyl unit, resulting in the release of two molecules of carbon dioxide. The citric acid cycle is the stage of respiration where the remaining carbon atoms that were originally in glucose at the start of glycolysis are converted into carbon dioxide. The CoA molecule that carried the acetyl group to the site of the citric acid cycle is released and participates again in pyruvate oxidation. The net reactants and products of one turn of the citric acid cycle are

$$1 \text{ acetyl-CoA} + 3 \text{ NAD}^+ + 1 \text{ FAD} + 1 \text{ ADP} +$$
$$1 \text{ P}_i + 2 \text{ H}_2\text{O} \rightarrow$$

$$2\text{CO}_2 + 3 \text{ NADH} + 1 \text{ FADH}_2 + 1 \text{ ATP} +$$
$$3 \text{ H}^+ + 1 \text{ CoA}$$

Because one molecule of glucose is converted to two molecules of pyruvate by glycolysis and each molecule of pyruvate is converted to one acetyl group, all the reactants and products in this equation should be doubled when the citric acid cycle is considered as a continuation of glycolysis and pyruvate oxidation. **Figure 6.14, p. 124,** presents a detailed view of the individual reactions of the citric acid cycle.

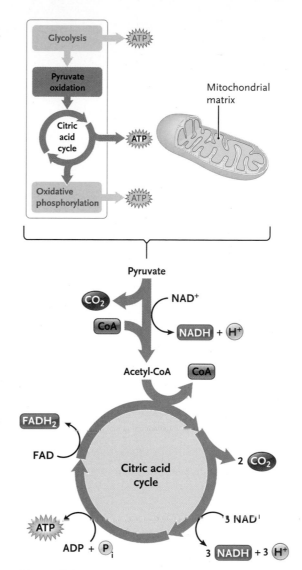

Figure 6.13
The reactions of pyruvate oxidation and the citric acid cycle. Each turn of the cycle oxidizes an acetyl group of acetyl-CoA to 2CO$_2$. Acetyl-CoA, NAD$^+$, FAD, and ADP enter the cycle; CoA, NADH, FADH$_2$, ATP, and CO$_2$ are released as products.

STUDY BREAK

1. What are the steps involved in converting pyruvate into acetyl-CoA?
2. What purpose is served by the citric acid cycle?

6.5 Oxidative Phosphorylation: Electron Transport and Chemiosmosis

Following the citric acid cycle, all the carbon atoms originally present in glucose have been completely oxidized and released as carbon dioxide. Besides ATP formed by substrate-level phosphorylation, the

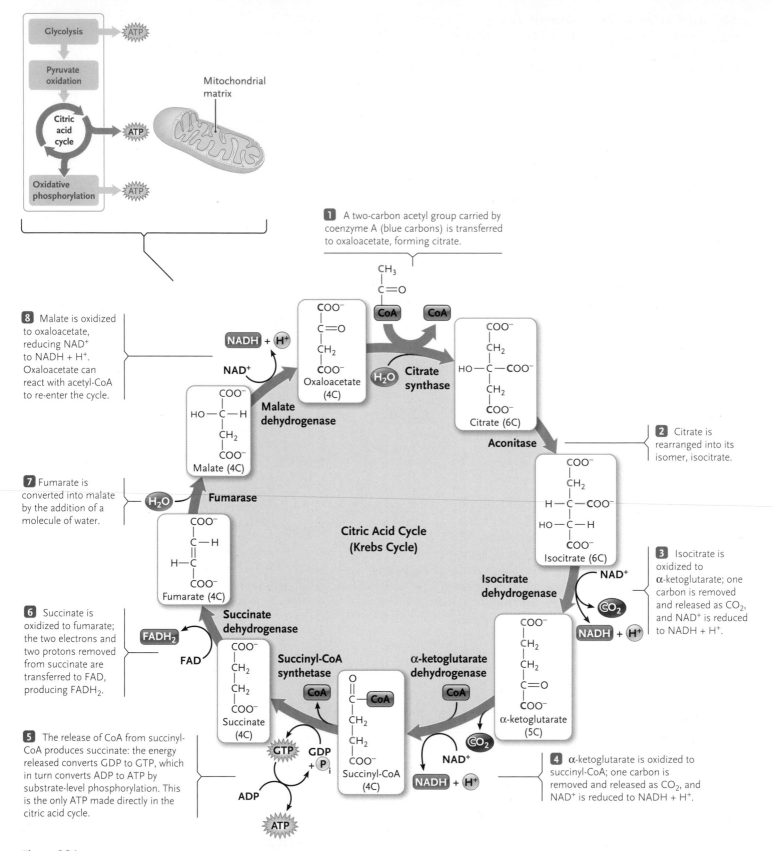

1 A two-carbon acetyl group carried by coenzyme A (blue carbons) is transferred to oxaloacetate, forming citrate.

8 Malate is oxidized to oxaloacetate, reducing NAD^+ to $NADH + H^+$. Oxaloacetate can react with acetyl-CoA to re-enter the cycle.

7 Fumarate is converted into malate by the addition of a molecule of water.

6 Succinate is oxidized to fumarate; the two electrons and two protons removed from succinate are transferred to FAD, producing $FADH_2$.

5 The release of CoA from succinyl-CoA produces succinate: the energy released converts GDP to GTP, which in turn converts ADP to ATP by substrate-level phosphorylation. This is the only ATP made directly in the citric acid cycle.

2 Citrate is rearranged into its isomer, isocitrate.

3 Isocitrate is oxidized to α-ketoglutarate; one carbon is removed and released as CO_2, and NAD^+ is reduced to $NADH + H^+$.

4 α-ketoglutarate is oxidized to succinyl-CoA; one carbon is removed and released as CO_2, and NAD^+ is reduced to $NADH + H^+$.

Citric Acid Cycle (Krebs Cycle)

Mitochondrial matrix

Figure 6.14

Reactions of the citric acid cycle. Acetyl-CoA, NAD^+, FAD, and ADP enter the cycle; CoA, NADH, $FADH_2$, ATP, and CO_2 are released as products. The CoA released in reaction 1 can cycle back for another turn of pyruvate oxidation. Enzyme names are in red.

potential energy originally present in glucose now exists in molecules of NADH and FADH$_2$. It is the role of the electron transport chain coupled with the process of chemiosmosis to extract the potential energy in these molecules and synthesize additional ATP.

6.5a The Electron Transport Chain Converts the Potential Energy in NADH and FADH$_2$ into a Proton-Motive Force

The respiratory electron transport chain **(Figure 6.15, p. 126)** comprises a system of components that in eukaryotes is found on the inner mitochondrial membrane. The chain facilitates the transfer of electrons from NADH$_2$ and FADH$_2$ to oxygen. The chain consists of four protein complexes: **complex I**, NADH dehydrogenase; **complex II**, succinate dehydrogenase; **complex III**, cytochrome complex; and **complex IV**, cytochrome oxidase. Whereas complex II is a single peripheral membrane protein, the remaining complexes are composed of multiple proteins. For example, about 40 individual proteins make up complex I.

Electron flow from one complex to another is facilitated by two mobile electron shuttles. Ubiquinone, which is a hydrophobic molecule found in the core of the membrane, shuttles electrons from complexes I and II to complex III. A second shuttle, cytochrome *c*, is located on the intermembrane space side of the membrane and transfers electrons from complex III to complex IV, cytochrome oxidase.

6.5b Electrons Move Spontaneously along the Electron Transport Chain

In an electron transport chain it is not the proteins themselves that transfer the electrons, but rather electron transfer is facilitated by nonprotein molecules called prosthetic groups. Protein subunits of each of complexes I, III, and IV bind a number of prosthetic groups very precisely to allow for electron transfer **(Figure 6.16, p. 127)**. Prosthetic groups are redox-active cofactors that alternate between reduced and oxidized states as they accept electrons from upstream molecules and subsequently donate electrons to downstream molecules. A common prosthetic group is the molecule heme, which is a component of the cytochromes, including cytochrome *c*. Heme is a component of many biologically important compounds, including hemoglobin, where it is critical to the molecule's ability to carry oxygen. Central to its function, a heme group contains a central redox-active iron atom that alternates between Fe^{2+} and Fe^{3+}.

During electron transport (see Figure 6.16, p. 127), one of the prosthetic groups of complex I, flavin mononucleotide (FMN), is reduced by electron donation from NADH on the matrix side of the inner membrane. FMN then donates the electron to the Fe/S (iron–sulfur) prosthetic group, which, in turn, donates the electron to ubiquinone. This process of reduction followed by oxidation of each carrier continues along the entire chain until, finally, the electrons are donated to oxygen (O$_2$), reducing it to water. The protons used in the formation of water are abundant in the aqueous environment of the cell.

A question concerning mechanism that we can ask at this stage is: why do electrons move down the chain? As shown in Figure 6.16, p. 127, the prosthetic groups and other electron carriers are organized in a very specific way—from high to low free energy. Any single component has a higher affinity for electrons than the preceding carrier in the chain. Overall, molecules such as NADH contain an abundance of free energy and can be readily oxidized, whereas O$_2$, the terminal electron acceptor of the chain, is strongly electronegative and can be easily reduced. As a consequence of this organization, electron movement along the chain is thermodynamically spontaneous, down a free energy gradient.

6.5c Chemiosmosis Powers ATP Synthesis by a Proton Gradient

Although the goal of cellular respiration is the synthesis of ATP, electron transport from NADH or FADH$_2$ to O$_2$ does not actually produce any ATP. Electrons are simply passed along a chain of electron carriers until they are donated to oxygen, producing water. To understand how ATP is formed let's go back and take another look at Figure 6.15, p. 126. As we have already mentioned, NADH has more free energy than O$_2$, so one can ask the question: where does this free energy go during electron transport? The energy that is released during electron transport is used to do work, specifically the work of transporting protons across the inner mitochondrial membrane from the matrix to the intermembrane space. As a consequence of this proton pumping across the inner membrane, which is essentially impermeable to protons, the H$^+$ concentration becomes much higher (and the pH lower) in the intermembrane space as compared to the matrix.

Proton translocation occurs at distinct sites along the electron transport chain (see Figure 6.15). Within complexes I and IV, specific protein components use the energy released from electron transport for proton pumping. In addition, as ubiquinone molecules accept electrons from complexes I and II, they pick up protons from the matrix. After migrating through the membrane and donating electrons to complex III, ubiquinone retains a neutral charge by releasing protons into the intermembrane space.

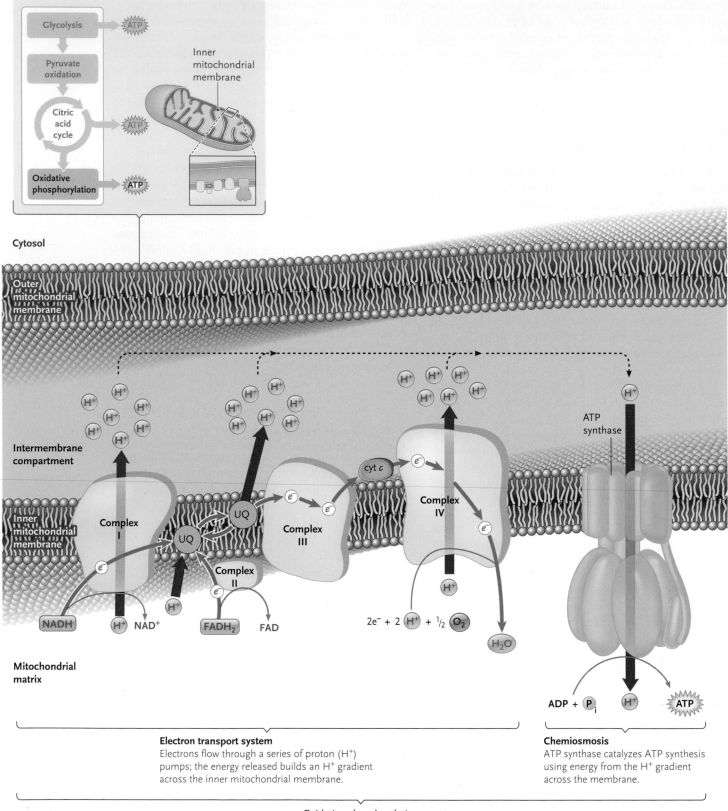

Figure 6.15

Oxidative phosphorylation: the mitochondrial electron transport chain and ATP synthase complex. The electron transfer system includes three major complexes, I, III, and IV. Two smaller electron carriers, ubiquinone (UQ) and cytochrome *c* (cyt *c*), act as shuttles between the major complexes, and succinate dehydrogenase (complex II) passes electrons to ubiquinone, bypassing complex I. Blue arrows indicate electron flow; red arrows indicate H+ movement. H+ is pumped from the matrix to the intermembrane compartment as electrons pass through complexes I and IV. H+ is also moved into the matrix by the cyclic reduction/oxidation of ubiquinone. Chemiosmotic synthesis of ATP involves the ATP synthase complex that uses the energy of the proton gradient to catalyze the synthesis of ATP.

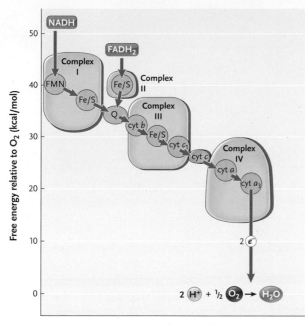

Figure 6.16

Redox components of the electron transport chain are organized from high to low free energy. Electron flow is spontaneous from high to low potential energy as electrons are passed from one redox molecule to the next.

The situation in which one side of the inner mitochondrial membrane has a higher concentration of protons than the other side represents potential energy that can be harnessed to do work. The situation is somewhat analogous to water behind a dam. The potential energy possessed by a proton gradient is derived from two factors. First, a chemical gradient exists across the membrane because the concentration of H^+ is not equal on both sides. Second, because protons are charged, there is an electrical difference, with the intermembrane compartment more positively charged than the matrix. The combination of a concentration gradient and a voltage difference across the membrane produces stored energy known as the **proton-motive force.**

Harnessing the proton-motive force to do work is referred to as **chemiosmosis.** It was first proposed as a mechanism to generate ATP by the British biochemist Peter Mitchell, who was later awarded a Nobel Prize in Chemistry for his work in this area (see *People behind Biology*). Whereas in mitochondria, the energy for chemiosmosis comes from the oxidation of energy-rich molecules such as NADH by the electron transport chain, chemiosmosis also applies to the generation of ATP in chloroplasts, where electron transport is driven by light energy. Chemiosmosis, however, does not only apply to the synthesis of ATP—the proton-motive force is also used, for example, to pump substances across membranes (see Chapter 5) and drive the rotation of flagella in bacteria.

The mode of ATP synthesis that is linked to the oxidation of energy-rich molecules by an electron transport chain is called **oxidative phosphorylation.** Compared to the substrate-level phosphorylation that occurs during glycolysis and the citric acid cycle, oxidative phosphorylation relies on the action of a large multiprotein complex that spans the inner mitochondrial membrane called **ATP synthase (Figure 6.17).**

6.5d ATP Synthase Is a Molecular Motor

ATP synthase is a lollipop-shaped complex consisting of a basal unit, which is embedded in the inner mitochondrial membrane, connected to a headpiece by a stalk (see Figure 6.17). The headpiece extends into the mitochondrial matrix. The basal unit forms a channel through which H^+ can pass freely. The proton-motive force is what propels protons in the intermembrane space through the channel in the enzyme's basal unit, down their concentration gradient, and into the matrix. Evidence indicates that the binding of individual protons to sites in the headpiece causes it to rotate in a way that catalyzes the formation of ATP from ADP and P_i. The spinning of the headpiece of ATP synthase represents the smallest molecular rotary motor known in nature.

In Chapter 5, we described active transport pumps that use energy from ATP to transport ions across membranes against their concentration gradients (see

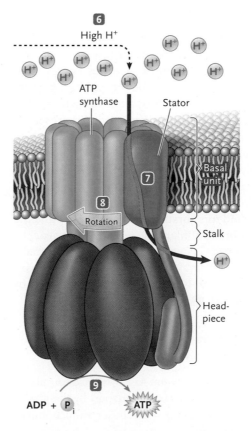

Figure 6.17

Detailed structure of ATP synthase—a molecular motor. The enzyme consists of a *basal unit*, which is embedded in the inner mitochondrial membrane, connected to a *headpiece* by a *stalk*, and with the *stator* bridging the basal unit and headpiece. Protons move through a channel between the basal unit and the stator, making the stalk and headpiece spin. This results in ATP synthesis.

Peter Mitchell was a British biochemist who in 1978 was awarded the Nobel Prize in Chemistry for what the Royal Swedish Academy of Sciences committee stated was "his contribution to the understanding of biological energy transfer through the formulation of the chemiosmotic theory."

Mitchell completed an undergraduate degree and a Ph.D. at Cambridge University, graduating with the latter in 1951. In 1955, he was invited to set up and direct a biochemical research unit in the Department of Zoology, Edinburgh University, where he was a faculty member until 1964. From 1964 onward, he was director of the Glynn Research Institute. Glynn is a mansion that Mitchell renovated and turned into a personal research institute, located near Bodmin in Cornwall, England.

By the 1950s, it was known that both the chloroplast and the mitochondrion contained electron transport chains and made ATP, but a solid theory on how the two were linked was elusive. The dominant theories were based on substrate-level phosphorylation, which was already well understood. It was thought that electron transport chains passed energy to a high-energy chemical intermediate, which, in turn, passed it on to ATP through an ATP synthase that was known to exist in both the chloroplast and the mitochondrion. But, of course, the problem was that no one could find this chemical intermediate. Moreover, the substrate-level phosphorylation idea could not explain troubling findings: Why did so many different reagents act as uncouplers? Why were the enzymes of oxidative phosphorylation associated with the mitochondrial membrane? Why did coupling seem so dependent on the maintenance of membrane structure?

Mitchell proposed the chemiosmotic theory in 1961 in an elegant paper published in *Nature*. It is hard to imagine now how revolutionary the paper was at the time. It contained very little experimental evidence and was opposed by almost the entire biochemical community, which was stuck believing in the high-energy intermediate concept. The paper was based on Mitchell's realization that the movement of ions across an electrochemical membrane potential could provide the energy needed to produce ATP. The basis of chemiosmosis is that the components of the electron transport chain are inserted into a membrane in only one way, which allows for protons to be transported in one direction during electron transport. The protons would flow back through the ATP synthase, causing synthesis of ATP. In Mitchell's model, the proton gradient across the membrane served as the high-energy intermediate—the elusive chemical intermediate could not be found because, of course, it did not exist.

Figure 5.18). An active transport pump is, in fact, an ATP synthase that is operating in reverse. It doesn't synthesize ATP but rather uses the free energy from the hydrolysis of ATP to provide the energy necessary to pump ions (such as protons) across a membrane.

Harnessing the potential energy that is present in a proton gradient to synthesize ATP is fundamental to almost all forms of life and developed early in the evolution of life. This is shown by the fact that the ATP synthase complex found in mitochondria is structurally very similar to the ATP synthase complexes found in the thylakoid membrane of the chloroplast and the plasma membrane of many bacteria and archaea.

CONCEPT FIX ATP is not a product of electron transport. Rather ATP is synthesized by chemiosmosis, which consumes the proton gradient generated by electron transport. ⬡

6.5e Electron Transport and Chemiosmosis Can Be Uncoupled

The generation of ATP by the ATP synthase complex is linked, or coupled, to electron transport by the proton gradient established across the inner mitochondrial membrane. A fundamental concept that is important to grasp is that electron transport and the chemiosmotic generation of ATP are separate and distinct processes and are not always completely coupled **(Figure 6.18).** For example, it is possible to have high rates of electron transport (and thus high rates of oxygen consumption) without the synthesis of ATP. This uncoupling of the two processes occurs when mechanisms prevent the formation of a proton-motive force. For example, a class of chemicals called ionophores form channels across membranes through which ions, including protons, can pass. Often called uncouplers, these chemicals are potentially lethal to many organisms because they allow for high rates of electron transport but prevent chemiosmotic ATP synthesis. It is interesting to note that in the 1930s, low concentrations of chemical uncouplers were commonly used as diet drugs. Although people did lose weight, overdoses resulting in death were not uncommon.

When electron transport is uncoupled from the chemiosmotic synthesis of ATP, the free energy released during electron transport is not conserved by the establishment of a proton-motive force but instead is lost as heat. Many organisms take advantage of this

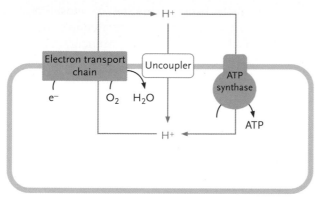

Figure 6.18

Uncoupling of electron transport and ATP synthesis. Respiratory electron transport results in the formation of a proton gradient across the membrane. Usually, this gradient is dissipated by protons flowing back to the matrix through the ATP synthase. Uncouplers, which may be specific chemicals or proteins, provide an alternative route for protons to flow back across the membrane. By circumventing the ATP synthase, no ATP is generated.

as a means of regulating body temperature by altering the expression of a group of transmembrane proteins. These *uncoupling proteins* are localized to the inner mitochondrial membrane and, similar to chemical uncouplers, form channels through which protons can freely flow. This mechanism of regulating body temperature is especially important in animals. For example, in hibernating mammals and in newborn infants, the activity of uncoupling proteins within mitochondria of brown adipose fat is an important mechanism of heat generation.

STUDY BREAK

1. Define proton-motive force, chemiosmosis, and oxidative phosphorylation.
2. What does it mean that electron transport and oxidative phosphorylation are coupled processes?

6.6 The Efficiency and Regulation of Cellular Respiration

In this section, we calculate the efficiency with which cellular respiration extracts the energy from glucose. As well, we discuss how this entire multienzyme pathway is regulated so that it remains flexible in the face of changing cellular demands for ATP and changes in food supply.

6.6a What Are the ATP Yield and Efficiency of Cellular Respiration?

Determining the total number of ATP molecules synthesized for each molecule of glucose oxidized is an important exercise that forces us to integrate all parts of the respiratory pathway. But before we look at the whole pathway, we first consider a question concerning oxidative phosphorylation: How many ATP molecules are produced by oxidative phosphorylation? Recent research suggests that for each NADH that is oxidized, and thus for each pair of electrons that travels down the electron transport chain, 10 H^+ are pumped into the inner membrane space. (Note: Don't try to figure out how you get 10 protons pumped from 2 electrons—it is not straightforward—wait until you take an advanced biochemistry course.) We also know that somewhere between 3 and 4 H^+ are needed to flow back through the ATP synthase for the synthesis of one molecule of ATP. So that gives between 2.5 and 3.3 molecules of ATP synthesized for every NADH oxidized by the electron transport chain. To make life easier, let's round off and say that for each NADH oxidized 3 ATP are synthesized. Because the oxidation of $FADH_2$ skips the proton-pumping complex I (look back at Figure 6.15, p. 126), only about two molecules of ATP are synthesized for each $FADH_2$ oxidized.

A detailed accounting of the ATP yield for each molecule of glucose oxidized is provided in **Figure 6.19, p. 130.** Recall that the products of glycolysis include two molecules of ATP and two molecules of NADH. Next, the oxidation of the two molecules of pyruvate generated by glycolysis results in the synthesis of 2 NADH. During the citric acid cycle, the two molecules of acetyl-CoA that are oxidized result in the synthesis of 2 ATP, along with 6 NADH and 2 $FADH_2$. That gives us a total of 10 NADH and 2 $FADH_2$ that can be oxidized by the electron transport chain. Recall that about 3 ATP are produced by oxidative phosphorylation for each NADH oxidized by the electron transport chain, while $FADH_2$ oxidation yields 2 ATP. So that gives a total of 34 ATP generated by oxidative phosphorylation as a result of the oxidation of 10 NADH and 2 $FADH_2$. So, adding up, we have 2 ATP from glycolysis, 2 ATP directly from the citric acid cycle, and 34 ATP from oxidative phosphorylation, yielding 38 molecules of ATP synthesized for each glucose oxidized!

The 38 ATP for each glucose oxidized is the maximum theoretical yield. There are three reasons, however, why this maximum is rarely achieved. First, while the maximum of 38 is true in bacteria, this is not the case in eukaryotic cells, where the theoretical maximum is only 36 ATP. This difference is due to the energy costs of transporting the NADH generated by glycolysis into the mitochondrion. The active transport system needed to move the electrons associated with NADH into the mitochondrion consumes 1 ATP for each molecule of NADH transported. Since 2 NADH are transported, the yield of ATP drops by two. The second reason why the yield is less than 38 ATP is that, electron transport and oxidative phosphorylation are rarely completely coupled to each other. Even under

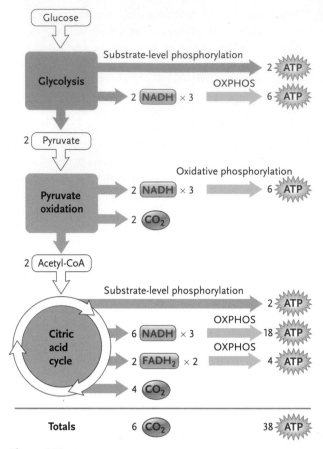

Figure 6.19

ATP yield from the oxidation of glucose. The maximum possible ATP yield from the oxidation of one molecule of glucose is 38. However, this yield is rarely achieved. (OXPHOS = Oxidative phosphorylation)

normal metabolic conditions, the inner mitochondrial membrane is somewhat leaky to protons, and thus not all the protons pumped across during electron transport pass back through the ATP synthase. Some re-enter the matrix by slowly diffusing directly through the inner mitochondrial membrane. The third reason why the theoretical maximum is not attained is that the proton-motive force generated by electron transport is used for other things besides simply generating ATP. As a source of potential energy, the proton-motive force can be harnessed to do other forms of work. For example, it is used to transport the pyruvate synthesized by glycolysis into the matrix.

So how efficient is cellular respiration at extracting the energy from glucose and converting it into ATP? We know how much energy is in glucose, but how much of that ends up in ATP? The phosphorylation of ADP to ATP requires about 7.3 kcal/mol. In eukaryotes, the theoretical maximum yield from that complete oxidation of a mole of glucose is 36 moles of ATP, so 36×7.3 gives a total of 263 kcal of energy. The complete oxidation of a mole of glucose releases exactly 686 kcal of energy. From these two numbers we can calculate the efficiency to be $263/686 \times 100 = 38\%$. In other words, 38% of the energy in glucose is converted into ATP. This may not seem amazingly high, but this value

is considerably better than that of most devices designed by human engineers—for example, an automobile extracts only about 25% of the energy in the fuel it burns. Recall from Chapter 4 that the second law of thermodynamics states that energy transformations can never be 100% efficient, as some of the energy is used to increase the entropy of the surroundings.

6.6b Fats, Proteins, and Carbohydrates Can Be Oxidized by Cellular Respiration

In addition to glucose and other six-carbon sugars, reactions leading from glycolysis through pyruvate oxidation also oxidize a range of other carbohydrates, as well as lipids and proteins, which enter the cellular respiratory pathway at various points (**Figure 6.20**).

Carbohydrates such as sucrose and other disaccharides are easily broken into monosaccharides such as glucose and fructose, which enter glycolysis at early steps. Starch is hydrolyzed by digestive enzymes into individual glucose molecules, whereas glycogen, a more complex carbohydrate, is broken down and converted by enzymes into glucose-6-phosphate, an early substrate molecule in glycolysis.

Among the fats, the triglycerides are major sources of electrons for ATP synthesis. Before entering the oxidative reactions, they are hydrolyzed into glycerol and individual fatty acids. The glycerol is converted to glyceraldehyde-3-phosphate before entering glycolysis. The fatty acids—and many other types of lipids—are split into two-carbon fragments, which enter the citric acid cycle as acetyl-CoA.

Proteins are hydrolyzed to amino acids before oxidation. The amino group ($-NH_2$) is removed, and the remainder of the molecule enters the respiratory pathway as pyruvate, acetyl units carried by coenzyme A, or intermediates of the citric acid cycle (see Figure 6.20). For example, the amino acid alanine is converted into pyruvate; leucine, into acetyl units; and phenylalanine, into fumarate, which enters the citric acid cycle.

6.6c Respiratory Intermediates Are Utilized for Anabolic Reactions

Organic molecules (carbohydrates, fats, proteins) are oxidized by cellular respiration and supply cells with the ATP required for growth and metabolism. In addition, organic molecules generated by the respiratory pathway are the carbon backbones (carbon skeletons) required to synthesize a range of essential molecules. The intermediates of glycolysis and the citric acid cycle are routinely diverted and used as the starting substrate for the anabolic pathways required to synthesize amino acids, fats, and the pyrimidine and purine bases needed for nucleic acid synthesis. As well, respiratory intermediates supply the carbon backbones for the array of hormones, growth factors, prosthetic groups, and cofactors that are essential to cell function.

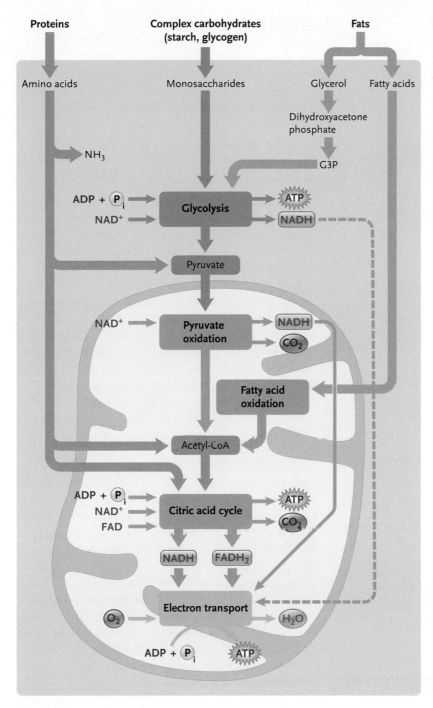

Figure 6.20

Major pathways that oxidize carbohydrates, fats, and proteins. Reactions that occur in the cytosol are shown against a tan background; reactions that occur in mitochondria are shown inside the organelle. Coenzyme A (CoA) funnels the products of many oxidative pathways into the citric acid cycle.

6.6d Cellular Respiration Is Controlled by Supply and Demand

Cellular respiration includes a large number of enzymes and transport systems and, in eukaryotic cells, numerous cellular compartments. The overall rate of cellular respiration, which is often measured as the rate of oxygen consumption, is tightly controlled so that ATP synthesis matches the requirements of the cell for chemical energy. This is an example of the concept of supply and demand—the cell does not waste valuable resources making more of a substance than it needs. Most metabolic pathways are regulated by supply and demand through the process of feedback inhibition: the end products of the pathway inhibit an enzyme early in the pathway. The concept of feedback inhibition was introduced in Chapter 4.

The rate of glucose oxidation by glycolysis is closely regulated by several mechanisms to match the cellular demands for ATP. A key enzyme early in glycolysis that is a major site of regulation is phosphofructokinase, which catalyses the conversion of fructose 6-phosphate to fructose 1,6-bisphosphate **(Figure 6.21, p. 132)**. Phosphofructokinase is an allosteric enzyme (see Chapter 4) and thus its activity can be adjusted by the binding of certain metabolic activators and inhibitors. Two of the key regulators of phosphofructokinase are ATP and AMP (adenosine monophosphate). Since ATP, ADP, and AMP are interconvertible,

$$ATP \rightleftharpoons ADP \rightleftharpoons AMP$$

That is, when ATP levels in the cell are low, ADP and AMP levels are higher, and vice versa. ATP is a known allosteric inhibitor of phosphofructokinase, so if excess ATP is present in the cytosol it binds to phosphofructokinase, inhibiting its action. The resulting decrease in the concentration of fructose 1,6-bisphosphate slows or stops the subsequent reactions of glycolysis and, as a consequence, the remainder of cellular respiration as well. The enzyme becomes active again when metabolic demands consume the excess ATP and the inhibition of phosphofructokinase is released. The increase in phosphofructokinase activity is not

The huge degree of metabolic flexibility is illustrated by the fact that many reactions illustrated in Figure 6.20 are reversible. For example, whereas fatty acids can be used as a source of energy by being oxidized to acetyl-CoA, excess acetyl-CoA can be removed from the respiration and used to synthesize the fatty acids needed for a range of cellular processes.

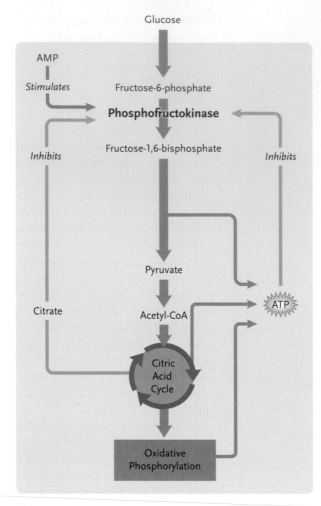

Figure 6.21

The control of cellular respiration. A major mechanism is allosteric control of the activity of the enzyme phosphofructokinase, which is found early in glycolysis. High levels of ATP and the citric acid cycle intermediate citrate allosterically inhibit phosphofructokinase. Alternatively, when ATP concentrations are low, the levels of ADP and AMP increase. AMP is an allosteric activator of the enzyme.

due solely to the release of ATP inhibition. AMP, which accumulates when ATP is being consumed for metabolism, is an allosteric activator of the enzyme (see Figure 6.21). Besides ATP and AMP, phosphofructokinase activity is also sensitive to the levels of citrate, which is the first product of the citric acid cycle. If the products of the citric acid cycle are in high demand, then citrate should not accumulate in the cell. Increased citrate concentrations suggest that the demand for ATP is low, which may occur, for example, under conditions of limited oxygen when the rate of oxidative phosphorylation is restricted. Alternatively, it may indicate that citrate is not required as a carbon skeleton for anabolic reactions. Overall, through various metabolic activators and inhibitors altering phosphofructokinase activity, the functional state of glycolysis and the citric acid cycle can be kept balanced.

Study Break

1. Give an accounting of the total ATP yield from the oxidation of a molecule of glucose.
2. Explain how the activity of the enzyme phosphofructokinase is controlled.

6.7 Oxygen and Cellular Respiration

A constant supply of oxygen is required to maintain the high rates of oxidative phosphorylation necessary to supply cells with sufficient ATP. Although humans need an almost constant supply of oxygen, other organisms can survive and even thrive in the absence of oxygen. There are two general mechanisms by which certain cells can oxidize fuel molecules and generate ATP in the absence of oxygen: fermentation and anaerobic respiration. The distinction between these two processes is that fermentation does not utilize an electron transport chain, whereas anaerobic respiration uses an electron transport chain that employs a molecule other than oxygen as the terminal electron acceptor.

6.7a In Eukaryotic Cells, Low Oxygen Levels Result in Fermentation

Following glycolysis, in eukaryotic cells cellular respiration can continue along one of two distinct pathways depending on whether or not oxygen is present **(Figure 6.22).** When oxygen is plentiful, the pyruvate and NADH produced by glycolysis are transported into the mitochondrion, where they are oxidized using the citric acid cycle and the electron transport chain. If, instead, oxygen is absent or in short supply, the pyruvate remains in the cytosol, where it is reduced, consuming the NADH generated by glycolysis by a series of reactions that are called **fermentation.**

Two types of fermentation reactions exist: lactate fermentation and alcohol fermentation. In **lactate fermentation,** pyruvate is converted into the three carbon compound lactate, which **(Figure 6.23a).** Occurs in many bacteria, in some plant tissues, and in certain animal tissues such as skeletal muscle cells. When vigorous contraction of muscle cells calls for more oxygen than the circulating blood can supply, lactate fermentation takes place. For example, lactate accumulates in the leg muscles of a sprinter during a 100 m race. The lactate temporarily stores electrons, and when the oxygen content of the muscle cells returns to normal levels, the reverse of the reaction in Figure 6.23a regenerates pyruvate and NADH. The pyruvate can then be used in the second stage of cellular respiration, and the NADH contributes its electron pair to the electron transfer system. Lactate is also the fermentation product of some bacteria; the sour taste of buttermilk, yogurt, and dill pickles is a sign of their activity.

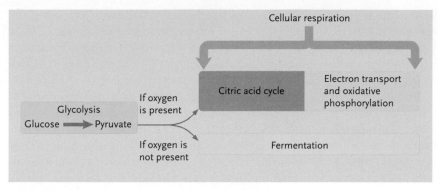

Figure 6.22

The metabolic path of pyruvate oxidation depends upon the presence of oxygen.

Alcohol fermentation (Figure 6.23b) occurs in microorganisms such as yeasts, which are single-celled fungi. In this reaction, pyruvate is oxidized in two successive reactions to a molecule of CO_2 and a molecule of ethyl alcohol as NADH is converted to NAD^+. Alcoholic fermentation by yeasts has widespread commercial applications. Bakers use the yeast *Saccharomyces cerevisiae* to make bread dough rise. They mix the yeast with a small amount of sugar and blend the mixture into the dough, where oxygen levels are low. As the yeast cells convert the sugar into ethyl alcohol and CO_2, the gaseous CO_2 expands and creates bubbles that cause the dough to rise. Oven heat evaporates the alcohol and causes further expansion of the bubbles, producing a light-textured product. Alcoholic fermentation is also the mainstay of

beer and wine brewing. Fruits are a natural home to wild yeasts **(Figure 6.24, p. 134)**; for example, winemakers rely on a mixture of wild and cultivated yeasts to produce wine. Alcoholic fermentation also occurs naturally in the environment; for example, overripe or rotting fruit will frequently start to ferment, and birds that eat the fruit may become too drunk to fly.

Overall, the reactions of fermentation play a critical role whenever organisms are exposed to conditions in which the oxygen concentration is too low to support oxidative phosphorylation. By consuming the NADH generated by glycolysis, fermentation reactions keep cytosolic NAD^+ levels high. This is of critical metabolic importance because NAD^+ is required for glycolysis (look back at figure 6.10 step 6). As long as there is sufficient NAD^+, glycolysis will continue to operate and generate ATP.

6.7b In Anaerobic Respiration, the Terminal Electron Acceptor Is Not Oxygen

Although they lack mitochondria, many bacteria and archaea have respiratory electron transport chains that are located on internal membrane systems derived

a. Lactate fermentation

b. Alcoholic fermentation

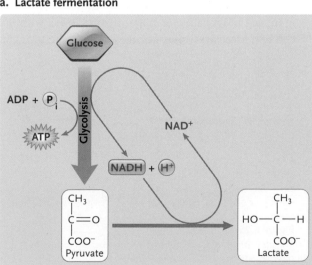

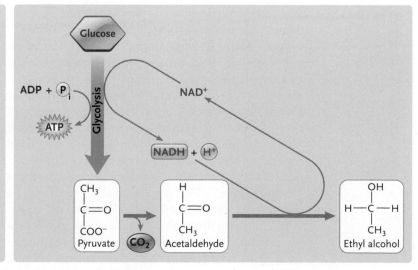

Figure 6.23

Fermentation reactions that produce (a) lactate and (b) ethyl alcohol. The fermentations, which occur in the cytosol, convert NADH to NAD^+, allowing the electron carrier to cycle back to glycolysis. This process keeps glycolysis running, with continued production of ATP.

Figure 6.24
Alcoholic fermentation in nature: wild yeast cells, visible as a dustlike coating on grapes.

from the plasma membrane. Some of these electron transport systems are very similar to those found in the mitochondria of eukaryotes and use O_2 as the terminal electron acceptor. Other bacteria and archaea, however, have respiratory chains that use a molecule other than O_2 as the terminal electron acceptor and are said to possess anaerobic (*an* = without; *aero* = air) respiration. Instead of O_2, sulfate (SO_4^{2-}), nitrate (NO_3^-), and the ferric ion (Fe^{3+}) are commonly used terminal electron acceptors. Generally, there is a huge diversity of molecules that have a high affinity for electrons that can be used as electron acceptors; likewise, a range of molecules besides glucose contain high amounts of chemical potential energy that can be used as substrates for cellular respiration. Even though the starting and ending points of cellular respiration may be different, cells are still able to use electron transport chains to create a proton-motive force that drives the synthesis of ATP. The advantage that aerobic respiration has, and the reason that it evolved to be the dominant form of respiratory metabolism, is that the affinity of oxygen for electrons is greater than that of many of the other electron acceptors; the consequence of this was increased efficiency at converting the energy in food molecules into ATP.

6.6c Organisms Differ with Respect to Their Ability to Use Oxygen

We can differentiate three different lifestyles depending on the requirements of an organism for oxygen. Many archaea, many bacteria, and most eukaryotes are **strict aerobes**—they have an absolute requirement for oxygen to survive and are unable to live solely by fermentation. To understand why this is, look back at Figure 6.19, p. 130. In the absence of oxygen, ATP is generated solely by substrate-level phosphorylation during glycolysis: 2 ATP generated for every glucose oxidized. By comparison, in the presence of oxygen, up to 38 ATP can be generated—that's 19 times more ATP for each glucose oxidized. As shown in Figure 6.19, p. 130, the difference is explained by the huge ATP yield of oxidative phosphorylation. Humans and other animals are especially sensitive to low oxygen environments because certain tissues, such as brain cells, have a huge energy requirement that is only met by constant and high rates of oxidative phosphorylation.

Other organisms, called **facultative anaerobes**, can switch between fermentation and full oxidative pathways, depending on the oxygen supply. Facultative anaerobes include *Escherichia coli*, the bacterium that inhabits the digestive tract of humans; the *Lactobacillus* bacteria used to produce buttermilk and yogurt; and *S. cerevisiae*, the yeast used in brewing and baking. Many cell types in higher organisms, including vertebrate muscle cells, are also facultatively anaerobic. Lastly, some bacteria, some archaea, and a few fungi are classified as **strict anaerobes** because they require an oxygen-free environment to survive. Strict anaerobes gain ATP from either fermentation or anaerobic respiration. Among these organisms are the bacteria that cause botulism, tetanus, and some other serious diseases. For example, the bacterium that causes botulism thrives in the oxygen-free environment of canned foods that prevents the growth of most other microorganisms.

6.7d The Paradox of Aerobic Life Is That Oxygen Is Essential and Toxic

As we mentioned above, some bacteria and archaea are strict anaerobes—they cannot live in an oxygen environment. But why can't they? Lacking the ability to use O_2 as an electron acceptor is one thing, but actually dying in the presence of O_2? The reason that strict anaerobes die in an oxygen environment is related to what is often called the *paradox of aerobic life:* although oxygen is absolutely essential to the survival of many organisms, oxygen is also potentially toxic.

It takes four electrons to completely reduce a molecule of O_2 to water **(Figure 6.25).** Partially reduced forms of O_2 are formed when O_2 accepts fewer electrons, producing what are called *reactive oxygen species* (ROS). These molecules, which include the compounds superoxide and hydrogen peroxide (see Figure 6.25), are powerful oxidizing molecules and readily remove electrons from proteins, lipids, and DNA, resulting in oxidative damage. If ROS levels within a cell are excessive, their strong oxidizing nature can

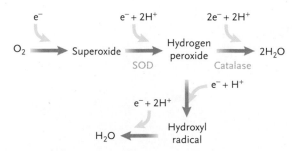

Figure 6.25
The conversion of O_2 to water is a four-electron reduction. If this occurs stepwise, it results in the formation of intermediates called reactive oxygen species (ROS), which are potentially harmful. Aerobic cells contain the enzymes superoxide dismutase (SOD) and catalase, which together quickly convert superoxide and hydrogen peroxide to water.

result in the destruction of many biological molecules and can be lethal. Because most cells contain an abundance of both O_2 and electron rich molecules (e.g. proteins, lipids, nucleic acids) the formation of ROS is a consequence of aerobic life that cannot be avoided.

To survive in an oxygen-rich environment, aerobic organisms have evolved an antioxidant defence system that includes both enzymes and nonenzyme molecules that have the role of intercepting and inactivating reactive oxygen molecules as they are produced within cells. Two of the major ROS-scavenging enzymes are superoxide dismutase and catalase (see Figure 6.25). Working in concert, superoxide dismutase converts the superoxide anion to hydrogen peroxide, which in turn is reduced to water by the action of catalase. In addition to enzymes, many cells have a range of antioxidants, including vitamin C and vitamin E, which act as reducing agents, safely and rapidly reducing reactive oxygen compounds to water. In recent years, excessive ROS formation has been implicated in a wide variety of degenerative diseases, including Parkinson's disease and Alzheimer dementia. In fact, it is thought that the progressive buildup of oxidative damage may underlie the aging process itself. This, in part, explains the huge interest in the possible protective value of a wide variety of antioxidant compounds, particularly those from certain fruits and vegetables.

So why do strict anaerobes die in the presence of oxygen? For one group, their inability to live in an oxygen environment is because they lack one or both of the enzymes superoxide dismutase and catalase, which results in a buildup of toxic reactive oxygen species within their cells if they were exposed to oxygen. Interestingly, some strict anaerobes do contain these enzymes, which are highly expressed when cells are placed in an oxygen environment. The inability of this second group of anaerobes to survive in an oxygen environment seems to be linked to oxygen itself inhibiting key metabolic enzymes.

As discussed in the last section, oxidative phosphorylation generates much more ATP than the substrate-level phosphorylation that takes place during glycolysis and the citric acid cycle. From this it is clear that the evolution of the electron transport system with oxygen as the terminal electron acceptor enabled

MOLECULE BEHIND BIOLOGY 6.2
Cyanide

Cyanide is an ion that consists of a carbon atom triple-bonded to an atom of nitrogen ($C \equiv N^-$). It is a very toxic metabolic poison acting as an irreversible inhibitor of the terminal enzyme of respiratory electron transport, cytochrome oxidase. By binding to the iron atom of the heme prosthetic groups in the enzyme, cyanide prevents electron flow to O_2, essentially inhibiting electron transport and subsequent chemiosmosis. Acute cyanide poisoning can result in death within minutes of exposure.

Cyanide is produced in small amounts by a range of microorganisms and is found in small amounts in apple seeds, almonds, and the pits of fruits such as peaches. In some plants, the production of cyanide in a form bound to sugars is thought to be a deterrent to herbivory. The presence of cyanide in the potato-like root of the cassava plant is of concern because it is a staple food in a number of tropical countries. The presence of cyanide glycosides is diminished by extensive soaking and cooking of the cassava root, but health problems associated with chronic cyanide poisoning remain quite common.

Cyanide has clear applications in a range of industries but especially in electroplating, metallurgy, and mining owing to the high solubility of gold $[Au(CN)_2]^-$ and silver $[Ag(CN)_2]^-$ cyanides in water. For these purposes, approximately 500 000 tonnes of highly toxic sodium cyanide are produced each year. In gold mining, the addition of a solution of sodium cyanide to ore containing low amounts of gold is effective at extracting the gold by bringing the gold into solution. The resulting formation of huge amounts of cyanide-contaminated water makes this form of gold mining highly controversial, yet it remains a very effective and cheap method of extraction.

In addition to a respiratory electron transport chain that is inhibited by cyanide, plants contain a pathway of electron transport that is resistant to cyanide. Instead of using cytochrome oxidase, this second pathway of respiration uses a terminal oxidase called the alternative oxidase. This alternative pathway of respiration is not linked to proton pumping like the normal respiratory chain; instead, electron flow simply generates heat. Intestinally, high levels of alternative oxidase in the flowers of some plant species are used to volatilize attractants for pollinators. This includes the aptly named skunk cabbage, which tells you that the attractants for pollinators are not necessarily pleasant.

In addition to being found in all plants, the alternative oxidase has been found in algae, some fungi, and, recently, some animal phyla. The physiological role of cyanide-resistant respiration in these species is being actively investigated by a number of research groups.

cells to extract far more energy from food molecules than other modes of metabolism. However, the evolution of the aerobic lifestyle required the development of antioxidants and enzymes such as catalase and superoxide dismutase to combat the harmful effects of oxygen, which include the inevitable formation of reactive oxygen species. In addition, it required that cytochrome oxidase, the last enzyme of the mitochondrial electron transport chain, develop a remarkable mode of catalysis. Looking back at Figure 6.15, p. 126, notice that the cytochrome oxidase complex donates electrons from the electron carrier cytochrome c to O_2. However, it does so in a way that, remarkably, leads to essentially no reactive oxygen generation. The enzyme is structurally quite complex, containing four redox centres (two hemes and two copper ions), each of which can store a single electron. When all centres are reduced, the enzyme simultaneously transfers all four electrons to O_2, producing two molecules of water. That cytochrome oxidase is the only enzyme that aerobic organisms, from bacterial to human, use as the terminal complex of electron transport indicates the chemical difficulty of carrying out the transfer of electrons to O_2 in a safe and controlled manner. Given that this single enzyme handles approximately 98% of the oxygen we metabolize, if the reaction resulted in significant amounts of partially reduced forms of oxygen (e.g., superoxide, hydrogen peroxide), aerobic life as we know it would have probably never evolved.

Review

Access an interactive eBook, chapter-specific interactive learning tools, including flashcards, quizzes, videos, and more in your Biology **CourseMate**, accessed through NelsonBrain.com **Aplia™** is an online interactive learning solution that helps you improve comprehension—and your grade—by integrating a variety of mediums and tools such as videos, tutorials, practice tests, and an interactive eBook.

6.1 The Chemical Basis of Cellular Respiration

- Glucose, like gasoline, is a good fuel because of the presence of C—H bonds, which contain electrons that can be easily removed and used to do work (see Figure 6.2).

- Oxidation–reduction reactions, called redox reactions, partially or completely transfer electrons from donor to acceptor atoms; the donor is oxidized as it releases electrons, and the acceptor is reduced (see Figure 6.4).

- Almost all organisms obtain energy for cellular activities through cellular respiration, the process of transferring electrons from donor organic molecules to a final acceptor molecule such as oxygen; the energy that is released drives ATP synthesis.

6.2 Cellular Respiration: An Overview

- Cellular respiration occurs in three stages: (1) in glycolysis, glucose is converted to two molecules of pyruvate; (2) in pyruvate oxidation and the citric acid cycle, pyruvate is converted to an acetyl compound that is oxidized completely to CO_2; and (3) in oxidative phosphorylation, high-energy electrons produced from the first two stages pass along an electron transport chain, with the energy released being used to establish a proton gradient across the membrane. This gradient is used to synthesize ATP (see Figure 6.7).

- Both eukaryotes and prokaryotes may undergo cellular respiration. In eukaryotes, however, most of the reactions of cellular respiration occur in mitochondria (see Figure 6.8).

6.3 Glycolysis: The Splitting of Glucose

- In glycolysis, which occurs in the cytosol, glucose (six carbons) is oxidized into two molecules of pyruvate (three carbons each). Electrons removed in the oxidation are delivered to NAD^+, producing NADH. The reaction sequence produces a net gain of two ATP, two NADH, and two pyruvate molecules for each molecule of glucose oxidized (see Figures 6.9 and 6.10).

- ATP molecules produced in the energy-releasing steps of glycolysis result from substrate-level phosphorylation, an enzyme-catalyzed reaction that transfers a phosphate group from a substrate to ADP (see Figure 6.11).

6.4 Pyruvate Oxidation and the Citric Acid Cycle

- In pyruvate oxidation, which occurs inside mitochondria, one pyruvate (three carbons) is oxidized to one acetyl group (two carbons) and 1 CO_2. Electrons removed in the oxidation are accepted by 1 NAD^+ to produce 1 NADH. The acetyl group is transferred to coenzyme A, which carries it to the citric acid cycle (see Figure 6.12).

- In the citric acid cycle, which occurs in the matrix of the mitochondrion, acetyl groups are oxidized completely to CO_2. Electrons removed in the oxidation are accepted by NAD^+ or FAD, and substrate-level phosphorylation produces ATP. For each acetyl group oxidized by the cycle, 2 CO_2, 1 ATP, 3 NADH, and 1 $FADH_2$ are produced (see Figures 6.13 and 6.14).

6.5 Oxidative Phosphorylation: Electron Transport and Chemiosmosis

- Electrons are passed from NADH and $FADH_2$ to the electron transport chain, which consists of four major protein complexes and two smaller shuttle carriers. As the electrons flow from one carrier to the next through the system, some of their energy is used by the complexes to pump protons across the inner mitochondrial membrane (see Figure 6.15).

- Two major protein complexes (I and IV) and the reduction/oxidation of ubiquinone contribute to the pumping of protons from the matrix to the intermembrane compartment, generating a proton gradient with a high concentration in the intermembrane compartment and a low concentration in the matrix.

- The proton gradient produced by the electron transfer system is used by ATP synthase as an energy source for synthesis of ATP from ADP and P_i. The ATP synthase is embedded in the inner mitochondrial membrane together with the electron transport chain (see Figure 6.17).

- Electron transport and the chemiosmotic synthesis of ATP are distinct and separate processes that are usually linked, or coupled, by the proton gradient. The complete uncoupling of the two results in high rates of electron transport (and oxygen consumption), without chemiosmotic ATP synthesis. Uncoupling results in heat generation (see Figure 6.18).

6.6 The Efficiency and Regulation of Cellular Respiration

- An estimated 3 ATP are synthesized as each electron pair travels from NADH to oxygen through the mitochondrial electron transport chain; about 2 ATP are synthesized as each electron pair travels through the system from $FADH_2$ to oxygen.

- In glycolysis, 2 ATP and 2 NADH are synthesized; during the oxidation of pyruvate and the citric acid cycle, 2 ATP, 8 NADH, and 2 $FADH_2$ are produced. That gives a total of 10 NADH and 2 $FADH_2$ that are oxidized by the electron transport chain, leading to the synthesis of about 34 ATP. This gives a total theoretical maximum ATP yield for each glucose oxidized of 38. For a number of reasons this maximum yield is rarely reached.

- The efficiency with which the energy in glucose is conserved in the synthesis of ATP is about 30% (see Figure 6.19).

- Besides simple sugars, energy can be extracted from fats, proteins and carbohydrates that enter the respiratory chain at different points (see Figure 6.20).

- A number of different molecules can activate and repress key steps of the respiratory pathway so that it can be controlled by supply and demand (see Figure 6.21).

6.7 Oxygen and Cellular Respiration

- Fermentation is a pathway of respiration that oxidizes fuel molecules in the absence of oxygen and does not involve oxidative phosphorylation (see Figure 6.22).

- During fermentation, pyruvate reduction in the cytosol consumes NADH. In so doing, NAD^+ is produced, which is required as a substrate for glycolysis. This allows glycolysis to continue to run, producing ATP by substrate-level phosphorylation (see Figure 6.23).

- In organisms with anaerobic respiratory pathways, the terminal electron acceptor of electron transport is a molecule other than oxygen. Anaerobic respiratory pathways are found only in archaea and bacteria.

- Many archaea, bacteria, and eukaryotes are strict aerobes. They have an absolute requirement for oxygen because they require the high-ATP yield of oxidative phosphorylation.

- Facultative aerobes can grow in the presence of oxygen and can grow in the absence of oxygen using fermentative pathways.

- Strict anaerobes cannot grow in the presence of oxygen.

- Although oxygen is required for aerobic life, paradoxically, oxygen is toxic to cells. Reactive oxygen species (ROS) are partially reduced forms of oxygen that can damage cells. The formation of ROS by the respiratory pathway is unavoidable (see Figure 6.24).

- Cells are protected from the toxicity of oxygen by both enzymatic and nonenzymatic antioxidants that detoxify ROS.

Questions

Self-Test Questions

1. Which of the following is found in organic molecules that are good fuels?
   a. Many C–H bonds
   b. Many C=C double bonds
   c. An abundance of oxygen
   d. A high molecular weight

2. Which of the following general statements about cellular respiration is correct?
   a. in cellular respiration oxygen is used as an electron donor
   b. since bacteria lack mitochondria, they do not perform cellular respiration.
   c. cellular respiration represents a series of reactions in which a carbon substrate is oxidized.
   d. the carbon dioxide produced during cellular respiration can be used as an energy source for metabolism.

3. Which of the following processes occurs during glycolysis?
   a. the oxidation of pyruvate.
   b. the reduction of glucose.
   c. oxidative phosphorylation.
   d. substrate-level phosphorylation.

4. Which of the following is an accurate statement about the proton-motive force?
   a. it needs to be high to synthesize ATP during the citric acid cycle.
   b. if protons were uncharged the proton motive force would be zero.
   c. along with multicellularity, it was a key development in eukaryotic cells.
   d. it represents the energy associated with a proton gradient across a membrane.

5. You are reading this text while breathing in oxygen and breathing out carbon dioxide. What two processes are the sources of the carbon dioxide?
   a. glycolysis and pyruvate oxidation
   b. glycolysis and oxidative phosphorylation
   c. pyruvate oxidation and the citric acid cycle
   d. citric acid cycle and oxidative phosphorylation

6. Under conditions of low oxygen, what key role is played by fermentation in overall metabolism?
   a. it regenerates the NAD^+ required for glycolysis.
   b. it synthesizes additional NADH for the citric acid cycle.
   c. it allows for pyruvate to be oxidized in mitochondria.
   d. by activating oxidative phosphorylation, it allows for the synthesis of extra ATP.

7. In cellular respiration, what does the term *uncoupled* specifically refer to?
   a. when the two parts of glycolysis are running independently of each other.
   b. when respiratory electron transport is operating, but chemiosmosis is inhibited.
   c. when respiratory electron transport is operating, but proton pumping is inhibited.
   d. when oxidative phosphorylation is occurring, but the proton-motive force remains high.

8. Phosphofructokinase (PFK) is regulated by a number of metabolites. Besides the ones mentioned in the text, which one of the following would also make sense?
   a. Pyruvate could function as an activator of PFK.
   b. Glucose could function as an inhibitor of PFK.
   c. ADP could function as an activator of PFK.
   d. Acetyl-CoA could act as an activator of PFK.

9. The breakdown of fats releases fatty acids. In what form do the carbon molecules enter the respiratory pathway?
   a. as NADH
   b. a glucose
   c. as pyruvate
   d. as citrate
   e. as acetyl-CoA

10. Which of the following statements about the "paradox of aerobic life" is correct?
   a. Humans are completely protected from the toxic effects of oxygen.
   b. Hydrogen peroxide is formed with a single electron is donated to O_2.
   c. Cytochrome oxidase is a major source of reactive oxygen species.
   d. Strict anaerobes often lack the enzymes superoxide dismutase and/or catalase.

Questions for Discussion

1. Respond to this statement: Respiration occurs in animals but not in plants.

2. In your opinion, are fermentations part of cellular respiration? Why or why not?

3. Why do you think nucleic acids are not oxidized extensively as a cellular energy source?

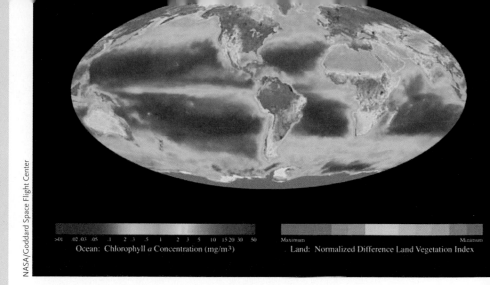

False-colour image estimating global marine and terrestrial photoautotroph abundance. Estimates of surface chlorophyll were achieved using data collected by the GeoEye Orb View-2 satellite (SeaWiFS project) and NASA/Goddard Space Flight Center.

Ocean: Chlorophyll a Concentration (mg/m³)

Land: Normalized Difference Land Vegetation Index

NASA/Goddard Space Flight Center

STUDY PLAN

7.1   Photosynthesis: An Overview

7.1a   Photosynthesis Can Be Divided into the Light Reactions and CO_2 Fixation

7.1b   In Eukaryotes, Photosynthesis Takes Place in Chloroplasts

7.2   The Photosynthetic Apparatus

7.2a   Electrons in Pigment Molecules Absorb Light Energy

7.2b   Chlorophylls and Carotenoids Cooperate in Light Absorption

7.2c   Photosynthetic Pigments Are Organized into Photosystems

7.2d   Photosystem II Uses Light Energy to Extract Electrons from Water

7.3   The Light Reactions

7.3a   Photosynthetic Electron Transport Synthesizes NADPH and Generates a Proton Gradient

7.3b   Light Is Used Specifically to Oxidize Chlorophyll

7.3c   In the Light Reactions, ATP Is Generated by Chemiosmosis

7.3d   The Stoichiometry of Linear Electron Transport

7.3e   Cyclic Electron Transport Generates ATP in the Absence of NADPH

7.4   The Calvin Cycle

7.4a   The Calvin Cycle Reduces Carbon Dioxide to a Carbohydrate

7.4b   G3P Is the Starting Point for the Synthesis of Many Other Organic Molecules

7.4c   Rubisco Is the Most Abundant Protein on Earth

7.5   Photorespiration and CO_2-Concentrating Mechanisms

7.5a   Rubisco Is an Ancient Enzyme That Is Inhibited by Oxygen

7.5b   Algae Pump Carbon Dioxide into Their Cells

7.5c   High Temperatures Exacerbate Photorespiration

7.5d C_4 Plants Spatially Separate the C_4 Pathway and the Calvin Cycle

7.5e   CAM Plants Temporally Separate the C_4 Pathway and the Calvin Cycle

7.6   Photosynthesis and Cellular Respiration Compared

7   Photosynthesis

WHY IT MATTERS

Earth can be considered a giant photoreceptor—a massive harvester of sunlight. Life on Earth depends entirely on energy from the Sun, not only to keep the planet at a suitable temperature but also to provide the energy required to sustain life. The energy of the Sun is actively captured by chlorophyll and related pigments present in photosynthetic organisms found in both terrestrial and aquatic habitats. This captured light energy is used to convert carbon dioxide into complex energy-rich molecules.

The amount of carbon dioxide that is converted into organic molecules by photosynthesis is staggering—approximately 11×10^{13} kg of carbon per year. And although we often think about photosynthesis in terms of plants and trees, about half of this carbon is fixed by photosynthetic microorganisms called phytoplankton that inhabit marine environments.

Looking at photosynthesis on a global scale (see opening figure), you may notice that, surprisingly, the abundance of phytoplankton (as estimated by chlorophyll concentration) is very low in the temperate regions of the Pacific and Atlantic oceans and higher as you move nearer the poles, especially the Arctic. The explanation for this distribution is that although the waters near the equator are warmer, which should increase phytoplankton growth, they are nutrient poor, being especially deficient in iron. By comparision, the waters around the poles are nutrient rich and support a large phytoplankton biomass.

As energy flows from the Sun through photosynthetic organisms to animals and to decomposers, the organic molecules made by photosynthesis are broken down into inorganic molecules again, and the chemical energy captured in photosynthesis is released as heat energy. Because the reactions capturing light energy are the first step on this pathway, photosynthesis is the vital link between the energy of sunlight and the vast majority of living organisms.

After an overview of photosynthesis, this chapter lays out the underlying chemistry of photosynthesis as well as the photophysical process of light absorption. These topics follow from the more cursory treatment found in Chapter 1. As well, the discussion of oxidation–reduction reactions and energy follows from their introduction in Chapters 4 and 6. Details of the two stages of photosynthesis, the light reactions and the Calvin cycle, are followed by a discussion of how various photosynthetic organisms have evolved mechanisms to cope with the problem of photorespiration. The chapter ends with an important section on comparing photosynthesis with the topic of the last chapter, cellular respiration.

7.1 Photosynthesis: An Overview

We can define **photosynthesis** as the conversion of carbon dioxide into organic molecules using light energy. Photosynthetic organisms are called **autotrophs** (*auto* = self, *trophos* = feeding) because they make all of their required organic molecules from carbon dioxide. While some autotrophs, called chemoautotrophs, use inorganic compounds as the source of energy, photosynthetic organisms use light energy to synthesize organic molecules and are thus classified as **photoautotrophs.**

Photoautotrophic organisms are known as Earth's *primary producers* **(Figure 7.1)**. This is because not only are the organic molecules synthesized by photosynthesis used by photosynthetic organisms, but also they represent the source of organic molecules for *consumers,* the animals that live by eating plants or other animals. Eventually, the bodies of both primary producers and consumers provide chemical energy for bacteria, fungi, and other *decomposers*. Recall from Chapter 3 that consumers and decomposers that require an already synthesized source of organic molecules to live are classified as **heterotrophs.**

Photosynthesis is found in the domains Bacteria and Eukarya but is not present in the Archaea.

Figure 7.1
Examples of photoautotrophs.

As discussed in Chapter 1, Archaea, including halobacteria, do harvest light energy and convert it into chemical energy. But since this light energy is not used to convert carbon dioxide into carbohydrate (sugars), it is not referred to as photosynthesis. It is more broadly defined as **phototrophy**, which includes any process that converts light energy into chemical energy.

7.1a Photosynthesis Can Be Divided into the Light Reactions and the Calvin Cycle

The conversion of carbon dioxide into carbohydrates that defines photosynthesis requires the integration of two distinct processes **(Figure 7.2)**: the light reactions and the Calvin cycle. The light reactions involve the

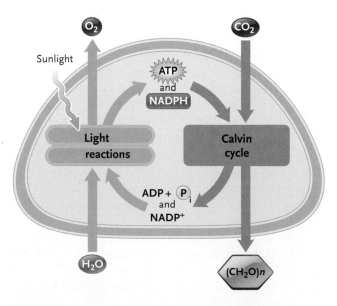

Figure 7.2
The light reactions and the Calvin cycle are the two stages of photosynthesis. The two are linked together by reactants and products. Both processes occur in the chloroplasts of photoautotrophic eukaryotes (plants and algae) as well as in photosynthetic bacteria.

capture of light energy by pigment molecules and the utilization of that energy to synthesize both NADPH (nicotinamide adenine dinucleotide phosphate) and ATP. In the Calvin cycle, the electrons and protons carried by NADPH and the energy of ATP are used to convert CO_2 into an organic form (a carbohydrate). This conversion, which is often referred to as *carbon fixation or CO₂ fixation,* is a reduction reaction with electrons (and protons) being added to CO_2. A common organic molecule formed by the reduction of CO_2 is a carbohydrate, which consists of carbon, hydrogen, and oxygen atoms in the ratio 1C:2H:1O:

$$CO_2 + H^+ + e^- \rightarrow (CH_2O)_n$$

Carbohydrate units are often symbolized as $(CH_2O)_n$, with the n indicating that different carbohydrates are formed from different multiples of the carbohydrate unit.

In most photosynthetic organisms, including plants, algae, and cyanobacteria, the source of the electrons required for CO_2 fixation is water. Recall from Chapter 3 that this is referred to as *oxygenic photosynthesis* because O_2 is produced as a by-product by the light-dependent splitting of water:

$$2H_2O + \text{light energy} \rightarrow 4H^+ + 4e^- + O_2$$

Three-carbon sugars are the major direct product of the Calvin cycle. These can be readily combined to form six-carbon monosaccharides, including glucose. Combining the two reactions above and multiplying through by six to produce a single molecule of glucose gives the overall balanced equation for photosynthesis as

$$6CO_2 + 12H_2O \rightarrow C_6H_{12}O_6 + 6O_2 + 6H_2O.$$

Although glucose is the major product of photosynthesis, it is important to realize that the reduced carbon produced by photosynthesis is also the source of the carbon for a huge range of other molecules, including lipids, proteins, and nucleic acids. In fact, one can consider all the organic molecules present in organisms as direct or indirect products of photosynthesis.

7.1b In Eukaryotes, Photosynthesis Takes Place in Chloroplasts

In photosynthetic eukaryotes, both the light reactions and the Calvin cycle take place within the chloroplast, a membrane-bound organelle that is formed from three membranes that define three distinct compartments **(Figure 7.3).** An *outer membrane* covers the entire surface of the organelle, whereas an *inner membrane* lies just inside the outer membrane. Between the outer and inner membranes is the *intermembrane compartment.* The aqueous environment within the inner membrane is the *stroma* of the chloroplast. Within the

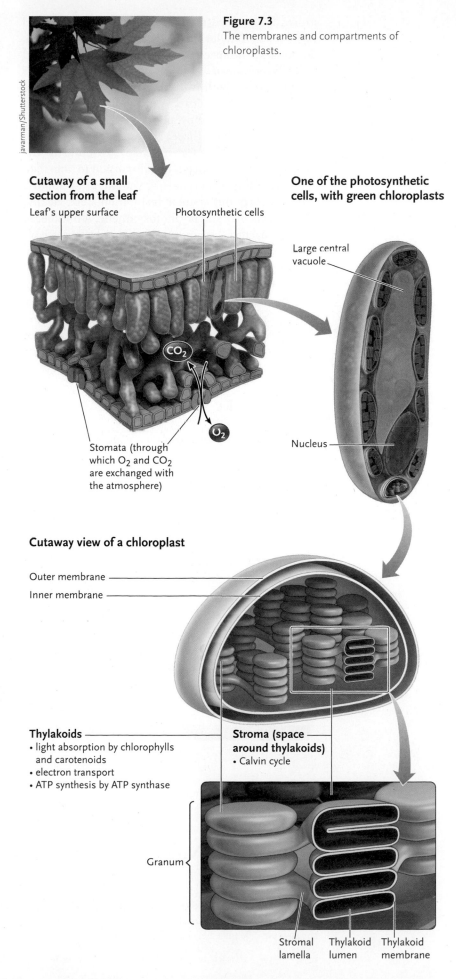

Figure 7.3
The membranes and compartments of chloroplasts.

javarman/Shutterstock

Cutaway of a small section from the leaf

Leaf's upper surface

Photosynthetic cells

CO_2

O_2

Stomata (through which O_2 and CO_2 are exchanged with the atmosphere)

One of the photosynthetic cells, with green chloroplasts

Large central vacuole

Nucleus

Cutaway view of a chloroplast

Outer membrane
Inner membrane

Thylakoids
• light absorption by chlorophylls and carotenoids
• electron transport
• ATP synthesis by ATP synthase

Stroma (space around thylakoids)
• Calvin cycle

Granum

Stromal lamella

Thylakoid lumen

Thylakoid membrane

stroma is the third membrane system, the *thylakoid membranes,* or thylakoids, which often form flattened, closed sacs. The space enclosed by a thylakoid is called the *thylakoid lumen.*

Embedded within the thylakoid membrane are the components that carry out the light reactions of photosynthesis: proteins, pigments, electron transfer carriers, and ATP synthase. The enzymes that catalyze the reactions of the Calvin cycle are found in the stroma of the chloroplast. It is important to note that, in the same way that organisms without mitochondria may still carry out cellular respiration, cells lacking chloroplasts may still be photosynthetic. A number of phyla of bacteria, including the cyanobacteria, have thylakoid membranes that are formed from infoldings of the plasma membrane and carry out carbon fixation in the cytosol of the cell. In most ways, photosynthesis carried out in cyanobacteria is biochemically identical to that found in the chloroplasts of plant leaves and is part of the evidence that indicates that chloroplasts are descended from free-living cyanobacteria (see Chapter 3).

STUDY BREAK

1. Why are photoautotrophs considered primary producers?
2. What is meant by the term *carbon fixation?*

7.2 The Photosynthetic Apparatus

Photosynthesis is initiated by light absorption by pigment molecules that are bound precisely to specific proteins. Together, these pigment–protein complexes are the basis of a sophisticated photochemical apparatus termed the *photosystem.*

7.2a Electrons in Pigment Molecules Absorb Light Energy

Photosynthesis requires the capture and utilization of light energy. As we did in Chapter 1, we can define light as that portion of the electromagnetic spectrum that humans can detect with their eyes **(Figure 7.4)**. The various forms of radiation that make up the electromagnetic spectrum differ in wavelength, ranging from very long radio waves, which have wavelengths in the range of 10 m to hundreds of kilometres, to gamma rays, which have wavelengths in the range of one hundredth to one millionth of a nanometre. The electromagnetic radiation that humans can detect (light or visible light) has wavelengths between about 400 nm, seen as blue light, and 700 nm, seen as red light (see Figure 7.4).

Although light can be described using the concept of a wave moving through space, the interaction of light with matter is best understood in terms of discrete packets of energy called photons (also called a

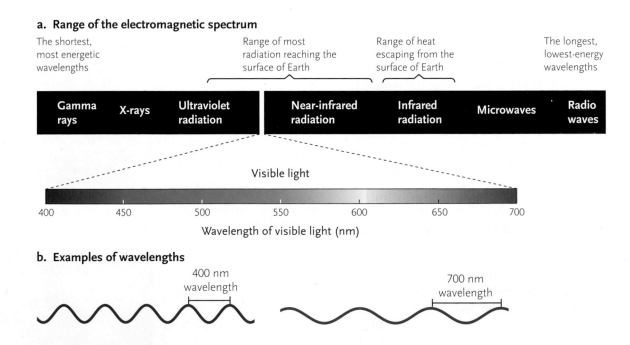

a. Range of the electromagnetic spectrum

The shortest, most energetic wavelengths

Range of most radiation reaching the surface of Earth

Range of heat escaping from the surface of Earth

The longest, lowest-energy wavelengths

| Gamma rays | X-rays | Ultraviolet radiation | Near-infrared radiation | Infrared radiation | Microwaves | Radio waves |

Visible light

400 450 500 550 600 650 700

Wavelength of visible light (nm)

b. Examples of wavelengths

400 nm wavelength

700 nm wavelength

Figure 7.4

The electromagnetic spectrum. (a) The electromagnetic spectrum ranges from gamma rays to radio waves; visible light, which includes the wavelengths used for photosynthesis, occupies only a narrow band of the spectrum. **(b)** Examples of wavelengths, showing the difference between the longest and shortest wavelengths of visible light.

quantum, plural *quanta*). A photon of light contains a fixed amount of energy that is inversely related to its wavelength: the shorter the wavelength, the greater the amount of energy photons of that wavelength contain. So, for example, the energy of a photon of blue light is greater than the energy found in a red photon of light.

To be used as a source of energy, photons of light must be absorbed by a molecule **(Figure 7.5)**. Absorption occurs when the energy of a photon is transferred to an electron within a molecule, moving the electron from the ground state to an excited state. In the excited state, the electron is farther away from the nucleus and thus it contains more energy. A major class of molecules that are very efficient at absorbing visible light are pigments because their structure results in a number of excitable electrons. The structures of a diversity of pigments are presented in Chapter 1, Figure 1.5.

Two important concepts about light absorption that we need to keep in mind are illustrated in

Figure 7.5a: (1) A single photon of light excites only a single electron within a pigment molecule, raising it from the ground state to an excited state. (2) A photon of light can only excite an electron when the energy of the photon matches the amount of energy required to raise the electron from the ground state to an excited state. If the energies do not match, then the photon is not absorbed.

After a pigment molecule absorbs a photon of light, one of three possible events can occur **(Figure 7.5b)**.

1. The excited electron from the pigment molecule returns to its ground state, releasing its energy either as heat or as an emission of light of a longer wavelength—a process called *fluorescence*.
2. The energy of the excited electron, but not the electron itself, is transferred to a neighbouring pigment molecule in a process called inductive resonance. This transfer excites the second molecule, while the first molecule returns to its ground state. Very little energy is lost in this energy transfer.
3. The excited electron is transferred from the pigment molecule to a nearby electron-accepting molecule called a primary acceptor.

The relative probabilities of these three events taking place depend on the environment surrounding the pigment molecule that absorbs the photon of light.

7.2b Chlorophylls and Carotenoids Cooperate in Light Absorption

In photosynthesis, light is absorbed by molecules of green pigments called chlorophylls and yellow-orange pigments called carotenoids. Chlorophylls are the major photosynthetic pigments in plants, green algae, and cyanobacteria. Chlorophyll is green in colour because a molecule of chlorophyll does not have an excited state that matches the energy of a green photon. Instead the green photon is either reflected or transmitted by the pigment, and it is this light that we detect with our eyes. Of the chlorophylls, the most dominant types are chlorophyll *a* and *b*, which are structurally only slightly different **(Figure 7.6, p. 144)**.

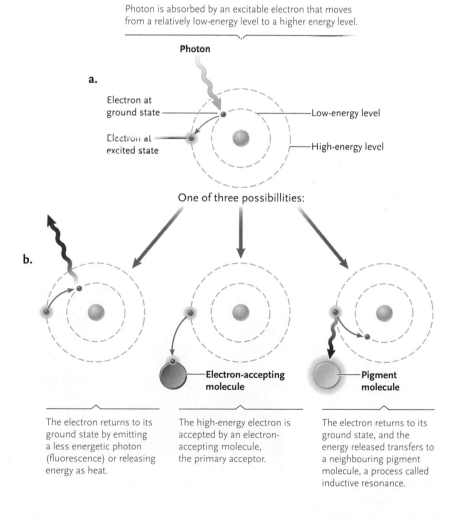

Figure 7.5

Three possible fates of an excited-state electron within a pigment molecule.

a. Chlorophyll structure

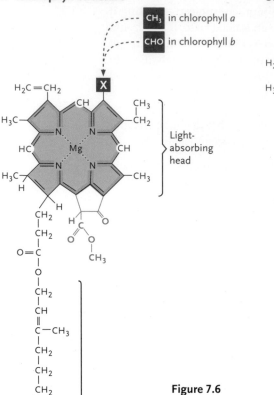

CH₃ in chlorophyll *a*

CHO in chlorophyll *b*

Light-absorbing head

Hydrophobic side chain

b. Carotenoid structure

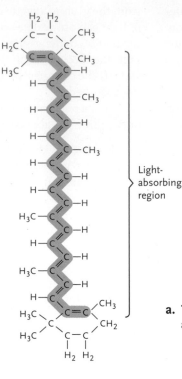

Light-absorbing region

Figure 7.6

Pigment molecules used in photosynthesis. **(a)** Chlorophylls *a* and *b*, which differ only in the side group attached at the X. **(b)** An example of a carotenoid. In both (a) and (b), the light-absorbing electrons are distributed among the bonds shaded in orange.

photosynthesis is usually determined by using a suspension of chloroplasts or algal cells and measuring the amount of O_2 released by photosynthesis at different wavelengths of visible light. Whenever an action spectrum for a physiological phenomenon is similar to the absorption spectrum of a specific pigment, it is highly suggestive that the physiological phenomenon depends upon light absorption by the specific pigment under study.

One of the earliest action spectra was produced in 1883 by Theodor Engelmann, who used only a light microscope and a glass prism to determine which wavelengths of light were most effective for photosynthesis **(Figure 7.8)**. Engelmann placed a strand of a green alga, *Spirogyra*, on a glass microscope slide, along with water containing bacteria that require oxygen to survive. He adjusted the prism so that it split a beam of

a. The absorption spectra of chlorophylls *a* and *b* and carotenoids

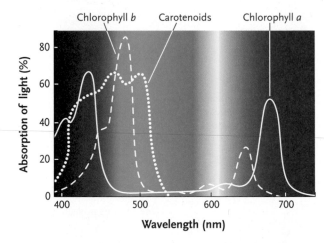

b. The action spectrum in higher plants, representing the combined effects of chlorophylls and carotenoids

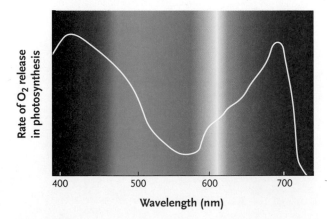

Figure 7.7

The absorption spectra of three photosynthetic pigments **(a)** and the action spectrum of photosynthesis **(b)** in plants. The absorption spectra in (a) were made from pigments that were extracted from cells and purified.

One can precisely determine the wavelengths of light absorbed by a pigment such as chlorophyll by producing an absorption spectrum for that pigment using an instrument called a spectrophotometer and a pure sample of a pigment. An **absorption spectrum** is a plot of the absorption of light as a function of wavelength. **Figure 7.7a** shows that chlorophyll *a* strongly absorbs blue and red light but does not absorb green or yellow light. The absorption spectra of the accessory pigments (chlorophyll *b* and carotenoids; see 7.7a) illustrate that these pigments expand the wavelengths of light that can be effectively captured and used for photosynthesis.

Photosynthesis depends on the absorption of light by chlorophylls and carotenoids, acting in combination. This is supported by the **action spectrum** for photosynthesis. An action spectrum is a plot of the effectiveness of light of particular wavelengths in driving a process **(Figure 7.7b)**. An action spectrum for

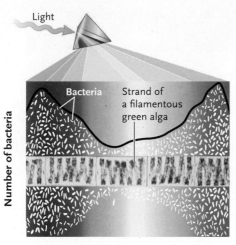

Light

Number of bacteria

Bacteria   Strand of
            a filamentous
            green alga

Wavelength

Figure 7.8
Engelmann's experiment revealed the action spectrum of light used in photosynthesis by *Spirogyra*, a green alga. The aerobic bacteria clustered along the algal strand in the regions where oxygen was released in greatest quantity—the regions in which photosynthesis proceeded at the greatest rate. Those regions corresponded to the colours (wavelengths) of light being absorbed most effectively by the alga—in this case, violet and red.

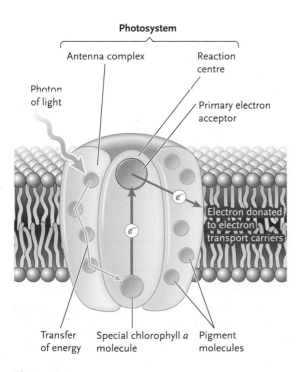

Photosystem

Antenna complex   Reaction
                         centre

Photon
of light

                         Primary electron
                         acceptor

                         Electron donated
                         to electron
                         transport carriers

Transfer   Special chlorophyll *a*   Pigment
of energy   molecule   molecules

Figure 7.9
Major components of a photosystem. A group of pigment proteins form an antenna complex that surrounds a reaction centre. Light energy absorbed anywhere in the antenna complex is conducted by inductive resonance to a special chlorophyll *a* molecule in the reaction centre. The absorbed light is converted to chemical energy when an excited electron from the chlorophyll *a* is transferred to a primary acceptor, also in the reaction centre. High-energy electrons are passed out of the photosystem to the electron transport system. The blue arrows show the path of energy flow.

light into its separate colours, which spread like a rainbow across the strand (see Figure 7.8). After a short time, he noticed that the bacteria had begun to cluster around the algal strand in different locations. The largest clusters were under the blue and violet light at one end of the strand and the red light at the other end. Very few bacteria were found in the green light.

7.2c Photosynthetic Pigments Are Organized into Photosystems

Photosynthetic pigments are required not only to absorb photons of light but also to transfer the energy to neighbouring molecules. To do this efficiently pigment molecules do not float freely within the thylakoid membrane but rather are bound very precisely to specific proteins. These pigment-proteins are organized within the thylakoid membrane into complexes called photosystems **(Figure 7.9)**. Each photosystem is composed of a large *antenna complex* (also called a *light-harvesting complex*) of pigment-proteins that surrounds a central *reaction centre*. The reaction centre of a photosystem comprises a small number of proteins that bind special chlorophyll *a* molecules as well as the primary electron acceptor (Figure 7.9). The function of a photosystem is to trap photons of light and use the energy to oxidize a reaction centre chlorophyll, with the electron being transferred to the primary electron acceptor. High rates of this oxidation–reduction reaction within the reaction centre are achieved by the large antenna complex of pigments absorbing light of a range of wavelengths and efficiently funnelling the energy to the reaction centre.

There are two different photosystems: photosystem I (PSI) and photosystem II (PSII). The specialized chlorophyll *a* in the reaction centre of photosystem I is called P700 (P = pigment) because its absorption maximum is at a wavelength of 700 nm. The reaction centre of photosystem II contains a specialized chlorophyll *a*, P680, which absorbs light maximally at 680 nm.

7.2d Photosystem II Uses Light Energy to Extract Electrons from Water

In Chapter 3, we discussed the evolutionary significance of the development of oxygenic photosynthesis and how it allowed organisms to use the most abundant substance on Earth, water, as a source of

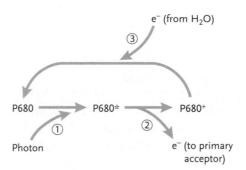

e^- (from H_2O)

③

P680 → P680* → P680+

①   ②

Photon e^- (to primary
              acceptor)

Figure 7.10
Diagram showing the sequence of the key events occurring within photosystem II. (**1**) Light energy from the antenna complex excites an electron within the reaction centre chlorophyll P680 producing P680*. (**2**) P680* is oxidized, forming P680+, by the primary electron acceptor. (**3**) P680+ is reduced back to P680 by an electron donated from water.

The D1 Protein Keeps Photosystem II Operating

Photosystem II can be considered the most important development in the evolution of life on Earth. Unlike anything that came before it, photosystem II meant that organisms that had it could harvest the energy of the Sun and use it to extract electrons from water. These electrons were used to convert CO_2 from the atmosphere into the organic building blocks of the cell. This ability to use water meant that life could thrive almost anywhere on the planet and led to an explosion in the conversion of CO_2 into organic molecules. By splitting water, photosystem II also produced O_2, which gradually accumulated in the atmosphere and led to the development of aerobic respiration. The process of aerobic respiration extracts 18 times more energy from sugar than the anaerobic pathway that came before it, resulting in an energy bounty that allowed the emergence of complex, multicellular

eukaryotic organisms. Because of this, photosystem II is known as the engine of life.

The splitting of water by photosystem II is the most energetically demanding reaction in all of biology. The reaction is carried out by a molecule, P680, that is found in the core of photosystem II, bound to a protein called D1. When photosystem II absorbs light, P680 is converted into the strongest known biological oxidant, $P680^+$, and this molecule is able to break apart H_2O, releasing electrons, protons, and O_2.

As a consequence of absorbing the energy of about 10 000 photons every second and generating powerful oxidants, photosystem II is constantly being damaged, which results in its inactivation. The major site of damage is the D1 protein, which is found in the core of the complex and binds P680. Over the course of two billion years of

evolution, organisms that have photosystem II have been unable to prevent the damage from occurring—but they have developed a highly specialized mechanism to repair it.

It takes only 20 minutes for a newly synthesized photosystem II complex to stop working because of damage to D1. However, damaged complexes are rapidly disassembled, the damaged D1 protein is removed and degraded, a newly synthesized D1 protein is inserted, and a functional photosystem is reassembled. This repair cycle is very efficient and depends on a high rate of D1 protein synthesis. It has been estimated that in the absence of this repair system, damage to photosystem II would lower the photosynthetic productivity of the planet by 95%. Thus, life on Earth could not have evolved to present-day levels of both abundance and complexity in the absence of a D1 repair mechanism.

---

electrons. By splitting water, these organisms released oxygen as a by-product, which slowly accumulated in the atmosphere. Oxygenic photosynthesis is the result of the development of photosystem II. The sequence of the key events that take place within photosystem II is as follows **(Figure 7.10, p. 145)**:

1. The absorption of photons by the antenna complex and funnelling of energy to the reaction centre result in an electron within P680 being excited. The excited state of the reaction centre chlorophyll P680 is denoted with an asterisk (P680*).

2. Once in the excited state, P680* can be easily oxidized to $P680^+$ by the primary electron acceptor. This oxidation–reduction reaction initiates electron transport.

3. $P680^+$ is reduced back to P680 by donation of an electron from water. This is facilitated by the oxygen-evolving complex, a protein that is found on the luminal side of photosystem II (see Figure 7.11).

STUDY BREAK

1. What is the difference between an absorption spectrum and an action spectrum?
2. Differentiate between P680, P680*, and $P680^+$.

7.3 The Light Reactions

Photosystem I and photosystem II are the two light-trapping components involved in photosynthetic electron transport in most photoautotrophs. In this section, we look in detail at how this particular electron transport chain operates and draw some analogies to respiratory electron transport.

7.3a Photosynthetic Electron Transport Synthesizes NADPH and Generates a Proton Gradient

Figure 7.11 shows the components of photosynthetic electron transport and the ATP synthase complex within the thylakoid membrane. As in all electron transport systems, the electron carriers of the photosynthetic system consist of nonprotein cofactors that alternate between being oxidized and reduced as electrons move through the system (see Chapter 6). The carriers, many of which are bound precisely to proteins, include the same types that act in mitochondrial electron transfer—cytochromes, quinones, and iron–sulfur centres.

Most of the electron carriers are organized into larger complexes embedded in the thylakoid membrane. The three major protein complexes of the

1 Absorption of light energy by photosystem II results in the oxidation of P680. The liberated electron is used to reduce the primary acceptor. P680+ is rapidly reduced back to P680 by an electron from H₂O transferred from the oxygen evolving complex.

2 From the primary acceptor the electron is passed to the mobile carrier molecule plastoquinone (PQ). As it accepts an electron from photosystem II, it picks up a proton from the stroma. PQ diffuses through the membrane before binding to the cytochrome complex, at which point it donates an electron and releases a proton into the thylakoid lumen. From the cytochrome complex the electron is donated to plastocyanin.

3 Absorption of light energy by photosystem I results in the oxidation of P700. The liberated electron is used to reduce the primary acceptor before being passed to ferredoxin. This single electron is then held by the NADP+ reductase complex. P700+ is reduced back to P700 by the electron that is coming from plastocyanin. Once a second electron travels along the chain and reaches NADP+ reductase complex, NADP+ is reduced to NADPH.

4 Proton pumping by plastoquinone (red arrows) creates a concentration gradient of H+ (a proton motive force) across the thylakoid membrane. The gradient is dissipated as H+ diffuses back into the stroma through the ATPase complex, which drives the synthesis of ATP from ADP and Pi.

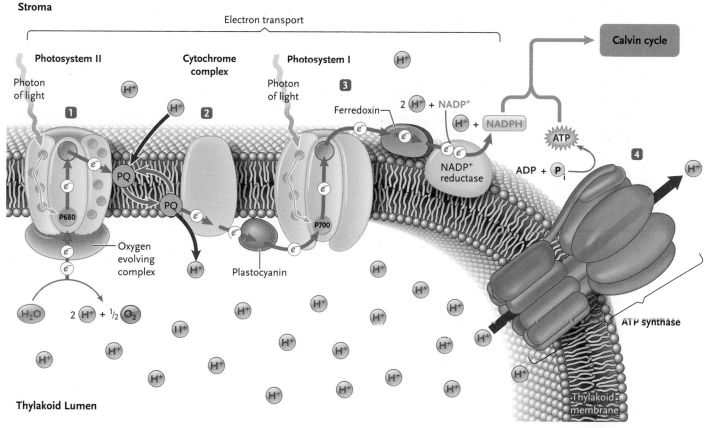

Figure 7.11

A model of the eukaryotic thylakoid membrane illustrating the major protein and redox cofactors required for photosynthetic electron transport and ATP synthesis.

electron transport chain are photosystem II, the cytochrome complex, and photosystem I. Electron flow between photosystem II and the cytochrome complex is facilitated by a pool of molecules of plastoquinone, which is similar in structure and function to the ubiquinone of respiratory electron transport (see Chapter 6). Electron flow from the cytochrome complex to photosystem I is linked by the mobile copper-containing protein plastocyanin.

From photosystem I, electrons are donated to an iron–sulfur protein called ferredoxin, which in turn donates electrons to the enzyme NADP+ reductase, which is found on the stromal side of the thylakoid membrane. The enzyme reduces NADP+ to NADPH

by using two electrons from electron transport and a proton from the surrounding aqueous environment. This pathway of electron flow from photosystem II through photosystem I to synthesize NADPH is referred to as **linear electron transport.**

7.3b Light Is Used Specifically to Oxidize Chlorophyll

All electron transport chains operate with electrons flowing spontaneously from molecules that are easily oxidized to molecules that are progressively more easily reduced. In the case of mitochondrial electron transport, recall that flow is from NADH,

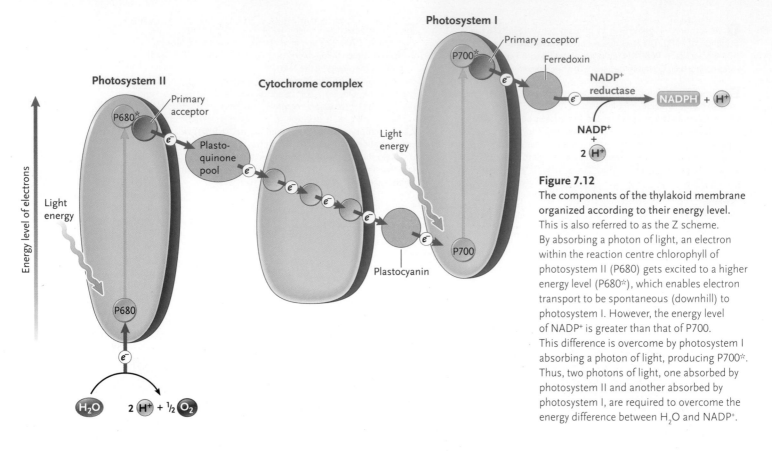

Photosystem I

Primary acceptor

Ferredoxin

Photosystem II

Primary acceptor

Cytochrome complex

Light energy

NADP+ reductase

NADPH + H+

NADP+ + 2 H+

Plasto-quinone pool

Light energy

Plastocyanin

P700

Energy level of electrons

Light energy

P680*

P680

H₂O   2 H+ + ½ O₂

Figure 7.12

The components of the thylakoid membrane organized according to their energy level. This is also referred to as the Z scheme. By absorbing a photon of light, an electron within the reaction centre chlorophyll of photosystem II (P680) gets excited to a higher energy level (P680*), which enables electron transport to be spontaneous (downhill) to photosystem I. However, the energy level of NADP+ is greater than that of P700. This difference is overcome by photosystem I absorbing a photon of light, producing P700*. Thus, two photons of light, one absorbed by photosystem II and another absorbed by photosystem I, are required to overcome the energy difference between H₂O and NADP+.

which is a source of electrons, to O_2, which has a very high affinity for electrons. In photosynthesis, electron transport occurs by the same principle; however, unlike NADH, the chlorophyll molecules in the reaction centres of photosystem II and photosystem I are not easily oxidized. So we can ask the question: what process gets a chlorophyll molecule into a state where it readily gives up an electron? Light absorption! The absorption of a photon of light within photosystem II and photosystem I and the funnelling of this high energy to the reaction centre is used to excite an electron within P680 or P700 **(Figure 7.12)**. By converting P680 into P680*, the absorption of light energy produces a molecule that is easily oxidized by the electron transport chain, and electron flow is a spontaneous process from P680* to photosystem I. A second photon of light absorbed by photosystem I results in the formation of P700*, which is easily oxidized by the primary electron acceptor of photosystem I, and in turn ferredoxin, before finally the electron is donated to NADP+ (see Figure 7.12).

7.3c In the Light Reactions, ATP Is Generated by Chemiosmosis

In a way analogous to respiratory electron transport, the flow of electrons along the photosynthetic electron transport chain is coupled to ATP synthesis by the buildup of a proton gradient. In photosynthetic electron transport, the proton gradient across the thylakoid membrane is

derived from three processes (see Figure 7.11, p. 147). First, protons are translocated into the lumen by the cyclic reduction and oxidation of plastoquinone as it migrates from photosystem II to the cytochrome complex and back again. Second, the gradient is enhanced by the addition of two protons to the lumen from the oxidation of water, which occurs on the luminal side of photosystem II. Third, the removal of one proton from the stroma for each NADPH molecule synthesized further decreases the H+ concentration in the stroma, thereby enhancing the gradient across the thylakoid membrane. The proton-motive force (see Section 6.5) established across the thylakoid membrane is used to synthesize ATP by chemiosmosis using the chloroplast ATP synthase. This multiprotein complex is structurally and functionally analogous to the ATP synthase used in oxidative phosphorylation in cellular respiration (see Figure 6.17, Chapter 6). Distinct from oxidative phosphorylation in cellular respiration, the process of using light to generate ATP is often referred to as *photophosphorylation*.

7.3d The Stoichiometry of Linear Electron Transport

We have described in detail the structure and function of the photosynthetic apparatus. Now it's time to go over the stoichiometry of the light reactions. To get a single electron down the electron transport chain from photosystem II (or water; it doesn't matter) to NADP+ takes two photons of light, one photon absorbed by photosystem II and a second by photosystem I. How many photons need to be absorbed by the photosynthetic apparatus to produce a single molecule of O_2? For all of these types of questions, we start by writing out a balanced chemical reaction, such as

$$2H_2O \rightarrow 4H^+ + 4e^- + O_2$$

The reaction shows that to produce one molecule of O_2 you need to oxidize two molecules of water, which results in the release of four electrons. Now to move a single electron down the electron transport chain requires the absorption of two photons. It follows then that to get four electrons from photosystem II to $NADP^+$, the photosynthetic apparatus needs to absorb a total of eight photons of light, four by each photosystem.

7.3e Cyclic Electron Transport Generates ATP in the Absence of NADPH

Photosystem I can function independently of photosystem II in what is called **cyclic electron transport (Figure 7.13).** In this process, electron flow from photosystem I to ferredoxin is not followed by electron donation to the $NADP^+$ reductase complex. Instead, reduced ferredoxin donates electrons back to the plastoquinone pool. In this manner, the plastoquinone pool gets continually reduced and oxidized and keeps moving protons across the thylakoid membrane without the involvement of electrons coming from photosystem II. Overall, cyclic electron transport only involves light absorption by

photosystem I, with the energy being used to establish a proton-motive force and generate ATP. Unlike linear electron transport, NADPH is not formed during cyclic electron transport.

Cyclic electron transport plays an important role in overall photosynthesis. The reduction of carbon dioxide by the Calvin cycle requires more ATP than NADPH, and the additional ATP molecules are provided by cyclic electron transport. Other energy-requiring reactions in the chloroplast also depend on ATP produced by the cyclic pathway.

STUDY BREAK

1. In which compartment of the chloroplast is NADPH generated?
2. Sketch out how the light reactions of photosynthesis generate ATP.

7.4 The Calvin Cycle

Recall from the last chapter that carbon dioxide is a fully oxidized carbon molecule and contains no usable energy. On the other hand, carbohydrate molecules such as glucose and sucrose are an abundant source of energy because they contain many C–H bonds. In the cytosol of photosynthetic bacteria and in the stroma of the

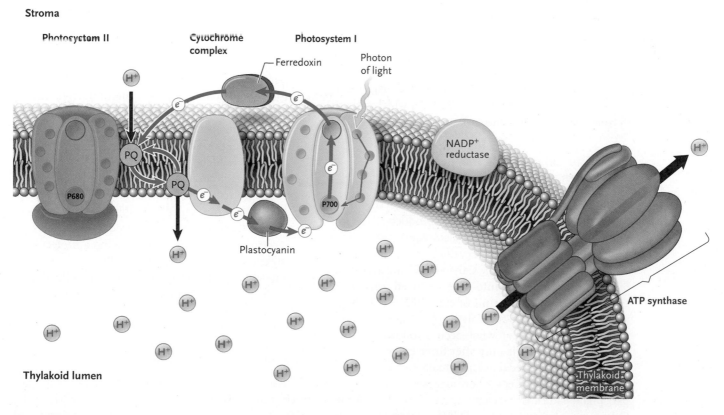

Figure 7.13

Cyclic electron transport. Electrons move in a circular pathway from photosystem I through ferredoxin back to the plastoquinone pool, through the cytochrome complex and plastocyanin and then back to photosystem I. In cyclic electron transport, photosystem II does not operate. The pathway generates proton pumping and thus leads to ATP production but does not result in the synthesis of NADPH.

PEOPLE BEHIND BIOLOGY 7.2

Norm Hüner, University of Western Ontario

A number of advances into our understanding of the regulation of photosynthesis have been elucidated by the research group of Norm Hüner, who holds a Tier 1 Canada Research Chair in Environmental Stress Biology at the University of Western Ontario in London.

Hüner's research has established that the photosynthetic apparatus has a dual role: not only does it function as the primary energy transformer of the biosphere, but it also acts as a sensor of environmental change in all photoautotrophs. Using a range of organisms, including plants, green algae, and cyanobacteria, Hüner's group has discovered that the relative redox state of photosynthetic electron transport acts as a natural sensor of the balance between energy input from the Sun and the demands for that energy by the metabolic processes of the organism. The redox

state of the photosynthetic apparatus can be readily assessed by measuring the *excitation pressure* on photosystem II using a fluorescence-based technique. Hüner's group has shown that changes in excitation pressure are a key trigger that initiates changes to a number of cellular processes, including gene expression, which enable photoautotrophs to readily acclimate to changes in light, temperature, and nutrient availability.

Hüner is the coauthor of an internationally acclaimed textbook entitled *Introduction to Plant Physiology*, which is currently in its fourth edition. As well, he has received more than 25 national and international awards and honours for his research, which include election as a fellow of the Academy of Science, Royal Society of Canada, and president of the Canadian Society of Plant Physiologists; an honorary

degree from the University of Umea, Sweden; and an honorary professorship from Xinjiang University, China.

In recent years, Hüner has been the lead investigator in the establishment of the Biotron Experimental Climate Change Research Centre, an international research facility on the campus of the University of Western Ontario. The research focus of this $30 million facility is the elucidation of the mechanisms by which plants, microbes, and insects sense and adjust to climate change. One of the unique aspects of the Biotron is that it gives researchers the ability to conduct control experiments on a much larger scale than possible in a conventional laboratory. This allows for the study of how changes to temperature, light, nutrients, and carbon dioxide concentrations may affect not only the growth of individual species, but also entire ecosystems.

chloroplast, a series of 11 enzyme-catalyzed reactions use NADPH to reduce CO_2 into sugar. The overall process is endergonic, requiring energy supplied by ATP. These 11 enzyme-catalyzed reactions are collectively known as the Calvin cycle (or light-independent reactions), which is the most common pathway on Earth by which carbon dioxide is transformed into carbohydrates.

7.4a The Calvin Cycle Reduces Carbon Dioxide to a Carbohydrate

Like other metabolic cycles, including the citric acid cycle, the Calvin cycle generates products that are removed from the cycle, but it also requires that molecules be regenerated so that cycling can continue.

During each turn of the Calvin cycle, one molecule of CO_2 is converted into one reduced carbon—essentially one (CH_2O) unit of carbohydrate. To help you better understand the Calvin cycle, **Figure 7.14** represents a summary of what occurs following three turns of the cycle. It is only after three carbon dioxide molecules get reduced that one actually generates a separate molecule—a three-carbon sugar glyceraldehyde-3-phosphate (G3P). By a reaction that is not part of the Calvin cycle, two molecules of G3P can synthesize one molecule of the six-carbon sugar glucose.

As shown in Figure 7.14, the Calvin cycle can be subdivided into three distinct phases: fixation, reduction, and

regeneration. The events that take place in each of these phases during ONE turn of the cycle are as follows:

Phase 1: Fixation. This phase involves the incorporation (i.e., fixing) of a carbon atom from CO_2 (one per turn) into one molecule of the five-carbon sugar ribulose-1,5-bisphosphate (RuBP) to produce two molecules of the three-carbon compound 3-phosphoglycerate.

Phase 2: Reduction. In this phase, each molecule of 3-phosphoglycerate gets an additional phosphate added from the breakdown of ATP. This produces a total of two molecules of 1,3-bisphosphoglycerate. Each of these molecules is subsequently reduced by electrons from NADPH, producing a molecule of glyceraldehyde-3-phosphate (G3P).

Phase 3: Regeneration. For each turn of the Calvin cycle, two molecules of G3P are produced—a total of six carbon atoms. In a multistep process, five of these carbons are rearranged to regenerate the single molecule of RuBP required for the next round of carbon fixation.

Let's work through Figure 7.14 (the key is to keep track of the carbons). In three turns of the Calvin cycle, $3CO_2$ (3 carbons) are incorporated into 3 molecules of RuBP (15 carbons), which produces 6 molecules of 3-phosphoglycerate (18 carbons). Each of these molecules is phosphorylated by a phosphate donated by ATP. In total, 6 ATP are consumed to phosphorylate the 6 molecules of 3-phosphoglycerate, generating 6 molecules of 1,3-bisphosphogly- cerate. Six molecules of NADPH are consumed in converting the 6 mol- ecules of 1,3-bisphosphoglycerate into 6 molecules of G3P (18 carbons). Five molecules of G3P (totalling 15 carbons) are used to regenerate 3 RuBP molecules (15 carbons), which requires 3 molecules of ATP. Thus, the cycle generates one surplus mol- ecule of G3P (three carbons) after every three turns. For the synthesis of this one extra G3P, the Calvin cycle requires a total of 9 molecules of ATP and 6 molecules of NADPH. Both ATP and NADPH are regenerated from ADP and NADP+, respectively, by the light reactions.

7.4b G3P Is the Starting Point for the Synthesis of Many Other Organic Molecules

The G3P molecule formed by three turns of the Calvin cycle is the starting point for the production of a wide variety of organic molecules. More complex carbohydrates, such as glucose and other monosaccharides, are made from G3P by reac- tions that, in effect, reverse the first half of glycolysis. Once produced, the monosaccharides may enter bio- chemical pathways that make disaccharides such as sucrose, polysaccharides such as starches and cellu- lose, and other complex carbohydrates. Other path- ways manufacture amino acids, fatty acids and lipids, proteins, and nucleic acids. The reactions forming these products occur both within chloroplasts and in the surrounding cytosol and nucleus.

Sucrose, a disaccharide consisting of glucose linked to fructose, is the main form in which the prod- ucts of photosynthesis circulate from cell to cell in plants. Organic nutrients are stored in most plants as sucrose, starch, or a combination of the two in propor- tions that depend on the plant species. Sugar cane and sugar beets, which contain stored sucrose in high con- centrations, are the main sources of the sucrose we use as table sugar.

7.4c Rubisco Is the Most Abundant Protein on Earth

Ribulose-1,5-bisphosphate carboxylase oxygenase, or Rubisco, is the enzyme of the Calvin cycle that cata- lyzes the fixation of CO_2 into organic form:

$$\text{Ribulose-1,5-bisphosphate (RuBP)} + CO_2 \rightarrow \text{2 3-phosphoglycerate}$$

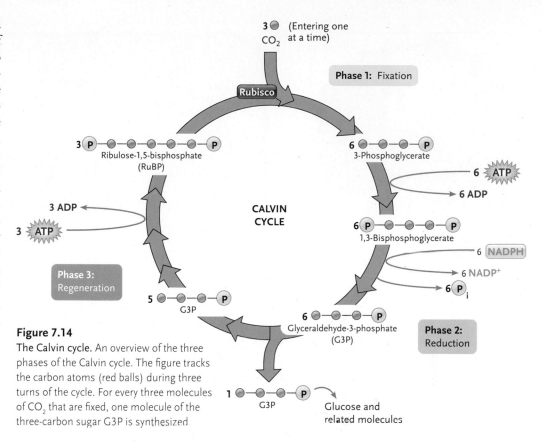

Figure 7.14

The Calvin cycle. An overview of the three phases of the Calvin cycle. The figure tracks the carbon atoms (red balls) during three turns of the cycle. For every three molecules of CO_2 that are fixed, one molecule of the three-carbon sugar G3P is synthesized

Rubisco is considered the most important enzyme of the biosphere because by catalyzing CO_2 fixation in all photoautotrophs, it provides the source of organic carbon molecules for most of the world's organisms. The enzyme converts a staggering 100 billion tonnes of CO_2 into carbohydrates annually. There are so many Rubisco molecules in chloroplasts that this one enzyme accounts for about 50% of the total protein content of plant leaves. This makes Rubisco easily the planet's most abundant protein, estimated to total some 40 million tonnes world- wide. Interestingly, the high abundance of Rubisco in photosynthetic cells is explained by the fact that this very important enzyme is catalytically very slow. Most enzymes can react with substrate molecules at a rate of many hundreds to many thousands of molecules per second, yet Rubisco only processes about 3 to 10 mol- ecules of carbon dioxide per second.

Isolation and purification of Rubisco from the chloroplast stroma has led to the elucidation of its three- dimensional structure. The molecule is cube shaped and contains eight small subunits and eight large subunits **(Figure 7.15a, p. 152).** Each of the large subunits contains an active site, which has defined binding sites for both CO_2 and RuBP. The small subunits do not have a role in catalysis but do serve an important regulatory role, although their exact function remains unknown.

The synthesis of Rubisco is quite remarkable as it requires the coordinated expression of genes in two different genomes **(Figure 7.15b, p. 152).** While the large subunit is encoded by a gene of the chloroplast genome, the small subunit is encoded by a gene that is found in

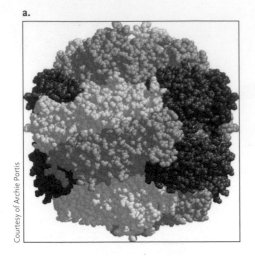

a.

Courtesy of Archie Portis

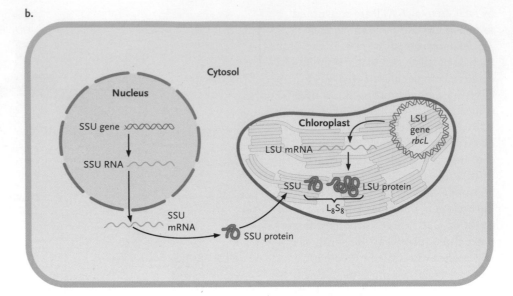

b.

Figure 7.15

Model of ribulose-1,5-bisphosphate carboxylase oxygenase (Rubisco). **(a)** The functional enzyme is composed of a total of 16 subunits: 8 large subunits (LSU) (shown in white and grey) and 8 small subunits (SSU) (shown in orange and blue). The synthesis of Rubsico **(b)** requires the coordination of two genomes. Each LSU is synthesized in the stroma of the chloroplast following the transcription of a gene coded by the chloroplast chromosome. The gene that encodes the SSU is found in the nucleus, with SSU monomers being synthesized by cytosolic ribosomes before being imported into the chloroplast.

the nucleus. After the small subunit polypeptide is synthesized in the cytosol, it is imported into the chloroplast, where it associates with large subunit monomers to make the functional enzyme.

The vast majority of the proteins found in chloroplasts (and mitochondria) are, in fact, encoded by the nuclear genome and thus are synthesized on ribosomes in the cytosol (see Chapter 3 for further discussion on this). They are then imported into the organelle using specific transport complexes that span the inner and outer membranes of these organelles. Many of the complexes of the electron transport chains of both mitochondria and chloroplasts are the products of both the nuclear genome and genes residing within the specific energy-transforming organelle.

STUDY BREAK

1. What does NADPH provide in the Calvin cycle?
2. Explain the synthesis of the enzyme Rubisco.

7.5 Photorespiration and CO₂-Concentrating Mechanisms

For being arguably the most important enzyme on the planet, Rubsico is surprisingly inefficient at fixing carbon dioxide. The cause of this inefficiency is that the active site of Rubisco is not specific to CO_2—a molecule

of O_2 can also bind to the active site and react with RuBP. When this occurs, one of the products is a two-carbon compound that is exported from the chloroplast and actually requires the cell to consume ATP to convert it into carbon dioxide, which is simply lost. This wasteful process is called **photorespiration** because it occurs in the light and is similar to cellular respiration in that it consumes O_2 and releases CO_2. In this section, we present details on the biochemistry of the reactions that Rubsico catalyses with O_2 and CO_2. As well, we discuss the key adaptations plants and algae have made to minimize photorespiration, and how photorespiration can be exacerbated by specific environmental conditions.

7.5a Rubisco Is an Ancient Enzyme That Is Inhibited by Oxygen

Before we discuss the biochemistry of photorespiration, a key question we could ask is: why would natural selection have led to the evolution of an enzyme that accepts a second substrate molecule that produces a wasteful product? Rubisco and Rubisco-like proteins evolved at least 3 billion years ago as the primary enzyme in the biosphere for reducing carbon dioxide into organic form. Support for this comes, in part, from Rubisco being found in a huge diversity of organisms, including many bacteria and archaea (while they don't carry out photosynthesis, archaea do have Rubisco). As discussed in Chapter 3, the atmosphere 3 billion years ago contained only trace amounts of O_2 and much higher levels of CO_2 than today. Under such conditions, an early form of Rubisco that had an active site that could bind O_2 as well as CO_2 would not have been detrimental to an organism. Photorespiration became a problem only as the levels of oxygen in the atmosphere increased. There is evidence that over time Rubisco has slowly evolved to be more specific for CO_2, but the inhibition by O_2 remains.

O_2 can directly compete with CO_2 for the active site of Rubisco, and as such is an excellent example of a competitive inhibitor of enzyme function (see Chapter 4). When oxygen binds to the active site of Rubisco, the enzyme acts as an *oxygenase* instead of a *carboxylase*. A comparison of the products of the carboxylation reaction and the oxygenation reaction of Rubisco is shown in **Figure 7.16.** Recall that the incorporation of a CO_2 molecule into RuBP leads to a net increase in carbon by producing two molecules of the three-carbon compound 3-phosphoglycerate. By comparison, the incorporation of O_2 into RuBP in the oxygenation reaction produces a single molecule of 3-phosphoglycerate and one molecule of the two-carbon compound phosphoglycolate. There is no carbon gain—five carbons in and five carbons out. However, what makes photorespiration perhaps even more detrimental is that photoautotrophs cannot use phosphoglycolate. In the process of breaking it down to salvage the carbon, a toxic compound called glycolate is produced. The elimination of glycolate through its oxidation results in the release of carbon dioxide. Thus, whereas the carboxylation reaction leads to carbon gain, the oxygenation reaction actually results in the cell losing carbon.

If we compare the carboxylation and oxygenation reactions of Rubisco under laboratory conditions, where we can keep the concentrations of both O_2 and CO_2 equal, then the carboxylation reaction will dominate because the active site of Rubisco has a greater affinity for CO_2 than O_2. In fact, the carboxylation reaction will occur about 80 times as quickly as the oxygenation reaction. However, unlike in the laboratory, the atmosphere does not contain equal amounts of the two gases—it contains approximately 21% O_2 and only about 0.04% CO_2. Because of this, under normal atmospheric concentrations and at moderate temperatures, the oxygenation reaction can occur about once for every three times the carboxylation reaction occurs. This means that 25% of the time, the wasteful oxygenation reaction occurs, which results in net carbon loss. To counter the extent to which the oxygenation reaction occurs, many species have evolved mechanisms to try to decrease the prevalence of the oxygenation reaction. The strategies involve using mechanisms that increase the CO_2/O_2 ratio at the site of Rubisco.

7.5b Algae Pump Carbon Dioxide into Their Cells

In aquatic environments, the concentration of CO_2 dissolved in the water is usually low, well below what is needed to saturate the active site of Rubisco. Yet, interestingly, bubbling additional CO_2 into a culture of algae does not usually lead to an increase in the rate of photosynthesis, which is what you would expect. The lack of response to additional CO_2 is explained by the presence of a *carbon-concentrating mechanism* that pumps inorganic carbon into algal cells. This means that even when the concentration of CO_2 in the water is low, the

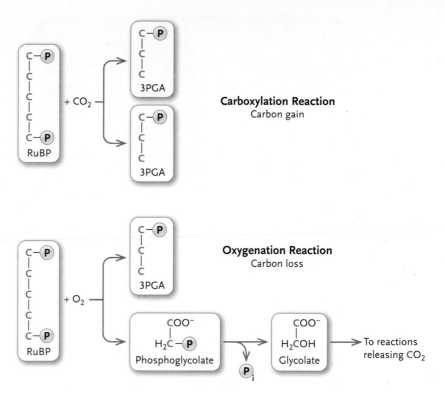

Figure 7.16

The enzyme Rubisco possesses both a carboxylase and an oxygenase activity. Compared with the usual carboxylase activity of the Calvin cycle, the oxygenase activity results in a net loss of carbon by the plant. Because oxygenase activity consumes O_2 and releases CO_2, it is also called photorespiration.

amount that is actually within the cells is kept very high by this active pumping mechanism.

A model for one type of carbon-concentrating mechanism is presented in **Figure 7.17, p. 154.** In aqueous environments of near-neutral pH, the dominant form of inorganic carbon is not CO_2 but rather the bicarbonate anion (HCO_3^-). In the system shown in Figure 7.17, p. 154, an ATP-dependent pump on the plasma membrane transports HCO_3^- into the cell, resulting in a concentration that is higher inside the cell than outside. Within the cytosol, the bicarbonate is rapidly converted into CO_2 by the enzyme carbonic anhydrase. The CO_2 then diffuses into the chloroplast to the site of Rubisco. This system results in a concentration of CO_2 at the site of Rubisco that is sufficiently high to essentially outcompete the O_2 that is present for the active site of Rubisco.

7.5c High Temperature Exacerbates Photorespiration

Compared to aquatic photoautotrophs, many terrestrial plants, especially those living in hot, dry climates, face not only the problem of photorespiration but also the problem of water loss. Interestingly, these two problems are linked.

The major photosynthetic organ of a plant is the leaf, and because of its high surface area, you would think that this would result in high rates of water loss due to evaporation. However, the surface of leaves is

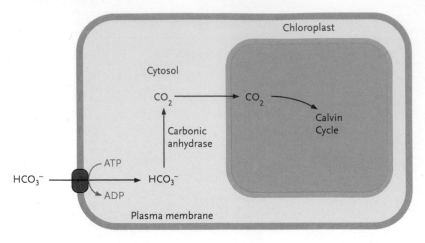

Figure 7.17

CO_2 concentration mechanism. Many aquatic photoautotrophs (e.g., algae) can increase their intracellular carbon dioxide concentrations through a mechanism that involves an ATP-dependent bicarbonate (HCO_3) pump on the plasma membrane. The bicarbonate is rapidly converted in the cytosol to CO_2 by the enzyme carbonic anhydrase.

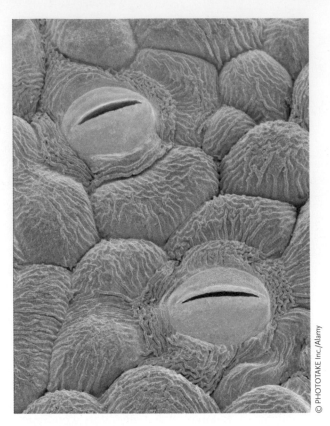

Figure 7.18

Stomata. Gas exchange and water loss by a plant are controlled by the presence of stomata. Each stoma is formed from two guard cells that control the opening and closing of the pore.

covered by a waxy cuticle that prevents water loss. But what prevents water loss also inhibits the rapid diffusion of carbon dioxide into the leaf. To enable high rates of gas exchange (CO_2 in and O_2 out) between the environment and the cells within the leaf, the surface of a leaf has small pores called stomata (singular, *stoma*) **(Figure 7.18).** The plant can regulate the size of the stomata from fully closed to fully open to balance the demands for gas exchange with the need to minimize water loss. As you may suspect, plants that are adapted to hot, dry climates are faced with a constant dilemma: they need to open their stomata to let CO_2 in for the Calvin cycle, but to conserve water, they need to keep the stomata closed. The dilemma is even harder to reconcile because photorespiration becomes a bigger problem the warmer the climate. The reason for this relates to the effect of temperature on the solubility of gases in solution (the stroma of the chloroplast is an aqueous environment). As shown in **Table 7.1,** the solubility of O_2 and CO_2 (and in fact all gases) decreases as the temperature increases. However, the solubility of CO_2 decreases more rapidly with an increase in temperature than O_2. So as growth temperature increases the CO_2/O_2 ratio decreases, and photorespiration takes away a greater proportion of the carbon from the plant.

At temperatures of about 35°C, as much as 50% of the plant's energy can be wasted by photorespiration.

7.5d C_4 Plants Spatially Separate the C_4 Pathway and the Calvin Cycle

Some plant species that are adapted to hot, dry climates have evolved a mode of carbon fixation that minimizes photorespiration. Besides having the Calvin cycle, these plants have a second carbon fixation pathway called the C_4 cycle **(Figure 7.19).** In this cycle, CO_2 initially combines with a three-carbon molecule, phosphoenolpyruvate (PEP), producing the four-carbon intermediate oxaloacetate. Oxaloacetate is then reduced to malate by electrons transferred from NADPH. After being transported to the site of the Calvin cycle, the malate gets oxidized to pyruvate, releasing CO_2. To complete the cycle, pyruvate is converted back into PEP in a reaction that consumes ATP. The oxygenation reaction of Rubisco is inhibited by the C_4 cycle because the conversion of malate to pyruvate actually generates CO_2, resulting in much higher concentrations of CO_2 at the site of Rubisco (see Figure 7.19).

The C_4 cycle gets its name because its first product, oxaloacetate, is a four-carbon molecule rather than the three-carbon phosphoglycerate, the first product of the

Table 7.1	Effect of Temperature on the Solubility of O_2 and CO_2		
Temperature (°C)	$[CO_2]$ (μM in solution)	$[O_2]$ (μM in solution)	$\dfrac{[CO_2]}{[O_2]}$
5	21.93	401.2	0.0547
15	15.69	319.8	0.0491
25	11.68	264.6	0.0441
35	9.11	228.2	0.0399

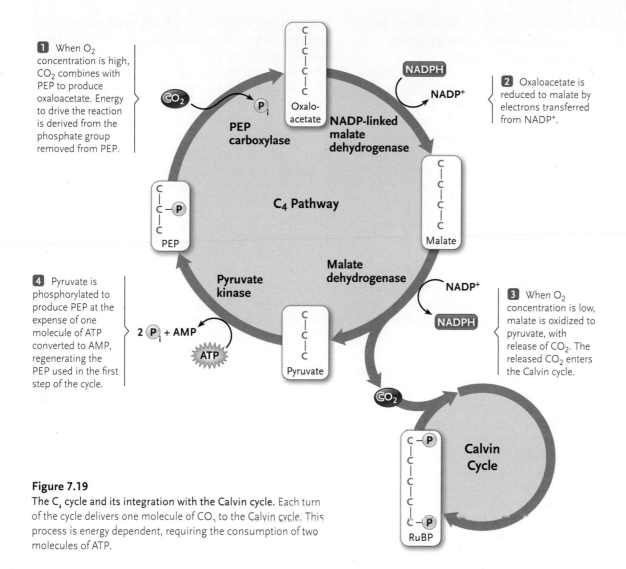

1 When O_2 concentration is high, CO_2 combines with PEP to produce oxaloacetate. Energy to drive the reaction is derived from the phosphate group removed from PEP.

2 Oxaloacetate is reduced to malate by electrons transferred from $NADP^+$.

4 Pyruvate is phosphorylated to produce PEP at the expense of one molecule of ATP converted to AMP, regenerating the PEP used in the first step of the cycle.

3 When O_2 concentration is low, malate is oxidized to pyruvate, with release of CO_2. The released CO_2 enters the Calvin cycle.

Figure 7.19

The C_4 cycle and its integration with the Calvin cycle. Each turn of the cycle delivers one molecule of CO_2 to the Calvin cycle. This process is energy dependent, requiring the consumption of two molecules of ATP.

Calvin cycle. One often talks in terms of the C_4 pathway and the C_3 pathway when distinguishing between plants that have the C_4 cycle and those that possess only the Calvin cycle. A key distinction between C_4 and C_3 metabolism concerns the carboxylation reactions. In the C_4 cycle, the initial carboxylation reaction that incorporates CO_2 into phosphoenolpyruvate is catalyzed by the enzyme *PEP carboxylase*. Unlike Rubisco, PEP carboxylase has much greater affinity for CO_2 and does not possess any oxygenase activity. It can efficiently catalyze the carboxylation of PEP regardless of the O_2 concentration near the enzyme.

Plants that possess C_4 metabolism include many tropical and several temperate crop species, including corn and sugar cane. In these species, the C_4 cycle occurs in mesophyll cells, which lie close to the surface of leaves and stems, where O_2 from the air is abundant (see Figure 7.19). The malate intermediate of the C_4 cycle diffuses from the mesophyll cells to *bundle sheath cells*, located in deeper tissues, where O_2 concentrations are lower. In these cells, in which the Calvin cycle operates, the malate enters chloroplasts and is converted to

pyruvate and CO_2. Because O_2 concentration is low and CO_2 concentration is high, the oxygenase activity of Rubisco is inhibited. The pyruvate produced by malate oxidation returns to the mesophyll cells to enter another turn of the C_4 cycle.

You may ask: if C_4 metabolism is so good at preventing photorespiration, why don't all plants use it? Looking back at Figure 7.19, notice that the C_4 pathway has an additional energy requirement. For each turn of the C_4 cycle, one molecule of ATP is required to regenerate PEP from pyruvate. In hot climates, photorespiration can decrease carbon fixation efficiency by over 50%, so the additional ATP requirement is worthwhile. As well, hot climates tend to receive a lot of sunlight, so the added ATP cost is easily met by absorbing more light energy and increasing the output of the light reactions. In temperate climates, the lower ambient temperatures mean that photorespiration is not as big of a problem (look back at Table 7.1), and the additional ATP requirement is often harder to meet given that these regions, on average, receive less sunlight. These differences in temperature and sunlight are the underlying reasons why, for example, in Florida, 70% of all native species are C_4 plants, while in Manitoba all native species are C_3 plants.

Not only do C_4 plants perform better where it is hot, but they also perform better where it is dry. Because PEP carboxylase has a very high affinity only for CO_2, C_4 plants are more efficient at fixing CO_2 than C_3 plants. As a consequence, they don't have to keep their stomata open as long as a C_3 plant to fix the same number of CO_2 molecules. Because this reduces water loss, C_4 plants are much better suited to arid conditions.

7.5e CAM Plants Temporally Separate the C_4 Pathway and the Calvin Cycle

Instead of running the Calvin and C_4 cycles simultaneously in different locations (spatial separation), some plants, such as pineapple, run the cycles at different times (temporal separation).

These plants are known as **CAM plants**, named for **crassulacean acid metabolism**, from the Crassulaceae family in which the adaptation was first observed. The plants in this group include many with thick, succulent leaves or stems, such as the cactus shown in **Figure 7.20.**

CAM plants typically live in regions that are hot and dry during the day and cool at night. Their fleshy leaves or stems have a low surface-to-volume ratio, and their stomata are reduced in number. Further, the stomata open only at night, when they release O_2 that accumulates from photosynthesis during the day and allow CO_2 to enter the leaves. The entering CO_2 is fixed by the C_4 pathway into malate, which accumulates throughout the night and is stored in large cell vacuoles.

Daylight initiates the second phase of the strategy. As the Sun comes up and the temperature rises, the stomata close, reducing water loss and cutting off the exchange of gases with the atmosphere. Malate diffuses

a. C_4 pathway in C_4 plants

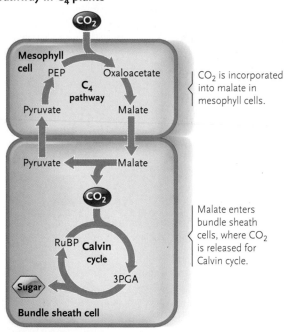

CO$_2$ is incorporated into malate in mesophyll cells.

Malate enters bundle sheath cells, where CO$_2$ is released for Calvin cycle.

b. CAM pathway in CAM plants

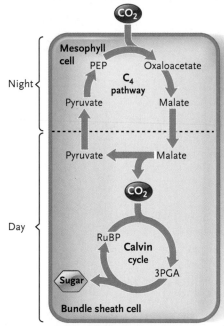

Stomata open at night; CO$_2$ converted into malate with minimal water loss.

Stomata close during day; CO$_2$ released from malate for Calvin cycle.

Figure 7.20

Two alternative processes of carbon fixation to minimize photorespiration. In each case, carbon fixation produces the four-carbon oxaloacetate, which is processed to generate the CO_2 that feeds into the Calvin (C_3) cycle. **(a)** In C_4 plants, carbon fixation and the Calvin cycle occur in different cell types: carbon fixation by the C_4 pathway takes place in mesophyll cells, while the Calvin cycle takes place in bundle sheath cells. **(b)** In CAM plants, carbon fixation and the Calvin cycle occur at different times in mesophyll cells: carbon fixation by the C_4 pathway takes place at night, while the Calvin cycle takes place during the day.

Zea mays (corn)

Photodisk/Getty Images

Opuntia basilaris (beavertail cactus)

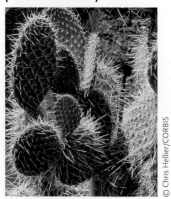

© Chris Hellier/CORBIS

from cell vacuoles into the cytosol, where it is oxidized to pyruvate, and CO_2 is released in high concentration. The high CO_2 concentration favours the carboxylase activity of Rubisco, allowing the Calvin cycle to proceed at maximum efficiency with little loss of organic carbon from photorespiration. The pyruvate produced by malate breakdown accumulates during the day; as night falls, it enters the C_4 reactions, converting it back to malate. During the night, oxygen is released by the plants, and more CO_2 enters.

Reduction of water loss by closure of the stomata during the hot daylight hours has the added benefit of making CAM plants highly resistant to dehydration. As a result, CAM species can tolerate extreme daytime heat and dryness.

STUDY BREAK

1. How does the enzyme carbonic anhydrase minimize photorespiration in aquatic photoautotrophs?
2. What is the chemical explanation for why photorespiration increases as the temperature increases?

7.6 Photosynthesis and Cellular Respiration Compared

A popular misconception is that photosynthesis occurs in plants, and cellular respiration occurs only in animals. In fact, both processes occur in plants, with photosynthesis confined to tissues containing chloroplasts and cellular respiration taking place in all cells. **Figure 7.21, p. 158,** presents side-by-side schematics of photosynthesis and cellular respiration to highlight their similarities and points of connection. Note that their overall reactions are basically the reverse of each other. That is, the reactants of photosynthesis—CO_2 and H_2O—are the products of cellular respiration, and the reactants of cellular respiration—glucose and O_2—are the products of photosynthesis. Both processes have key phosphorylation reactions involving an electron transfer system—photophosphorylation in photosynthesis and oxidative phosphorylation in cellular respiration—followed by the chemiosmotic synthesis of ATP. Further, G3P is found in the pathways of both processes. In photosynthesis, it is a product of the Calvin cycle and is used for the synthesis of sugars and other organic fuel molecules. In cellular respiration, it is an intermediate generated in glycolysis in the conversion of glucose to pyruvate. Thus, G3P is used by anabolic pathways when it is generated by photosynthesis, and it is a product of a catabolic pathway in cellular respiration.

In this chapter, you have seen how photosynthesis supplies the organic molecules used as fuels by almost all the organisms of the world. It is a story of electron flow: electrons, pushed to high energy levels by the absorption of light energy, are added to CO_2, which is fixed into carbohydrates and other fuel molecules. The high-energy electrons are then removed from the fuel molecules by the oxidative reactions of cellular respiration, which use the released energy to power the activities of life. Among the most significant of these activities are cell growth and division, the subjects of the next chapter.

Review

Access an interactive eBook, chapter-specific interactive learning tools, including flashcards, quizzes, videos, and more in your Biology **CourseMate**, accessed through NelsonBrain.com **Aplia™** is an online interactive learning solution that helps you improve comprehension—and your grade—by integrating a variety of mediums and tools such as videos, tutorials, practice tests, and an interactive eBook.

7.1 Photosynthesis: An Overview

- Photosynthesis is the use of light energy to convert carbon dioxide into an organic form.
- Photoautotrophs are the primary producers of the planet as they use the energy of sunlight to drive synthesis of organic molecules from simple inorganic molecules such as CO_2. The organic molecules are used by the photosynthetic organisms themselves as fuels; they also form the primary energy source for animals, fungi, and other heterotrophs.
- Photosynthesis can be divided into the light reactions and the Calvin cycle. In eukaryotes, both stages take place inside chloroplasts. The light reactions, which occur on the thylakoid membrane of chloroplasts (in eukaryotes), use the energy of light to drive the synthesis of NADPH and ATP. These are consumed by the Calvin cycle, which fixes CO_2 into carbohydrates (see Figure 7.2).

7.2 The Photosynthetic Apparatus

- The absorption of light energy by pigment molecules results in electrons within the pigment being raised to a higher-energy (excited) state. There are three fates of this excited state: energy loss, transfer of the energy, or oxidation of the pigment (loss of the electron) (see Figure 7.5).
- Chlorophylls and carotenoids, the photon-absorbing pigments in eukaryotes and cyanobacteria, together absorb light energy at a range of wavelengths, enabling a wide spectrum of light to be used (see Figures 7.6 and 7.7)
- Photosynthetic pigments are organized into two types of photosystems: photosystem II and photosystem I. Each photosystem consists of a reaction centre surrounded by an antenna complex. Energy trapped by pigments in the antenna is funnelled to the reaction centre, where it is used to oxidize a special reaction centre chlorophyll (denoted by P680 for photosystem II and P700 for photosystem I). The oxidation of reaction centre

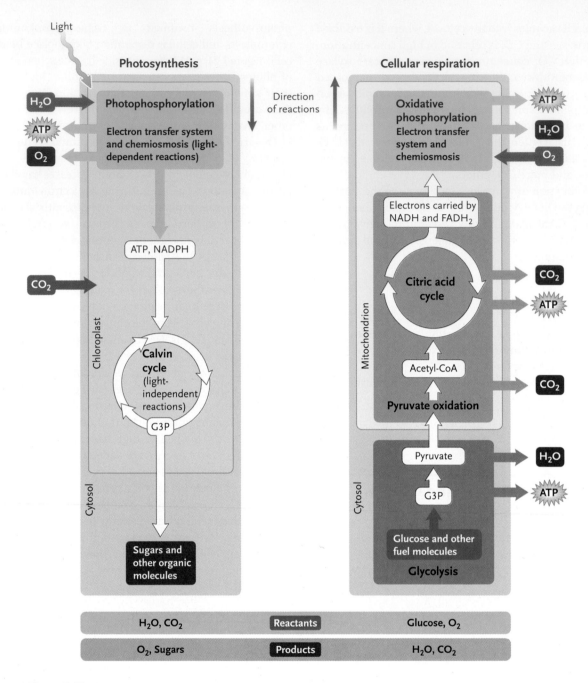

Figure 7.21

Schematic diagrams of the process of photosynthesis (left) and cellular respiration (right). Cellular respiration is shown upside down with respect to the direction of reactions to help illustrate the similarities of the process with photosynthesis.

chlorophyll is coupled to the reduction of the primary electron acceptors within each reaction centre (see Figure 7.9).

- Within photosystem II, light energy is funnelled to the reaction centre, where it excites P680, forming P680*. Oxidation of P680* forms P680+, which is reduced back to P680 by donation of an electron from water. O_2 is produced as a by-product and is released into the atmosphere (see Figure 7.10).

7.3 The Light Reactions

- The photosynthetic electron transport chain (the light reactions) uses the energy of light absorbed by photosystem II and photosystem I to generate reducing power in the form of NADPH. Electrons released by the oxidation of the reaction centre chloro-

phyll of photosystem II are passed along an electron transport chain. To get all the way down the chain, electrons become excited again at photosystem I, and then they are delivered to $NADP^+$ as final electron acceptor. $NADP^+$ is reduced to NADPH (see Figure 7.11).

- In a way similar to respiratory electron transport, the process of photosynthetic electron transport results in the establishment of a proton gradient, in this case, across the thylakoid membrane. The proton gradient is used to generate ATP through chemiosmosis using the ATP synthase complex embedded in the thylakoid membrane (see Figure 7.11).

- Besides linear electron transport from photosystem II through photosystem I, electrons can also flow in a cycle around photosystem I, building the H^+ concentration and allowing extra ATP to be produced, but no NADPH (see Figure 7.13).

7.4 The Calvin Cycle

- In the Calvin cycle, CO_2 is reduced and converted into carbohydrate by the addition of electrons and hydrogen carried by the NADPH produced in the light-dependent reactions. ATP, also derived from the light-dependent reactions, provides energy. The key enzyme of the light-independent reactions is Rubisco (RuBP carboxylase/oxygenase), which catalyzes the reaction that combines CO_2 with a molecule of ribulose-1,5-bisphosphate (RuBP), producing two molecules of the three-carbon compound 3-phosphoglycerate (see Figure 7.14).

- For three turns of the Calvin cycle, one molecule of the three-carbon sugar glyceraldehyde-3-phosphate (G3P) is synthesized. G3P is the starting point for synthesis of glucose (requires two G3P molecules), sucrose, starch, and other organic molecules.

7.5 Photorespiration and CO_2-Concentrating Mechanisms

- Oxygen is a competitive inhibitor of Rubisco—it can compete with CO_2 for the active site. As an oxygenase, Rubisco catalyzes the combination of RuBP with O_2 rather than CO_2, forming toxic products that cannot be used in photosynthesis. The toxic products are eliminated by reactions that release carbon in inorganic form as CO_2, greatly reducing the efficiency of photosynthesis. The entire process is called photorespiration because it uses oxygen and releases CO_2 (see Figure 7.16).

- To avoid photorespiration, a range of plants and algae have evolved mechanisms to decrease the amount of O_2 that is present at the site of Rubisco and carbon fixation.

- In aquatic photoautotrophs, an ATP-dependent process pumps bicarbonate (HCO_3^-) into the cell, which is converted to CO_2 through the action of the enzyme carbonic anhydrase. This makes the CO_2/O_2 ratio greater at the site of Rubisco (Figure 7.17).

- Some plants have evolved C_4 metabolism whereby CO_2 from the air is first fixed by a carboxylase that does not have oxygenase activity into the four-carbon compound that occurs in mesophyll cells (the site of the Calvin cycle in C_3 plants). Following transport into bundle sheath cells, decarboxylation of a related four-carbon compound releases CO_2 at the site of Rubisco. This results in the CO_2/O_2 ratio being very high (see Figures 7.19 and 7.20).

- CAM plants also first fix CO_2 into oxaloacetate and then generate CO_2 for the Calvin cycle. Here both the carbon fixation and the Calvin cycle occur in mesophyll cells, but they are separated by time; initial carbon fixation occurs at night and the Calvin cycle occurs during the day (see Figure 7.20).

7.6 Photosynthesis and Cellular Respiration Compared

- Photosynthesis occurs in the cells of plants that contain chloroplasts, whereas cellular respiration occurs in all cells. The overall reactions of the two processes are essentially the reverse of each other, with the reactants of one being the products of the other (see Figure 7.21).

Questions

Self-Test Questions

1. What is the correct definition of the term *autotroph*?
   a. an organism that uses light energy to live.
   b. an organism that can synthesize carbohydrates.
   c. an organism that consumes the molecules found in other organisms.
   d. an organism that synthesizes organic molecules using inorganic carbon.

2. Why is chlorophyll green in colour?
   a. Because chlorophyll only absorbs green photons of light.
   b. Because green photons of light excite electrons within chlorophyll.
   c. Because chlorophyll lacks an excited state that matches the energy of a green photon.
   d. Because green photons of light are not of high enough energy to excite electrons in chlorophyll.

3. Which statement about light reactions is correct?
   a. The light reactions cause an increase in the pH of the thylakoid lumen.
   b. $O2$ is the source of electrons that result in the reduction of $P680^+$ back to P680.
   c. Ferredoxin shuttles electrons from the cytochrome complex to photosystem I.
   d. The electrons that pass along the electron transport chain come from the oxidation of P680.
   e. Chlorophyll molecules in the antenna complexes of the photosystems are oxidized by light absorption.

4. What is the minimum number of photons that need to be absorbed by the photosystems to reduce three molecules of $NADP^+$ to NADPH by the photosynthetic electron transport chain?
   a. 3   c. 12
   b. 6   d. 18

5. Which of the following statements correctly distinguishes between linear electron transport and cyclic electron transport?
   a. NADH is generated only during linear electron transport.
   b. Photosystem I is used only during linear electron transport.
   c. Photosystem II is required only during cyclic electron transport.
   d. A proton-motive force is generated only during cyclic electron transport.

6. The Calvin cycle is sometimes called the light-independent reactions. This is missleading since the Calvin cycle will stop operating after a plant is placed in the dark. Why will it stop?
   a. Rubisco is rapidly degraded in the dark.
   b. NAD^+ generated by the light reactions is needed to activate PGA.
   c. In the dark, oxygen builds up in the chloroplast and inhibits Rubisco activity.
   d. The Calvin cycle requires a constant supply of ATP generation by the light reactions.

7. Which of the following statements about the Calvin cycle is correct?
   a. The cycle stops if the regeneration of RuBP is prevented.
   b. After three turns one molecule of glucose is synthesized.
   c. It takes three turns of the cycle to fix one molecule of CO_2.
   d. It takes nine molecules of ATP to fix one molecule of CO_2.

8. Why don't C_4 plants photorespire?
   a. They lack mitochondria.
   b. They express high levels of carbonic anhydrase.
   c. The CO_2/O_2 ratio in their chloroplasts is very high.
   d. The Rubisco in their chloroplasts only has affinity for CO_2.

9. Compared to C_3 plants, one often find C_4 plants in drier habitats. Why is that?
   a. They have a larger root system.
   b. They can keep their stomata closed at all times.
   c. They don't have to keep their stomata open as long.
   d. Unlike C_3 plants, the leaves of C_4 plants are covered by a waxy cuticle.

10. In what way are the light reactions of photosynthesis similar to aerobic respiration?
   a. Both processes synthesize NADPH.
   b. Both processes use substrate phosphorylation to synthesize ATP.
   c. Chemiosmosis using the proton-motive force occurs in both.
   d. Both require oxygen as the final electron acceptor of electron transport.

Questions for Discussion

1. Like other accessory pigments, the carotenoids extend the range of wavelengths absorbed in photosynthesis. They also protect plants from a potentially lethal process known as *photooxidation*. This process begins when excitation energy in chlorophylls drives the conversion of oxygen into reactive oxygen species (ROS) (See Chapter 6), substances that can damage organic compounds and kill cells. When plants that cannot produce carotenoids are grown in light, they bleach white and die. Given this observation, what molecules in the plants are likely to be destroyed by photooxidation?

2. Exposing plants to light at low temperatures increases the damage to photosystem II. Why do you think this is the case?

3. If global warming raises the temperature of our climate significantly, will C3 plants or C4 plants be favored by natural selection? How will global warming change the geographical distributions of plants?

A cell in mitosis (fluorescence micrograph). The spindle (red) is separating copies of the cell's chromosomes (green) before cell division.

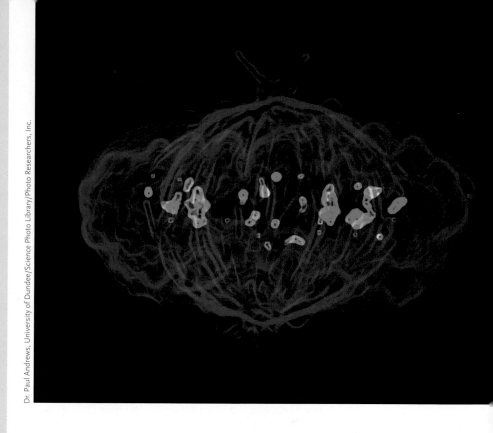

Dr. Paul Andrews, University of Dundee/Science Photo Library/Photo Researchers, Inc.

STUDY PLAN

8.1 The Cycle of Cell Growth and Division: An Overview

8.2 The Cell Cycle in Prokaryotic Organisms

8.2a Replication Occupies Most of the Cell Cycle in Rapidly Dividing Prokaryotic Cells

8.2b Replicated Chromosomes Are Distributed Actively to the Halves of the Prokaryotic Cell

8.2c Mitosis Has Evolved from an Early Form of Binary Fission

8.3 Mitosis and the Eukaryotic Cell Cycle

8.3a Chromosomes Are the Genetic Units Divided by Mitosis

8.3b Interphase Extends from the End of One Mitosis to the Beginning of the Next Mitosis

8.3c After Interphase, Mitosis Proceeds in Five Stages

8.3d Cytokinesis Completes Cell Division by Dividing the Cytoplasm between Daughter Cells

8.4 Formation and Action of the Mitotic Spindle

8.4a Animals and Plants Form Spindles in Different Ways

8.4b Mitotic Spindles May Move Chromosomes by a Combination of Two Mechanisms

8.5 Cell Cycle Regulation

8.5a Cyclins and Cyclin-Dependent Kinases Are the Internal Controls That Directly Regulate Cell Division

8.5b Internal Checkpoints Stop the Cell Cycle if Stages Are Incomplete

8.5c External Controls Coordinate the Mitotic Cell Cycle of Individual Cells with the Overall Activities of the Organism

8.5d Most Cells in a Multicellular Body Cannot Divide Indefinitely

8.5e Cell Cycle Controls Are Lost in Cancer

8.5f Some Cells Are Programmed to Die

8 Cell Cycles

WHY IT MATTERS

As the rainy season recedes in Northern India, rice paddies and other flooded areas begin to dry. These shallow seasonal pools have provided an environment of slow-moving warm water for zebrafish (*Danio rerio*) to spawn **(Figure 8.1, p. 162).** Over the past few months, many millions of cell divisions have fuelled the growth and development of single fertilized eggs into the complex multicellular tissues and organs of these small, boldly striped fish. Most cells in the adults have now stopped dividing and are dedicated to particular functions.

Moving into the fast-running streams that feed the Ganges River, the young zebrafish encounter larger predators, such as knifefish (*Notopterus notopterus*). Imagine for a moment that a zebrafish is attacked by a knifefish; the prey narrowly escapes but not without leaving one of its fins behind in the mouth of the predator. In an amazing feat of cell cycle regulation, the entire zebrafish fin will be regenerated—skin, nerves, muscles, bones, and all—within a week!

As a model system for vertebrate development, the zebrafish has provided a popular tool for researchers to identify the stages of regeneration at the molecular level. (See *The Purple Pages* for more information about zebrafish as model organisms.) In the first step,

Figure 8.1
Zebrafish (*Danio rerio*)

cells lost to wear (shedding skin and gut lining) and tear (wound repair, virus infection) **(Figure 8.2)**. Although the cell division cycle is conceptually simple—grow, divide, grow, divide—repeat for billions of years—regulation of this process must be precise and complex. If cells divide too quickly, daughter cells may be too small or lacking essential cytoplasm or genetic material. If cells divide too slowly, they may grow inefficiently large or accumulate extra chromosomes. All dividing cells must meet the challenge of closely

a.

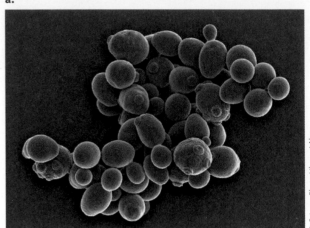

b.

c.

Figure 8.2
Actively dividing cells provide for increased population size of yeast **(a)**, growth of skin **(b)**, and conifer needles. **(c)**

existing skin cells migrate to close the wound and prevent bleeding. Then cells under the new skin form a temporary tissue called a blastema. Blastema cells divide up to 50 times as fast as usual, providing large numbers of daughter cells capable of maturing into new bone, nerve, muscle, and blood vessel cells in response to signal proteins produced by the skin. Once the regenerated fin has reached its normal size and shape, the new cells stop growing and dividing.

The remarkable ability of eukaryotic cells to coordinate their growth and division, always yielding daughter cells in a timely fashion with a complete set of genetic material, is the focus of this chapter. In particular, we intend for you to appreciate how this coordination is achieved through the interplay of three cellular processes: (1) DNA replication, (2) a dynamically changing cytoskeleton, and (3) cell cycle "checkpoints." To provide a hint of what the ancestral cell division process may have been like, the chapter opens with a look at cell division in prokaryotic organisms and the simpler eukaryotes.

8.1 The Cycle of Cell Growth and Division: An Overview

While regenerating a lost body part is certainly dramatic at the scale of an individual organism, we invite you now to consider the wider, grander, view of the relevance of the cell division cycle. Scientists have known since the early nineteenth century that all life on Earth is composed of cells and their products. All cells, in all organisms that have ever lived, are descended from previous cells in an unbroken chain of cell division stretching billions of years into the past. New progeny cells are needed for expanding population size (single-celled organisms), multicellular tissue growth (new leaves), asexual reproduction, and replacement of

coordinating their growth, DNA replication, and cell division in the face of a changing environment.

Although this chapter highlights the characteristics of dividing cells, it is important for you to realize that most cells in the body of a multicellular organism are *not* destined to divide any time soon, if ever. In fact, some cells may even be programmed to die immediately!

8.2 The Cell Cycle in Prokaryotic Organisms

A newly formed prokaryotic cell, such as the bacterium *Escherichia coli,* must double in size, replicate its circular chromosome, and then move each of the resulting two daughter chromosomes into its own progeny cell during cell division. The entire mechanism of prokaryotic cell division, called **binary fission**, that is, splitting or dividing into two parts, can be thought of in three periods, as shown in **Figure 8.3.** Following birth, cells may grow for some time before initiating DNA synthesis (B period). Once the chromosomes are replicated and separated to opposite ends of the cell (C period), the membrane pinches together between them and two daughter cells are formed (D period).

8.2a Replication Occupies Most of the Cell Cycle in Rapidly Dividing Prokaryotic Cells

All bacteria and archaea use DNA as their hereditary information, and the vast majority of species package it all in a single, circular chromosome of double-stranded DNA (Figure 8.3, step 1). Although the chromosome is shown extended in Figure 8.3 for the purposes of illustration, it is actually compacted in a central region called the **nucleoid** throughout the cell cycle (see Figure 2.7, Chapter 2). When nutrients are abundant, prokaryotic cells have no need for a B period since they can grow quickly enough to divide their cytoplasm as soon as DNA replication is complete and chromosomes are separated. Under such optimal conditions, populations of *E. coli* cells can double every 20 minutes.

8.2b Replicated Chromosomes Are Distributed Actively to the Halves of the Prokaryotic Cell

In the 1860s, François Jacob of The Pasteur Institute in Paris, France, proposed a model for the segregation of bacterial chromosomes to the daughter cells in which the two chromosomes attach to the plasma membrane near the middle of the cell and separate as a new plasma membrane is added between the two sites during cell elongation. The essence of this model is that chromosome separation is passive. However, current research indicates that bacterial chromosomes rapidly separate in an active way that is linked to DNA replication events and is independent of cell elongation. The new model is summarized in the C period of Figure 8.3.

Replication of the bacterial chromosome commences at a specific region called the **origin of replication** (*ori*). The *ori* is in the middle of the cell, where the enzymes for DNA replication are located. Once the *ori* has been duplicated, the two new origins migrate toward the two opposite ends (poles) of the cell as replication continues for the rest of the chromosome (see Figure 8.3, step 3). The mechanism that propels the two replicated chromosomes to their respective ends of the cell is still unknown. Next, cytoplasmic division is associated with an inward constriction of a **cytokinetic ring** of cytoskeletal proteins. New plasma membrane and cell wall material is assembled to divide the cell into two equal parts (see Figure 8.3, step 5).

8.2c Mitosis Has Evolved from an Early Form of Binary Fission

The prokaryotic mechanism works effectively because most prokaryotic organisms have only a single chromosome. Thus, if a daughter cell receives at least one copy of the chromosome, its genetic information is complete. By contrast, the genetic information of eukaryotes is

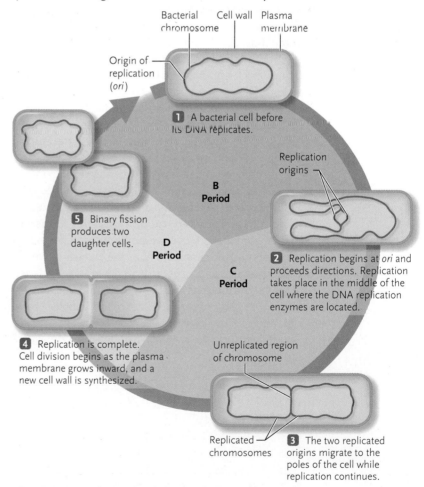

Figure 8.3
The bacterial cell cycle. During the B period, from birth to the initiation of DNA replication, the cell grows in size. The chromosome is replicated and the resulting daughter chromosomes move to opposite ends during the C period. Then the cell divides by binary fission during the D period. In very fast growing cultures, the B period may be nonexistent; cells may be born with chromosomes that are already partly replicated!

divided among several chromosomes, with each chromosome containing a much greater length of DNA than a prokaryotic chromosome does. If a daughter cell fails to receive a copy of even one chromosome, the effects are usually lethal. It is also important to note that, during most of the cell cycle, eukaryotic chromosomes are contained within the nuclear membrane. Bacteria and archaea do not have an internal membrane around their nucleoid. Therefore, eukaryotic cellular and chromosomal architecture demands a quite different mechanism for distributing chromosomes to daughter cells. Mitosis is that different mechanism, and we will examine this process in detail later in the chapter (see **Figure 8.7, p. 168**). For now, just be aware that one of the central innovations of the evolution of mitosis is the ability to hold the two newly created molecules of double-stranded DNA (now called **chromatids**) together following DNA synthesis. This enables cells to keep track of such long replicated chromosomes and to orient them relative to the cytoskeleton at the proper time to ensure precise distribution to daughter cells. In most higher eukaryotes, the nuclear membrane disintegrates at the time when chromosomes are being distributed and then reforms around them in daughter cells.

Variations in the mitotic apparatus in modern-day organisms illuminate possible intermediates in the evolutionary pathway to mitosis from some ancestral type of binary fission. For example, in many primitive eukaryotes, such as dinoflagellates (a type of single-celled alga), the nuclear envelope remains intact during mitosis, and the chromosomes bind to the inner membrane of the nuclear membrane. When the nucleus divides, the chromosomes are segregated.

A more advanced form of the mitotic apparatus is seen in yeasts and diatoms (another type of single-celled alga). In these organisms, a **spindle** of microtubules made of polymerized tubulin protein forms and chromosomes segregate to daughter nuclei without the disassembly and reassembly of the nuclear envelope. Current evidence suggests that the type of mitosis seen in yeasts and diatoms and the type of mitosis in animals and higher plants described later in this chapter evolved separately from a common ancestral type.

STUDY BREAK

What are the three main steps in binary fission of prokaryotic organisms?

8.3 Mitosis and the Eukaryotic Cell Cycle

As long as eukaryotes require their daughter cells to be exact genetic copies of the parental cell, mitosis serves very well to divide the replicated DNA equally and precisely. This is the result of three elegantly interrelated systems. One component is an elaborate master program of molecular checks and balances that ensures an orderly and timely progression through the cell cycle (see Figure 8.18). Within the overall regulation of the cell cycle, the process of DNA synthesis replicates each DNA chromosome into two copies with almost perfect fidelity (see Section 12.3). The final system is a structural and mechanical web of interwoven "cables" and "motors" of the cytoskeleton that separates the DNA copies precisely into the daughter cells (see **Figure 8.13, p. 172**). We begin with a look at the behaviour of chromosomes during the cell cycle.

8.3a Chromosomes Are the Genetic Units Divided by Mitosis

In all eukaryotes, the hereditary information of the nucleus is distributed among several linear, double-stranded DNA molecules. These DNA molecules are combined with proteins that stabilize the DNA, assist in packaging DNA during cell division, and influence the expression of individual genes. Each chromosome (*chroma* = colour, when stained with dyes used in light microscopy; *soma* = body; **Figure 8.4**) in a cell is composed of one of these DNA molecules, along with its associated proteins.

Most eukaryotes have two copies of each type of chromosome in their nuclei, and their chromosome complement is said to be **diploid**, or $2n$. For example, humans have 23 different pairs of chromosomes for a diploid number of 46 chromosomes ($2n = 46$). Other eukaryotes, mostly microorganisms, may have only one copy of each type of chromosome in their nucleus, so their chromosome complement is said to be **haploid**, or n. Baker's yeast (*Saccharomyces cerevisiae*) is an example of an organism that can grow as a diploid

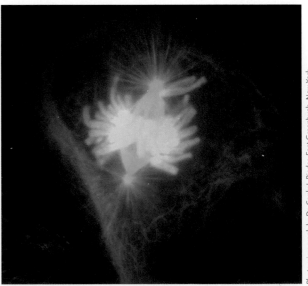

Figure 8.4
Eukaryotic chromosomes (stained blue) during mitosis.

Photomicrograph by Dr. Conly L Rieder, East Greenbush, New York

$(2n = 32)$ and as a haploid $(n = 16)$. Still others, such as many plant species, have three, four, or even more complete sets of chromosomes in each cell. The number of chromosome sets is called the **ploidy** of a cell or species. See Chapter 19 for a look at the role of ploidy in the formation of new species.

Replication of the DNA of each individual chromosome creates two new, identical, molecules called **sister chromatids.** Newly formed sister chromatids are held together at a region called the centromere until mitosis separates them, placing one in each of the two daughter nuclei. As a result of this precise division, each daughter nucleus receives exactly the same number and types of chromosomes, and contains the same genetic information, as the parent cell entering the division. The equal distribution of daughter chromosomes to each of the two cells that result from cell division is called **chromosome segregation.**

CONCEPT FIX The double-strandedness of DNA, the mechanism of cell division, and new vocabulary can lead to confusion about just how many chromosomes are in a particular cell at a particular time. Let's pick the fruit fly *Drosophila melanogaster* as an example organism because all of its genes are contained in only four different chromosomes. Every body cell in a fruit fly for instance, is diploid $(2n)$ and therefore contains two of each of the four distinct *Drosophila* chromosomes—for a total of eight. Each of these eight chromosomes is composed of one double-stranded DNA molecule of the type shown in Figure 12.6, Chapter 12. If the cell is preparing to divide, DNA synthesis, as shown in Figure 12.7, Chapter 12, creates two identical DNA molecules from each of the eight originals. The two new DNA molecules created from each original chromosome remain attached to one another and are now called sister chromatids. (Someone once suggested that these two new molecules should be called twin chromatids because they are identical.) Now here comes the confusing part. Since sister chromatids remain attached to each other at their centromeres following DNA synthesis, the pair of them is still referred to as just one chromosome. Before replication, one chromosome is composed of one DNA molecule; after replication, one chromosome is composed of two DNA molecules. You should see that DNA replication increases the amount of DNA in the nucleus but it does not increase the number of chromosomes. Our *Drosophila* cell has eight DNA molecules in the nucleus before DNA synthesis and eight pairs of molecules after. There are eight chromosomes before DNA synthesis and eight replicated chromosomes after. During cell division, each of the two daughter cells receives one of the two sister chromatids from each replicated chromosome. You should therefore agree to the rather counterintuitive claim that two daughter cells can each receive eight chromosomes even though there were only eight chromosomes in the original cell. ⬡

The precision of chromosome replication and segregation in the mitotic cell cycle creates a group of cells called a clone. Except for rare chance mutations, all cells of a clone are genetically identical. Since all the diverse cell types of a complex multicellular organism arose by mitosis from a single zygote, they should all contain the same genetic information. Forensic scientists rely on this feature of organisms when, for instance, they match the genetic profile of a small amount of tissue (e.g., cells in dog saliva recovered from a bite victim) with that of a blood sample from the suspected animal.

STUDY BREAK

1. What are the three interrelated systems that contribute to the eukaryotic cell cycle?
2. What is a chromosome composed of?

8.3b Interphase Extends from the End of One Mitosis to the Beginning of the Next Mitosis

If cells show an alternating phase of growth and division, they can be thought of as moving through a cell *cycle*. Although the cell cycle is usually a smooth continuum of change in nature, it is helpful to describe discrete *phases* for discussion purposes. Internal regulatory controls trigger each phase, ensuring that the processes of one phase are completed successfully before the next phase can begin. Various internal mechanisms also regulate the overall number of cycles that a cell is allowed. These internal controls may be subject to various external influences caused by other cells or viruses as well as signal molecules, including hormones, growth factors, and death factors.

If we choose to let the formation of a new daughter cell mark the beginning of the cell cycle, then the first and longest phase is **interphase.** During interphase, the cell grows and replicates its DNA in preparation for mitosis (also called the *M phase*) and cytokinesis **(Figure 8.5, p. 167).** Interphase begins as a daughter cell from a previous division cycle enters an initial period of cytoplasmic growth. During this initial growth stage, called the **G$_1$ phase** of the cell cycle, the cell makes various RNAs, proteins, and other types of cellular molecules but not nuclear DNA (the G in G$_1$ stands for *gap,* referring to the absence of DNA synthesis). Then, if the cell is going to divide, DNA replication begins, initiating the **S phase** of the cell cycle (S stands for *synthesis,* meaning DNA synthesis).

During the S phase, the cell duplicates the chromosomal proteins as well as the DNA and continues the synthesis of other cellular molecules. As the S phase is completed, the cell enters the **G$_2$ phase** of the cell cycle (G$_2$ refers to the second gap, during which there is no DNA synthesis). During G$_2$, the cell continues to synthesize RNAs and proteins, including those required for mitosis, and the cell continues to grow. At the end of G$_2$,

How can investigators safely test whether a particular substance is toxic to human cells or whether it can cure or cause cancer? One widely used approach is to work with **cell cultures**—living cells grown in laboratory vessels. Many types of prokaryotic and eukaryotic cells can be grown in this way.

When cell cultures are started from single cells, they form **clones:** barring mutations, all the individuals descended from the original cell are genetically identical. Clones are ideal for experiments in genetics, biochemistry, molecular biology, and medicine because the cells lack genetic differences that could affect the experimental results.

Microorganisms such as yeasts and many bacteria are easy to grow in laboratory cultures. For example, the human intestinal bacterium *E. coli* can be grown in solutions (growth media) that contain only an organic carbon source such as glucose, a nitrogen source, and inorganic salts. The cells may be grown in liquid suspensions or on the surface of a solid growth medium such as an agar gel (agar is a polysaccharide extracted from an alga). Many thousands of bacterial strains are used in a wide variety of experimental studies.

Many types of plant cells can also be cultured as clones in specific growth media. With the addition of plant growth hormones, complete plants can often be grown from single cultured cells. Growing plants from cultured cells is particularly valuable in genetic engineering, in which genes introduced into cultured cells can be tracked in fully developed plants. Plants that have been engineered successfully can then be grown simply by planting their seeds.

Animal cells vary in what is needed to culture them. For many types, the culture medium must contain essential amino acids—that is, the amino acids that the cells cannot make for themselves. In addition, mammalian cells require specific growth factors provided by adding blood serum, the fluid part of the blood left after red and white blood cells are removed.

Even with added serum, many types of normal mammalian cells cannot be grown in long-term cultures. Eventually, the cells stop dividing and die. By contrast, tumour cells often form cultures that grow and divide indefinitely.

The first successful culturing of cancer cells was performed in 1951 in the laboratory of George and Margaret Gey (Johns Hopkins University, Baltimore, Maryland). Gey and Gey's cultures of normal cells died after a few weeks, but the researchers achieved success with a culture of tumour cells from a cancer patient. The cells in culture continued to grow and divide; in fact, descendants of those cells are still being cultured and used for research today. The cells were given the code name *HeLa*, from the first two letters of the patient's first and last names—Henrietta Lacks. Unfortunately, the tumour cells in Lacks's body also continued to grow, and she died within two months of her cancer diagnosis.

Other types of human cells have since been grown successfully in culture, derived from either tumour cells or normal cells that have been "immortalized" by inducing genetic changes that transformed them into tumour-like cells.

---

which marks the end of interphase, mitosis begins. During all the steps of interphase, the chromosomes are relatively loose, but organized, in the nucleus **(Figure 8.6)**.

Usually, G_1 is the only phase of the cell cycle that varies in length for a given species. Thus, whether cells divide rapidly or slowly depends primarily on the length of G_1. Once DNA replication begins, most mammalian cells take about 10 to 12 hours to proceed through the S phase, about 4 to 6 hours to go through G_2, and about 1 to 4 hours to complete mitosis. G_1 is also the stage in which many cell types stop dividing. This state of division arrest is often designated the **G_0 phase** (see Figure 8.5). For example, in humans, cells of the nervous system normally enter G_0 once they are fully mature.

The events of interphase are an important focus of research, particularly the regulatory controls for the transition from the G_1 phase to the S phase and, with it, the commitment to cell division. Understanding the molecular events that regulate the G_1/S phase transition is important because one of the hallmarks of cancer is the loss of normal control of that transition.

CONCEPT FIX Since the emphasis of this chapter is on the behaviour of chromosomes, your attention might get focused on the events of mitosis such that you assume nothing much happens during interphase. Cells are not just "resting up" for the next round of mitosis. During interphase, an appropriate suite of genes is actively expressed to support cell growth and metabolism. It is also during interphase that DNA is replicated. ⬡

8.3c After Interphase, Mitosis Proceeds in Five Stages

If you were to watch a cell going through mitosis **(Figures 8.7, p. 168, and 8.8, p. 170),** you would notice several dramatic changes that signal the progression through different stages: prophase (*pro* = before), prometaphase (*meta* = between), metaphase, anaphase (*ana* = back), and telophase (*telo* = end).

Prophase. During **prophase**, the greatly extended chromosomes that were replicated during interphase

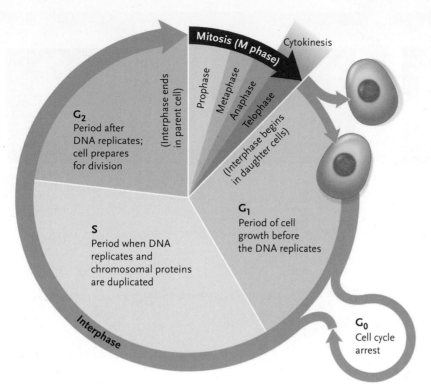

Figure 8.5

The cell cycle. The length of G_1 varies, but for a given cell type, the timing of S phase, G_2 phase, and mitosis is usually relatively uniform. Cytokinesis (red segment) usually begins while mitosis is in progress and reaches completion as mitosis ends. Cells in a state of division arrest are considered to enter a side loop (or shunt) from G_1 phase called G_0 phase.

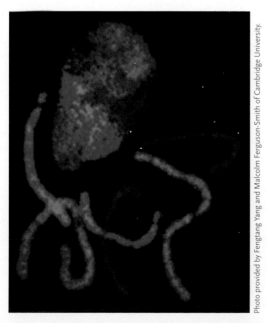

Photo provided by Fengtang Yang and Malcolm Ferguson-Smith of Cambridge University.

Figure 8.6

Chromosomes from the muntjac deer are individually "painted" with fluorescent stain. Note that there are two cells in this picture. The metaphase cell shows two copies of each of three long, condensed chromosomes. The interphase nucleus shows the DNA of different chromosomes organized in close proximity rather than randomly distributed.

begin to *condense* into compact, rodlike structures (see chromatin packaging in Section 12.5). Each diploid human cell, although only about 40 to $50 \mu m$ in diameter, contains $2 m$ of DNA distributed among 23 pairs of chromosomes. Condensation during prophase packs these long DNA molecules into units small enough to be divided successfully during mitosis. As they condense, the chromosomes appear as thin threads under the light microscope. The word *mitosis* (*mitos* = thread) is derived from this threadlike appearance.

While condensation is in progress, the nucleolus becomes smaller and eventually disappears in most species. The disappearance reflects a shutdown of all types of RNA synthesis, including the ribosomal RNA made in the nucleolus.

In the cytoplasm, the **mitotic spindle** (**Figure 8.9, p. 170;** see also **Figure 8.13**) begins to form between the two centrosomes as they start migrating toward the opposite ends of the cell to form the **spindle poles.** The spindle develops as bundles of microtubules that radiate from the spindle poles.

Prometaphase. At the end of prophase, the nuclear envelope breaks down, heralding the beginning of **prometaphase.** Bundles of spindle microtubules grow from centrosomes at the opposing spindle poles toward the centre of the cell. Some of the developing spindle enters the former nuclear area and attaches to the chromosomes.

Although replicated chromosomes are seldom visible as a double structure at this point, it is important for you to remember that each one is made up of two identical sister chromatids held together only at their **centromeres.** By this time, a complex of several proteins, a **kinetochore,** has formed on each chromatid at the centromere. Kinetochore microtubules bind to the kinetochores. These connections determine the outcome of mitosis because they attach the sister chromatids of each chromosome to microtubules leading to the opposite spindle poles (see Figure 8.9, p. 170). Microtubules that do not attach to kinetochores overlap those from the opposite spindle pole.

Metaphase. During **metaphase,** the spindle reaches its final form and the spindle microtubules move the chromosomes into alignment at the spindle midpoint,

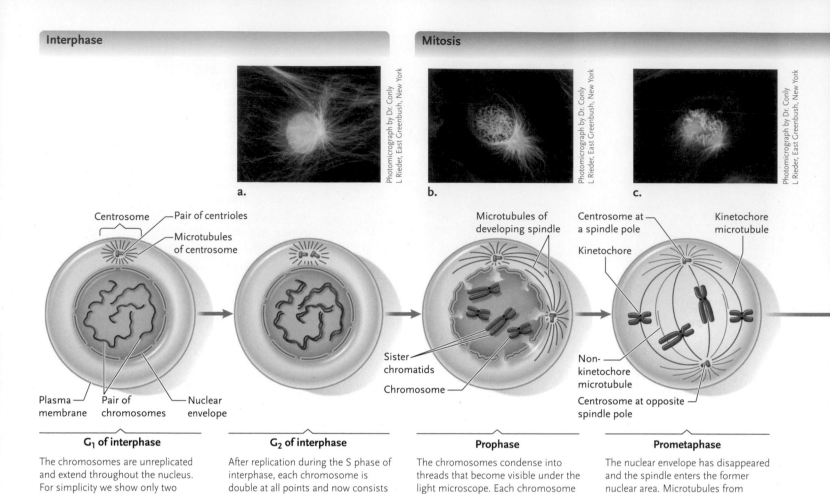

a. Photomicrograph by Dr. Conly L Rieder, East Greenbush, New York

b. Photomicrograph by Dr. Conly L Rieder, East Greenbush, New York

c. Photomicrograph by Dr. Conly L Rieder, East Greenbush, New York

G₁ of interphase

The chromosomes are unreplicated and extend throughout the nucleus. For simplicity we show only two pairs of chromosomes. One of each pair was inherited from one parent, and the other was inherited from the other parent.

G₂ of interphase

After replication during the S phase of interphase, each chromosome is double at all points and now consists of two sister chromatids. The centrioles within the centrosome have also doubled into pairs.

Prophase

The chromosomes condense into threads that become visible under the light microscope. Each chromosome is double as a result of replication. The centrosome has divided into two parts, which are generating the spindle as they separate.

Prometaphase

The nuclear envelope has disappeared and the spindle enters the former nuclear area. Microtubules from opposite spindle poles attach to the two kinetochores of each chromosome.

Figure 8.7

The stages of mitosis. Triple-stained immunoflourescent light micrographs show mitosis in an animal cell (salamander lung). The chromosomes are blue, the spindle and cytoplasmic microtubules are yellow-green, and the intermediate filaments are red. **(a)** Interphase. Microtubules focus on the centrosome, located adjacent to the nucleus. **(b)** Prophase. Chromosomes are well condensed, the nuclear envelope is intact, and the microtubules are organized into radial arrays. **(c)** Prometaphase. The nuclear envelope has broken down to allow the chromosomes to interact with the microtubules originating from two separate centrosomes. **(d)** Metaphase. All of the replicated chromosomes are aligned on the equator of the mature mitotic spindle. **(e)** Anaphase/telophase. Chromosomes have been equally segregated and have decondensed to form two independent daughter nuclei. This cell has just begun cytokinesis. **(f)** The end result of mitosis: two genetically identical daughter cells.

also called the metaphase plate. The chromosomes complete their condensation in this stage and assume their characteristic shape as determined by the location of the centromere and the length and thickness of the chromatid arms.

Only when the chromosomes are all assembled at the spindle midpoint, with the two sister chromatids of each one attached to microtubules leading to opposite spindle poles, can metaphase give way to actual separation of chromatids.

CONCEPT FIX Although you probably think of chromosomes as X shapes, it is important to realize that few chromosomes ever actually look like this. Only chromosomes with their centromere near the middle could ever appear as an X. Only during (pro)metaphase are chromosomes condensed enough to take on any shape at all. ◗

The complete collection of metaphase chromosomes, arranged according to size and shape, forms the **karyotype** of a given species. In many cases, the karyotype is so distinctive that a species can be identified from this characteristic alone. **Figure 8.10, p. 170,** shows a human karyotype.

Anaphase. During **anaphase,** sister chromatids separate and move to opposite spindle poles. The first signs of chromosome movement can be seen at the centromeres as the kinetochores are the first sections to move toward opposite poles. The movement continues until the separated chromatids, now called daughter chromosomes,

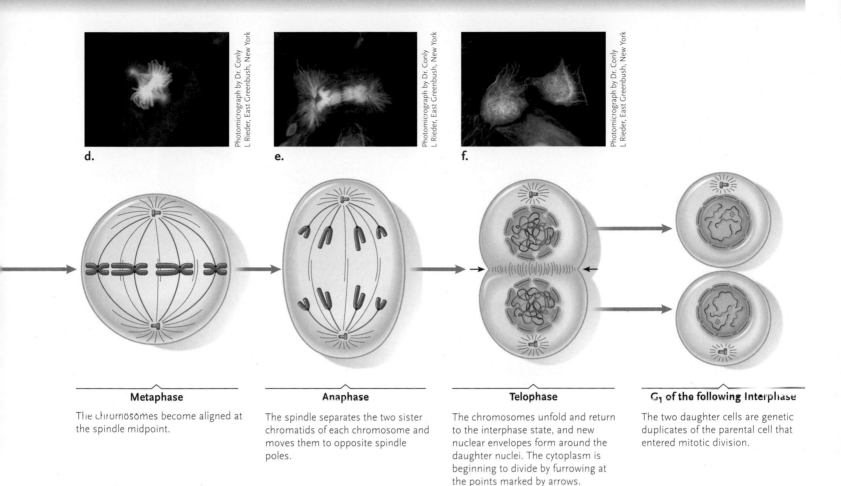

Photomicrograph by Dr. Conly
L Rieder, East Greenbush, New York

Photomicrograph by Dr. Conly
L Rieder, East Greenbush, New York

Photomicrograph by Dr. Conly
L Rieder, East Greenbush, New York

d.   e.   f.

Metaphase	**Anaphase**	**Telophase**	**G₁ of the following Interphase**
The chromosomes become aligned at the spindle midpoint.	The spindle separates the two sister chromatids of each chromosome and moves them to opposite spindle poles.	The chromosomes unfold and return to the interphase state, and new nuclear envelopes form around the daughter nuclei. The cytoplasm is beginning to divide by furrowing at the points marked by arrows.	The two daughter cells are genetic duplicates of the parental cell that entered mitotic division.

have reached the two poles. At this point, chromosome segregation has been completed.

Telophase. During **telophase**, the spindle disassembles and the chromosomes at each spindle pole decondense and return to the extended state typical of interphase. As decondensation proceeds, the nucleolus reappears, RNA transcription resumes, and a new nuclear envelope forms around the chromosomes at each pole, producing the two daughter nuclei. At this point, nuclear division is complete, and the cell has two nuclei.

8.3d Cytokinesis Completes Cell Division by Dividing the Cytoplasm between Daughter Cells

Cytokinesis, the division of the cytoplasm, usually follows the nuclear division stage of mitosis and produces two daughter cells, each containing one of the daughter nuclei. In most cells, cytokinesis begins during telophase or even late anaphase. By the time cytokinesis is completed, the daughter nuclei have progressed to the interphase stage and entered the G_1 phase of the next cell cycle.

Cytokinesis proceeds by different pathways in the different kingdoms of eukaryotic organisms. In animals, protists, and many fungi, a groove, the **furrow**, girdles the cell and gradually deepens until it cuts the cytoplasm into two parts. In plants, a new cell wall, called the **cell plate**, forms between the daughter nuclei and grows laterally until it divides the cytoplasm. In both cases, the plane of cytoplasmic division is determined by the layer of microtubules that persist at the former spindle midpoint.

Furrowing. In furrowing, the layer of microtubules that remains at the former spindle midpoint expands laterally until it stretches entirely across the dividing cell **(Figure 8.11, p. 171)**. As the layer develops, a band of microfilaments forms just inside the plasma membrane, forming a belt that follows the inside boundary of the cell in the plane of the microtubule layer (microfilaments are discussed in Section 2.3f). Powered by motor proteins, the microfilaments slide together, tightening the band and constricting the cell. The constriction forms a groove—the furrow—in the plasma membrane. The furrow gradually deepens, much like the tightening of a drawstring, until the daughter cells

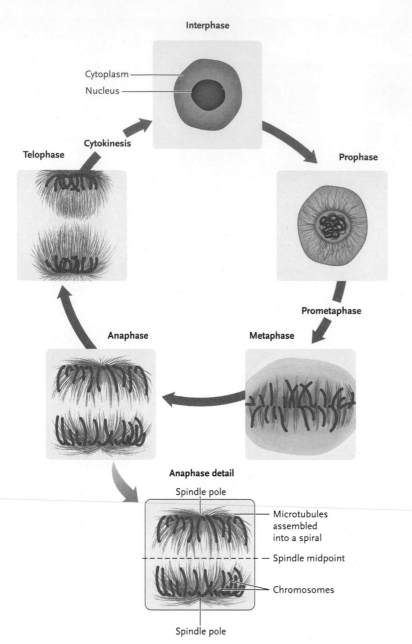

Figure 8.8
Mitosis in the blood lily *Haemanthus*. The chromosomes are stained blue; the spindle microtubules are stained red.

Interphase

Cytoplasm
Nucleus

Cytokinesis
Telophase
Prophase

Anaphase
Metaphase
Prometaphase

Anaphase detail

Spindle pole

Microtubules assembled into a spiral

Spindle midpoint

Chromosomes

Spindle pole

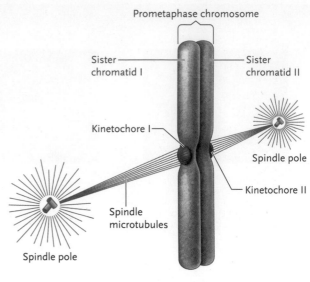

Prometaphase chromosome

Sister chromatid I
Sister chromatid II

Kinetochore I
Spindle pole
Kinetochore II

Spindle microtubules

Spindle pole

Figure 8.9
Spindle connections made by chromosomes at mitotic prometaphase. The two kinetochores of the chromosome connect to opposite spindle poles, ensuring that the chromatids are separated and moved to opposite spindle poles during anaphase.

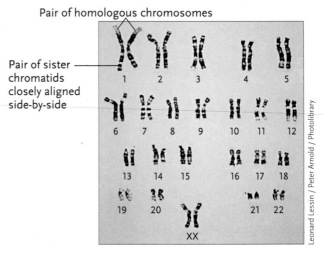

Pair of homologous chromosomes

Pair of sister chromatids closely aligned side-by-side

Leonard Lessin / Peter Arnold / Photolibrary

Figure 8.10
Karyotype of a human female. Note the two X chromosomes.

are completely separated. The cytoplasmic division isolates the daughter nuclei in the two cells and, at the same time, distributes the organelles and other structures (which have also doubled) approximately equally.

Cell Plate Formation. In cell plate formation, the layer of microtubules that persists at the former spindle midpoint serves as an organizing site for vesicles produced by the endoplasmic reticulum (ER) and Golgi complex **(Figure 8.12)**. As the vesicles collect, the layer expands until it spreads entirely across the dividing cell. During this expansion, the vesicles fuse together and their contents assemble into a new cell wall—the cell plate—stretching completely across the former spindle midpoint. The junction separates the cytoplasm

and its organelles into two parts and isolates the daughter nuclei in separate cells. The plasma membranes that line the two surfaces of the cell plate are derived from the vesicle membranes.

STUDY BREAK

1. During which stage(s) of the cell cycle is a chromosome composed of two chromatids?
2. What are the conditions under which a chromosome could appear as an X shape under the microscope?
3. How does cytokinesis differ in plant and animal cells?

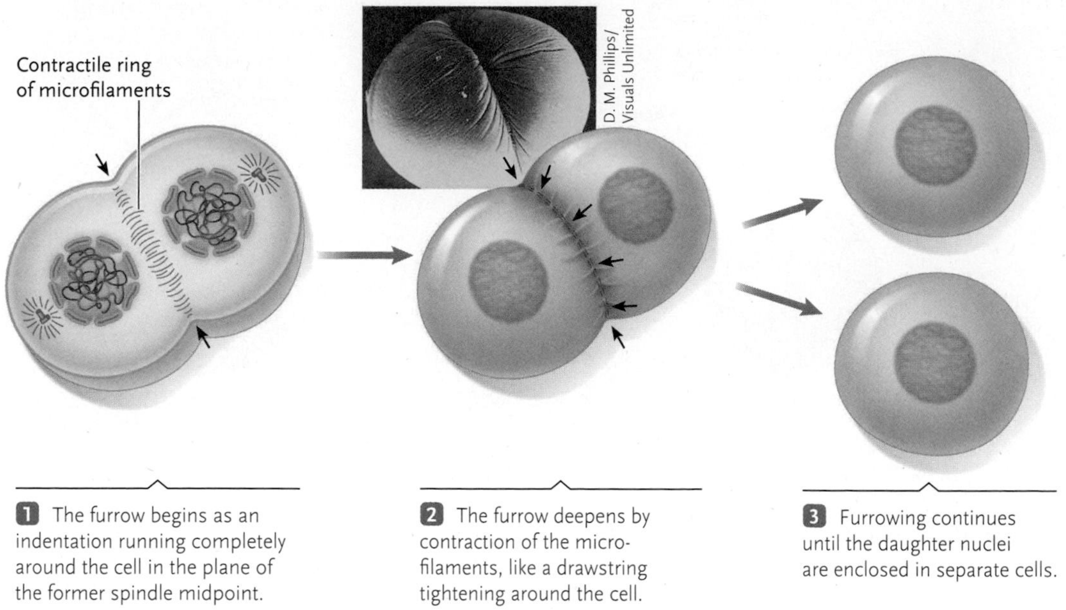

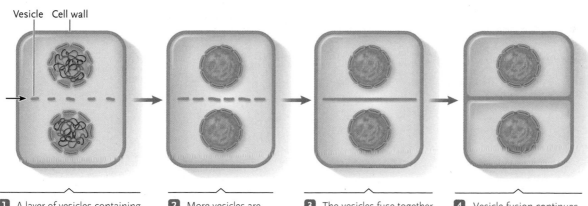

D. M. Phillips/
Visuals Unlimited

Figure 8.11
Cytokinesis by furrowing. The micrograph shows a furrow developing in the first division of a fertilized egg cell.

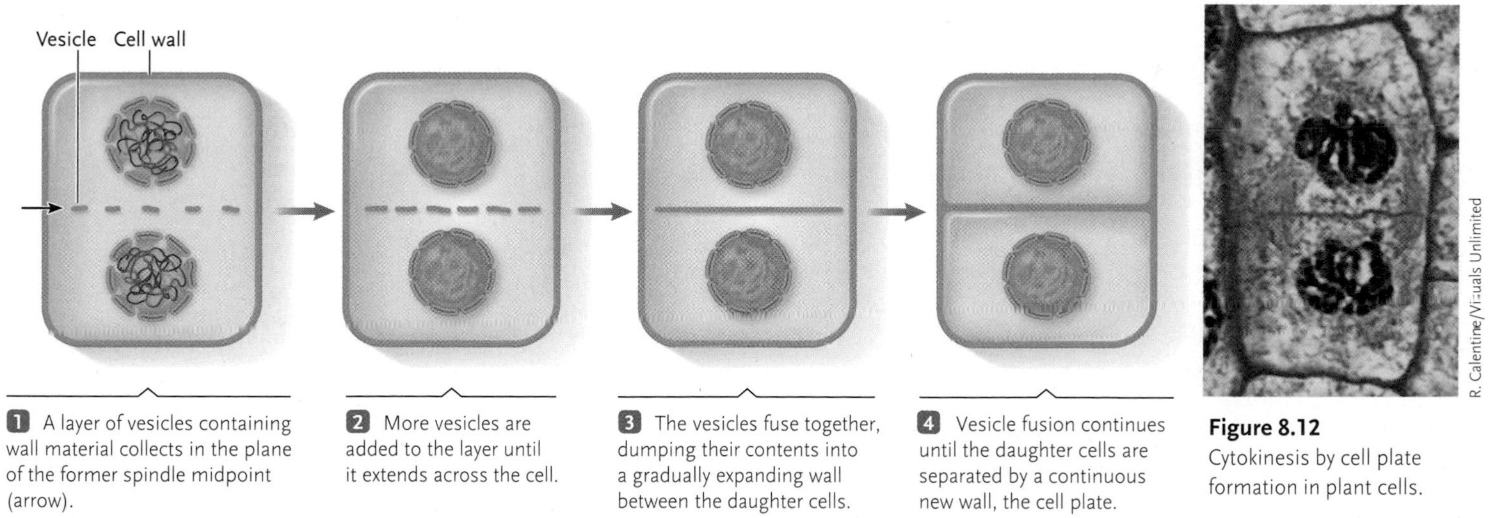

Contractile ring
of microfilaments

1 The furrow begins as an indentation running completely around the cell in the plane of the former spindle midpoint.

2 The furrow deepens by contraction of the microfilaments, like a drawstring tightening around the cell.

3 Furrowing continues until the daughter nuclei are enclosed in separate cells.

Vesicle   Cell wall

1 A layer of vesicles containing wall material collects in the plane of the former spindle midpoint (arrow).

2 More vesicles are added to the layer until it extends across the cell.

3 The vesicles fuse together, dumping their contents into a gradually expanding wall between the daughter cells.

4 Vesicle fusion continues until the daughter cells are separated by a continuous new wall, the cell plate.

R. Calentine/Visuals Unlimited

Figure 8.12
Cytokinesis by cell plate formation in plant cells.

8.4 Formation and Action of the Mitotic Spindle

The mitotic spindle is central to both mitosis and cytokinesis. The spindle is made up of microtubules and their proteins, and its activities depend on their changing patterns of organization during the cell cycle.

Microtubules form a major part of the interphase cytoskeleton of eukaryotic cells. (Section 2.3f outlines the patterns of microtubule organization in the cytoskeleton.) As mitosis approaches, the microtubules disassemble from their interphase arrangement and reorganize into the spindle, which grows until it fills almost the entire cell. This reorganization follows one of two pathways in different organisms, depending on the presence or absence of a *centrosome* during interphase. However, once organized, the basic function of the spindle is the same, regardless of whether a centrosome is present.

8.4a Animals and Plants Form Spindles in Different Ways

Animal cells and many protists have a **centrosome**, a site near the nucleus from which microtubules radiate outward in all directions (**Figure 8.13, p. 172,** step 1). The centrosome is the main **microtubule organizing centre (MTOC)** of the cell, anchoring the microtubule cytoskeleton during interphase and positioning many of the cytoplasmic organelles. The centrosome contains a pair of **centrioles**, usually arranged at right angles to each other. Although centrioles originally appeared to be important in the construction of the mitotic spindle, it has now been shown that they can be removed with no ill effect. The primary function of centrioles is actually to generate the microtubules needed for flagella or cilia, the whiplike extensions that provide cell motility.

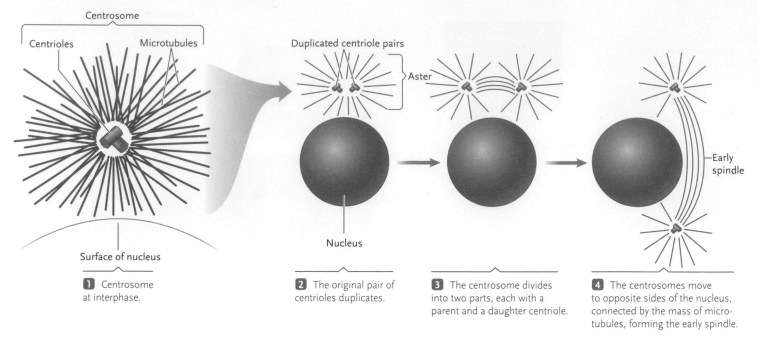

1 Centrosome at interphase.

2 The original pair of centrioles duplicates.

3 The centrosome divides into two parts, each with a parent and a daughter centriole.

4 The centrosomes move to opposite sides of the nucleus, connected by the mass of microtubules, forming the early spindle.

Figure 8.13

The centrosome and its role in spindle formation.

When DNA replicates during the S phase of the cell cycle, the centrioles within the centrosome also duplicate, producing two pairs of centrioles (see Figure 8.13, step 2). As prophase begins in the M phase, the centrosome separates into two parts (step 3). The duplicated centrosomes, with the centrioles inside them, continue to separate until they reach opposite ends of the nucleus (step 4). As the centrosomes move apart, the microtubules between them lengthen and increase in number.

By late prophase, when the centrosomes are fully separated, the microtubules that extend between them form a large mass around one side of the nucleus called the early spindle. When the nuclear envelope subsequently breaks down at the end of prophase, the spindle moves into the region formerly occupied by the nucleus and continues growing until it fills the cytoplasm. The microtubules that extend from the centrosomes also grow in length and extent, producing radiating arrays that appear starlike under the light microscope. Initially named by early microscopists, **asters** are the centrosomes at the spindle tips, which form the poles of the spindle. By dividing the duplicated centrioles, the spindle ensures that, when the cytoplasm divides during cytokinesis, the daughter cells each receive a pair of centrioles.

No centrosome or centrioles are present in angiosperms (flowering plants) or in most gymnosperms, such as conifers. Instead, the spindle forms from microtubules that assemble in all directions from multiple MTOCs surrounding the entire nucleus (see prophase in Figure 8.8). When the nuclear envelope breaks down at the end of prophase, the spindle moves into the former nuclear region, as in animals.

8.4b Mitotic Spindles May Move Chromosomes by a Combination of Two Mechanisms

When fully formed at metaphase, the spindle may contain from hundreds to many thousands of microtubules, depending on the species **(Figure 8.14)**. In almost all eukaryotes, these microtubules are divided into two groups. Some, called kinetochore microtubules, connect the chromosomes to the spindle poles **(Figure 8.15a)**. Others, called nonkinetochore microtubules, extend between the spindle poles without connecting to chromosomes; at the spindle midpoint, the microtubules from one pole overlap with the microtubules from the opposite pole **(Figure 8.15b)**. The separation of the chromosomes at anaphase appears to result from a combination of separate but coordinated movements produced by the two types of microtubules.

The exact mechanism by which chromosomes move is still uncertain; at one time, it was believed that microtubules pulled the chromosomes toward the poles of dividing cells. However, subsequent data suggest that chromosomes "walk" themselves to the poles along stationary microtubules, using motor proteins in their kinetochores **(Figure 8.16)**. The tubulin subunits of the kinetochore microtubules disassemble as the kinetochores pass along them; thus, the microtubules become shorter as the movement progresses (see Figure 8.15a).

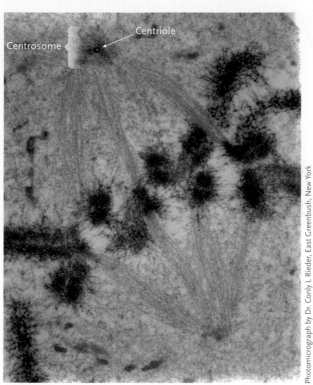

Centrosome

Centriole

Figure 8.14
A fully developed spindle in a mammalian cell. Only microtubules connected to chromosomes have been caught in the plane of this section. One of the centrioles is visible in cross section in the centrosome at the top of the micrograph (arrow). Original magnification × 14 000.

Photomicrograph by Dr. Conly L Rieder, East Greenbush, New York

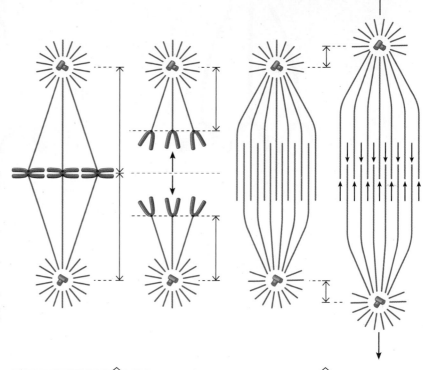

a. The kinetochore microtubules connected to the kinetochores of the chromosomes become shorter, lessening the distance from the chromosomes to the poles.

b. Sliding of the nonkinetochore microtubules in the zone of overlap at the spindle midpoint pushes poles farther apart and increases the total length of the spindle.

Figure 8.15
The two microtubule-based movements of the anaphase spindle.

The movement is similar to pulling yourself, hand over hand, up a rope as it falls apart behind you.

Evidence supporting kinetochore-based movement comes from experiments in which researchers tagged kinetochore microtubules with a microscopic beam of ultraviolet light, producing bleached sites that could be seen in the light microscope **(Figure 8.17, p. 174).** As the chromosomes moved to the spindle poles, the bleached sites stayed in the same place. This result showed that the kinetochore microtubules do not move much with respect to the poles during the anaphase movement.

In nonkinetochore microtubule-based movement, the entire spindle is lengthened, pushing the poles farther apart (see Figure 8.15b). The pushing movement is presumably produced by microtubules sliding over one another in the zone of overlap, powered by proteins acting as microtubule motors. In many species, the nonkinetochore microtubules also push the poles apart by growing in length as they slide.

STUDY BREAK

1. What is the role of the centrosome?
2. What is the role of the kinetochore?

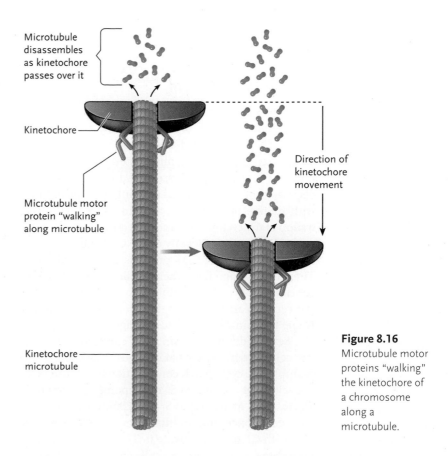

Microtubule disassembles as kinetochore passes over it

Kinetochore

Microtubule motor protein "walking" along microtubule

Direction of kinetochore movement

Kinetochore microtubule

Figure 8.16
Microtubule motor proteins "walking" the kinetochore of a chromosome along a microtubule.

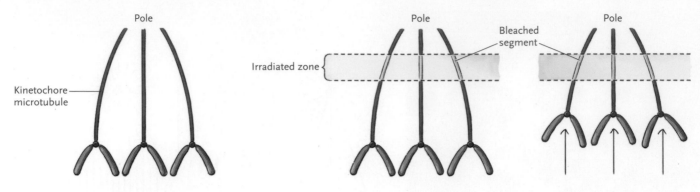

Figure 8.17

Experiment demonstrating that kinetochore microtubules remain stationary as chromosomes move during anaphase.

8.5 Cell Cycle Regulation

We have noted that a number of internal and external regulatory mechanisms control the mitotic cell cycle. As part of the internal controls, the cell cycle has built-in **checkpoints** to prevent critical phases from beginning until the previous phases are completed. Hormones, growth factors, and other external controls coordinate the cell cycle with the needs of an organism by stimulating or inhibiting division. Some key research contributing to our understanding of cell cycle regulation, particularly defining the genes involved and their protein products, was done using yeast. *The Purple Pages* section describes yeast and its role in research in more detail.

8.5a Cyclins and Cyclin-Dependent Kinases Are the Internal Controls That Directly Regulate Cell Division

Cyclin-dependent kinases (CDKs) are major players in the regulation of cell division, directly affecting progression through the cell cycle. CDKs are protein kinases, enzymes that add phosphate groups to target proteins. CDK enzymes are called cyclin dependent because they are "switched on" only when combined with another protein called a **cyclin.** Since the concentration of the cyclins rises and falls during the cell cycle, so does the enzyme activity of the CDKs (even though the concentration of CDK proteins remains constant). The name *cyclin* reflects these cyclic fluctuations in its concentration. R. Timothy Hunt, of the Imperial Cancer Research Fund in London, U.K., received a Nobel Prize in 2001 for discovering cyclins.

Several different cyclin:CDK combinations regulate cell cycle transitions at different checkpoints. For example, the cyclin:CDK combination that controls the cell cycle at the G_1-to-S checkpoint is shown in **Figure 8.18.** At the G_1-to-S checkpoint, cyclin E has reached a concentration high enough to form a complex with CDK2 and activate it. The CDK2 then phosphorylates a number of cell cycle control target proteins, which trigger the cell to make the transition into the S phase. After the transition is made, the cyclin E is degraded, less is available for binding to CDK2, and therefore kinase activity decreases. CDK2 becomes activated again when cyclin E levels rise at the next G_1-to-S checkpoint, after mitosis. Similar events, with a different cyclin:CDK combination, occur to release the G_2-to-M checkpoint referred to below.

8.5b Internal Checkpoints Stop the Cell Cycle if Stages Are Incomplete

The cyclin:CDK combinations directly control the cell cycle, but other factors within the cell act as indirect controls by altering the activity of the cyclin:CDK complexes. At each key checkpoint, regulatory events block the cyclin:CDK complex from triggering the associated cell cycle transition until the actions of a previous phase are successfully completed. For example, the cyclin B:CDK1 complex stimulates the cell to enter the M phase out of the G_2 phase. However, until the cell is ready to enter mitosis, phosphorylation of a site on CDK1 keeps it inactive even though it is bound to cyclin B. When the cell is ready, a phosphatase removes the inhibitory phosphate, the CDK1 becomes active, and the cell is moved into mitosis.

Control at checkpoints is exercised in many circumstances. For instance, if some of the DNA remains unreplicated during the S phase, the cell slows its progress during the G_2 phase to allow more time for replication to be completed. Similarly, if radiation or chemicals damage DNA, inhibitory events prevent the onset of S phase to give the cell an opportunity to repair the damage.

8.5c External Controls Coordinate the Mitotic Cell Cycle of Individual Cells with the Overall Activities of the Organism

The internal controls that regulate the cell cycle are modified by signal molecules that originate from outside the dividing cells. In animals, these signal

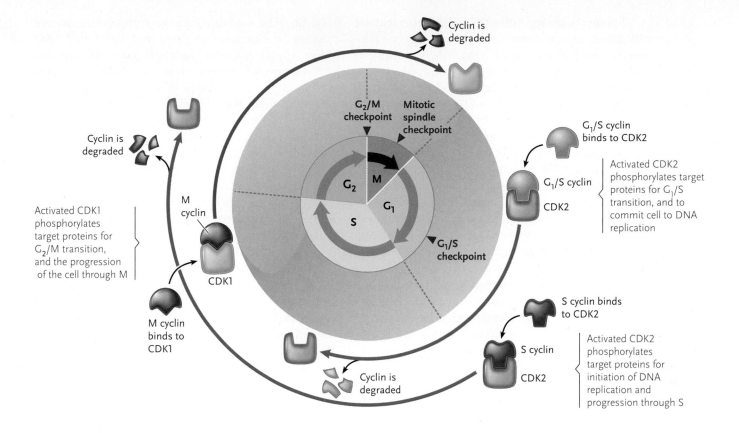

Figure 8.18

Cyclin:CDK control of the G_1-to-S and G_2-to-M transitions of the cell cycle.

molecules include the peptide hormones and similar proteins called growth or death factors.

Many of these external factors bind to receptors at the cell surface, which respond by triggering reactions inside the cell. These reactions often include steps that add phosphate groups to the cyclin:CDK complexes, thereby affecting their function. The overall effect is to speed, slow, or stop the progress of cell division, depending on the particular hormone or factor and the internal pathway that is stimulated. Some growth factors are even able to break the arrest of cells shunted into the G_0 stage and return them to active division. (Hormones, growth factors, and other signal molecules are part of the cell communication system, as discussed in Chapter 5.)

Cell-surface receptors in animal cells also recognize contact with other cells or with molecules of the extracellular matrix. The contact triggers internal reaction pathways that inhibit division by arresting the cell cycle, usually in the G_1 phase. The response, called **contact inhibition,** stabilizes cell growth in fully developed organs and tissues. As long as the cells of most tissues are in contact with one another or with the extracellular matrix, they are shunted into the G_0 phase and prevented from dividing. If the contacts are broken, the freed cells often enter rounds of division.

Contact inhibition is easily observed in cultured mammalian cells grown on a glass or plastic surface.

In such cultures, division proceeds until all the cells are in contact with their neighbours in a continuous, unbroken, single layer. At this point, division stops. If a researcher then scrapes some of the cells from the surface, cells at the edges of the "wound" are released from inhibition and divide until they form a continuous layer and all the cells are again in contact with their neighbours.

8.5d Most Cells in a Multicellular Body Cannot Divide Indefinitely

In 1961, Leonard Hayflick and Paul Moorhead reported that normal human skin cells eventually stopped dividing when grown in artificial culture. This loss of proliferative ability over time is called **cellular senescence,** and scientists have been searching for the *Hayflick factors* that are responsible for it. We consider two candidates: DNA damage and telomere shortening.

The progressive accumulation of random damage to a cell's DNA sequence, or its chromosome structure, or even the genes coding for the enzyme machinery needed to repair such damage, is perhaps the most intuitive Hayflick factor. One would expect "older" cells to have diminished function if they have suffered mutations in genes controlling critical activities.

Telomeres are repetitive DNA sequences that are added to the ends of chromosomes by the enzyme telomerase. Since DNA replication machinery is unable to replicate the entire ends of linear chromosomes, telomere sequence is lost at each round of replication (see Figure 12.18, Chapter 12). Once telomeres diminish to a certain minimum length, cells stop dividing (senesce) and may die.

You might wonder why we do not just take a pill to stimulate our telomerase, rejuvenate our cells, and extend our life span. It turns out that cellular senescence is an important antitumour mechanism. Some researchers have stimulated the telomerase of cultured cells: they become "immortal" and divide out of control. Mice that have been engineered to lack telomerase, and therefore suffer faster senescence, are significantly *resistant* to cancer. It seems that by the time cells are short on telomeres, many of them are also a long way toward cancerous growth, as described below.

8.5e Cell Cycle Controls Are Lost in Cancer

Cancer occurs when cells lose the normal controls that determine when and how often they will divide. Cancer cells divide continuously and uncontrollably, producing a rapidly growing mass called a tumour **(Figure 8.19)**. Cancer cells also typically lose their adhesions to other cells and often become actively mobile. As a result, in a process called metastasis, they tend to break loose from an original tumour, spread throughout the body, and grow into new tumours in other body regions. Metastasis is promoted by changes that defeat contact inhibition and alter the cell surface molecules that link cells together or to the extracellular matrix.

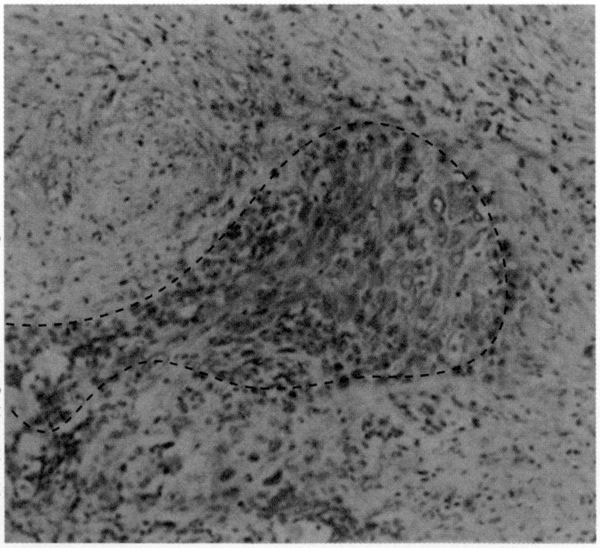

Growing tumours damage surrounding normal tissues by compressing them and interfering with blood supply and nerve function. Tumours may also break through barriers such as the outer skin, internal cell layers, or the gut wall. The breakthroughs cause bleeding, open the body to infection by microorganisms, and destroy the separation of body compartments necessary for normal function. Both compression and breakthroughs can cause pain that, in advanced cases, may become extreme. As tumours increase in mass, the actively growing and dividing cancer cells may deprive normal cells of their required nutrients, leading to generally impaired body functions, muscular weakness, fatigue, and weight loss.

Cancer cells have typically accumulated mutations in a variety of different genes that promote uncontrolled cell division or metastasis. Before they undergo mutation, many of these genes code for components of the cyclin:CDK system that regulates cell division; others encode proteins that regulate gene expression, form cell surface receptors, or make up elements of the signalling pathways controlled by the receptors. When mutated, the genes, called **oncogenes**, encode altered versions of these products.

For example, a mutation in a gene that codes for a surface receptor might result in a protein that is constantly active even without binding the intended extracellular signal molecule. As a result, the internal reaction pathways triggered by the receptor, which induce cell division, are continually stimulated. Another mutation, this time in a cyclin gene, could result in increased cyclin:CDK binding that triggers DNA replication and the rest of the cell cycle. Cancer, oncogenes, and the alterations that convert normal genes to oncogenes are discussed in further detail in Chapter 14.

8.5f Some Cells Are Programmed to Die

Normal development of multicellular organisms is a highly regulated balance between cell proliferation and cell death. Programmed cell death, called **apoptosis**, appears to be a very ancient mechanism common to all multicellular eukaryotes studied so far. Initiation of cell death can result from either internal or external signals. The nematode *Caenorhabditis elegans* is one useful model organism to study this signalling because all adult animals have exactly the same number of cells **(Figure 8.20a)**.

In addition, the fate of each of these cells, from the zygote to the adult, can be tracked with a light microscope. Detailed studies of the 1090 cells that are generated to form an adult reveal that 131 of them not only stop dividing—they stop living.

The apoptosis machinery in *C. elegans* is available in all its cells, waiting in an inactive state for the right trigger. The main "executioner" enzyme is one of a family of normally inactive proteases, called **caspases**,

Courtesy of Professor Pierre Chambon, Institut de Génétique et de Biologie Moléculaire et Cellulaire, University of Strasbourg. Reprinted by permission from Nature 348:699. Copyright 1990 Macmillan Magazines, Ltd.

Figure 8.19
A mass of tumour cells (dashed line) embedded in normal tissue. As is typical, the tumour cells appear to be more densely packed because they have less cytoplasmic volume than normal cells. Original magnification × 270.

MOLECULE BEHIND BIOLOGY 8.2

Roscovitine

Screening of a wide variety of artificially modified adenine molecules has led to the discovery of a group of compounds related to plant cytokinin hormones that selectively inhibit CDKs by competing for (and blocking) their ATP binding site. The example shown below, roscovitine, has antitumour and antiviral activity resulting from stimulation of cell death in affected cells. Note the adenine in each molecule (rectangle).

FIGURE 1
(a) *Roscovitine.* **(b)** *The plant cytokinin hormone zeatin.* **(c)** *ATP.*

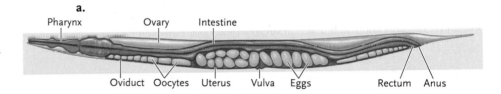

and is coded by the *cell death abnormal* gene, *CED-3* **(Figure 8.20b)**. If a cell is destined to die by apoptosis, the cascade begins when internal developmental cues stimulate expression of a gene called *egg laying deficient, EGL-1*. EGL-1 protein then binds to CED-9 protein, resulting in the release of bound CED-4 protein and the formation of an active apoptosome. CED-3 caspase is thus activated, and cell death ensues. The causes of death are nuclear DNA degradation and disrupted mitochondrial function. The corpses of dead cells are engulfed and eaten by neighbouring cells. The 2002 Nobel Prize in Physiology or Medicine was awarded jointly to Sydney Brenner, Robert Horvitz, and John Sulston for their discoveries concerning "genetic regulation of organ development and programmed cell death" in *C. elegans*. The Experimental Research Organisms (see *The Purple Pages*) section describes *C. elegans* and its role in research in more detail.

Removing cells that are surplus for development is one function of apoptosis, but why are other cells programmed to die? We hope you will agree that it would be beneficial for an organism to provoke apoptosis in cells suffering severe DNA damage, viral infection, or mutations leading to uncontrolled division. Sometimes perfectly normal and healthy cells die by apoptosis. For instance, the cells that make up xylem elements in the vascular tissue of woody plants actually function as "skeletons." They must die to fulfill their function as hollow, water-conducting pipes.

The overview of the cell cycle and its regulation presented in this chapter only hints at the complexity of cell growth and division. The likelihood of any given cell dividing is determined by weighing a variety of internal signals in the context of external

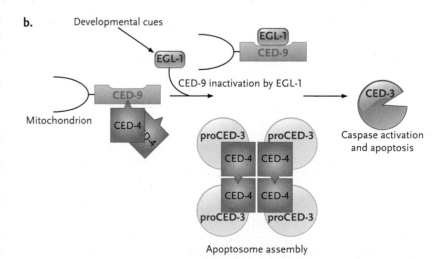

Figure 8.20
(a) The adult nematode "worm" *Caenorhabditis elegans* is about 1 mm long and is composed of 959 living cells. **(b)** The main cascade of programmed cell death in *C. elegans*. Cells destined to die express EGL-1 protein that, by binding to mitochondrial-bound CED-9, releases CED-4 protein. A complex of CED-4 then activates the main "executioner" caspase protease enzyme, CED-3.

cues from the environment. If a cell is destined to divide, then the problem of accurately replicating and partitioning its DNA requires a highly regulated, intricately interrelated series of mechanisms. Although male Australian Jack Jumper ants (*Myrmecia pilosula*) have only one chromosome to deal with, think of the problems faced by the fern *Ophioglossum pycnostichum*, which has 1260 chromosomes in each cell!

STUDY BREAK

1. Explain how the *activity* of CDKs can rise and fall with each turn of the cell cycle, whereas the *concentration* of these enzymes remains constant.
2. What observation do Hayflick factors explain?
3. What is metastasis?

PEOPLE BEHIND BIOLOGY 8.3
Dr. John Dick, University of Toronto

One of the best places to find actively cycling cells in a vertebrate body is in bone marrow. It is here that hematopoietic stem cells divide to produce progeny cells capable of proliferating and differentiating into the various specialized cells needed to maintain the liquid tissue called blood.

One of the best places to try to understand this developmental process, as well as the mechanisms underlying human blood disorders and cancer (leukemia), is the laboratory of John Dick at the University of Toronto. Dick is a professor of medical genetics and microbiology, a fellow of the Royal Society of Canada, and Canada Research Chair in Stem Cell Biology. Originally from rural Manitoba, he now heads a team of coworkers and international collaborators from his office in the MaRS

Discovery District in downtown Toronto.

One of Dick's most powerful tools, one that gained him international recognition, is his system for modelling the production of blood by establishing human hematopoietic cells in mice. That is, he creates mice that make human blood instead of their usual mouse blood. Mice that make human blood also show human blood disorders, and Dick's team has been able to study the initiation and progression of human leukemia entirely in mice. This mouse model system provides an opportunity to better understand the genetic changes involved in leukemia and the effectiveness of emerging therapies.

Dick's sustained success arises from his ability to locate stem cells and understand their biology. His

original discovery of the role of aberrant stem cells at the root of leukemia is now seen as the opening line of a story that is fundamentally altering the prevailing view of cancer and its treatment. If Dick is correct in his hypothesis that many cancers are initiated and fed by the progeny of relatively slow cycling, genetically aberrant stem cells (as is suggested by a growing body of research), then traditional therapies designed to indiscriminately kill rapidly cycling cancer cells are understandably "hit and miss." Dick has been able to identify and sort colon cancer cells into two fractions: those that can reproduce new tumours and those that cannot. This ability to specifically target cancer stem cells will be at the centre of the development of anticancer therapies.

Review

Access an interactive eBook, chapter-specific interactive learning tools, including flashcards, quizzes, videos, and more in your Biology **CourseMate**, accessed through NelsonBrain.com **Aplia™** is an online interactive learning solution that helps you improve comprehension—and your grade—by integrating a variety of mediums and tools such as videos, tutorials, practice tests, and an interactive eBook.

8.1 The Cycle of Cell Growth and Division: An Overview

- In mitotic cell division, DNA replication is followed by the equal separation—that is, segregation—of the replicated DNA molecules and their delivery to daughter cells. The process ensures that the two cell products of a division have the same genetic information as the parent cell entering division.

- Mitosis is the basis for growth and maintenance of body mass in multicelled eukaryotes and for the reproduction of many single-celled eukaryotes.

- The chromosomes of eukaryotic cells are individual, linear DNA molecules with associated proteins.

- DNA replication and the duplication of chromosomal proteins convert each chromosome into a structure composed of two exact copies known as sister chromatids.

8.2 The Cell Cycle in Prokaryotic Organisms

- Prokaryotic cells undergo a cycle of binary fission involving coordinated cytoplasmic growth, DNA replication, and cell division, producing two daughter cells from an original parent cell.

- Replication of the bacterial chromosome consumes most of the time in the cell cycle and begins at a single site called the origin through reactions catalyzed by enzymes located in the middle of the cell. Once the origin of replication (*ori*) is duplicated, the two origins actively migrate to the two ends of the cell. Division of the cytoplasm then occurs through a partition of cell wall material that grows inward until the cell is separated into two parts (see Figure 8.3).

8.3 Mitosis and the Eukaryotic Cell Cycle

- Mitosis and interphase constitute the mitotic cell cycle. Mitosis occurs in five stages. In prophase (stage 1), the chromosomes condense into short rods and the spindle forms in the cytoplasm (see Figures 8.7 and 8.8).

- In prometaphase (stage 2), the nuclear envelope breaks down, the spindle enters the former nuclear area, and the sister chromatids of each chromosome make connections to opposite spindle poles. Each chromatid has a kinetochore that attaches to spindle microtubules (see Figures 8.7 and 8.8).

- In metaphase (stage 3), the spindle is fully formed and the chromosomes, moved by the spindle microtubules, become aligned at the metaphase plate (see Figure 8.7).

- In anaphase (stage 4), the spindle separates the sister chromatids and moves them to opposite spindle poles. At this point, chromosome segregation is complete (see Figures 8.7 and 8.8).

- In telophase (stage 5), the chromosomes decondense and return to the extended state typical of interphase. A new nuclear envelope forms around the chromosomes (see Figures 8.7 and 8.8).

- Cytokinesis, the division of the cytoplasm, completes cell division by producing two daughter cells, each containing a daughter nucleus produced by mitosis (see Figures 8.7 and 8.8).

- Cytokinesis in animal cells proceeds by furrowing, in which a band of microfilaments just under the plasma membrane contracts, gradually separating the cytoplasm into two parts (see Figure 8.11).

- In plant cytokinesis, cell wall material is deposited along the plane of the former spindle midpoint; the deposition continues until a continuous new wall, the cell plate, separates the daughter cells (see Figure 8.12).

8.4 Formation and Action of the Mitotic Spindle

- In animal cells, the centrosome divides and the two parts move apart. As they do so, the microtubules of the spindle form

between them. In plant cells with no centrosome, the spindle microtubules assemble around the nucleus (see Figure 8.13).

- In the spindle, kinetochore microtubules run from the poles to the kinetochores of the chromosomes, and nonkinetochore microtubules run from the poles to a zone of overlap at the spindle midpoint without connecting to the chromosomes (see Figure 8.15).

- During anaphase, the kinetochores move along the kinetochore microtubules, pulling the chromosomes to the poles. The nonkinetochore microtubules slide over each other, pushing the poles farther apart (see Figures 8.15 and 8.16).

8.5 Cell Cycle Regulation

- The cell cycle is controlled directly by complexes of cyclins and a cyclin-dependent protein kinase (CDK). A CDK is activated when combined with a cyclin and then adds phosphate groups to target proteins, activating them. The activated proteins trigger the cell to progress to the next cell cycle stage. Each major stage of the cell cycle begins with activation of one or more cyclin:CDK complexes and ends with deactivation of the complexes by breakdown of the cyclins (see Figure 8.18).

- Important internal controls create checkpoints to ensure that the reactions of one stage are complete before the cycle proceeds to the next stage.

- External controls are based primarily on surface receptors that recognize and bind signals such as peptide hormones and growth factors, surface groups on other cells, or molecules of the extracellular matrix. The binding triggers internal reactions that speed, slow, or stop cell division.

- Most cells in multicellular eukaryotes progressively lose the ability to divide over time by a process called cellular senescence. Factors that contribute to senescence include accumulating DNA damage and shortening telomeres.

- In cancer, control of cell division is lost and cells divide continuously and uncontrollably, forming a rapidly growing mass of cells that interferes with body functions. Cancer cells also break loose from their original tumour (metastasize) to form additional tumours in other parts of the body.

- Certain cells may undergo a programmed cell death called apoptosis. Such a fate is appropriate for cells that are, for instance, surplus for development, damaged, infected, or functional only after death.

Self-Test Questions

1. Which of the following situations is characteristic of cell division in bacteria?
   a. Several chromatids are separated at anaphase.
   b. Binary fission produces four daughter cells.
   c. Replication begins at the *ori*, and the two new DNA molecules separate.
   d. The daughter cells receive different genetic information from the parent cell.

2. When does the mass of DNA in an elephant cell increase during the cell cycle?
   a. M phase (mitosis)
   b. G_1 phase
   c. G_2 phase
   d. S phase

3. Honeybee eggs that are not fertilized develop into fertile, haploid males called drones. Fertilized eggs can develop into diploid females, one of which might become a queen. (Fertilized eggs might also become males, but they are taken out and killed by the drones.)

   If the queen has 32 chromosomes in her body cells, how many chromatids will be present in a G_2 drone cell?
   a. 8
   b. 16
   c. 32
   d. 64

4. Which of the following is the major microtubule-organizing centre of the animal cell?
   a. the centrosome, composed of centrioles
   b. the chromatin, composed of chromatids
   c. the chromosomes, composed of centromeres
   d. the spindle, composed of actin

5. For one given oak tree cell, which of the following is more plentiful at the end of S phase than at the beginning?
   a. nuclei
   b. chromatids
   c. chromosomes
   d. CDK2 molecules

6. Which of the following statements about mitosis is true?
   a. In prophase, the spindle separates sister chromatids and pulls them apart.
   b. Chromosomes congregate near the centre of the cell during metaphase.
   c. Both the animal cell furrow and the plant cell plate form at their former spindle poles.
   d. Cytokinesis describes the movement of chromosomes.

7. While researching an assignment on the Internet, you come across the following passage: "The cell cycle has a DNA synthesis phase (S phase) that doubles the normal full number of chromosomes from diploid ($2n$) to tetraploid ($4n$). This is followed by a G2 cell phase that biochemically prepares the cell for the mitotic or M phase, which includes cytokinesis."

   In what way is the author of the above passage mistaken?
   a. DNA synthesis does not occur in S phase.
   b. S phase does not increase ploidy from $2n$ to $4n$.
   c. G2 does not follow S phase.
   d. Cytokinesis is not part of mitotic cell division.

8. Which of the following statements about cell cycle regulation is true?
   a. Caspase is inactivated by cyclin binding.
   b. Cyclin binding activates CDKs to degrade target proteins.
   c. Telomere shortening promotes cell cycling.
   d. Stem cells divide more often than other somatic cells.

9. Which of the following is a characteristic of cancer cells?
   a. avoidance of metastasis
   b. avoidance of Hayflick factors
   c. contact inhibition
   d. cycle arrest at checkpoints

10. Imagine that you are in a job interview for a pharmaceutical company and are asked to suggest a good mechanism for an anticancer drug. Which of the following mechanisms would you suggest?
    a. decreased apoptosis
    b. decreased binding of cyclin to CDK
    c. increased CDK activity
    d. increased telomerase

Questions for Discussion

1. You have a means of measuring the amount of DNA in a single cell. You first measure the amount of DNA during G_1. At what point(s) during the remainder of the cell cycle would you expect the amount of DNA per cell to change?

2. A cell has 38 chromosomes. After mitosis and cell division, 1 daughter cell has 39 chromosomes and the other has 37. What might have caused these abnormal chromosome numbers? What effects do you suppose this might have on cell function? Why?

3. Taxol (Bristol-Myers Squibb, New York), a substance derived from the Pacific yew (*Taxus brevifolia*), is effective in the treatment of breast and ovarian cancers. It works by stabilizing microtubules, thereby preventing them from disassembling. Why would this activity slow or stop the growth of cancer cells?

4. Many chemicals in the food we eat potentially have effects on cancer cells. Chocolate, for example, contains a number of flavonoid compounds, which act as natural antioxidants. Design an experiment to determine whether any of the flavonoids in chocolate inhibit the cell cycle of breast cancer cells growing in culture.

5. The genes and proteins involved in cell cycle regulation are very different in bacteria and archaea versus those in eukaryotes. However, both prokaryotic and eukaryotic organisms use similar molecular regulatory reactions to coordinate DNA synthesis with cell division. What does this observation mean from an evolutionary perspective?

Mating octopuses.

© VOLVOX Inc. Tsuneo Nakamura Marine Photo Office

STUDY PLAN

9.1   Mechanism of Genetic Recombination

9.2   Genetic Recombination in Bacteria

9.2a   Genetic Recombination Occurs in *E. coli*

9.2b   Bacterial Conjugation Brings DNA of Two
Cells into Close Proximity

9.2c   Transformation and Transduction Provide
Additional Sources of DNA for
Recombination

9.3   Genetic Recombination in Eukaryotes: Meiosis

9.3a   Meiosis Occurs in Different Places in
Different Organismal Life Cycles

9.3b   Meiosis Changes Both Chromosome
Number and DNA Sequence

9.3c   Meiosis Produces Four Genetically Different
Daughter Cells

9.3d   Several Mechanisms Contribute to Genetic
Diversity

9.4   Mobile Elements

9.4a   Insertion Sequence Elements and
Transposons Are the Two Major Types of
Prokaryotic Mobile Elements

9.4b   Transposable Elements Were First
Discovered in Eukaryotes

9.4c   Eukaryotic Transposable Elements Are
Classified as Transposons or
Retrotransposons

9.4d   Retrotransposons Are Similar to
Retroviruses

9   Genetic Recombination

WHY IT MATTERS

A couple clearly shows mutual interest. First, he caresses her with one arm, then another—then another, another, and another. She reciprocates. This interaction goes on for hours—a hug here, a squeeze there. At the climactic moment, the male reaches deftly under his mantle and removes a packet of sperm, which he inserts under the mantle of the female. For every one of his sperm that successfully performs its function, a fertilized egg can develop into a new octopus.

For the octopus, sex is an occasional event, preceded by a courtship ritual that involves intermingled tentacles. For another marine animal, the slipper limpet, sex is a lifelong group activity. Slipper limpets are relatives of snails. Like many other animals, a slipper limpet passes through a free-living immature stage before it becomes a sexually mature adult. When the time comes for an immature limpet to transform into an adult, it settles onto a rock or other firm surface. If the limpet settles by itself, it develops into a female. If instead it settles on top of a female, it develops into a male. If another slipper limpet settles down on that male, it, too, becomes a male. Adult slipper limpets almost always live in such piles, with the one on the bottom always being a female. All the male limpets continually contribute sperm that fertilizes eggs shed by the female. If the one female dies, the surviving male at the bottom of the pile changes into a female and reproduction continues.

The life history of these octopuses and slipper limpets illustrates a tension in biology between sameness and difference. On the one hand, the growth and repair of their multicellular tissues depend on faithful replication of deoxyribonucleic acid (DNA) during mitotic cell division, as described in the previous chapter. At the level of the organism, it is important that all the individual cells in the body of a slipper limpet, for example, are genetically identical. However, on the other hand, at the level of the population, it is important that the individual limpets are genetically *different* from one another. If populations have genetic variability, they have the potential to evolve. Natural selection can act on this variability such that certain variants leave more offspring than others. Over time, the relative proportion of different variants will change. This is evolution in action.

The ultimate source of genetic diversity is mutation of the DNA sequence, often resulting from errors during DNA replication. Since mutations are relatively rare, diversity is amplified through various mechanisms that shuffle existing mutations into novel combinations. This process, of literally cutting and pasting DNA backbones into new combinations, is called genetic recombination and is very widespread in nature. Genetic recombination allows "jumping genes" to move, inserts some viruses into the chromosome of their hosts, underlies the spread of antibiotic resistance among bacteria and archaea, and is at the heart of meiosis in eukaryotic organisms. Genetic recombination puts the "sexual" in sexual reproduction; without genetic recombination, reproduction is asexual, and offspring are simply identical clones of their parent. We begin this chapter with a look at the basic mechanism of DNA recombination.

9.1 Mechanism of Genetic Recombination

Biologists who study genetic recombination have developed several models to precisely explain the process in various situations. In its most general sense, genetic recombination requires the following: two DNA molecules that differ from one another, a mechanism for bringing the DNA molecules into close proximity, and a collection of enzymes to

"cut," "exchange," and "paste" the DNA back together. **Figure 9.1** conveys a very simple model for recombination that, although lacking the details of more sophisticated models, highlights the basic steps involved.

The elegant double helix of DNA represented in Figure 9.1 is one of the most widely recognized biological molecules; you should be able to discern the "backbone" of the helix winding around the interior "steps" of paired bases. The sugar–phosphate backbone is held together by strong covalent bonds, whereas the bases pair with their partners through relatively weak hydrogen bonds. (If these ideas are new to you, see Chapter 12 for a more comprehensive look at DNA structure.) Figure 9.1a shows two similar double helixes lying close together as the first step in recombination. Most of the recombination discussed in this chapter occurs between regions of DNA that are very similar, but not identical, in the sequence of bases. Such regions, which may be as short as a few base pairs or as long as an entire chromosome, are called **homologous**. Homology allows different DNA molecules to line up and recombine precisely. Once homologous regions of DNA are paired, enzymes break a covalent bond in each of the four sugar–phosphate backbones. The free ends of each backbone are then exchanged

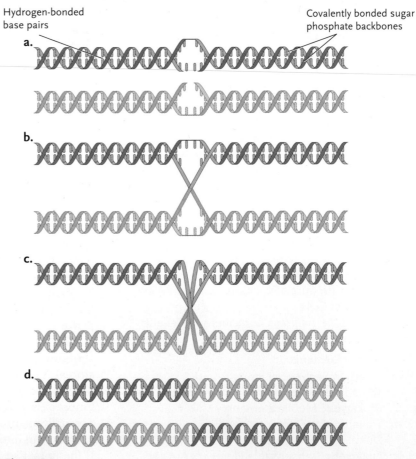

Hydrogen-bonded base pairs

Covalently bonded sugar phosphate backbones

a.

b.

c.

d.

Figure 9.1

A simplified model of genetic recombination. **(a)** Two molecules of DNA with similar sequence are brought into close proximity. **(b)** Enzymes nick the DNA backbones, exchange the ends, and reattach them. **(c** and **d)** In this case, the final result is two recombined DNA molecules.

and reattached to those of the other DNA molecule, as shown in Figure 9.1b, c. The result is two recombined molecules in which the originally red DNA is now covalently bound to blue DNA, and vice versa. In this chapter, we consider all the steps shown in Figure 9.1 to make up a single recombination event. This idea is worth restating: cutting and pasting *four* DNA backbones results in *one* recombination event.

As we move through diverse examples of recombination in this chapter, from plasmids to meiotic crossing-over to transposons, the characteristics of the participating DNA molecules will be different, the enzymes will change, and the results of recombination will have quite different consequences for the organism in question. However, you can always return to Figure 9.1 to remind yourself of the basic underlying mechanism.

STUDY BREAK

What would happen if two circular DNA molecules were involved in a single recombination event?

9.2 Genetic Recombination in Bacteria

Genetic recombination was historically first associated with meiosis in sexually reproducing eukaryotes. Genetic and microscopic research in the early decades of the twentieth century characterized recombination and culminated in the construction of the first genetic maps of chromosomes. However, by the middle of that century, improved techniques for studying the genetics of prokaryotic organisms (and their viruses) enabled researchers to look for evidence of genetic recombination even though these organisms do not reproduce sexually by meiosis. The data showed that, for particular bacteria, there are mechanisms to bring DNA from different cells together and that this DNA recombines to create offspring that are different from either parent cell. Bacteria clearly have a type of sex in their lives. It may be surprising for you to learn that, in some types of bacterial recombination, one of the participating cells is dead. Watch for this.

Escherichia coli, the most extensively studied prokaryotic organism, is named in honour of its discoverer, a Viennese pediatrician named Theodor Escherich, who isolated it from dirty diapers during an outbreak of diarrhea in 1885. Ready availability and ease of growth in the laboratory have made *E. coli* a workhorse of bacterial genetics that has helped lay the foundations for our understanding of the role of DNA as the genetic material, as well as the molecular structure, expression, and recombination of genes. (See more information about *E. coli* as a model research organism in *The Purple Pages.*)

9.2a Genetic Recombination Occurs in *E. coli*

In 1946, two scientists at Yale University, Joshua Lederberg and Edward L. Tatum, set out to determine if genetic recombination occurs in bacteria, using *E. coli* as their experimental organism. In essence, they were testing whether bacteria have a kind of sexuality in their reproduction process. In order to understand Lederberg and Tatum's work, you first need to know how bacteria are grown in the laboratory.

E. coli and many other bacteria can be grown in a **minimal medium** containing water, an organic carbon source such as glucose, and a selection of inorganic salts, including one, such as ammonium chloride, that provides nitrogen. The growth medium can be in liquid form or in the form of a gel made by adding agar to the liquid medium. (Agar is a polysaccharide material, indigestible by most bacteria, that is extracted from algae.) Since it is not practical to study a single bacterium for most experiments, researchers developed techniques for starting bacterial cultures from a single cell, generating cultures with a large number of genetically identical cells. Cultures of this type are called **clones.** To start bacterial clones, the scientist spreads a drop of a bacterial culture over a sterile agar gel in a culture dish. The culture is diluted enough to ensure that cells will be widely separated on the agar surface. Each cell divides many times to produce a clump of identical cells called a *colony.* Cells can be removed from a colony and introduced into liquid media or spread on agar and grown in essentially any quantity.

Now, in order for Lederberg and Tatum to detect genetic recombination, they needed some sort of detectable differences that could be shown to occur in changing combinations. The difference that proved most useful was related to nutrition. Cells require various amino acids for synthesis of proteins. Strains that are able to synthesize the necessary amino acids are called **prototrophs.** Mutant strains that are unable to synthesize amino acids are called **auxotrophs;** they can grow only if the required amino acid is provided for them in the growth medium. A strain that cannot manufacture its own arginine is represented by the genetic shorthand *argA⁻*. In this shorthand, *argA* refers to one of the genes that govern a cell's ability to synthesize arginine from simple inorganic molecules. A given strain of bacteria might carry this gene in its normal form, *argA⁺*, or its mutant form, *argA⁻*. These alternative forms of the gene are called alleles and might differ by as little as one base pair in their respective DNA sequences. Prokaryotic cells typically have one circular chromosome that carries one particular allele for each of their genes.

Using mutagens such as X-rays or ultraviolet light, Lederberg and Tatum isolated two different strains of *E. coli* carrying distinctive combinations of alleles for various metabolic genes. See **Figure 9.2, p. 184,** to understand how replica plating could

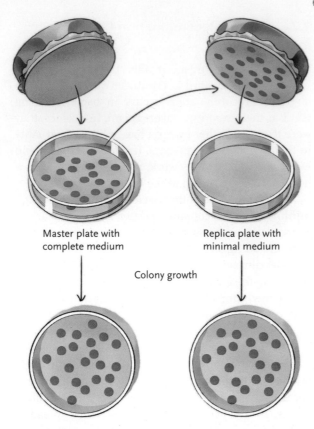

Figure 9.2
Replica plating transfers cells from complete media to minimal media where auxotrophs fail to grow.

Master plate with complete medium

Replica plate with minimal medium

Colony growth

isolate these auxotrophic strains. One particular strain could grow only if the vitamin biotin and the amino acid methionine were added to the culture medium. A second mutant strain did not need biotin or methionine but could grow only if the amino acids

leucine and threonine were added along with the vitamin thiamine. These two multiple-mutant strains of *E. coli* were represented in genetic notation as follows:

Strain 1   bio⁻ met⁻ leu⁺ thr⁺ thi⁺

Strain 2   bio⁺ met⁺ leu⁻ thr⁻ thi⁻

Lederberg and Tatum mixed about 100 million cells of the two mutant strains together and placed them on a minimal medium **(Figure 9.3)**. Several hundred colonies grew, even though, individually, none of the original cells carried all of the normal alleles needed for growth. You might be thinking, "They are mutants. Maybe some of the originally mutated alleles went back to normal." This possibility was easily discounted by plating large numbers of cells from each original strain onto minimal medium separately. If mutation were responsible for the initial results with mixed cultures, then colonies should have also appeared when strains were plated separately. There were none. Some form of recombination between the DNA molecules of the two parental types must have produced the necessary combination with normal alleles for each of the five genes:

bio⁺ met⁺ leu⁺ thr⁺ thi⁺

9.2b Bacterial Conjugation Brings DNA of Two Cells into Close Proximity

How was DNA from two different bacterial cells able to recombine? We will see in Section 9.3 that genetic recombination in eukaryotes occurs in diploid cells by an exchange of segments between pairs of chromosomes. However, bacteria are haploid organisms; each

Figure 9.3
Experimental evidence for genetic recombination in bacteria.

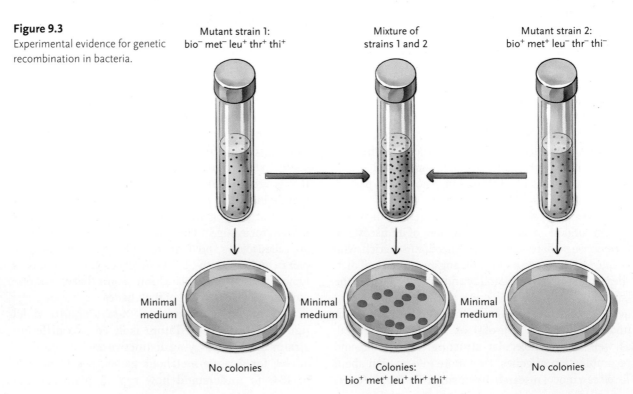

Mutant strain 1:
bio⁻ met⁻ leu⁺ thr⁺ thi⁺

Mixture of strains 1 and 2

Mutant strain 2:
bio⁺ met⁺ leu⁻ thr⁻ thi⁻

Minimal medium

Minimal medium

Minimal medium

No colonies

Colonies:
bio⁺ met⁺ leu⁺ thr⁺ thi⁺

No colonies

cell typically has its own single, circular chromosome. So where do the "pairs" of chromosomes come from in bacteria? Although bacterial cells were first thought to bring their DNA together by fusing two cells together, it was later established that transfer of genetic information is unidirectional, from one donor cell to a recipient cell. Instead of fusing, bacterial cells *conjugate*. That is, cells contact each other by a long tubular structure called a *sex pilus* and then form a cytoplasmic bridge **(Figure 9.4a, b).** During **conjugation**, a copy of part of the DNA of one cell moves through the cytoplasmic bridge into the other cell. Once DNA from one cell enters the other, genetic recombination can occur. Through this unidirectional transfer of a part of the chromosome, conjugation facilitates a kind of sexual reproduction in prokaryotic organisms.

The F Factor and Conjugation. Conjugation is initiated by a bacterial cell that contains a small circle of DNA in addition to the main circular chromosomal DNA **(Figures 9.5 and 9.6, p. 186).** Such small circles are called plasmids, and this particular one is known as the *fertility* plasmid or the *F factor*. Like all plasmids, the F factor carries several genes as well as a replication origin that permits a copy to be passed on to each daughter cell during the usual process of bacterial cell

a. Attachment by sex pilus

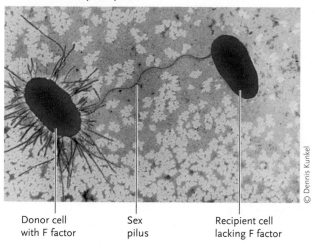

Donor cell with F factor Sex pilus Recipient cell lacking F factor

© Dennis Kunkel

b. Cytoplasmic bridge formed

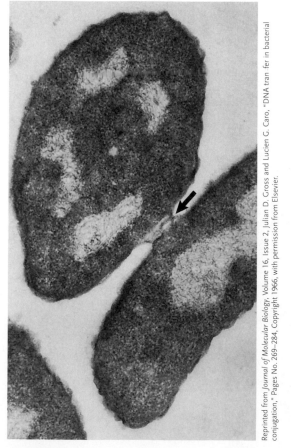

Reprinted from *Journal of Molecular Biology,* Volume 16, Issue 2, Julian D. Gross and Lucien G. Caro, "DNA transfer in bacterial conjugation," Pages No. 269–284, Copyright 1966, with permission from Elsevier.

a. Bacterial DNA released from cell

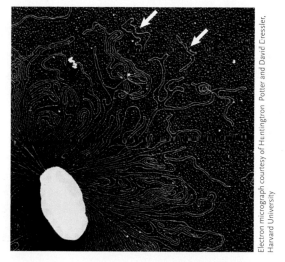

Electron micrograph courtesy of Hentingtron Potter and David Cressler, Harvard University

b. Plasmid

Prof. Stanley Cohen/SPL/Photo Researchers, Inc.

Figure 9.4
Conjugating *E. coli* cells. **(a)** Initial attachment of two cells by the sex pilus. **(b)** A cytoplasmic bridge (arrow) has formed between the cells, through which DNA moves from one cell to the other.

Figure 9.5
Electron micrographs of DNA released from a disrupted bacterial cell. **(a)** Plasmids (arrows) near the mass of chromosomal DNA. **(b)** A single plasmid at higher magnification (colourized).

a. Transfer of the F factor

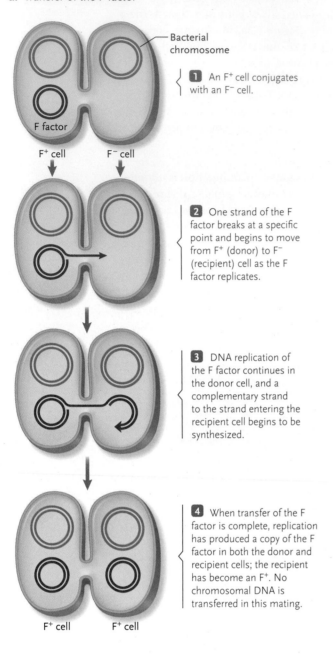

Bacterial chromosome

1 An F+ cell conjugates with an F− cell.

F factor

F+ cell   F− cell

2 One strand of the F factor breaks at a specific point and begins to move from F+ (donor) to F− (recipient) cell as the F factor replicates.

3 DNA replication of the F factor continues in the donor cell, and a complementary strand to the strand entering the recipient cell begins to be synthesized.

4 When transfer of the F factor is complete, replication has produced a copy of the F factor in both the donor and recipient cells; the recipient has become an F+. No chromosomal DNA is transferred in this mating.

F+ cell   F+ cell

b. Transfer of bacterial genes

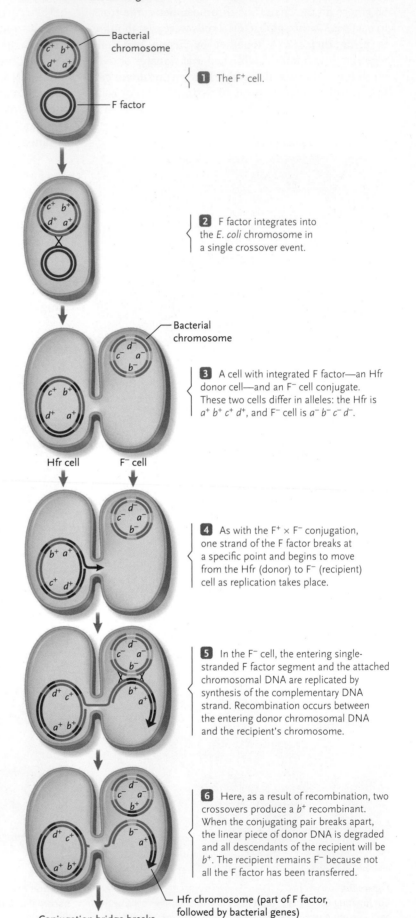

Bacterial chromosome

1 The F+ cell.

F factor

2 F factor integrates into the *E. coli* chromosome in a single crossover event.

Bacterial chromosome

3 A cell with integrated F factor—an Hfr donor cell—and an F− cell conjugate. These two cells differ in alleles: the Hfr is $a^+ b^+ c^+ d^+$, and F− cell is $a^- b^- c^- d^-$.

Hfr cell   F− cell

4 As with the F+ × F− conjugation, one strand of the F factor breaks at a specific point and begins to move from the Hfr (donor) to F− (recipient) cell as replication takes place.

5 In the F− cell, the entering single-stranded F factor segment and the attached chromosomal DNA are replicated by synthesis of the complementary DNA strand. Recombination occurs between the entering donor chromosomal DNA and the recipient's chromosome.

6 Here, as a result of recombination, two crossovers produce a b^+ recombinant. When the conjugating pair breaks apart, the linear piece of donor DNA is degraded and all descendants of the recipient will be b^+. The recipient remains F− because not all the F factor has been transferred.

Conjugation bridge breaks.
F− is a b^+ recombinant.

Hfr chromosome (part of F factor, followed by bacterial genes)

Figure 9.6
Transfer of genetic material during conjugation between *E. coli* cells.
(a) Transfer of the F factor during conjugation between F+ and F− cells.
(b) Transfer of bacterial genes and the production of recombinants during conjugation between Hfr and F− cells.

division. This is an example of *vertical* inheritance from one generation to the next that you are familiar with. However, during conjugation, the F factor also has the ability to be copied and passed directly from the donor cell to the recipient cell. This is an example of *horizontal* inheritance.

Donor cells are called **F⁺ cells** because they contain the F factor. They are able to mate with recipient cells but not with other donor cells. Recipient cells lack the F factor and, hence, are called **F⁻ cells.** The F factor carries about 20 genes. Several of them encode proteins of the **sex pilus,** also called the **F pilus** (plural **pili**) (see Figures 9.4, p. 185, and 9.6a, step 1).

During conjugation, the F plasmid replicates using a special type of DNA replication called *rolling circle*. To understand this mechanism, first picture a site, called the origin of transfer, on the F plasmid. Then imagine a break in just one strand of the double helix at this site. Now, imagine gently pulling the free end of the single strand of DNA away from the F factor, through the cytoplasmic bridge, and into the recipient cell. As the single strand is pulled, the remaining strand—still a circle—"rolls" like the spool on a tape dispenser. DNA synthesis fills in the complementary bases to ensure that the F factor is double stranded in both the donor and the recipient cells. When the entire F factor strand has transferred and replicated, it circularizes again (see Figure 9.6a, step 4). It is important to understand that although the recipient cell becomes F⁺, no chromosomal DNA is transferred between cells in this process. *That is, no genetic recombination occurs between the DNA of two different cells in such a mating.*

So why are we including F factor conjugation in this chapter if it does not recombine DNA of different cells? The answer lies in the Hfr cells described in the next section.

Hfr Cells and Genetic Recombination. In some F⁺ cells, the F factor comes into close proximity with the main chromosome and, lining up in a short region of homology, undergoes a recombination event. When two circular DNA molecules recombine (by the mechanism shown in Figure 9.1, p. 182), they simply fuse together into one larger circle. In this way, the F factor actually becomes a part of the main bacterial chromosome (see Figure 9.6b, step 2). These special donor cells are known as **Hfr cells** (Hfr = high-frequency recombination). It is important not to be confused at this point; although a recombination event integrated the F factor into the host chromosome, this is recombination within one cell, not between the chromosomes of different cells. Hfr cells are called "high-frequency recombination" because they can promote recombination between DNA of different cells by "exporting" copies of chromosomal genes to another cell, as described below.

When the F factor is integrated into the bacterial chromosome, its genes are still available for expression. Therefore, these Hfr cells make sex pili and can conjugate with an F⁻ cell. Figure 9.6b, step 3, shows an Hfr × F⁻ mating where the two cell types differ in alleles for the genes *a*, *b*, *c*, and *d*. Note that a segment of the F factor moves through the conjugation bridge into the recipient, bringing the single-stranded chromosomal DNA behind it (see Figure 9.6b, steps 4 and 5). This is, again, rolling circle replication in which both donor and recipient cells restore the DNA to double-strandedness. In this situation, the circle that rolls is the entire Hfr donor chromosome! Although DNA transfer often continues long enough for several genes to enter the recipient cell, the fragile conjugation bridge soon breaks. It is rare for the entire donor chromosome to be transferred.

At this point, it is important to recall that when the F factor transfers by itself, as described in the previous section, the recipient cells often become F⁺. However, in Hfr cells, the origin of transfer is near the middle of the integrated F factor. As a result, only half of the F factor DNA is transferred at the front of the chromosomal DNA. (Think of the engine of a train.) The other half of the F factor (the dining car at the end of the train) can follow only after the rest of the entire chromosome (see Figure 9.6b, steps 4 to 6). As a result, it is very unusual for a recipient cell to obtain the entire F factor and become Hfr as well. Most likely, the recipient cell will become a **partial diploid;** it will have two copies of only those genes that came through the conjugation bridge on the donor chromosomal DNA segment.

For our example, the recipient cell in Figure 9.6b, step 5, has become, for the moment, $a^+ b^+/a^- b^-$. Although the DNA carrying + alleles for genes *a* and *b* differs slightly from that carrying − alleles, these regions are homologous and can pair for recombination. In fact, Figure 9.6 shows two recombination events, one on either side of the *b* gene, resulting in the exchange of the donor allele with that of the recipient (see Figure 9.6b, step 5). As a result, the recipient cell has become an $a^- b^+$ recombinant. Since enzymes in the recipient cell degrade the linear Hfr chromosome soon after recombination occurs, any incoming alleles that are not recombined onto the chromosome are lost. Following recombination, the bacterial DNA replicates and the cell divides normally, producing a clone of cells with the new combination of alleles.

In other pairs in the mating population, recombination events at different locations would lead to different recombinant recipients; perhaps the *a* gene could recombine with the homologous recipient gene, or both *a* and *b* genes could recombine to give $a^+ b^+$ recipients. The various genetic recombinants observed in the Lederberg and Tatum experiment described earlier were produced in this general way.

Mapping Genes by Conjugation. The use of conjugation for genetic mapping was discovered by two scientists, François Jacob (the same scientist who proposed the operon model for the regulation of gene expression in bacteria; see Section 14.1) and Elie L. Wollman, at the Pasteur Institute in Paris. They began their experiments by mating Hfr and F cells that differed in a number of alleles. At regular intervals after conjugation commenced, they removed some of the cells and agitated them in a blender to break apart mating pairs. They then cultured the separated cells and analyzed them for recombinants. They found that the longer they allowed cells to conjugate before separation, the greater the number of donor genes that entered the recipient and produced recombinants. By noting the order and time at which genes were transferred, Jacob and Wollman were able to map and assign the relative positions of several genes in the E. coli chromosome.

9.2c Transformation and Transduction Provide Additional Sources of DNA for Recombination

The discovery of conjugation and genetic recombination in E. coli showed that genetic recombination is not restricted to eukaryotes. Further discoveries demonstrated that DNA can transfer from one bacterial cell to another by two additional mechanisms, transformation and transduction. Like conjugation, these mechanisms transfer DNA in one direction and create partial diploids in which recombination can occur between alleles in the homologous DNA regions. Unlike conjugation, in which both donor and recipient cells are living, transformation and transduction enable recipient cells to recombine with DNA obtained from dead donors.

Transformation. In **transformation**, bacteria simply take up pieces of DNA that are released into the environment as other cells disintegrate. Fred Griffith, a medical officer in the British Ministry of Health, London, discovered this phenomenon in 1928 while trying to understand how bacteria cause pneumonia in mice. Cells of the virulent strains of *Streptococcus pneumoniae* were surrounded by a polysaccharide capsule, whereas the nonvirulent strains were not. Griffith found that a mixture of heat-killed virulent cells plus living nonvirulent cells still caused pneumonia. One interpretation of this observation was that the living nonvirulent cells had been transformed to virulence by something released from the dead cells. In 1944, Oswald Avery and his colleagues at New York University found that the substance derived from the killed virulent cells, the substance capable of transforming nonvirulent bacteria to the virulent form, was DNA (discussed in Section 12.1).

Subsequently, geneticists established that in the transformation of *Streptococcus*, the linear DNA fragments taken up from disrupted virulent cells recombine with the chromosomal DNA of the nonvirulent cells in much the same way as genetic recombination takes place in conjugation. In this case, the recombination introduces the normal allele for capsule formation into the DNA of the nonvirulent cells; expression of that normal allele generates a capsule around the cell and its descendants, making them virulent.

Only some species of bacteria can take up DNA from the surrounding medium by natural mechanisms, and E. coli is not one of them. Fortunately for molecular biologists, E. coli cells can be induced to take up DNA in the laboratory by a variety of artificial transformation techniques involving exposure to calcium ions and/or pulses of electric current. Artificial transformation is often used to insert recombinant DNA plasmids into E. coli cells as part of cloning or genetic engineering techniques. (DNA cloning and genetic engineering are discussed further in Chapter 15.)

Transduction. In **transduction**, DNA is transferred from donor to recipient cells inside the head of an infecting bacterial virus. The infection cycles of viruses that infect bacteria, called **bacteriophages** (or just phages), are described in Chapter 21. For the purposes of this chapter, the basic details of phage infection are shown in **Figure 9.7, p. 189 and Figure 9.8, p. 190.** In general, transduction begins when new phages assemble within an infected bacterial cell; they sometimes incorporate fragments of the host cell DNA along with, or instead of, the viral DNA. After the host cell is killed, the new phages that are released may then attach to another cell and inject the bacterial DNA (and the viral DNA if it is present) into that recipient cell. The introduction of this DNA, as in conjugation and transformation, makes the recipient cell a partial diploid and allows recombination to take place. Recipients are not killed because they have received bacterial DNA rather than infective viral DNA. Lederberg and his graduate student, Norton Zinder, then at the University of Wisconsin at Madison, discovered transduction in 1952 in experiments with the bacterium *Salmonella typhimurium* and phage P22. Lederberg received a Nobel Prize in 1958 for his discovery of conjugation and transduction in bacteria.

There are two different types of transduction, generalized and specialized, arising from the different infection cycles of the phage involved. **Generalized transduction,** in which all donor genes are equally likely to be transferred, is associated with some **virulent bacteriophages,** which kill their host cells during each cycle of infection (the **lytic cycle**). Notice in Figure 9.7 that, during infection by the virulent phage, the host bacterial chromosome is degraded to provide raw material for synthesis of new phage chromosomes. However, sometimes a fragment of host chromosome avoids degradation and is packed into the head of a new phage *by mistake*. This particular phage now contains a small random sample of bacterial genes *instead of* phage genes. When the host cell is burst to release the new phage, this *transducing phage* can mechanically infect a recipient cell. However, it will deliver a linear

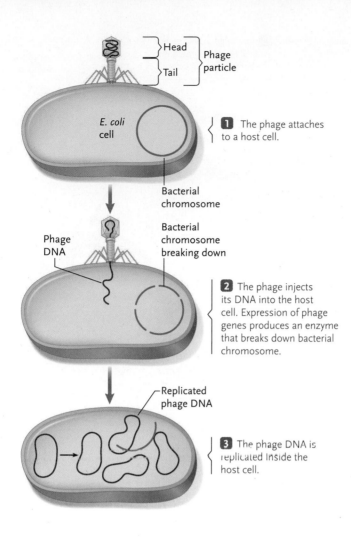

1 The phage attaches to a host cell.

2 The phage injects its DNA into the host cell. Expression of phage genes produces an enzyme that breaks down bacterial chromosome.

3 The phage DNA is replicated inside the host cell.

4 Viral head and tail units are synthesized.

5 The phage DNA, head, and tail units assemble into complete phage particles. Note that a piece of undegraded bacterial DNA has been packaged by mistake.

6 The cell ruptures, releasing the new phage particles. One progeny phage carries bacterial DNA instead of phage DNA.

7 Bacterial DNA is injected into the next host where it can recombine with similar regions on the host chromosome.

Figure 9.7

Generalized transduction. Movement of bacterial DNA from one cell to another inside the head of a lytic bacteriophage.

piece of DNA from the donor cell rather than an infectious phage chromosome. The newly infected (and incredibly lucky) recipient cell will survive; incoming DNA may then pair, and recombine, with homologous regions on the recipient chromosome.

One of the most extensively studied bacteriophages is phage lambda (λ), which infects *E. coli*. Again, a mistake in the infection cycle can result in the transfer of bacterial genes from a donor to a recipient cell. However, in this case, a different type of mistake, in a different infection cycle, gives rise to a different type of transduction: **specialized transduction** (shown in Figure 9.8, p. 190). Lambda is a **temperate bacteriophage.** That is, when lambda first infects a new host, it determines whether this cell is likely to be a robust and

long-lived host. Is it starving? Is it suffering from DNA damage? If the host cell passes this molecular health checkup, then the lambda chromosome lines up with a small region of homology on the bacterial chromosome and a phage-coded enzyme catalyzes a single recombination event. The phage is thus integrated into the host chromosomal DNA and, in this state, is called a **prophage.** (Overall, this mechanism is very similar to the integration of the F factor discussed previously.) The prophage is then replicated and passed to daughter cells along with the rest of the bacterial chromosome as long as conditions remain favourable (the **lysogenic cycle** in Figure 9.8, p. 190).

If, however, the host cell becomes inhospitable (perhaps as a result of ultraviolet-induced DNA

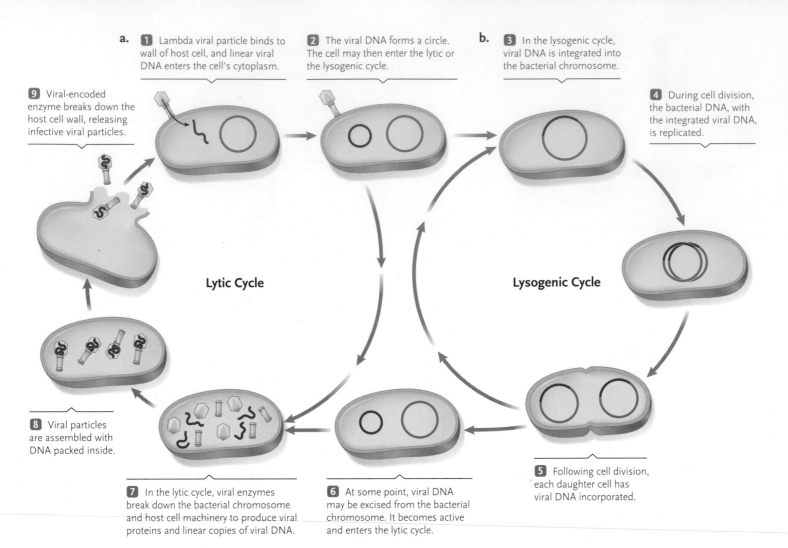

a.

1 Lambda viral particle binds to wall of host cell, and linear viral DNA enters the cell's cytoplasm.

2 The viral DNA forms a circle. The cell may then enter the lytic or the lysogenic cycle.

b.

3 In the lysogenic cycle, viral DNA is integrated into the bacterial chromosome.

9 Viral-encoded enzyme breaks down the host cell wall, releasing infective viral particles.

4 During cell division, the bacterial DNA, with the integrated viral DNA, is replicated.

Lytic Cycle

Lysogenic Cycle

8 Viral particles are assembled with DNA packed inside.

7 In the lytic cycle, viral enzymes break down the bacterial chromosome and host cell machinery to produce viral proteins and linear copies of viral DNA.

6 At some point, viral DNA may be excised from the bacterial chromosome. It becomes active and enters the lytic cycle.

5 Following cell division, each daughter cell has viral DNA incorporated.

Figure 9.8
The infective cycle of lambda, an example of a temperate phage, which can go through the lytic cycle **(a)** or the lysogenic cycle **(b)**.

damage), the prophage activates several genes, releases itself from the chromosome by a recombination event, and proceeds to manufacture new phages, which are released as the cell bursts as a result of lytic growth.

In specialized transduction, the "mistake" occurs when the prophage is excised from the chromosome. Sometimes this recombination event is imprecise; bacterial DNA is removed from the host chromosome, and some prophage DNA is left behind. As a result, this bacterial DNA is packaged into new phages and carried to recipient cells. Since the transducing phage is defective, having left some of its genes behind in the host, it does not kill its new host. You should be able to see that in the case of specialized transduction only bacterial genes that are close to the integration site of the phage will likely be incorporated into the phage chromosome by the recombination mistake. Typically, only genes coding for galactose and biotin metabolism are transferred at high frequency by phage lambda.

Conjugation, transformation, and transduction are all ways in which DNA from two different bacterial cells is brought into close proximity. Homologous regions may then pair and recombine to give rise to a recipient cell that carries a different collection of alleles than it had previously. Overall, these processes create

more diversity in the DNA sequence among members of a population than would arise by mutation and binary fission alone. More diversity leads to a higher likelihood that at least some individuals will be well suited to survival in a changing environment.

These basic principles also apply to single-celled and multicellular eukaryotes. The next section of this chapter introduces genetic recombination in eukaryotes as it occurs within the overall process of meiosis. Notice how DNA from two different individuals is brought close together in the same cell following fertilization. Also watch for extensive similarity of the DNA sequence (homology) that now extends the full length of large linear chromosomes. Finally, notice the genetic recombination at the centre of this process, which generates novel chromosomes with new combinations of alleles.

STUDY BREAK

1. Contrast the characteristics of F⁻, F⁺, and Hfr cells.
2. Explain why all genes have an equal likelihood of transfer by generalized transduction but not by specialized transduction.

9.3 Genetic Recombination in Eukaryotes: Meiosis

The octopuses and slipper limpets described at the opening of this chapter are engaged in forms of **sexual reproduction**, the production of offspring through the union of male and female **gametes**—for example, eggs and sperm cells in animals. Sexual reproduction depends on **meiosis**, a specialized process of cell division that recombines DNA sequences and produces cells with half the number of chromosomes present in the **somatic cells** (body cells) of a species. The derivation of the word *meiosis* (*meioun* = to diminish) reflects this reduction. At **fertilization**, the nuclei of an egg and a sperm cell fuse, producing a cell called the **zygote**, in which the chromosome number typical of the species is restored. Without the halving of chromosome number by the meiotic divisions, fertilization would double the number of chromosomes in each subsequent generation.

Both meiosis and fertilization also mix genetic information into new combinations; thus, none of the offspring of a mating pair are likely to be genetically identical to either their parents or their siblings. This genetic variability is the raw material for the process of evolution as described in Chapters 16 and 18.

The biological foundations of sexual reproduction are the mixing of genetic information into new combinations and the halving of the chromosome number, both of which occur through meiosis, as well as the restoration of the original chromosome number by fertilization. Intermingled tentacles in octopuses, communal sex among limpets, clouds of pollen in the wind, and the courting and mating rituals of humans are nothing more or less than variations of the means for achieving fertilization, thus bringing DNA together for recombination.

9.3a Meiosis Occurs in Different Places in Different Organismal Life Cycles

Although the life cycle of nearly all eukaryotes alternates between a stage with one basic set of chromosomes (haploid) and a stage with two basic sets of chromosomes (diploid), **Figure 9.9** shows that evolution has produced wide variety in the relative timing of mitosis, meiosis, and fertilization among different species.

CONCEPT FIX The life cycles of plants, algae, and fungi may be unfamiliar to you and can be better understood by focusing your attention on the function of the cells that are the immediate products of meiosis. You may assume that "gametes are made by meiosis." This assumption is true—but only for yourself and other animals. In the life cycle of houseplants and some of the fungi living in the soil in the park, the haploid products of meiosis are spores, not gametes.

a. Animal life cycles

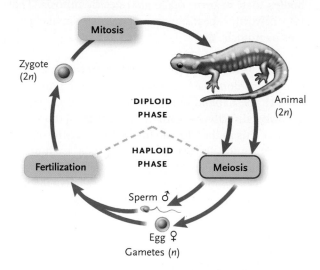

b. All land plants and some fungi and algae (fern shown; relative length of the two phases varies widely in plants)

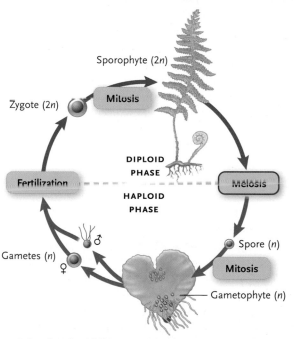

c. Other fungi and algae

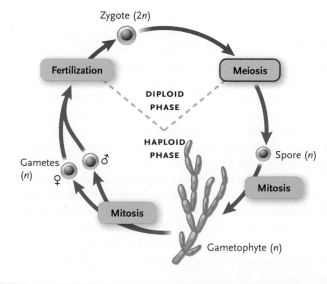

Figure 9.9
Variations in the time and place of meiosis and mitosis in life cycle of eukaryotes. The diploid phase of the life cycles is shaded in red; the haploid phase is shaded in yellow. *n* refers to the haploid number of chromosomes; 2*n* refers to the diploid number. **(a)** Meiosis in animal life cycles. Zygotes divide by mitosis. **(b)** Meiosis in most plants and some fungi and algae. Spores and zygotes divide by mitosis. **(c)** Meiosis in other fungi and algae. Spores divide by mitosis.

These spores divide by mitosis to form multicellular bodies that, in turn, make gametes by mitosis. That idea is worth repeating: many organisms make gametes by mitosis. ⬡

Animals. Animals follow the pattern in which the diploid phase dominates the life cycle (see Figure 9.9a, p. 191), the haploid phase is reduced, and meiosis is followed directly by gamete formation. (You could think of this as the "diploid life cycle" since the diploid stage is multicellular.) In male animals, each of the four nuclei produced by meiosis is enclosed in a separate cell by cytoplasmic divisions, and each of the four cells differentiates into a functional sperm cell. In female animals, only one of the four nuclei becomes functional as an egg cell nucleus.

Fertilization restores the diploid phase of the life cycle. Thus, animals are haploids only as sperm or eggs, and no mitotic divisions occur during the haploid phase of the life cycle.

Most Plants and Some Fungi. Most plants and some algae and fungi follow the life cycle pattern shown in Figure 9.9b, p. 191. These organisms alternate between haploid and diploid generations in which, depending on the organism, either generation may dominate the life cycle, and mitotic divisions occur in both phases. (You could think of this as the "alternating-generations life cycle" since both the diploid and the haploid stages can be multicellular.) In these organisms, fertilization produces the diploid generation, in which the individuals are called **sporophytes** (*spora* = seed; *phyta* = plant). After the sporophytes grow to maturity by mitotic divisions, some of their cells undergo meiosis, producing haploid, genetically different, reproductive cells called **spores.** The spores are not gametes; they germinate and grow directly by mitotic divisions into a generation of haploid individuals called **gametophytes** (*gameta* = gamete). At maturity, the nuclei of some cells in gametophytes develop into egg or sperm nuclei. All the egg or sperm nuclei produced by a particular gametophyte are genetically identical because they arise through mitosis; meiosis does not occur in gametophytes. Fusion of a haploid egg and sperm nucleus produces a diploid zygote nucleus that divides by mitosis to produce the diploid sporophyte generation again.

In all plants (except bryophytes), the diploid sporophyte generation is the most visible part of the plant. The gametophyte generation is reduced to an almost microscopic stage that develops in the reproductive parts of the sporophytes—in flowering plants, in the structures of the flower. The female gametophyte remains in the flower; the male gametophyte is released from flowers as microscopic pollen grains. When pollen contacts a flower of the same species, it releases a haploid nucleus that fertilizes a haploid egg cell of a female gametophyte in the flower. The resulting cell, the zygote, reproduces by mitosis to form a sporophyte.

Sphagnum moss (commonly known as "peat moss") is a good example of a plant in which the gametophyte is the most visible and familiar stage of the life cycle. In this case, the sporophyte is reduced and develops from a zygote within the body of the gametophyte. Vast peatlands of *Sphagnum* gametophytes are industrially harvested in many parts of the world for fuel and horticultural use.

Most Fungi. The life cycle of most fungi and algae follows the third life cycle pattern (see Figure 9.9c, p. 191). In these organisms, the diploid phase is limited to a single cell, the zygote, produced by fertilization. Immediately after fertilization, the diploid zygote undergoes meiosis to produce the haploid phase. Mitotic divisions occur only in the haploid phase. (You could think of this as the "haploid life cycle" since the haploid stage is multicellular.)

During fertilization, two haploid gametes, usually designated simply as positive (+) and negative (−) because they are similar in structure, fuse to form a diploid nucleus. This nucleus immediately enters meiosis, producing four haploid cells. These cells develop directly or after one or more mitotic divisions into haploid spores. These spores germinate to produce haploid individuals which grow or increase in number by mitotic divisions. Eventually, positive and negative gametes are formed in these individuals by differentiation of some of the cells produced by the mitotic divisions. Because the gametes are produced by mitosis, all the gametes of an individual are genetically identical.

🔧 **CONCEPT FIX** We are emphasizing that zygotes arising from fertilization contain DNA from two different parents in close proximity so that recombination may occur. However, note carefully that, in the life cycles of the animals and plants you are likely familiar with, it is not this single-celled fertilized zygote that undergoes recombination. It is only after many rounds of replication by mitosis that certain cells in the resulting multicellular body are destined to divide by meiosis. That is when and where recombination occurs. ⬡

9.3b Meiosis Changes Both Chromosome Number and DNA Sequence

In order to understand the mechanism of meiosis, it is helpful to keep the big picture in mind. Chapter 8 made the point that the essence of mitotic cell division is *sameness*. That is, chromosomes are replicated and partitioned to ensure that cells produced by the process have the same number of chromosomes, with the same DNA sequence, as the cell that began the process. In this way, somatic cells are produced for most of the requirements of haploid or diploid multicellular organisms. However, the essence of meiosis is *difference*—actually two kinds of difference: halved chromosome number and recombined chromosomal DNA sequence. The products of meiosis are not intended to contribute to the body of the organisms that make them. In multicellular animals and plants, you would find that meiosis occurs only in specialized tissues that produce gametes and spores, respectively.

Both types of difference mentioned above arise from the very different behaviour of chromosomes in meiosis relative to mitosis. If you understand the significance of the chromosome pairs in diploid organisms as described below, then the differences in chromosome behaviour in meiosis and mitosis will make sense more easily.

As discussed in Section 9.1, the two representatives of each chromosome in a diploid cell constitute a *homologous pair (homo* = same; *logos* = information)— they have the same genes, arranged in the same order in the DNA of the chromosomes. One chromosome of each homologous pair, the **paternal chromosome**, is derived from the male parent of the organism, and the other chromosome, the **maternal chromosome**, is derived from its female parent. Although two homologous chromosomes carry the same genes arranged in the same order, different *versions* of these genes, **alleles**, may be present on either chromosome. Recall from the bacterial conjugation material at the beginning of this chapter that different alleles of a given gene have similar, but distinct, DNA sequences. They therefore likely encode variations of the given ribonucleic acid (RNA) or protein gene product, which may then have a different structure, different biochemistry, or both.

For example, all the different breeds of dogs normally have 78 chromosomes in their cells, made up of 39 homologous pairs. However, each individual has a unique combination of the alleles carried by the two chromosomes of each homologous pair. The distinct set of alleles, arising from the mixing mechanisms of meiosis and fertilization in the parents, gives each individual offspring its own unique combination of inherited traits, including attributes such as size, coat colour, susceptibility to certain diseases and disorders, and aspects of behaviour and intelligence.

One of the more dramatic accomplishments of meiosis in an organism like a dog is the separation of the members of each homologous pair into different cells, thereby reducing the diploid or 2*n* number of chromosomes to the haploid or *n* number. Each cell produced by meiosis carries only one member of each homologous pair. An egg or sperm cell contains 39 chromosomes, one of each pair. When the egg and sperm combine in sexual reproduction to produce the zygote—the first cell of the new puppy—the diploid number of 78 chromosomes (39 pairs) is regenerated. The processes of DNA replication and mitotic cell division ensure that this diploid number is maintained in the body cells as the zygote divides and develops (see Chapter 8).

The second significant consequence of meiotic cell division is, of course, genetic recombination of the actual DNA sequence on chromosomes. Referring back to Figure 9.1, p. 182, recall that recombination involves the precise breaking of covalently bonded DNA backbones, exchanging the "ends" with those of the other homologue and reforming the bonds. As a result, each chromosome passed on to offspring is composed of a novel mixture of both maternal and paternal DNA sequence.

The following sections describe how the ability of homologues to find their respective partners, and pair intimately along their length, allows both the partitioning of homologues into separate cells and the process of recombination to occur during the first part of the two-step process of meiosis.

9.3c Meiosis Produces Four Genetically Different Daughter Cells

Cells that are destined to divide by meiosis (called **meiocytes**) move through their last turn of the cell cycle as usual, replicating DNA and making more chromosomal proteins during S phase. (See Chapter 12 for details of DNA replication.) The resulting G_2 cells carry replicated chromosomes, each composed of two identical sister chromatids **(Figure 9.10, p. 194)**. Following this premeiotic interphase, cells enter the first of the two meiotic divisions: meiosis I and meiosis II. During meiosis I, chromosomes behave dramatically differently than they do during mitosis. That is, early in meiosis I, homologous chromosomes find their partners and pair lengthwise, gene for gene, in a process called synapsis. During this intimate pairing, recombination occurs, and chromosomal segments are exchanged. As the meiocyte continues through to the end of the first division, the members of each homologous pair are moved into one or the other of the two daughter cells. These daughter cells still contain replicated chromosomes (composed of two chromatids each); however, the number of such chromosomes is only half that of the original meiocyte. That is, the cells now have the haploid number of chromosomes but each chromosome still has two chromatids.

During the second meiotic division, meiosis II, the sister chromatids are separated into different cells, further reducing the amount of DNA in each product of meiosis. A total of four cells, each with the haploid number of chromosomes and a novel collection of alleles, is the final result of the two meiotic divisions.

CONCEPT FIX Notice that the chromosome in the cells at the bottom of Figure 9.10, p. 194, is an unreplicated, single structure. Since these cells are haploid, sometimes people come to believe that all chromosomes in haploid cells are unreplicated, single structures, while all chromosomes in diploid cells are double structures with two chromatids each. However, Figure 9.10, p. 194,

Figure 9.10

Production of four haploid nuclei by the two meiotic divisions. For simplicity, just one pair of homologous chromosomes is followed through the divisions.

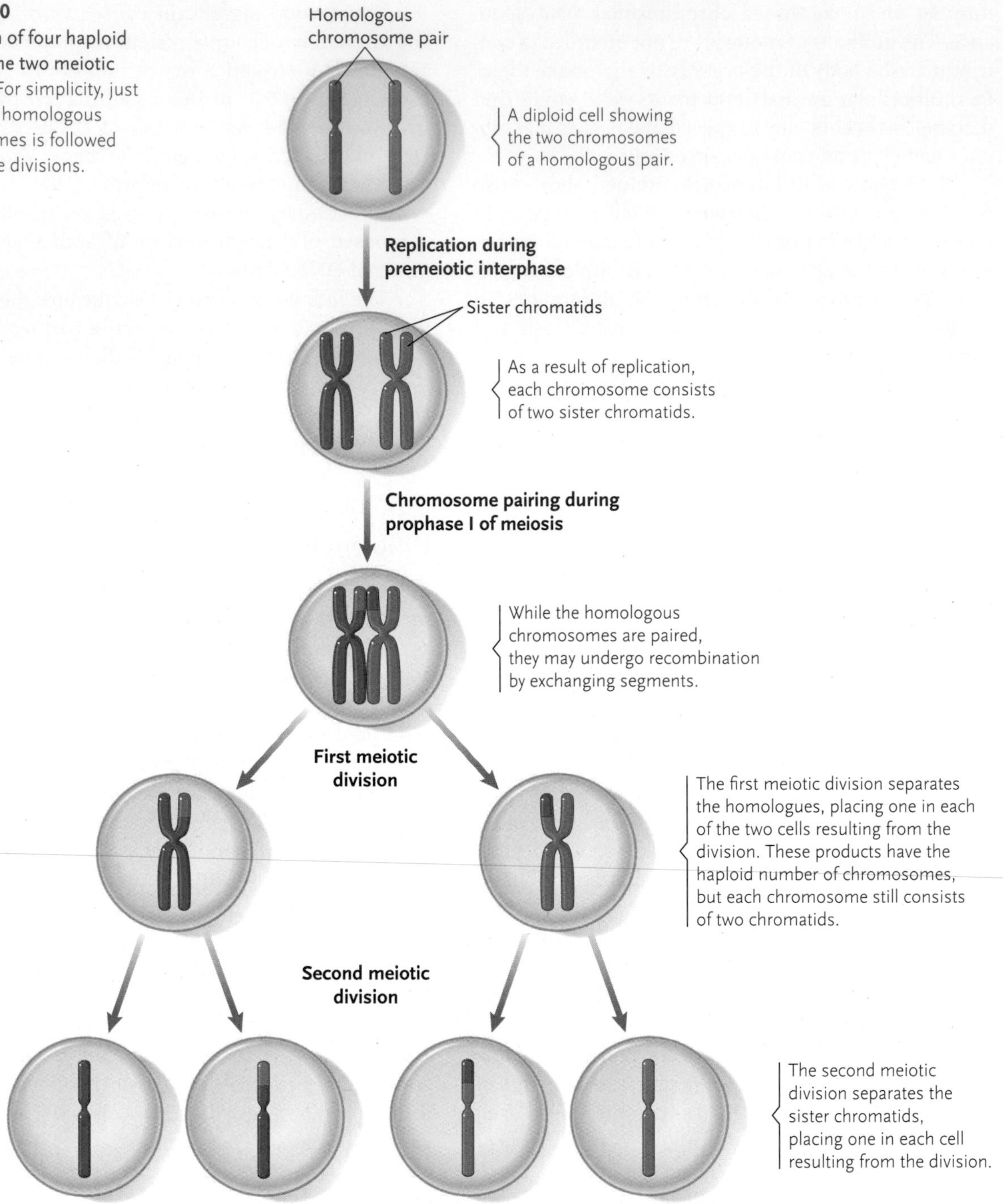

Homologous chromosome pair

A diploid cell showing the two chromosomes of a homologous pair.

Replication during premeiotic interphase

Sister chromatids

As a result of replication, each chromosome consists of two sister chromatids.

Chromosome pairing during prophase I of meiosis

While the homologous chromosomes are paired, they may undergo recombination by exchanging segments.

First meiotic division

The first meiotic division separates the homologues, placing one in each of the two cells resulting from the division. These products have the haploid number of chromosomes, but each chromosome still consists of two chromatids.

Second meiotic division

The second meiotic division separates the sister chromatids, placing one in each cell resulting from the division.

clearly shows that the top cell is diploid, even though its two chromosomes are unreplicated. Following meiosis I, the cells are haploid, even though their single chromosome is replicated. Ploidy is determined only by the number of chromosomes; it is not influenced by whether the chromosomes are replicated or not. ⬡

For convenience, biologists separate each meiotic division into the same key stages as mitosis: prophase, prometaphase, metaphase, anaphase, and telophase. The stages are identified as belonging to the two divisions, meiosis I and meiosis II, by a I or a II, as in prophase I and prophase II. A brief interphase called **interkinesis** separates the two meiotic divisions, *but no DNA replication occurs during interkinesis.*

Prophase I. At the beginning of prophase I, the replicated chromosomes, each consisting of two sister chromatids, begin to fold and condense into threadlike structures in the nucleus (**Figure 9.11, p. 196**, step 1). The two chromosomes of each homologous pair then come together and line up side by side in a zipperlike way; this process is called **pairing** or **synapsis** (step 2). The fully paired homologues are called **tetrads**, referring to the fact that each homologous pair consists of four chromatids. *Note that chromosomes do not behave like this in mitosis.*

While they are paired, the chromatids of homologous chromosomes physically exchange segments (step 3). This physical exchange, genetic recombination, is the step that mixes the alleles of the homologous chromosomes into new combinations and contributes to the generation of variability in sexual reproduction. (This is the process, described in Chapter 11, that underlies recombination frequency mapping.) As prophase I finishes, a spindle forms in the cytoplasm by the same basic mechanisms described in Chapter 8.

Prometaphase I. In prometaphase I, the nuclear envelope breaks down and the spindle enters the former nuclear area (see Figure 9.11, p. 196, step 4). The two chromosomes of each pair attach to kinetochore microtubules that are anchored to opposite spindle poles. That is, both sister chromatids of one homologue attach to microtubules leading to one spindle pole, whereas both sister chromatids of the other homologue attach to microtubules leading to the opposite pole. *Notice, again, how this is different from the spindle attachments during mitosis.*

Metaphase I and Anaphase I. At metaphase I, movements of the spindle microtubules have aligned the recombined tetrads on the equatorial plane—the *metaphase plate*—between the two spindle poles (see Figure 9.11, p. 197, step 5). Then the two chromosomes of each homologous pair separate and move to opposite spindle poles during anaphase I (step 6). The movement segregates homologous pairs, delivering a haploid set of chromosomes to each pole of the spindle. However, all the chromosomes at the poles are still double structures composed of two sister chromatids joined at their centromeres.

Telophase I and Interkinesis. Telophase I is a brief, transitory stage in which there is little or no change in the chromosomes (see Figure 9.11, p. 197, step 7). New nuclear envelopes form in some species but not in others. Telophase I is followed by an interkinesis in which the single spindle of the first meiotic division disassembles and the microtubules reassemble into two new spindles for the second division. Recall that there is no DNA replication between the first and the second division.

Prophase II, Prometaphase II, and Metaphase II. During prophase of meiosis II, the chromosomes condense (see Figure 9.11, p. 196, step 8). During prometaphase II, the nuclear envelope breaks down, the spindle enters the former nuclear area, and spindle microtubules leading to opposite spindle poles attach to the two kinetochores of each chromosome. At metaphase II, movements of the chromosomes within the spindle bring them to rest at the metaphase plate (step 9).

CONCEPT FIX Although the separation of chromatids during meiosis II is superficially similar to that in a mitotic division, it is important to remember that these two processes are quite distinct. Meiosis II is not "just like mitosis." Meiosis II occurs only in reproductive tissue, there is no immediately preceding DNA replication phase, and the resulting daughter cells are not genetically identical. ⬡

Anaphase II and Telophase II. Anaphase II begins as the sister chromatids of each chromosome separate from each other and move to opposite spindle poles (see Figure 9.11, p. 197, step 10). At the completion of anaphase II, the separated chromatids—now called chromosomes—have been segregated to the two poles. During telophase II, the chromatids decondense to the extended interphase state, the spindles disassemble, and new nuclear envelopes form around the masses of chromatin (step 11). The result is four haploid cells, each with a nucleus containing half the number of chromosomes present in the cell at the beginning of meiosis. These chromosomes all carry various new combinations of maternal and paternal alleles.

Failure in Chromosome Segregation. Rarely, chromosome segregation fails at either meiosis I or II. For example, during meiosis I, both chromosomes of a homologous pair may connect to the same spindle pole in anaphase I. In the resulting nondisjunction, as it is called, the spindle fails to separate the homologous chromosomes of the tetrad. As a result, one pole receives both chromosomes of the homologous pair, whereas the other pole has no copies of that chromosome. Meiosis II will proceed to separate the chromatids of the extra chromosome as usual, with the result that gametes will have two copies of this chromosome (instead of one). A failure at meiosis II, in which chromatids do not separate to opposite poles, also results in gametes with abnormal numbers of chromosomes. Zygotes that receive an extra chromosome from an abnormal gamete therefore have three copies of a given chromosome instead of two. In humans, most zygotes of this kind do not result in live births. One exception is Down syndrome, which can result from three copies of chromosome 21. Down syndrome involves characteristic alterations in body and facial structure, developmental delays, and significantly reduced fertility due to extra genetic information (see Chapter 11 for a more detailed discussion of Down syndrome).

Sex Chromosomes. In many eukaryotes, including most animals, one or more pairs of chromosomes, called the sex chromosomes, are different in male and female individuals of the same species. For example, in fruit flies, the cells of females contain a pair of sex chromosomes called the *XX pair*. Male flies contain a pair of sex chromosomes that consist of one X chromosome and a smaller chromosome called the Y chromosome. The two X chromosomes in females are fully homologous, whereas the male X and Y chromosomes are homologous only through a short region. The X and Y chromosomes behave as homologues (i.e., they pair where homologous, recombine, and move together to the metaphase plate) during meiosis in males. As a result of meiosis, a gamete formed by females may receive either member of the XX pair. A gamete formed by males receives either an X or a Y chromosome.

Prophase I

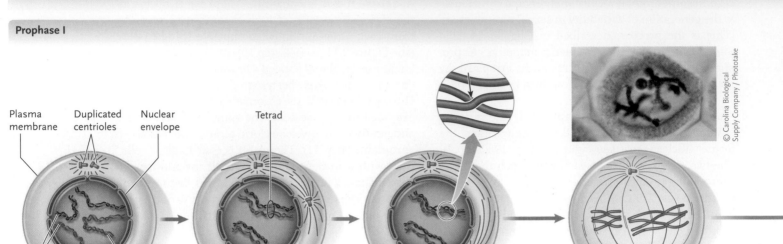

Plasma membrane | Duplicated centrioles | Nuclear envelope

Homologous chromosomes | Two sister chromatids

Tetrad

Condensation of chromosomes

1 At the beginning of prophase I the chromosomes begin to condense into threadlike structures. Each consists of two sister chromatids, as a result of DNA replication during premeiotic interphase. The chromosomes of two homologous pairs, one long and one short, are shown.

Synapsis

2 Homologous chromosomes come together and pair.

Recombination

3 While they are paired, the chromatids of homologous chromosomes undergo recombination by exchanging segments. The enlarged circle shows a site undergoing recombination (arrow).

Prometaphase I

4 In prometaphase I, the nuclear envelope breaks down, and the spindle moves into the former nuclear area. Kinetochore microtubules connect to the chromosomes—kinetochore microtubules from one pole attach to both sister kinetochores of one duplicated chromosome, and kinetochore microtubules from the other pole attach to both sister kinetochores of the other duplicated chromosome.

© Carolina Biological Supply Company / Phototake

Second meiotic division

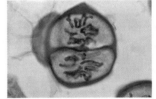

© Carolina Biological Supply Company / Phototake

Figure 9.11

The meiotic divisions. The artwork summarizes the behaviour of chromosomes in a hypothetical animal cell having two homologous pairs of chromosomes ($2n = 4$). Photomicrographs show comparable stages in the anther cells of a lily plant.

Prophase II

8 The chromosomes condense and a spindle forms.

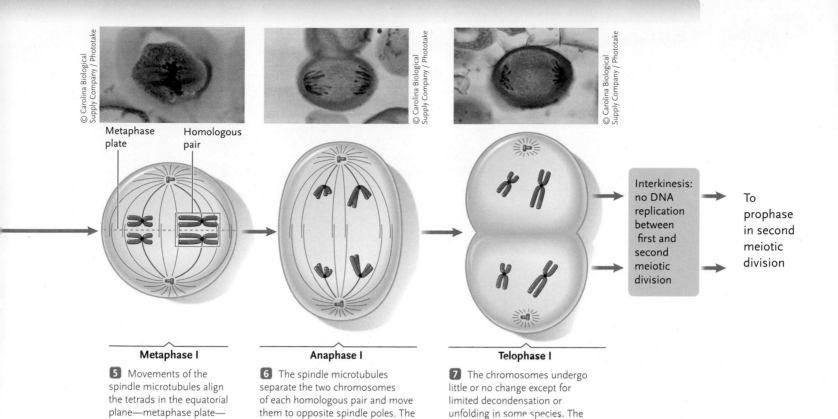

Metaphase I

5 Movements of the spindle microtubules align the tetrads in the equatorial plane—metaphase plate—between the two spindle poles.

Anaphase I

6 The spindle microtubules separate the two chromosomes of each homologous pair and move them to opposite spindle poles. The poles now contain the haploid number of chromosomes. However, each chromosome at the poles still contains two chromatids.

Telophase I

7 The chromosomes undergo little or no change except for limited decondensation or unfolding in some species. The spindle of the first meiotic division disassembles, and two new spindles form for the second division.

Interkinesis: no DNA replication between first and second meiotic division

To prophase in second meiotic division

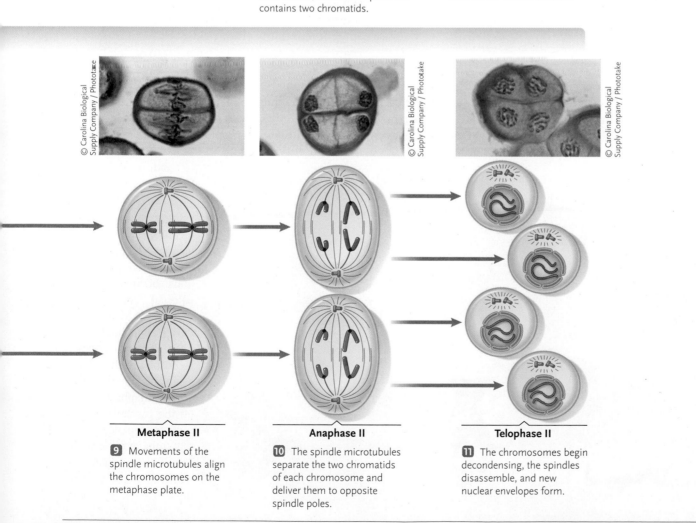

Metaphase II

9 Movements of the spindle microtubules align the chromosomes on the metaphase plate.

Anaphase II

10 The spindle microtubules separate the two chromatids of each chromosome and deliver them to opposite spindle poles.

Telophase II

11 The chromosomes begin decondensing, the spindles disassemble, and new nuclear envelopes form.

MOLECULE BEHIND BIOLOGY 9.1

Bisphenol A and the Grandmother Effect

Although this chapter documents the role of meiosis in generating genetically diverse offspring, one type of diversity that must be avoided is differences in chromosome number. Cells (or organisms) that have more, or fewer, than the normal number of chromosomes are called *aneuploid;* agents that promote this problem are known as *aneugens.* The formation of gametes by meiosis is under hormonal control in mammals, and it is not surprising to learn that synthetic chemicals influencing the action of reproductive hormones can be aneugenic. Bisphenol A, a chemical monomer used in the manufacture of polycarbonate plastics and resins, binds to estrogen receptors in mice. Exposure to relatively high concentrations has been shown to elevate the incidence of aneuploid gametes and offspring. Since meiosis is active in females before they are born, exposure of pregnant mouse mothers resulted in aneuploid gametes produced by their daughters, which, in turn, gave rise to aneuploid grandchildren.

Canada has declared BPA a toxic substance and banned its use in baby bottles.

FIGURE 1
Bisphenol A

(See Chapter 11 for a discussion of the inheritance of genes on sex chromosomes.)

The sequence of steps in the two meiotic divisions accomplishes the major outcomes of meiosis: the generation of genetic variability and the reduction in chromosome number. (Figure 9.16 reviews the two meiotic divisions and compares them with the single division of mitosis.)

9.3d Several Mechanisms Contribute to Genetic Diversity

Figure 9.12
Genetic variability as shown in the appearance of domestic cats.

The generation of genetic variability by meiosis is a prime evolutionary advantage of sexual reproduction **(Figure 9.12).** Such variability increases the chance that at least some offspring will have combinations of alleles that will be successful in surviving and reproducing in changing environments. In fact, some scientists argue that meiosis exists not to create just any variability but to generate "repaired" chromosomes to be passed on to the next generation (see "People behind Biology"). As you work through the ideas in this section, try to envision how you could pass a "perfect" copy of chromosome 6 to your children even if both copies of chromosome 6 you inherited from your parents are damaged.

The variability produced by sexual reproduction is apparent all around us, particularly in the human population. Except for identical twins, no two humans look alike, act alike, or have identical biochemical and physiological characteristics, even if they are members of the same immediate family. Other species that reproduce sexually show equivalent variability arising from meiosis.

During meiosis and fertilization, genetic variability arises from four sources: (1) genetic recombination of homologous chromosomes, (2) the differing combinations of maternal and paternal chromosomes segregated to the poles during anaphase I, (3) the differing combinations of recombinant chromatids segregated to the poles during anaphase II, and (4) the particular sets of male and female gametes that unite in fertilization. The four mechanisms, working together, produce so much total

PEOPLE BEHIND BIOLOGY 9.2

Dr. Aurora Nedelcu, University of New Brunswick

Whereas the octopuses and limpets mentioned at the opening of this chapter have no choice but to undergo meiosis and follow the remaining steps of their sexual life cycle, bacteria, archaea, and many lower eukaryotes become sexual only in response to suboptimal environmental conditions, such as elevated temperature or nutrient deficiency. This observation led Aurora Nedelcu and her colleagues in The Green Lab at the University of New Brunswick to gather evidence to test the hypothesis that sex originally evolved as one of several responses available to cells dealing with stress.

A variety of external stresses all eventually cause internal oxidative stress resulting from increased concentration of damaging reactive oxygen species (ROS). Using her multicellular algal model system (*Volvox carteri*), Nedelcu has shown that stress-induced increase in ROS does indeed stimulate the expression of sex-related genes **(Figure 1)**. She believes that the cells experiencing oxidative stress "turn on" their sex genes in order to benefit from the possibility that meiotic recombination will repair DNA damage caused by ROS.

Photo by Oana Marcu

FIGURE 1
Volvox carteri under heat stress. ROS indicated by green fluorescence.

variability that no two products of meiosis produced by the same or different individuals and no two zygotes produced by union of the gametes are likely to have the same genetic makeup. Each of these sources of variability is discussed in further detail in the following sections. **(Figure 9.16, p. 202–203)** contrasts the genetically identical daughter cells arising from mitosis with the diverse daughter cells produced by meiosis.

Genetic Recombination. Recombination, the key genetic event of prophase I, starts when homologous chromosomes pair **(Figure 9.13,** step 1). Recall that although hom-

ologous chromosomes have the same genes in the same order, they likely carry different versions of those genes (alleles). This means that the underlying DNA sequence is similar enough to form the basis of meiotic pairing, yet different enough to generate novel combinations after recombination. (Recall Lederberg's multiple auxotrophic *E. coli* mutants here; the idea is the same.) As the homologous chromosomes pair, they are held together tightly by a protein framework called the synaptonemal complex **(Figure 9.14, p. 200).** Supported by this framework, regions of homologous chromatids exchange segments, producing new combinations of alleles (see Figure 9.13,

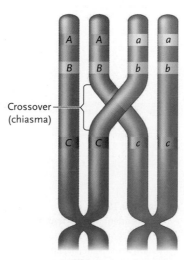
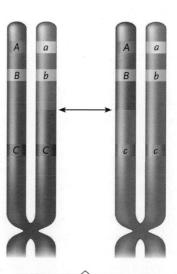

Homologous pair

Sister chromatids | Sister chromatids

Crossover (chiasma)

1 Homologous chromosomes pair.

2 Homologous chromatids exchange segments.

3 Homologous chromosomes separate at first meiotic division.

Figure 9.13
Effects of the exchange between chromatids that accomplishes genetic recombination. Although the closest chromatids are shown crossing over, any pair of nonsister chromatids may recombine. The letters indicate two alleles (e.g., *A* and *a*) for each of three genes. In the meiocyte, the alleles are in the combination of *A–B–C* and *a–b–c* on their respective homologues. As a result of this recombination event, two of the chromatids, the recombinants, have a new combination: *a–b–C* and *A–B–c*.

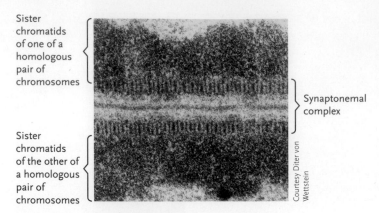

Sister chromatids of one of a homologous pair of chromosomes

Sister chromatids of the other of a homologous pair of chromosomes

Synaptonemal complex

Courtesy Diter von Wettstein

Figure 9.14

The synaptonemal complex as seen in a meiotic cell of the fungus *Neotiella*.

step 2). Recall that the exchange process is very precise and involves the breakage and rejoining of DNA molecules by enzymes (Figure 9.1, p. 182). When the exchange is complete toward the end of prophase I, the synaptonemal complex disassembles and disappears. If you now follow meiosis I and II through to the end in your mind, notice that each of the four resulting nuclei receives one of these four chromatids (see Figure 9.13, p. 199, step 3); two receive unchanged "parental" chromatids, and two receive chromatids that have new combinations of alleles due to recombination; these are called *recombinants*.

The physical effect of recombination can be seen later in prophase I, when increased condensation of the chromosomes thickens the chromosomes enough to make them visible under the light microscope (see Figure 9.11, p. 196, steps 3 and 4). Regions in which nonsister chromatids cross one another, called **crossovers** or **chiasmata** (singular, *chiasma* = crosspiece), clearly show that two of the four chromatids have exchanged segments. Because of the shape produced, the recombination process is also called **crossing-over.**

Note that illustrations of recombination usually show chromosomes "paired" side by side, with only the closest chromatids participating in recombination (see Figure 9.13, p. 199); however, chromosomes actually pair "one on top of the other" such that any two of the four chromatids can participate in a given recombination event. Recombination takes place largely at random, at almost any position along the chromosome arms. Several events likely occur at various locations along all chromatids.

CONCEPT FIX Notice in Figure 9.13, p. 199 that a recombination event does not just "switch" the alleles of a given gene in a localized area. Rather, all of the DNA sequence stretching from the site of recombination to the ends of the participating chromatids is exchanged. ⬡

Random Segregation. Random segregation of chromosomes of maternal and paternal origin accounts for the second major source of genetic variability in meiosis. Recall that the maternal and paternal members of each homologous pair are different in that they typically carry different alleles of many of the genes on that

chromosome. During prometaphase I, spindle microtubules make connections to kinetochores. For each homologous pair, one chromosome makes spindle connections leading to one pole and the other chromosome connects to the opposite pole in a random choice. In making these connections, all the maternal chromosomes may connect to one pole and all the paternal chromosomes may connect to the opposite pole. Or, as is much more likely, a random combination of maternal and paternal chromosomes will be segregated to a given spindle pole **(Figure 9.15).**

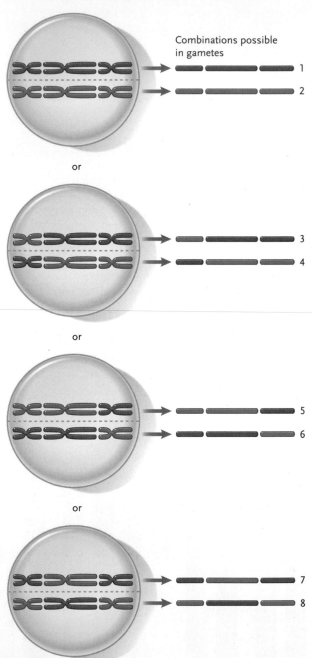

Combinations possible in gametes

1
2

or

3
4

or

5
6

or

7
8

Figure 9.15

Independent assortment. Possible outcomes of the random spindle connections of three pairs of chromosomes at metaphase I of meiosis. Maternal chromosomes are red; paternal chromosomes are blue. There are four possible patterns of connections, giving eight possible combinations of maternal and paternal chromosomes in gametes (labelled 1–8).

The number of possible random combinations depends on the number of chromosome pairs in a species. For example, the 39 chromosome pairs in dogs allow 2^{39} different combinations of maternal and paternal chromosomes to be delivered to the poles, producing potentially 550 billion genetically different gametes from this source of variability alone. Note that this random partitioning of maternal and paternal chromosomes is responsible for the independent assortment of the alleles of two genes in Mendel's experiments with garden peas described in Chapter 10.

Alternative Combinations at Meiosis II. If you look carefully at the cells drawn in metaphase II in Figure 9.13, you will see that the chromosomes are still replicated, and, as a result of recombination in prophase I, each chromosome carries one recombinant chromatid and one nonrecombinant chromatid. Notice that, in this case, the chromosomes have aligned at metaphase II with both recombinant chromatids attached to the same spindle pole. However, since the attachment of spindles to kinetochores is random at this stage, you should be able to see that it is just as likely that these chromosomes *could* have lined up, with the smaller chromosome sending its recombinant chromatid to one pole and the larger chromosome sending its recombinant chromatid to the opposite pole. The resulting daughter cells will be genetically different, depending on how the chromosomes align in metaphase II.

Random Fertilization. The haploid products of meiosis are genetically diverse. The random combination of these cells (or their descendants) during fertilization is a matter of chance that amplifies the variability of sexual reproduction. For example, if we consider only the variability available from random separation of homologous chromosomes at meiosis I along with that from random fertilization, the possibility that two children of the same human parents could receive the same combination of maternal and paternal chromosomes is 1 chance out of $(2^{23})^2$ or 1 in about 70 trillion, a number that far exceeds the number of humans who have ever lived. The further variability introduced by recombination and shuffling at meiosis II makes it practically impossible for humans and most other sexually reproducing organisms to produce genetically identical gametes or offspring. The only exception is identical twins (or identical triplets, identical quadruplets, and so forth), which arise not from the combination of identical gametes during fertilization but from mitotic division of a single fertilized egg into separate cells that give rise to genetically identical individuals.

We have just seen that meiosis has three outcomes that are vital to sexual reproduction. This process reduces the chromosomes to the haploid number so that

they can be brought together with those of another individual without doubling the usual chromosome number during fertilization. Through genetic recombination and random separation of maternal and paternal chromosomes, meiosis produces genetic variability in gametes; further variability is provided by the random combination of gametes in fertilization. These ideas form the "mechanics" that underlie the patterns of inheritance of traits in sexually reproducing organisms discovered by Mendel and described in Chapter 10.

STUDY BREAK

1. Which phase (diploid or haploid) dominates the respective life cycles of animals, plants, and fungi?
2. What are the two functions of meiosis?
3. What are the four sources of genetic variability in sexually reproducing organisms?
4. What is nondisjunction, and how does it occur?

9.4 Mobile Elements

Our examples have so far involved two participating DNA molecules that have always been at least partially homologous and that have always originated from two different individuals. However, one of the most interesting examples of genetic recombination in nature shows neither of these characteristics. All organisms appear to contain particular segments of DNA, called **mobile elements**, that can move from one place to another; they cut and paste sections of DNA using a type of recombination that does *not necessarily require homology*. Sometimes called *jumping genes,* these elements normally move from place to place *within the genome of a given cell*. The following section describes these fascinating elements in more detail.

9.4a Insertion Sequence Elements and Transposons Are the Two Major Types of Prokaryotic Mobile Elements

Mobile elements are also known by the more specific term **transposable elements (TEs)**, and their mechanism of movement, involving nonhomologous recombination, is called **transposition**. Transposition usually occurs at a low frequency in either of two ways, depending on the type of element: (1) a cut-and-paste process, in which the TE leaves its original location and transposes to a new location **(Figure 9.17a, p. 204)**, and (2) a copy-and-paste process, in which a copy of a TE transposes to a new location, leaving the original TE behind **(Figure 9.17b, p. 204).** For most TEs, transposition starts with contact between the TE and the target site.

This also means that TEs do not exist free of the DNA in which they are integrated; hence, the popular name *jumping genes* is actually inaccurate. TEs are never "in the air" between one location and another. TEs are important because of the genetic changes they cause. For example, they produce mutations by transposing into genes and knocking out their functions, and they increase or decrease gene expression by transposing into regulatory sequences of genes. As such, TEs are biological mutagens that increase genetic variability.

Bacterial TEs were discovered in the 1960s. They have been shown to move from site to site within the bacterial chromosome, between the bacterial chromosome and plasmids, and between plasmids. The frequency of transposition is low but constant for a given TE. Some bacterial TEs insert randomly, at any point in the DNA, whereas others recognize certain sequences as "hot spots" for insertion and insert preferentially at these locations.

The two major types of bacterial TEs are **insertion sequences (IS)** and **transposons.** Insertion sequences are the simplest TEs. They are relatively small and contain only genes for their transposition, notably the gene for **transposase,** an enzyme that catalyzes some of the recombination reactions for inserting or removing the TE from the DNA **(Figure 9.18, p. 204).** At each of the two ends of an IS is a short **inverted repeat** sequence—the same DNA sequence running in opposite directions

(shown by directional arrows in the figure). The inverted repeat sequences enable the transposase enzyme to identify the ends of the TE when it catalyzes transposition. The inverted repeat sequence is an IS element on both the F factor and the bacterial chromosome that provides the homology needed for the creation of the Hfr strains described in Section 9.2.

The second type of bacterial TE, called a transposon, has an inverted repeat sequence at each end enclosing a central region with one or more genes. In a number of bacterial transposons, the inverted repeat sequences are insertion sequences, which provide the transposase for movement of the element (see Figure 9.18, p. 204). Additional genes in the central region typically code for antibiotic resistance; they can originate from the main bacterial chromosome or from plasmids. These non-IS genes included in transposons are carried along as the TEs move from place to place.

Many antibiotics, such as penicillin, erythromycin, tetracycline, ampicillin, and streptomycin, which were once successful in curing bacterial infections, have lost much of their effectiveness because of resistance genes carried in transposons. Movements of the transposons, particularly to plasmids that can be transferred by conjugation within and between bacterial species, greatly increase the spread of genes, providing antibiotic resistance to infecting cells. Resistance genes have made many bacterial diseases difficult or impossible to treat with standard antibiotics.

Figure 9.16

Comparison of key steps in meiosis and mitosis. Both diagrams use an animal cell as an example. Maternal chromosomes are shown in red; paternal chromosomes are shown in blue.

Meiosis I

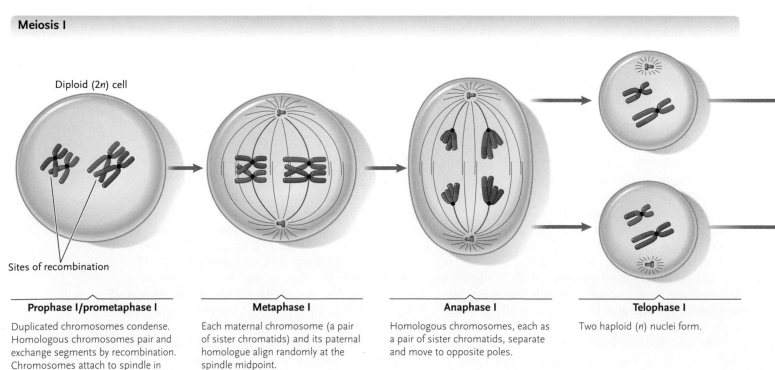

Diploid (2*n*) cell

Sites of recombination

Prophase I/prometaphase I	**Metaphase I**	**Anaphase I**	**Telophase I**
Duplicated chromosomes condense. Homologous chromosomes pair and exchange segments by recombination. Chromosomes attach to spindle in homologous pairs.	Each maternal chromosome (a pair of sister chromatids) and its paternal homologue align randomly at the spindle midpoint.	Homologous chromosomes, each as a pair of sister chromatids, separate and move to opposite poles.	Two haploid (*n*) nuclei form.

9.4b Transposable Elements Were First Discovered in Eukaryotes

TEs were first discovered in a eukaryote, maize (corn), in the 1940s by Barbara McClintock, a geneticist working at the Cold Spring Harbor Laboratory in New York. McClintock noted that some mutations affecting kernel and leaf colour appeared and disappeared rapidly under certain conditions. Mapping the alleles by linkage studies produced a surprising result: the map positions changed frequently, indicating that the alleles could move from place to place in the corn chromosomes.

Some of the movements were so frequent that changes in their effects could be noticed at different times in a single developing kernel **(Figure 9.19, p. 205).**

When McClintock first reported her results, her findings were regarded as an isolated curiosity, possibly applying only to corn. This was because the then-prevailing opinion among geneticists was that genes are fixed in the chromosomes and do not move to other locations. Her conclusions were widely accepted only after TEs were detected and characterized in bacteria in the 1960s. By the 1970s, further examples of TEs were discovered in other eukaryotes, including yeast

Mitosis

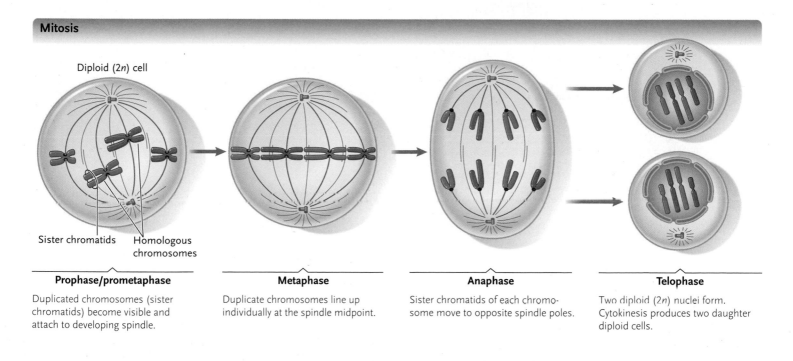

Prophase/prometaphase

Duplicated chromosomes (sister chromatids) become visible and attach to developing spindle.

Metaphase

Duplicate chromosomes line up individually at the spindle midpoint.

Anaphase

Sister chromatids of each chromosome move to opposite spindle poles.

Telophase

Two diploid (2*n*) nuclei form. Cytokinesis produces two daughter diploid cells.

Meiosis II

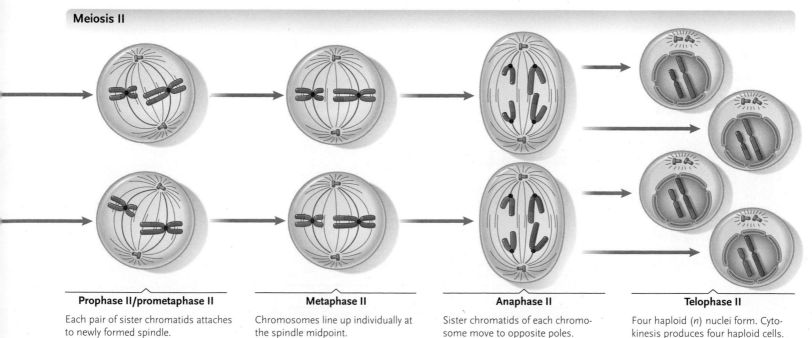

Prophase II/prometaphase II

Each pair of sister chromatids attaches to newly formed spindle.

Metaphase II

Chromosomes line up individually at the spindle midpoint.

Anaphase II

Sister chromatids of each chromosome move to opposite poles.

Telophase II

Four haploid (*n*) nuclei form. Cytokinesis produces four haploid cells.

a. Cut-and-paste transposition

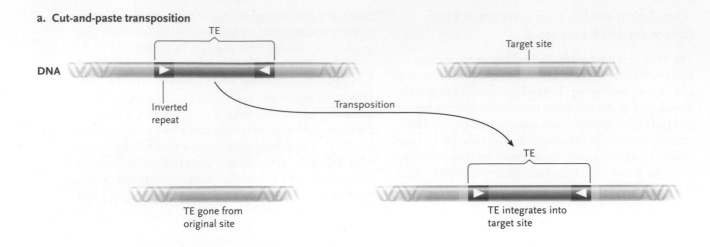

b. Copy-and-paste transposition

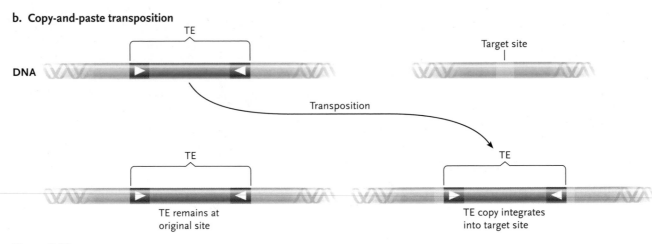

Figure 9.17

Two transposition processes for transposable elements. **(a)** Cut-and-paste transposition, in which the TE leaves one location in the DNA and moves to a new location. **(b)** Copy-and-paste transposition, in which a copy of the TE moves to a new location, leaving the original TE behind.

a. IS element

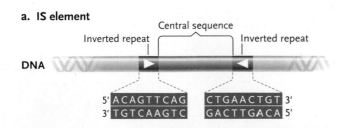

b. Transposon

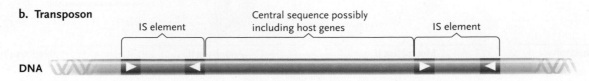

Figure 9.18

Types of bacterial transposable elements. **(a)** Insertion sequence (IS element).
(b) Transposon in which the central sequence is transposed by flanking IS elements.

Figure 9.19
Barbara McClintock and corn kernels showing different colour patterns due to the movement of transposable elements. As TEs move into or out of genes, controlling pigment production in developing kernels, the ability of cells and their descendants to produce the dark pigment is destroyed or restored. The result is random patterns of pigmented and colourless (yellow) segments in individual kernels.

and mammals. McClintock was awarded a Nobel Prize in 1983 for her pioneering work, after these discoveries confirmed her early findings that TEs are probably universally distributed among both prokaryotic and eukaryotic organisms.

9.4c Eukaryotic Transposable Elements Are Classified as Transposons or Retrotransposons

Eukaryotic TEs fall into two major classes: transposons and retrotransposons. They are distinguished by the way the TE sequence moves from place to place in the DNA. Eukaryotic transposons are similar to bacterial transposons in their general structure and in the ways they transpose. However, members of the other class of eukaryotic TEs, the **retrotransposons,** transpose by a copy-and-paste mechanism that is unlike any of the other TEs we have discussed. Retrotransposons have this name because transposition occurs via an intermediate RNA copy of the TE **(Figure 9.20).** First, the retrotransposon, which is a DNA element integrated into the chromosomal DNA, is transcribed into a complementary RNA copy. Next,

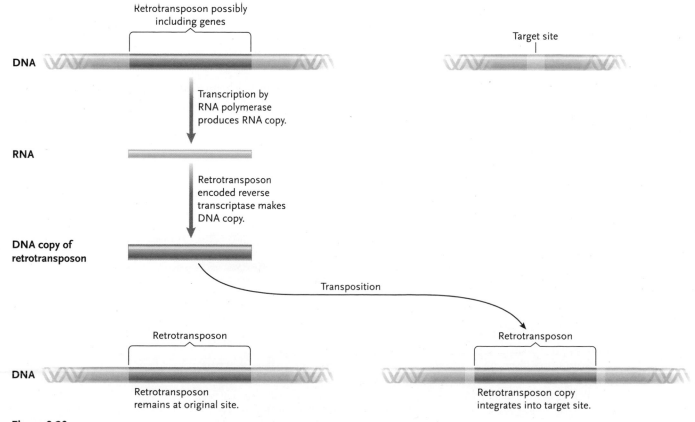

Figure 9.20
Transposition of a eukaryotic retrotransposon to a new location by means of an intermediate RNA copy.

an enzyme called **reverse transcriptase**, which is encoded by one of the genes of the retrotransposon, uses the RNA as a template to make a DNA copy of the retrotransposon.

The DNA copy is then inserted into the DNA at a new location, leaving the original in place. This insertion step involves breaking and rejoining DNA backbones, as we have seen several times in this chapter.

Once TEs are inserted into chromosomes, they become more or less permanent residents, duplicated and passed on during cell division along with the rest of the DNA. TEs inserted into the DNA of reproductive cells may be inherited, thereby becoming a permanent part of the genetic material of a species. Long-standing TEs are subject to mutation along with other sequences in the DNA. Such mutations may accumulate in a TE, gradually altering it into a nonmobile, residual sequence in the DNA. The DNA of many eukaryotes, including humans, contains a surprising amount of nonfunctional TE sequence likely created in this way.

9.4d Retrotransposons Are Similar to Retroviruses

The RNA to DNA reverse transcription associated with retrotransposon movement is strikingly similar to that employed by a class of eukaryotic viruses called **retroviruses.** When a retrovirus infects a host cell, a reverse transcriptase carried in the virus particle is released and copies the single-stranded RNA genome into a double-stranded DNA copy. The viral DNA is then inserted into the host DNA (by genetic recombination), where it is replicated and passed to progeny cells during cell division. Similar to the prophage of bacteria, the inserted viral DNA is known as a **provirus (Figure 9.21).**

Retroviruses are found in a wide range of organisms, with most so far identified in vertebrates. You, as well as other humans and mammals, contain several retroviruses in your genome as proviruses. In total, retrotransposons and retroviruses of all types occupy some 40% of the human genome!

Although many of the retroviruses do not produce infectious virus particles, they sometimes cause DNA rearrangements such as deletions and translocations. Such changes may alter the relative position of DNA sequences on the chromosome and, in turn, disturb the normal regulation of gene expression. Given your knowledge of transduction by bacterial viruses described earlier in this chapter, you will not be surprised to hear that retroviruses sometimes pick up host eukaryotic genes and move them to recipients. Such genes may become abnormally active through the effects of regulatory sequences located in the TE itself or the DNA nearby. Certain forms of cancer have been linked to this type of abnormal activation of genes that are important in regulating cell division (see Section 14.4). In one of the most dramatic examples, a cellular gene is transported to an infected cell by the avian sarcoma retrovirus. The cellular gene is overexpressed in the new environment, resulting in uncontrolled growth of infected cells, leading to tumours in infected birds.

STUDY BREAK

Among eukaryotic mobile elements, how do transposons, retrotransposons, and retroviruses differ?

This has been a long chapter. We hope that, taken together, all of these ideas will help you understand the balance that biology must strike between the

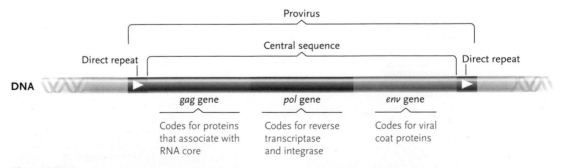

Figure 9.21
A mammalian retrovirus in the provirus form in which it is inserted into chromosomal DNA. The direct repeats at either end contain sequences capable of acting as enhancer, promoter, and termination signals for transcription. The central sequence contains genes coding for proteins, concentrated in the **gag, pol,** and **env** regions. The provirus of human immunodeficiency virus (HIV), the virus that causes acquired immune deficiency syndrome (AIDS), takes this form.

stability and the plasticity of the genetic material. On the one hand, DNA must be faithfully replicated and passed to the next generation. Lack of quality control at this step would allow widespread random mutations to undermine the selection and preservation of good combinations of alleles. On the other hand, any system that made only perfectly "photocopied" DNA available for the next generation would be doomed as well; a wide variety of diverse genetic "solutions" are needed for a population to survive in constantly changing environments that are impossible to anticipate in advance.

Genetic recombination is central to many processes that contribute changes to the sequence of DNA in all forms of life. (And we did not even discuss interesting examples of developmental genetic recombination in infecting parasites or the cells of the developing immune system, or foreign DNA taken up by rotifers.) The genetic elements discussed in this chapter, particularly plasmids and retroviruses, often act as natural genetic engineers by moving genes between species. Chapter 15 describes how human genetic engineers manipulate and clone DNA and how they analyze genomes at the DNA level.

Review

 Access an interactive eBook, chapter-specific interactive learning tools, including flashcards, quizzes, videos, and more in your Biology **CourseMate**, accessed through NelsonBrain.com **Aplia™** is an online interactive learning solution that helps you improve comprehension—and your grade—by integrating a variety of mediums and tools such as videos, tutorials, practice tests, and an interactive eBook.

9.1 Mechanism of Genetic Recombination

- Genetic recombination requires two DNA molecules that differ from one another, a mechanism for bringing the DNA molecules into close proximity, and a collection of enzymes to cut, exchange, and paste the DNA back together.
- Homology allows DNA on different molecules to line up and recombine precisely.
- Enzymatic cutting and pasting of both DNA backbones from each of the two DNA molecules is required for each recombination event (see Figure 9.1).

9.2 Genetic Recombination in Bacteria

- Study of bacterial recombination requires strains carrying different alleles.
- Lederberg and Tatum mutated bacteria to create strains that were different in their ability to manufacture certain amino acids and vitamins.
- In bacteria, the DNA of the bacterial chromosome may recombine with DNA brought into close proximity from another cell.
- Three primary mechanisms bring DNA into bacterial cells from the outside: conjugation, transformation, and transduction.
- In conjugation, two bacterial cells form a cytoplasmic bridge allowing at least some of the DNA of one cell to move into the other cell. The donated DNA can then recombine with homologous sequences of the recipient cell's DNA.
- *E. coli* bacteria that are able to act as DNA donors in conjugation have an F plasmid, making them F⁺; recipients have no F plasmid and are F⁻. In Hfr strains of *E. coli*, the F plasmid is a part of the main chromosome. As a result, genes from the main chromosome can be transferred into F⁻ cells along with a portion of the F plasmid DNA (see Figure 9.6).
- In transformation, intact cells of some species absorb pieces of DNA released from cells that have disintegrated. The entering DNA fragments can recombine with the recipient cell's DNA.
- In transduction, DNA is transferred from one cell to another "by mistake" inside the head of an infecting virus (see Figure 9.7).
- Since generalized transduction transfers random fragments of the host chromosome, all host genes are transferred at equal frequency. Specialized transduction only transfers genes lying close to the point of insertion of the prophage (see Figure 9.8).

9.3 Genetic Recombination in Eukaryotes: Meiosis

- The time and place of meiosis follow one of three major pathways in the life cycles of eukaryotes, which reflect the portions of the life cycle spent in the haploid and diploid phases and whether mitotic divisions intervene between meiosis and the formation of gametes (see Figure 9.9).
- Animals have a diploid life cycle in which the diploid phase is multicellular and the haploid phase is unicellular. Meiosis is followed by gamete formation.
- Plants and some fungi have an alternating-generations life cycle in which either haploid or diploid phases are multicellular and both of which divide by mitosis. The diploid sporophytes are produced by fertilization, and the haploid gametophytes are produced by mitotic divisions of the spores formed by meiosis.
- Most fungi exhibit a haploid life cycle in which the haploid phase is multicellular and the diploid phase is limited to a single cell produced by fertilization, which then immediately undergoes meiosis.
- In animals, the products of meiosis are haploid gametes. The diploid phase of the life cycle is then restored when one gamete fuses with another at fertilization. In plants, meiosis occurs in some of the cells of the diploid sporophytes and produces a generation of haploid spores. These spores then divide by mitosis to produce multicellular gametophytes. Gametes are formed from mitotic division of specific sporophyte tissues.
- The functions of meiosis are to reduce the chromosome number (from diploid to haploid) and to generate genetic diversity in sexually reproducing organisms (see Figure 9.10).
- Meiosis occurs only in eukaryotes that reproduce sexually and only in organisms that are at least diploid—that is, organisms

that have at least two representatives of each chromosome (see Figure 9.11).

- DNA replicates and the chromosomal proteins are duplicated during the premeiotic interphase, producing two copies, the sister chromatids, of each chromosome.

- During prophase I of the first meiotic division (meiosis I), the replicated chromosomes condense and come together and pair as the spindle forms in the cytoplasm.

- While they are paired, the chromatids of homologous chromosomes undergo recombination by breaking the covalent bonds of the DNA backbones, matching complementary sequences on non-sister chromatids, exchanging the ends, and restoring the bonds.

- During prometaphase I, the nuclear envelope breaks down, the spindle enters the area of the former nucleus, and kinetochore microtubules leading to opposite spindle poles attach to one kinetochore of each pair of sister chromatids of homologous chromosomes.

- At metaphase I, spindle microtubule movements have aligned the tetrads on the metaphase plate, the equatorial plane between the two spindle poles. The connections of kinetochore microtubules to opposite poles ensure that the homologous pairs separate and move to opposite spindle poles during anaphase I, reducing the chromosome number to the haploid value. Each chromosome at the poles still contains two chromatids.

- Telophase I and interkinesis are brief and transitory stages; no DNA replication occurs during interkinesis. During these stages, the remaining single spindle of the first meiotic division disassembles and the microtubule subunits are available to reassemble into two new spindles for the second division.

- During prophase II, the chromosomes condense and the spindle reorganizes. During prometaphase II, the nuclear envelope breaks down, the spindle enters the former nuclear area, and spindle microtubules leading to opposite spindle poles attach to the two kinetochores of each chromosome. At metaphase II, the chromosomes become aligned on the metaphase plate. The connections of kinetochore microtubules to opposite spindle poles ensure that during anaphase II, the chromatids of each chromosome are separated and segregate to those opposite spindle poles.

- During telophase II, the chromosomes decondense to their extended interphase state, the spindles disassemble, and new nuclear envelopes form. The result is four haploid cells, each containing half the number of chromosomes present in a G_1 nucleus of the same species. In animals, these products of meiosis function as gametes that fuse in fertilization; in plants, these products function as spores that divide by mitosis to form gametophytes.

- Meiosis II differs from mitosis in that meiosis II occurs only in reproductive tissue, is not preceded by an S phase, and results in genetically different daughter cells (see Figure 9.16).

- Nondisjunction occurs when both members of a pair of homologous chromosomes connect to spindles from the same pole. Following anaphase, one pole then receives both copies of the pair, and the other pole receives none. The overall results (following normal meiosis II) are haploid products of meiosis that have two copies of the given chromosome. After fertilization, the resulting zygote will therefore have three copies of the chromosome instead of two.

- In many eukaryotes, including most animals, one or more pairs of chromosomes, called the sex chromosomes, are different in male and female individuals of the same species.

- Recombination is the first source of the genetic variability produced by meiosis. During recombination, chromatids generate new combinations of alleles by physically exchanging segments. The exchange process involves precise breakage and joining of DNA molecules. It is catalyzed by enzymes and occurs while the homologous chromosomes are held together tightly by the synaptonemal complex. The crossovers visible between the chromosomes at late prophase I reflect the exchange of chromatid segments that occurred during the molecular steps of genetic recombination (see Figures 9. 13 and 9.14).

- The random segregation of homologous chromosomes is the second source of genetic variability produced by meiosis. The homologous pairs separate at anaphase I of meiosis, creating random combinations of maternal and paternal chromosomes travelling to each of the two spindle poles (see Figure 9.15).

- Random segregation of the chromatids of replicated chromosomes at meiosis II is a third mechanism for generating diversity.

- Random joining of male and female gametes in fertilization is the fourth source of genetic variability.

9.4 Mobile Elements

- Both prokaryotic and eukaryotic organisms contain TEs (transposable elements)—DNA sequences that can move from place to place in the DNA. The TEs may move from one location in the DNA to another or generate duplicated copies that insert in new locations while leaving the parent copy in its original location (see Figure 9.17).

- Genes of the host cell DNA may become incorporated into a TE and may be carried with it to a new location. There the genes may become abnormally active when placed near sequences that control the activity of genes within the TE or near the control elements of active host genes (see Figure 9.18).

- Eukaryotic TEs occur as transposons, which release from one location in the DNA and insert at a different site, or as retrotransposons, which move by making an RNA copy, which is then used to assemble a DNA copy that is inserted at a new location. The parent copy remains at the original location. Like retrotransposons, retroviruses make a DNA copy of their RNA genome and insert this into the host's chromosome. Retroviruses may have evolved from retrotransposons (see Figure 9.20).

- TE-instigated abnormal activation of genes regulating cell division has been linked to the development of some forms of cancer in humans and other complex animals.

Questions

Self-Test Questions

1. If recombination occurred in a bacterium undergoing transformation as shown in the figure, what would be the final genotype of the bacterial chromosome?

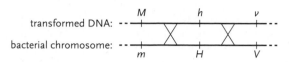

   a. *MHv*
   b. *MHv*
   c. *mHV*
   d. *mhV*

2. Which of the following events turns F⁺ cells into Hfr (high-frequency recombination) cells?
   a. replication of the F factor by rolling circle replication
   b. recombination between the F factor and the recipient chromosome
   c. transfer of the F factor to a recipient cell
   d. integration of the F factor into the host chromosome

3. Which of the following describes an aspect of bacterial conjugation?
   a. Recipient cells incorporate single-stranded DNA from donors into their chromosome.
   b. DNA from dead donor bacteria is transferred to live recipient cells.
   c. Genes are transferred in a particular order from donors to recipients.
   d. A virus is required for the transfer of DNA from donors to recipient cells.

4. If a virus is in the lysogenic phase of its life cycle, what is it doing?
   a. bursting the host cell
   b. transducing genes into a bacterial cell
   c. assembling viral particles for cell rupture
   d. being expressed and/or copied as a part of the host DNA

5. If the diploid number of an organism is 6, which stage of cell division does the figure below represent?

   a. mitotic metaphase
   b. meiotic metaphase I
   c. meiotic metaphase II
   d. could be either mitotic metaphase or meiotic metaphase II

6. Imagine that you are helping your younger brother with his biology homework. You notice that he has written down in his notes that "Plants are haploid and make gametes by mitosis. Animals are diploid and make gametes by meiosis." What should your response be?
   a. Yes, plants make gametes by mitosis and most animals make gametes by meiosis. However, animals and plants both have a haploid and a diploid stage of their life cycle.
   b. Yes, both plants and animals make gametes. The difference is that plant gametes divide by mitosis but animal gametes do not.
   c. Yes, plants are simpler organisms than animals and have fewer chromosomes in their cells.
   d. Yes, plants and animals use meiosis for different purposes. Animals make gametes by meiosis while plants make zygotes.

7. As a result of genetic recombination, each of the chromosomes of your family dog contains a different combination of alleles compared to those of its brothers and sisters. When did this recombination occur?
   a. when your dog's parents made gametes
   b. when your dog was a newly fertilized, single-celled zygote
   c. when your dog grew from a zygote to a multicellular organism
   d. when your dog reached sexual maturity

8. The number of human chromosomes in a cell in prophase I of meiosis is ___ and in telophase II is ___.
   a. 92; 46
   b. 46; 23
   c. 23; 23
   d. 23; 16

9. Consider a penguin gamete. The amount of DNA (pg) in this gamete is defined as 1*C*. The number of chromosomes in this gamete is defined as 1*n*. That is, the value of *C* and the value of *n* are equal in a penguin gamete. During which other stage of penguin cell division would the value of *C* and the value of *n* also be equal?
   a. during G_1; both *n* and *C* equal 2
   b. during G_2; both *n* and *C* equal 4
   c. during metaphase of meiosis II; both *n* and *C* equal 1
   d. during metaphase of mitosis; both *n* and *C* equal 2

10. Which of the following is a feature of mobile elements?
    a. They have no negative impact on host cells.
    b. They have inverted repeat sequences at their centre.
    c. They make use of recombination that does not require extensive homology.
    d. They are a kind of virus.

Questions for Discussion

1. You set up an experiment like the one carried out by Lederberg and Tatum, mixing millions of *E. coli* of two strains with the following genetic constitutions.

   Strain 1: bio^- met^- thr^+ leu^+

   Strain 2: bio^+ met^+ thr^- leu^-

   Among the bacteria obtained after mixing, you find some cells that do not require threonine, leucine, or biotin to grow but still need methionine. How might you explain this result?

2. You have a technique that allows you to measure the amount of DNA in a cell nucleus. You establish the amount of DNA in a sperm cell of an organism as your baseline. Which multiple of this amount would you expect to find in a nucleus of this organism at G_2 of premeiotic interphase? At telophase I of meiosis? During interkinesis? At telophase II of meiosis?

3. Mutations are changes in DNA sequences that can create new alleles. In which cells of an individual, somatic or meiotic cells, would mutations be of greatest significance to that individual? What about to the species to which the individual belongs?

4. Sometimes pieces of chromosomes can be exchanged in a kind of rearrangement called a reciprocal translocation. Imagine the case in a diploid organism where the end of one chromosome 4 was exchanged for the end of a chromosome 12. The other chromosomes 4 and 12 remained uninvolved and normal in structure. What shape might these four chromosomes take as they tried to pair during meiosis I?

5. Experimental systems have been developed in which transposable elements can be induced to move under the control of a researcher. Following the induced transposition of a yeast TE element, two mutants were identified with altered activities of enzyme X. One of the mutants lacked enzyme activity completely, whereas the other had five times the enzyme activity of normal cells. Both mutants were found to have the TE inserted into the gene for enzyme X. Propose hypotheses for how the two different mutant phenotypes were produced.

Rabbits, showing genetic variation in coat colour.

Biosphoto / Gunther Michel / Photolibrary

STUDY PLAN

10.1 The Beginnings of Genetics: Mendel's Garden Peas

10.1a Mendel Chose True-Breeding Garden Peas for His Experiments

10.1b Mendel First Worked with Single-Character Crosses

10.1c Mendel's Single-Character Crosses Led Him to Propose the Principle of Segregation

10.1d Mendel Could Predict Both Classes and Proportions of Offspring from His Hypotheses

10.1e Mendel Used a Testcross to Check the Validity of His Hypotheses

10.1f Mendel Tested the Independence of Different Genes in Crosses

10.1g Mendel's Research Founded the Field of Genetics

10.1h Sutton's Chromosome Theory of Inheritance Related Mendel's Genes to Chromosomes

10.2 Later Modifications and Additions to Mendel's Hypotheses

10.2a In Incomplete Dominance, Dominant Alleles Do Not Completely Compensate for Recessive Alleles

10.2b In Codominance, the Effects of Different Alleles Are Equally Detectable in Heterozygotes

10.2c In Multiple Alleles, More Than Two Alleles of a Gene Are Present in a Population

10.2d In Epistasis, Genes Interact, with the Activity of One Gene Influencing the Activity of Another Gene

10.2e In Polygenic Inheritance, a Character Is Controlled by the Common Effects of Several Genes

10.2f In Pleiotropy, Two or More Characters Are Affected by a Single Gene

10 Mendel, Genes, and Inheritance

WHY IT MATTERS

Parties and champagne were among the last things on Ernest Irons's mind on New Year's Eve, 1904. Irons, a medical intern, was examining a blood specimen from a new patient and was sketching what he saw through his microscope—peculiarly elongated red blood cells **(Figure 10.1, p. 212)**. He and his supervisor, James Herrick, had never seen anything like them. The shape of the cells was reminiscent of a sickle, a cutting tool with a crescent-shaped blade.

The patient had complained of weakness, dizziness, shortness of breath, and pain. His father and two sisters had died from mysterious ailments that had damaged their lungs or kidneys. Did those deceased family members also have sickle-shaped red cells in their blood? Was there a connection between the abnormal cells and the ailments? How did the cells become sickled?

The medical problems that baffled Irons and Herrick killed their patient when he was only 32 years old. The patient's symptoms were characteristic of a genetic disorder now called *sickle cell disease*. This disease develops when a person has received two copies of a gene (one from each parent) that codes for an altered subunit of hemoglobin, the oxygen-transporting protein in red blood cells. When oxygen

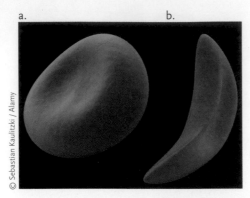

Figure 10.1
Red blood cell shape in sickle cell disease.
(a) A normal red blood cell. **(b)** A sickled red blood cell.

Figure 10.2
Gregor Mendel (1822–1884), the founder of genetics.

supplies are low, the altered hemoglobin forms long, fibrous, crystal-like structures that push red blood cells into the sickle shape. The altered protein differs from the normal protein by just a single amino acid.

The sickled red blood cells are too elongated and inflexible to pass through the capillaries, the smallest vessels in the circulatory system. As a result, the cells block the capillaries. The surrounding tissues become starved for oxygen and saturated with metabolic wastes, causing the symptoms experienced by Irons and Herrick's patient. The problem worsens as oxygen concentration falls in tissues and more red blood cells are pushed into the sickled form. (You will learn more about sickle cell disease in this chapter and in Chapter 11.)

Researchers have studied sickle cell disease in great detail at both the molecular and the clinical level. You may find it curious, however, that our understanding of sickle cell disease—and all other heritable traits—actually began with studies of pea plants in a monastery garden.

Fifty years before Ernest Irons sketched sickled red blood cells, a scholarly monk named Gregor Mendel **(Figure 10.2)** used garden peas to study patterns of inheritance. To test his hypotheses about inheritance, Mendel bred generation after generation of pea plants and carefully observed the patterns by which parents transmit traits to their offspring. Through his experiments and observations, Mendel discovered the fundamental rules that govern inheritance. His discoveries and conclusions founded the science of genetics and still have the power to explain many of the puzzling and sometimes devastating aspects of inheritance that continue to occupy our attention.

10.1 The Beginnings of Genetics: Mendel's Garden Peas

Until about 1900, scientists and the general public believed in the **blending theory of inheritance**, which suggested that hereditary traits blend evenly in

offspring through mixing of the parents' blood, much like the effect of mixing coffee and cream. Even today, many people assume that parental characteristics such as skin colour, body size, and facial features blend evenly in their offspring, with the traits of the children appearing about halfway between those of their parents. Yet if blending takes place, why don't extremes, such as very tall and very short individuals, gradually disappear over generations as repeated blending takes place? Also, why do children with blue eyes keep turning up among the offspring of brown-eyed parents?

Gregor Mendel's experiments with garden peas, performed in the 1860s, provided the first answers to these questions and many more. Mendel was an Augustinian monk who lived in a monastery in Brünn, now part of the Czech Republic. But he had an unusual education for a monk in the mid-nineteenth century. He had studied mathematics, chemistry, zoology, and botany at the University of Vienna under some of the foremost scientists of his day. He grew up on a farm and was well aware of agricultural principles and their application. He kept abreast of breeding experiments published in scientific journals. Mendel also won several awards for developing improved varieties of fruits and vegetables.

In his work with peas, Mendel studied a variety of heritable characteristics called **characters**, such as flower colour or seed shape. A variation in a character, such as purple or white flower colour, is called a **trait**. Mendel established that characters are passed to offspring in the form of discrete hereditary factors, which are now known as genes. Mendel observed that rather than blending evenly, many parental traits appear unchanged in offspring, whereas others disappear in one generation to reappear unchanged in the next. Although Mendel did not know it, the inheritance patterns he observed are the result of the segregation of chromosomes, on which the genes are located, to gametes in meiosis (see Chapter 9). Mendel's methods illustrate, perhaps as well as any experiments in the history of science, how rigorous scientific work is conducted: through observation, making hypotheses, and testing the hypotheses with experiments. Although others had studied inheritance patterns before him, Mendel's most important innovation was his quantitative approach to science, specifically his rigour and statistical analysis in an era when qualitative, purely descriptive science was the accepted practice. In this chapter, we will pay particular attention to the experimental aspect of Mendel's approach to explaining inheritance.

10.1a Mendel Chose True-Breeding Garden Peas for His Experiments

Mendel chose the garden pea (*Pisum sativum*) for his research because the plant could be grown easily in the monastery garden, without elaborate equipment. As in other flowering plants, gametes are produced in structures of the flowers **(Figure 10.3)**. The male gametes are sperm nuclei contained in the pollen, which is produced in the *anthers* of the flower. The female gametes are egg cells, produced in the *carpel* of the flowers. Normally, pea plants **self-fertilize** (also known as **self-pollinate** or, more simply, *self*): sperm nuclei in pollen produced by anthers fertilize egg cells housed in the carpel of the same flower. However, for his experiments, Mendel prevented self-fertilization by cutting off the anthers. Pollen to fertilize these flowers then had to come from a different plant. This technique is called **cross-pollination** or, more simply, a *cross*. This technique allowed Mendel to test the effects of mating pea plants of different parental types.

To begin his experiments, Mendel chose pea plants that were known to be **true-breeding** (also called *pure-breeding*); that is, when self-fertilized or, more simply, *selfed*, they passed traits without change from one generation to the next.

10.1b Mendel First Worked with Single-Character Crosses

Flower colour was among the seven characters Mendel selected for study; one true-breeding variety of peas had purple flowers, and the other true-breeding variety had white flowers (see Figure 10.3). Would these traits blend evenly if plants with purple flowers were cross-pollinated with plants with white flowers?

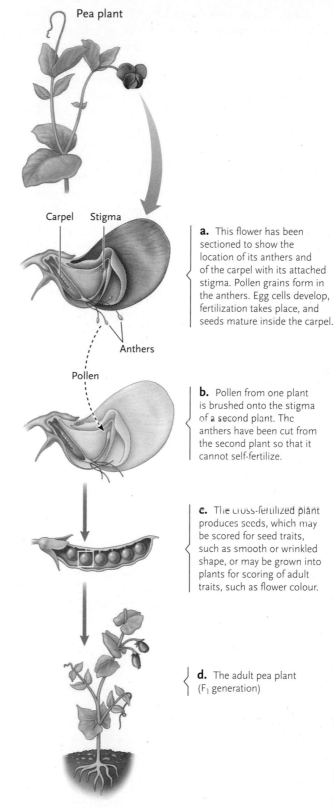

a. This flower has been sectioned to show the location of its anthers and of the carpel with its attached stigma. Pollen grains form in the anthers. Egg cells develop, fertilization takes place, and seeds mature inside the carpel.

b. Pollen from one plant is brushed onto the stigma of a second plant. The anthers have been cut from the second plant so that it cannot self-fertilize.

c. The cross-fertilized plant produces seeds, which may be scored for seed traits, such as smooth or wrinkled shape, or may be grown into plants for scoring of adult traits, such as flower colour.

d. The adult pea plant (F₁ generation)

Figure 10.3
The garden pea (*Pisum sativum*), the focus of Mendel's experiments.

To answer this question, Mendel took pollen from the anthers of plants with purple flowers and placed it in the flowers of white-flowered plants. He placed the pollen on the *stigma*, the part of the carpel that receives pollen in flowers (see Figure 10.3). He also performed the reciprocal experiment by placing pollen from white-flowered plants on the stigmas of purple-flowered plants. Seeds were the result of the crosses; each seed contains a zygote, or embryo, that will develop into a new pea plant. The plants that develop from the seeds produced by the cross—the first generation of offspring from the cross—are the **F₁ generation** (F stands for *filial; filius* = son). The plants used in the initial cross are called the parental or **P generation.** The plants that grew from the F₁ seeds all formed purple flowers, as if the trait for white flowers had disappeared. The flowers showed no evidence of blending.

Mendel then allowed the purple-flowered F₁ plants to self, producing seeds that represented the **F₂ generation.** When he planted the F₂ seeds produced by this cross, the white-flowered trait reappeared; both purple-flowered and white-flowered plants were produced. Mendel counted 705 plants with purple flowers and 224 with white flowers, in a ratio that he noted was close to 3:1, or about 75% purple-flowered plants and 25% white-flowered plants.

Mendel made similar crosses that involved six other characters, each with pairs of traits **(Figure 10.4);** for example, the character of seed colour has the traits

yellow and green. In all cases, he observed a uniform F₁ generation, in which only one of the two traits was present. In the F₂ generation, the missing trait reappeared, and both traits were present among the offspring. Moreover, the trait present in the F₁ generation was present in a definite, predictable proportion among the F₂ offspring.

10.1c Mendel's Single-Character Crosses Led Him to Propose the Principle of Segregation

Using his knowledge of mathematics, Mendel developed a set of hypotheses to explain the results of his crosses. His first hypothesis was that *the adult plants carry a pair of factors that govern the inheritance of each character.* He correctly deduced that for each character, an organism inherits one factor from each parent.

In modern terminology, Mendel's factors are called *genes,* which are located on chromosomes. The different versions of a gene that produce different traits of a character are called **alleles.** Thus, there are

Figure 10.4
Mendel's crosses with seven different characters in peas, including his results and the calculated ratios of offspring.

Character	Traits crossed	F₁	F₂		Ratio
Seed shape	round × wrinkled	All round	5474 round	1850 wrinkled	2.96:1
Seed colour	yellow × green	All yellow	6022 yellow	2001 green	3.01:1
Pod shape	inflated × constricted	All inflated	882 inflated	299 constricted	2.95:1
Pod colour	green × yellow	All green	428 green	152 yellow	2.82:1
Flower colour	purple × white	All purple	705 purple	224 white	3.15:1
Flower position	axial (along stems) × terminal (at tips)	All axial	651 axial	207 terminal	3.14:1
Stem length	tall × dwarf	All tall	787 tall	277 dwarf	2.84:1

two alleles of the gene that govern flower colour in garden peas: one allele for purple flowers and the other allele for white flowers. Organisms with two copies of each gene are now known as diploids; the two alleles of a gene in a diploid individual may be identical or different.

How can the disappearance of one of the traits, such as white flowers, in the F_1 generation and its reappearance in the F_2 generation be explained? Mendel deduced that the trait that had seemed to disappear in the F_1 generation was actually present but was masked in some way by the "stronger" allele. Mendel called the masking effect **dominance.** Accordingly, Mendel's second hypothesis stated that *if an individual's pair of genes consists of different alleles, one allele is dominant over the other, recessive, allele.*

CONCEPT FIX What makes an allele dominant? In the case of flower colour in Mendel's peas, the purple allele is declared to be dominant simply because, when both alleles are present, the flowers are purple rather than white. More generally, when an organism carries two different alleles, the dominant allele is simply the one that determines the appearance of the organism. In the years since Mendel's work, the underlying mechanisms of dominance have been discovered. For example, notice the round versus wrinkled pea seed shape character shown in Figure 10.4. We now know that round seeds contain a branched form of starch called amylopectin, while wrinkled seeds do not. In the DNA of pea plants there is a gene that codes for an enzyme that produces amylopectin. At some time in the past, a mutation in this gene created an alternative, mutant, version. This mutant allele codes for an enzyme that is nonfunctional and produces no amylopectin. Therefore, plants that contain both of these alleles produce both the functional and the nonfunctional enzymes. The functional enzyme creates amylopectin, resulting in round seeds. Since the allele coding the functional enzyme determines the appearance of the seeds in such plants, it is called the dominant allele. *Notice that dominant alleles do not directly inhibit recessive alleles.*

As a third hypothesis, Mendel proposed the following: the pairs of alleles that control a character **segregate** (separate) as gametes are formed; half the gametes carry one allele, and the other half carry the other allele. This hypothesis is now known as Mendel's **Principle of Segregation.** During fertilization, fusion of the haploid maternal and paternal gametes produces a diploid nucleus called the zygote nucleus. The zygote nucleus receives one allele for the character from the male gamete and one allele for the same character from the female gamete, reuniting the pairs.

Mendel's three hypotheses explained the results of the crosses as summarized in **Figure 10.5, p. 216.** Both alleles of the flower colour gene in the true-breeding parent plant with purple flowers are the same. The symbol P is used here to designate this allele, with the capital letter indicating that it is dominant, which gives this true-breeding parent the PP combination of alleles. Such an individual is called a **homozygote** (*homo* = same) and is said to be **homozygous** for the P allele. Therefore, when the individual produces gametes and the paired alleles separate during meiosis, all the gametes from this individual will receive a P allele (step 1 to step 2 in Figure 10.5, p. 216).

In the original true-breeding parent with white flowers, both alleles of the flower colour gene are also the same. Here the symbol p is used to designate this allele, with the lowercase letter indicating that it is recessive, which gives this true-breeding plant the homozygous pp combination of alleles. These alleles also separate during meiosis, leading to gametes that all contain one p allele.

All the F_1 plants produced by crossing purple-flowered and white-flowered plants—the cross $PP \times pp$—received the same combination of alleles: P from one parent and p from the other (step 3 in Figure 10.5, p. 216). An individual of this type, with two different alleles of a gene, is called a **heterozygote** (*hetero* = different) and is said to be **heterozygous** for the trait. Because P is dominant over p, all the Pp plants have purple flowers, even though they also carry the allele for white flowers. An F_1 heterozygote produced from a cross that involves a single character is called a **monohybrid** (*mono* = one; *hybrid* = an offspring of parents with different traits).

According to Mendel's hypotheses, all the Pp plants in the F_1 generation produce two kinds of gametes. Because the heterozygous Pp pair separates during meiosis I, half of the gametes receive the P allele and half receive the p allele (step 4 to step 5 of Figure 10.5, p. 216). Step 5 of Figure 10.5, p. 216, shows how these gametes can combine during selfing of F_1 plants. Generally, a cross between two individuals that are each heterozygous for the same pair of alleles—$Pp \times Pp$ here—is called a **monohybrid cross.** The gametes are entered in both the rows and columns in Figure 10.5, p. 216; the cells show the possible combinations. Combining two gametes that both carry the P allele produces a PP F_2 plant; combining P from one parent and p from the other produces a Pp plant; and combining p from both F_1 parents produces a pp F_2 plant. The homozygous PP and heterozygous Pp plants in the F_2 generation have purple flowers, the dominant trait; the homozygous pp offspring have white flowers, the recessive trait.

Mendel's hypotheses explain how individuals may differ genetically but still look the same. The PP and Pp plants, although genetically different, both have purple flowers. In modern terminology, **genotype** refers to the *genetic constitution of an organism*, and **phenotype** (Greek *phainein* = to show) refers to its *outward appearance*. In this case, the two different genotypes PP and Pp produce the same purple-flower phenotype.

Figure 10.5

Mendel's experiment illustrating the principle of segregation for flower colour in peas.

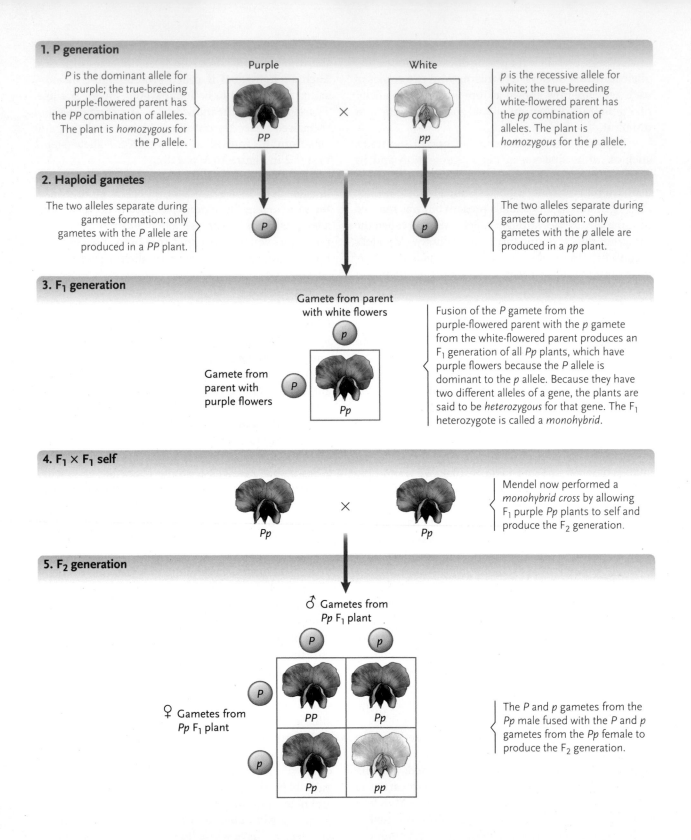

1. P generation

Purple   White

P is the dominant allele for purple; the true-breeding purple-flowered parent has the *PP* combination of alleles. The plant is *homozygous* for the *P* allele.

PP × *pp*

p is the recessive allele for white; the true-breeding white-flowered parent has the *pp* combination of alleles. The plant is *homozygous* for the *p* allele.

2. Haploid gametes

The two alleles separate during gamete formation: only gametes with the *P* allele are produced in a *PP* plant.

P   *p*

The two alleles separate during gamete formation: only gametes with the *p* allele are produced in a *pp* plant.

3. F₁ generation

Gamete from parent with white flowers

p

Gamete from parent with purple flowers

P

Pp

Fusion of the *P* gamete from the purple-flowered parent with the *p* gamete from the white-flowered parent produces an F₁ generation of all *Pp* plants, which have purple flowers because the *P* allele is dominant to the *p* allele. Because they have two different alleles of a gene, the plants are said to be *heterozygous* for that gene. The F₁ heterozygote is called a *monohybrid*.

4. F₁ × F₁ self

Pp × *Pp*

Mendel now performed a *monohybrid cross* by allowing F₁ purple *Pp* plants to self and produce the F₂ generation.

5. F₂ generation

♂ Gametes from *Pp* F₁ plant

P   *p*

♀ Gametes from *Pp* F₁ plant

P

p

PP   *Pp*

Pp   *pp*

The *P* and *p* gametes from the *Pp* male fused with the *P* and *p* gametes from the *Pp* female to produce the F₂ generation.

Thus, the results of Mendel's crosses support his three hypotheses:

1. The genes that govern genetic characters are present in two copies in individuals.
2. If different alleles are present in an individual's pair of genes, one allele is dominant over the other.
3. The two alleles of a gene segregate and enter gametes singly.

10.1d Mendel Could Predict Both Classes and Proportions of Offspring from His Hypotheses

Mendel could predict both classes and proportions of offspring from his hypotheses. To understand how Mendel's hypotheses allowed him to predict the proportions of offspring resulting from a genetic cross, let's review the mathematical rules that govern probability—that is, the possibility that an outcome will occur if it is a matter of chance, as in the random fertilization of an egg by a sperm cell that contains one allele or another.

In the mathematics of probability, the likelihood of an outcome is predicted on a scale of 0 to 1. An outcome that is certain to occur has a probability of 1, and an outcome that cannot possibly happen has a probability of 0. The standard game die, a cube with one of the numbers 1 through 6 on each face, is a familiar model to demonstrate working with probability. In general, we determine the probability of any given outcome (rolling a 4) by dividing that outcome by the total number of possible outcomes. For obtaining 4 in rolling a die, the probability is 1 divided by 6, or 1/6. The likelihood of rolling an even number (2 or 4 or 6) is 3/6 = 1/2. The probabilities of all the possible outcomes, when added together, must equal 1.

The Product Rule in Probability. If you roll two dice together, what is the chance of rolling double fours? Because the outcome of one die has no effect on the outcome of the other one, the two rolls are independent. When two or more events are independent, the probability that they will both occur is calculated using the **product rule**—their individual probabilities are multiplied. That is, the probability that events A and B *both* will occur equals the probability of event A *multiplied* by the probability of event B. For example, the probability of getting a 4 on the first die is 1/6; the probability of a 4 on the second die is also 1/6 **(Figure 10.6)**.

a. Likelihood of rolling a double four.

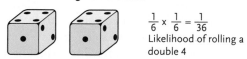

$$\frac{1}{6} \times \frac{1}{6} = \frac{1}{36}$$
Likelihood of rolling a double 4

b. Likelihood of rolling a seven in any combination.

Figure 10.6
Rules of probability. **(a)** For each die, the probability of a 4 is 1/6. Because the outcome of one die is independent of that of the other, the combined probability of rolling a 4 on both dice at the same time is calculated by multiplying the individual probabilities (product rule). **(b)** Since there are six different outcomes, each of which adds up to 7, the total likelihood of rolling a 7 is calculated by adding the individual probabilities (sum rule).

Because the events are independent, the probability of getting a 4 on both dice is 1/6 × 1/6 = 1/36. Applying this principle to human families, the sex of one child has no effect on the sex of the next child; therefore, the probability of having four girls in a row is the product of their individual probabilities (very close to 1/2 for each birth): 1/2 × 1/2 × 1/2 × 1/2 = 1/16.

The Sum Rule in Probability. Another relationship, the **sum rule**, applies when several different events all give the same outcome; that is, the probability that *either* event A *or* event B *or* event C will occur equals the probability of event A *plus* the probability of event B *plus* the probability of event C. Returning to the two dice example, what is the probability of rolling a 7? Several different events all give the same total. One could make a total of 7 from a 1 on the first die and a 6 on the second, or a 5 on the first and a 2 on the second, or a 4 on the first and a 3 on the second. Each of these three combinations would be expected to occur at a frequency of 1/6 × 1/6 = 1/36. You should be able to see three more possible combinations that are just the reciprocal of the first three, that is, 6 on the first die and 1 on the second, and so on, for a total of six different ways to roll a 7. That is, there are six ways of obtaining the same outcome. Therefore, for the probability of rolling a 7, we sum the individual probabilities to get the final probability: 1/36 + 1/36 + 1/36 + 1/36 + 1/36 + 1/36 = 6/36 = 1/6. On average, you could expect to roll a combination of numbers totalling 7 once in every six attempts.

Probability in Mendel's Crosses. Since the randomness inherent in meiosis is comparable to the randomness inherent in rolling dice, the same rules of probability just discussed apply to genes carried on chromosomes in Mendel's crosses. For example, in the crosses that involve the purple-flowered and white-flowered traits, half of the gametes of the F_1 generation contain the *P* allele of the gene and half contain the *p* allele (see Figure 10.5). To produce a *PP* zygote, two *P* gametes must combine. The probability of selecting a *P* gamete from one F_1 parent is 1/2, and the probability of selecting a *P* gamete from the other F_1 parent is also 1/2. Therefore, the probability of producing a *PP* zygote from this monohybrid cross is 1/2 × 1/2 = 1/4. That is, by the product rule, one-fourth of the offspring of the F_1 cross *Pp* × *Pp* are expected to be *PP*, which have purple flowers **(Figure 10.7a, p. 218)**. By the same line of reasoning, one-fourth of the F_2 offspring are expected to be *pp*, which have white flowers **(Figure 10.7b, p. 218)**.

What about the production of *Pp* offspring? The cross *Pp* × *Pp* can produce *Pp* in two different ways. A *P* gamete from the first parent can combine with a *p* gamete from the second parent (*Pp*), or a *p* gamete from the first parent can combine with a *P* gamete from the second parent (*pP*) **(Figure 10.7c, p. 218)**. Because there are two different ways to get the same outcome,

CHAPTER 10 MENDEL, GENES, AND INHERITANCE

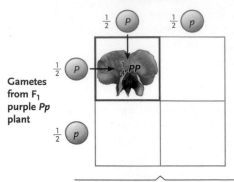

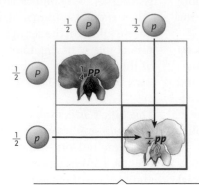

a. To produce an F$_2$ plant with the *PP* genotype, two *P* gametes must combine. The probability of selecting a *P* gamete from one F$_1$ parent is $\frac{1}{2}$, and the probability of selecting a *P* gamete from the other F$_1$ parent is also $\frac{1}{2}$. Using the product rule, the probability of producing purple-flowered *PP* plant from a *Pp* × *Pp* cross is $\frac{1}{2} \times \frac{1}{2} = \frac{1}{4}$.

b. To produce an F$_2$ plant with the *pp* genotype, two *p* gametes must combine. The probability of selecting a *p* gamete from one F$_1$ parent is $\frac{1}{2}$, and the probability of selecting a *p* gamete from the other F$_1$ parent is also $\frac{1}{2}$. Using the product rule, the probability of producing white-flowered *pp* plant from a *Pp* × *Pp* cross is $\frac{1}{2} \times \frac{1}{2} = \frac{1}{4}$.

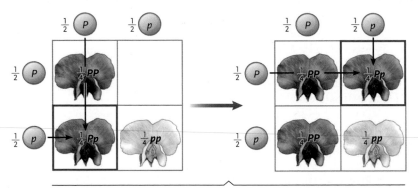

c. To produce an F$_2$ plant with the *Pp* genotype, a *P* gamete must combine with a *p* gamete. The cross *Pp* × *Pp* can produce *Pp* offspring in two different ways: (1) a *P* gamete from the first parent can combine with a *p* gamete from the second parent; or (2) a *p* gamete from the first parent can combine with a *P* gamete from the second parent. We apply the sum rule to obtain the combined probability: each of the ways to get *Pp* has an individual probability of $\frac{1}{4}$, so the probability of *Pp*, purple-flowered offspring is $\frac{1}{4} + \frac{1}{4} = \frac{1}{2}$.

Figure 10.7

Punnett square method for predicting offspring and their ratios in genetic crosses. The example is the F$_1$ × F$_1$ cross of purple-flowered plants from Figure 10.5, p. 216. Each cell shows the genotype and proportion of one type of F$_2$ plant.

we apply the sum rule to obtain the combined probability. Each of the ways to get *Pp* has an individual probability of 1/4; when we add these individual probabilities, we have 1/4 + 1/4 = 1/2. Therefore, half of the offspring are expected to be *Pp*, which have purple flowers. We could get the same result from the requirement that all of the individual probabilities must add up to 1. If the probability of *PP* is 1/4 and the probability of *pp* is 1/4, then the probability of the remaining possibility, *Pp*, must be 1/2, because the total of the individual probabilities must add up to 1: 1/4 + 1/4 + 1/2 = 1.

What if we want to know the probability of obtaining purple flowers in the cross *Pp* × *Pp*? In this case, the rule

of addition applies, because there are two ways to get purple flowers: genotypes *PP* and *Pp*. Adding the individual probabilities of these combinations, 1/4 *PP* + 1/2 *Pp*, gives a total of 3/4, indicating that three-fourths of the F$_2$ offspring are expected to have purple flowers. Because the total probabilities must add up to 1, the remaining one-fourth of the offspring is expected to have white flowers (1/4 *pp*). These proportions give the ratio 3:1, which is close to the ratio Mendel obtained in his cross.

In Figure 10.7 we have just stepped through the **Punnett square** method for determining the genotypes of offspring and their expected proportions. To use the Punnett square, write the probability that meiosis will produce gametes with each type of allele from one parent at the top of the diagram and write the chance of obtaining each type of allele from the other parent on the left side. Then fill in the cells by combining the alleles from the top and from the left and multiplying their individual probabilities.

10.1e Mendel Used a Testcross to Check the Validity of His Hypotheses

Mendel realized that he could assess the validity of his hypotheses by determining whether they could be used successfully to *predict* the outcome of a cross of a different type than he had tried so far. Accordingly, he crossed an F$_1$ plant with purple flowers, assumed to have the heterozygous genotype *Pp*, with a true-breeding white-flowered plant, with the homozygous genotype *pp* (**Figure 10.8**, Experiment 1). There are two expected classes of offspring, *Pp* and *pp*, both with a probability of 1/2. Thus, the phenotypes of the offspring are expected to be 1 purple-flowered : 1 white-flowered. Mendel's actual results closely approach the expected 1:1 ratio. Mendel also made the same type of cross with all the other traits used in his study, including those traits affecting seed shape, seed colour, and plant height, and found the same 1:1 ratio.

A cross between an individual with the dominant phenotype and a homozygous recessive individual, such as the one described, is called a **testcross**. Geneticists use a testcross as a standard test to determine whether an individual with a dominant trait is a heterozygote or a homozygote, because these cannot be distinguished phenotypically. If the offspring of the testcross are of two types, with half displaying the dominant trait and half the recessive trait, then the individual in question must be a heterozygote (see

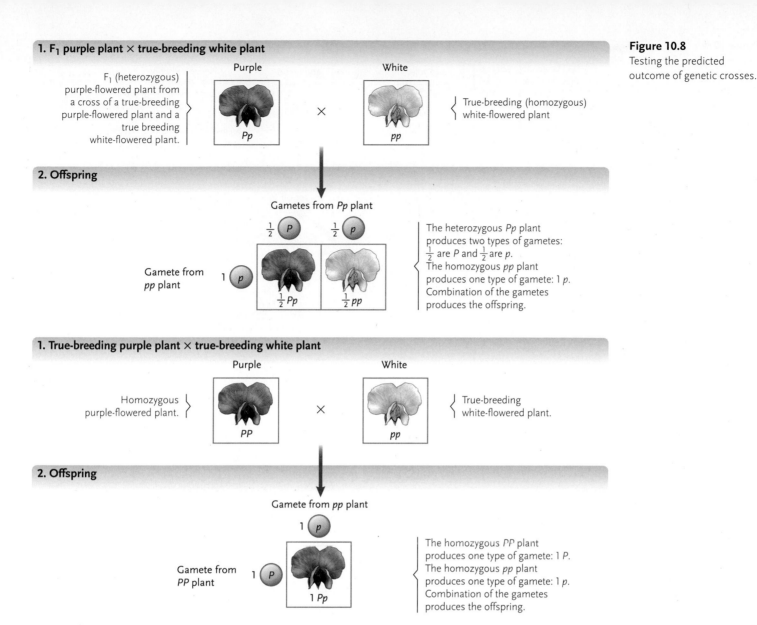

Figure 10.8
Testing the predicted
outcome of genetic crosses.

1. F₁ purple plant × true-breeding white plant

F₁ (heterozygous)
purple-flowered plant from
a cross of a true-breeding
purple-flowered plant and a
true breeding
white-flowered plant.

Purple

White

True-breeding (homozygous)
white-flowered plant

Pp   ×   *pp*

2. Offspring

Gametes from *Pp* plant

$\frac{1}{2}$ P $\frac{1}{2}$ p

Gamete from
pp plant   1 p

$\frac{1}{2}$ Pp $\frac{1}{2}$ pp

The heterozygous *Pp* plant
produces two types of gametes:
$\frac{1}{2}$ are *P* and $\frac{1}{2}$ are *p*.
The homozygous *pp* plant
produces one type of gamete: 1 *p*.
Combination of the gametes
produces the offspring.

1. True-breeding purple plant × true-breeding white plant

Purple   White

Homozygous
purple-flowered plant.

True-breeding
white-flowered plant.

PP   ×   *pp*

2. Offspring

Gamete from *pp* plant

1 p

Gamete from
PP plant   1 P

1 *Pp*

The homozygous *PP* plant
produces one type of gamete: 1 *P*.
The homozygous *pp* plant
produces one type of gamete: 1 *p*.
Combination of the gametes
produces the offspring.

Figure 10.8, Experiment 1). If all the offspring display the dominant trait, the individual in question must be a homozygote. For example, the cross *PP × pp* gives all *Pp* progeny, which show the dominant purple phenotype (see Figure 10.8, Experiment 2).

Obviously, the testcross method cannot be used for humans. However, it can be used in reverse by noting the traits present in families over several generations and working backward to deduce whether a parent must have been a homozygote or a heterozygote (see also Chapter 11).

10.1f Mendel Tested the Independence of Different Genes in Crosses

Mendel next asked what happens in crosses when more than one character is involved. Would the alleles of different characters be inherited independently, or would they interact to alter their expected proportions in offspring?

To answer these questions, Mendel crossed parental stocks that had differences in two of the hereditary characters he was studying: seed shape and seed colour. His single-character crosses had shown that each was controlled by a pair of alleles. For seed shape, the *RR* or *Rr* genotype produces round seeds and the *rr* genotype produces wrinkled seeds. For seed colour, yellow is dominant. The homozygous *YY* and heterozygous *Yy* genotypes produce yellow seeds; the homozygous *yy* genotype produces green seeds.

Mendel crossed plants that bred true for the production of round and yellow seeds (*RR YY*) with plants that bred true for the production of wrinkled and green seeds (*rr yy*) **(Figure 10.9, p. 220)**. The cross, *RR YY × rr yy*, yielded an F₁ generation that consisted of all round yellow seeds, with the genotype *Rr Yy*. A zygote produced from a cross that involves two characters is called a **dihybrid** (*di* = two).

Mendel then planted the F₁ seeds, grew the plants to maturity, and selfed them; that is, he crossed the F₁

Figure 10.9

Mendel's experiment illustrating the principle of independent assortment for seed shape and seed colour in peas.

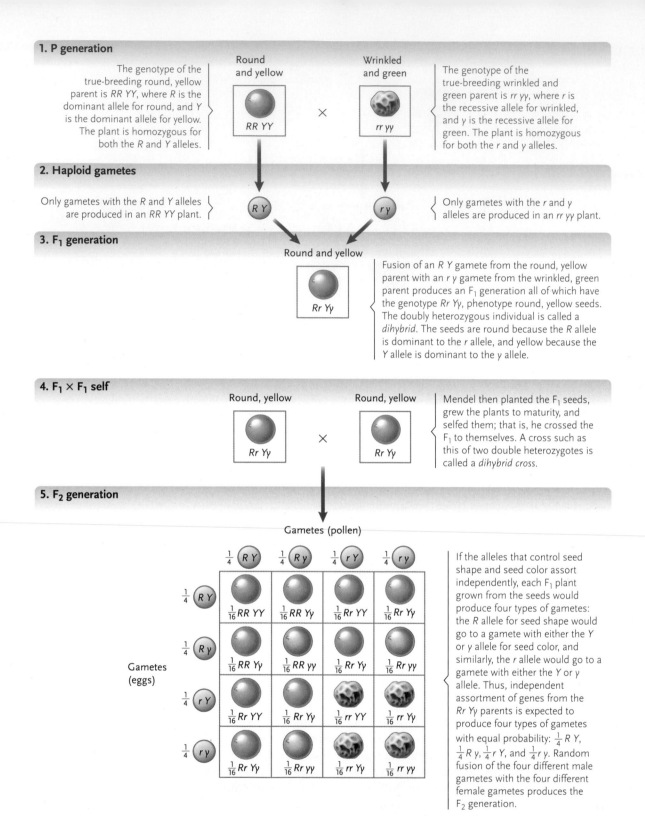

1. P generation

The genotype of the true-breeding round, yellow parent is *RR YY*, where *R* is the dominant allele for round, and *Y* is the dominant allele for yellow. The plant is homozygous for both the *R* and *Y* alleles.

Round and yellow

RR YY

×

Wrinkled and green

rr yy

The genotype of the true-breeding wrinkled and green parent is *rr yy*, where *r* is the recessive allele for wrinkled, and *y* is the recessive allele for green. The plant is homozygous for both the *r* and *y* alleles.

2. Haploid gametes

Only gametes with the *R* and *Y* alleles are produced in an *RR YY* plant.

R Y

r y

Only gametes with the *r* and *y* alleles are produced in an *rr yy* plant.

3. F₁ generation

Round and yellow

Rr Yy

Fusion of an *R Y* gamete from the round, yellow parent with an *r y* gamete from the wrinkled, green parent produces an F₁ generation all of which have the genotype *Rr Yy*, phenotype round, yellow seeds. The doubly heterozygous individual is called a *dihybrid*. The seeds are round because the *R* allele is dominant to the *r* allele, and yellow because the *Y* allele is dominant to the *y* allele.

4. F₁ × F₁ self

Round, yellow

Rr Yy

×

Round, yellow

Rr Yy

Mendel then planted the F₁ seeds, grew the plants to maturity, and selfed them; that is, he crossed the F₁ to themselves. A cross such as this of two double heterozygotes is called a *dihybrid cross*.

5. F₂ generation

Gametes (pollen)

	$\frac{1}{4}$ *R Y*	$\frac{1}{4}$ *R y*	$\frac{1}{4}$ *r Y*	$\frac{1}{4}$ *r y*
$\frac{1}{4}$ *R Y*	$\frac{1}{16}$ *RR YY*	$\frac{1}{16}$ *RR Yy*	$\frac{1}{16}$ *Rr YY*	$\frac{1}{16}$ *Rr Yy*
$\frac{1}{4}$ *R y*	$\frac{1}{16}$ *RR Yy*	$\frac{1}{16}$ *RR yy*	$\frac{1}{16}$ *Rr Yy*	$\frac{1}{16}$ *Rr yy*
$\frac{1}{4}$ *r Y*	$\frac{1}{16}$ *Rr YY*	$\frac{1}{16}$ *Rr Yy*	$\frac{1}{16}$ *rr YY*	$\frac{1}{16}$ *rr Yy*
$\frac{1}{4}$ *r y*	$\frac{1}{16}$ *Rr Yy*	$\frac{1}{16}$ *Rr yy*	$\frac{1}{16}$ *rr Yy*	$\frac{1}{16}$ *rr yy*

Gametes (eggs)

If the alleles that control seed shape and seed color assort independently, each F₁ plant grown from the seeds would produce four types of gametes: the *R* allele for seed shape would go to a gamete with either the *Y* or *y* allele for seed color, and similarly, the *r* allele would go to a gamete with either the *Y* or *y* allele. Thus, independent assortment of genes from the *Rr Yy* parents is expected to produce four types of gametes with equal probability: $\frac{1}{4}$ *R Y*, $\frac{1}{4}$ *R y*, $\frac{1}{4}$ *r Y*, and $\frac{1}{4}$ *r y*. Random fusion of the four different male gametes with the four different female gametes produces the F₂ generation.

plants to themselves. A cross between two individuals that are heterozygous for two pairs of alleles—here *Rr Yy* × *Rr Yy*—is called a **dihybrid cross** (see Figure 10.9). The seeds produced by these plants, representing the F₂ generation, included 315 round yellow seeds, 101 wrinkled yellow seeds, 103 round green seeds, and 32 wrinkled green seeds. Mendel noted that these numbers were close to a 9:3:3:1 ratio (3:1 for round : wrinkled, and 3:1 for yellow : green).

This 9:3:3:1 ratio was consistent with Mendel's previous findings if he added one further hypothesis: *The alleles of the genes that govern the two characters segregate independently during formation of gametes.* That is, the allele for seed shape that the gamete receives (*R* or *r*) has no influence on which allele for seed colour it receives (*Y* or *y*) and vice versa. The two events are completely independent. Mendel termed this assumption **independent assortment**; it is now known as Mendel's **Principle of Independent Assortment.**

To understand the effect of independent assortment in the cross, assume that the *RR YY* parent produces only *R Y* gametes and the *rr yy* parent produces only *r y* gametes. In the F_1 generation, all possible combinations of these gametes produce only one genotype, *Rr Yy*, in the offspring. As observed, all the F_1 will be round yellow seeds.

If the alleles that control seed shape and seed colour assort independently in gamete formation, each F_1 plant grown from the seeds will produce four types of gametes. As shown in **Figure 10.10, p. 222**, the random alignment of homologous chromosome pairs in meiosis I ensures that the *R* allele for seed shape can be delivered independently to a gamete with either the *Y* or the *y* allele for seed colour, and, similarly, the *r* allele can be delivered to a gamete with either the *Y* or the *y* allele. Thus, the independent assortment of genes from the *Rr Yy* parents allows the organism to produce, overall, four types of gametes with equal probability: 1/4 *R Y*, 1/4 *R y*, 1/4 *r Y*, and 1/4 *r y*. These gametes and their probabilities are entered as the row and column headings of the Punnett square in Figure 10.9.

Filling in the cells of the diagram (see Figure 10.9) gives 16 combinations of alleles, all with an equal probability of 1 in every 16 offspring. Of these, the genotypes *RR YY*, *RR Yy*, *Rr YY*, and *Rr Yy* all have the same phenotype: round yellow seeds. These combinations occur in 9 of the 16 cells in the diagram, giving a total probability of 9/16. The genotypes *rr YY* and *rr Yy*, which produce wrinkled yellow seeds, are found in three cells, giving a probability of 3/16 for this phenotype. Similarly, the genotypes *RR yy* and *Rr yy*, which yield round green seeds, occur in three cells, giving a probability of 3/16. Finally, the genotype *rr yy*, which produces wrinkled green seeds, is found in only one cell and therefore has a probability of 1/16.

These probabilities of round yellow seeds, wrinkled yellow seeds, round green seeds, and wrinkled green seeds, in a 9:3:3:1 ratio, closely approximate the actual results of 315:101:108:32 obtained by Mendel. Thus, Mendel's first three hypotheses, with the added hypothesis of independent assortment, explain the observed results of his dihybrid cross. Mendel's testcrosses completely confirmed his hypotheses; for example, the testcross *Rr Yy × rr yy* produced 55 round yellow seeds, 51 round green seeds, 49 wrinkled yellow seeds, and 53 wrinkled green seeds. This distribution corresponds well to the expected 1:1:1:1 ratio in the offspring. (Try to set up a Punnett square for this cross and predict the expected classes of offspring and their frequencies.)

Mendel's first three hypotheses provided a coherent explanation of the pattern of inheritance for alternate traits of the same character, such as purple and white for flower colour. His fourth hypothesis, independent assortment, addressed the inheritance of traits for different characters, such as seed shape, seed colour, and flower colour, and showed that, instead of being inherited together, the traits of different characters were distributed independently to offspring.

10.1g Mendel's Research Founded the Field of Genetics

Mendel's techniques and conclusions were so advanced for his time that their significance was not immediately appreciated. Mendel's success was based partly on a good choice of experimental organism. He was also lucky. The characters he chose all segregate independently; that is, none of them are physically near each other on the chromosomes, a condition that would have given ratios other than 9:3:3:1, showing that they do not assort independently.

We now know that Mendel's findings demonstrated the patterns by which genes and chromosomes determine inheritance. Yet, when Mendel first reported his findings during the nineteenth century, the structure and function of chromosomes and the patterns by which they are separated and distributed to gametes were unknown; meiosis remained to be discovered. In addition, his use of mathematical analysis was a new and radical departure from the usual biological techniques of his day.

Mendel reported his results to a small group of fellow intellectuals in Brünn and presented his results in 1866 in a natural history journal published in the city. His article received little notice outside of Brünn, and those who read it were unable to appreciate the significance of his findings. His work was overlooked until the early 1900s, when three investigators—Hugo de Vries in Holland, Carl Correns in Germany, and Erich von Tschermak in Austria—independently performed a series of breeding experiments similar to Mendel's and reached the same conclusions. These investigators, in searching through previously published scientific articles, were surprised to discover Mendel's article about his experiments conducted 34 years earlier. Each gave credit to Mendel's discoveries, and the quality and far-reaching implications of his work were at last realized. Mendel died in 1884, 16 years before the rediscovery of his experiments and conclusions; thus, he never received the recognition that he so richly deserved during his lifetime.

Mendel was unable to relate the behaviour of his "factors" (genes) to cell structures because the critical information he required was not obtained until later, through the discovery of meiosis during the 1890s. The next section describes how a genetics student familiar with meiosis was able to make the connection between Mendel's factors and chromosomes.

10.1h Sutton's Chromosome Theory of Inheritance Related Mendel's Genes to Chromosomes

By the time Mendel's results were rediscovered in the early 1900s, critical information from studies of meiosis was available. It was not long before a genetics student, Walter Sutton, recognized the similarities between the inheritance of the genes discovered by Mendel and the behaviour of chromosomes in meiosis and fertilization (Figure 10.10).

In a historic article published in 1903, Sutton, then a graduate student at Columbia University in New York, drew all the necessary parallels between genes and chromosomes:

- Chromosomes occur in pairs in sexually reproducing, diploid organisms, as do the alleles of each gene.
- The chromosomes of each pair are separated and delivered singly to gametes, as are the alleles of a gene.
- The separation of any pair of chromosomes in meiosis and gamete formation is independent of the separation of other pairs (see Figure 10.10), as in the independent assortment of the alleles of different genes in Mendel's dihybrid crosses.

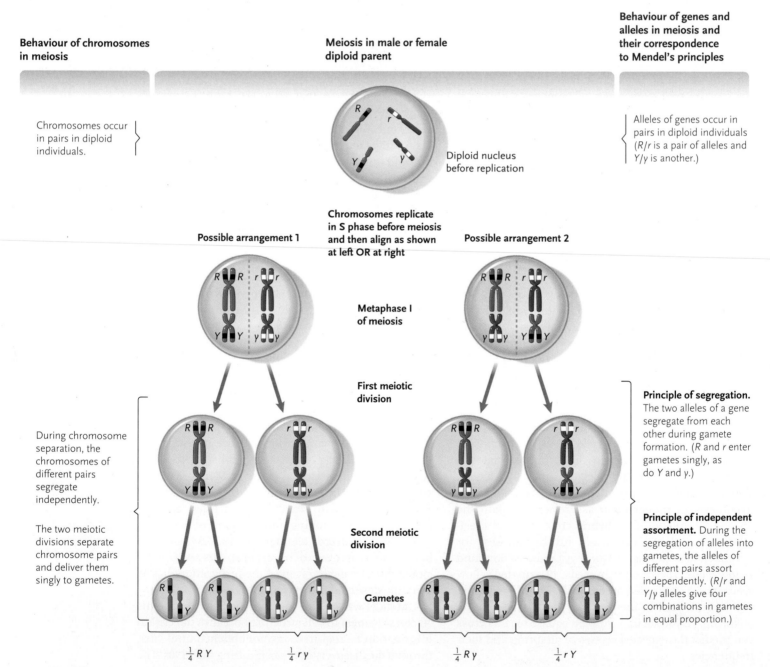

Behaviour of chromosomes in meiosis

Chromosomes occur in pairs in diploid individuals.

During chromosome separation, the chromosomes of different pairs segregate independently.

The two meiotic divisions separate chromosome pairs and deliver them singly to gametes.

Meiosis in male or female diploid parent

Diploid nucleus before replication

Chromosomes replicate in S phase before meiosis and then align as shown at left OR at right

Possible arrangement 1

Possible arrangement 2

Metaphase I of meiosis

First meiotic division

Second meiotic division

Gametes

$\frac{1}{4}RY$ $\frac{1}{4}ry$ $\frac{1}{4}Ry$ $\frac{1}{4}rY$

Behaviour of genes and alleles in meiosis and their correspondence to Mendel's principles

Alleles of genes occur in pairs in diploid individuals (R/r is a pair of alleles and Y/y is another.)

Principle of segregation. The two alleles of a gene segregate from each other during gamete formation. (R and r enter gametes singly, as do Y and y.)

Principle of independent assortment. During the segregation of alleles into gametes, the alleles of different pairs assort independently. (R/r and Y/y alleles give four combinations in gametes in equal proportion.)

Figure 10.10

The parallels between the behaviour of chromosomes and genes and alleles in meiosis. The gametes show four different combinations of alleles produced by independent segregation of chromosome pairs.

- Finally, one member of each chromosome pair is derived in fertilization from the male parent, and the other member is derived from the female parent, in an exact parallel with the two alleles of a gene.

From this total coincidence in behaviour, Sutton correctly concluded that genes and their alleles are carried on the chromosomes, a conclusion known today as the **chromosome theory of inheritance.**

The exact parallel between the principles set forth by Mendel and the behaviour of chromosomes and genes during meiosis is shown in Figure 10.10 for an *Rr Yy* diploid. For a cross of *Rr Yy* × *Rr Yy*, when the gametes fuse randomly, the progeny will show a phenotypic ratio of 9:3:3:1. This mechanism explains the same ratio of gametes and progeny as the *Rr Yy* × *Rr Yy* cross in Figure 10.9, p. 220.

The particular site on a chromosome at which a gene is located is called the **locus** (plural, *loci*) of the gene. The locus is a particular DNA sequence that encodes a protein or ribonucleic acid (RNA) product responsible for the phenotype controlled by the gene. A locus for a gene with two alleles, *A* and *a*, on a homologous pair of chromosomes is shown in **Figure 10.11.** At the molecular level, different alleles consist of small differences in the DNA sequence of a gene, which may result in functional differences in the protein or RNA product encoded by the gene. These differences are detected as distinct phenotypes in the offspring of a cross.

All of the genetics research conducted since the early 1900s has confirmed Mendel's basic hypotheses about inheritance. This research has shown that Mendel's conclusions apply to all types of organisms, from yeast and fruit flies to humans, and has led to the rapidly growing field of human genetics. In humans, a number of easily seen traits show inheritance patterns that follow Mendelian principles **(Figure 10.12);** for example, albinism, the lack of normal skin colour,

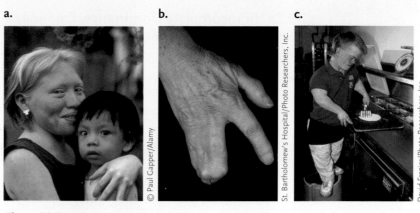

a.   **b.**   **c.**

Figure 10.12

Human traits showing inheritance patterns that follow Mendelian principles. **(a)** Lack of normal skin colour (albinism). **(b)** Webbed fingers. **(c)** Achondroplasia or short-limbed dwarfism.

is recessive to normal skin colour, and fingers with webs between them are recessive to normally separated fingers. Similarly, achondroplasia, the most frequent form of short-limb dwarfism, is a recessive trait that involves abnormal bone growth. Many human disorders that cannot be seen easily also show simple inheritance patterns. For instance, cystic fibrosis, in which a defect in the membrane transport of chloride ions leads to pulmonary and digestive dysfunctions and reduced life span, is a recessive trait.

The post-Mendel research has demonstrated additional patterns of inheritance (see the next section) that were not anticipated by Mendel and, in some circumstances, require modifications or additions to his hypotheses.

STUDY BREAK

1. What characteristics of the garden pea made this organism a good model system for Mendel?
2. How does independent assortment explain Mendel's dihybrid cross data?
3. How is an allele related to a locus?

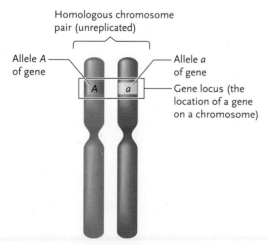

Figure 10.11

A locus, the site occupied by a gene on a pair of homologous chromosomes. Two alleles, *A* and *a*, of the gene are present at this locus in the homologous pair. These alleles have differences in the DNA sequence of the gene.

10.2 Later Modifications and Additions to Mendel's Hypotheses

The rediscovery of Mendel's research in the early 1900s produced an immediate burst of interest in genetics. The research that followed greatly expanded our understanding of genes and their inheritance. That research fully supported Mendel's hypotheses, but also revealed many variations on the basic principles he had outlined. The following sections discuss each of these extensions of Mendel's fundamental principles.

10.2a In Incomplete Dominance, Dominant Alleles Do Not Completely Compensate for Recessive Alleles

Incomplete dominance occurs when the effects of recessive alleles can be detected to some extent in heterozygotes. Flower colour in snapdragons shows incomplete dominance (**Figure 10.13**). If true-breeding red-flowered and white-flowered snapdragon plants are crossed, all the F_1 offspring have pink flowers (see Figure 10.13). The pink colour might make it appear that the pure red and white colours have blended—mixing red and white makes pink. However, when two F_1 plants are crossed, the red and white traits both

Figure 10.13
Experiment showing incomplete dominance in the inheritance of flower colour in snapdragons.

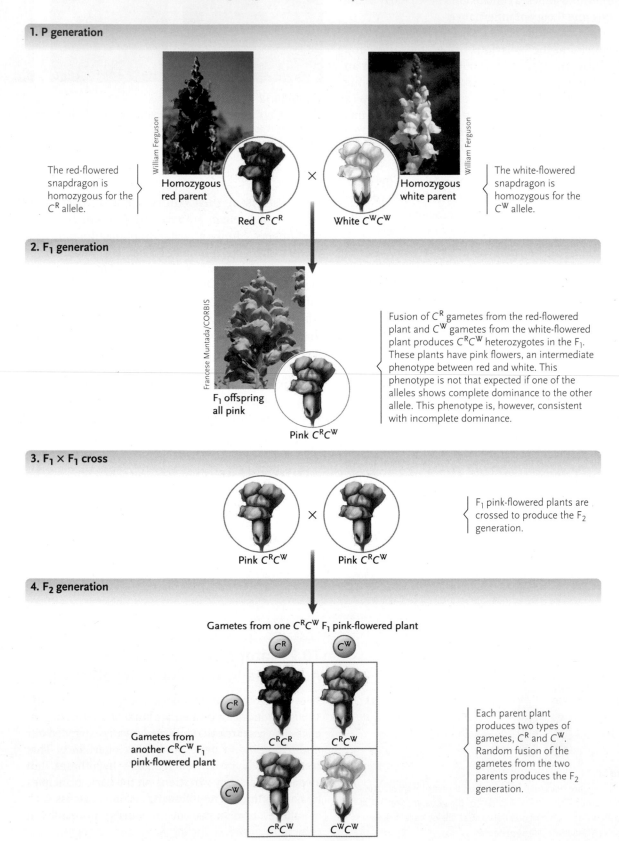

1. P generation

The red-flowered snapdragon is homozygous for the C^R allele.

Homozygous red parent

Red $C^R C^R$

The white-flowered snapdragon is homozygous for the C^W allele.

Homozygous white parent

White $C^W C^W$

2. F₁ generation

F_1 offspring all pink

Pink $C^R C^W$

Fusion of C^R gametes from the red-flowered plant and C^W gametes from the white-flowered plant produces $C^R C^W$ heterozygotes in the F_1. These plants have pink flowers, an intermediate phenotype between red and white. This phenotype is not that expected if one of the alleles shows complete dominance to the other allele. This phenotype is, however, consistent with incomplete dominance.

3. F₁ × F₁ cross

Pink $C^R C^W$ ×   Pink $C^R C^W$

F_1 pink-flowered plants are crossed to produce the F_2 generation.

4. F₂ generation

Gametes from one $C^R C^W$ F_1 pink-flowered plant

C^R C^W

Gametes from another $C^R C^W$ F_1 pink-flowered plant

C^R

C^W

$C^R C^R$ $C^R C^W$

$C^R C^W$ $C^W C^W$

Each parent plant produces two types of gametes, C^R and C^W. Random fusion of the gametes from the two parents produces the F_2 generation.

FOCUS ON RESEARCH 10.1
Why Mendel's Dwarf Pea Plants Were So Short

Two independent research teams worked out the molecular basis for one of the seven characters Mendel studied—dwarfing, which is governed by stem length in garden peas. The investigators, including Diane Lester and her colleagues at the University of Tasmania in Australia and David Martin and his coworkers at Oregon State University, were interested in learning the molecular differences in the alleles of the gene that produced tall or dwarf plants. The dominant T allele (T = tall) of the gene produces plants of normal height; the recessive t allele produces dwarf plants with short stems. How can a single gene control the overall height of a plant?

Lester's team discovered that the gene encodes an enzyme that carries out a preliminary step in the synthesis of the plant hormone gibberellin, which, among other effects, causes the stems of plants to elongate. Martin's group cloned the gene and determined its complete DNA sequence. (Cloning techniques and DNA sequencing are described in Sections 15.1 and 15.3.) Comparisons of the DNA sequences from the T and t alleles revealed two versions of the enzyme that catalyzes gibberellin synthesis that differ by only a single amino acid. Lester's group found that the faulty enzyme encoded by the t allele carries out its step (addition of a hydroxyl group to a

precursor) much more slowly than the enzyme encoded by the normal T allele. As a result, plants with the t allele have only about 5% as much gibberellin in their stems as T plants. The reduced gibberellin levels limit stem elongation, producing the dwarf plants.

Thus, the methods of molecular biology allowed contemporary researchers to study a gene first discovered in the mid-nineteenth century. The findings leave little doubt that a change in a single amino acid leads to the dwarf phenotype Mendel observed in his monastery garden.

---

reappear in the F_2 generation, which has red, pink, and white flowers in numbers approximating a 1:2:1 ratio.

This outcome can be explained by incomplete dominance between a C^R allele for red colour and a C^W allele for white colour. When one allele is not completely dominant to the other, we use a superscript to signify the character. In this case, C signifies the character for flower colour and the superscripts indicate the alleles (R for red and W for white). Therefore, the initial cross is $C^R C^R$ (red) × $C^W C^W$ (white), which produces $C^R C^W$ F_1 (pink) plants. The C^R allele encodes an enzyme that produces a red pigment, but two alleles ($C^R C^R$) are necessary to produce enough of the active form of the enzyme to produce fully red flowers. The enzyme is completely inactive in $C^W C^W$ plants, which produce colourless flowers that appear white because of the scattering of light by cell walls and other structures. With their single C^R allele, the $C^R C^W$ heterozygotes of the F_1 generation can produce only enough pigment to give the flowers a pink colour. When the pink $C^R C^W$ F_1 plants are crossed, the fully red and white colours reappear, together with the pink colour, in the F_2 generation, in a ratio of 1/4 $C^R C^R$ (red), 1/2 $C^R C^W$ (pink), and 1/4 $C^W C^W$ (white). This ratio is exactly the same as the ratio of genotypes produced from a cross of two heterozygotes in Mendel's experiments (for example, see Figure 10.7, p. 218).

Some human disorders show incomplete dominance. For example, sickle cell disease (see the introduction to this chapter) is characterized by an alteration in the hemoglobin molecule that changes the shape of red blood cells when oxygen levels are low. An individual with sickle cell disease is homozygous for a

recessive allele that encodes a defective form of one of the polypeptides of the hemoglobin molecule. Individuals heterozygous for that recessive allele and the normal allele have a condition known as *sickle cell trait,* which is a milder form of the disease because the individuals still produce normal polypeptides from the normal allele.

Familial hypercholesterolemia is another example of incomplete dominance. The gene involved encodes the low-density lipoprotein (LDL) receptor, a cell membrane protein responsible for removing excess cholesterol from the blood. Individuals with familial hypercholesterolemia are homozygous for a defective LDL receptor gene, produce no LDL receptors, and have a severe form of the disease. These individuals have six times the normal level of cholesterol in the blood and therefore are very prone to atherosclerosis (hardening of the arteries). Many individuals with familial hypercholesterolemia have heart attacks as children. Heterozygous individuals have half the normal number of receptors, which results in a milder form of the disease. Their symptoms are twice the normal blood cholesterol level, an unusually high risk of atherosclerosis, and a high risk of heart attacks before age 35.

Many alleles that appear to be completely dominant are actually incomplete in their effects when analyzed at the biochemical or molecular level. For example, for pigments that produce fur or flower colours, biochemical studies often show that even though heterozygotes may produce enough pigment to make them look the same externally as homozygous dominants, a difference in the amount of pigment is

MOLECULE BEHIND BIOLOGY 10.2

Phenylthiocarbamide (PTC)

Have you ever sat down to a plate of Brussels sprouts, only to find that they taste unpleasantly bitter? This sensation arises because receptors in the membranes of taste cells on your tongue are binding to compounds such as isothiocyanate (which is toxic to your thyroid in large doses). Much of our understanding of the molecular nature of bitter taste perception has grown out of an accidental observation that a synthetic chemical, phenylthiocarbamide (PTC), tastes intensely bitter to some people and yet is taste-

less to others. PTC "nontasters" make up 20 to 30% of almost all populations of humans, chimps, and gorillas studied. Although several genes influence the limits of PTC detection, one particular member of the bitter receptor gene family on human chromosome 7 is mainly responsible for PTC tasting ability. The two most common alleles of this gene, "taster" and "nontaster," show a codominant inheritance pattern in families. Since PTC is not found in nature, it is likely that the two very common alleles

detect naturally occurring toxic compounds containing the bitter-tasting thiourea chemical structure shown in the diagram (N − C = S).

FIGURE 1

The chemical structure of phenylthiocarbamide (PTC). Note the N − C = S component.

---

measurable at the biochemical level. Thus, whether dominance between alleles is complete or incomplete often depends on the level at which the effects of the alleles are examined.

A similar situation occurs in humans who carry the recessive allele that causes Tay–Sachs disease. Children who are homozygous for the recessive allele do not have a functional version of an enzyme that breaks down gangliosides, a type of membrane lipid. As a result, gangliosides accumulate in the brain, leading to mental impairment and eventually to death. Heterozygotes are without symptoms of the disease, even though they have one copy of the recessive allele. However, at the biochemical level, reduced breakdown of gangliosides can be detected in heterozygotes, evidently due to a reduced quantity of the active enzyme. **CONCEPT FIX** Since all of Mendel's traits show "simple" or "complete" dominance, you might get the idea that most traits in nature are governed by one dominant and one recessive allele. However, the above examples illustrate that only a minority of human genetic disorders show such simple dominance. ⬢

10.2b In Codominance, the Effects of Different Alleles Are Equally Detectable in Heterozygotes

Codominance occurs when alleles have approximately equal effects in individuals, making the two alleles equally detectable in heterozygotes. The inheritance of the human blood types M, MN, and N is an example of codominance. These are different blood types from the familiar blood types of the ABO blood group. The L^M and L^N alleles of the MN blood group gene that control this character encode different forms of a glycoprotein molecule located on the surface of red blood cells. If

the genotype is $L^M L^M$, only the M form of the glycoprotein is present and the blood type is M; if it is $L^N L^N$, only the N form is present and the blood type is N. In heterozygotes with the $L^M L^N$ genotype, both glycoprotein types are present and can be detected, producing the blood type MN. Because each genotype has a different phenotype, the inheritance pattern for the MN blood group alleles is generally the same as for incompletely dominant alleles. That is, you would not be able to distinguish between codominance and incomplete dominance just by comparing the ratio of offspring from crosses.

The MN blood types do not affect blood transfusions and have relatively little medical importance. However, they have been invaluable in tracing human evolution and prehistoric migrations, and they are frequently used in initial tests to determine the paternity of a child. Among their primary advantages in research and paternity determination is that the genotype of all individuals, including heterozygotes, can be detected directly—and inexpensively—from their phenotype, with no requirement for further genetic tests or analysis.

10.2c In Multiple Alleles, More Than Two Alleles of a Gene Are Present in a Population

One of Mendel's major and most fundamental assumptions was that alleles occur in pairs in individuals; in the pairs, the alleles may be the same or different. After the rediscovery of Mendel's principles, it soon became apparent that although alleles do indeed occur in pairs in individuals, **multiple alleles** (more than two different alleles of a gene) may be present if all the individuals of a population are taken into account. For example, for a gene B, there could be the normal allele,

B, and several alleles with alterations in the gene named, for example, b_1, b_2, b_3, and so on. Some individuals in a population may have the *B* and b_1 alleles of a gene; others, the b_2 and b_3 alleles; still others, the b_3 and b_5 alleles; and so on, for all possible combinations. Thus, although any one individual can have only two alleles of the gene, there are more than two alleles in the population as a whole. One of the genes that plays a part in the acceptance or rejection of organ transplants in humans has more than 200 different alleles!

The multiple alleles of a gene each contain nucleotide differences at one or more locations in their DNA sequences **(Figure 10.14)**, and these often cause detectable alterations in the structure and function of gene products encoded by the alleles. Despite the presence of multiple alleles at the population level, each diploid individual still has only two of the alleles, allowing gametes to be predicted and traced through crosses by the usual methods.

Human ABO Blood Group. The human ABO blood group provides a real example of multiple alleles, in a system that also exhibits both dominance and codominance. Karl Landsteiner, an Austrian biochemist, discovered the ABO blood group in 1901 while investigating the fact that attempts to transfer whole blood from one person to another were sometimes fatal. Landsteiner found that only certain combinations of four blood types, designated A, B, AB, and O, can be mixed safely in transfusions **(Table 10.1).**

Landsteiner determined that, in certain combinations, red blood cells from one blood type are agglutinated or clumped by an agent in the serum of another type (the serum is the fluid in which the blood cells are suspended). The clumping was later found to depend on the action of an antibody in the blood serum. (Antibodies, protein molecules that interact with specific substances called antigens, are discussed in Chapter 43.)

Table 10.1	Blood Types of the Human ABO Blood Group		
Blood Type	Antigens	Antibodies	Blood Types Accepted in a Transfusion
A	A	Anti-B	A or O
B	B	Anti-A	B or O
AB	A and B	None	A, B, AB, or O
O	None	Anti-A, anti-B	O

The antigens responsible for the blood types of the ABO blood group are the carbohydrate parts of glycoproteins located on the surfaces of red blood cells (unrelated to the glycoprotein carbohydrates responsible for the blood types of the MN blood group). People with type A blood have *antigen A* on their red blood cells, and people with type B blood have *antigen B* on their red blood cells. At the same time, people with type A blood have antibodies against antigen B, and people with type B blood have antibodies against antigen A. People with type O blood have neither antigen A nor antigen B on their red blood cells, but they have antibodies against both of these antigens. People with type AB blood have neither anti-A nor anti-B antibodies, but they have both the A and B antigens, and their red blood cells are clumped by antibodies in the blood of all the other groups.

The four blood types—A, B, AB, and O—are produced by different combinations of multiple (three) alleles of a single gene *I* **(Figure 10.15)**. The three alleles, designated I^A, I^B, and *i*, produce the following blood types:

$$I^A I^A = \text{type A blood}$$
$$I^A i = \text{type A blood}$$
$$I^A I^B = \text{type AB blood}$$
$$I^B I^B = \text{type B blood}$$
$$I^B i = \text{type B blood}$$
$$ii = \text{type O blood}$$

In addition, I^A and I^B are codominant alleles that are each dominant to the *i* allele.

B allele   5′...A T G C A G A T A C C G A T T A C A G A C C A T A G G...3′
3′...T A C G T C T A T G G C T A A T G T C T G G T A T C C...5′

b_1 allele   5′...A T G C A G A G A C C G A T T A C A G A C C A T A G G...3′
3′...T A C G T C T C T G G C T A A T G T C T G G T A T C C...5′

b_2 allele   5′...A T G C A G A T A C C G A C T A C A G A C C A T A G G...3′
3′...T A C G T C T A T G G C T G A T G T C T G G T A T C C...5′

b_3 allele   5′...A T G C A G A T A C C G A T T A C A G T C C A T A G G...3′
3′...T A C G T C T A T G G C T A A T G T C A G G T A T C C...5′

Figure 10.14

Multiple alleles. Multiple alleles consist of small differences in the DNA sequence of a gene at one or more points, which result in detectable differences in the structure of the protein encoded by the gene. The *B* allele is the normal allele, which encodes a protein with normal function. The three *b* alleles each have alterations of the normal protein-coding DNA sequence that may adversely affect the function of that protein.

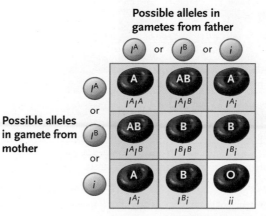

Possible alleles in gametes from father

Figure 10.15

Inheritance of the blood types of the human ABO blood group. Note that although there are three possible alleles in the population, each individual parent carries only two.

10.2d In Epistasis, Genes Interact, with the Activity of One Gene Influencing the Activity of Another Gene

The genetic characters discussed so far in this chapter, such as flower colour, seed shape, and the blood types of the ABO group, are all produced by the alleles of single genes, with each gene functioning on its own. This is not the case for every trait. In **epistasis** (*epi* = on or over; *stasis* = standing or stopping), genes interact, with one or more alleles of a gene at one locus inhibiting or masking the effects of one or more alleles of a gene at a different locus. The result of epistasis is that some expected phenotypes do not appear among offspring.

Labrador retrievers may have black, chocolate brown, or yellow fur (**Figure 10.16**). The different colours result from variations in the amount and distribution in hairs of a brownish black pigment called melanin. One gene, coding for an enzyme involved in melanin production, determines how much melanin is produced. The dominant *B* allele of this gene produces black fur colour in *BB* or *Bb* Labs; less pigment is produced in *bb* dogs, which are chocolate brown. However, another gene at a different locus determines whether the black or chocolate colour appears at all, by controlling the deposition of pigment in hairs. The dominant *E* allele of this second gene permits pigment deposition, so that the black colour in *BB* or *Bb* individuals, or the chocolate colour in *bb* individuals, actually appears in the fur. Pigment deposition is almost completely blocked in homozygous recessive *ee* individuals, so the fur lacks melanin and has a yellow colour whether the genotype for the *B* gene is *BB*, *Bb*, or *bb*. Thus, the *E* gene is said to be epistatic to the *B* gene.

Epistasis by the *E* gene eliminates some of the expected classes from crosses among Labs. Rather than two separate classes, as would be expected from a dihybrid cross without epistasis, the *BB ee, Bb ee, bB ee,* and *bb ee* genotypes produce a single yellow phenotype, giving the distribution 9/16 black, 3/16 chocolate, and 4/16 yellow. That is, the ratio is 9:3:4 instead of the expected 9:3:3:1 ratio. Many other dihybrid crosses that involve epistatic interactions produce distributions that differ from the expected 9:3:3:1 ratio.

In human biology, researchers believe that gene interactions and epistasis are common. The current thinking is that epistasis is an important factor in determining an individual's susceptibility to common human diseases. That is, the different degrees of susceptibility are the result of different gene interactions in the individuals. A specific example is insulin resistance, a disorder in which muscle, fat, and liver cells do not use insulin correctly, with the result that glucose and insulin levels become high in the blood. This disorder is believed to be determined by several genes often interacting with one another.

A. Black labrador

Erik Lam / Shutterstock

B. Chocolate brown labrador

cen / Shutterstock

C. Yellow labrador

cen / Shutterstock

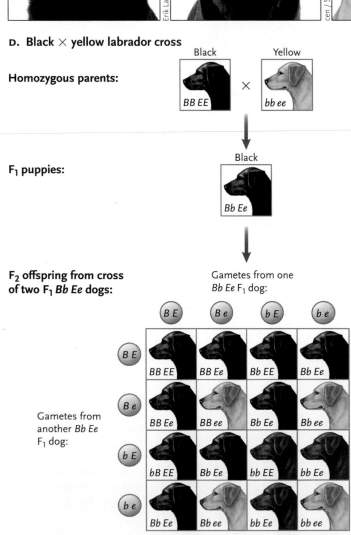

D. Black × yellow labrador cross

Homozygous parents:

Black   Yellow

BB EE × *bb ee*

F_1 puppies:

Black

Bb Ee

F_2 offspring from cross of two F_1 *Bb Ee* dogs:

Gametes from one *Bb Ee* F_1 dog:

BE   Be   bE   be

Gametes from another *Bb Ee* F_1 dog:

BE | BB EE | BB Ee | Bb EE | Bb Ee
Be | BB Ee | BB ee | Bb Ee | Bb ee
bE | bB EE | Bb Ee | bb EE | bb Ee
be | Bb Ee | Bb ee | bb Ee | bb ee

F_2 phenotypic ratio is 9 black : 3 chocolate : 4 yellow

Figure 10.16
An example of epistasis: the inheritance of coat colour in Labrador retrievers.

10.2e In Polygenic Inheritance, a Character Is Controlled by the Common Effects of Several Genes

Some characters follow a pattern of inheritance in which there is a more or less even gradation of types, forming a continuous distribution, rather than "on" or "off" (discontinuous) effects such as the production of only purple or white flowers in pea plants. For example, human adults range from short to tall, in a continuous distribution of height between limits of about 1 and 2 m. Typically, a continuous distribution of this type is the result of **polygenic inheritance**, in which several to many different genes contribute to the same character. Other characters that undertake a similar continuous distribution include skin colour and body weight in humans, ear length in corn, seed colour in wheat, and colour spotting in mice. These characters are also known as **quantitative traits.**

Polygenic inheritance can be detected by defining classes of variation, such as human body height of 180 cm in one class, 181 cm in the next class, 182 cm in the next class, and so on. The number of individuals in each class is then plotted as a graph. If the plot produces a bell-shaped curve, with fewer individuals at the extremes and the greatest numbers clustered around the midpoint, it is a good indication that the trait is quantitative **(Figure 10.17).**

The expression of a genetic phenotype can be influenced by the environment; this is particularly common with quantitative traits like body size. For example, poor nutrition during infancy and childhood is one environmental factor that can limit growth and prevent individuals from reaching the height expected from purely genetic contributions; good nutrition can have the opposite effect. Thus, the average young adult in Japan today is several inches taller than the average adult in the 1930s, when nutrition was poorer.

CONCEPT FIX At first glance, the wide variation shown in a quantitative trait might appear to support the old idea that the characteristics of parents are blended in their offspring. Commonly, people believe that the children in a family with one tall and one short parent will be of intermediate height. Although the children of such parents are indeed most likely to be of intermediate height, careful genetic analysis of hundreds of such families shows that their offspring actually range over a continuum from short to tall,

a. Students at Brigham Young University, arranged according to height

Dan Fairbanks/Brigham Young University

Figure 10.17
Continuous variation in height due to polygenic inheritance.

b. Actual distribution of individuals in the photo according to height

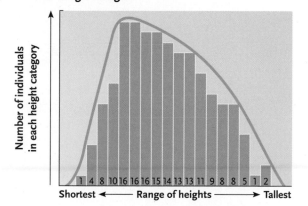

c. Idealized bell-shaped curve for a population that displays continuous variation in a trait

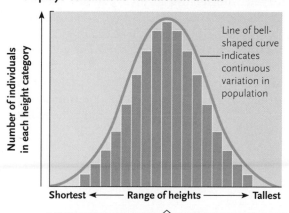

Line of bell-shaped curve indicates continuous variation in population

If the sample in the photo included more individuals, the distribution would more closely approach this ideal.

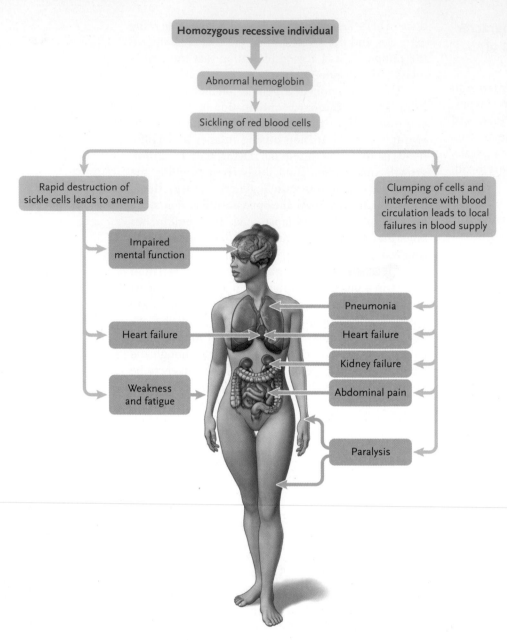

Figure 10.18

Pleiotropy, as demonstrated by the wide-ranging, multiple effects of the single mutant allele responsible for sickle cell disease. (Not all effects are shown.)

support the idea of blending or even mixing of parental traits in quantitative characteristics such as body size or skin colour. ⬡

10.2f In Pleiotropy, Two or More Characters Are Affected by a Single Gene

In the previous section, we saw several genes affecting the same trait. In this section we see the reverse situation: single genes affecting more than one character of an organism in a process called **pleiotropy.** For example, sickle cell disease (see earlier discussion) is caused by a recessive allele of a single gene that affects hemoglobin structure and function. However, the altered hemoglobin protein, the primary phenotypic change of the sickle cell mutation, leads to blood vessel blockage, which can damage many tissues and organs in the body and thus affect many body functions, producing wide-ranging symptoms such as fatigue, abdominal pain, heart failure, paralysis, and pneumonia **(Figure 10.18).** Physicians recognize these wide-ranging pleiotropic effects as symptoms of sickle cell disease.

CONCEPT FIX Although Mendel's simple, single gene experiments in peas provided a valuable scientific model for understanding inheritance, modern analyses in a wide variety of organisms are finding that many traits are quantitative and most genes have some pleiotropic effects. ⬡

The next chapter describes additional patterns of inheritance that were not anticipated by Mendel, including the effects of recombination during meiosis. These additional patterns also extend, rather than contradict, Mendel's fundamental principles.

forming a typical bell-shaped curve. Some children are not intermediate relative to their parents; they are either taller or shorter than both parents. Careful analysis of the inheritance of skin colour produces the same result. Although the skin colour of children is most often intermediate between that of their parents, a typical bell-shaped distribution is obtained in which some children at the extremes are lighter or darker than either parent. Thus, genetic analysis does not

STUDY BREAK

1. Distinguish between alleles that are incompletely dominant and those that are codominant.
2. How might you know that a trait is polygenic?

PEOPLE BEHIND BIOLOGY 10.3

Dr. Charles Scriver, Professor Emeritus, McGill University, Montréal

A *paradigm* is a particular way of thinking about a subject, and as Charles Scriver began his career, the way of thinking about genetic disease was beginning to shift. The old paradigm of "nothing can be done" was giving way to an understanding that disease phenotypes have both a genetic *and* an environmental component. Through a combination of basic research, public education, newborn-screening programs, and online archiving of hundreds of mutations, Scriver brought this paradigm shift to our understanding of the underlying biology, treatment, and prevention of diseases such as phenylketonuria, vitamin D-deficient rickets, Tay–Sachs disease, and thalassemia.

Review

Access an interactive eBook, chapter-specific interactive learning tools, including flashcards, quizzes, videos, and more in your Biology **CourseMate**, accessed through NelsonBrain.com **Aplia™** is an online interactive learning solution that helps you improve comprehension—and your grade—by integrating a variety of mediums and tools such as videos, tutorials, practice tests, and an interactive eBook.

10.1 The Beginnings of Genetics: Mendel's Garden Peas

- Mendel made a good choice of experimental organism in that garden peas offered simple cultivation; clearly defined, true-breeding characters (such as flower colour or seed shape); and an opportunity to make controlled pollinations.

- By analyzing his results quantitatively, Mendel showed that traits are passed from parents to offspring as hereditary factors (now called genes and alleles) in predictable ratios and combinations, disproving the notion of blended inheritance (see Figures 10.3, 10.4, and 10.5).

- Mendel realized that his results with crosses involving single characters (monohybrid crosses) could be explained if three hypotheses were true: (1) the genes that govern genetic characters occur in pairs in individuals; (2) if different alleles of a gene are present in a pair within an individual, one allele is dominant over the other; and (3) the two alleles of a gene segregate and enter gametes singly (see Figures 10.5 and 10.7).

- Mendel confirmed his hypotheses by a testcross between an F1 heterozygote and a homozygous recessive parent. This type of testcross is still used to determine whether an individual is homozygous or heterozygous for a dominant allele (see Figure 10.8).

- To explain the results of his crosses with individuals showing differences in two characters—dihybrid crosses—Mendel added an additional hypothesis: the alleles of the genes that govern the two characters segregate independently during formation of gametes (see Figure 10.9). That is, the dihybrid cross $Aa\ Bb \times Aa\ Bb$ can be treated as two separate monohybrid crosses: $Aa \times Aa$ and $Bb \times Bb$. The monohybrid crosses would give phenotypic ratios of $3/4\ A\_\_: 1/4\ aa$ and $3/4\ B\_\_: 1/4\ bb$, respectively. The standard dihybrid ratios arise from combinations of these monohybrid ratios. That is, $9/16\ A\_\_\ B\_\_$ results from $3/4$ $A\_\_ \times 3/4\ B\_\_$, $3/16\ aa\ B\_\_$ results from $1/4\ aa \times 3/4\ B\_\_$, and so on.

- Walter Sutton was the first person to note the similarities between the inheritance of genes and the behaviour of chromosomes in meiosis and fertilization. These parallels made it obvious that genes and alleles are carried on the chromosomes, and are called the chromosome theory of inheritance (see Figure 10.10).

- A locus is the particular site where a given gene is found on the chromosomes of an organism (see Figure 10.11). An allele is just a particular version of the DNA sequence of a gene. Therefore, if an individual were heterozygous for the stem length gene of Mendel's peas, it would have a T allele on one homologue and a t allele on the other. These two alleles would each be located at exactly the same locus on their respective chromosomes.

10.2 Later Modifications and Additions to Mendel's Hypotheses

- Incomplete dominance arises when, in a heterozygote, the activity of one allele is insufficient to compensate for the inactivity of another. Codominance arises when, in a heterozygote, both alleles are equally active. In both cases, the phenotype of heterozygotes is different from that of either homozygote (see Figure 10.13).

- Many genes may have multiple alleles if all the individuals in a population are taken into account. However, any diploid individual in a population has only two alleles of these genes, which are inherited and passed on according to Mendel's principles (see Figures 10.14 and 10.15).

- In epistasis, genes interact, with alleles of one locus inhibiting or masking the effects of alleles at a different locus. The result is that some expected phenotypes do not appear among offspring (see Figure 10.16).

- A character that is subject to polygenic inheritance shows a more or less continuous variation from one extreme to another. Plotting the distribution of such characters among individuals typically produces a bell-shaped curve (see Figure 10.17).

- In pleiotropy, one gene affects more than one character of an organism (see Figure 10.18).

Questions

Self-Test Questions

1. Imagine an organism with the genotype *Rr*. If the diagrams below represent the replicated chromosomes of this organism early in meiosis, which one shows the correct location of the *R* and *r* alleles?

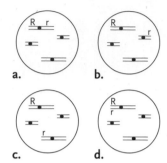

2. Kernel colour in corn is influenced by the *C* gene. The dominant *C* allele produces coloured kernels, and plants homozygous for the recessive *c* allele have colourless (white) kernels. What gamete genotypes, and in what proportions, would be produced by the plants in the following crosses? What kernel colour, and in what proportions, would be expected in the offspring of the crosses?
   a. $CC \times Cc$
   b. $Cc \times Cc$
   c. $Cc \times cc$

3. In peas, the allele *T* produces tall plants and the allele *t* produces dwarf plants. The *T* allele is dominant to *t*. If a tall plant is crossed with a dwarf and the offspring are distributed about equally between tall and dwarf plants, what are the genotypes of the parents?

4. The ability of humans to taste the bitter chemical phenylthiocarbamide (PTC) is a genetic trait. People with at least one copy of the normal, dominant allele of the *PTC* gene can taste PTC; those who are homozygous for a mutant, recessive allele cannot taste it. Could two parents able to taste PTC have a nontaster child? Could nontaster parents have a child able to taste PTC? A pair of taster parents, both of whom had one parent able to taste PTC and one nontaster parent, is expecting their first child. What are the chances that the child will be either able or unable to taste PTC? Suppose the first child is a nontaster; what is the chance that their second child will also be unable to taste PTC?

5. One gene has the alleles *A* and *a*; another gene has the alleles *B* and *b*. Alleles of the *A* and *B* genes assort independently. For each of the following genotypes, what genotypes of gametes will be produced, and in what proportions?
   a. *AA BB*
   b. *Aa BB*
   c. *Aa bb*
   d. *Aa Bb*

6. Which genotypes, and in what frequencies, will be present in the offspring from the following matings?
   a. *AA BB* × *aa BB*
   b. *Aa Bb* × *Aa Bb*
   c. *Aa Bb* × *aa bb*
   d. *Aa BB* × *AA Bb*

7. In addition to the two genes in question 4, assume you now study a third independently assorting gene that has the alleles *C* and *c*. For each of the following genotypes, indicate what types of gametes will be produced.
   a. *AA BB CC*
   b. *Aa BB cc*
   c. *Aa BB Cc*
   d. *Aa Bb Cc*

8. Imagine that you are helping a friend with genetics problems. He has drawn the Punnett square below to answer questions about a dihybrid cross: *Mm Hh* × *Mm Hh*. Use the principles of meiosis to explain why this diagram is incorrect.

	M	H	h	m
M				
h				
H				
m				

9. A man is homozygous dominant for alleles at 10 different genes that assort independently. How many genotypically different types of sperm cells can he produce? A woman is homozygous recessive for the alleles of 8 of these 10 genes, but she is heterozygous for the other 2 genes. How many genotypically different types of eggs can she produce? What hypothesis can you suggest to describe the relationship between the number of different possible gametes and the number of heterozygous and homozygous genes that are present?

10. In guinea pigs, an allele for rough fur (*R*) is dominant over an allele for smooth fur (*r*); an allele for black coat (*B*) is dominant over that for white (*b*). You have an animal with rough, black fur. What cross would you use to determine whether the animal is homozygous for these traits? What phenotype would you expect in the offspring if the animal were homozygous?

11. You cross a lima bean plant from a variety that breeds true for green pods with another lima bean from a variety that breeds true for yellow pods. You note that all the F_1 plants have green pods. These green-pod F_1 plants, when crossed to each other, yield 675 plants with green pods and 217 with yellow pods. How many genes likely control pod colour in this experiment? Give the alleles letter designations. Which is dominant?

12. Some recessive alleles have such a detrimental effect that they are lethal when present in both chromosomes of a pair. Homozygous recessives cannot survive, and die at some point during embryonic development. Suppose that the allele *r* is lethal in the homozygous *rr* condition. What genotypic ratios would you expect among the living offspring of the following crosses?
    a. $RR \times Rr$
    b. $Rr \times Rr$

13. In garden peas, the genotypes *GG* and *Gg* produce green pods and *gg* produces yellow pods; *TT* and *Tt* plants are tall and *tt* plants are dwarfed; *RR* and *Rr* produce round seeds and *rr* produces wrinkled seeds. If a plant of a true-breeding tall variety with green pods and round seeds is crossed with a plant of a true-breeding dwarf variety with yellow pods and wrinkled seeds, what phenotypes are expected, and in what ratios, in the F_1 generation? What phenotypes, and in what ratios, are expected if F_1 individuals are crossed?

14. In chickens, a gene called *F* influences leg feathering. Feathered legs are produced by a dominant allele *F*, while featherless legs result in individuals who are homozygous for the *f* allele. A second gene, *P*, on another chromosome,

influences comb shape. The dominant allele *P* produces pea combs; a recessive allele *p* of this gene causes single combs. A breeder makes the following crosses with birds 1, 2, 3, and 4; all parents have feathered legs and pea combs.

Cross	Offspring
1 × 2	all feathered, pea comb
1 × 3	3/4 feathered; 1/4 featherless, all pea comb
1 × 4	9/16 feathered, pea comb; 3/16 featherless, pea comb; 3/16 feathered, single comb; 1/16 featherless, single comb

What are the genotypes of the four birds?

15. A mixup in a hospital ward causes a mother with O and MN blood types to think that a baby given to her really belongs to someone else. Tests in the hospital show that the doubting mother is able to taste PTC (see question 3). The baby given to her has O and MN blood types and has no reaction when the bitter PTC chemical is placed on its tongue. The mother has four other children with the following blood types and tasting abilities for PTC.
    a. type A and MN blood, taster
    b. type B and N blood, nontaster
    c. type A and M blood, taster
    d. type A and N blood, taster

    Without knowing the father's blood types and tasting ability, can you determine whether the child is really hers? (Assume that all her children have the same father.)

16. In cats, the genotype *AA* produces tabby fur colour; *Aa* is also a tabby, and *aa* is black. Another independently assorting gene at a different locus is epistatic to the gene for fur colour. When present in its dominant *W* form (*WW* or *Ww*), this gene blocks the formation of fur colour and all the offspring are white; *ww* individuals develop normal fur colour. What fur colours, and in what proportions, would you expect from the cross *Aa Ww* × *Aa Ww*?

17. Having malformed hands with shortened fingers is a dominant trait controlled by a single gene; people who are homozygous for the recessive allele have normal hands and fingers. Having woolly hair is a dominant trait controlled by a different, independently assorting gene; homozygous recessive individuals have normal, nonwoolly hair. Suppose a woman with normal hands and nonwoolly hair marries a man who has malformed hands and woolly hair. Their first child has normal hands and nonwoolly hair. What are the genotypes of the mother, the father, and the child? If this couple has a second child, what is the probability that it will have normal hands and woolly hair?

Questions for Discussion

1. The eyes of brown-eyed people are not alike but rather vary considerably in shade and pattern. What do you think causes these differences?

2. Explain how individuals of an organism that are phenotypically alike can produce different ratios of progeny phenotypes.

3. ABO blood type tests can be used to exclude paternity. Suppose a defendant who is the alleged father of a child takes a blood-type test and the results do not exclude him as the father. Do the results indicate that he is the father? What arguments could a lawyer make based on the test results to exclude the defendant from being the father? (Assume the tests were performed correctly.)

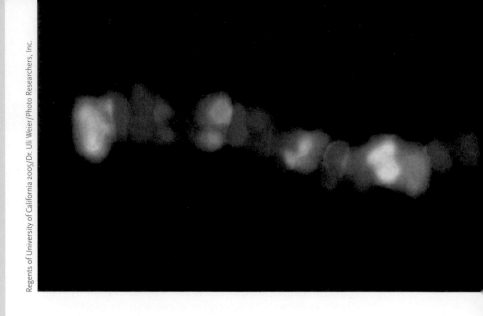

Fluorescent probes bound to specific sequences along human chromosome 10 (light micrograph). New ways of mapping chromosome structure yield insights into the inheritance of normal and abnormal traits.

Regents of University of California 2005/Dr. Uli Weier/Photo Researchers, Inc.

STUDY PLAN

11.1 Genetic Linkage and Recombination

11.1a The Principles of Linkage and Recombination Were Determined with *Drosophila*

11.1b Recombination Frequency Can Be Used to Map Chromosomes

11.1c Widely Separated Linked Genes Assort Independently

11.2 Sex-Linked Genes

11.2a Females Are XX and Males Are XY in Both Humans and Fruit Flies

11.2b Human Sex Determination Depends on the *SRY* Gene

11.2c Sex-Linked Genes Were First Discovered in *Drosophila*

11.2d Sex-Linked Genes in Humans Are Inherited as They Are in *Drosophila*

11.2e Inactivation of One X Chromosome Evens Out Gene Effects

11.3 Chromosomal Alterations That Affect Inheritance

11.3a Deletions, Duplications, Translocations, and Inversions Are the Most Common Chromosomal Alterations

11.3b The Number of Entire Chromosomes May Also Change

11.4 Human Genetics and Genetic Counselling

11.4a In Autosomal Recessive Inheritance, Heterozygotes Are Carriers and Homozygous Recessives Are Affected by the Trait

11.4b In Autosomal Dominant Inheritance, Only Homozygous Recessives Are Unaffected

11.4c Males Are More Likely to Be Affected by X-Linked Recessive Traits

11.4d Human Genetic Disorders Can Be Predicted, and Many Can Be Treated

11.5 Nontraditional Patterns of Inheritance

11.5a Cytoplasmic Inheritance Follows the Pattern of Inheritance of Mitochondria or Chloroplasts

11.5b In Gene Imprinting, an Allele Inherited from One of the Parents Is Expressed whereas the Other Allele Is Silent

11 Genes, Chromosomes, and Human Genetics

WHY IT MATTERS

Imagine being 10 years old and trapped in a body that each day becomes more shrivelled, frail, and old. You are just tall enough to peer over the top of the kitchen counter, and you weigh less than 16 kg. Already you are bald, and you probably have only a few more years to live. But if you are like Mickey Hayes or Fransie Geringer **(Figure 11.1)**, you still have not lost your courage or your childlike curiosity about life. Like them, you still play, laugh, and celebrate birthdays.

Progeria, the premature aging that afflicts Mickey and Fransie, is caused by a genetic error that occurs once in every 8 million human births. The error is perpetuated each time cells of the embryo—then of the child—duplicate their chromosomes and divide. The outcome of that rare mistake is an acceleration of aging and a greatly reduced life expectancy.

Progeria affects both boys and girls. Usually, symptoms begin to appear before the age of 2. The rate of body growth declines to abnormally low levels. Skin becomes thinner, muscles become flaccid, and limb bones start to degenerate. Children with progeria never reach

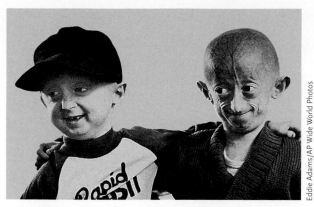

Figure 11.1

Two boys, both younger than 10, who have progeria, a genetic disorder characterized by accelerated aging and extremely reduced life expectancy.

11.1a The Principles of Linkage and Recombination Were Determined with *Drosophila*

In the early part of the twentieth century, Thomas H. Morgan and coworkers at Columbia University used the fruit fly, *Drosophila melanogaster,* as a model organism to investigate Mendel's principles in animals. (For more information about *Drosophila* as a model research organism, see *The Purple Pages.*) Groups of genes that tended to assort together in crosses were believed to be carried on the same chromosome. It was an undergraduate student named Alfred Sturtevant, working in Morgan's lab, who developed the insight that resulted in the construction of the first genetic map showing the relative order of genes on a chromosome. This map also estimated the distance separating the genes. These brilliant and far-reaching hypotheses were typical of Morgan's group, which founded genetics research in the United States, developed *Drosophila* as a research organism, and made discoveries that were likely as significant to the development of genetics as those of Mendel.

Although it is tempting to assume that genetic maps could be made simply by looking down a microscope, finding the genes, and measuring the distance between them, the technology to do this was simply not available. Instead, Morgan's group used an indirect measure of distance. They reasoned that genes sitting relatively far apart on a chromosome would be more likely to be separated from one another during meiotic crossing-over than genes lying closer together. Figure 9.13, Chapter 9, illustrates this process of recombination occurring in the space separating two genes as they appear on chromosomes paired during meiosis. Obviously, if recombination is to be used as a measure of the distance separating genes, it must be detectable. That is why the organism used in Figure 9.13, Chapter 9, is heterozygous for all genes; the chromatids resulting from recombination are then different from the original, nonrecombinant, ones and can be identified. Following meiosis I and II, each of the four different chromatids will become a chromosome in a separate gamete (review the basic mechanisms of meiosis in Figure 9.10, Chapter 9,). Which chromosome, recombinant or not, is carried by a given gamete is most clearly revealed only in offspring resulting from fertilization with a homozygous recessive gamete. That is why, in the cross originally done by Morgan in 1911, you will notice that one parent is heterozygous and the other is homozygous recessive **(Figure 11.2, p. 236).**

To understand the following crosses, you need to learn to work with the genetic symbolism developed by Morgan instead of the *A/a* system used in Chapter 10. Although *Drosophila* notation might appear counterintuitive at first, understanding a few basic principles will help you see the logic behind it. First, note that geneticists working with fruit flies have all agreed on a "normal," or "wild-type," genotype; any change from

puberty, and most die in their early teens from a stroke or heart attack brought on by hardening of the arteries, a condition typical of advanced age.

The plight of Mickey and Fransie provides a telling and tragic example of the dramatic effects that gene defects can have on living organisms. The characteristics of each individual, from humans to pine trees to protozoa, depend on the combination of genes, alleles, and chromosomes inherited from its parents, as well as on environmental effects. This chapter delves into genes and the role of chromosomes in inheritance.

11.1 Genetic Linkage and Recombination

In the historic experiments described in the previous chapter, Gregor Mendel carried out crosses with seven different characters in garden peas, controlled by seven different genes. He found that his observations from crosses were consistent with the hypothesis that each of the genes assorted independently of all of the others. If Mendel had extended his study to additional characters, he would soon have found exceptions to this principle. This should not be surprising because an organism has many more genes than chromosomes. Conceptually, then, chromosomes contain many genes, with each gene at a particular location, or locus. Genes located on different chromosomes assort independently during meiosis because the two chromosomes behave independently of one another during as they line up on the metaphase plate (see Chapter 9 for a review of chromosome behaviour during meiosis). Genes located on the same chromosome may be inherited together in genetic crosses— that is, they do not assort independently—because the chromosome is inherited as a single physical entity in meiosis. Genes on the same chromosome are known as **linked genes,** and the phenomenon is called **linkage.**

Figure 11.2
Evidence for gene linkage.

QUESTION: Do the purple-eye vestigial-wing genes of *Drosophila* assort independently?

EXPERIMENT: Morgan crossed true-breeding wild-type flies with red eyes and normal wings with purple-eyed, vestigial-winged flies. The F₁ dihybrids were all wild-type in phenotype. Next he crossed the F₁ dihybrid flies with purple-eyed, vestigial-winged flies (this is a testcross) and analyzed the phenotypes of the progeny.

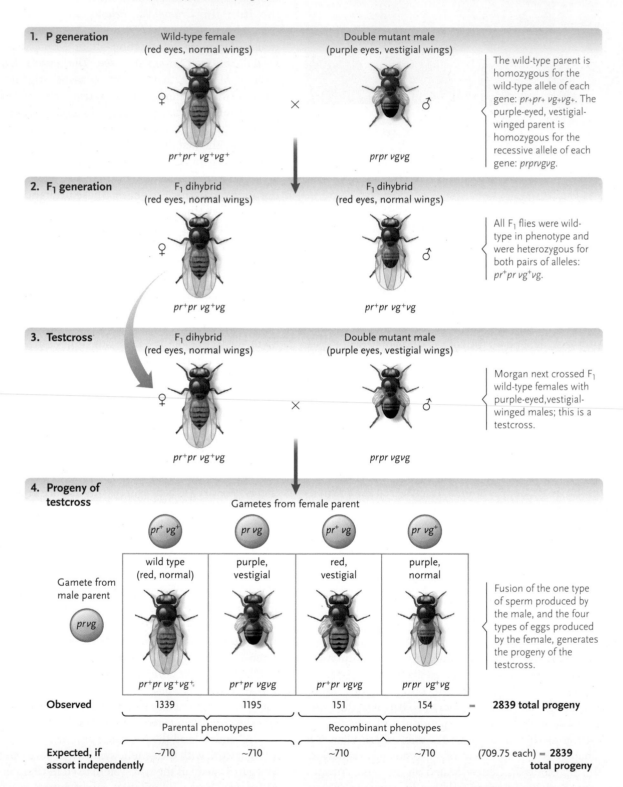

1. P generation

Wild-type female (red eyes, normal wings) × Double mutant male (purple eyes, vestigial wings)

♀ $pr^+pr^+\ vg^+vg^+$ ♂ $prpr\ vgvg$

The wild-type parent is homozygous for the wild-type allele of each gene: $pr_+pr_+\ vg_+vg_+$. The purple-eyed, vestigial-winged parent is homozygous for the recessive allele of each gene: $prprvgvg$.

2. F₁ generation

F₁ dihybrid (red eyes, normal wings)   F₁ dihybrid (red eyes, normal wings)

♀ $pr^+pr\ vg^+vg$ ♂ $pr^+pr\ vg^+vg$

All F₁ flies were wild-type in phenotype and were heterozygous for both pairs of alleles: $pr^+pr\ vg^+vg$.

3. Testcross

F₁ dihybrid (red eyes, normal wings) × Double mutant male (purple eyes, vestigial wings)

♀ $pr^+pr\ vg^+vg$ ♂ $prpr\ vgvg$

Morgan next crossed F₁ wild-type females with purple-eyed, vestigial-winged males; this is a testcross.

4. Progeny of testcross

Gametes from female parent

| $pr^+\ vg^+$ | $pr\ vg$ | $pr^+\ vg$ | $pr\ vg^+$ |

Gamete from male parent $pr\ vg$

wild type (red, normal)	purple, vestigial	red, vestigial	purple, normal
$pr^+pr\ vg^+vg^+$	$pr^+pr\ vgvg$	$pr^+pr\ vgvg$	$prpr\ vg^+vg$

Fusion of the one type of sperm produced by the male, and the four types of eggs produced by the female, generates the progeny of the testcross.

Observed	1339	1195	151	154	= **2839 total progeny**

Parental phenotypes — Recombinant phenotypes

| **Expected, if assort independently** | ~710 | ~710 | ~710 | ~710 | (709.75 each) = **2839 total progeny** |

RESULTS: 2534 of the testcross progeny flies were parental: wild-type or purple, vestigial, while 305 of the progeny were recombinant: red, vestigial or purple, normal. If the genes assorted independently, the expectation is for a 1:1:1:1 ratio for testcross progeny: approximately 1420 of both parental and recombinant progeny.

CONCLUSION: The purple-eye and vestigial-wing genes do not assort independently. The simplest alternative is that the two genes are linked on the same chromosome.

wild type is, by definition, a mutant. Mutant alleles are named based on the altered phenotype of the organism that expresses them. The names for dominant mutant alleles are written with the first letter in uppercase, whereas those for recessive mutant alleles are written with the first letter in lowercase. For example, a dominant mutant allele transforming an antenna into a leg is called Antennapedia (*Antp*), whereas a recessive mutant allele altering eye colour is called vermilion (*v*). The notation for a wild-type allele is always made by simply adding a superscripted plus (+) sign to the mutant allele notation. You know you understand this system if you agree that *Antp*+ refers to a *recessive* allele giving a normal phenotype when homozygous.

Morgan began a specific breeding program using true-breeding fruit flies with normal red eyes and normal wing length (genotype *pr*+*pr*+ *vg*+*vg*+), along with a true-breeding fly with the recessive traits of purple eyes and vestigial (that is, short and crumpled) wings (genotype *prpr vgvg*) (Figure 11.2, step 1).

The F₁ (first-generation) offspring were all dihybrid *pr*+*pr vg*+*vg*, and because of the dominance of the wild-type alleles, they all had red eyes and normal wings (see Figure 11.2, step 2). Morgan then selected these wild-type F₁ females as the dihybrid parent and mated them to homozygous recessive males (with purple eyes and vestigial wings) as the testcross parent. If the purple and vestigial genes were carried on different chromosomes, Mendel's principle of independent assortment (see Section 10.1) would predict four classes of phenotypes in the offspring, in the approximate 1:1:1:1 ratio of red eyes, normal wings: purple, vestigial: red, vestigial: purple, normal. Given over 2800 offspring from several females, about 700 should have been in each class. However, Morgan observed two types of progeny in which the counts were much higher than 700 (red, normal and purple, vestigial) and two types with counts that were much lower (red, vestigial, and purple, normal (see Figure 11.2, step 4).

Morgan's hypothesis to explain this non-Mendelian distribution is illustrated in **Figure 11.3, p. 238.** He suggested that the two genes are linked genetically—physically associated on the same chromosome. That is, *pr* and *vg* are linked genes. He further hypothesized that the behaviour of these linked genes is explained by *chromosome recombination* during meiosis. Furthermore, he proposed that the frequency of this recombination is a function of the distance between linked genes.

The *pr*+*pr vg*+*vg* F₁ dihybrid parents produce four types of gametes (see Figure 11.3, p. 238). The two parental gametes, *pr*+ *vg*+ and *pr vg*, are generated by simple segregation of the chromosomes during meiosis without any crossing-over (recombination) between the genes. The two recombinant gametes, *pr*+ *vg* and *pr vg*+, result from crossing-over between the homologous chromatids when they are paired in prophase I of meiosis (see Figures 9.10 and 9.13, Chapter 9). The offspring of the cross are produced by fusion of each of these four gametes with a *pr vg* gamete produced by the *prpr vgvg* male parent. The

phenotypes of the offspring directly reflect the genotypes of the gametes produced by the dihybrid parent.

CONCEPT FIX Students of genetics sometimes assume that the wild-type and purple vestigial offspring in the above cross are called "parental" because they *look like* the parents. However, the term *parental* actually refers to genotype, not phenotype; parental offspring are the ones that *inherit chromosomes that were NOT involved in recombination in the dihybrid parent.* Parental offspring, therefore, do not always resemble the parents of the cross. ⬢

Although Morgan could not look down a microscope and measure the distance between genes directly, he could look down a microscope and identify the phenotypes of recombinant offspring from dihybrid fruit fly testcrosses. Thus, the relative frequency of recombinant progeny became his "measure" of the distance separating genes. The example in Figure 11.3, p. 238 reveals that purple eyes and vestigial wings are on the same chromosome and are separated by a recombinant offspring frequency distance of 10.7%.

11.1b Recombination Frequency Can Be Used to Map Chromosomes

The recombinant offspring frequency of 10.7% for the *pr* and *vg* genes of *Drosophila* means that 10.7% of the gametes originating from the *pr*+*pr vg*+*vg* parent contained recombined chromosomes (i.e., either *pr*+ *vg* or *pr vg*+). That recombinant offspring frequency is characteristic for those two genes. In other crosses that involve linked genes, Morgan found that the recombinant offspring frequency was characteristic of the two particular genes involved, and varied from less than 1% up to a maximum of 50% (see the next section).

From these observations, Alfred Sturtevant realized that the variation in recombinant offspring frequencies could be used as a means of mapping genes on chromosomes. Sturtevant himself later recalled his light-bulb moment:

> I suddenly realized that the variations in the strength of linkage already attributed by Morgan to difference in the spatial separation of the gene offered the possibility of determining sequence in the linear dimensions of a chromosome. I went home and spent most of the night (to the neglect of my other homework) producing the first chromosome map.

Therefore, recombinant offspring frequencies can be used to make a **linkage map** of a chromosome showing the relative locations of genes. For example, assume that the three genes *a*, *b*, and *c* are carried together on the same chromosome. Crosses reveal a 9.6% frequency of recombinants for *a* and *b*, an 8% frequency for *a* and *c*, and a 2% frequency for *b* and *c*. These recombinant offspring frequencies allow the

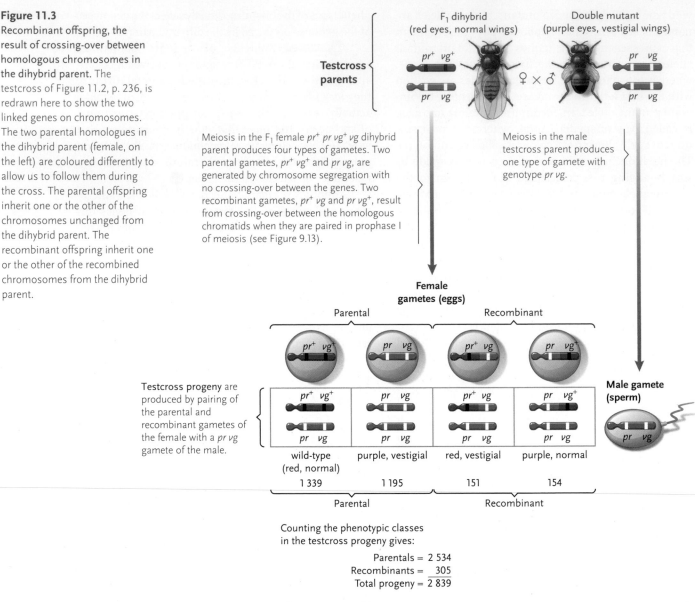

Figure 11.3

Recombinant offspring, the result of crossing-over between homologous chromosomes in the dihybrid parent. The testcross of Figure 11.2, p. 236, is redrawn here to show the two linked genes on chromosomes. The two parental homologues in the dihybrid parent (female, on the left) are coloured differently to allow us to follow them during the cross. The parental offspring inherit one or the other of the chromosomes unchanged from the dihybrid parent. The recombinant offspring inherit one or the other of the recombined chromosomes from the dihybrid parent.

Meiosis in the F₁ female pr^+ pr vg^+ vg dihybrid parent produces four types of gametes. Two parental gametes, pr^+ vg^+ and pr vg, are generated by chromosome segregation with no crossing-over between the genes. Two recombinant gametes, pr^+ vg and pr vg^+, result from crossing-over between the homologous chromatids when they are paired in prophase I of meiosis (see Figure 9.13).

Meiosis in the male testcross parent produces one type of gamete with genotype pr vg.

Counting the phenotypic classes in the testcross progeny gives:

Parentals = 2 534
Recombinants = 305
Total progeny = 2 839

The percentage of the progeny that are recombinants, the recombination frequency =

$$\frac{305 \text{ recombinants}}{2\ 839 \text{ total progeny}} \times 100 = 10.7\%$$

genes to be arranged in only one sequence on the chromosomes as follows:

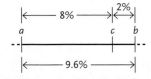

You will note that the *a–b* recombinant offspring frequency does not exactly equal the sum of the *a–c* and *c–b* frequencies. This is because genes farther apart on a chromosome are more likely to have more than one crossover occur between them. Whereas a single crossover between two genes gives recombinant chromatids, a double crossover (two single crossovers occurring in the same meiosis) between two genes gives the parental arrangement of alleles (and is therefore undetect-

able and would not be counted). You can see this simply by drawing single and double crossovers between two genes on a piece of paper. In our example, the undetectable double crossovers that occur between *a* and *b* have slightly decreased the overall recombinant offspring frequency between these two genes.

Using this method, Sturtevant created the first linkage map showing the arrangement of six genes on the *Drosophila* X chromosome. (A partial linkage map of a *Drosophila* chromosome is shown in **Figure 11.4**.)

Since the time of Morgan, many *Drosophila* genes and those of other eukaryotic organisms widely used for genetic research, including *Neurospora* (a fungus), yeast, maize (corn), and the mouse, have been mapped using the same approach. Recombinant offspring frequencies, together with the results of other techniques, have been used to create linkage maps of the locations of genes in the DNA of prokaryotic organisms such as *Escherichia coli*.

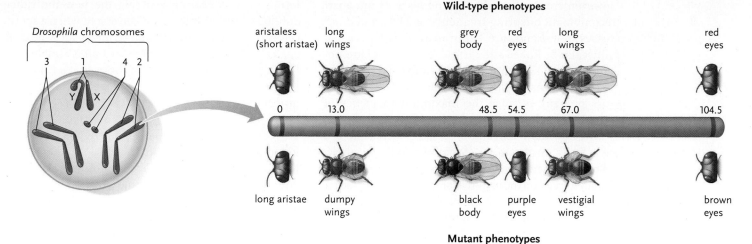

Figure 11.4

Relative map locations of several genes on chromosome 2 of *Drosophila*, as determined by frequencies of recombinant offspring from dihybrid testcrosses. For each gene, the diagram shows the normal or wild-type phenotype on the top and the mutant phenotype on the bottom. Mutant alleles at two different locations alter wing structure, one producing the dumpy-wing phenotype and the other the vestigial-wing phenotype; the normal allele at these locations results in normal long-wing structure. Mutant alleles at two different locations also alter eye colour.

The unit of a linkage map, called a **map unit** (abbreviated mu), is equivalent to a recombinant offspring frequency of 1%. The map unit is also called the **centimorgan** (cM) in honour of Morgan's discoveries of linkage and recombination. Map units are not absolute physical distances such as micrometres or nanometres; rather, they are *relative*, showing the positions of genes with respect to each other. One of the reasons that the units are relative and not absolute distances is that the frequency of crossing-over giving rise to recombinant offspring varies to some extent from one position to another along chromosomes.

In recent years, DNA sequencing of whole genomes has supplemented the linkage maps of a number of species. This shows the precise physical locations of genes right down to the number of base pairs separating them.

11.1c Widely Separated Linked Genes Assort Independently

Genes can be so widely separated on a chromosome that recombination is almost certain to occur at some point between them in every cell undergoing meiosis. When this is the case, the genes assort independently even though they are on the same chromosome. The map distance separating them will be 50 mu. (Fifty map units reflect 50% recombinant offspring. This the same proportion of recombinant offspring observed when genes are on different chromosomes.)

To understand why this is, first recall Figure 9.13, Chapter 9, showing that a recombination event in a given cell creates 2 recombinant and 2 nonrecombinant chromatids. Next, imagine 100 meiocytes going through meiosis as usual to yield 400 gametes. If a recombination event occurred in the space separating 2 given genes in 10 of those cells, then 20 recombinant chromatids would be produced during prophase I.

Twenty gametes would eventually receive recombinant chromosomes, and 20/400 = 5% of the total testcross progeny would be recombinant. We would conclude that these genes are 5 mu apart. Now assume that a recombination event occurs along the chromosome in the space separating the two genes in *every one of the 100* cells going through meiosis. Two hundred recombinant offspring would result out of the total of 400; 50% would be recombinants; 50 mu would separate the genes.

Linkage between such widely separated genes can still be detected, however, by testing their linkage to one or more genes that lie between them. For example, the genes *a* and *c* in **Figure 11.5** are located so far apart that they assort independently and show no linkage.

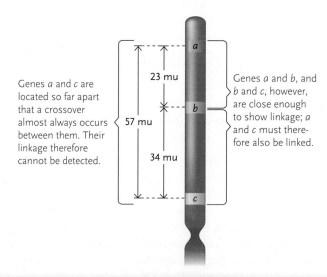

Figure 11.5

Genes far apart on the same chromosome. Genes *a* and *c* are far apart and will not show linkage, suggesting that they are on different chromosomes. However, linkage between such genes can be established by noting their linkage to another gene or genes located between them—gene *b* here.

However, crosses that show *a* and *b* are 23 mu apart (recombinant offspring frequency of 23%), and other crosses show *b* and *c* are 34 mu apart. Therefore, *a* and *c* must also be linked and carried on the same chromosome at 23 + 34 = 57 mu apart. Obviously, we could not see a recombinant offspring frequency of 57% in testcross progeny because the maximum frequency of recombinant chromatids is 50%, as described above.

We now know that some of the genes Mendel studied are actually on the same chromosome. For example, although the genes for flower colour and seed colour are actually located on the same chromosome, they are so far apart that frequent recombination between them made them assort independently in Mendel's analysis.

STUDY BREAK

1. What type of cross is typically used to discover whether two genes are linked or not?
2. How can two genes be on the same chromosome and yet assort independently (as if they were on separate chromosomes)?

11.2 Sex-Linked Genes

In many organisms, one or more pairs of chromosomes are different in males from those in females. Genes located on these chromosomes, the *sex chromosomes,* are called **sex-linked genes;** they are inherited differently in males and females.

CONCEPT FIX Note that the word "linked" in the phrase "sex-linked gene" means only that the gene is on a sex chromosome. The use of the word "linked" when considering two or more genes means that the genes are on the same chromosome. Linked genes might be on a sex chromosome or an autosome. ⬣

Chromosomes other than the sex chromosomes are called **autosomes;** genes on these chromosomes have the same patterns of inheritance in both sexes. In humans, chromosomes 1 to 22 are the autosomes.

11.2a Females Are XX and Males Are XY in Both Humans and Fruit Flies

In most species with sex chromosomes, females have two copies of a chromosome known as the **X chromosome,** forming a fully homologous XX pair, whereas males have only one X chromosome. Another chromosome, the Y chromosome, occurs in males but not in females. The Y chromosome has a short region of homology with the X chromosome that allows them to pair during meiosis. The XX human chromosome complement is shown in Figure 8.10, Chapter 8.

Each normal gamete produced by an XX female carries an X chromosome. Half the gametes produced by an XY male carry an X chromosome and half carry a Y. When a sperm cell carrying an X chromosome fertilizes an X-bearing egg cell, the new individual develops into an XX female. Conversely, when a sperm cell carrying a Y chromosome fertilizes an X-bearing egg cell, the combination produces an XY male. The Punnett square (see **Figure 11.6**) shows that fertilization is expected to produce females and males with an equal probability of 1/2. This expectation is closely matched in the human and *Drosophila* populations.

Other sex chromosome arrangements have been found, as in some insects with XX females and XO males (the O means there is no Y chromosome). In birds, butterflies, and some reptiles, the situation is reversed: males have a homologous pair of sex chromosomes (ZZ instead of XX), and females have the equivalent of an XY combination (ZW).

11.2b Human Sex Determination Depends on the *SRY* Gene

One gene carried on the Y chromosome, *SRY* (for sex-determining region of the Y), appears to be the master switch that directs development toward maleness at an

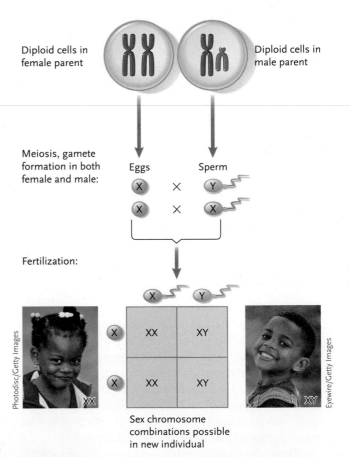

Figure 11.6

Sex chromosomes and the chromosomal basis of sex determination in humans. Females have two X chromosomes and therefore all gametes (eggs) have the X sex chromosome. Males have one X and one Y chromosome and therefore produce equal numbers of gametes containing an X chromosome versus a Y chromosome. Males transmit their Y chromosome to their sons, but not to their daughters. Males receive their X chromosome only from their mother.

MOLECULE BEHIND BIOLOGY 11.1

Drosopterin

The brick-red eyes of wild-type fruit flies owe their colour to a mixture of two types of pigment: bright red drosopterin and brown ommochrome. Drosopterin is the final product of a multistep biochemical pathway beginning with guanine. Mutations can alter the function of enzymes that act at different steps in this pathway to result in novel eye colours such as purple, brown, and sepia.

early point in embryonic development. For the first month or so of embryonic development in humans and other mammals, the rudimentary structures that give rise to reproductive organs and tissues are the same in XX or XY embryos. After 6 to 8 weeks, the *SRY* gene becomes active in XY embryos, producing a protein that regulates the expression of other genes, thereby stimulating part of these structures to develop as testes. As a part of stimulation by hormones secreted in the developing testes and elsewhere, tissues degenerate that would otherwise develop into female structures such as the vagina and oviducts. The remaining structures develop into the penis and scrotum. In XX embryos, which do not have a copy of the *SRY* gene, development proceeds toward female reproductive structures. The rudimentary male structures degenerate in XX embryos because the hormones released by the developing testes in XY embryos are not present. Further details of the *SRY* gene and its role in human sex determination are presented in Chapter 34.

CONCEPT FIX Although the X and Y chromosomes are called *sex chromosomes,* only a few genes they carry have any influence on sex determination or sexual function. For instance, most of the roughly 2 400 known genes on the human X chromosome code for phenotypes needed by both sexes, such as colour perception, blood clotting, and DNA replication. Conversely, genes governing structures needed by only one sex or the other, such as breast development, penis structure, and facial hair, are coded on autosomes. If you are male, you have inherited the genes needed for uterine development and you will pass them along to your offspring to be used by daughters. You do not express these genes in your body. If you are female, a comparable situation is the case for genes coding for penis structure, and so on. You inherited these genes but you don't express them. ⬡

11.2c Sex-Linked Genes Were First Discovered in *Drosophila*

Since males and females have different sets of sex chromosomes, the genes carried on these chromosomes can be inherited in a distinctly non-Mendelian pattern called sex linkage. Sex linkage arises from two differences between males and females: (1) males have one X chromosome and therefore one allele for each gene on this chromosome (males are hemizygous for X-linked genes, *hemi* = half); females have two copies of the X chromosome and therefore two alleles for all genes on the X chromosome; (2) males also have one copy of the Y chromosome and one allele for each gene on this chromosome; females have no Y chromosome and therefore no Y alleles at all. Y chromosomes are present in males but not females.

Morgan discovered sex-linked genes and their pattern of sex linkage in 1910. The story of discovery started when he found a male fly in his stocks with white eyes instead of the normal red eyes **(Figure 11.7)**. He crossed the white-eyed male with a true-breeding female with red eyes and observed that all the F_1 flies had red eyes **(Figure 11.8a, p. 242)**. He concluded that the white-eye trait was recessive. Next, he allowed the F_1 flies to interbreed. Based on Mendel's principles, he expected that both male and female F_2 flies would show a 3:1 ratio of red-eyed flies to white-eyed flies. Morgan was surprised to find that all the F_2 females had red eyes, *but half of the F_2 males had red eyes and half had white eyes* **(Figure 11.8b, p. 242)**.

Morgan hypothesized that the alleles segregating in the cross were of a gene located on the X chromosome—now termed a sex-linked gene. The white-eyed male parent in the cross had the genotype $X^w Y$: an X chromosome with a white (X^w) allele, and no other allele of that gene on the Y chromosome. The red-eyed female parent in the cross had the genotype

a. **b.**

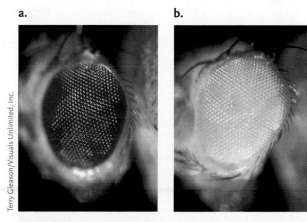

Figure 11.7

Eye colour phenotypes in *Drosophila*. **(a)** Normal, red wild-type eye colour. **(b)** Mutant white eye colour caused by a recessive allele of a sex-linked gene carried on the X chromosome.

Figure 11.8
Evidence for sex-linked genes.

QUESTION: How is the white-eye gene of *Drosophila* inherited?

EXPERIMENT: Morgan crossed a white-eyed male *Drosophila* with a true-breeding female with red eyes and then crossed the F_1 flies to produce the F_2 generation. He also performed the reciprocal cross in which the phenotypes were switched in the parental flies—true-breeding white-eyed female × red-eyed male.

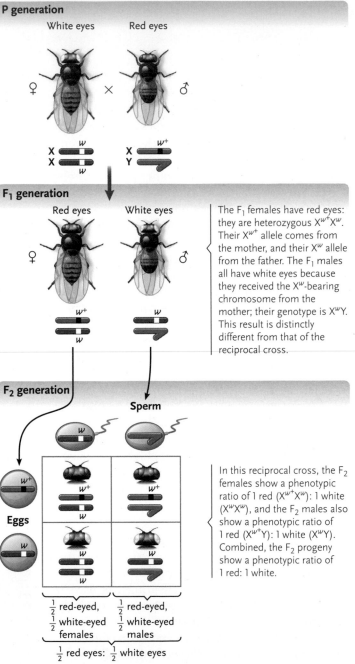

A. True-breeding red-eyed female × white-eyed male

P generation

Red eyes (wild type) × White eyes

F₁ generation

Red eyes, Red eyes

All F_1 flies have red eyes, indicating that the white-eye trait is recessive. The F_1 females inherit one X from each parent; their genotype is $X^{w^+}X^w$, and their phenotype is red eyes because the X^{w^+} allele is dominant. The F_1 males inherit their X chromosome from their mothers; their genotype is $X^{w^+}Y$, and their phenotype is red eyes.

F₂ generation

Sperm / Eggs

The F_2 females receive an X^{w^+} allele from the F_1 father and either an X^{w^+} or X^w allele from the F_1 mother; both these genotypes result in red eyes. The F_2 males inherit their one X chromosome from the F_1 mother whose genotype is $X^{w^+}X^w$. Therefore, F_2 males are half $X^{w^+}Y$ (red eyes) and half X^wY (white eyes). Females and males together show a phenotypic ratio of 3 red: 1 white.

All red-eyed females / $\frac{1}{2}$ red-eyed, $\frac{1}{2}$ white-eyed males

$\frac{3}{4}$ red eyes: $\frac{1}{4}$ white eyes

B. White-eyed female × red-eyed male

P generation

White eyes × Red eyes

F₁ generation

Red eyes, White eyes

The F_1 females have red eyes: they are heterozygous $X^{w^+}X^w$. Their X^{w^+} allele comes from the mother, and their X^w allele from the father. The F_1 males all have white eyes because they received the X^w-bearing chromosome from the mother; their genotype is X^wY. This result is distinctly different from that of the reciprocal cross.

F₂ generation

Sperm / Eggs

In this reciprocal cross, the F_2 females show a phenotypic ratio of 1 red ($X^{w^+}X^w$): 1 white (X^wX^w), and the F_2 males also show a phenotypic ratio of 1 red ($X^{w^+}Y$): 1 white (X^wY). Combined, the F_2 progeny show a phenotypic ratio of 1 red: 1 white.

$\frac{1}{2}$ red-eyed, $\frac{1}{2}$ white-eyed females / $\frac{1}{2}$ red-eyed, $\frac{1}{2}$ white-eyed males

$\frac{1}{2}$ red eyes: $\frac{1}{2}$ white eyes

RESULTS: Differences were seen in both the F_1 and F_2 generations for the red ♀ × white ♂ and white ♀ × red ♂ crosses.

CONCLUSION: The segregation pattern for the white-eye trait showed that the white-eye gene is a sex-linked gene located on the X chromosome.

$X^{w^+}X^{w^+}$: each X chromosome carries the dominant normal allele for red eyes, X^{w^+}.

We can follow the alleles in this cross (see Figure 11.8a). The F_1 flies of a cross $X^{w^+}X^{w^+} \times X^wY$ are produced as follows. The X chromosome of each male comes from his mother; therefore, his genotype is $X^{w^+}Y$, and his phenotype is red eyes. The females each receive one X from each parent; therefore, her genotype is $X^{w^+}X^w$, and her phenotype is red eyes due to the dominance of the X^{w^+} allele.

In the F_2 generation, each female receives an X^{w^+} allele from her father (F_1) and either an X^{w^+} or X^w allele from her mother (F_1); these genotypes result in red eyes (see Figure 11.8a). Each male receives his one X chromosome from his mother (F_1), which has the genotype $X^{w^+}X^w$. Therefore, F_2 males are half $X^{w^+}Y$ (red eyes) and half X^wY (white eyes).

Morgan also made a *reciprocal cross* of the one just described; that is, the phenotypes were switched between the parents. The reciprocal cross here was a white-eyed female (X^wX^w) with a red-eyed male ($X^{w^+}Y$) (see Figure 11.8b). All F_1 males had white eyes because they received the X^w-bearing chromosome from their mother; thus, their genotype is X^wY. The F_1 females have red eyes; they are all heterozygous $X^{w^+}X^w$. *This result is clearly different from the reciprocal cross shown in Figure 11.8a.*

In the F_2 generation of this second cross, both male and female flies showed a 1:1 ratio of red eyes to white eyes (see Figure 11.8b). Again, this result differs markedly from that of the cross in Figure 11.8a.

In summary, Morgan's work showed that there is a distinctive pattern in the phenotypic ratios for reciprocal crosses in which the gene involved is on the X chromosome. A key indicator of this sex linkage is when all male offspring of a cross between a true-breeding mutant female and a wild-type male have the mutant phenotype. As we have seen, this occurs because a male receives his X chromosome from his female parent.

11.2d Sex-Linked Genes in Humans Are Inherited as They Are in *Drosophila*

For obvious reasons, experimental genetic crosses cannot be conducted with humans. However, a similar analysis can be made by interviewing and testing living members of a family and reconstructing the genotypes and phenotypes of past generations from family records. The results are summarized in a chart called a **pedigree**, which shows all parents and offspring for as many generations as possible, the sex of individuals in the different generations, and the presence or absence of the trait of interest. Females are designated by a circle and males by a square; a solid circle or square indicates the presence of the trait.

In humans, as in fruit flies, sex-linked recessive traits appear more frequently among males than females because males need to receive only one copy of the allele on the X chromosome inherited from their mothers to develop the trait. Females must receive two copies of the recessive allele, one from each parent, to express the trait. Two examples of human sex-linked traits are red–green colour-blindness, a recessive trait in which the affected individual is unable to distinguish between the colours red and green because of a defect in light-sensing cells in the retina, and hemophilia, a recessive trait in which affected individuals have a defect in blood clotting.

CONCEPT FIX Colour-blindness does not mean that people see only black and white. The inability to see any colour at all is very rare. As shown in Figure 11.16, p. 252 colour-blindness reduces the variety of colours that can be distinguished. ⬡

People with hemophilia are "bleeders"; that is, they bleed uncontrollably if they are injured because a protein required for forming blood clots is not produced in functional form. Males are bleeders if they receive an X chromosome that carries the recessive allele. The disease also develops in females with the recessive allele on both of their X chromosomes—a rare combination. With luck and good care, affected people can reach maturity, but their lives are tightly circumscribed by the necessity to avoid injury. Even internal bleeding from slight bruises can be fatal. The disease, which affects about 1 in 7 000 males, can be treated by injection of the required clotting protein.

Hemophilia has had effects reaching far beyond individuals who inherit the disease. The most famous cases occurred in the royal families of Europe descended from Queen Victoria of England **(Figure 11.9, p. 244)**. The disease was not recorded in Queen Victoria's ancestors, so the recessive allele for the trait probably appeared as a spontaneous mutation in the queen or one of her parents. Queen Victoria was heterozygous for the recessive hemophilia allele; that is, she was a **carrier**, meaning that she carried the mutant allele and could pass it on to her offspring, but she did not have symptoms of the disease. A carrier is indicated in a pedigree by a male or female symbol with a central dot.

Note in Queen Victoria's pedigree in Figure 11.9, p. 244 that Leopold, Duke of Albany, had hemophilia, as did his grandson, Rupert, Viscount Trematon. The trait appears in males in alternate generations (i.e., it skips a generation) because it passes with the X chromosome from mother to son. Mothers do not express the trait because they are heterozygous carriers. The sons, in turn, must pass the X chromosome with the affected allele to their daughters (and the Y chromosome to their sons), as did the Duke of Albany. The appearance of a trait in the males of alternate generations therefore suggests that the allele under study is recessive and carried on the X chromosome.

At one time, 18 of Queen Victoria's 69 descendants were affected males or female carriers. Because so many sons of European royalty were affected, the trait influenced the course of history. In Russia, Crown Prince Alexis was one of Victoria's descendants with hemophilia. His affliction drew together his parents, Czar Nicholas II and Czarina Alexandra (a granddaughter of Victoria and a carrier), and the hypnotic monk Rasputin, who manipulated the family to his advantage by convincing them that only he could control the boy's bleeding. The situation helped trigger the Russian Revolution of 1917, which ended the Russian monarchy and led to the establishment of a Communist government in the former Soviet Union, a significant event in twentieth-century history.

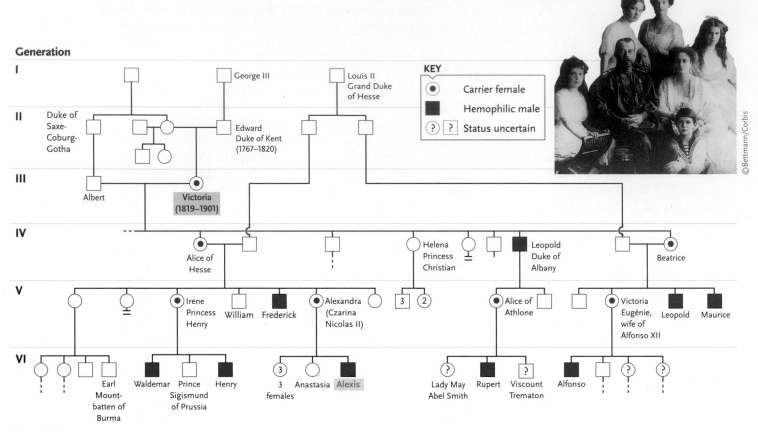

Generation

KEY
- ⊙ Carrier female
- ■ Hemophilic male
- ⊙ ? Status uncertain

Figure 11.9

Inheritance of hemophilia in descendants of Queen Victoria of England. The photograph shows the Russian royal family in which the son, Crown Prince Alexis, had hemophilia. His mother was a carrier of the mutated gene.

Hemophilia affected only sons in the royal lines but could have affected daughters if a hemophiliac son had married a carrier female. Because the disease is rare in the human population as a whole, the chance of such a mating is so low that only a few hemophiliac females have been recorded.

11.2e Inactivation of One X Chromosome Evens out Gene Effects

Although mammalian females have twice as many copies of genes carried on the X chromosome as males, it is unlikely that they require twice as much of the products of those genes. Theoretically, products from genes on the X chromosome could be equalized in males and females if (1) expression of genes on the single male X chromosome were doubled, or (2) expression of genes on both female X chromosomes were halved, or (3) one X chromosome were "turned off" in females. All of these dosage compensation mechanisms are known in nature, but mammals use the latter; females with two X chromosomes inactivate most of the genes on one X chromosome or the other in most body cells.

As a result of the equalizing mechanism, the activity of most genes carried on the X chromosome is essentially the same in the cells of males and females. The inactivation occurs by a condensation process that folds and packs the chromatin of one of the two X chromosomes into a tightly coiled state similar to the condensed state of chromosomes during cell division. The inactive, condensed X chromosome can be seen within the nucleus in cells of females as a dense mass of chromatin called the **Barr body**.

The inactivation occurs during embryonic development. Which of the two X chromosomes becomes inactive in a particular embryonic cell line is a random event. But once one of the X chromosomes is inactivated in a cell, that same X is inactivated in all descendants of the cell. Thus, within one female, one of the X chromosomes is active in particular cells and inactive in others and vice versa.

If the two X chromosomes carry different alleles of a gene, one allele will be active in cell lines in which one X chromosome is active, and the other allele will be active in cell lines in which the other X chromosome is active. For many sex-linked alleles, such as the recessive allele that causes hemophilia, random inactivation of either X chromosome has little overall whole-body effect in heterozygous females because the dominant allele is active in enough of the critical cells to produce a normal phenotype. However, for some genes, the inactivation of either X chromosome in heterozygotes produces recognizably different effects in distinct regions of the body.

For example, the orange and black patches of fur in calico cats result from inactivation of one of the two X chromosomes in regions of the skin of heterozygous females **(Figure 11.10)**. Males, which get only one of the two alleles, normally have either black or orange fur. Similarly, in humans, females who are heterozygous for an allele on the X chromosome that blocks development of sweat glands may have a patchy distribution of skin areas with and without the glands. Females with the patchy distribution are not seriously affected and may be unaware of the condition.

As we have seen, the discovery of genetic linkage, recombination, and sex-linked genes led to the elaboration and expansion of Mendel's principles of inheritance. Next, we examine what happens when patterns of inheritance are modified by changes in the chromosomes.

STUDY BREAK

1. What are the differences in sex chromosomes that underlie sex linkage inheritance patterns?
2. How could you determine if a given gene is sex-linked or not?

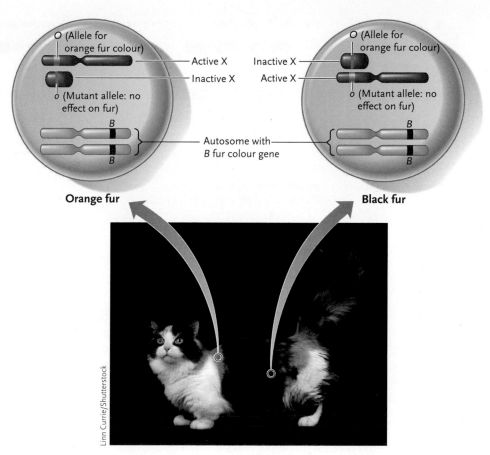

Figure 11.10

A female cat with the calico colour pattern in which patches of orange and black fur are produced by random inactivation of one of the two X chromosomes. Two genes control the black and orange colours: the *O* gene on the X chromosome is for orange fur colour, and the *B* gene on an autosome is for black fur colour. A calico cat has the genotype *Oo BB* (or *Oo Bb*). An orange patch results when the X chromosome carrying the mutant *o* allele is inactivated. In this case, the *O* gene masks the expression of the *B* gene and orange fur is produced. (This in an example of epistasis; see Section 10.2d.) A black patch results when the X chromosome carrying the *O* allele is inactivated. In this case, the mutant *o* allele cannot mask *B* gene expression and black fur results. The white patches result from interactions with a third, autosomal, gene that entirely blocks pigment deposition in the fur.

11.3 Chromosomal Alterations That Affect Inheritance

Although chromosomes are relatively stable structures, they are sometimes altered by breaks in the DNA, which can be generated by agents such as radiation or certain chemicals or by enzymes encoded in some infecting viruses. The broken chromosome fragments may be lost or they may reattach to the same or different chromosomes. The resulting changes in chromosome structure may have genetic consequences if alleles are eliminated, mixed in new combinations, duplicated, or placed in new locations by the alterations in cell lines that lead to the formation of gametes.

Genetic changes may also occur through changes in chromosome number, including addition or loss of one or more chromosomes or even entire sets of chromosomes. Both chromosomal alterations and changes in chromosome number can be a source of disease and disability, as well as a source of variability during evolution.

11.3a Deletions, Duplications, Translocations, and Inversions Are the Most Common Chromosomal Alterations

Chromosomal alterations after breakages occur in four major forms **(Figure 11.11, p. 246)**:

- A **deletion** occurs if a broken segment is lost from a chromosome.
- A **duplication** occurs if a segment is broken from one chromosome and inserted into its homologue. In the receiving homologue, the alleles in the inserted fragment are added to the ones already there.
- A **translocation** occurs if a broken segment is attached to a different, nonhomologous chromosome.
- An **inversion** occurs if a broken segment reattaches to the same chromosome from which it was lost, but in reversed orientation, so that the order of genes is reversed.

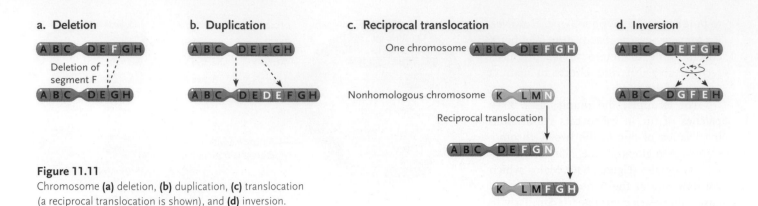

Figure 11.11

Chromosome **(a)** deletion, **(b)** duplication, **(c)** translocation (a reciprocal translocation is shown), and **(d)** inversion.

To be inherited, chromosomal alterations must occur or be included in cells of the germ line leading to development of eggs or sperm.

Deletions and Duplications. A deletion (see Figure 11.11a) may cause severe problems if the missing segment contains genes that are essential for normal development or cellular functions. For example, one deletion from human chromosome 5 typically leads to severe mental retardation and a malformed larynx. The cries of an affected infant sound more like a meow than a human cry—hence the name of the disorder, *cri-du-chat* (meaning "cat's cry").

A duplication (see Figure 11.11b) may have effects that vary from harmful to beneficial, depending on the genes and alleles contained in the duplicated region. Although most duplications are likely to be detrimental, some have been important sources of evolutionary change. That is, because there are duplicate genes, one copy can mutate into new forms without seriously affecting the basic functions of the organism. For example, mammals have genes that encode several types of hemoglobin that are not present in vertebrates such as sharks that evolved earlier; the additional hemoglobin genes of mammals are believed to have appeared through duplications, followed by mutations in the duplicates that created new and beneficial forms of hemoglobin as further evolution took place. Duplications sometimes arise during recombination in meiosis, if crossing-over occurs unequally, so that a segment is deleted from one chromosome of a homologous pair and inserted into the other.

Translocations and Inversions. In a translocation, a segment breaks from one chromosome and attaches to another, nonhomologous, chromosome. In many cases, a translocation is reciprocal, meaning that two non-homologous chromosomes exchange segments (see Figure 11.11c). Reciprocal translocations resemble genetic recombination, except that the two chromosomes involved in the exchange do not contain the same genes.

For example, a particular cancer of the human immune system, Burkitt lymphoma, is caused by a translocation that moves a segment of human chromosome 8 to the end of chromosome 14. The break does not interrupt any genes required for normal cell function, but the translocated segment contains a gene that influences cell division. Although this cell division gene is precisely regulated at its normal location, it is overexpressed in the new location. This can result in uncontrolled cell division and the development of a cancer in certain tissues.

In an inversion, a chromosome segment breaks and then reattaches to the same chromosome, but in reverse order (see Figure 11.11d). Inversions have essentially the same effects as translocations—genes may be broken internally by the inversion, with loss of function, or they may be transferred intact to a new location within the same chromosome, producing effects that range from beneficial to harmful.

Inversions and translocations have been important factors in the evolution of plants and some animals, including insects and primates. For example, five of the chromosome pairs of humans show evidence of translocations and inversions that are not present in one of our nearest primate relatives, gorillas. Therefore, the changes must have occurred after the gorilla and human evolutionary lineages split.

11.3b The Number of Entire Chromosomes May Also Change

At times, whole single chromosomes are lost or gained from cells entering or undergoing meiosis, resulting in a change of chromosome number. Most often, these changes occur through **nondisjunction**, the failure of homologous pairs to separate during the first meiotic division, or through misdivision, the failure of chromatids to separate during the second meiotic division (see Chapter 9 and **Figure 11.12**). As a result, products of meiosis are produced that lack one or more chromosomes or contain extra copies of the chromosomes. *Note that failure of homologues to disjoin in meiosis I does not affect meiosis II; chromatids will most likely separate normally in meiosis II.* Fertilization by such gametes produces an individual with extra or missing chromosomes. Such individuals are called **aneuploids**, whereas individuals with a normal set of chromosomes are called **euploids.**

Changes in chromosome number can also occur through duplication of entire sets, meaning individuals may receive one or more extra copies of the entire haploid

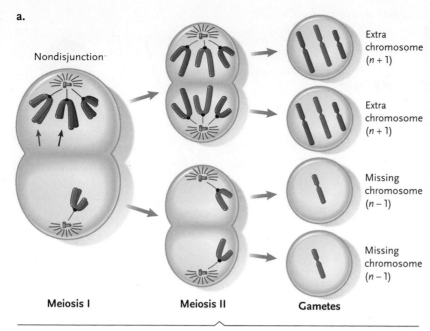

a.

Nondisjunction

Meiosis I   Meiosis II   Gametes

Extra chromosome (*n* + 1)

Extra chromosome (*n* + 1)

Missing chromosome (*n* − 1)

Missing chromosome (*n* − 1)

Nondisjunction during the first meiotic division causes both chromosomes of one pair to be delivered to the same pole of the spindle. The nondisjunction produces two gametes with an extra chromosome and two with a missing chromosome.

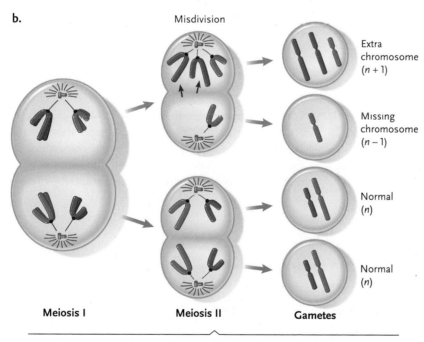

b.

Misdivision

Meiosis I   Meiosis II   Gametes

Extra chromosome (*n* + 1)

Missing chromosome (*n* − 1)

Normal (*n*)

Normal (*n*)

Misdivision during the second meiotic division produces two normal gametes, one gamete with an extra chromosome, and one gamete with a missing chromosome.

Figure 11.12

(a) Nondisjunction during the first meiotic division and **(b)** misdivision during the second meiotic division.

complement of chromosomes. Such individuals are called **polyploids.** *Triploids* have three copies of each chromosome instead of two; *tetraploids* have four copies of each chromosome. Multiples higher than tetraploids also occur.

Aneuploids. The effects of addition or loss of whole chromosomes vary depending on the chromosome and the species. In animals, aneuploidy of autosomes usually

produces debilitating or lethal developmental abnormalities. These abnormalities also occur in humans; addition or loss of an autosomal chromosome causes embryos to develop so abnormally that they are aborted naturally. For reasons that are not understood, aneuploidy is as much as 10 times as frequent in humans as in other mammals. Of human embryos that have been miscarried and examined, about 70% are aneuploids.

In some cases, autosomal aneuploids survive. This is the case with humans who receive an extra copy of chromosome 21—one of the smallest chromosomes **(Figure 11.13a, p. 248).** Many of these individuals survive well into adulthood. The condition produced by the extra chromosome, called *Down syndrome* or *trisomy 21,* is characterized by short stature and some degree of mental retardation. About 40% of individuals with Down syndrome have heart defects, and skeletal development is slower than normal. Most do not mature sexually and remain sterile. However, with attentive care and appropriate educational opportunities, individuals with Down syndrome can successfully participate in many activities.

Most Down syndrome arises from nondisjunction or misdivision of chromosome 21 during meiosis, primarily in women (about 5% of nondisjunctions that lead to Down syndrome occur in men). The nondisjunction occurs more frequently as women age, increasing the chance that a child may be born with the syndrome **(Figure 11.13b, p. 248).** Around the world, about 1 in every 800 children is born with Down syndrome, making it one of the most common serious human genetic defects.

Aneuploidy of sex chromosomes can also arise by nondisjunction or misdivision during meiosis **(Figure 11.14** and **Table 11.1, p. 248).** Unlike autosomal aneuploidy, which usually has drastic effects on survival, altered numbers of X and Y chromosomes are often tolerated, producing individuals who progress through embryonic development and grow to adulthood. In the case of multiple X chromosomes, the X-chromosome inactivation mechanism converts all

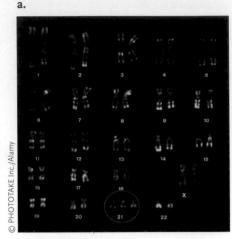

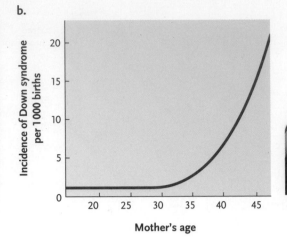

Figure 11.13

Down syndrome. **(a)** The chromosomes of a human female with Down syndrome showing three copies of chromosome 21 (circled in red). **(b)** The incidence of Down syndrome increases with the age of the mother, as determined in a study conducted in Victoria, Australia, between 1942 and 1957.

but one of the X chromosomes to a Barr body, so the dosage of active X-chromosome genes is the same as in normal XX females and XY males. Triple X females may be taller than usual and may be at higher risk for learning disability, reduced muscle tone, and menstrual irregularities.

Because sexual development in humans is pushed toward male or female reproductive organs primarily by the presence or absence of the *SRY* gene on the Y chromosome, people with a Y chromosome are externally malelike, no matter how many X chromosomes are present. If no Y chromosome is present, X chromosomes in various numbers give rise to femalelike individuals. (Table 11.1 lists the effects of some alterations in sex chromosome number.) Similar abnormal combinations of sex chromosomes also occur in other animals, including *Drosophila,* with varying effects on viability.

Polyploids. Polyploidy often originates from failure of the spindle to function normally during mitosis in cell lines leading to germ-line cells. In these divisions, the spindle fails to separate the duplicated chromosomes, which are therefore incorporated into a single nucleus with twice the usual number of chromosomes. Eventually, meiosis

Figure 11.14

Some abnormal combinations of sex chromosomes resulting from nondisjunction of X chromosomes in females.

Table 11.1	Effects of Unusual Combinations of Sex Chromosomes in Humans	
Combination of Sex Chromosomes	**Approximate Frequency**	**Effects**
XO	1 in 5 000 births	Turner syndrome: females with underdeveloped ovaries; sterile; intelligence and external genitalia are normal; typically, individuals are short in stature with underdeveloped breasts
XXY	1 in 2 000 births	Klinefelter syndrome: male external genitalia with very small and underdeveloped testes; sterile; intelligence usually normal; sparse body hair and some development of the breasts; similar characteristics in XXXY and XXXXY individuals
XYY	1 in 1 000 births	XYY syndrome: apparently normal males but often taller than average
XXX	1 in 1 000 births	Triple-X syndrome: apparently normal female with normal or slightly retarded mental function

PEOPLE BEHIND BIOLOGY 11.2

Dr. Irene Ayako Uchida, Professor Emeritus, McMaster University

In the early 1940s, the world was at war and Irene Uchida was studying English literature at the University of British Columbia and writing for a student newspaper. On returning home from a visit to Japan, she was prevented from continuing her studies. Fearing a Japanese invasion, and suspecting the Japanese people living on the Pacific coast to be a threat to national security, the Canadian government forced Uchida's family and thousands of other Japanese-Canadians to relocate to internment camps in the interior of British Columbia. During this difficult time, Uchida was head of a school for the children of internees. She was later able to resume her education, this time at the University of Toronto, where she was encouraged to take up the field of genetics rather than her intended career in social work. Graduating with a Ph.D. in 1951, Uchida became a pioneer in the emerging field of medical cytogenetics and an international authority on the relationship between radiation and trisomies such as 18 and 21 (Down syndrome).

takes place and produces products with two copies of each chromosome instead of one. Fusion of one such gamete with a normal haploid gamete produces a triploid zygote, and fusion of two such gametes produces a tetraploid zygote.

The effects of polyploidy vary widely between plants and animals. In plants, polyploids are often hardier and more successful in growth and reproduction than the diploid plants from which they were derived. As a result, polyploidy is common and has been an important source of variability in plant evolution. About half of all flowering plant species are polyploids, including important crop plants such as wheat and other cereals, cotton, and strawberries. One particularly widespread use of polyploids is in triploid bananas. Since triploid plants have difficulty disjoining homologues properly in meiosis, they are often sterile or, in this case, seedless.

By contrast, polyploidy is uncommon among animals because it usually has lethal effects during embryonic development. For example, in humans, all but about 1% of polyploids die before birth, and the few who are born die within a month. The lethality is probably due to disturbance of animal developmental pathways, which are typically much more complex than those of plants.

We now turn to a description of the effects of altered alleles on human health and development.

STUDY BREAK

What mechanisms are responsible for (a) duplication of a chromosome segment, (b) generation of a Down syndrome individual, (c) a chromosome translocation, and (d) polyploidy?

11.4 Human Genetics and Genetic Counselling

We have already noted a number of human genetic traits and conditions caused by mutant alleles or chromosomal alterations (see **Table 11.2** for a more detailed list). All of

Table 11.2	Examples of Human Genetic Traits
Trait	Adverse Health Effects
Autosomal Recessive Inheritance	
Albinism	Absence of pigmentation (melanin)
Attached earlobes	None
Cystic fibrosis	Excess mucus in lungs and digestive cavities
Sickle cell disease	Severe tissue and organ damage
Galactosemia	Brain, liver, and eye damage
Phenylketonuria	Mental retardation
Tay–Sachs disease	Mental retardation, death
Autosomal Dominant Inheritance	
Free earlobes	None
Achondroplasia	Defective cartilage formation that causes dwarfism
Early balding in males	None
Campodactyly	Rigid, bent small fingers
Curly hair	None
Huntington disease	Progressive, irreversible degeneration of nervous system
Syndactyly	Webbing between fingers
Polydactyly	Extra digits
Brachydactyly	Short digits
Progeria	Premature aging
X-Linked Inheritance	
Hemophilia A	Deficient blood clotting
Red–green colour-blindness	Inability to distinguish red from green
Testicular feminizing syndrome	Absence of male organs, sterility
Changes in Chromosome Structure	
Cri-du-chat	Mental retardation, malformed larynx
Changes in Chromosome Number	
Down syndrome	Mental retardation, heart defects

these traits are of interest as examples of patterns of inheritance that amplify and extend Mendel's basic principles. Those with harmful effects are also important because of their impact on human life and society.

11.4a In Autosomal Recessive Inheritance, Heterozygotes Are Carriers and Homozygous Recessives Are Affected by the Trait

Sickle cell disease and cystic fibrosis are examples of human traits caused by recessive alleles on autosomes. Alleles of these particular traits code for defective proteins that function poorly, if at all. Many other human genetic traits follow a similar pattern of inheritance (see Table 11.2). These traits are passed on according to the pattern known as **autosomal recessive inheritance,** in which individuals who are homozygous for the dominant allele are free of symptoms and are not carriers; heterozygotes are usually symptom free but are carriers. People who are homozygous for the recessive allele show the trait.

Between 10% and 15% of African Americans in the United States are carriers of sickle cell disease—that is, they have the sickle cell trait (see Section 10.2f). Although carriers make enough normal hemoglobin through the activity of the dominant allele to be essentially unaffected, the mutant, sickle cell form of the hemoglobin molecule is also present in their red blood cells. Carriers can be identified by a simple test for the mutant hemoglobin. In countries where malaria is common, including several countries in Africa, sickle cell carriers are less susceptible to contracting malaria, which helps explain the increased proportions of the recessive allele among races that originated in malarial areas.

Cystic fibrosis, one of the most common genetic disorders among people of Northern European descent, is another autosomal recessive trait **(Figure 11.15).** About 1 in every 25 people from this line of descent is an unaffected carrier with one copy of the recessive allele, and about 1 in 2 500 is homozygous for the recessive allele. The homozygous recessives have an altered membrane transport protein that results in excess Cl⁻ (chloride ions) in the extracellular fluids. Through pathways that are not completely understood, the alteration in chloride transport causes thick, sticky mucus to collect in airways of the lungs, in the ducts of glands such as the pancreas, and in the digestive tract. The accumulated mucus impairs body functions and, in the lungs, promotes pneumonia and other infections. With current management procedures, the life expectancy for a person with cystic fibrosis is about 40 years. The prevalence of cystic fibrosis alleles may have a similar explanation to those for sickle cell disease; heterozygotes may enjoy some resistance to infectious diseases such as tuberculosis or cholera.

Another autosomal recessive disease, *phenylketonuria* (PKU), appears in about 1 of every 15 000 births.

© Kristiina Paul

Figure 11.15
A child affected by cystic fibrosis. Daily chest thumps, back thumps, and repositioning dislodge thick mucus that collects in airways to the lungs.

Affected individuals cannot produce an enzyme that converts the amino acid phenylalanine to another amino acid, tyrosine. As a result, phenylalanine builds up in the blood and is converted into other products, including phenylpyruvate. Elevations in both phenylalanine and phenylpyruvate damage brain tissue and can lead to mental retardation. However, if diagnosed early enough, an affected infant can be placed on a phenylalanine-restricted diet, which can prevent the PKU symptoms. Screening newborns for PKU is routine in the developed world and is becoming more established in the developing world as well. This is a wonderful example of how the expression of a genetic trait can be influenced by the environment.

You may have seen warnings on certain foods and drinks for phenylketonuriacs (individuals with PKU) not to use them. This is because they contain the artificial sweetener aspartame (trade name NutraSweet). Aspartame is a small molecule consisting of the amino acids aspartic acid and phenylalanine. Aspartame binds to taste receptors, signalling that the substance is sweet. Once ingested, aspartame is broken down and phenylalanine is released in amounts that might be harmful for people with PKU.

11.4b In Autosomal Dominant Inheritance, Only Homozygous Recessives Are Unaffected

Some human traits follow a pattern of **autosomal dominant inheritance** (see Table 11.2). In this case, the allele that causes the trait is dominant, and people who are either homozygous or heterozygous for the dominant

FOCUS ON RESEARCH 11.3
Achondroplastic Dwarfing by a Single Amino Acid Change

Researchers recently found that the gene responsible for achondroplastic dwarfing is on chromosome 4.

The gene codes for a receptor that binds the *fibroblast growth factor (FGF)*, a growth hormone that stimulates a wide range of mammalian cells to grow and divide. This fibroblast growth factor receptor (FGFR) gene is active in chondrocytes—cells that form cartilage and bone.

Arnold Munnich and his colleagues isolated the gene that encodes the FGFR and obtained its DNA sequence. They found two versions of the gene's sequence with a single difference—one version had an adenine–thymine (A-T) base pair and the other had a guanine–cytosine (G-C) base pair at the same position in the DNA sequence. The change substitutes arginine for glycine at one position in the amino acid sequence of the encoded protein. Arginine and glycine have very different chemical properties. The substitution occurs in a segment of the protein that extends across the membrane, connecting a hormone-binding site outside the cell with a site inside the cell that triggers the internal response.

The investigators then looked for the A-T–to–G-C substitution in the mutant form of the gene on chromosome 4 that causes achondroplastic dwarfing. The substitution was present in copies of the gene isolated from 6 families of achondroplastic dwarfs but absent in 120 people who lack the trait. This result supported the hypothesis that a mutant allele of the FGFR on chromosome 4 is responsible for achondroplastic dwarfism.

How does the single amino acid substitution cause dwarfing? The cause is not known exactly. The change may inhibit the transmission of the signal triggered by a hormone binding to the receptor on the outer membrane. As a result, chondrocytes divide improperly and inhibit normal elongation of the limb bones. This helps explain why the achondroplasia mutation is dominant.

Identification of the gene responsible for achondroplastic dwarfing opens the future to finding a cure for the condition, possibly through gene therapy for infants or young children who carry the mutation.

allele are affected. Individuals homozygous for the recessive normal allele are unaffected.

Achondroplasia, a type of dwarfing that occurs in about 1 in 10 000 people, is caused by an autosomal dominant allele of a gene on chromosome 4. Of individuals with the dominant allele, only heterozygotes survive embryonic development; homozygous dominants are usually stillborn. When limb bones develop in heterozygous children, cartilage formation is defective, leading to disproportionately short arms and legs. The trunk and head, however, are of normal size. Affected adults are usually not much more than 122 cm tall. Achondroplastic dwarfs are of normal intelligence, are fertile, and can have children.

11.4c Males Are More Likely to Be Affected by X-Linked Recessive Traits

Red–green colour-blindness (**Figure 11.16, p. 252**) and hemophilia have already been presented as examples of human traits that demonstrate **X-linked recessive inheritance**, that is, traits due to inheritance of recessive alleles carried on the X chromosome. Another X-linked recessive human disease trait is Duchenne muscular dystrophy. In affected individuals, muscle tissue begins to degenerate late in childhood; by the onset of puberty, most individuals with this disease are unable to walk. Muscular weakness progresses, with later involvement of the heart muscle; the average life expectancy for individuals with Duchenne muscular dystrophy is 25 years.

11.4d Human Genetic Disorders Can Be Predicted, and Many Can Be Treated

Each year, roughly 8 million children around the world are born with a severe disease or disability with a significant genetic component. The rate of such births in middle- and low-income countries is double that for high-income countries. Why might this be? One contributing factor has already been mentioned: in areas where malaria is endemic, the frequency of the sickle cell allele tends to be higher and the incidence of newborn sickle cell disease is higher. Nutritional deficiencies, consanguinous (blood relative) marriage practices, and higher numbers of children born to older mothers may also elevate birth defect rates in certain societies. In addition to improvements in basic financial, health, and nutritional standards, programs offering genetic counselling, prenatal diagnosis, and genetic screening can help reduce the suffering associated with genetic disorders.

Genetic counselling allows prospective parents to assess the possibility that they might have an affected child. For example, parents may seek counselling if they, a close relative, or one of their existing children has a genetic disorder. Genetic counselling begins with identification of parental genotypes through family pedigrees or direct testing for an altered protein or DNA sequence. With this information in hand, counsellors can often predict the chances of having a child with the trait in question. Couples can then make an informed decision about whether to have a child.

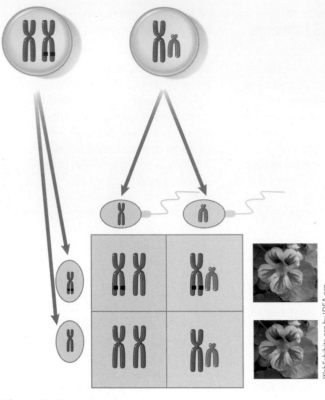

Figure 11.16
Punnett square showing sex-linked recessive inheritance of colour-blindness in humans. Note that the mother carries the defective allele on one of her X chromosomes but is unaffected. Half of her daughters will be carriers and half of her sons will be colour-blind. Images indicate how the normal and colour-blind sons perceive a particular flower and leaves.

WebExhibits.org by IDEA.org

Genetic counselling is often combined with techniques of **prenatal diagnosis**, in which cells derived from a developing embryo or its surrounding tissues or fluids are tested for the presence of mutant alleles or chromosomal alterations. In **amniocentesis**, cells are obtained from the amniotic fluid—the watery fluid surrounding the embryo in the mother's uterus **(Figure 11.17)**. In **chorionic villus sampling**, cells are obtained from portions of the placenta that develop from tissues of the embryo. More than 100 genetic disorders can now be detected by these tests. If prenatal diagnosis detects a serious genetic defect, the prospective parents can reach an informed decision about whether to continue the pregnancy, including religious and moral considerations, as well as genetic and medical advice.

Once a child is born, inherited disorders are identified by **genetic screening**, in which biochemical or molecular tests for disorders are routinely applied to children and adults or to newborn infants in hospitals. The tests can detect inherited disorders early enough to start any available preventive measures before symptoms develop. As mentioned previously, worldwide newborn screening for PKU identifies affected children in time for them to avoid the debilitating symptoms of this disease. The first generation of people to survive childhood with PKU are now adults.

The characters and traits described so far in this chapter all depend on genes carried by chromosomes in the nucleus. But what of the genes located on DNA in mitochondria and chloroplasts? The following section addresses such interesting cases.

Figure 11.17
Amniocentesis, a procedure used for prenatal diagnosis of genetic defects. The procedure is complicated and costly, and, therefore, it is used primarily in high-risk cases.

In amniocentesis, a syringe needle is inserted carefully through the uterine wall and a sample of amniotic fluid is taken. The procedure is generally performed before 12 weeks of development because of the risk to the fetus. Cells from the fetus in the extracted fluid are analyzed for genetic defects or chromosomal mutations.

Embryo and fetus develop surrounded by amniotic fluid to cushion it against shock

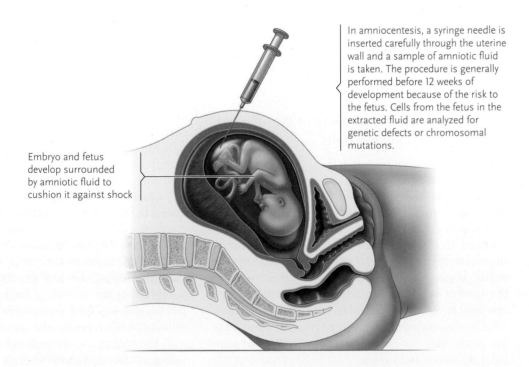

11.5 Nontraditional Patterns of Inheritance

We consider two examples of nontraditional patterns of inheritance in this section. In **cytoplasmic inheritance**, the pattern of inheritance follows that of genes in the cytoplasmic organelles: mitochondria or chloroplasts. In **genomic imprinting**, the expression of an allele of a particular nuclear gene is based on whether an individual organism inherits the allele from the male or female parent.

11.5a Cytoplasmic Inheritance Follows the Pattern of Inheritance of Mitochondria or Chloroplasts

Organelle DNA contains genes and alleles that, like nuclear genes, are also subject to being mutated. Mutant genes in some cases result in altered phenotypes, but the inheritance pattern of these mutant genes is fundamentally different from that of mutant genes carried on chromosomes in the nucleus. The two major differences are as follows: (1) ratios typical of Mendelian segregation are *not* found because genes are not segregating by meiosis, and (2) genes usually show uniparental inheritance from generation to generation. In *uniparental inheritance,* all progeny (both males and females) inherit the genotype of only one of the parents. For most multicellular eukaryotes, the mother's genotype is passed on in a phenomenon called *maternal inheritance.* Maternal inheritance occurs because the amount of cytoplasm in the female gamete usually far exceeds that in the male gamete. Hence, a zygote receives most of its cytoplasm, including mitochondria and (in plants) chloroplasts, from the female ("egg" parent) and little from the male parent.

CONCEPT FIX Many people believe that they inherit half of their DNA from each of their parents. Although this idea is roughly true for nuclear DNA, recall that mitochondria also contain DNA and they are inherited exclusively from mothers. You have considerably more of your mother's DNA than your father's.

In humans, several inherited diseases have been traced to mutations in mitochondrial genes **(Table 11.3).** Recall that the mitochondrion plays a critical role in synthesizing adenosine triphosphate (ATP), the energy source for many cellular reactions. The mutations producing the diseases in Table 11.3 are in mitochondrial

Table 11.3	Some Human Diseases Caused by Mutations in Mitochondrial Genes
Disease	**Symptoms**
Kearns–Sayre syndrome	May include muscle weakness, mental deficiencies, abnormal heartbeat, short stature
Leber hereditary optic neuropathy	Vision loss from degeneration of the optic nerve, abnormal heartbeat
Mitochondrial myopathy and encephalomyopathy	May include seizures, strokelike episodes, hearing loss, progressive dementia, abnormal heartbeat, short stature
Myoclonic epilepsy	Vision and hearing loss, uncoordinated movement, jerking of limbs, progressive dementia, heart defects

genes that encode components of the ATP-generating system of the organelle. The resulting mitochondrial defects are especially destructive to the organ systems most dependent on mitochondrial reactions for energy: the central nervous system, skeletal and cardiac muscle, the liver, and the kidneys. These inherited diseases show maternal inheritance.

11.5b In Gene Imprinting, the Allele Inherited from One of the Parents Is Expressed whereas the Other Allele Is Silent

Genomic imprinting is a phenomenon in which the expression of an allele of a gene is determined by the parent that contributed it. In some cases, the paternally derived allele is expressed; in others, the maternally derived allele is expressed. The silent allele—the one that is not expressed—is called the *imprinted allele.* The imprinted allele is not inactivated by mutation. Rather, it is silenced by chemical modification (methylation) of certain bases in its sequence.

As an example of how imprinting is involved in human disease, Prader–Willi syndrome (PWS) and Angelman syndrome (AS) in humans are each caused by genomic imprinting of a particular gene on a chromosome inherited from one parent, coincident with deletion of the same gene on the homologous chromosome inherited from the other parent. The syndromes differ with respect to the gene imprinted. Both PWS and AS occur in about 1 in 15 000 births and are characterized by serious developmental, mental, and behavioural problems. PWS individuals are compulsive overeaters (leading to obesity), have short stature, have small hands and feet, and show mild to moderate mental retardation. AS individuals are hyperactive, are unable to speak, have seizures, show severe mental retardation, and display a happy disposition with bursts of laughter.

How is genomic imprinting responsible for these two syndromes? PWS is caused when an individual has a normal maternally derived chromosome 15 and a paternally derived chromosome 15 with a deletion of a small region of several genes that includes the PWS gene. The PWS gene is imprinted, and therefore silenced, on maternally derived chromosomes. As a result, when there is no PWS gene on the paternally derived chromosome, there is no PWS gene activity and PWS results. Similarly, AS is caused when an individual has a normal paternally derived chromosome 15 and a maternally derived chromosome 15 with a deletion of the same region; that region also includes the AS gene, the normal function of which is also required for normal development. In this case, genomic imprinting silences the AS gene on the paternally derived chromosome, and because there is no AS gene on the maternally derived chromosome, there is no AS gene activity and AS syndrome develops.

CONCEPT FIX Although imprinted traits can show a *parent of origin effect,* imprinting is not the same as sex-linkage. Imprinted traits are not necessarily carried on sex chromosomes and any given sex-linked allele can be inherited from either a mother or a father. ⬡

The mechanism of imprinting involves the modification of the DNA in the region that controls the expression of a gene by the addition of methyl ($-CH_3$) groups to cytosine nucleotides. The methylation of the control region of a gene usually prevents it from being expressed. The regulation of gene expression by methylation of DNA is discussed further in Section 14.2c. Genomic imprinting occurs in the gametes where the allele destined to be inactive in the new embryo after fertilization—either the father's or the mother's, depending on the gene—is methylated. That methylated (silenced) state of the gene is passed on as the cells grow and divide to produce the somatic (body) cells of the organism.

A number of cancers are associated with the failure to imprint genes. For instance, the mammalian *Igf2* (insulin growth factor 2) gene encodes a growth factor, a molecule that stimulates cells to grow and divide. *Igf2* is an imprinted gene, with the paternally derived allele "on" and the maternally derived allele "off." In some cases, the imprinting mechanism for this gene does not work, resulting in both alleles of *Igf2* being active, a phenomenon known as **loss of imprinting.** The resulting double dose of the growth factor disrupts the cell division cycle, increasing the risk of uncontrolled growth and cancer.

In this chapter, we have discussed genes and the role of chromosomes in inheritance. In the next chapter, we will turn to the molecular structure and function of the genetic material and learn about the molecular mechanism by which DNA is replicated.

STUDY BREAK

Which inheritance pattern would suggest that a trait is coded by the mitochondrial genome?

Review

Access an interactive eBook, chapter-specific interactive learning tools, including flashcards, quizzes, videos, and more in your Biology **CourseMate**, accessed through NelsonBrain.com **Aplia™** is an online interactive learning solution that helps you improve comprehension—and your grade—by integrating a variety of mediums and tools such as videos, tutorials, practice tests, and an interactive eBook.

11.1 Genetic Linkage and Recombination

- Genes consist of sequences of nucleotides in DNA and are arranged linearly in chromosomes.

- Genes carried on the same chromosome are linked together in their transmission from parent to offspring. Linked genes are inherited in patterns similar to those of single genes, except for changes in the linkage due to recombination (see Figure 11.2).

- As a result of recombination, the order of a particular collection of alleles linked on any given chromosome is mixed up as a result of exchange with corresponding alleles on the other homologous chromosome. The exchanges occur while homologues pair during prophase I of meiosis.

- The likelihood of recombination between any two genes located on the same chromosome pair reflects the physical distance between them on the chromosome. The greater this distance, the greater the chance that chromatids will exchange segments at points between the genes and the greater the frequency of recombinant products of meiosis (gametes in animals, spores in plants).

- The relationship between separation and recombinant offspring frequencies is used to produce chromosome maps in which

genes are assigned relative locations with respect to each other (see Figure 11.4).

- Testcrosses ($AaBb \times aabb$) can be used to detect linkage. If all progeny classes are equally frequent, then the genes are not linked.

- Genes carried on the same chromosome may not show genetic linkage (i.e., assort independently) if they are quite far apart.

11.2 Sex-Linked Genes

- Sex linkage is a pattern of inheritance produced by genes carried on sex chromosomes: chromosomes that differ between males and females. Sex-linked inheritance patterns arise because, in humans and fruit flies, females have two copies of the X chromosome and therefore two alleles for each gene. Males have only one copy of the X chromosome and therefore only one allele for each gene. Only males have an allele for genes carried on the Y chromosome.

- Sex linkage is suggested by a particular, non-Mendelian pattern of inheritance when the progeny of reciprocal crosses are different (see Figure 11.8).

- Since males have only one X chromosome, any recessive alleles that they inherit on that X chromosome will be expressed. Females must receive two copies of the recessive allele, one from each parent, to develop the trait (see Figures 11.6–11.8).

- In mammals, inactivation of one of the two X chromosomes in cells of the female makes the dosage of X-linked genes the same in males and females (see Figure 11.10).

- Parents can influence the expression of certain alleles in their offspring through DNA methylation called imprinting.

11.3 Chromosomal Alterations That Affect Inheritance

- Inheritance is influenced by processes that delete, duplicate, or invert segments within chromosomes or translocate segments between chromosomes (see Figure 11.11).

- Chromosomes also change in number by addition or removal of individual chromosomes or entire sets of chromosomes. Changes in single chromosomes usually occur through nondisjunction, in which homologous pairs fail to separate during meiosis I, or by misdivision when sister chromatids fail to separate during meiosis II. As a result, one set of meiotic products receives an extra copy of a chromosome and the other set is deprived of the chromosome.

- Polyploids have one or more extra copies of the entire chromosome set. Polyploids usually arise when the spindle fails to function during meiosis in cell lines leading to gamete formation, producing zygotes that contain double the number of chromosomes typical for the species (see Figures 11.12–11.14).

11.4 Human Genetics and Genetic Counselling

- Three modes of inheritance are most significant in human heredity: autosomal recessive, autosomal dominant, and X-linked recessive inheritance.

- In autosomal recessive inheritance, males or females carry a recessive allele on an autosome. Heterozygotes are carriers that are usually unaffected, but homozygous individuals show symptoms of the trait. Affected children born to unaffected parents suggest autosomal recessive inheritance.

- In autosomal dominant inheritance, a dominant gene is carried on an autosome. Individuals that are homozygous or heterozygous for the trait show symptoms of the trait; homozygous recessives are normal.

- In X-linked recessive inheritance, a recessive allele for the trait is carried on the X chromosome. Male individuals with the recessive allele on their X chromosome or female individuals with the recessive allele on both X chromosomes show symptoms of the trait. Heterozygous females are carriers but usually show no symptoms of the trait.

- Genetic counselling, based on identification of parental genotypes by constructing family pedigrees and prenatal diagnosis, allows prospective parents to reach an informed decision about whether to have a child or continue a pregnancy.

11.5 Nontraditional Patterns of Inheritance

- Cytoplasmic inheritance depends on genes carried on DNA in mitochondria or chloroplasts. Cytoplasmic inheritance follows the maternal line: it parallels the inheritance of the cytoplasm in fertilization, in which most or all of the cytoplasm of the zygote originates from the egg cell. That is, all of the offspring of affected mothers would be affected; none of the offspring of affected fathers would be affected.

- Genomic imprinting is a phenomenon in which the expression of an allele of a gene is determined by the parent that contributed it. In some cases, the allele inherited from the father is expressed; in others, the allele from the mother is expressed. The silencing of the other allele is often the result of methylation of the region adjacent to the gene tha is responsible for controlling the expression of that gene.

Questions

Self-Test Questions

1. In humans, red–green colour-blindness is an X-linked recessive trait. If a man with normal vision and a colour-blind woman have a son, what is the chance that the son will be colour-blind? What is the chance that a daughter will be colour-blind?

2. The following pedigree shows the pattern of inheritance of red–green colour-blindness in a family. Females are shown as circles and males as squares; the squares or circles of individuals affected by the trait are filled in black.

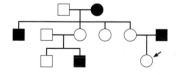

What is the chance that a son of the third-generation female indicated by the arrow will be colour-blind if the father is a normal man? If the father is colour-blind?

3. Individuals affected by a condition known as polydactyly have extra fingers or toes. The following pedigree shows the pattern of inheritance of this trait in one family:

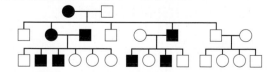

From the pedigree, can you tell if polydactyly comes from a dominant or recessive allele? Is the trait sex linked? As far as you can determine, what is the genotype of each person in the pedigree with respect to the trait?

4. A number of genes carried on the same chromosome are tested and show the following crossover frequencies. What is their sequence in the map of the chromosome?

Genes	Crossover Frequencies between Them
C and A	7%
B and D	3%
B and A	4%
C and D	6%
C and B	3%

5. In *Drosophila*, two genes, one for body colour and one for eye colour, are carried on the same chromosome. The wild-type grey body colour is dominant to black body colour, and wild-type red eyes are dominant to purple eyes. You make a cross between a fly with a grey body and red eyes and a fly with a black body and purple eyes. Among the offspring, about half have grey bodies and red eyes and half have black bodies and purple eyes. A small percentage have (a) black bodies and red eyes or (b) grey bodies and purple eyes. Which alleles are carried together on the chromosomes in each of the flies used in the cross? Which alleles are carried together on the

chromosomes of the F₁ flies with black bodies and red eyes, and those with grey bodies and purple eyes?

6. Another gene in *Drosophila* determines wing length. The dominant wild-type allele of this gene produces long wings; a recessive allele produces vestigial (short) wings. A female that is true-breeding for red eyes and long wings is mated with a male that has purple eyes and vestigial wings. F₁ females are then crossed with purple-eyed, vestigial-winged males. From this second cross, a total of 600 offspring are obtained with the following combinations of traits:

    252 with red eyes and long wings
    276 with purple eyes and vestigial wings
     42 with red eyes and vestigial wings
     30 with purple eyes and long wings

Are the genes linked, unlinked, or sex linked? If they are linked, how many map units separate them on the chromosome?

Drosophila with vestigial wings

7. One human gene, which is suspected to be carried on the Y chromosome, controls the length of hair on men's ears. One allele produces nonhairy ears, and another produces hairy ears. If a man with hairy ears has sons, what percentage will also have hairy ears? What percentage of his daughters will have hairy ears?

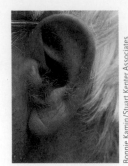

Male with hairy ears

8. You conduct a cross in *Drosophila* that produces only half as many male as female offspring. What might you suspect as a cause?

Questions for Discussion

1. Can a linkage map be made for a haploid organism that reproduces sexually?

2. Crossing-over does not occur between any pair of homologous chromosomes during meiosis in male *Drosophila*. From what you have learned about meiosis and crossing-over, propose one hypothesis for why this might be the case.

3. Even though X inactivation occurs in XXY (Klinefelter syndrome) humans, they do not have the same phenotype as normal XY males. Similarly, even though X inactivation occurs in XX individuals, they do not have the same phenotype as XO (Turner syndrome) humans. Why might this be the case?

4. All mammals have evolved from a common ancestor. However, the chromosome number varies among mammals. By what mechanism might this have occurred?

5. Assume that genes *a*, *b*, *c*, *d*, *e*, and *f* are linked. Explain how you would construct a linkage map that shows the order of these six genes and the map units between them.

A digital model of DNA (based on data generated by X-ray crystallography).

STUDY PLAN

12.1 Establishing DNA as the Hereditary Molecule

12.1a Experiments Began When Griffith Found a Substance That Could Genetically Transform Pneumonia Bacteria

12.1b Avery and His Coworkers Identified DNA as the Molecule That Transforms Avirulent Rough *Streptococcus* to the Virulent Smooth Form

12.1c Hershey and Chase Found the Final Evidence Establishing DNA as the Hereditary Molecule

12.2 DNA Structure

12.2a Watson and Crick Brought Together Information from Several Sources to Work Out DNA Structure

12.2b The New Model Proposed That Two Polynucleotide Chains Wind into a DNA Double Helix

12.3 DNA Replication

12.3a Meselson and Stahl Showed That DNA Replication Is Semiconservative

12.3b DNA Polymerases Are the Primary Enzymes of DNA Replication

12.3c Helicases Unwind DNA for New DNA Synthesis, and Other Proteins Stabilize the DNA at the Replication Fork

12.3d RNA Primers Provide the Starting Point for DNA Polymerase to Begin Synthesizing a New DNA Chain

12.3e One New DNA Strand Is Synthesized Continuously; the Other, Discontinuously

12.3f Multiple Enzymes Coordinate Their Activities in DNA Replication

12.3g Multiple Replication Origins Enable Rapid Replication of Large Chromosomes

12.3h Telomerases Solve a Special Replication Problem at the Ends of Linear DNA Molecules in Eukaryotes

12.4 Mechanisms That Correct Replication Errors

12.4a Proofreading Depends on the Ability of DNA Polymerases to Reverse and Remove Mismatched Bases

12.4b DNA Repair Corrects Errors That Escape Proofreading

12.5 DNA Organization in Eukaryotic versus Prokaryotic Cells

12.5a Histones Pack Eukaryotic DNA at Successive Levels of Organization

12.5b Many Nonhistone Proteins Have Key Roles in the Regulation of Gene Expression

12.5c DNA Is Organized More Simply in Prokaryotes than in Eukaryotes

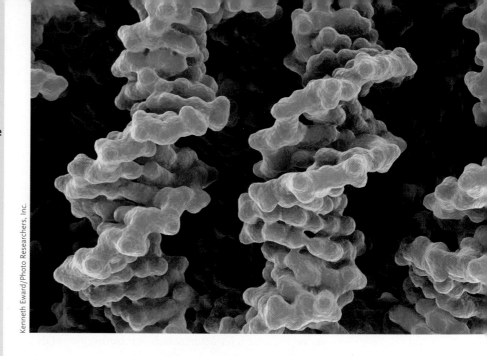

Kenneth Eward/Photo Researchers, Inc.

12 DNA Structure, Replication, and Organization

WHY IT MATTERS

Imagine a scene 40 000 years ago in what is now called the Drachenlock Cave in Switzerland. Flickering torchlight reflects from a collection of large bear skulls as a Neanderthal shaman arranges one, then the next, to face toward the entrance to the cave. Now fast-forward to the present to find cave bear bones and teeth once again carefully arranged by human hands, this time on the bench of a modern, ultraclean research laboratory. The scientist is completely covered by a protective gown, gloves, and a face mask. The surface of the specimens is bleached and irradiated with high-intensity ultraviolet light. A small drill bores into the interior of a molar tooth, where researchers hope to recover ancient DNA (aDNA) from *Ursus spelaeus,* a long-extinct relative of modern bears.

As much as characterization of aDNA sequences promises to enhance our understanding of the genetic history and composition of modern populations, this field is overshadowed by two significant problems: DNA damage and contamination. The double helix of DNA is subject to breakages in one or both strands in addition to inappropriate cross-linking and chemical modification of individual bases. Living cells very successfully prevent or repair most of this DNA damage, but post-mortem degradation can be extensive after thousands of years. Sustained cold temperatures preserve aDNA relatively well, facilitating successful recovery of sequences from frozen mammoths and bison in permafrost, penguins in ice, and the human "Ice Man" frozen in a glacier. Ancient bacterial DNA sequences have been recovered from 500 000-year-old sections of ice cores.

The natural degradation of DNA over time usually means that aDNA sequences remaining in a given tissue sample are very rare and therefore prone to contamination by DNA from modern or ancient sources—hence the need for ultraclean laboratories, decontamination procedures, and authentication protocols. Suspicions of contamination have clouded some of the most dramatic reports of aDNA recovery from specimens 10 to 100 million years old.

As the future brings better techniques for the recovery and characterization of authentic aDNA sequences on Earth, we will undoubtedly turn these skills toward the search for evidence of past or present life on other planets. The Martian polar ice caps are very cold and very persistent, providing ideal conditions for preservation of DNA from any organisms that may have inhabited the Red Planet in the past.

Our current ability to find, characterize, and manipulate DNA arises ultimately from the work of a Swiss physician and physiological chemist, Johann Friedrich Miescher. In 1868, Miescher was engaged in a study of the composition of the cell nucleus. He collected pus cells from discarded bandages and extracted large quantities of an acidic substance with a high phosphorus content. He called the unusual substance *nuclein*. Nuclein is now known by its modern name, **deoxyribonucleic acid**, or **DNA**, the molecule that is the genetic material of all living organisms and, as indicated by ancient DNA studies, all extinct organisms as well.

At the time of Miescher's discovery, scientists knew nothing about the molecular basis of heredity and very little about genetics. Although Mendel had already published the results of his genetic experiments with garden peas, the significance of his findings was not widely known or appreciated. It was not known which chemical substance in cells actually carries the instructions for reproducing parental traits in offspring. Not until 1952, more than 80 years after Miescher's discovery, did scientists fully recognize that the hereditary molecule was DNA.

After DNA was established as the hereditary molecule, the focus of research changed to the three-dimensional structure of DNA. Among the scientists striving to work out the structure were James D. Watson, a young American postdoctoral student at Cambridge University in England, and the Englishman Francis H.C. Crick, then a graduate student at Cambridge University. Using chemical and physical information about DNA, in particular Rosalind Franklin's analysis of the arrangement of atoms in DNA, the

Figure 12.1

James D. Watson and Francis H.C. Crick demonstrating their 1953 model for DNA structure, which revolutionized the biological sciences.

two investigators assembled molecular models from pieces of cardboard and bits of wire. Eventually, they constructed a model for DNA that fit all the known data **(Figure 12.1)**. Their discovery was of momentous importance in biology. The model enabled scientists to understand key processes in cells for the first time in terms of the structure and interaction of molecules. For example, the model immediately made it possible to understand how genetic information is stored in the structure of DNA and how DNA replicates. Unquestionably, the discovery launched a molecular revolution within biology, making it possible for the first time to relate the genetic traits of living organisms to a universal molecular code present in the DNA of every cell. In addition, Watson and Crick's discovery opened the way for numerous advances in fields such as medicine, forensics, pharmacology, and agriculture and eventually gave rise to the current rapid growth of the biotechnology industry.

12.1 Establishing DNA as the Hereditary Molecule

In the first half of the twentieth century, many scientists believed that proteins were the most likely candidates for the hereditary molecules because they appeared to offer greater opportunities for information coding than did nucleic acids. That is, proteins contain 20 types of amino acids, whereas nucleic acids have only 4 different nitrogenous bases available for coding. Other scientists believed that nucleic acids were the hereditary molecules. In this section, we describe the experiments showing that DNA, not protein, is the genetic material.

12.1a Experiments Began When Griffith Found a Substance That Could Genetically Transform Pneumonia Bacteria

In 1928, Frederick Griffith, a British medical officer, observed an interesting phenomenon in his experiments with the bacterium *Streptococcus pneumoniae,* which causes a severe form of pneumonia in mammals. Griffith was trying to make a vaccine to prevent pneumonia infections in the epidemics that occurred after World War I. He used two strains of the bacterium in his attempts. The smooth strain, *S,* has a polysaccharide capsule surrounding each cell and forms colonies that appear smooth and glossy when grown on a culture plate. When he injected the *S* strain into mice, it was virulent (highly infective, or pathogenic), causing pneumonia and killing the mice in a day or two (**Figure 12.2,** step 1). The rough strain, *R,* does not have a polysaccharide capsule and forms colonies with a nonshiny, rough appearance. When Griffith injected the *R* strain into mice, it was avirulent (not infective, or nonpathogenic); the mice lived (step 2). Evidently, the capsule was responsible for the virulence of the *S* strain. We now know that the capsule hinders the ability of the host's immune system to detect the *Streptococcus* cells. The smooth strain could therefore live long enough to multiply and cause fatal pneumonia.

If Griffith killed the *S* bacteria by heating before injecting them into the mice, the mice remained healthy (step 3). However, quite unexpectedly, Griffith found that if he injected living *R* bacteria along with the heat-killed *S* bacteria, many of the mice died (step 4). Also, he was able to isolate living *S* bacteria with polysaccharide capsules from the infected mice. In some way, living *R* bacteria had acquired the ability to make the polysaccharide capsule from the dead *S* bacteria, and they had changed—transformed—into virulent *S* cells. The transformed bacteria were altered permanently; the smooth, infective trait was stably inherited by the descendants of the transformed bacteria. Griffith called the conversion of *R* bacteria to *S* bacteria *transformation* and the agent responsible the *transforming principle.* What was the nature of the molecule responsible for the transformation? Carbohydrates, lipids, proteins, and nucleic acids are the four main types of biological macromolecules. The structure of carbohydrates and lipids tends to be highly repetitive and therefore not very likely to carry information. However, proteins and nucleic acids are built of various combinations of different amino acids and nucleotides, respectively. This gives them a complexity of structure that makes them likely candidates for carrying the information needed for transformation.

QUESTION: What is the nature of the genetic material?

EXPERIMENT: Frederick Griffith studied the conversion of a nonvirulent (noninfective) *R* form of the bacterium *Streptococcus pneumoniae* to a virulent (infective) *S* form. The *S* form has a capsule surrounding the cell, giving colonies of it on a laboratory dish a smooth, shiny appearance. The *R* form has no capsule, so the colonies have a rough, nonshiny appearance. Griffith injected the bacteria into mice and determined how the mice were infected.

1. Mice injected with live *S* cells (control to show effect of *S* cells)

2. Mice injected with live *R* cells (control to show effect of *R* cells)

RESULT: Mice die. Live *S* cells in their blood; shows that *S* cells are virulent.

RESULT: Mice live. No live *R* cells in their blood; shows that *R* cells are nonvirulent. Evidently the capsule is responsible for virulence of the *S* strain.

3. Mice injected with heat-killed *S* cells (control to show effect of dead *S* cells)

4. Mice injected with heat-killed *S* cells plus live *R* cells

RESULT: Mice live. No live *S* cells in their blood; shows that live *S* cells are necessary to be virulent to mice.

RESULT: Mice die. Live *S* cells in their blood; shows that living *R* cells can be converted to virulent *S* cells with some factor from dead *S* cells.

CONCLUSION: Griffith concluded that some molecules released when *S* cells were killed could change living nonvirulent *R* cells genetically to the virulent *S* form. He called the molecule the *transforming principle* and the process of genetic change *transformation.*

Figure 12.2
Griffith's experiment with infective and noninfective strains of *Streptococcus pneumoniae.*

12.1b Avery and His Coworkers Identified DNA as the Molecule That Transforms Avirulent Rough *Streptococcus* to the Virulent Smooth Form

In the 1940s, Oswald Avery, a physician and medical researcher at the hospital at the Rockefeller Institute for Medical Research in New York, and his coworkers Colin MacLeod and Maclyn McCarty performed an experiment designed to identify the chemical nature of the transforming principle that can change the avirulent *Rough* form of *Streptococcus* bacteria into the infective *Smooth* form. Rather than working with mice, they attempted to reproduce the transformation using bacteria growing in culture tubes. They used heat to kill virulent *S* bacteria and then treated the macromolecules extracted from the cells with enzymes that break down each of the three main candidate molecules for the hereditary material—protein; DNA; and the other nucleic acid, ribonucleic acid (RNA). When they destroyed proteins or RNA, the researchers saw no effect; the extract of *S* bacteria still transformed *R* bacteria into virulent *S* bacteria—the cells had polysaccharide capsules and produced smooth colonies on culture plates. When they destroyed DNA, however, no transformation occurred—no smooth colonies were seen on culture plates.

In 1944, Avery and his colleagues published their discovery that the transforming principle was DNA. At the time, many scientists firmly believed that the genetic material was protein. So although their findings were clearly revolutionary, Avery and his colleagues presented their conclusions in the paper cautiously, offering several interpretations of their results. Although some scientists accepted these data almost immediately, others remained unconvinced. After all, it seemed unlikely that a molecule like DNA, with only four different components (adenine, thymine, cytosine, and guanine), could hold the complex information required of the genetic material in a cell. Protein, with its 20 different amino acid components, seemed a far superior medium for coding information. Those who believed that the genetic material was protein argued that it was possible that not all protein was destroyed by Avery's enzyme treatments, and, as contaminants in their DNA transformation reaction, these remaining proteins were, in fact, responsible for the transformation. Further experiments were needed to convince all scientists that DNA is the hereditary molecule.

12.1c Hershey and Chase Found the Final Evidence Establishing DNA as the Hereditary Molecule

A final series of elegant experiments conducted in 1952 by bacteriologist Alfred D. Hershey and his laboratory assistant Martha Chase at the Cold Spring Harbor Laboratory removed any remaining doubts that DNA is the hereditary molecule. Hershey and Chase studied the infection of the bacterium *Escherichia coli* by bacteriophage T2. *E. coli* is a bacterium normally found in the intestines of mammals. **Bacteriophages** (or simply **phages;** see Chapter 9 and 21) are viruses that infect bacteria. A **virus** is an infectious agent that contains either DNA or RNA surrounded by a protein coat. Viruses cannot reproduce except in a host cell. When a virus infects a cell, it can use the cell's resources to produce more virus particles.

The phage replication cycle begins when a phage attaches to the surface of a bacterium. For phages such as T2, the infected cell quickly stops producing its own molecules and instead starts making progeny phages. After about 100 to 200 phages are assembled inside the bacterial cell, a viral enzyme breaks down the cell wall, killing the cell and releasing the new phages. The whole cycle takes approximately 90 minutes.

The T2 phage that Hershey and Chase studied consists of only a core of DNA surrounded by proteins. Therefore, one of these molecules must be the genetic material that enters the bacterial cell and directs the infective cycle within. But which one? Hershey and Chase prepared two batches of phages, one with the protein tagged with a radioactive label and the other with the DNA tagged with a radioactive label. To obtain labelled phages, they added T2 to *E. coli* growing in the presence of either the radioactive isotope of sulfur (^{35}S) or the radioactive isotope of phosphorus (^{32}P) (**Figure 12.3,** step 1). The progeny phages produced in the ^{35}S medium had labelled proteins and unlabelled DNA because sulfur is a component of proteins but not of DNA. The phages produced in the ^{32}P medium had labelled DNA and unlabelled proteins because phosphorus is a component of DNA but not of proteins.

Hershey and Chase then infected separate cultures of *E. coli* with the two types of labelled phages (step 2). After a short period to allow the genetic material to enter the bacterial cell, they mixed the bacteria in a kitchen blender. They reasoned that only the genetic material was injected into the bacterial cell, leaving the rest of the phage outside. By mixing the cells in a blender, they could shear off the phage parts that did not enter the bacteria and collect them separately for analysis.

When they infected the bacteria with phages that contained labelled protein coats, they found no radioactivity in the bacterial cells but could easily measure it in the material removed by the blender (step 3, top). They also found no radioactivity in the progeny phages (step 4, top). However, if the infecting phages contained radioactive DNA, they found radioactivity inside the infected bacteria but none in the phage coats removed by the blender (step 3, bottom). In addition, radioactivity *was* seen in the progeny phages (step 4, bottom). The results were unequivocal: the genetic material of the phage was DNA, not protein.

When taken together, the experiments of Griffith, Avery and his coworkers, and Hershey and Chase established that DNA, not proteins, carries genetic information. Their research also established the term *transformation,* which is still used in molecular biology. **Transformation** is the conversion of a cell's hereditary type by the uptake of DNA released by the breakdown of another cell, as in the Griffith and Avery experiments.

Figure 12.3
The Hershey and Chase experiment demonstrating that DNA is the hereditary molecule.

QUESTION: Is DNA or protein the genetic material?

EXPERIMENT: Hershey and Chase performed a definitive experiment to show whether DNA or protein is the genetic material. They used phage T2 for their experiment; it consists only of DNA and protein.

1. They infected *E. coli* growing in the presence of radioactive ^{32}P or ^{35}S with phage T2. The progeny phages were either labelled in their protein with ^{35}S (top), or in their DNA with ^{32}P (bottom).

2. Separate cultures of *E. coli* were infected with the radioactively labelled phages.

3. After a short period of time to allow the genetic material to enter the bacterial cell, the bacteria were mixed in a blender. The blending sheared from the cell surface the phage coats that did not enter the bacteria. The components were analyzed for radioactivity.

4. Progeny phages analyzed for radioactivity.

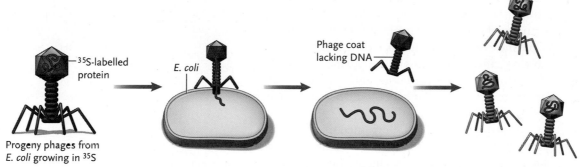

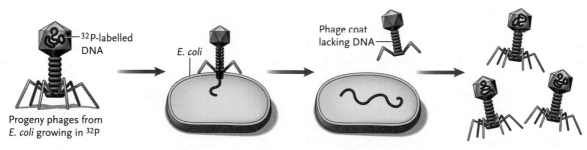

CONCLUSION: ^{32}P, the isotope used to label DNA, was found within phage-infected cells and in progeny phages, indicating that DNA is the genetic material. ^{35}S, the radioisotope used to label proteins, was found in phage coats after infection but was not found in the infected cell or in progeny phages, showing that protein is not the genetic material.

Having identified DNA as the hereditary molecule, scientists turned next to determining its structure.

STUDY BREAK

How did Hershey and Chase exploit the reproductive cycle of a phage to gain evidence for DNA as the hereditary material?

12.2 DNA Structure

The experiments that established DNA as the hereditary molecule were followed by a highly competitive scientific race to discover the structure of DNA. The race ended in 1953 when Watson and Crick elucidated the structure of DNA, ushering in a new era of molecular biology.

12.2a Watson and Crick Brought Together Information from Several Sources to Work Out DNA Structure

Before Watson and Crick began their research, other investigators had established that DNA contains four different nucleotides. Each nucleotide consists of the five-carbon sugar *deoxyribose* (carbon atoms on deoxyribose are numbered with primes from 1′ to 5′); a phosphate group; and one of the four nitrogenous bases—adenine (A), guanine (G), thymine (T), and cytosine (C) **(Figure 12.4).** Two of the bases, **adenine** and **guanine**, are *purines,* nitrogenous bases built from a pair of fused rings of carbon and nitrogen atoms. The other two bases, **thymine** and **cytosine**, are *pyrimidines,* built from a single carbon ring. An organic chemist, Erwin Chargaff, measured the amounts of nitrogenous bases in DNA and discovered that they occur in definite ratios. He observed that the number of purines equals the number of pyrimidines, but, more specifically, the amount of adenine equals the amount of thymine, and the amount of guanine equals the amount of cytosine; these relationships are known as *Chargaff's rules.*

Researchers had also determined that DNA contains nucleotides joined to form a *polynucleotide chain.* In a polynucleotide chain, the deoxyribose sugars are linked by phosphate groups in an alternating sugar–phosphate–sugar–phosphate pattern, forming a **sugar–phosphate backbone** (highlighted in grey in Figure 12.4). Each phosphate group is a "bridge" between the 3′ carbon of one sugar and the 5′ carbon of the next sugar; the entire linkage, including the bridging phosphate group, is called a *phosphodiester bond.*

The polynucleotide chain of DNA has polarity, or directionality. That is, the two ends of the chain are not the same: at one end, a phosphate group is bound to the 5′ carbon of a deoxyribose sugar, whereas at the other end, a hydroxyl group is bonded to the 3′ carbon of a deoxyribose sugar (see Figure 12.4). Consequently, the two ends are called the **5′ end** and the **3′ end**, respectively.

These were the known facts when Watson and Crick began their collaboration in the early 1950s. However, the number of polynucleotide chains in a DNA molecule and the manner in which they fold or twist in DNA were unknown. Watson and Crick themselves did not conduct experiments to study the structure of DNA; instead, they used the research data of others for their analysis, relying heavily on data gathered by physicist Maurice H.F. Wilkins and research associate Rosalind Franklin **(Figure 12.5a),** at King's College, London. These researchers were using **X-ray diffraction** to study the structure of DNA **(Figure 12.5b).** In X-ray diffraction, an X-ray beam is directed at a molecule in the form of a regular solid, ideally in the form

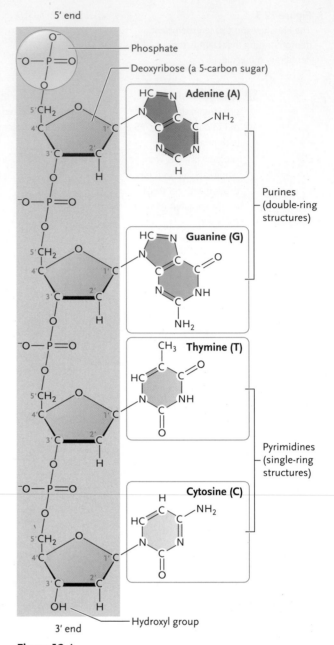

Figure 12.4

The four nucleotide subunits of DNA, linked into a polynucleotide chain. The sugar–phosphate backbone of the chain is highlighted in grey. The connection between adjacent deoxyribose sugars is a phosphodiester bond. The polynucleotide chain has polarity: at one end (5′), a phosphate group is bound to the 5′ carbon of a deoxyribose sugar, whereas at the other end (3′), a hydroxyl group is bound to the 3′ carbon of a deoxyribose sugar.

of a crystal. Within the crystal, regularly arranged atoms bend and reflect the X-rays into smaller beams that exit the crystal at definite angles determined by the arrangement of atoms in the structure of the crystal. If a photographic film is placed behind the crystal, the exiting beams produce a pattern of exposed spots. From that pattern, researchers can deduce the positions of the atoms in the crystal.

Wilkins and Franklin did not have DNA crystals to work with, but they were able to obtain X-ray diffraction

Franklin's DNA diffraction pattern

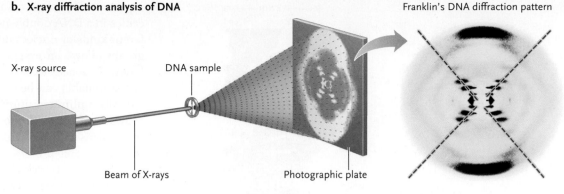

X-ray source

DNA sample

Beam of X-rays

Photographic plate

Figure 12.5

X-ray diffraction analysis of DNA. **(a)** Rosalind Franklin. **(b)** The X-ray diffraction method to study DNA and the diffraction pattern Rosalind Franklin obtained. The X-shaped pattern of spots (dashed lines) was correctly interpreted by Franklin to indicate that DNA has a helical structure similar to a spiral staircase.

patterns from a sample of DNA molecules that had been pulled out into a fibre (see Figure 12.5). The patterns indicated that the DNA molecules within the fibre were cylindrical and about 2 nm in diameter. Separations between the spots showed that major patterns of atoms repeat at intervals of 0.34 nm and 3.4 nm within the DNA. Franklin correctly interpreted an X-shaped distribution of spots in the diffraction pattern (see dashed lines in Figure 12.5) to mean that DNA has a helical structure.

12.2b The New Model Proposed That Two Polynucleotide Chains Wind into a DNA Double Helix

Watson and Crick constructed scale models of the four DNA nucleotides and fitted them together in different ways until they arrived at an arrangement that satisfied both Wilkins's and Franklin's X-ray data and Chargaff's chemical analysis. Watson and Crick's trials led them to a double-stranded model for DNA structure in which two polynucleotide chains twist around each other in a right-handed way, like a double-spiral staircase **(Figure 12.6, p. 264).** They were the first to propose the famous double-helix model for DNA.

In the **double-helix model**, the two sugar–phosphate backbones are separated from each other by a regular distance. The bases extend into and fill this central space. A purine and a pyrimidine, if paired together, are exactly wide enough to fill the space between the backbone chains in the double helix. However, a purine–purine base pair is too wide to fit the space exactly, and a pyrimidine–pyrimidine pair is too narrow. From Chargaff's data, Watson and Crick proposed that the purine–pyrimidine base pairs in DNA are A-T and G-C pairs. That is, wherever an A occurs in one strand, a T must be opposite it in the other strand; wherever a G occurs in one strand, a C must be opposite it. This feature of DNA is called **complementary base-pairing**, and one strand is said to be

complementary to the other. The base pairs, which fit together like pieces of a jigsaw puzzle, are stabilized by hydrogen bonds—two between A and T and three between G and C (see Figure 12.6, p. 264; hydrogen bonds are discussed in *The Purple Pages*). The hydrogen bonds between the paired bases, repeated along the double helix, hold the two strands together in the helix.

CONCEPT FIX Although this text follows the generally common convention of referring to the DNA double helix as a *DNA molecule,* you should be aware that this terminology is, strictly speaking, inaccurate. If a molecule is defined as a collection of atoms connected by covalent bonds, then *each* of the two sugar–phosphate backbones of the double helix qualifies as a molecule. The double helix is technically composed of *two* polynucleotide molecules held together by hydrogen bonds. ⬡

The base pairs lie in flat planes almost perpendicular to the long axis of the DNA helix. In this state, each base pair occupies a length of 0.34 nm along the long axis of the double helix (see Figure 12.6, p. 264). This spacing accounts for the repeating 0.34 nm pattern noted in the X-ray diffraction patterns. The larger 3.4 nm repeat pattern was interpreted to mean that each full turn of the double helix takes up 3.4 nm along the length of the molecule; therefore, 10 base pairs are packed into a full turn.

Watson and Crick also realized that the two strands of a double helix fit together in a stable chemical way only if they are **antiparallel**, that is, only if they run in opposite directions (see Figure 12.6, p. 264, arrows). In other words, the *3′ end* of one strand is opposite the *5′ end* of its complementary strand. This antiparallel arrangement is highly significant for the process of replication, which is discussed in the next section.

As hereditary material, DNA must faithfully store and transmit genetic information for the entire life cycle of an organism. Watson and Crick recognized that this information is coded into the DNA by the particular sequence of the four nucleotides. This sequence

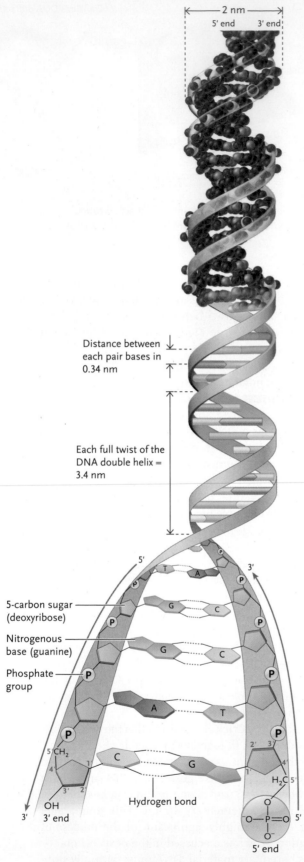

2 nm

5' end   3' end

Distance between
each pair bases in
0.34 nm

Each full twist of the
DNA double helix =
3.4 nm

5' 3'

T   A

5-carbon sugar
(deoxyribose)

G   C

Nitrogenous
base (guanine)

G   C

Phosphate
group   P

A   T

P   P

5' CH₂

C   G

H₂C 5'

OH

Hydrogen bond

3'   3' end

O—P=O   5'

5' end

Figure 12.6

DNA double helix. Arrows and labelling of the ends show that the two polynucleotide chains of the double helix are antiparallel—that is, they have opposite polarity in that they run in opposite directions. In the space-filling model at the top, the spaces occupied by atoms are indicated by spheres. There are 10 base pairs per turn of the helix; only 8 base pairs are visible because the other 2 are obscured where the backbones pass over each other.

is preserved by robust covalent bonds between the molecules in a DNA double helix. Although only four different kinds of nucleotides exist, combining them in groups allows an essentially infinite number of different sequences to be "written," just as the 26 letters of the alphabet can be combined in groups to write a virtually unlimited number of words. Chapter 13 shows how taking the four nucleotides in groups of three forms enough words to spell out the structure of any conceivable protein.

Watson and Crick announced their model for DNA structure in a brief but monumental paper published in the journal *Nature* in 1953. Watson and Crick shared a Nobel Prize with Wilkins in 1962 for their discovery of the molecular structure of DNA. Rosalind Franklin might have been a candidate for a Nobel Prize had she not died of cancer at age 38 in 1958. (The Nobel Prize is given only to living investigators.) Unquestionably, Watson and Crick's discovery of DNA structure opened the way to molecular studies of genetics and heredity, leading to our modern understanding of gene structure and action at the molecular level.

STUDY BREAK

1. Which bases in DNA are purines? Which are pyrimidines?
2. What bonds form between complementary base pairs? Between a base and the deoxyribose sugar?
3. Which features of the DNA molecule did Watson and Crick describe?

12.3 DNA Replication

Once they had discovered the structure of DNA, Watson and Crick realized immediately that complementary base-pairing could explain how DNA replicates **(Figure 12.7)**. They imagined that, for replication, the hydrogen bonds between the two strands break, allowing them to unwind and separate. Each strand then acts as a template for the synthesis of its partner. When replication is complete, there are two double helices, each with one strand derived from the parental DNA molecule base-paired with a newly synthesized one. Most important, each of the two new double helices consists of the identical base-pair sequences as the parental DNA.

The model of replication Watson and Crick proposed is termed **semiconservative replication (Figure 12.8a, p. 266)**. Other scientists proposed two other models for replication. In the *conservative replication model*, each of the two strands of original DNA serves as a template for a new DNA double helix **(Figure 12.8b, p. 266)**. After the two complementary copies separate from their templates, they wind together into an

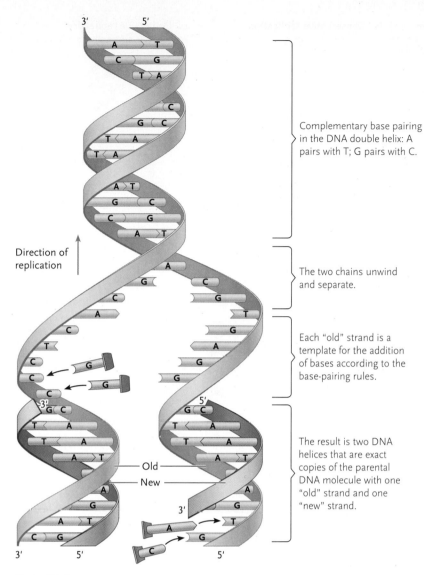

Direction of replication

Complementary base pairing in the DNA double helix: A pairs with T; G pairs with C.

The two chains unwind and separate.

Each "old" strand is a template for the addition of bases according to the base-pairing rules.

The result is two DNA helices that are exact copies of the parental DNA molecule with one "old" strand and one "new" strand.

Old
New

Figure 12.7

Watson and Crick's model for DNA replication. The original DNA is shown in grey. A new polynucleotide chain (red) is assembled on each original chain as they unwind. The template and complementary copy chains remain together when replication is complete, producing DNA double helices that are half old and half new. The model is known as the semiconservative model for DNA replication.

all "new" DNA double helix. In the *dispersive replication model,* neither parental molecule remains intact; both chains of each replicated double helix contain old and new segments **(Figure 12.8c, p. 266).**

12.3a Meselson and Stahl Showed That DNA Replication Is Semiconservative

A definitive experiment published in 1958 by Matthew Meselson and Franklin Stahl of the California Institute of Technology demonstrated that DNA replication is semiconservative **(Figure 12.9, p. 267).** In their experiment, Meselson and Stahl had to be able to distinguish parental DNA molecules from newly synthesized DNA. To do this, they used a nonradioactive "heavy" nitrogen isotope to tag the parental DNA. The heavy isotope, ^{15}N, has one more neutron in its nucleus than

the normal ^{14}N isotope. Molecules containing ^{15}N are measurably heavier (denser) than molecules of the same type containing ^{14}N.

As the first step in their experiment, Meselson and Stahl grew *E. coli* bacteria in a culture medium containing the heavy ^{15}N isotope (see Figure 12.9, p. 267, step 1). The heavy isotope was incorporated into the nitrogenous bases of DNA, resulting in the entire DNA being labelled with ^{15}N. Then they transferred the bacteria to a culture medium containing the light ^{14}N isotope (step 2). All new DNA synthesized after the transfer contained the light isotope. Just before the transfer to the medium with the ^{14}N isotope, and after each round of replication following the transfer, they took a sample of the cells and extracted the DNA (step 3).

Meselson and Stahl then mixed the DNA samples with cesium chloride (CsCl) and centrifuged the mixture at very high speed (step 4). During the centrifugation, the CsCl forms a density gradient and DNA double helices move to a position in the gradient where their density matches that of the CsCl. Therefore, DNA of different densities is separated into bands, with the densest DNA settling closer to the bottom of the tube. In Figure 12.9, p. 267, "Result" shows the outcome of these experiments, and "Conclusions" shows why the results were compatible with only the semiconservative replication model.

12.3b DNA Polymerases Are the Primary Enzymes of DNA Replication

During replication, complementary polynucleotide chains are assembled from individual deoxyribonucleotides by enzymes known as DNA polymerases. More than one kind of DNA polymerase is required for DNA replication in all cells. *Deoxyribonucleoside triphosphates* are the substrates for the polymerization reaction catalyzed by DNA polymerases **(Figure 12.10, p. 268).** A nucleoside triphosphate is a nitrogenous base linked to a sugar, which is linked, in turn, to a chain of three phosphate groups (see Figure 4.11, Chapter 4). You have encountered a nucleoside triphosphate before; namely the ATP produced in cellular respiration (see

Figure 12.8

(a) Semiconservative, (b) conservative, and (c) dispersive models for DNA replication.

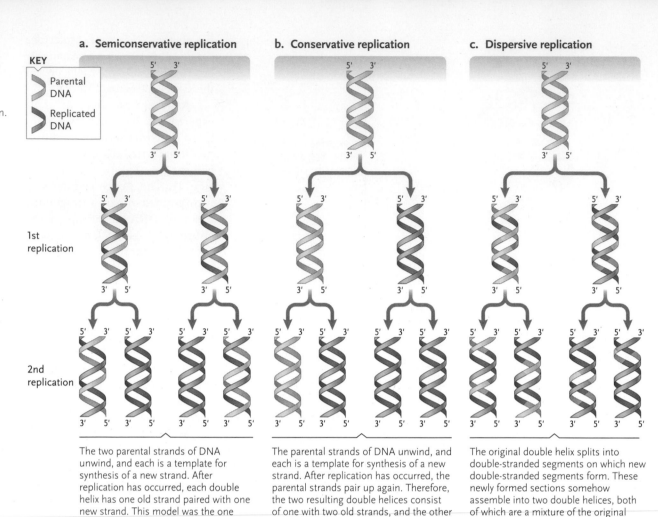

a. Semiconservative replication

The two parental strands of DNA unwind, and each is a template for synthesis of a new strand. After replication has occurred, each double helix has one old strand paired with one new strand. This model was the one proposed by Watson and Crick themselves.

b. Conservative replication

The parental strands of DNA unwind, and each is a template for synthesis of a new strand. After replication has occurred, the parental strands pair up again. Therefore, the two resulting double helices consist of one with two old strands, and the other with two new strands.

c. Dispersive replication

The original double helix splits into double-stranded segments on which new double-stranded segments form. These newly formed sections somehow assemble into two double helices, both of which are a mixture of the original double-stranded DNA interspersed with new double-stranded DNA.

Chapter 6). In that case, the sugar is ribose, making ATP a ribonucleoside triphosphate. The deoxyribonucleoside triphosphates used in DNA replication have the sugar *deoxyribose* rather than the sugar *ribose*. Because four different bases are found in DNA—adenine (A), guanine (G), cytosine (C), and thymine (T)—four different deoxyribonucleoside triphosphates are used for DNA replication. In keeping with the ATP naming convention, the deoxyribonucleoside triphosphates for DNA replication are given the short names dATP, dGTP, dCTP, and dTTP, where the "d" stands for "deoxyribose."

Figure 12.10 presents a section of a DNA polynucleotide chain being replicated, showing how DNA polymerase catalyzes the assembly of a new DNA strand that is complementary to the template strand. To understand Figure 12.10, remember that the carbons in the deoxyriboses of nucleotides are numbered with primes. Each DNA strand has two distinct ends: the 5′ end has an exposed phosphate group attached to the 5′ carbon of the sugar, and the 3′ end has an exposed hydroxyl group attached to the 3′ carbon of the sugar. As you learned earlier, because of the antiparallel nature of the DNA strands within a double helix, the

5′ end of one strand is opposite the 3′ end of the other. DNA polymerase can add a nucleotide *only to the 3′* end of an existing nucleotide chain. As a new DNA strand is assembled, a 3′ –OH group is always exposed at its "newest" end; the "oldest" end of the new chain has an exposed 5′ phosphate. DNA polymerases are therefore said to assemble nucleotide chains in the 5′ → 3′ direction.

Because of the antiparallel nature of DNA, the template strand is "read" in the 3′ → 5′ direction for this new synthesis. DNA polymerases of bacteria, archaeans, and eukaryotes all consist of several polypeptide subunits arranged to form different domains (see polypeptides in *The Purple Pages*). The polymerases share a shape that is said to resemble a partially closed human right hand in which the template DNA lies over the "palm" in a groove formed by the "fingers" and "thumb" **(Figure 12.11a, p. 269)**. The palm domain is evolutionarily related among the polymerases of bacteria, archaea, and eukaryotes, while the finger and thumb domains are different sequences in each of these three types of organisms. The template strand does not pass through the tunnel formed by the thumb and finger domains, however. Instead, the template

Figure 12.9

The Meselson and Stahl experiment demonstrating the semiconservative model to be correct.

QUESTION: Does DNA replicate semiconservatively?

EXPERIMENT: Matthew Meselson and Franklin Stahl proved that the semiconservative model of DNA replication is correct and that the conservative and dispersive models are incorrect.

1. Bacteria grown in ^{15}N (heavy) medium. The heavy isotope is incorporated into the bases of DNA, resulting in all the DNA being heavy, that is, labelled with ^{15}N.

2. Bacteria transferred to ^{14}N (light) medium and allowed to grow and divide for several generations. All new DNA is light.

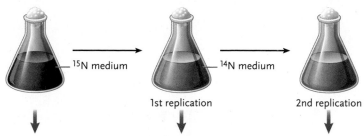

^{15}N medium → ^{14}N medium
1st replication → 2nd replication

3. DNA extracted from bacteria cultured in ^{15}N medium and after each generation in ^{14}N medium.

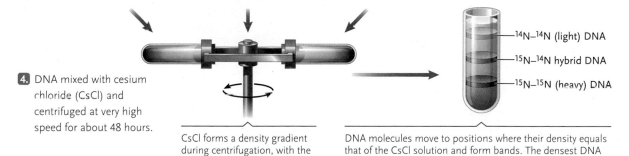

4. DNA mixed with cesium chloride (CsCl) and centrifuged at very high speed for about 48 hours.

$^{14}N–^{14}N$ (light) DNA
$^{15}N–^{14}N$ hybrid DNA
$^{15}N–^{15}N$ (heavy) DNA

CsCl forms a density gradient during centrifugation, with the highest density at the bottom of the tube.

DNA molecules move to positions where their density equals that of the CsCl solution and form bands. The densest DNA ends up closest to the bottom of the tube. Shown are the positions of differently labelled DNA molecules. Experimentally the bands are detected by absorbance of UV light.

RESULT: Meselson and Stahl obtained the following results:

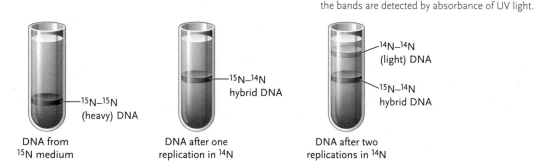

$^{15}N–^{15}N$ (heavy) DNA
$^{15}N–^{14}N$ hybrid DNA
$^{14}N–^{14}N$ (light) DNA
$^{15}N–^{14}N$ hybrid DNA

DNA from ^{15}N medium
DNA after one replication in ^{14}N
DNA after two replications in ^{14}N

CONCLUSIONS: The predicted DNA banding patterns for the three DNA replication models were as follows:

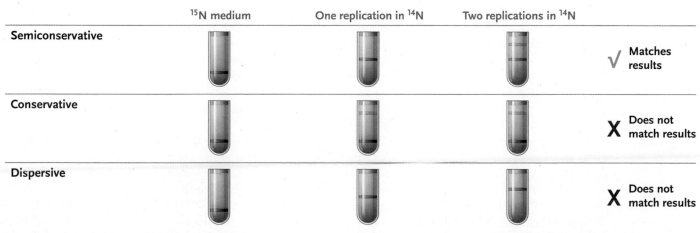

	^{15}N medium	One replication in ^{14}N	Two replications in ^{14}N	
Semiconservative				√ Matches results
Conservative				X Does not match results
Dispersive				X Does not match results

The results support the semiconservative model.

CHAPTER 12 DNA STRUCTURE, REPLICATION, AND ORGANIZATION

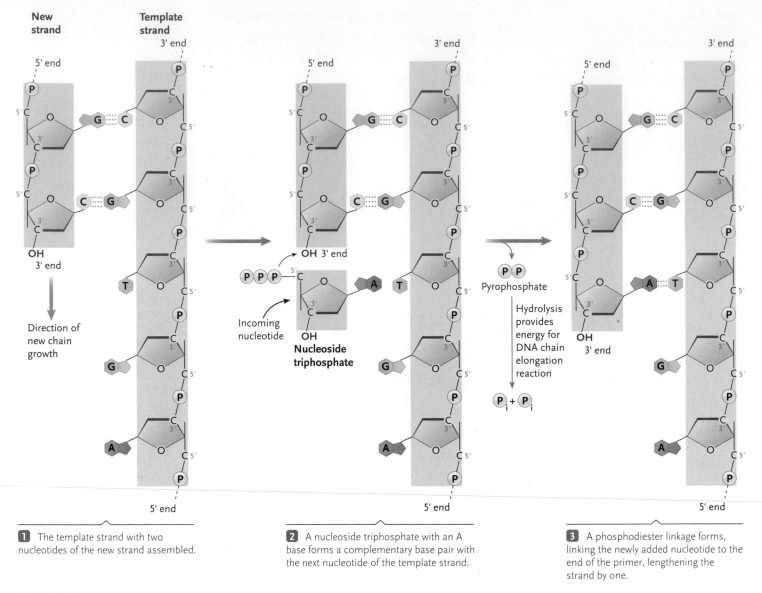

1 The template strand with two nucleotides of the new strand assembled.

2 A nucleoside triphosphate with an A base forms a complementary base pair with the next nucleotide of the template strand.

3 A phosphodiester linkage forms, linking the newly added nucleotide to the end of the primer, lengthening the strand by one.

Figure 12.10

Reactions assembling a complementary chain in the 5′ → 3′ direction on a template DNA strand, showing the phosphodiester linkage created when the DNA polymerase enzyme adds each nucleotide to the chain.

strand and the 3′ –OH of the new strand meet at the active site for the polymerization reaction of DNA synthesis, located in the palm domain. A nucleotide is added to the new strand when an incoming dNTP enters the active site carrying a base complementary to the template strand base positioned in the active site. By moving along the template strand, one nucleotide at a time, DNA polymerase extends the new DNA strand, as we saw in Figure 12.10.

Figure 12.11b shows the representation of DNA polymerase used in the following DNA replication figures, and it also shows a sliding DNA clamp. The **sliding DNA clamp** is a protein that encircles the DNA and binds to the rear of the DNA polymerase in terms of the enzyme's forward movement during replication. The function of the sliding DNA clamp is to tether the DNA polymerase to the template strand. Tethering the

DNA polymerase makes replication more efficient because without it, the enzyme will detach from the template after only a few dozen polymerizations. But, with the clamp, many tens of thousands of polymerizations occur before the enzyme detaches. Overall, the rate of DNA synthesis is much faster because of the sliding DNA clamp.

In sum, the key molecular events of DNA replication are as follows:

1. The two strands of the DNA molecule unwind for replication to occur.
2. DNA polymerase can add nucleotides only to an existing chain.
3. The overall direction of new synthesis is in the 5′ → 3′ direction, which is a direction antiparallel to that of the template strand.

a. Bacterial DNA polymerase

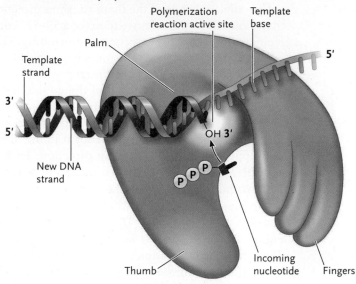

b. How a DNA polymerase and sliding clamp is shown in the book

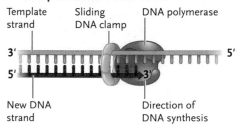

Figure 12.11

DNA polymerase structure. **(a)** Stylized drawing of a bacterial DNA polymerase. The enzyme viewed from the side resembles a human right hand. The polymerization reaction site lies on the palm. When the incoming nucleotide is added, the thumb and fingers close over the site to facilitate the reaction. **(b)** How DNA polymerase is shown in subsequent figures of DNA replication. The figure also shows a sliding DNA clamp tethering the DNA polymerase to the template strand.

4. Nucleotides enter into a newly synthesized chain according to the A-T and G-C complementary base-pairing rules.

The following sections describe how enzymes and other proteins conduct these molecular events. Our focus is on the well-characterized replication system of *E. coli*. Replication in archaeans and eukaryotes is highly similar, although there are differences in the replication machinery. The replication machinery of archaeans is strikingly similar to that of eukaryotes and is clearly different from that of bacteria.

12.3c Helicases Unwind DNA for New DNA Synthesis, and Other Proteins Stabilize the DNA at the Replication Fork

In semiconservative replication, the two strands of the parental DNA molecule unwind and separate to expose the template strands for new DNA synthesis

(**Figure 12.12, p. 270**). Unwinding of the DNA for replication occurs at a small, specific sequence in the bacterial chromosome known as the **origin of replication** (*ori*). Specific proteins bind to an *ori* sequence and, in turn, promote binding of **DNA helicase**, which unwinds the DNA strands. The unwinding produces a Y-shaped structure called a **replication fork**, which consists of the two unwound template strands transitioning to double-helical DNA.

Single-stranded binding proteins (SSBs) coat the exposed single-stranded DNA segments, stabilizing the DNA and keeping the two strands from pairing back together (see Figure 12.12, p. 270). The SSBs are displaced as the replication enzymes make the new polynucleotide chain on the template strands. For circular chromosomes, such as the genomes of most bacteria, unwinding the DNA will eventually cause the still-wound DNA ahead of the unwinding to become highly twisted. You can visualize this phenomenon with some string. Take two equal lengths of string and twist them around each other. Now tie the two ends of each string together. You have created a model of a circular DNA double helix. Pick anywhere in the circle and pull apart the two pieces of string. The more you pull, the more the region where the two strings are still together becomes highly twisted. In the cell, the twisting of DNA during replication is relieved by **topoisomerase**. This enzyme cuts the DNA ahead of the replication fork, turns the DNA on one side of the break in the opposite direction of the twisting force, and rejoins the two strands (see Figure 12.12, p. 270).

12.3d RNA Primers Provide the Starting Point for DNA Polymerase to Begin Synthesizing a New DNA Chain

If DNA polymerases can only add nucleotides to the 3′ end of an existing strand, how can a new strand begin when there is no existing strand in place? The answer lies in a short chain a few nucleotides long called a **primer** that is made of RNA instead of DNA (**Figure 12.13, p. 270**). The primer is synthesized by the enzyme **primase**. Primase then leaves the template, and DNA polymerase takes over, extending the RNA primer with DNA nucleotides as it synthesizes the new

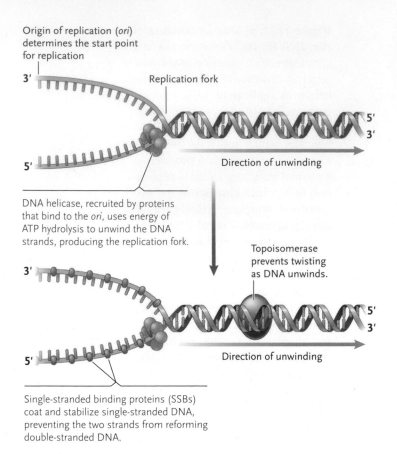

Origin of replication (*ori*) determines the start point for replication

3′

Replication fork

5′
3′

Direction of unwinding

DNA helicase, recruited by proteins that bind to the *ori*, uses energy of ATP hydrolysis to unwind the DNA strands, producing the replication fork.

Topoisomerase prevents twisting as DNA unwinds.

3′

5′
3′

Direction of unwinding

5′

Single-stranded binding proteins (SSBs) coat and stabilize single-stranded DNA, preventing the two strands from reforming double-stranded DNA.

Figure 12.12

The roles of DNA helicase, single-stranded binding proteins (SSBs), and topoisomerase in DNA replication.

Figure 12.13

Initiation of a new DNA strand by synthesis of a short RNA primer by primase, and the extension of the primer as DNA by DNA polymerase.

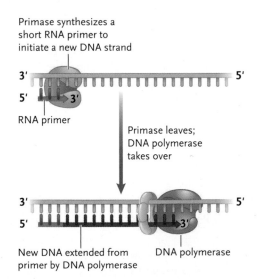

Primase synthesizes a short RNA primer to initiate a new DNA strand

3′
5′

5′
3′

RNA primer

Primase leaves; DNA polymerase takes over

3′
5′

5′
3′

New DNA extended from primer by DNA polymerase

DNA polymerase

DNA chain. RNA primers are removed and replaced with DNA later in replication.

12.3e One New DNA Strand Is Synthesized Continuously; the Other, Discontinuously

DNA polymerases synthesize a new DNA strand on a template strand in the 5′ → 3′ direction. Because the two strands of a DNA double helix are antiparallel, only one of the them runs in a direction that allows DNA polymerase to make a 5′ → 3′ complementary copy in the direction of unwinding. That is, on this template strand—top strand in **Figure 12.14**—new DNA is synthesized continuously in the direction of unwinding of the double helix. However, the other template strand—bottom strand in Figure 12.14—runs in the opposite direction; this means DNA polymerase has to copy it in the direction opposite to the unwinding direction. How is new DNA polymerized in the direction opposite to the unwinding? The polymerases make this strand in short lengths that are synthesized in the direction opposite to that of DNA unwinding (see Figure 12.14). The short lengths produced by this **discontinuous replication** are then covalently linked into a single continuous polynucleotide chain. The short lengths are called **Okazaki fragments**, after Reiji Okazaki, the scientist who first detected them. The new DNA strand synthesized in the direction of DNA unwinding is called the **leading strand** of DNA replication; the template for that strand is the **leading strand template.** The strand synthesized discontinuously in the opposite direction is called the **lagging strand**; the template strand for that strand is the **lagging strand template.**

12.3f Multiple Enzymes Coordinate Their Activities in DNA Replication

Figure 12.15, p. 272 shows how the enzymes and proteins we have introduced act in a coordinated way to replicate DNA. Primase initiates all new strands by synthesizing an RNA primer. **DNA polymerase III,** the main polymerase, extends the primer by adding DNA nucleotides. For the lagging strand, **DNA polymerase I** removes the RNA primer at the 5′ end of the previous newly synthesized Okazaki fragment, replacing the RNA nucleotides one by one with DNA nucleotides. RNA nucleotide removal uses the 5′ → 3′ exonuclease activity of the enzyme. (An exonuclease removes nucleotides from the end of a molecule; the primer is digested from its 5′ end toward its 3′ end.) DNA polymerase I stops replacing RNA and leaves the template when it encounters the first DNA nucleotide that was synthesized in the Okazaki fragment (Figure 12.15, p. 272). Therefore, the DNA base replacing the last RNA base of the primer ends up right beside the first DNA base of the Okazaki fragment. The needed covalent bond in the backbone is made by DNA ligase (*ligare* = to tie).

The replication process continues in the same way until the entire DNA double helix is copied. **Table 12.1, p. 273** summarizes the activities of the major enzymes replicating DNA. Replication advances at a rate of about 500 to 1000 nucleotides per second in

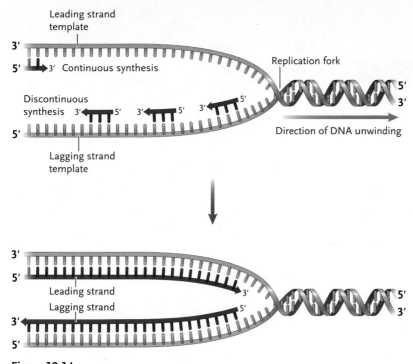

Figure 12.14

Replication of antiparallel template strands at a replication fork. Synthesis of the new DNA strand on the top template strand is continuous. Synthesis on the new DNA strand on the bottom template strand is discontinuous—short lengths of DNA are made, which are then joined into a continuous chain. The overall effect is synthesis of both strands in the direction of replication fork movement.

E. coli and other bacteria, and at a rate of about 50 to 100 per second in eukaryotes. The entire process is so rapid that the RNA primers and nicks left by discontinuous synthesis persist for only seconds or fractions of a second. A short distance behind the fork, the new DNA chains are fully continuous and wound into complete DNA double helices. Each helix consists of one "old" and one "new" polynucleotide. Researchers identified the enzymes that replicate DNA through experiments with a variety of bacteria and eukaryotes and with viruses that infect both types of cells. Experiments with the bacterium *E. coli* have provided the most complete information about DNA replication, particularly in the laboratory of Arthur Kornberg at Stanford University. Kornberg received a Nobel Prize in 1959 for his discovery of the mechanism for DNA synthesis.

MOLECULE BEHIND BIOLOGY 12.1

Acyclic Nucleoside Phosphonates as Antiviral Drugs

Viruses are obligate parasites that exploit the cellular machinery of infected host cells for replication and gene expression. Such intimate association with host biochemistry makes it difficult for scientists to find an exclusively viral "target" for antiviral drug binding.

However, herpes viruses provide such a target when, once inside the nucleus of an infected cell, they tran-

scribe a gene coding for their own distinctive DNA polymerase. This novel polymerase replicates viral DNA, drawing from the cellular pool of nucleotide triphosphates.

It has been possible to selectively "poison" viral DNA replication with acyclic nucleoside phosphonates such as cidofovir (shown below) because they (1) are converted to their triphosphate form by infected cells, (2) are

then selectively incorporated into viral DNA (instead of the normal nucleotides) by viral polymerase, and (3) block further DNA synthesis.

These drugs are part of a large class of compounds called base analogues that are incorporated into DNA by "mistake." Compare the structures below with those of the standard bases shown in Figure 12.4, p. 262, and notice why these drugs are called "acyclic."

Cidofovir   Adefovir dipivoxil   Tenofovir disoproxil fumarate

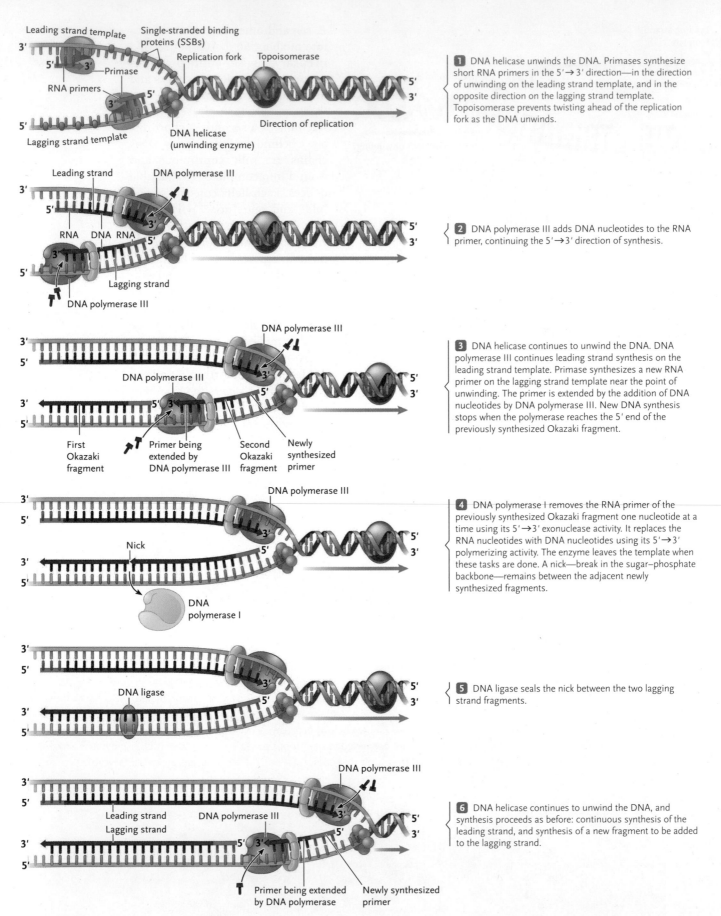

1 DNA helicase unwinds the DNA. Primases synthesize short RNA primers in the 5' → 3' direction—in the direction of unwinding on the leading strand template, and in the opposite direction on the lagging strand template. Topoisomerase prevents twisting ahead of the replication fork as the DNA unwinds.

2 DNA polymerase III adds DNA nucleotides to the RNA primer, continuing the 5'→3' direction of synthesis.

3 DNA helicase continues to unwind the DNA. DNA polymerase III continues leading strand synthesis on the leading strand template. Primase synthesizes a new RNA primer on the lagging strand template near the point of unwinding. The primer is extended by the addition of DNA nucleotides by DNA polymerase III. New DNA synthesis stops when the polymerase reaches the 5' end of the previously synthesized Okazaki fragment.

4 DNA polymerase I removes the RNA primer of the previously synthesized Okazaki fragment one nucleotide at a time using its 5' →3' exonuclease activity. It replaces the RNA nucleotides with DNA nucleotides using its 5' →3' polymerizing activity. The enzyme leaves the template when these tasks are done. A nick—break in the sugar–phosphate backbone—remains between the adjacent newly synthesized fragments.

5 DNA ligase seals the nick between the two lagging strand fragments.

6 DNA helicase continues to unwind the DNA, and synthesis proceeds as before: continuous synthesis of the leading strand, and synthesis of a new fragment to be added to the lagging strand.

Figure 12.15

Molecular model of DNA replication. The drawings simplify the process. In reality, the enzymes assemble at the fork, replicating both strands from that position as the template strands fold and pass through the assembly.

Table 12.1	Major Enzymes of DNA Replication
Enzyme	**Activity**
Helicase	Unwinds DNA helix
Single-stranded binding proteins	Stabilize single-stranded DNA and prevent the two strands at the replication fork from reforming double-stranded DNA
Topoisomerase	Avoids twisting of the DNA ahead of the replication fork (in circular DNA) by cutting the DNA, turning the DNA on one side of the break in the direction opposite to that of the twisting force, and rejoining the two strands
Primase	Assembles RNA primers in the 5′ → 3′ direction to initiate a new DNA strand
DNA polymerase III	Main replication enzyme in *E. coli*; extends the RNA primer by adding DNA nucleotides to it
DNA polymerase I	*E. coli* enzyme that uses its 5′ → 3′ exonuclease activity to remove the RNA of the previously synthesized Okazaki fragment, and uses its 5′ → 3′ polymerization activity to replace the RNA nucleotides with DNA nucleotides
Sliding clamp	Tethers DNA polymerase III to the DNA template, making replication more efficient
DNA ligase	Seals nick left between adjacent bases after RNA primers replaced with DNA

12.3g Multiple Replication Origins Enable Rapid Replication of Large Chromosomes

Unwinding at an *ori* within a DNA molecule actually produces two replication forks: two Ys joined together at their tops to form a **replication bubble**. Typically, each of the replication forks moves away from the ori as DNA replication proceeds, with the events at each fork mirroring those in the other **(Figure 12.16, p. 274)**. For small circular genomes, such as those found in many bacteria and archaeans, there is a single ori. Eukaryotic genomes, by contrast, are distributed among several linear chromosomes, each of which can be very long. The average human chromosome, for instance, is about 25 times as long as the *E. coli* chromosome. Nonetheless, replication of long, eukaryotic chromosomes is relatively rapid—sometimes faster than the *E. coli* chromosome—because there are many, sometimes hundreds, of origins of replication along eukaryotic chromosomes. Replication initiates at each origin, forming a replication bubble at each **(Figure 12.17, p. 274)**. Movement of the two forks in opposite directions from each origin extends the replication bubbles until the forks eventually meet along the chromosomes to produce fully replicated DNA molecules. Normally, a replication origin is activated only once during the S phase of a eukaryotic cell cycle, so no portion of the DNA is replicated more than once.

12.3h Telomerases Solve a Special Replication Problem at the Ends of Linear DNA Molecules in Eukaryotes

The requirement for an RNA primer to initiate DNA replication (see Figures 12.13, p. 270 and 12.15, p. 272) results in the linear chromosomes of eukaryotes getting shorter at each round of replication. Think about the end of a linear DNA molecule. New DNA synthesis on the 3′ → 5′ template strand must be started with an RNA primer. When that primer is subsequently removed, as usual, a gap will be left in its place at the 5′ end of the new DNA strand **(Figure 12.18, p. 275)**. Everywhere else on the chromosome, such gaps are filled in by DNA polymerase by elongating the 3′ end of a neighbouring nucleotide. However, at the very ends of chromosomes, there is no existing nucleotide chain that can be elongated. Therefore, DNA polymerase cannot fill in the gap with the required DNA nucleotides and the resulting newly synthesized strand will be too short. (You should agree that this problem occurs on both ends of the chromosome, just on opposite strands of the double helix.) When these new, now shortened, DNA strands are used as a template for the next round of DNA replication, the resulting chromosomes will be shorter still. Indeed, when most somatic cells go through the cell cycle, their chromosomes shorten with each division. Such loss of DNA sequences can eventually have lethal consequences for the cell.

Figure 12.16

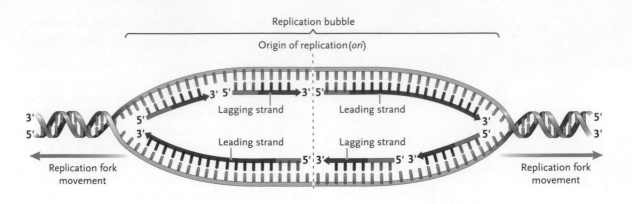

Figure 12.17
Replication from multiple origins in the linear chromosomes of eukaryotes.

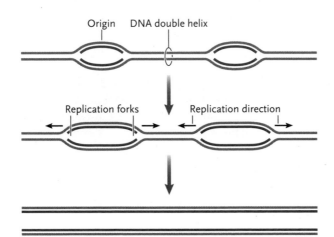

Most eukaryotic chromosomes can afford to lose some DNA sequence because a buffer of highly repetitive noncoding DNA protects genes near the ends of chromosomes. This region of noncoding DNA is called the **telomere** (*telo* = end, *mere* = segment). A telomere consists of a short DNA sequence that is repeated hundreds to thousands of times. In humans, the repeated sequence, the *telomere repeat,* is 5'-TTAGGG-3' on the template strand (the top strand in Figure 12.18, step 1). With each replication, a fraction of the telomere repeats is lost by the mechanism described above but the genes are unaffected. The buffering fails only when the entire telomere is lost.

The length of telomeres can be maintained by the action of an unusual enzyme, called **telomerase**, which adds DNA to the ends of chromosomes. Since telomerase makes DNA, it is a type of DNA polymerase. Recall that DNA polymerases require a free 3' OH to extend, a supply of dNTPs, and a template strand. If you look closely at Figure 12.18, you might predict that telomerase elongates the 5' end of the bottom strand to fill in the gap. Although this solution appears easiest, it is impossible since *there are no known polymerases capable of elongating a 5' end*. So, instead, telomerase must elongate the available 3' end of the top strand.

But now there is a different problem—what to use for a template strand? The lack of a template on the chromosome is solved by *telomerase carrying its own template* in the form of single-stranded RNA molecule. Telomerase adds a telomere repeat to the 3' end of the DNA using the RNA as a template (see Figure 12.18). Then it shifts toward the end of the chromosome and adds another, and another. Once several hundred repeats are added to the top strand, it is primed and used as a template as usual. When the RNA primer is removed, there will be a single-stranded region at the end of the chromosome as before.

CONCEPT FIX It is important to understand that telomerase does not directly prevent the mechanism that causes the shortening of chromosomes. Telomerase just acts against this mechanism by lengthening chromosomes. ⬡

In most multicellular organisms, telomerase is not active in somatic cells, meaning telomeres shorten when such cells divide. As a result, somatic cells are capable of only a certain number of mitotic divisions before they stop dividing and die. Telomerase is normally active only in the rapidly dividing cells of the early embryo, and in germ cells to ensure that chromosomes of gametes have telomeres restored before passing to the next generation.

Telomerase explains how cancer cells can divide indefinitely and not be limited to a certain number of divisions as a result of telomere shortening. For many cancers, as normal cells develop into cancer cells, their telomerases are reactivated, preserving chromosome length during the rapid divisions characteristic of cancer. A positive side of this discovery is that it may lead to an effective cancer treatment if a means can be found to switch off the telomerases in tumour cells. The chromosomes in the rapidly dividing cancer cells would then eventually shorten to the length at which they break down, leading to cell death and elimination of the tumour. Elizabeth Blackburn, Carol Greider, and Jack Szostak were awarded a Nobel Prize in 2009 for their discovery of how chromosomes are protected by telomeres and the enzyme telomerase.

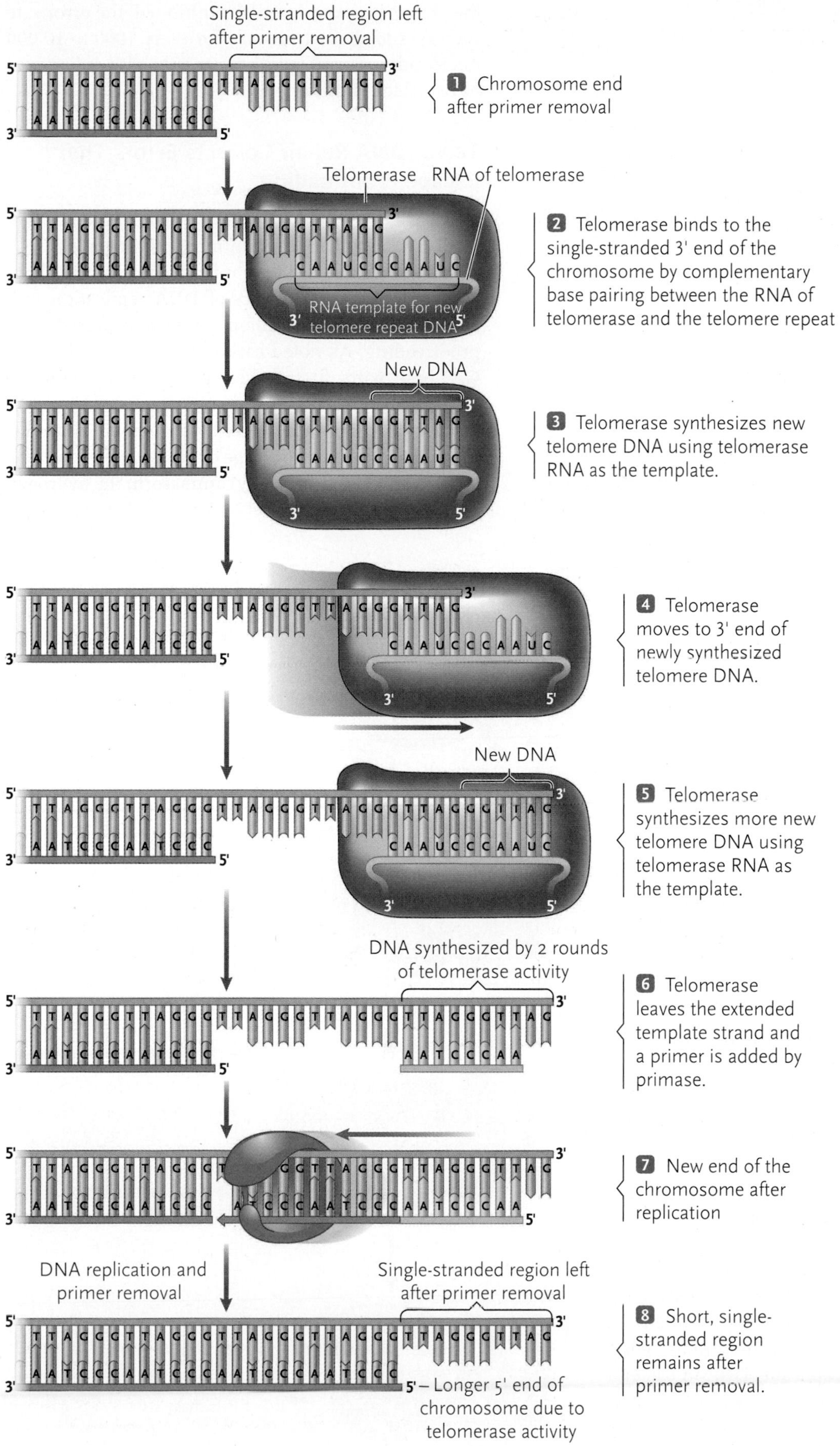

Figure 12.18
Addition of telomere repeats to the 3' end of a eukaryotic linear chromosome by telomerase.

Single-stranded region left after primer removal

1 Chromosome end after primer removal

Telomerase   RNA of telomerase

2 Telomerase binds to the single-stranded 3' end of the chromosome by complementary base pairing between the RNA of telomerase and the telomere repeat

RNA template for new telomere repeat DNA

New DNA

3 Telomerase synthesizes new telomere DNA using telomerase RNA as the template.

4 Telomerase moves to 3' end of newly synthesized telomere DNA.

New DNA

5 Telomerase synthesizes more new telomere DNA using telomerase RNA as the template.

DNA synthesized by 2 rounds of telomerase activity

6 Telomerase leaves the extended template strand and a primer is added by primase.

7 New end of the chromosome after replication

DNA replication and primer removal

Single-stranded region left after primer removal

8 Short, single-stranded region remains after primer removal.

Longer 5' end of chromosome due to telomerase activity

STUDY BREAK

1. What is the importance of complementary base-pairing to DNA replication?
2. Why is a primer needed for DNA replication on both strands?
3. Two DNA polymerases are used in DNA replication. What are their roles?
4. Why are telomeres important?

12.4 Mechanisms That Correct Replication Errors

DNA polymerases make very few errors as they assemble new molecules. Most of the mistakes that do occur, called **base-pair mismatches**, are corrected, either by a proofreading mechanism carried out during replication by the DNA polymerases themselves or by a DNA repair mechanism that corrects mismatched base pairs after replication is complete.

12.4a Proofreading Depends on the Ability of DNA Polymerases to Reverse and Remove Mismatched Bases

The **proofreading mechanism**, first proposed in 1972 by Arthur Kornberg and Douglas L. Brutlag of Stanford University in California, depends on the ability of DNA polymerases to back up and remove mispaired nucleotides from a DNA strand. Only when the most recently added base is correctly paired with its complementary base on the template strand can the DNA polymerases continue to add nucleotides to a growing chain. The correct pairs allow the fully stabilizing hydrogen bonds to form **(Figure 12.19,** step 1). If a newly added nucleotide is mismatched (step 2), the DNA polymerase reverses using a built-in deoxyribonuclease to remove the newly added incorrect nucleotide (step 3). The enzyme resumes working forward, now inserting the correct nucleotide (step 4).

Several experiments have confirmed that the major DNA polymerases of replication can actually proofread their work in this way. For example, when the primary DNA polymerase that replicates DNA in bacteria is intact, with its reverse activity working, its overall error rate is astonishingly low—only about 1 mispair persists in the DNA for every 1 million nucleotides assembled in the test tube. If the proofreading activity of the enzyme is experimentally inhibited, the error rate increases to about 1 mistake for every 1000 to 10 000 nucleotides assembled. Experiments with eukaryotes have yielded similar results.

12.4b DNA Repair Corrects Errors That Escape Proofreading

Any base-pair mismatches that remain after proofreading face still another round of correction by **DNA repair mechanisms**. These **mismatch repair** mechanisms increase the accuracy of DNA replication well beyond the one-in-a-million errors that persist after proofreading. As noted earlier, the "correct" A-T and G-C base pairs fit together like pieces of a jigsaw puzzle, and their dimensions separate the sugar–phosphate backbone chains by a constant distance. Mispaired bases are too large or small to maintain the correct separation, and they cannot form the hydrogen

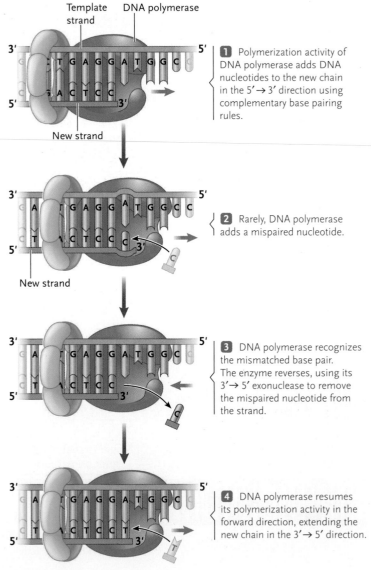

1. Polymerization activity of DNA polymerase adds DNA nucleotides to the new chain in the 5′ → 3′ direction using complementary base pairing rules.

2. Rarely, DNA polymerase adds a mispaired nucleotide.

3. DNA polymerase recognizes the mismatched base pair. The enzyme reverses, using its 3′ → 5′ exonuclease to remove the mispaired nucleotide from the strand.

4. DNA polymerase resumes its polymerization activity in the forward direction, extending the new chain in the 3′ → 5′ direction.

Figure 12.19
Proofreading by a DNA polymerase.

bonds characteristic of the normal base pairs. As a result, base mismatches distort the structure of the DNA helix. These distortions provide recognition sites for the enzymes catalyzing mismatch repair.

The repair enzymes move along the double helix, "scanning" the DNA for distortions in the newly synthesized nucleotide chain. If the enzymes encounter a distortion, they remove a portion of the new chain, including the mismatched nucleotides **(Figure 12.20, step 1)**. The gap left by the removal (step 2) is then filled by a DNA polymerase, using the template strand as a guide (step 3). The repair is completed by a DNA ligase, which seals the nucleotide chain into a continuous DNA molecule (step 4).

The same repair mechanisms also detect and correct alterations in DNA caused by the damaging effects of chemicals and radiation, including the ultraviolet light in sunlight. Some idea of the importance of the repair mechanisms comes from the unfortunate plight of individuals with *Xeroderma pigmentosum,* a hereditary disorder in which the repair mechanism is faulty. Because of the effects of unrepaired alterations in their DNA, skin cancer can develop quickly in these individuals if they are exposed to sunlight.

The rare replication errors that remain in DNA after proofreading and DNA repair are a primary source of **mutations,** differences in DNA sequence that appear and remain in the replicated copies. When a mutation occurs in a gene, it can alter the property of the protein encoded by the gene, which, in turn, may alter how the organism functions. Hence, mutations are highly important to the evolutionary process because they are the ultimate source of the variability in offspring acted on by natural selection.

We now turn from DNA replication and error correction to the arrangements of DNA in eukaryotic and prokaryotic cells. These arrangements organize superstructures that fit the long DNA molecules into the microscopic dimensions of cells and also contribute to the regulation of DNA activity.

STUDY BREAK

Why is a proofreading mechanism important for DNA replication?

12.5 DNA Organization in Eukaryotic versus Prokaryotic Cells

Enzymatic proteins are the essential catalysts of every step in DNA replication. In addition, numerous proteins of other types organize the DNA in both eukaryotic and prokaryotic cells in addition to controlling its expression.

In eukaryotes, two major types of proteins, the histone and nonhistone proteins, are associated with DNA structure and regulation in the nucleus. These proteins are known collectively as the **chromosomal proteins** of eukaryotes. The complex of DNA and its associated proteins, termed **chromatin,** is the structural building block of a chromosome.

By comparison, the single DNA molecule of a prokaryotic cell is more simply organized and has fewer associated proteins. However, prokaryotic DNA is still associated with two classes of proteins with functions similar to those of the eukaryotic histones and nonhistones: one class that organizes the DNA structurally and one that regulates gene activity. We begin this section with the major DNA-associated proteins of eukaryotes as they relate to packaging. The role of chromatin structure in gene regulation is addressed in Chapter 14.

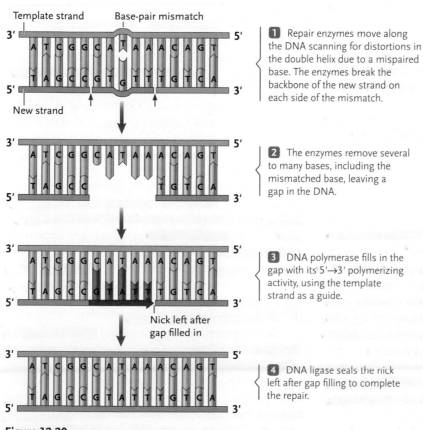

Figure 12.20
Repair of mismatched bases in replicated DNA.

1 Repair enzymes move along the DNA scanning for distortions in the double helix due to a mispaired base. The enzymes break the backbone of the new strand on each side of the mismatch.

2 The enzymes remove several to many bases, including the mismatched base, leaving a gap in the DNA.

3 DNA polymerase fills in the gap with its 5'→3' polymerizing activity, using the template strand as a guide.

4 DNA ligase seals the nick left after gap filling to complete the repair.

PEOPLE BEHIND BIOLOGY 12.2
Dr. Robert (Bob) Haynes, York University, Toronto

In 1944, the Austrian physicist Erwin Schrödinger published *What Is Life?* This small book speculated about the theoretical nature of the genetic material and prompted several physicists to turn their creativity to solving fundamental problems in the field of biology.

Cross-fertilization of these scientific disciplines energized research into the molecular biology of the gene and, specifically through the career of Bob Haynes, provided pioneering insights into the ways in which cells suffer and respond to DNA damage. Subsequent research has revealed that a breakdown in repair of DNA damage has important implications for cancer, aging, certain genetic diseases, and exposure to physical and chemical mutagens.

Born in 1931, Haynes earned undergraduate and Ph.D. degrees in biophysics from the University of Western Ontario before working as a postdoctoral fellow in physics at St. Bartholomew's Hospital Medical College, University of London. He joined the Biophysics Departments of the University of Chicago and the University of California at Berkeley before returning to Canada in 1968 as chair of the Biology Department at York University in Toronto. Upon his death in 1998, Haynes was a fellow of the Royal Society of Canada and an officer of the Order of Canada in recognition of his broad contributions to research in environmental mutagenesis, international leadership, and science education.

12.5a Histones Pack Eukaryotic DNA at Successive Levels of Organization

The **histones** are a class of small, positively charged (basic) proteins that are complexed with DNA in the chromosomes of eukaryotes. (Most other cellular proteins are larger and are neutral or negatively charged.) The histones link to DNA by an attraction between their positive charges and the negatively charged phosphate groups of the DNA.

Five types of histones exist in most eukaryotic cells: H1, H2A, H2B, H3, and H4. The amino acid sequences of these proteins are highly similar among eukaryotes, suggesting that they perform the same functions in all eukaryotic organisms.

One function of histones is to pack DNA molecules into the narrow confines of the cell nucleus. For example, each human cell nucleus contains 2 m of DNA. Combination with the histones compacts this length so much that it fits into nuclei that are only about 10 μm in diameter.

Histones and DNA Packing. The histones pack DNA at several levels of chromatin structure. In the most fundamental structure, called a **nucleosome**, two molecules each of H2A, H2B, H3, and H4 combine to form a beadlike, eight-protein **nucleosome core particle** around which DNA winds for almost two turns **(Figure 12.21)**. A short segment of DNA, the **linker**, extends between one nucleosome and the next. Under the electron microscope, this structure looks like beads on a string. The diameter of the beads (the nucleosomes) gives this structure its name—the **10 nm chromatin fibre** (see Figure 12.21).

Each nucleosome and linker includes about 200 base pairs of DNA. Nucleosomes compact DNA by a factor of about 7; that is, a length of DNA becomes about one-seventh the length when it is wrapped into nucleosomes.

Histones and Chromatin Fibres. The fifth histone, H1, brings about the next level of chromatin packing. One H1 molecule binds both to the nucleosomes and to the linker DNA. This binding causes the nucleosomes to package into a coiled structure 30 nm in diameter, called the **30 nm chromatin fibre** or **solenoid**, with about six nucleosomes per turn (see Figure 12.21).

The arrangement of DNA in nucleosomes and solenoids compacts the DNA and probably also protects it from chemical and mechanical damage. In the test tube, DNA wound into nucleosomes and chromatin fibres is much more resistant to degradation by deoxyribonuclease (a DNA-digesting enzyme) than when it is not bound to histone proteins.

Packing at Still Higher Levels: Euchromatin and Heterochromatin. In interphase nuclei, chromatin fibres are loosely packed in some regions and densely packed in others. The loosely packed regions are known as **euchromatin** (*eu* = true, regular, or typical), and the densely packed regions are called **heterochromatin** (*hetero* = different). Chromatin fibres also fold and pack into the thick, rodlike chromosomes that become visible during mitosis and meiosis.

Several experiments indicate that heterochromatin represents large blocks of genes that have been turned off and placed in a compact storage form. For example, recall the process of X-chromosome inactivation in mammalian females (see Section 11.2). As one of the two X chromosomes becomes inactive in cells early in development, it packs down into a block of heterochromatin called the *Barr body,* which is large enough to see

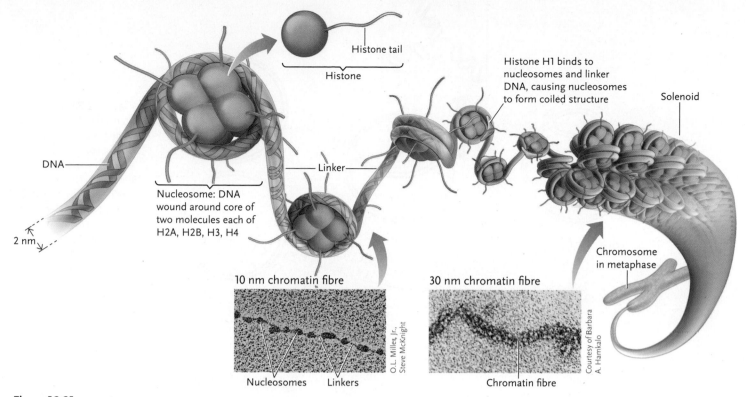

Figure 12.21
Levels of organization in eukaryotic chromatin and chromosomes.

under the light microscope. These findings support the idea that, in addition to organizing nuclear DNA, histones play a role in regulating gene activity.

12.5b Many Nonhistone Proteins Have Key Roles in the Regulation of Gene Expression

Nonhistone proteins are loosely defined as all the proteins associated with DNA that are not histones. Nonhistones vary widely in structure; most are negatively charged or neutral, but some are positively charged. They range in size from polypeptides smaller than histones to some of the largest cellular proteins.

Many nonhistone proteins help control the expression of individual genes. (The regulation of gene expression is the subject of Chapter 14.) For example, expression of a gene requires that the enzymes and proteins for that process be able to access the gene in the chromatin. If a gene is packed into heterochromatin, it is unavailable for activation. If the gene is in the more extended euchromatin, it is more accessible. Many nonhistone proteins affect gene accessibility by modifying histones to change how they associate with DNA in chromatin, either loosening or tightening the association. Other nonhistone proteins are regulatory proteins that activate or repress the expression of a gene. Yet others are components of the enzyme–protein complexes that are needed for the expression of any gene.

12.5c DNA Is Organized More Simply in Prokaryotes than in Eukaryotes

Several features of DNA organization in prokaryotic cells differ fundamentally from eukaryotic DNA. In contrast to the linear DNA in eukaryotes, the primary DNA molecule of most prokaryotic cells is circular, with only one copy per cell. In parallel with eukaryotic terminology, the DNA molecule is called a **bacterial chromosome.** The chromosome of the best-known bacterium, *E. coli*, includes about 1360 μm of DNA, which is equivalent to 4.6 million base pairs. There are exceptions: some bacteria have two or more different chromosomes in the cell, and some bacterial chromosomes are linear.

Replication begins from a single origin in the DNA circle, forming two forks that travel around the circle in opposite directions. Eventually, the forks meet at the opposite side from the origin to complete replication **(Figure 12.22, p. 280).**

Inside prokaryotic cells, the DNA circle is packed and folded into an irregularly shaped mass called the **nucleoid** (shown in Figure 2.7, Chapter 2). The DNA of the nucleoid is suspended directly in the cytoplasm with no surrounding membrane.

Many prokaryotic cells also contain other DNA molecules, called **plasmids,** in addition to the main chromosome of the nucleoid. Most plasmids are circular, although some are linear. Plasmids have replication origins and are duplicated and distributed to daughter cells

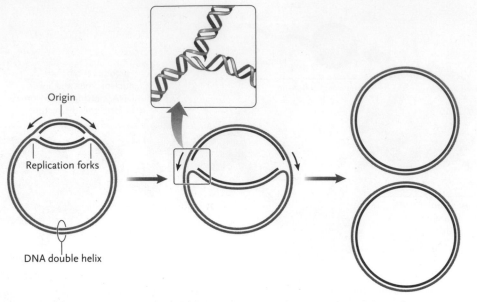

Figure 12.22
Replication from a single origin of replication in a circular bacterial chromosome.

Figure 12.23
Transfer of F factor by rolling circle replication during conjugation. One of the two strands of the plasmid is nicked and the 5′ end moves from the donor into a recipient cell. The remaining circular strand "rolls" like a tape dispenser. DNA synthesis is continuous in the donor cell and discontinuous in the recipient (arrows), resulting in two complete plasmids.

together with the bacterial chromosome during cell division. Chapter 9 describes the process of conjugation, in which plasmids are replicated while being transferred from a donor cell to a recipient cell. The DNA is replicated by a mechanism called rolling circle replication, in which one strand of the plasmid is cut and travels into a recipient cell as a linear molecule; the other strand remains circular in the donor cell **(Figure 12.23)**. DNA replication restores both strands to double-strandedness, and the linear molecule recircularizes. Although rolling circle replication follows the usual rules of DNA replication, notice that the leading and lagging strand synthesis occur in separate cells rather than at one replication fork.

Although bacterial DNA is not organized into nucleosomes, there are positively charged proteins that combine with bacterial DNA. Some of these proteins help organize the DNA into loops, thereby providing some compaction of the molecule. Bacterial DNA also combines with many types of genetic regulatory proteins that have functions similar to those of the nonhistone proteins of eukaryotes (see Chapter 14).

With this description of prokaryotic DNA organization, our survey of DNA structure and its replication and organization is complete. The next chapter revisits the same structures and discusses how they function in the expression of information encoded in DNA.

STUDY BREAK

1. What is the structure of the nucleosome?
2. What is the role of histone H1 in eukaryotic chromosome structure?

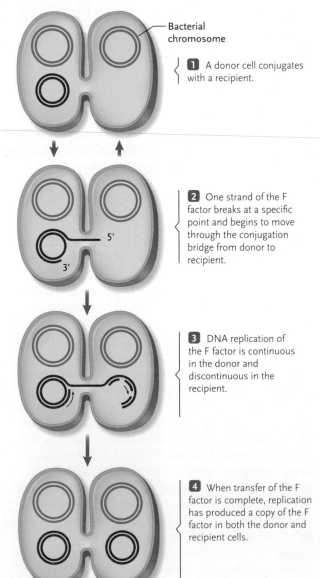

Bacterial chromosome

1 A donor cell conjugates with a recipient.

2 One strand of the F factor breaks at a specific point and begins to move through the conjugation bridge from donor to recipient.

3 DNA replication of the F factor is continuous in the donor and discontinuous in the recipient.

4 When transfer of the F factor is complete, replication has produced a copy of the F factor in both the donor and recipient cells.

Review

CourseMate Access an interactive eBook, chapter-specific interactive learning tools, including flashcards, quizzes, videos, and more in your Biology **CourseMate**, accessed through NelsonBrain.com **Aplia™** is an online interactive learning solution that helps you improve comprehension—and your grade—by integrating a variety of mediums and tools such as videos, tutorials, practice tests, and an interactive eBook.

12.1 Establishing DNA as the Hereditary Molecule

- Griffith found that a substance derived from killed virulent *Streptococcus pneumoniae* bacteria could transform nonvirulent living *S. pneumoniae* bacteria to the virulent type (Figure 12.2).

- Avery and his coworkers showed that DNA, and not protein or RNA, was the molecule responsible for transforming *S. pneumoniae* bacteria into the virulent form.

- Hershey and Chase showed that the DNA of a phage, not the protein, enters bacterial cells to direct the life cycle of the virus. Taken together, the experiments of Griffith, Avery and his coworkers, and Hershey and Chase established that DNA is the hereditary molecule (Figure 12.3).

12.2 DNA Structure

- Watson and Crick discovered that a DNA molecule consists of two polynucleotide chains twisted around each other into a right-handed double helix. Each nucleotide of the chains consists of deoxyribose; a phosphate group; and one of adenine, thymine, guanine, and cytosine. The deoxyribose sugars are linked by phosphate groups to form an alternating sugar–phosphate backbone. The two strands are held together by hydrogen bonded adenine–thymine (A-T) and guanine–cytosine (G-C) base pairs. Each full turn of the double helix involves 10 base pairs (Figures 12.4 and 12.6).

- The two strands of the DNA double helix are antiparallel.

12.3 DNA Replication

- DNA is duplicated by semiconservative replication, in which the two strands of a parental DNA molecule unwind and each serves as a template for the synthesis of a complementary copy (Figures 12.7–12.9).

- Several enzymes catalyze DNA replication. Helicase unwinds the DNA; primase synthesizes an RNA primer used as a starting point for nucleotide assembly by DNA polymerases. DNA polymerases assemble nucleotides into a polymer, one at a time, in a sequence complementary to the sequence of bases in the template. After a DNA polymerase removes the primers and fills in the resulting gaps, DNA ligase closes the remaining single-strand nicks (Figures 12.10–12.12 and 12.15).

- As the DNA helix unwinds, only one template runs in a direction that allows the new DNA strand to be made continuously in the direction of unwinding. The other template strand is copied in short lengths that run in the direction opposite to unwinding.

The short lengths produced by this discontinuous replication are then linked into a continuous strand (Figures 12.14 and 12.15).

- DNA synthesis begins at sites that act as replication origins and proceeds from the origins as two replication forks moving in opposite directions (Figures 12.16 and 12.17).

- The ends of eukaryotic chromosomes consist of telomeres: short sequences repeated hundreds to thousands of times. These repeats provide a buffer against chromosome shortening during replication. Although most somatic cells show this chromosome shortening, some cell types do not because they have a telomerase enzyme that adds telomere repeats to the chromosome ends (Figure 12.18).

12.4 Mechanisms That Correct Replication Errors

- In proofreading, the DNA polymerase reverses and removes the most recently added base if it is mispaired as a result of a replication error. The enzyme then resumes DNA synthesis in the forward direction (Figure 12.19).

- In DNA mismatch repair, enzymes recognize distorted regions caused by mispaired base pairs and remove a section of DNA that includes the mispaired base from the newly synthesized nucleotide chain. A DNA polymerase then resynthesizes the section correctly, using the original template chain as a guide (Figure 12.20).

12.5 DNA Organization in Eukaryotes and Prokaryotes

- Eukaryotic chromosomes consist of DNA complexed with histone and nonhistone proteins.

- In eukaryotic chromosomes, DNA is wrapped around a core consisting of two molecules each of histones H2A, H2B, H3, and H4 to produce a nucleosome. Linker DNA connects adjacent nucleosomes. The chromosome structure in this form is the 10 nm chromatin fibre. The binding of histone H1 causes the nucleosomes to package into a coiled structure called the 30 nm chromatin fibre (Figure 12.21).

- Chromatin is distributed between euchromatin, a loosely packed region in which genes are active in RNA transcription, and heterochromatin, densely packed masses in which genes, if present, are inactive. Chromatin also folds and packs to form thick, rodlike chromosomes during nuclear division.

- Nonhistone proteins help control the expression of individual genes.

- The bacterial chromosome is a closed, circular double helix of DNA; it is packed into the nucleoid region of the cell. Replication begins from a single origin and proceeds in both directions. Many bacteria also contain plasmids, which replicate independently of the host chromosome (Figure 12.22).

- Bacterial DNA is organized into loops through interaction with proteins. Other proteins similar to eukaryotic nonhistones regulate gene activity in prokaryotic organisms.

Questions

Self-Test Questions

1. Working on the Amazon River, a biologist isolated DNA from two unknown organisms, P and Q. He discovered that the adenine content of P was 15% and the cytosine content of Q was 42%. Which of the following conclusions can be drawn?
   a. The amount of adenine in Q is 42%.
   b. The amount of guanine in P is 15%.
   c. The amount of guanine and cytosine combined in P is 70%.
   d. The amount of thymine in Q is 21%.

2. The Hershey and Chase experiment involved infecting bacterial cells with radioactively labelled viruses. What did this experiment show?
   a. ^{35}S-labelled DNA ended up inside the virus progeny.
   b. ^{32}P-labelled DNA entered bacterial cells.
   c. ^{35}S-labelled protein was incorporated into bacterial cells.
   d. ^{32}P-labelled protein was incorporated into virus coats.

3. Which of the following would appear on a list of pyrimidines?
   a. cytosine and thymine
   b. cytosine and guanine
   c. adenine and thymine
   d. adenine and guanine

4. Which of the following statements about DNA replication is true?
   a. DNA polymerase III extends an RNA primer.
   b. Some DNA polymerases can add new bases to the 5′ end of a growing strand.
   c. Each eukaryotic chromosome has a single origin of replication.
   d. Okazaki fragments are made only of RNA.

5. Which of the following statements about DNA structure is true?
   a. Each DNA strand has a 3′ OH on one end and a 5′ OH on the other end.
   b. Each strand of the double helix runs parallel to the other.
   c. The binding of adenine to thymine is through three hydrogen bonds.
   d. Bonds between components of the backbone (i.e., sugar–phosphate) are stronger than those between one strand and the other.

6. In the Meselson and Stahl experiment, the DNA in the parental generation was all ^{15}N^{15}N, and after one round of replication, the DNA was all ^{15}N^{14}N. What ratio of DNA would be seen after three rounds of replication?
   a. one ^{15}N^{14}N : one ^{14}N^{14}N
   b. one ^{15}N^{14}N : two ^{14}N^{14}N
   c. one ^{15}N^{14}N : three ^{14}N^{14}N
   d. one ^{15}N^{14}N : four ^{14}N^{14}N

7. Since DNA is synthesized in the 5′ → 3′ direction, which of the following must be true?
   a. The template must be read in the 5′ → 3′ direction.
   b. Polymerase must add successive nucleotides to the 3′ –OH end of the newly forming chain.
   c. Ligase must unwind the two DNA strands in opposite directions.
   d. Primase must add RNA nucleotides to the growing 5′ end.

8. Which of the following is a characteristic of telomerase?
   a. It is active in cancer cells.
   b. It is more active in adult than in embryonic cells.
   c. It has telomeres made of RNA.
   d. It shortens the ends of chromosomes.

9. What does the process of mismatch repair accomplish?
   a. It seals Okazaki fragments with ligase into a continual DNA strand.
   b. It removes RNA primers and replaces them with the correct DNA.
   c. It restores DNA sequence that is lost during the replication of the ends of chromosomes.
   d. It replaces incorrect bases that escape proofreading by DNA polymerase.

10. The DNA of prokaryotic organisms differs from that of eukaryotes. In what way?
    a. Prokaryotic DNA is surrounded by densely packed histones; eukaryotic DNA is not.
    b. Prokaryotic DNA has many sites for the initiation of DNA replication; eukaryotic DNA does not.
    c. Prokaryotic DNA is typically single stranded; eukaryotic DNA is typically double stranded.
    d. Prokaryotic DNA is rarely packaged in linear chromosomes, eukaryotic DNA is commonly packaged in linear chromosomes.

Questions for Discussion

1. Chargaff's data suggested that adenine pairs with thymine and guanine pairs with cytosine. What other data available to Watson and Crick suggested that adenine–guanine and cytosine–thymine pairs normally do not form?

2. Exposing cells to radioactive thymidine can label eukaryotic chromosomes during the S phase of interphase. If cells are exposed to radioactive thymidine during the S phase, would you expect both or only one of the sister chromatids of a duplicated chromosome to be labelled at metaphase of the following mitosis (see Section 8.3)?

3. If the cells in question 2 finish division and then enter another round of DNA replication in a medium that has been washed free of radioactive label, would you expect both or only one of the sister chromatids of a duplicated chromosome to be labelled at metaphase of the following mitosis?

4. During replication, an error uncorrected by proofreading or mismatch repair produces a DNA molecule with a base mismatch at the indicated position:

   AATTCCGACTCCTATGG

   TTAAGGTTGAGGATACC

   ↑

   This DNA molecule is received by one of the two daughter cells produced by mitosis. In the next round of replication and division, the mutation appears in only one of the two daughter cells. Develop a hypothesis to explain this observation.

5. Strains of bacteria that are resistant to an antibiotic sometimes appear spontaneously among other bacteria of the same type that are killed by the antibiotic. In view of the information in this chapter about DNA replication, what might account for the appearance of this resistance?

Transcription of a eukaryotic gene to produce messenger RNA (mRNA), a type of RNA that acts as a template for protein synthesis. The DNA of the gene unwinds from the nucleosome (left side) and is copied by an RNA polymerase (centre) into mRNA (exiting the top).

© LookatSciences/Phototake

STUDY PLAN

13.1 The Connection between DNA, RNA, and Protein

13.1a Genes Specify Either Protein or RNA Products

13.1b The Pathway from Gene to Polypeptide Involves Transcription and Translation

13.1c The Genetic Code Is Written in Three-Letter Words Using a Four-Letter Alphabet

13.2 Transcription: DNA-Directed RNA Synthesis

13.2a Transcription Proceeds in Three Steps

13.2b Transcription of Non-Protein-Coding Genes Occurs in a Similar Way

13.3 Processing of mRNAs in Eukaryotes

13.3a Eukaryotic Protein-Coding Genes Are Transcribed into Precursor mRNAs That Are Modified in the Nucleus

13.3b Introns Are Removed during Pre-mRNA Processing to Produce Translatable mRNA

13.3c Introns Contribute to Protein Variability

13.4 Translation: mRNA-Directed Polypeptide Synthesis

13.4a tRNAs Are Small RNAs of a Highly Distinctive Structure That Bring Amino Acids to the Ribosome

13.4b Ribosomes Are rRNA–Protein Complexes That Work as Automated Protein Assembly Machines

13.4c Translation Initiation Brings the Ribosomal Subunits, an mRNA, and the First Aminoacyl–tRNA Together

13.4d Polypeptide Chains Grow during the Elongation Stage of Translation

13.4e Termination Releases a Completed Polypeptide from the Ribosome

13.4f Multiple Ribosomes Simultaneously Translate a Single mRNA

13.4g Newly Synthesized Polypeptides Are Processed and Folded into Finished Form

13.4h Finished Proteins Are Sorted to the Cellular Locations Where They Function

13.4i Mutations Can Affect Protein Structure and Function

13 Gene Structure and Expression

WHY IT MATTERS

The marine mussel *Mytilus* **(Figure 13.1, p. 284)** lives in one of the most demanding environments on the Earth—it clings permanently to rocks pounded by surf day in and day out, constantly in danger of being dashed to pieces or torn loose by foraging predators. The mussel is remarkably resistant to disturbance. If you try to pry one loose, you will find how difficult it is to tear the tough, elastic fibres that hold it fast. They are even hard to cut with a knife.

The fibres holding mussels to rocks are proteins secreted by the muscular foot of the animal. The proteins include keratin (an intermediate filament protein) and another resinous protein. Along with other proteins, they form a tough, adhesive material called byssus.

Byssus is one of the world's premier underwater adhesives. It fascinates biochemists, adhesive manufacturers, dentists, and surgeons looking for better ways to hold repaired body parts together. Genetic engineers are inserting segments of mussel deoxyribonucleic acid (DNA) into yeast cells, which reproduce in large numbers and serve as "factories," translating the mussel genes into proteins. Among the proteins produced are those of byssus, allowing investigators to figure out how to use or imitate the mussel glue for human

Figure 13.1
The marine mussel *Mytilus* and its natural habitat.

needs. This exciting work, like the mussel's own byssus building, starts with one of life's universal truths: *Every protein is assembled on ribosomes according to instructions dictated by genes coded in DNA.*

In this chapter, we trace the basic process that produces proteins in all organisms, beginning with the instructions encoded in DNA and leading through ribonucleic acid (RNA) to the sequence of amino acids in a protein. Many enzymes and other proteins are players as well as products in this story, as are several kinds of RNA and the cell's protein-making machines, the ribosomes. As your understanding of the fundamental elements of all protein production grows, be sure to notice the differences in the kinds of information coded in DNA, differences in the mechanisms in prokaryotic cells versus eukaryotes, and differences in the structure of genes that code for protein versus those that code for RNA.

13.1 The Connection between DNA, RNA, and Protein

Although the relationship between proteins and nucleic acids was once uncertain, it is now common knowledge that proteins are encoded by genes made of DNA. In this section, you will learn how that connection was discovered. We also present an overview of the molecular steps needed to go from gene to protein: transcription and translation.

13.1a Genes Specify Either Protein or RNA Products

How do we know that genes encode—that is, specify the amino acid sequence of—proteins? Two key pieces of research involving defects in metabolism illustrated this connection unequivocally. The first began in 1896 with Archibald Garrod, an English physician. He studied *alkaptonuria,* a human disease that does little harm but is detected easily by the fact that a patient's urine turns black when exposed to oxygen. Garrod and William Bateson, a geneticist, studied families of patients with the disease and concluded that it is an inherited trait.

Garrod also found that people with alkaptonuria excrete a particular compound, homogentisic acid, in their urine. Garrod concluded that normal people are able to metabolize the homogentisic acid, whereas people with alkaptonuria cannot. By 1908, Garrod had concluded that the disease was an inborn error of metabolism. Garrod's work was the first to show a specific relationship between genes and metabolism.

In the second piece of research, George Beadle and Edward Tatum, working in the 1940s with the orange bread mould *Neurospora crassa,* collected data showing a direct relationship between genes and enzymes. Beadle and Tatum chose *Neurospora* for their work because it is a haploid fungus with simple nutritional needs. That is, wild-type *Neurospora*—the form of the mould found in nature—grows readily on a minimal medium (MM) consisting of a number of inorganic salts, sucrose, and a vitamin. The researchers reasoned that the fungus uses only simple chemicals in the medium to synthesize all of the more complex molecules needed for growth and reproduction, including amino acids for proteins and nucleotides for DNA and RNA.

Beadle and Tatum exposed spores of wild-type *Neurospora* to X-rays that caused mutations. They found that some of the treated spores would not germinate and grow unless MM was supplemented with additional nutrients, such as amino acids or vitamins. Mutant strains that are unable to grow on MM are called auxotrophs (*auxo* = increased; *troph* = eater), or nutritional mutants. Beadle and Tatum hypothesized that each auxotrophic strain had a defect in a gene coding for an enzyme needed to synthesize a nutrient that now had to be added to the MM. The wild-type strain could make the nutrient for itself from raw materials in the MM, but the mutant strain could grow only if the researchers supplied the nutrient. By testing to see if each mutant strain would grow on MM supplemented with a given nutrient, Beadle and Tatum discovered which specific nutrient each mutant needed to grow and, therefore, which gene defect it had. For example, a mutant that required the addition of the amino acid arginine to grow had a defect in a gene for an enzyme involved in the synthesis of arginine. Such arginine auxotrophs are known as *arg* mutants. The assembly of arginine from raw materials is a multi-step "assembly-line" process with a different enzyme catalyzing each step. Therefore, different *arg* mutants might have defects in different enzymes and therefore have blocks at different steps in the assembly line. (This is conceptually similar to Lederberg's work with auxotrophic bacteria described in Chapter 9.)

Beadle and Tatum determined where in the arginine synthesis pathway each of four mutants (*argE, argF, argG,* and *argH*) was blocked. They tested whether each mutant could grow on MM or on MM supplemented with one of ornithine, citrulline, argininosuccinate (three compounds known to be involved in the synthesis of arginine), or and arginine itself (**Figure 13.2**). While none of the four

QUESTION: Do genes specify enzymes?

EXPERIMENT: Test *arg* mutants of the orange bread mould *Neurospora crassa* for growth on MM (minimal medium), MM + ornithine, MM + citrulline, MM + argininosuccinate, and MM + arginine. *Arg* mutants are unable to synthesize the amino acid arginine, which is essential for growth.

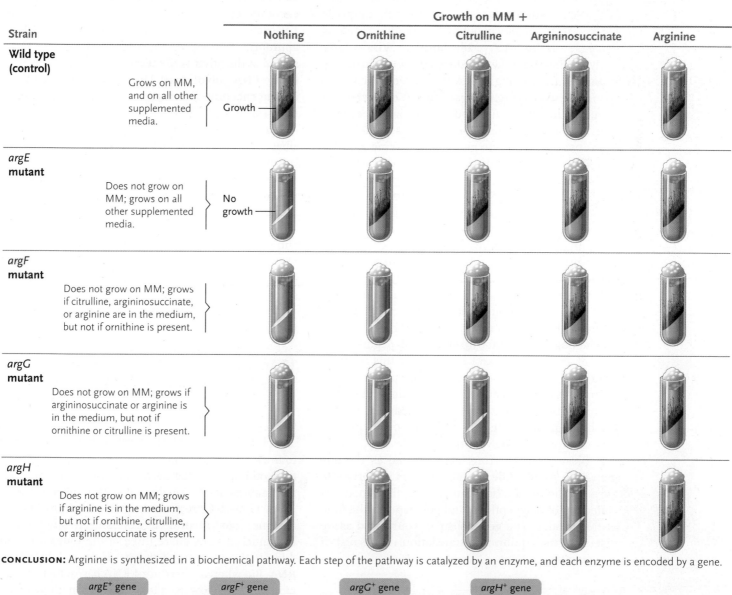

CONCLUSION: Arginine is synthesized in a biochemical pathway. Each step of the pathway is catalyzed by an enzyme, and each enzyme is encoded by a gene.

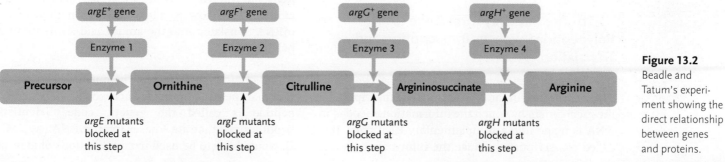

Figure 13.2
Beadle and Tatum's experiment showing the direct relationship between genes and proteins.

mutants could grow on MM because it was lacking arginine, they all grew well on MM + arginine. Each of the *arg* mutants showed a different pattern of growth on the supplemented MM (see Figure 13.2, p. 285). Beadle and Tatum deduced that the biosynthesis of arginine occurred in a number of steps, with each step controlled by a gene that encoded the enzyme for the step (see Figure 13.2, p. 285, bottom). For example, the *argH* mutant grows on MM + arginine but not on MM + any of the other three compounds; this means that the mutant is blocked at the last step in the pathway, which produces arginine. Similarly, the *argG* mutant grows on MM + arginine or argininosuccinate but not on MM + any of the other supplements; this means that *argG* is blocked in the pathway before argininosuccinate is made (see Figure 13.2, p. 285, bottom). With similar analysis, the researchers deduced the whole pathway from precursor to arginine and showed which gene encoded the enzyme that carried out each step. In sum, Beadle and Tatum had shown the direct relationship between genes and enzymes, which they put forward as the **one gene–one enzyme hypothesis**. Their experiment was a keystone in the development of molecular biology. As a result of their work, they were awarded a Nobel Prize in 1958.

It is important to understand that protein structure and function are now known to be more complex than suggested by the work of Beadle and Tatum. Many proteins consist of more than one subunit. Each of these subunits is a separate molecule, called a polypeptide, that is coded by a separate gene. Polypeptides can assemble to create a functional cluster of molecules called a protein. For instance, the protein hemoglobin is made up of four polypeptides, two each of an α subunit and a β subunit; this composition gives the protein its functional property of transporting oxygen rather than catalyzing a chemical reaction. Two different genes are needed to encode the hemoglobin protein: one for the α polypeptide and one for the β polypeptide. Beadle and Tatum's hypothesis was therefore later restated as the **one gene–one polypeptide hypothesis.** It is important to keep the distinction between protein, the functional collection of polypeptides, and polypeptide, the molecule encoded by a gene, clear in your mind as we discuss transcription and translation in the rest of this chapter.

13.1b The Pathway from Gene to Polypeptide Involves Transcription and Translation

The pathway from gene to polypeptide has two major steps, transcription and translation. **Transcription** is the mechanism by which the information encoded in DNA is made into a complementary RNA copy. It is called transcription because the information in one nucleic acid type is transferred to another nucleic acid type. **Translation** is the use of the information encoded in the RNA to assemble amino acids into a polypeptide. It is called translation because the information in a nucleic acid, in the form of nucleotides, is converted into a different kind of molecule—amino acids. In 1956, Francis Crick gave the name Central Dogma to the flow of information from DNA to RNA to protein.

In transcription, the enzyme RNA polymerase creates an RNA sequence that is complementary to the DNA sequence of a given gene. The process follows the same basic rules of complementary base-pairing and nucleic acid chemistry that we first encountered in DNA replication (see Chapter 12). For each of the several thousand genes that will be appropriate to express in a given cell, one DNA strand or the other is the **template strand** and is read by the RNA polymerase. The RNA transcribed from a gene encoding a polypeptide is called **messenger RNA (mRNA)**.

In translation, an mRNA associates with a **ribosome**, a particle on which amino acids are linked into polypeptide chains. As the ribosome moves along the mRNA, the amino acids specified by the mRNA are joined one by one to form the polypeptide encoded by the gene.

The processes of transcription and translation are similar in prokaryotic and eukaryotic cells **(Figure 13.3).** One key difference is that, whereas prokaryotic cells can transcribe and translate a given gene simultaneously, eukaryotic cells transcribe and process mRNA in the nucleus before exporting it to the cytoplasm for translation on ribosomes.

13.1c The Genetic Code Is Written in Three-Letter Words Using a Four-Letter Alphabet

Conceptually, the transcription of DNA into RNA is straightforward. The DNA "alphabet" consists of the four letters A, T, G, and C, representing the four DNA nucleotide bases, adenine, thymine, guanine, and cytosine, and the RNA alphabet consists of the four letters A, U, G, and C, representing the four RNA bases, adenine, uracil, guanine, and cytosine. In other words, both nucleic acids share three of the four bases but differ in the other one: T in DNA is equivalent to U in RNA. But whereas there are 4 RNA bases, there are 20 amino acids. How is nucleotide information in an mRNA translated into the amino acid sequence of a polypeptide?

Breaking the Genetic Code. The nucleotide information that specifies the amino acid sequence of a polypeptide is called the **genetic code.** Scientists hypothesized that the 4 bases in an mRNA (A, U, G, C) would have to be used in combinations of at least

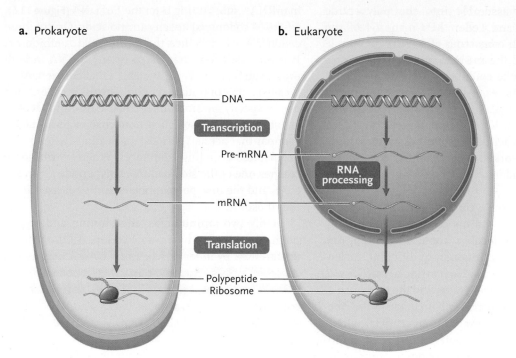

a. Prokaryote

b. Eukaryote

DNA

Transcription

Pre-mRNA

RNA processing

mRNA

Translation

Polypeptide
Ribosome

Figure 13.3

Transcription and translation in **(a)** prokaryotic and **(b)** eukaryotic cells. In prokaryotic cells, RNA polymerase synthesizes an mRNA molecule that is immediately available for translation on ribosomes. In eukaryotes, RNA polymerase synthesizes a precursor–mRNA (pre-mRNA molecule) containing extra segments that are removed by RNA processing to produce a translatable mRNA. That mRNA exits the nucleus through a nuclear pore and is translated on ribosomes in the cytoplasm. Note that only a small segment of DNA is shown. In prokaryotic cells the chromosome is circular.

3 to provide the capacity to code for 20 amino acids. One- and two-letter words were eliminated because if the code used one-letter words, only 4 different amino acids could be specified (that is, 4^1); if two-letter words were used, only 16 different amino acids could be specified (that is, 4^2). But if the code used three-letter words, 64 different amino acids could be specified (that is, 4^3), more than enough to specify 20 amino acids. We know now that the genetic code is indeed a three-letter code; each three-letter word (triplet) is called a **codon. Figure 13.4** illustrates the relationship among a gene, codons in an mRNA, and the amino acid sequence of a polypeptide. Genetic information in DNA is first transcribed into complementary three-letter RNA codons (the RNA complement to adenine [A] in the template strand is uracil [U] instead of thymine [T]).

CONCEPT FIX The template strand for a given gene is always read 3′ to 5′. For gene *a* in Figure 13.4, the bottom strand is the template, and is therefore read left to right. However, the template for gene *b* might be the top strand; RNA polymerase would then have to read right to left. ⬡

How do the codons correspond to the amino acids? Marshall Nirenberg and Philip Leder of the National Institutes of Health (NIH) in the United States established the identity of most of the codons in 1964. These researchers found that short, artificial mRNAs of codon length—three nucleotides—could bind to ribosomes in a test tube and cause a single transfer RNA (tRNA), with its linked amino acid, to bind to the ribosome. (As we will discuss in Section 13.4, tRNAs are a special class of RNA molecules that bring amino acids to

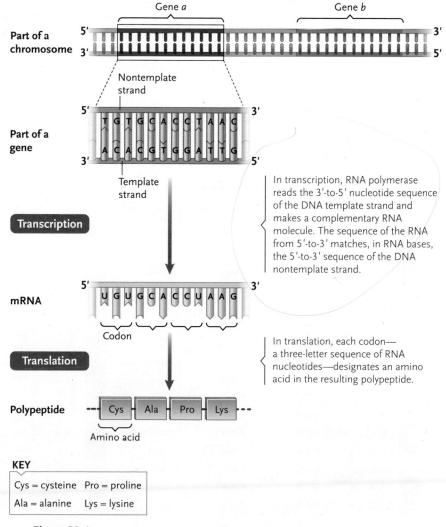

Gene *a*   Gene *b*

Part of a chromosome   5′   3′
                        3′   5′

Nontemplate strand

Part of a gene   5′ T G T G C A C C T A A C 3′
                  3′ A C A C G T G G A T T G 5′

Template strand

Transcription

In transcription, RNA polymerase reads the 3′-to-5′ nucleotide sequence of the DNA template strand and makes a complementary RNA molecule. The sequence of the RNA from 5′-to-3′ matches, in RNA bases, the 5′-to-3′ sequence of the DNA nontemplate strand.

mRNA   5′ U G U G C A C C U A A G 3′

Codon

Translation

In translation, each codon—a three-letter sequence of RNA nucleotides—designates an amino acid in the resulting polypeptide.

Polypeptide - - - Cys — Ala — Pro — Lys - - -

Amino acid

KEY

Cys = cysteine	Pro = proline
Ala = alanine	Lys = lysine

Figure 13.4

Relationship among a gene, codons in an mRNA, and the amino acid sequence of a polypeptide.

the ribosome for assembly into the polypeptide chain.) Nirenberg and Leder then made 64 of the short mRNAs, each consisting of a different, single codon. They added the mRNAs, one at a time, to a mixture in a test tube containing ribosomes and all the different tRNAs, each linked to its own amino acid. The idea was that, from the mixture of tRNAs, each single-codon mRNA would link to the tRNA carrying the amino acid corresponding to the codon. The experiment worked for 50 of the 64 codons, allowing those codons to be assigned to amino acids definitively.

Another approach, carried out in 1966 by H. Ghobind Khorana and his coworkers, used long, artificial mRNA molecules containing only one nucleotide repeated continuously or different nucleotides in repeating patterns. Each artificial mRNA was added to ribosomes in a test tube, and the sequence of amino acids in the polypeptide chain made by the ribosomes was analyzed. For example, an artificial mRNA containing only uracil nucleotides in the sequence UUUUUU... resulted in a polypeptide containing only the amino acid phenylalanine; they deduced that UUU must be the codon for phenylalanine. Khorana's approach, combined with the results of Nirenberg and Leder's experiments, identified the coding assignments of all the codons. Nirenberg and Khorana received a Nobel Prize in 1968 for solving the nucleic acid code.

Features of the Genetic Code. By convention, scientists write the codons in the 5′ → 3′ direction as they appear in mRNAs, substituting U for the T of DNA **(Figure 13.5).** Of the 64 codons, 61 specify amino acids. One of these codons, AUG, specifies the amino acid methionine. It is the first codon translated in any mRNA in both prokaryotic cells and eukaryotes. In that position, AUG is called a **start** or **initiator codon.** The three codons that do not specify amino acids—UAA, UAG, and UGA—are **stop codons** (also called **nonsense** or **termination codons**) that act as "periods" indicating the end of a polypeptide-encoding sentence. When a ribosome reaches one of the stop codons, polypeptide synthesis stops and the new polypeptide chain is released from the ribosome.

Only two amino acids, methionine and tryptophan, are specified by a single codon. All the rest are represented by at least two; some by as many as six. In other words, there are many synonyms in the nucleic acid code, a feature known as **degeneracy** (or redundancy). For example, UGU and UGC both specify cysteine, and CCU, CCC, CCA, and CCG all specify proline.

Another feature of the genetic code is that it is **commaless;** that is, the words of the nucleic acid code are sequential, with no indicators such as commas or spaces to mark the end of one codon and the beginning of the next. Therefore, the code can be read correctly only by starting at the right place—at the first base of the first three-letter codon at the beginning of a coded message (the start codon)—and reading three nucleotides at a time. In other words, there is only one correct **reading frame** for each mRNA. For example, if you read the message SADMOMHASMOPCUTOFFBOYTOT three letters at a time, starting with the first letter of the first "codon," you would find that a mother reluctantly had her small child's hair cut. However, if you start incorrectly at the second letter of the first codon, you read the gibberish message ADM OMH ASM OPC UTO FFB OYT OT.

The code is also **universal.** With a few exceptions, the same codons specify the same amino acids in all living organisms, and even in viruses. The universality of the nucleic acid code indicates that it was established in its present form very early in the evolution of life and has remained virtually unchanged through billions of years of evolutionary history. Consistency in the genetic code makes genetic engineering possible. In Chapter 15, you will see how genes from one organism can be transferred to, and interpreted, by another.

Second base of codon

First base of codon	U	C	A	G	Third base of codon
U	UUU Phe	UCU Ser	UAU Tyr	UGU Cys	U
U	UUC Phe	UCC Ser	UAC Tyr	UGC Cys	C
U	UUA Leu	UCA Ser	UAA	UGA	A
U	UUG Leu	UCG Ser	UAG	UGG Trp	G
C	CUU Leu	CCU Pro	CAU His	CGU Arg	U
C	CUC Leu	CCC Pro	CAC His	CGC Arg	C
C	CUA Leu	CCA Pro	CAA Gln	CGA Arg	A
C	CUG Leu	CCG Pro	CAG Gln	CGG Arg	G
A	AUU Ile	ACU Thr	AAU Asn	AGU Ser	U
A	AUC Ile	ACC Thr	AAC Asn	AGC Ser	C
A	AUA Ile	ACA Thr	AAA Lys	AGA Arg	A
A	AUG Met	ACG Thr	AAG Lys	AGG Arg	G
G	GUU Val	GCU Ala	GAU Asp	GGU Gly	U
G	GUC Val	GCC Ala	GAC Asp	GGC Gly	C
G	GUA Val	GCA Ala	GAA Glu	GGA Gly	A
G	GUG Val	GCG Ala	GAG Glu	GGG Gly	G

KEY

Ala	= alanine
Arg	= arginine
Asn	= asparagine
Asp	= aspartic acid
Cys	= cysteine
Gln	= glutamine
Glu	= glutamic acid
Gly	= glycine
His	= histidine
Ile	= isoleucine
Leu	= leucine
Lys	= lysine
Met	= methionine
Phe	= phenylalanine
Pro	= proline
Ser	= serine
Thr	= threonine
Trp	= tryptophan
Tyr	= tyrosine
Val	= valine

Figure 13.5
The genetic code, written as the codons appear in mRNA being read 5′ to 3′. The AUG initiator codon, which codes for methionine, is shown in green; the three terminator codons are boxed in red.

STUDY BREAK

1. On the basis of their work with auxotrophic mutants of the fungus *Neurospora crassa,* Beadle and Tatum proposed the one gene–one enzyme hypothesis. Why was this hypothesis updated subsequently to the one gene–one polypeptide hypothesis?
2. Why is the sequence of bases in the mRNA different to that in the DNA of a given gene?

13.2 Transcription: DNA-Directed RNA Synthesis

Transcription is the process by which information coded in sequential DNA bases is transferred to a complementary RNA strand. Although certain aspects of this mechanism **(Figure 13.6, p. 290)** are similar to those of DNA replication (see Figure 12.15, Chapter 12), it is important for you to understand how these processes are different. In transcription,

- for a given gene, *only one of the two DNA nucleotide strands acts as a template* for synthesis of a complementary copy, instead of both, as in replication.
- only a relatively small part of a DNA molecule—the sequence encoding a single gene—serves as a template, rather than all of both strands, as in DNA replication.
- RNA polymerases catalyze the assembly of nucleotides into an RNA strand, rather than the DNA polymerases that catalyze replication.
- the RNA molecules resulting from transcription are single polynucleotide chains, not double ones, as in DNA replication.
  wherever adenine appears in the DNA template chain, a uracil is matched to it in the RNA transcript instead of thymine as in DNA replication.

Although the mechanism of transcription is similar in prokaryotic cells and eukaryotes, watch for the important differences pointed out in this section.

13.2a Transcription Proceeds in Three Steps

Figure 13.6, p. 290, illustrates the general structure of a eukaryotic protein-coding gene and shows how it is transcribed. The gene consists of two main parts, a **promoter,** which is a control sequence for transcription, and a **transcription unit**, the section of the gene that is copied into an RNA molecule. Transcription takes place in three steps: (1) initiation, in which the molecular machinery that carries out transcription assembles at the promoter and begins synthesizing an RNA copy of the gene; (2) elongation, in which the RNA polymerase moves along the gene extending the RNA chain; and (3) termination, in which transcription ends and the RNA molecule—the transcript—and the RNA polymerase are released from

the DNA template. Roger Kornberg of Stanford University in California received a Nobel Prize in 2006 for describing the molecular structure of the eukaryotic transcription apparatus and how it acts in transcription.

Similarities and differences in transcription of eukaryotic and bacterial protein-coding genes are as follows:

- Gene organization is the same, although the specific sequences in the promoter where the transcription apparatus assembles differ.
- In eukaryotes, RNA polymerase II, the enzyme that transcribes protein-coding genes, cannot bind directly to DNA; it is recruited to the promoter once proteins called **transcription factors** have bound. In bacteria, RNA polymerase binds directly to DNA; it is directed to the promoter by a protein factor that is then released once transcription begins.
- Elongation is essentially identical in the two types of organisms.
- In prokaryotic cells, there are two types of specific DNA sequences called **terminators** that signal the end of transcription of the gene. Both types of terminator sequences act *after they are transcribed.* In the first case, the terminator sequence on the mRNA uses complementary base-pairing with itself to form a "hairpin." In the second case, a protein binds to a particular terminator sequence on the mRNA. Both of these mechanisms trigger the termination of transcription and the release of the RNA and RNA polymerase from the template. In eukaryotes, there are no equivalent "transcription terminator" sequences. Instead, the 3′ end of the mRNA is specified by a different process, which is discussed in a later section.

Once an RNA polymerase molecule has started transcription and progressed past the beginning of a gene, another molecule of RNA polymerase may start transcribing as soon as there is room at the promoter. In most genes this process continues until there are many RNA polymerase molecules spaced closely along a gene, each making an RNA transcript.

13.2b Transcription of Non-Protein-Coding Genes Occurs in a Similar Way

Non-protein-coding genes include, for example, those for tRNAs and rRNAs. In eukaryotes, RNA polymerase II transcribes protein-coding genes, RNA polymerase III transcribes tRNA genes and the gene for one of the four rRNAs, and RNA polymerase I transcribes the genes for the three other rRNAs. The promoters for these non-protein-coding genes are different from those of protein-coding genes, being specialized for the assembly of the transcription machinery that involves the correct RNA polymerase type. In bacteria a single type of RNA polymerase transcribes all types of genes. The promoters for bacterial non-protein-coding genes are essentially the same as those of protein-coding genes.

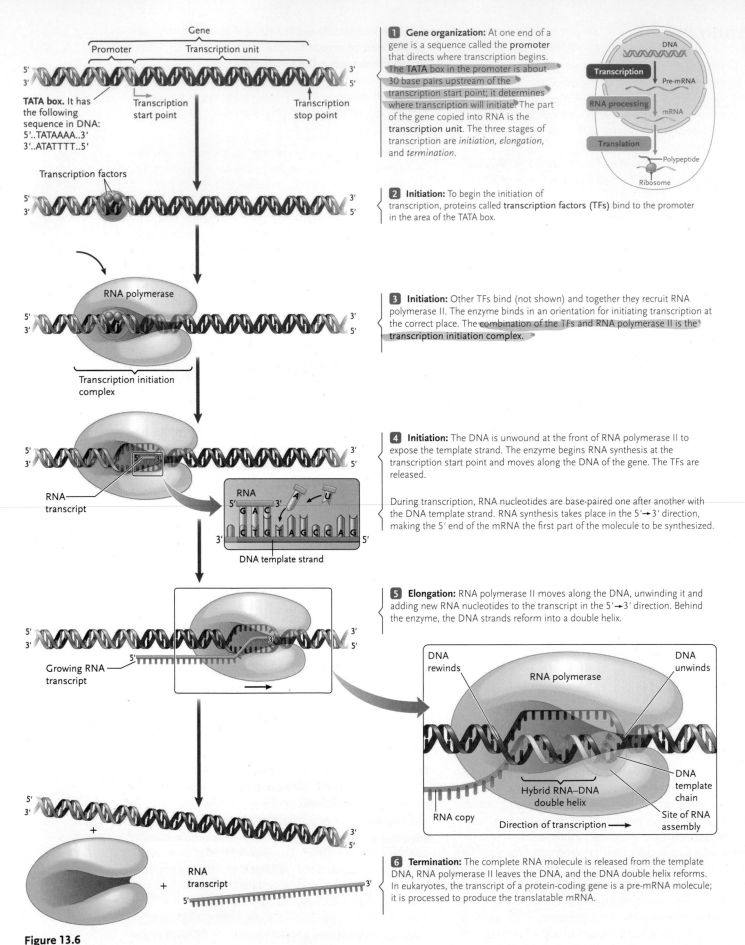

1 **Gene organization:** At one end of a gene is a sequence called the **promoter** that directs where transcription begins. The TATA box in the promoter is about 30 base pairs upstream of the transcription start point; it determines where transcription will initiate. The part of the gene copied into RNA is the **transcription unit.** The three stages of transcription are *initiation*, *elongation*, and *termination.*

2 **Initiation:** To begin the initiation of transcription, proteins called **transcription factors (TFs)** bind to the promoter in the area of the TATA box.

3 **Initiation:** Other TFs bind (not shown) and together they recruit RNA polymerase II. The enzyme binds in an orientation for initiating transcription at the correct place. The combination of the TFs and RNA polymerase II is the **transcription initiation complex.**

4 **Initiation:** The DNA is unwound at the front of RNA polymerase II to expose the template strand. The enzyme begins RNA synthesis at the transcription start point and moves along the DNA of the gene. The TFs are released.

During transcription, RNA nucleotides are base-paired one after another with the DNA template strand. RNA synthesis takes place in the 5'→3' direction, making the 5' end of the mRNA the first part of the molecule to be synthesized.

5 **Elongation:** RNA polymerase II moves along the DNA, unwinding it and adding new RNA nucleotides to the transcript in the 5'→3' direction. Behind the enzyme, the DNA strands reform into a double helix.

6 **Termination:** The complete RNA molecule is released from the template DNA, RNA polymerase II leaves the DNA, and the DNA double helix reforms. In eukaryotes, the transcript of a protein-coding gene is a pre-mRNA molecule; it is processed to produce the translatable mRNA.

Figure 13.6

Transcription of a eukaryotic protein-coding gene. Transcription has three stages: initiation, elongation, and termination. RNA polymerase moves along the gene, separating the two DNA strands to allow RNA synthesis in the 5'→3' direction using the 3'→5' DNA strand as template.

13.3 Processing of mRNAs in Eukaryotes

Although mRNAs obviously contain regions that code for protein, they also contain noncoding regions that, although not specifying an amino acid, nevertheless play key roles in the process of protein synthesis. For instance, in prokaryotic mRNAs the coding region is flanked by untranslated ends, the 5' untranslated region (5' UTR) and a 3' untranslated region (3' UTR). These same elements are present in eukaryotic mRNAs along with additional types of noncoding elements. The following section looks at the structure and function of genes, with particular focus on the synthesis of mRNA in eukaryotes.

13.3a Eukaryotic Protein-Coding Genes Are Transcribed into Precursor mRNAs That Are Modified in the Nucleus

A eukaryotic protein-coding gene is typically transcribed into a **precursor mRNA (pre-mRNA)** that must be processed in the nucleus to produce translatable mRNA (see **Figures 13.3, p. 287, 13.7, and 13.8, p. 292**). The mature mRNA exits the nucleus and is translated by ribosomes in the cytoplasm.

Modifications of Pre-mRNA and mRNA Ends. At the 5' end of the pre-mRNA is the 5' guanine cap, consisting of a guanine-containing nucleotide that is reversed so that its 3'–OH group faces the beginning rather than the end of the molecule. A capping enzyme adds this 5' cap to the pre-mRNA (without the need for complementary base-pairing) soon after RNA polymerase II begins transcription. The cap, which is connected to the rest of the chain by three phosphate groups, remains when pre-mRNA is processed to mRNA. The cap protects the mRNA from degradation and is the site where ribosomes attach at the start of translation.

Transcription of a eukaryotic protein-coding gene is terminated differently from that of a prokaryotic gene (Figure 13.7). The eukaryotic gene has no terminator sequence in the

DNA that, after transcription into RNA, signals RNA polymerase to stop transcribing. Instead, near the 3' end of the gene is a DNA sequence that is transcribed into the pre-mRNA. Proteins bind to this *polyadenylation signal* in the RNA and cleave it just downstream.

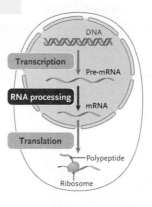

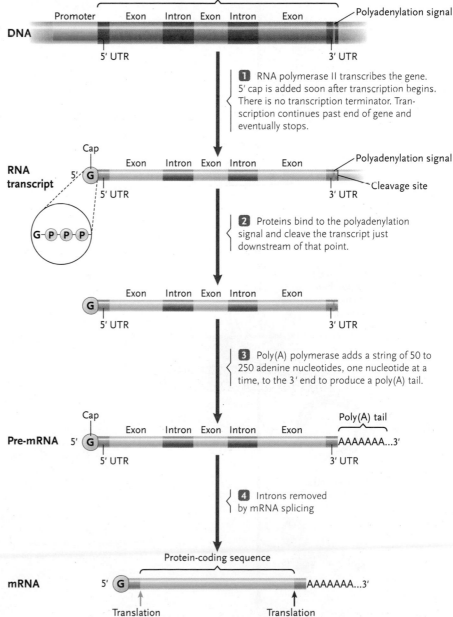

Figure 13.7
Relationship between a eukaryotic protein-coding gene, the pre-mRNA transcribed from it, and the mRNA processed from the pre-mRNA.

This signals the RNA polymerase to stop transcription. Then the enzyme poly(A) polymerase adds a chain of 50 to 250 adenine nucleotides, one nucleotide at a time, to the newly created 3′ end of the pre-mRNA.

CONCEPT FIX No complementary base-pairing with a template is needed for this particular type of RNA synthesis. There is no "poly(T)" sequence in the DNA corresponding to the poly(A) sequence in the pre-mRNA.

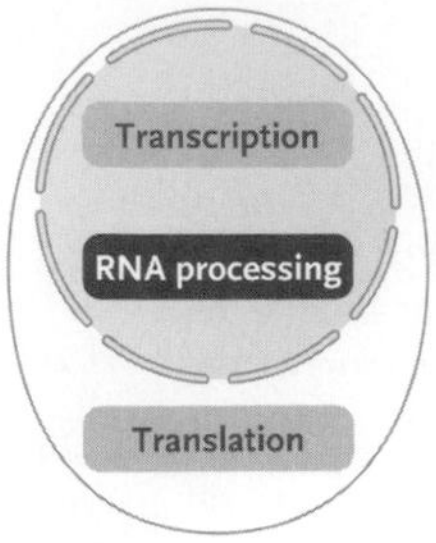

Figure 13.8

mRNA splicing—the removal from pre-mRNA of introns and joining of exons in the spliceosome.

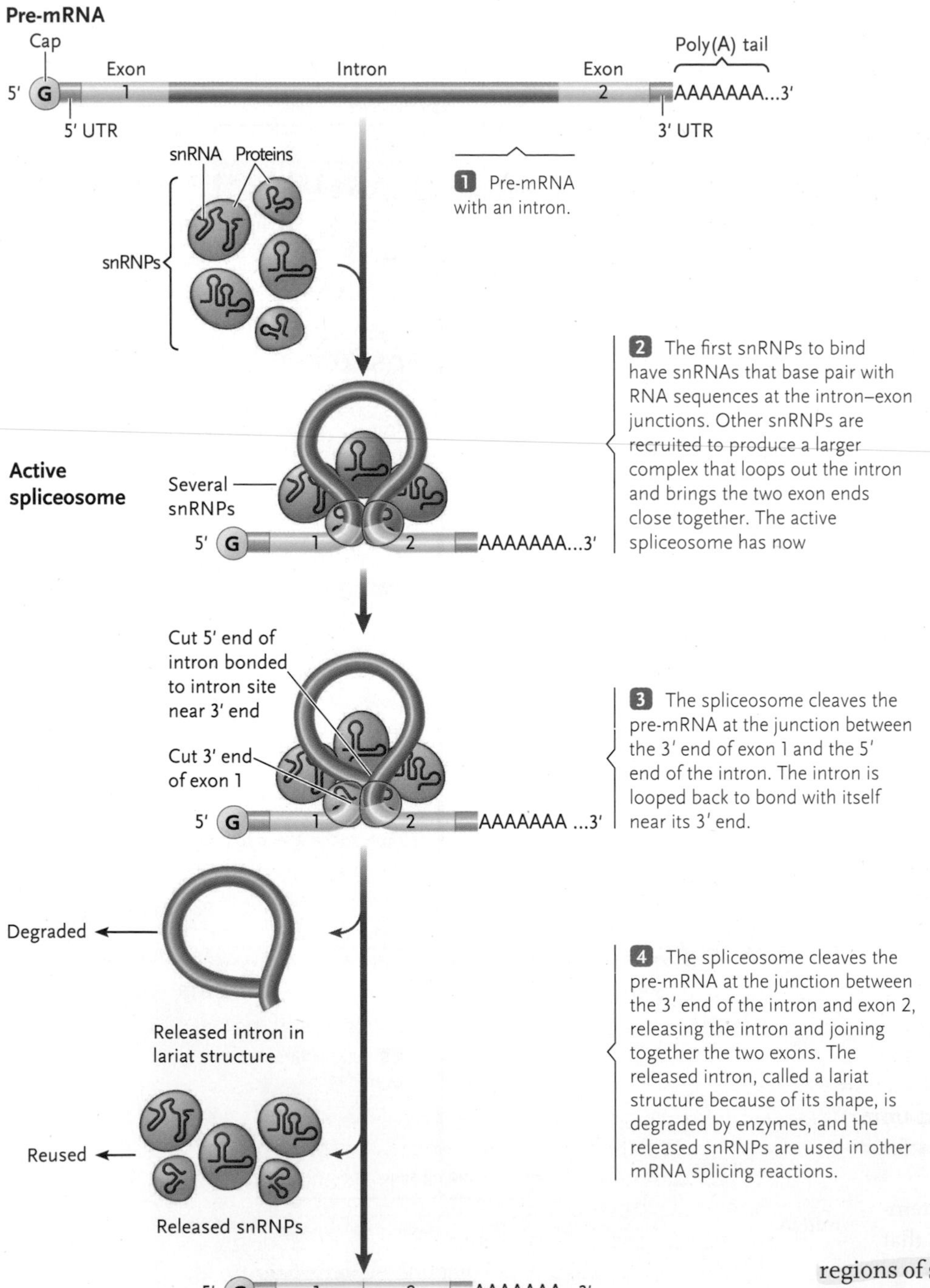

The string of adenine nucleotides, called the **poly (A) tail**, enables the mRNA produced from the pre-mRNA to be translated efficiently and protects it from attack by RNA-digesting enzymes in the cytoplasm.

Sequences Interrupting the Protein-Coding Sequence. The transcription unit of a protein-coding gene—the RNA-coding sequence—also contains non-protein-coding sequences called **introns** that interrupt the protein-coding sequence (shown in Figure 13.8). The introns are transcribed into pre-mRNAs but are removed from pre-mRNAs during processing in the nucleus. The amino acid–coding sequences that are retained in finished mRNAs are called **exons**. The mechanisms by which introns originated in genes remain a mystery.

Introns were discovered by several methods, including direct comparisons between the nucleotide sequences of mature mRNAs and either pre-mRNAs or the genes encoding them. Although many eukaryotic genes do not contain introns, most have at least one; some contain more than 60. In humans, introns are, on average, 6 times the length of exons. The original discoverers of introns, Richard Roberts and Phillip Sharp, received a Nobel Prize in 1993 for their findings.

13.3b Introns Are Removed during Pre-mRNA Processing to Produce Translatable mRNA

A process called **mRNA splicing**, which occurs in the nucleus, removes introns from pre-mRNAs and joins exons together. As an illustration of one type of mRNA splicing, Figure 13.8 shows the processing of a pre-mRNA with a single intron to produce a mature mRNA. mRNA splicing takes place in a **spliceosome**, a complex formed between the pre-mRNA and a handful of **small ribonucleoprotein particles**. A ribonucleoprotein particle is a complex of RNA and proteins. The small ribonucleoprotein particles involved in mRNA splicing are located in the nucleus; each consists of a relatively short *small nuclear RNA* (snRNA) bound to a number of proteins. The particles are therefore known as snRNPs, pronounced "snurps." The snRNPs bind in a particular order to an intron in the pre-mRNA and form the active spliceosome. The spliceosome cleaves the pre-mRNA to release the intron, and joins the flanking exons.

Complementary base-pairing between regions of snRNA and mRNA ensures that the cutting and splicing are so exact that not a single base of an intron is retained in the finished mRNA, nor is a single base removed from the exons. Without this precision, removing introns would change the reading frame of the coding portion of the mRNA, producing the wrong codons from the point of a mistake onward.

13.3c Introns Contribute to Protein Variability

Introns seem wasteful in terms of the energy and raw materials required to replicate and transcribe them and the elaborate cellular machinery required to remove them during pre-mRNA processing. Why are they present in mRNA-encoding genes? Among a number of possibilities, introns may provide a selective advantage to organisms by increasing the coding capacity of existing genes through a process called alternative splicing and in a process that generates new proteins called exon shuffling.

Alternative Splicing. The removal of introns from a given pre-mRNA is not absolute. That is, in particular tissues or sexes, or under certain environmental conditions, different regions of a given pre-mRNA may be identified as introns and removed in different combinations to produce different mature mRNAs. *Regions that are exon in one situation may well be removed as intron in another situation* (Figure 13.9). As an example, the pre-mRNA transcript of the mammalian α-tropomyosin gene is spliced in various ways in different tissues—smooth muscle (for example, muscles of the intestine and bladder), skeletal muscle (for example, biceps, glutes), fibroblast (connective tissue cell that makes collagen), liver, and brain—to produce different forms of the α-tropomyosin protein. Figure 13.9 shows the splicing of the α-tropomyosin pre-mRNA to the mRNAs found in smooth muscle and skeletal muscle. Exons 2 and 12 are found only in the smooth muscle mRNA, whereas exons 3, 10, and 11 are found only in the skeletal muscle mRNA.

The mechanism, called **alternative splicing**, greatly increases the number and variety of proteins encoded in the cell nucleus without increasing the size of the genome. For example, current data suggest that three-quarters of all human pre-mRNAs are subjected to alternative splicing. In each case, the different mRNAs produced from the parent pre-mRNA are translated to produce a family of related proteins with various combinations of amino acid sequences derived from the exons. Each protein in the family, then, varies in its function. Alternative splicing helps us understand why humans have only about 20 000 genes but can make over 100 000 proteins. As a result of alternative splicing, the number of diverse protein products far exceeds the number of genes. Ultimately, it is the diversity of

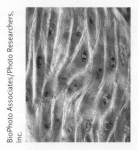

Smooth muscle: Found in walls of tubes and cavities of the body, including blood vessels, the stomach and intestine, the bladder, and the uterus. Contraction of smooth muscles typically produces a squeezing motion.

BioPhoto Associates/Photo Researchers, Inc.

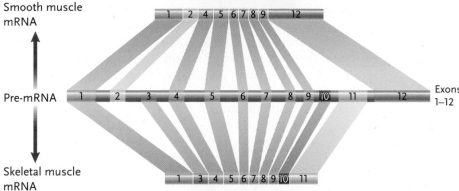

Smooth muscle mRNA

Pre-mRNA

Skeletal muscle mRNA

Exons 1–12

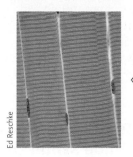

Ed Reschke

Skeletal muscle: Most muscles of this type are attached by tendons to the skeleton. Their function is locomotion and movement of body parts. The human body has more than 600 skeletal muscles, ranging in size from the small muscles that move the eyeballs to the large muscles that move the legs.

Figure 13.9

Alternative splicing of the α-tropomyosin pre-mRNA to distinct mRNA forms found in smooth muscle and skeletal muscle. All of the introns are removed in both mRNA splicing pathways, but exons 3, 10, and 11 are also removed to produce the smooth muscle mRNA, and exons 2 and 12 are also removed to produce the skeletal muscle mRNA.

proteins available, not the amount or diversity of DNA sequence, that determines the relative complexity of an organism's functions.

The polypeptides made from the two related tropomyosin mRNAs in Figure 13.9 have some identical stretches of amino acids, along with others that differ. As described in *The Purple Pages*, the primary structure of a protein—its amino acid structure—directs the folding of the chain into its three-dimensional shape. Therefore, the two forms of tropomyosin fold into related, but different, shapes. In its role in muscle contraction in smooth muscles and skeletal muscles, tropomyosin interacts with other proteins. The interactions depend upon the specific structural form of the tropomyosin, and, as you might expect, the two forms participate in different types of muscle action; typically smooth muscles perform squeezing actions in blood vessels and internal organs, whereas skeletal muscles pull on the bones of the skeleton to move body parts.

Alternative splicing causes us to further reconsider the one gene–one polypeptide hypothesis introduced earlier in the chapter. We must now accept the fact that for some genes at least, one gene may specify a number of polypeptides, each of which has a related function.

Exon Shuffling. Another advantage provided by introns may come from the fact that intron–exon junctions often fall at points dividing major functional regions in encoded proteins. The functional divisions may have allowed new proteins to evolve by exon shuffling, a process by which existing protein regions or domains, already selected for due to their useful functions, are mixed into novel combinations to create new proteins. Evolution by this mechanism would produce new proteins with novel functions much more quickly than by changes in individual nucleotides at random points.

STUDY BREAK

1. What are the similarities and differences between pre-mRNAs and mRNAs?
2. What is the role of base-pairing in mRNA splicing?
3. How is it possible for an organism to produce more proteins than it has genes for?

13.4 Translation: mRNA-Directed Polypeptide Synthesis

Translation is the assembly of amino acids into polypeptides on ribosomes. In prokaryotic organisms, translation takes place throughout the cell, whereas in eukaryotes it occurs in the cytoplasm. (However, a few specialized genes are transcribed and translated in mitochondria and chloroplasts.)

Figure 13.10 summarizes the translation process. In prokaryotic cells, the mRNA produced by transcription is not confined within a nucleus and is therefore available immediately for translation. However, for eukaryotes the mRNA produced by splicing of the pre-mRNA first exits the nucleus and is then translated in the cytoplasm. In translation,

the mRNA associates with a ribosome and another type of RNA, transfer RNA (tRNA), which brings amino acids to the complex to be joined, one by one, into the polypeptide chain. The sequence of amino acids in the polypeptide chain is determined by the sequence of codons in the mRNA. The mRNA is read from the 5′ end to the 3′ end; the polypeptide is assembled from the N-terminal to the C-terminal end.

In this section, we will start by discussing the key players in the process, the tRNAs and ribosomes, and then walk through the translation process from a start codon to a stop codon.

13.4a tRNAs Are Small RNAs of a Highly Distinctive Structure That Bring Amino Acids to the Ribosome

Transfer RNAs (tRNAs) bring amino acids to the ribosome for addition to the polypeptide chain.

tRNA Structure. tRNAs are small RNAs, about 75 to 90 nucleotides long (mRNAs are typically hundreds of nucleotides long), with a highly distinctive

Figure 13.10

An overview of translation, in which ribosomes assemble amino acids into a polypeptide chain. The figure shows a ribosome in the process of translation. A tRNA molecule with an amino acid bound to it is entering the ribosome on the right. The anticodon on the tRNA will pair with the codon in the mRNA. Its amino acid will then be added to the growing polypeptide that is currently attached to the tRNA in the middle of the ribosome. As it assembles a polypeptide chain, the ribosome moves from one codon to the next along the mRNA in the 5′→3′ direction.

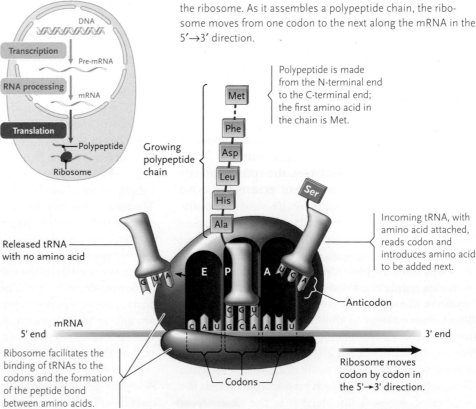

Polypeptide is made from the N-terminal end to the C-terminal end; the first amino acid in the chain is Met.

Growing polypeptide chain

Released tRNA with no amino acid

Incoming tRNA, with amino acid attached, reads codon and introduces amino acid to be added next.

Anticodon

Ribosome facilitates the binding of tRNAs to the codons and the formation of the peptide bond between amino acids.

mRNA
5′ end
3′ end

Codons

Ribosome moves codon by codon in the 5′→3′ direction.

PEOPLE BEHIND BIOLOGY 13.1

Dr. Steve Zimmerly, University of Calgary

Steve Zimmerly and his colleagues think they know where introns came from.

Biology students (and researchers) often wonder about the origins of introns, and to investigate this question, Zimmerly collected and analyzed a large number of examples of a type of intron called "Group II" from plant organelles and bacteria. Group II introns have two fascinating abilities. First, they can splice themselves out of RNA without the need for snRNPs. Second, they are mobile; these elements can copy themselves and insert at a new location **(Figure 1)**.

The Zimmerly lab proposed a model for intron evolution that suggests the introns in nuclear genes of higher eukaryotes evolved from mobile Group II introns originating in prokaryotic cells. These Group II introns may have spread to eukaryotes at the time when their bacterial hosts were engulfed by eukaryotic cells to become endosymbiotic mitochondria and chloroplasts. Over evolutionary time, the nuclear introns lost their mobility and became dependent on spliceosomes for accurate splicing.

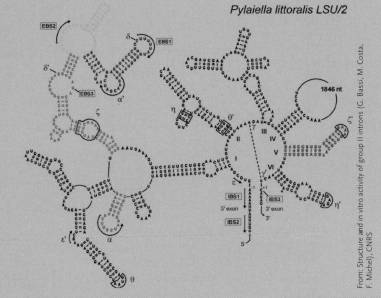

Pylaiella littoralis LSU/2

From: Structure and in vitro activity of group II introns (G. Bassi, M. Costa, F. Michel), CNRS

FIGURE 1

Sequence of a Group II intron showing extensive complementary base-pairing with itself.

structure that accomplishes their role in translation **(Figure 13.11, p. 296)**. All tRNAs can base-pair with themselves to wind into four double-helical segments, forming a cloverleaf pattern in two dimensions. At the tip of one of the double-helical segments is the **anticodon**, the three-nucleotide segment that base-pairs with a codon in mRNAs. At the other end of the cloverleaf, opposite the anticodon, is a free 3′ end of the molecule that links to the amino acid corresponding to the anticodon. For example, a tRNA that is linked to serine (Ser) pairs with the codon 5′-AGU-3′ in mRNA (see Figure 13.11, p. 296). The anticodon of the tRNA that pairs with this codon is 3′-UCA-5′.

CONCEPT FIX The anticodon and codon pair in an antiparallel manner, as do the two strands in the DNA helix. We will therefore write anticodons in the 3′→5′ direction to make it easy to see how they pair with codons, which are normally written 5′→3′. ⬢

The tRNA cloverleaf folds in three dimensions into the L-shaped structure shown in Figure 13.11b, p. 296. The anticodon and the segment binding the amino acid are located at the opposite ends of the L structure.

Recall that 61 of the 64 codons of the genetic code specify an amino acid. Does this mean that 61 different tRNAs read the sense codons? The answer is no. Francis Crick's **wobble hypothesis** proposed that the complete set of 61 sense codons can be read by fewer than 61 distinct tRNAs because of the particular pairing properties of the bases in the anticodons. That is, the pairing of the anticodon with the first two nucleotides of the codon is always precise, but the anticodon has more flexibility in pairing with the third nucleotide of the codon. In many cases, the same tRNA's anticodon can read codons that have either U or C in the third position; for example, a tRNA carrying phenylalanine can read both codons 5′-UUU-3′ and

a. A tRNA molecule in two dimensions (yeast alanine tRNA)

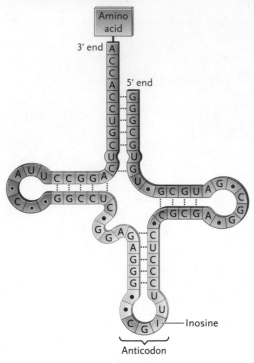

Inosine

Anticodon

b. A tRNA molecule in three dimensions

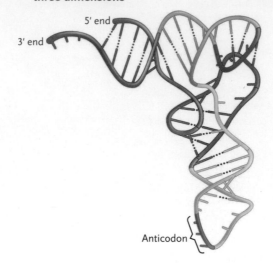

Anticodon

c. How an aminoacyl–tRNA complex is shown in this book

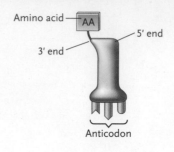

Anticodon

Figure 13.11

tRNA structure. The red dots show sites where bases are chemically modified into other forms; chemical modification of certain bases is typical of tRNAs. This tRNA has the purine inosine (I) in the anticodon, which has relatively loose base-pairing ability, allowing this single tRNA to pair with each of three alanine codons: 5′-GCU-3′, 5′-GCC-3′, and 5′-GCA-3′. This tRNA also has the unusual base pair G–U. Unusual base pairs, allowed by the greater flexibility of short RNA chains, are common in tRNAs.

5′-UUC-3′. Similarly, the same tRNA's anticodon can read two codons that have A or G in the third position; for example, a tRNA carrying glutamine can pair with both 5′-CAA-3′ and 5′-CAG-3′ codons. The special purine, called inosine, in the alanine tRNA shown in Figure 13.11a, allows even more extensive wobble by allowing the tRNA to pair with codons that have one of U, C, and A in the third position.

Addition of Amino Acids to Their Corresponding tRNAs. The correct amino acid must be present on a tRNA if translation is to be accurate. The process of adding an amino acid to a tRNA is called **aminoacylation** (literally, the addition of an amino acid) or charging (because the process adds free energy as the amino acid–tRNA combinations are formed).

The finished product of charging, a tRNA linked to its "correct" amino acid, is called an **aminoacyl–tRNA**. A collection of different enzymes called **aminoacyl–tRNA synthetases** catalyzes aminoacylation as shown in **Figure 13.12**. This energy in the aminoacyl–tRNA eventually drives the formation of the peptide bond linking amino acids during translation.

With the tRNAs attached to their corresponding amino acids, our attention moves to the ribosome, where the amino acids are removed from tRNAs and linked into polypeptide chains.

13.4b Ribosomes Are rRNA–Protein Complexes That Work as Automated Protein Assembly Machines

Ribosomes are ribonucleoprotein particles that carry out protein synthesis by translating mRNA into chains of amino acids. Like some automated machines, such as those forming complicated metal parts by a series of machining steps, ribosomes use an information tape—an mRNA molecule—as the directions required to accomplish a task. For ribosomes, the task is to join amino acids into ordered sequences to make a polypeptide chain.

In prokaryotic cells, ribosomes carry out their assembly functions throughout the cell. In eukaryotes, ribosomes function only in the cytoplasm, either suspended freely in the cytoplasmic solution or attached to the membranes of the endoplasmic reticulum (ER), the system of membrane-bound tubular or flattened sacs in the cytoplasm. A finished ribosome is made up of two parts of dissimilar size, called the *large* and *small ribosomal subunits* (**Figure 13.13**). Each subunit is made up of a combination of ribosomal RNA (rRNA) and ribosomal proteins.

CONCEPT FIX The endosymbiotic origin of chloroplasts and mitochondria in eukaryotic cells is reflected by the fact that these organelles still code for their own "prokaryotic" ribosomes that are distinct from those in the cytoplasm. ⬡

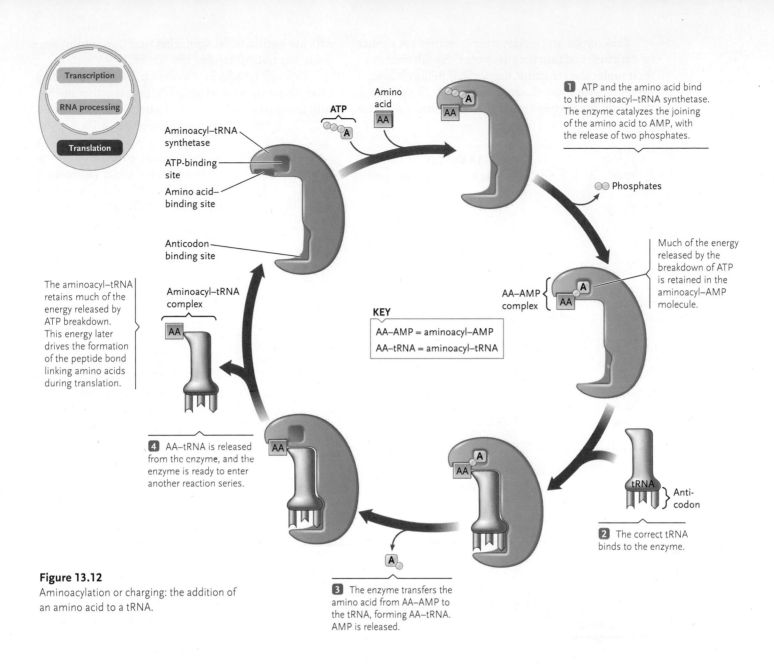

Figure 13.12

Aminoacylation or charging: the addition of an amino acid to a tRNA.

KEY

AA–AMP = aminoacyl–AMP

AA–tRNA = aminoacyl–tRNA

1 ATP and the amino acid bind to the aminoacyl–tRNA synthetase. The enzyme catalyzes the joining of the amino acid to AMP, with the release of two phosphates.

Phosphates

Much of the energy released by the breakdown of ATP is retained in the aminoacyl–AMP molecule.

AA–AMP complex

2 The correct tRNA binds to the enzyme.

Anticodon

3 The enzyme transfers the amino acid from AA–AMP to the tRNA, forming AA–tRNA. AMP is released.

4 AA–tRNA is released from the enzyme, and the enzyme is ready to enter another reaction series.

The aminoacyl–tRNA retains much of the energy released by ATP breakdown. This energy later drives the formation of the peptide bond linking amino acids during translation.

Aminoacyl–tRNA complex

Aminoacyl–tRNA synthetase

ATP-binding site

Amino acid–binding site

Anticodon binding site

Amino acid

ATP

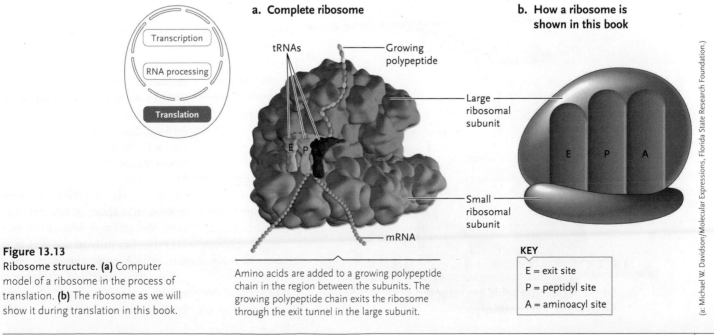

a. Complete ribosome

tRNAs

Growing polypeptide

Large ribosomal subunit

Small ribosomal subunit

mRNA

Amino acids are added to a growing polypeptide chain in the region between the subunits. The growing polypeptide chain exits the ribosome through the exit tunnel in the large subunit.

b. How a ribosome is shown in this book

KEY

E = exit site

P = peptidyl site

A = aminoacyl site

Figure 13.13

Ribosome structure. **(a)** Computer model of a ribosome in the process of translation. **(b)** The ribosome as we will show it during translation in this book.

(a: Michael W. Davidson/Molecular Expressions, Florida State Research Foundation.)

Prokaryotic and eukaryotic ribosomes are similar in structure and function. However, the differences in their molecular structure, particularly in the ribosomal proteins, give them distinct properties. For example, the antibiotics streptomycin and erythromycin are effective antibacterial agents because they inhibit bacterial, but not eukaryotic, ribosomes.

To fulfill its role in translation, the ribosome has special binding sites active in bringing together mRNA with aminoacyl–tRNAs (see Figure 13.13, p. 297, and refer also to Figure 13.10, p. 294). One such site is where the mRNA threads a bent path through the ribosome. The **A site** (aminoacyl site) is where the incoming aminoacyl–tRNA (carrying the next amino acid to be added to the polypeptide chain) binds to the mRNA. The **P site** (peptidyl site) is where the tRNA carrying the growing polypeptide chain is bound. The **E site** (exit site) is where an exiting tRNA binds as it leaves the ribosome.

13.4c Translation Initiation Brings the Ribosomal Subunits, an mRNA, and the First Aminoacyl–tRNA Together

There are three major stages of translation: *initiation, elongation,* and *termination*. During initiation, the translation components assemble on the start codon of the mRNA. In elongation, the assembled complex reads the string of codons in the mRNA one at a time while joining the specified amino acids into the polypeptide. Termination completes the translation process when the complex disassembles after the last amino acid of the polypeptide specified by the mRNA has been added to the polypeptide.

Figure 13.14 illustrates the steps of translation initiation in eukaryotes. In bacteria, translation initiation is similar in using a special initiator Met–tRNA and GTP, but the way in which the ribosome assembles at the start codon is different than in eukaryotes. Rather than scanning from the 5′ end of the mRNA, the small ribosomal subunit, the initiator Met–tRNA and GTP bind directly to the region of the mRNA with the AUG start codon. This initiation complex is then guided by the **ribosome binding site**—a short, specific RNA

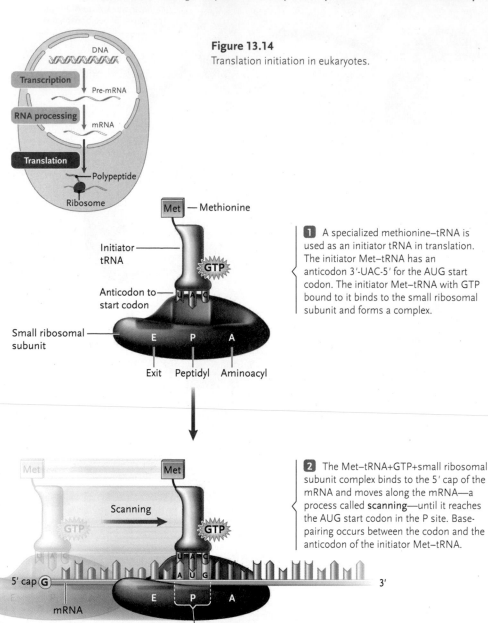

Figure 13.14
Translation initiation in eukaryotes.

1 A specialized methionine–tRNA is used as an initiator tRNA in translation. The initiator Met–tRNA has an anticodon 3′-UAC-5′ for the AUG start codon. The initiator Met–tRNA with GTP bound to it binds to the small ribosomal subunit and forms a complex.

2 The Met–tRNA+GTP+small ribosomal subunit complex binds to the 5′ cap of the mRNA and moves along the mRNA—a process called **scanning**—until it reaches the AUG start codon in the P site. Base-pairing occurs between the codon and the anticodon of the initiator Met–tRNA.

3 The large ribosomal subunit binds and GTP is hydrolyzed, completing initiation. The ribosome is ready for the next stage of translation, elongation.

sequence—just upstream of the start codon on the mRNA that base-pairs with a complementary sequence of rRNA in the small ribosomal subunit. The large ribosomal subunit then binds to the small subunit to complete the ribosome. GTP hydrolysis then begins translation.

After the initiator tRNA pairs with the AUG initiator codon, the subsequent stages of translation simply read the codons one at a time on the mRNA. The initiator tRNA–AUG pairing thus establishes the correct **reading frame**—the series of codons for the polypeptide encoded by the mRNA. This is often referred to as the open reading frame.

13.4d Polypeptide Chains Grow during the Elongation Stage of Translation

The central reactions of translation take place in the elongation stage, which adds amino acids one at a time to a growing polypeptide chain. The individual steps of elongation depend on the binding properties of the P, A, and E sites of the ribosome. The P site, with one exception, can bind only to a **peptidyl–tRNA**, that is, a tRNA linked to a growing polypeptide chain containing two or more amino acids. The exception is the initiator tRNA, which is recognized by the P site as a peptidyl–tRNA even though it carries only a single amino acid, methionine. The A site can bind only to an aminoacyl–tRNA. The tRNA that was previously in the P site is shifted to the E site and then leaves the ribosome.

Figure 13.15 shows the elongation cycle of translation. The cycle begins at the point when an initiator

Figure 13.15
Translation elongation. A protein elongation factor (EF) complexes with the aminoacyl–tRNA to bring it to the ribosome, and another EF is needed for ribosome translocation. For simplicity, the EFs are not shown in the figure.

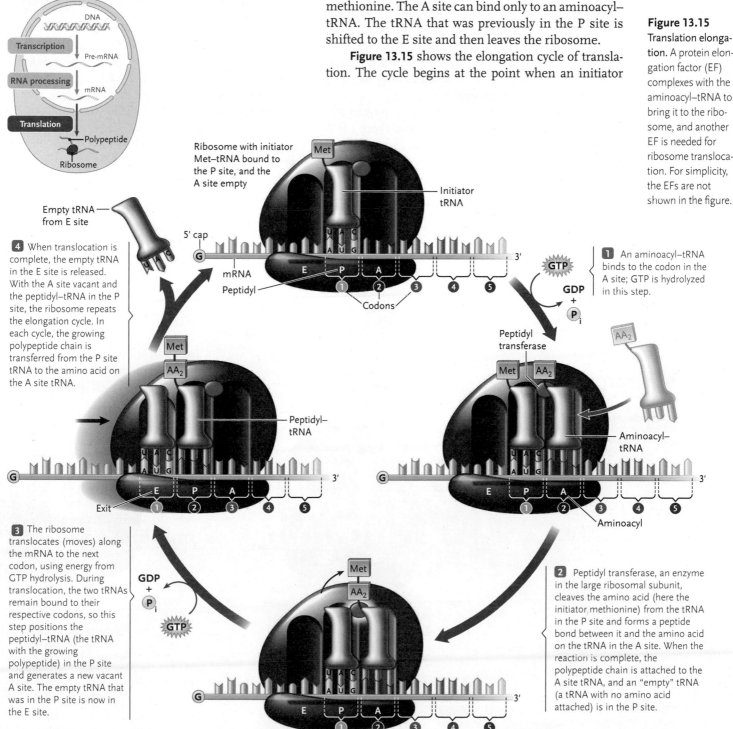

4 When translocation is complete, the empty tRNA in the E site is released. With the A site vacant and the peptidyl–tRNA in the P site, the ribosome repeats the elongation cycle. In each cycle, the growing polypeptide chain is transferred from the P site tRNA to the amino acid on the A site tRNA.

Empty tRNA from E site

Ribosome with initiator Met–tRNA bound to the P site, and the A site empty

Initiator tRNA

5′ cap

mRNA

Peptidyl

Codons

1 An aminoacyl–tRNA binds to the codon in the A site; GTP is hydrolyzed in this step.

GTP

GDP + P$_i$

Peptidyl transferase

Peptidyl–tRNA

Aminoacyl–tRNA

Aminoacyl

Exit

3 The ribosome translocates (moves) along the mRNA to the next codon, using energy from GTP hydrolysis. During translocation, the two tRNAs remain bound to their respective codons, so this step positions the peptidyl–tRNA (the tRNA with the growing polypeptide) in the P site and generates a new vacant A site. The empty tRNA that was in the P site is now in the E site.

GDP + P$_i$

GTP

2 Peptidyl transferase, an enzyme in the large ribosomal subunit, cleaves the amino acid (here the initiator methionine) from the tRNA in the P site and forms a peptide bond between it and the amino acid on the tRNA in the A site. When the reaction is complete, the polypeptide chain is attached to the A site tRNA, and an "empty" tRNA (a tRNA with no amino acid attached) is in the P site.

tRNA with its attached methionine is bound to the P site, and the A site is empty (top of figure). The first step in each round of the cycle is the binding of the appropriate aminoacyl–tRNA to the codon in the A site of the ribosome (step 1). This binding is facilitated by a protein **elongation factor (EF)** that is bound to the aminoacyl–tRNA and that is released once the tRNA binds to the codon. Another EF is used when the ribosome translocates along the mRNA to the next codon (step 3). Each EF is released after its job is completed. GTP hydrolysis is used to power the ribosome along the mRNA. In elongation, a peptide bond is formed between the C-terminal end of the growing polypeptide on the P site tRNA and the amino acid on the A site tRNA (step 2). **Peptidyl transferase** catalyzes this reaction. As we noted in an earlier example of the splicing reaction, researchers have demonstrated that the enzyme activity in the large ribosomal subunit is not a protein but a ribozyme (catalytic RNA) within the large subunit.

The elongation cycle is quite similar in prokaryotic cells and eukaryotes, turning at the rate of about 1 to 3 times per second in eukaryotes versus 15 to 20 times per second in bacteria.

13.4e Termination Releases a Completed Polypeptide from the Ribosome

Translation termination is similar in prokaryotic and eukaryotic cells; it takes place when one of the stop codons on the mRNA, UAG, UAA, or UGA arrives in the A site of a ribosome **(Figure 13.16)**. A protein **release factor (RF;** also called a **termination factor)** binds in the A site and causes the ribosome to disassemble into its subunits.

CONCEPT FIX Since the termination factor is a protein, and not a tRNA, it cannot base-pair with the stop codon. It has a similar shape as tRNA and simply wins the competition to occupy the A site of the ribosome since there are no competing tRNAs that recognize termination codons.

13.4f Multiple Ribosomes Simultaneously Translate a Single mRNA

Once the first ribosome has begun translation, another one can assemble with an initiator tRNA as soon as there is room at the 5′ UTR of the mRNA. Ribosomes continue to attach as translation continues and become spaced along the mRNA like beads on a string. The entire structure of an mRNA molecule and the multiple ribosomes attached to it is known as a **polysome** (a contraction of *polyribosome;* **Figure 13.17, p. 302**). The multiple ribosomes greatly increase the overall rate of polypeptide synthesis from a single mRNA. The total number of ribosomes in a polysome depends on the length of the coding region of its mRNA molecule, ranging from a minimum of one or two ribosomes on the smallest mRNAs to as many as 100 on the longest mRNAs.

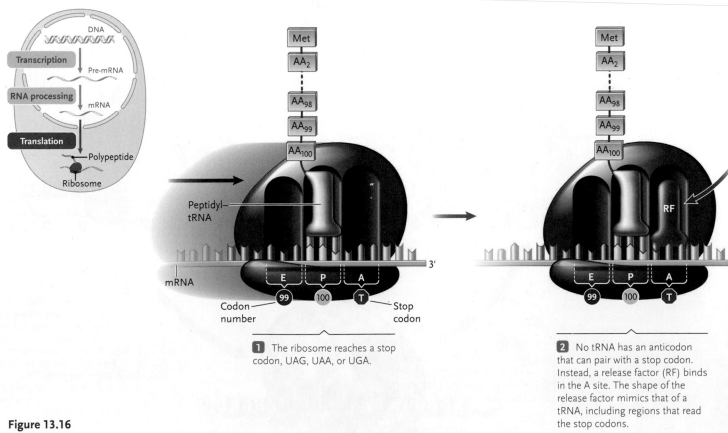

Figure 13.16
Translation termination.

1 The ribosome reaches a stop codon, UAG, UAA, or UGA.

2 No tRNA has an anticodon that can pair with a stop codon. Instead, a release factor (RF) binds in the A site. The shape of the release factor mimics that of a tRNA, including regions that read the stop codons.

MOLECULE BEHIND BIOLOGY 13.2

Amanitin

Alpha-amanitin is one of several potent toxins found in various species of the mushroom *Amanita* **(Figure 1)**. Although composed of many amino acid backbones linked in a ring, this interesting molecule is not a protein. It is the product of a metabolic pathway; it is not produced by translation. In the laboratory, amanitin is a useful inhibitor of eukaryotic RNA polymerase. However, on the dinner table, amanitin is a powerful poison. People suffering from amanitin poisoning show extensive, and usually fatal, liver and kidney damage.

a.

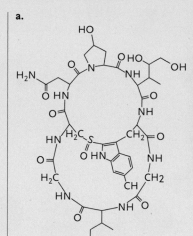

b.

Jens Ottoson/Shutterstock

FIGURE 1
(a) *The very striking double circular structure of amanitin.* (b) *Amanita phalloides.*

In prokaryotic cells, because of the absence of a nuclear envelope, transcription and translation are typically coupled. As soon as the 5′ end of a new mRNA emerges from the RNA polymerase, ribosomal subunits attach and initiate translation. By the time the mRNA is completely transcribed, it is covered with ribosomes from end to end, each assembling a copy of the encoded polypeptide. Meanwhile, several other RNA polymerases have likely begun transcribing the same gene, each one trailing a collection of translating

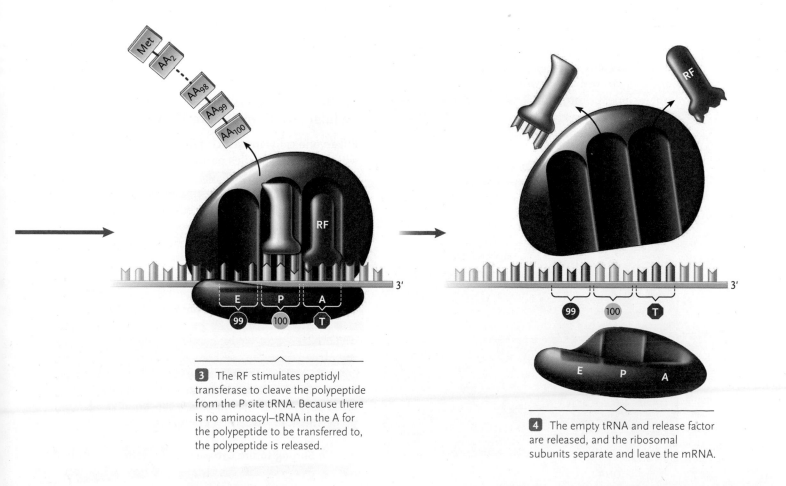

3 The RF stimulates peptidyl transferase to cleave the polypeptide from the P site tRNA. Because there is no aminoacyl–tRNA in the A for the polypeptide to be transferred to, the polypeptide is released.

4 The empty tRNA and release factor are released, and the ribosomal subunits separate and leave the mRNA.

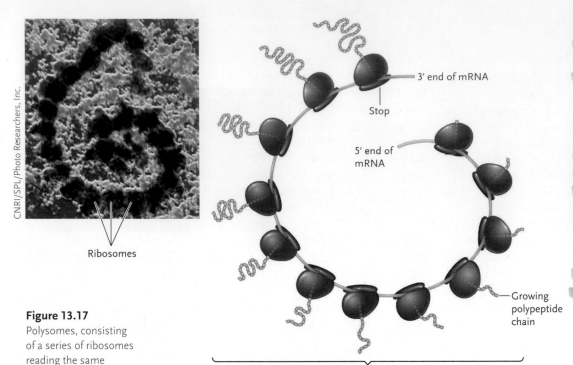

Figure 13.17

Polysomes, consisting of a series of ribosomes reading the same mRNA.

Ribosomes

3' end of mRNA

Stop

5' end of mRNA

Growing polypeptide chain

Polysome

onins assist the folding process by combining with the folding protein, promoting correct three-dimensional structures and inhibiting incorrect ones.

In some cases, the same initial polypeptide may be processed by alternative pathways that produce different mature polypeptides, usually by removing different, long stretches of amino acids from the interior of the polypeptide chain. Alternative processing is another mechanism, distinct from alternative splicing of mRNA, that increases the number of proteins encoded by a single gene.

Other proteins are processed into an initial, inactive form that is later activated at a particular time or location by removal of a covering segment of the amino acid chain. The digestive enzyme pepsin, for example, is made by cells lining the stomach in an inactive form called pepsinogen. When the cells secrete pepsinogen into the stomach, the high acidity of that organ triggers removal of a segment of amino acids, thus converting the enzyme into an active form that rapidly degrades food proteins in food particles. The initial production of the protein as inactive pepsinogen protects the cells that make it from having their own proteins degraded by the enzyme.

ribosomes **(Figure 13.18).** Such a system allows prokaryotic cells to regulate the production very quickly in response to changing environmental conditions.

13.4g Newly Synthesized Polypeptides Are Processed and Folded into Finished Form

Most eukaryotic proteins are in an inactive, unfinished form when ribosomes release them. Processing reactions that convert the new proteins into the finished form include the removal of amino acids from the ends or interior of the polypeptide chain and the addition of larger organic groups, including carbohydrate or lipid structures.

Proteins fold into their final three-dimensional shapes as the processing reactions take place. For many proteins, helper proteins called chaperones or chaper-

13.4h Finished Proteins Are Sorted to the Cellular Locations Where They Function

Eukaryotic cells are structurally compartmentalized, with various organelles performing specialized functions. Therefore, every protein that is made must be delivered to its appropriate compartment. Without a sorting and delivery system, cells would wind up as a jumble of proteins floating about in the cytoplasm, with none of the spatial organization that makes cellular life possible.

Although translation of all proteins begins on free ribosomes in the cytosol, there are three types of final destination compartments where the final products may be needed: (1) the cytosol; (2) the endomembrane system, which includes the endoplasmic reticulum (ER), Golgi complex, lysosomes, secretory vesicles, the nuclear envelope, and the plasma membrane; and (3) other membrane-bound organelles distinct from the endomembrane system, including the nucleus, mitochondria, chloroplasts, and microbodies (for example, peroxisomes).

Protein Sorting to the Cytoplasm. Proteins that function in the cytosol are simply released from ribosomes

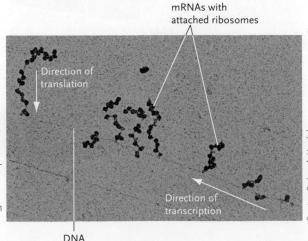

Figure 13.18

Simultaneous transcription and translation in progress in an electron microscope preparation extracted from *E. coli*, × 5 700 000.

mRNAs with attached ribosomes

Direction of translation

Direction of transcription

DNA

once translation is completed. Examples of proteins that function in the cytoplasm include are cytoskeleton proteins (for example, tubulin and keratin), and the enzymes that carry out glycolysis (see Section 6.3).

Protein Sorting to the Endomembrane System. The endomembrane system is a major traffic network for proteins. Polypeptides that sort to the endomembrane system begin their synthesis on free ribosomes in the cytosol and produce a short segment of amino acids called a **signal sequence** (also called a **signal peptide**) near their N-terminal ends. As **Figure 13.19** shows, the signal sequence is recognized by a signal recognition particle that initiates a series of steps that ultimately result in the polypeptide entering the lumen (interior) of the rough ER. This mechanism is called **cotranslational import** because import of the polypeptide into the ER occurs simultaneously with translation of the mRNA encoding the polypeptide.

CONCEPT FIX Ribosomes engaged in cotranslational import stud the surface of the ER and give rise to the term *rough*. Note that ribosomes do not sit on the rough ER waiting for mRNA to translate. Rather, they only associate with the ER *after* they have begun translation as free ribosomes in the cytosol. ◉

The signal sequence was discovered in 1975 by Günter Blobel, B. Dobberstein, and colleagues at Rockefeller University in New York when they observed that proteins sorted through the endomembrane system initially contain extra amino acids at their N-terminal ends. Blobel received a Nobel Prize in 1999 for his work with the mechanism of sorting proteins in cells.

Once inside the lumen of the rough ER, proteins fold into their final form. They also have, or obtain, a type of tag—a postal code if you will—that targets each protein for sorting to its final destination. Depending on the protein and its destination, the tag may be an amino acid sequence already coded in the protein, or a functional group or short sugar chain added to the protein in the lumen. Some proteins remain in the ER, whereas others are transported to the Golgi complex where they may be modified further. From the Golgi complex, proteins are packaged into vesicles, which may deliver them to lysosomes, secrete them from the cell (digestive enzymes, for example), or deposit them in the plasma membrane (cell surface receptors, for instance).

Protein Sorting to the Nucleus, Mitochondria, Chloroplasts, and Microbodies. Proteins are sorted to the nucleus, mitochondria, chloroplasts, and microbodies after they have been made on free ribosomes in the cytosol. This mechanism of sorting is called **posttranslational import**. Proteins destined for the mitochondria, chloroplasts, and microbodies have short amino acid sequences called **transit sequences** at their N-terminal ends that target them to the appropriate organelle. The protein is taken up into the correct organelle by interactions between its transit sequences and organelle-specific transport

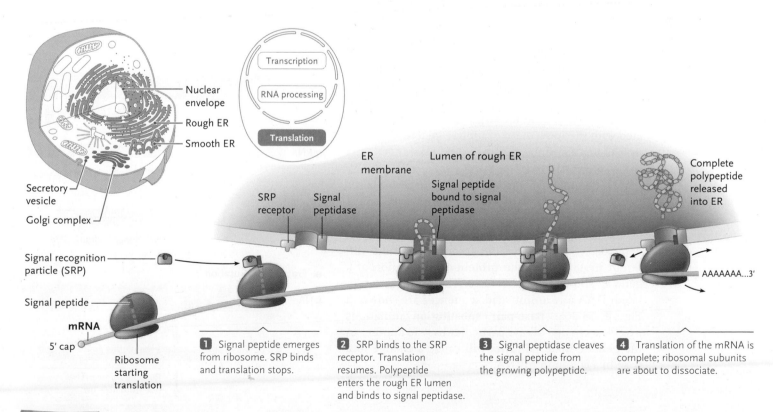

Transcription

RNA processing

Translation

Nuclear envelope
Rough ER
Smooth ER
Secretory vesicle
Golgi complex
Signal recognition particle (SRP)
Signal peptide
mRNA
5' cap
Ribosome starting translation

ER membrane
Lumen of rough ER
SRP receptor
Signal peptidase
Signal peptide bound to signal peptidase
Complete polypeptide released into ER
AAAAAAA...3'

1 Signal peptide emerges from ribosome. SRP binds and translation stops.

2 SRP binds to the SRP receptor. Translation resumes. Polypeptide enters the rough ER lumen and binds to signal peptidase.

3 Signal peptidase cleaves the signal peptide from the growing polypeptide.

4 Translation of the mRNA is complete; ribosomal subunits are about to dissociate.

Figure 13.19

The signal mechanism directing proteins to the ER. The figure shows several ribosomes at different stages of translation of the mRNA.

complexes in the membrane of the appropriate organelle. A transit peptidase enzyme within the organelle then removes the transit sequence.

Proteins sorted to the nucleus, such as the enzymes for DNA replication and RNA transcription, have short amino acid sequences called **nuclear localization signals**. A cytosolic transport protein binds to the signal and moves the nuclear protein to the nuclear pore complex where it is then transported into the nucleus. The localization signal is never removed from nuclear proteins because they need to reenter the nucleus each time the nuclear envelope breaks down and reforms during the cell division cycle.

Although prokaryotic cells are structurally simpler than eukaryotes, the same basic system of molecular sorting signals distributes proteins throughout prokaryotic cells. In prokaryotic organisms, signals similar to the ER-directing signals of eukaryotes direct newly synthesized bacterial proteins to the plasma membrane (bacteria do not have ER membranes); further information built into the proteins keeps them in the plasma membrane or allows them to enter the cell wall or to be secreted outside the cell. Proteins without sorting signals remain in the cytoplasm. The similarity of mechanisms across all cells suggests that protein sorting is a very ancient evolutionary innovation.

13.4i Mutations Can Affect Protein Structure and Function

To this point in the chapter, we have been building an understanding of how the sequence of DNA bases in genes is directly related to the structure and function of the polypeptides that they encode. We will close the chapter with consideration of how various types of small changes in the DNA sequence might affect protein structure. (Contrast these small changes with the rather large-scale changes associated with the movement of mobile genetic elements in Chapter 9 and the chromosomal rearrangements in Chapter 11.)

Mutations are changes in the sequence of bases in the genetic material. How will mutations affect protein structure and function? Your understanding of this chapter should lead you to respond, "It depends." For instance, let's consider several different mutations in the protein-coding region of a gene as shown in **Figure 13.20**. The normal (unmutated) DNA and amino acid sequences are shown in Figure 13.20a. **Base-pair substitution mutations** involve a change of one particular base to another in the genetic material. This will cause a change in a base in a codon in mRNA.

Figure 13.20

Effects of base-pair mutations in protein-coding genes on the amino acid sequence of the encoded polypeptide.

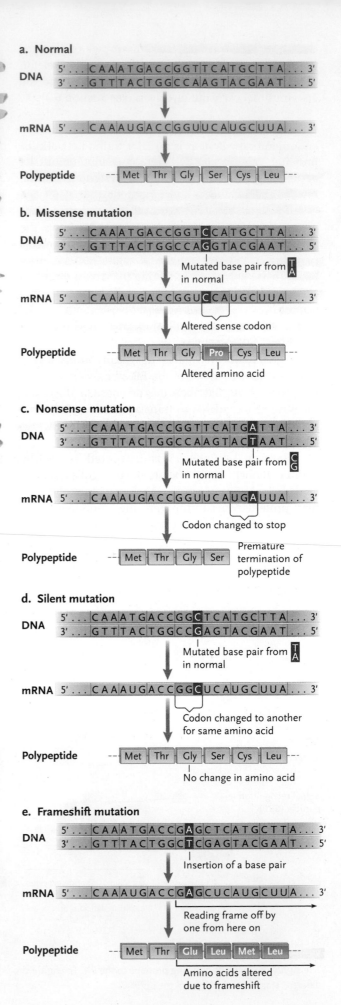

If a mutation alters the codon to specify a different amino acid, then the resulting protein will have a different amino acid sequence. We call this a **missense mutation** because although an amino acid is placed in the polypeptide, it is the wrong one (see Figure 13.20b). Whether the polypeptide's function is altered significantly or not depends on which amino acid is changed and what it is changed to. A missense mutation in the gene for one of the two hemoglobin polypeptides **(Figure 13.21)** results in the genetic disease sickle cell anemia, described in Chapter 10.

A second type of base-pair substitution mutation is a **nonsense mutation** (see Figure 13.20c). In this case, the mutation changes a sense (amino acid–coding) codon to a nonsense (termination) codon in the mRNA. Translation of an mRNA containing a nonsense mutation results in a premature "stop" and a shorter-than-normal polypeptide. This polypeptide will likely be partially functional at best.

Because of the degeneracy of the genetic code, some base-pair substitution mutations do not alter the amino acid specified by the gene because the changed codon specifies the same amino acid as in the normal polypeptide. Such mutations are known as **silent mutations** (see Figure 13.20d).

If a single base pair is deleted or inserted in the coding region of a gene, the reading frame of the resulting mRNA is altered. That is, after that point, the ribosome reads codons that are not the same as for the normal mRNA, typically producing a completely different amino acid sequence in the polypeptide from then on. This type of mutation is called a **frameshift mutation** (see Figure 13.20e; insertion mutation shown); the resulting polypeptide is usually nonfunctional because of the significantly altered amino acid sequence. The protein may be longer or shorter than usual depending on where the stop codons occur in the shifted reading frame.

Both transcription and translation are steps in the process of gene expression, the realization of the gene's coded information in the makeup and activities of a cell. However, we will see in the next chapter that the flow of information is not one way; organisms and cells also exert control over how their genes are expressed.

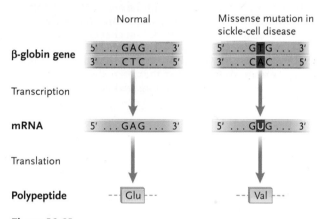

Figure 13.21

Missense mutation in a gene for one of the two polypeptides of hemoglobin that is the cause of sickle cell disease.

STUDY BREAK

1. How does translation initiation occur in eukaryotes versus prokaryotic cells?
2. Distinguish among the E, P, and A sites of the ribosome.
3. How are proteins directed to different parts of a eukaryotic cell?

Review

CourseMate Access an interactive eBook, chapter-specific interactive learning tools, including flashcards, quizzes, videos, and more in your Biology **CourseMate**, accessed through NelsonBrain.com

aplia Aplia™ is an online interactive learning solution that helps you improve comprehension—and your grade—by integrating a variety of mediums and tools such as videos, tutorials, practice tests, and an interactive eBook.

13.1 The Connection between DNA, RNA, and Protein

- In their genetic experiments with *Neurospora crassa,* Beadle and Tatum found a direct correspondence between gene mutations and alterations of enzymes. Their one gene–one enzyme hypothesis is now restated as the one gene–one polypeptide hypothesis (Figure 13.2).
- The pathway from genes to proteins involves transcription and then translation. In transcription, a sequence of nucleotides in DNA is copied into a complementary sequence in an RNA molecule. In translation, the sequence of nucleotides in an mRNA molecule specifies an amino acid sequence in a polypeptide (Figure 13.4).

- The genetic code is a triplet code. AUG at the beginning of a coded message establishes a reading frame for reading the codons three nucleotides at a time. The code is redundant: most of the amino acids are specified by more than one codon (Figure13.5).
- The genetic code is essentially universal.
- Aside from genes that code for protein through translation of mRNA, other genes code directly for RNA products (such as tRNA, rRNA, and snRNA) that are not translated.

13.2 Transcription: DNA-Directed RNA Synthesis

- Transcription is the process by which information coded in DNA is transferred to a complementary RNA copy (Figure 13.6).
- Transcription begins when an RNA polymerase binds to a promoter sequence in the DNA and starts synthesizing an RNA molecule. The enzyme then adds RNA nucleotides in sequence according to the DNA template. At the end of the transcribed sequence, the enzyme and the completed RNA transcript release from the DNA template. The mechanism of termination is different in eukaryotes and prokaryotic cells.

In addition to sequences coding for amino acids, the DNA of protein-coding genes also contains several types of sequences that regulate transcription and translation.

13.3 Processing of mRNAs in Eukaryotes

- A gene encoding an mRNA molecule includes the promoter, which is recognized by the regulatory proteins and transcription factors that promote DNA unwinding and the initiation of transcription by an RNA polymerase. Transcription in eukaryotes produces a pre-mRNA molecule that consists of a 5′ cap, the 5′ untranslated region, interspersed exons (amino acid–coding segments) and introns, the 3′ untranslated regions, and the 3′ poly(A) tail. All are copied from DNA except the 5′ cap and poly (A) tail, which are added during transcription (Figure 13.7).

- Introns in pre-mRNAs are removed to produce functional mRNAs by splicing. snRNPs bind to the introns, loop them out of the pre-mRNA, clip the intron at each exon boundary, and join the adjacent exons together (Figure 13.8).

- Many pre-mRNAs are subjected to alternative splicing, a process that joins exons in different combinations to produce different mRNAs encoded by the same gene. Translation of each mRNA produced in this way generates a protein with a different function (Figure 13.9).

13.4 Translation: mRNA-Directed Polypeptide Synthesis

- Translation is the assembly of amino acids into polypeptides. Translation occurs on ribosomes. The P, A, and E sites of the ribosome are used for the stepwise addition of amino acids to the polypeptide as directed by the mRNA (Figures 13.10 and 13.13).

- Amino acids are brought to the ribosome attached to specific tRNAs. Amino acids are linked to their corresponding tRNAs by aminoacyl-tRNA synthetases. By matching amino acids with tRNAs, the reactions also provide the ultimate basis for the accuracy of translation (Figures 13.14 and 13.15).

- Translation proceeds through the stages of initiation, elongation, and termination. In initiation, a ribosome assembles with an mRNA molecule and an initiator methionine-tRNA. In elongation, amino acids linked to tRNAs are added one at a time to the growing polypeptide chain. In termination, the new polypeptide is released from the ribosome and the ribosomal subunits separate from the mRNA (Figure 13.16).

- After they are synthesized on ribosomes, polypeptides are converted into finished form by processing reactions, which include removal of one or more amino acids from the protein chains, addition of organic groups, and folding guided by chaperones.

- Proteins are distributed in cells by means of signals spelled out by amino acid sequences at the N-terminal end of the newly translated polypeptide (Figure 13.19).

- Mutations in the DNA template alter the mRNA and can lead to changes in the amino acid sequence of the encoded polypeptide. A missense mutation changes one codon to one that specifies a different amino acid, a nonsense mutation changes a codon to a stop codon, and a silent mutation changes one codon to another codon that specifies the same amino acid. A base-pair insertion or deletion is a frameshift mutation that alters the reading frame beyond the point of the mutation, leading to a different amino acid sequence from then on in the polypeptide (Figures 13.20 and 13.21).

Questions

Self-Test Questions

1. Which statement about the following pathway is true?

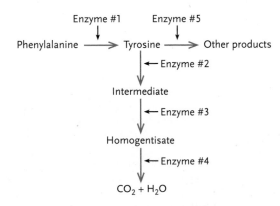

   a. A mutation for enzyme #1 causes tyrosine to build up.
   b. A mutation for enzyme #2 prevents tyrosine from being synthesized.
   c. A mutation at enzyme #3 prevents homogentistate from being synthesized.
   d. A mutation for enzyme #4 could hide a mutation in enzyme #1.

2. Which of the following statements describes *eukaryotic* mRNA?
   a. It uses snRNPs to cut out introns and seal together translatable exons.
   b. It is translated by ribosomes as it is being transcribed by RNA polymerase.
   c. It has a guanine cap on its 3′ end and a poly (A) tail on its 5′ end.
   d. It is a polymer of adenine, thymine, guanine, and cytosine bases.

3. A segment strand of DNA has a base sequence of 5′-GCATTAGAC-3′. What would be the sequence of an RNA molecule complementary to that sequence?
   a. 5′-GUCTAATGC-3′
   b. 5′-GCAUUAGAC-3′
   c. 5′-CGTAATCTG-3′
   d. 5′-GUCUAAUGC-3′

4. Which of the following statements about the initiation phase of translation in prokaryotic cells is true?
   a. GTP is synthesized.
   b. A region of the 5′ UTR of mRNA binds to rRNA.
   c. 5′-UAC-3′ on the Met tRNA binds 3′-AUG-5′ on mRNA.
   d. tRNA attaches first to the small ribosomal subunit.

5. Which of the following types of bonding involves complementary base-pairing?
   a. tRNA to amino acid
   b. signal peptide to signal recognition particle
   c. release factor to stop codon
   d. DNA to RNA during transcription of rRNA gene

6. Translation is in progress, with methionine bound to a tRNA in the P site, and a phenylalanine bound to a tRNA in the A site. What is the order of the next steps in the elongation cycle?
   a. the ribosome translocates → a new aminoacyl-tRNA enters the A site → peptidyl transferase catalyzes a peptide bond between the two amino acids → empty tRNA is released from the ribosome
   b. peptidyl transferase catalyzes a peptide bond between the two amino acids → a new aminoacyl-tRNA enters the A site → empty tRNA is released from the ribosome → the ribosome translocates
   c. peptidyl transferase catalyzes a peptide bond between the two amino acids → the ribosome translocates → empty tRNA is released from the ribosome → a new aminoacyl-tRNA enters the A site
   d. the ribosome translocates → peptidyl transferase catalyzes a peptide bond between the two amino acids → empty tRNA is released from the ribosome → a new aminoacyl-tRNA enters the A site

7. Which of the following statements about translation is true?
   a. ATP is the preferred energy source during various stages of translation.
   b. Peptide bond formation between amino acids is catalyzed by a ribozyme.
   c. When the mRNA codon UGG reaches the ribosome, there is no tRNA to bind to it.
   d. Forty-two amino acids of a protein are encoded by 84 nucleotides of the mRNA.

8. Which of the following items binds to the SRP receptor and to the signal sequence to guide a newly synthesized protein to be secreted to its proper channel?
   a. a ribosome
   b. a signal peptidase
   c. a signal recognition particle
   d. a rough endoplasmic reticulum

9. A part of an mRNA molecule with the sequence 5'-UGC GCA-3' is being translated by a ribosome. The following activated tRNA molecules are available. Which two of them can correctly bind the mRNA, resulting in a dipeptide?

tRNA Anticodon	Amino Acid
3'-GGC-5'	Proline
3'-CGU-5'	Alanine
3'-UGC-5'	Threonine
3'-CCG-5'	Glycine
3'-ACG-5'	Cysteine
3'-CGG-5'	Alanine

   a. cysteine–alanine
   b. proline–cysteine
   c. glycine–proline
   d. threonine–glycine

10. If a single base insertion mutation occurred within the first exon of a eukaryotic gene, what would be the likely result?
    a. improper splicing by spliceosome
    b. a longer mature mRNA
    c. a failure of the initiation of translation
    d. a silent mutation

Questions for Discussion

1. Would you expect rRNA genes to have start codons? Why or why not?

2. A mutation appears that alters an anticodon in a tRNA from AAU to AUU. What effect will this change have on protein synthesis in cells carrying this mutation?

3. The normal form of a gene is shown below, starting with the start codon (3' and 5' UTR are not visible):

   5'-ATGCCCGCCTTTGCTACTTGGTAG-3'

   3'-TACGGGCGGAAACGATGAACCATC-5'

   When this gene is transcribed, the result is the following mRNA molecule:

   5'-AUGCCCGCCUUUGCUACUUGGUAG-3'

   In a mutated form of the gene, two extra base pairs (underlined) are inserted:

   5'-ATGCCCGCCTAATTGCTACTTGGTAG-3'

   3'-TACGGGCGGATTAACGATGAACCATC-5'

   What effect will this mutation have on the structure of the protein encoded in the gene?

4. A geneticist is attempting to isolate mutations in the genes for four enzymes acting in a metabolic pathway in the bacterium *Escherichia coli*. The end product E of the pathway is absolutely essential for life:

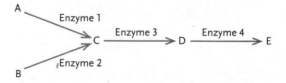

   The geneticist has been able to isolate mutations in the genes for enzymes 1 and 2, but not for enzymes 3 and 4. Develop a hypothesis to explain why.

5. How could you show experimentally that the genetic code is universal, namely, that it is the same in bacteria as it is in eukaryotes such as fungi, plants, and animals?

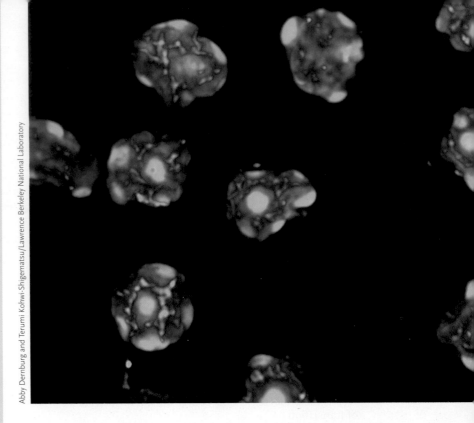

Abby Dernburg and Terumi Kohwi-Shigematsu/Lawrence Berkeley National Laboratory

Chromatin remodelling proteins (gold) binding to chromatin (blue). Chromatin remodelling, a change in chromosome structure in the region of a gene, is a key step in the activation of genes in eukaryotes.

STUDY PLAN

14.1   Regulation of Gene Expression in Prokaryotic Cells

14.1a   The Operon Is a Unit of Transcription

14.1b   The *lac* Operon for Lactose Metabolism Is Transcribed When an Inducer Inactivates a Repressor

14.1c   Transcription of the *lac* Operon Is Also Controlled by a Positive Regulatory System

14.1d   Transcription of the *trp* Operon Genes for Tryptophan Biosynthesis Is Repressed When Tryptophan Activates a Repressor

14.2   Regulation of Transcription in Eukaryotes

14.2a   In Eukaryotes, Regulation of Gene Expression Occurs at Several Levels

14.2b   Regulation of Transcription Initiation Involves the Effects of Proteins Binding to a Gene's Promoter and Regulatory Sites

14.2c   Methylation of DNA Can Control Gene Transcription

14.2d   Chromatin Structure Plays an Important Role in Whether a Gene Is Active or Inactive

14.3   Posttranscriptional, Translational, and Posttranslational Regulation

14.3a   Posttranscriptional Regulation Controls mRNA Availability

14.3b   Translational Regulation Controls the Rate of Protein Synthesis

14.3c   Posttranslational Regulation Controls the Availability of Functional Proteins

14.4   The Loss of Regulatory Controls in Cancer

14.4a   Cancers Are Genetic Diseases

14.4b   Three Main Classes of Genes Are Implicated in Cancer

14.4c   Cancer Develops Gradually by Multiple Steps

14 Control of Gene Expression

WHY IT MATTERS

A human egg cell is almost completely inactive metabolically when it is released from the ovary. It remains quiescent as it travels down a fallopian tube leading from the ovary to the uterus, carried along by movements of cilia lining the walls of the tube **(Figure 14.1)**. It is here, in the fallopian tube, that the egg meets sperm cells and embryonic development begins. Within seconds after the cells unite, the fertilized egg breaks its quiescent state and begins a series of divisions that continues as the egg moves through the fallopian tube and enters the uterus. Subsequent divisions produce specialized cells that *differentiate* into the distinct types tailored for the myriad specific functions in the body, from muscle cells to cells of the lens of the eye.

At first glance, you might think it most efficient for the cells in each differentiated tissue to retain only those genes needed to carry out its specific function; that is, liver cells might be expected to have a different collection of genes than bone cells. However, biochemical and cytogenetic analyses do not support this model and have, in fact, demonstrated that all nucleated cells of a developing embryo retain essentially the same set of genes that was created in the original single-celled zygote at fertilization. Structural and functional

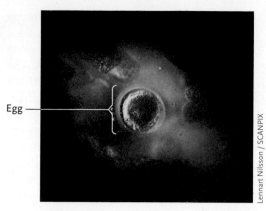

Figure 14.1

A human egg at the time of its release from the ovary. The outer layer appearing light blue in colour is a coat of polysaccharides and glycoproteins that surrounds the egg. Within the egg, genes and regulatory proteins are poised to enter the pathways initiating embryonic development.

Lennart Nilsson / SCANPIX

differences in cell types result from the presence or absence of the *products resulting from expression of genes* rather than the presence or absence of the genes themselves. As you saw in the previous chapter, all gene expression initially results in RNA products made by transcription. One type of RNA product, mRNA, further directs the synthesis of protein products by translation. But what determines when the product is produced, where, and how much? For example, the products of some genes, known as housekeeping genes, are expressed in nearly all cells, whereas the products of other genes may be found only in certain cell types at specific times under particular environmental conditions. To illustrate this point, consider that all cells contain genes coding for the rRNA molecules needed for ribosome function, as well as genes coding for various hemoglobin polypeptides. While rRNA gene products are abundant in all cells, particular hemoglobins are found only in those cells that give rise to red blood cells in the fetus, newborn, or adult.

The material in the previous chapter on transcription and translation hinted at possible regulatory mechanisms of gene expression. Usually, when we say that a gene is "turned on," we mean that it is more likely to be transcribed actively. Beyond transcription, the expression of gene products is subject to further controls affecting the processing of ribonucleic acid (RNA), possible translation into protein, and the activity and "life span" of the product itself.

You saw in the previous chapter that transcription and translation are coincident in prokaryotic cells. This enables a rapid response to environmental conditions through regulation of transcription initiation. Eukaryotes, particularly multicellular organisms, exhibit a variety of mechanisms not used by prokaryotic organisms. In this chapter, we examine the mechanisms of transcriptional regulation and its fine-tuning by additional controls at the posttranscriptional, translational, and posttranslational levels. Our discussion begins with bacterial systems, where researchers first discovered a mechanism for transcriptional regulation, and then moves to eukaryotic systems, where the regulation of gene activity is more complex. The chapter closes with a look at the loss of regulatory controls in cancer cells. The ways in which genes regulate development is discussed in Chapters 29 and 34.

14.1 Regulation of Gene Expression in Prokaryotic Cells

Transcription and translation are closely regulated in prokaryotic cells in ways that reflect prokaryotic life histories. Prokaryotic organisms tend to be single-celled and relatively simple, with generation times measured in minutes. Rather than the complex patterns of long-term cell differentiation and development typical of multicellular eukaryotes, prokaryotic cells typically undergo rapid and reversible alterations in biochemical pathways that allow them to adapt quickly to changes in their environment.

The bacterium *Escherichia coli*, for example, can find itself in the intestinal tract of a cow one minute and then in a treated municipal water supply soon after. Sugars such as lactose might be more available in the aquatic environment, and genes coding for enzymes needed to metabolize this energy source must be turned on. Other nutrients, such as the amino acid tryptophan, may be abundant in the intestinal tract. Therefore, genes coding for enzymes needed to manufacture the amino acid from scratch must be turned off. A versatile and responsive control system allows the bacterium to make the most efficient use of the particular array of nutrients and energy sources available at any given time.

14.1a The Operon Is a Unit of Transcription

For a typical metabolic process, several genes are involved, and they must be regulated in a coordinated fashion. For example, three genes encode proteins for the metabolism of lactose by *E. coli*. In the absence of lactose, the three genes are transcribed very little, whereas in the presence of lactose, the genes are transcribed quite actively. That is, the on/off control of these genes is at the level of transcription.

In 1961, François Jacob and Jacques Monod of the Pasteur Institute in Paris proposed the *operon model* for the control of the expression of genes for lactose metabolism in *E. coli*. Subsequently, data have shown the operon model to be widely applicable to the regulation of gene expression in bacteria and their viruses. Jacob and Monod received the Nobel Prize in 1965 for their explanation of bacterial operons and their regulation by repressors.

An **operon** is a cluster of prokaryotic genes and the DNA sequences involved in their regulation. The promoter, as we saw in the previous chapter, is a region where the RNA polymerase begins transcription. Another regulatory DNA sequence in the operon is the **operator**, a short segment that is a binding sequence for a **regulatory protein**. A gene that is separate from the operon encodes the regulatory protein. Some operons are controlled by a regulatory protein termed a **repressor**, which, when bound to the DNA, reduces the likelihood that genes will be transcribed. Other operons are controlled by a regulatory protein termed an **activator**, which, when bound to the DNA, increases the likelihood that genes will be transcribed. Many operons are controlled by more than one regulatory mechanism, and a number of the repressors or activators control more than one operon. The result is a complex network of superimposed controls that provides regulation of transcription, allowing almost instantaneous global responses to changing environmental conditions.

Each operon, which can contain several to many genes, is transcribed as a unit from the promoter into a single messenger RNA (mRNA), and, as a result, the mRNA contains codes for several proteins. The cluster of genes transcribed into a single mRNA is called a **transcription unit**. A ribosome translates the entire mRNA from one end to the other, sequentially making each protein encoded in the mRNA. Typically, the proteins encoded by genes in the same operon catalyze steps in the same process, such as enzymes acting in sequence in a biochemical pathway.

14.1b The *lac* Operon for Lactose Metabolism Is Transcribed When an Inducer Inactivates a Repressor

Jacob and Monod researched the genetic control of lactose metabolism in *E. coli* through a series of brilliantly creative genetic and biochemical approaches. Their studies showed that metabolism of lactose as an energy source involves three genes: *lacZ, lacY,* and *lacA* **(Figure 14.2)**. These three genes are adjacent to one another on the chromosome in the order *Z-Y-A*. The genes are transcribed as a unit into a single mRNA starting with the *lacZ* gene; the promoter for the transcription unit is upstream of *lacZ*. The *lacZ* gene encodes the enzyme β-galactosidase, which catalyzes the conversion of the disaccharide sugar, lactose, into the monosaccharide sugars, glucose and galactose. These sugars are then further metabolized by other enzymes, producing energy for the cell by glycolysis and Kreb's cycle. The *lacY* gene encodes a permease enzyme that transports lactose actively into the cell, and the *lacA* gene encodes a transacetylase enzyme, the function of which is more relevant to metabolism of compounds other than lactose.

Jacob and Monod called the cluster of genes and adjacent sequences that control their expression the *lac operon* (see Figure 14.2). They coined the name *operon* from the key DNA sequence they discovered for regulating transcription of the operon—the operator. The operator was named because it controls the operation of the genes adjacent to it. For the *lac* operon, the operator is a short DNA sequence between the promoter and the *lacZ* gene.

These two investigators showed that the *lac* operon was controlled by a regulatory protein that they termed the *Lac repressor*. The Lac repressor is encoded by the regulatory gene *lacI*, which is nearby but separate from the *lac* operon (see Figure 14.2), and is synthesized in active form. When lactose is absent from the medium, the Lac repressor binds to the operator, thereby blocking the RNA polymerase from binding to the promoter **(Figure 14.3a)**. Repressor binding is a kind of equilibrium; while it is bound to the operator most of the time, it occasionally comes off. In moments when the repressor is not bound, polymerase can successfully transcribe. As a result, *there is always a low concentration of lac operon gene products in the cell.*

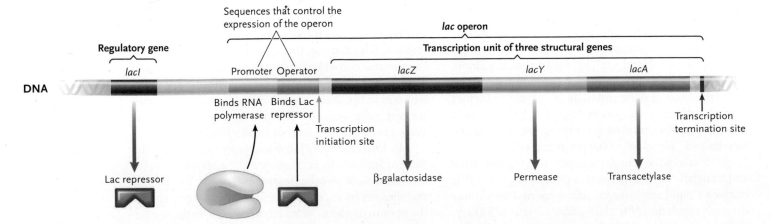

Figure 14.2

The *E. coli lac* operon. The *lacZ, lacY,* and *lacA* genes encode the enzymes taking part in lactose metabolism. The separate regulatory gene, *lacI*, encodes the Lac repressor, which plays a pivotal role in the control of the operon. The promoter binds RNA polymerase, and the operator binds the activated Lac repressor. The transcription unit, which extends from the transcription initiation site to the transcription termination site, contains the genes.

a. Lactose absent from medium: structural genes expressed at very low levels

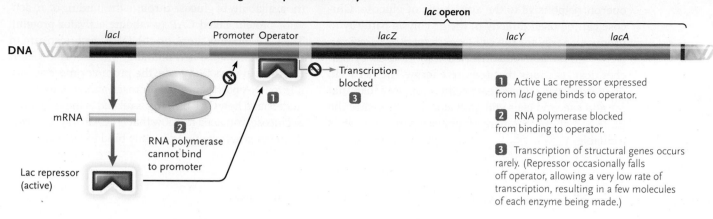

❶ Active Lac repressor expressed from *lacI* gene binds to operator.

❷ RNA polymerase blocked from binding to operator.

❸ Transcription of structural genes occurs rarely. (Repressor occasionally falls off operator, allowing a very low rate of transcription, resulting in a few molecules of each enzyme being made.)

b. Lactose present in medium: structural genes expressed at high levels

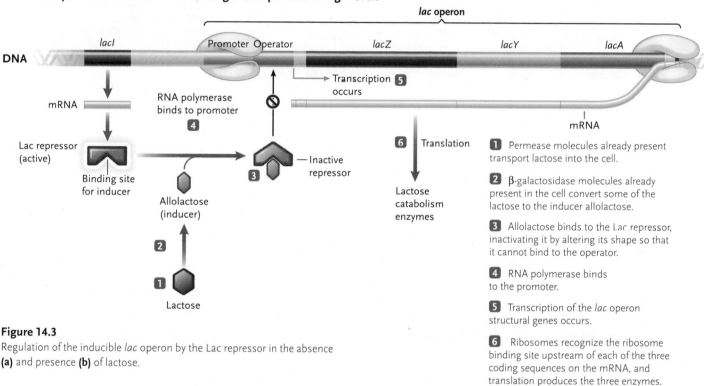

❶ Permease molecules already present transport lactose into the cell.

❷ β-galactosidase molecules already present in the cell convert some of the lactose to the inducer allolactose.

❸ Allolactose binds to the Lac repressor, inactivating it by altering its shape so that it cannot bind to the operator.

❹ RNA polymerase binds to the promoter.

❺ Transcription of the *lac* operon structural genes occurs.

❻ Ribosomes recognize the ribosome binding site upstream of each of the three coding sequences on the mRNA, and translation produces the three enzymes.

Figure 14.3
Regulation of the inducible *lac* operon by the Lac repressor in the absence **(a)** and presence **(b)** of lactose.

When lactose is added to the medium, the *lac* operon is turned on and all three enzymes are synthesized rapidly **(Figure 14.3b)**. How does this occur? Lactose enters the cell and the low levels of β-galactosidase molecules already present convert some of it to *allolactose,* an isomer of lactose. Allolactose is an **inducer** for the *lac* operon. It binds to the Lac repressor, altering its shape so that the repressor can no longer bind to the operator DNA. With the repressor out of the way, RNA polymerase is then able to bind freely to the promoter and transcribe the three genes at a dramatically elevated rate. Because an inducer molecule increases its expression, the *lac* operon is called an **inducible operon.**

As the lactose is used up, the regulatory system switches the *lac* operon off. That is, the absence of

lactose means that there are no allolactose inducer molecules to inactivate the repressor; the repressor binds to the operator, reducing transcription of the operon. These controls are aided by the fact that bacterial mRNAs are very short-lived, about three minutes on average. This quick turnover permits the cytoplasm to be cleared quickly of the mRNAs transcribed from an operon. The enzymes themselves also have short lifetimes and are quickly degraded.

14.1c Transcription of the *lac* Operon Is Also Controlled by a Positive Regulatory System

Several years after Jacob and Monod proposed their negatively regulated operon model for the lactose metabolism genes, researchers found a *positive gene regulation* system that makes expression of the *lac* operon responsive to the availability of glucose. Glucose can be used directly in the glycolysis pathway to produce energy for the cell (see Chapter 6). However, lactose must first be converted into glucose by biochemical reactions that require energy. The net yield of energy from other sugars is therefore less than that for glucose, and cells will grow best if they ensure the preferential metabolism of glucose whenever it is available.

Figure 14.4a shows that the *lac* operon is sensitive to the availability of glucose through the binding of an activator protein called CAP (catabolite activator protein). The CAP binding site is on the DNA, just upstream of the *lac* promoter. When bound at this site, CAP bends the DNA in ways that make the promoter more accessible to RNA polymerase and transcription increases. To understand how CAP binding is related to the availability of glucose, you need to know that (1) CAP is synthesized in an inactive form that can only bind to DNA *after* it is

a. Lactose present and glucose low or absent: structural genes expressed at very high levels

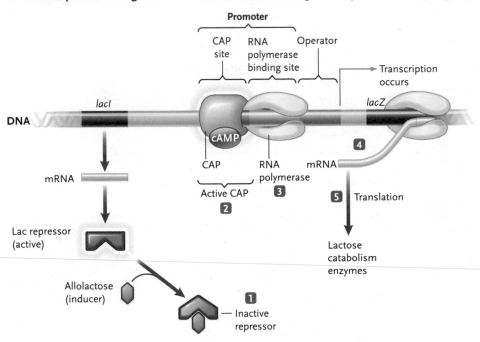

1. Lactose converted to the inducer, allolactose, which inactivates Lac repressor.

2. Active adenylyl cyclase synthesizes cAMP to high levels. cAMP binds to activator CAP, activating it. Activated CAP binds to CAP site in the promoter.

3. RNA polymerase binds efficiently to the promoter.

4. Genes of operon transcribed to high levels.

5. Translation produces high amounts of enzymes.

b. Lactose present and glucose present: structural genes expressed at low levels

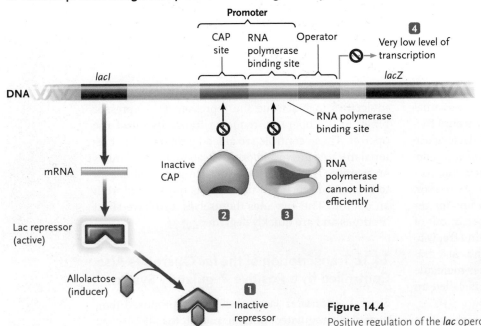

1. Lactose converted to the inducer, allolactose, which inactivates Lac repressor.

2. Catabolism of incoming glucose leads to inactivation of adenylyl cyclase, which causes the amount of cAMP in the cell to drop to a level too low to activate CAP. Inactive CAP cannot bind to the CAP site.

3. RNA polymerase is unable to bind to the promoter efficiently.

4. Transcription occurs at a low level: because the Lac repressor is not present to block RNA polymerase from binding to the promoter, the level of transcription is higher than when lactose is absent, but far lower than when lactose is present and glucose is absent.

Figure 14.4
Positive regulation of the *lac* operon through binding of the CAP activator protein.

activated by binding with cyclic AMP (cAMP is a nucleotide that plays a role in regulating cellular processes in both prokaryotic and eukaryotic cells), and (2) cAMP levels are inversely related to the uptake of glucose from the growth medium; when glucose is abundant, cAMP levels tend to be low (meaning CAP is mostly inactive). When glucose is absent from the environment, cAMP concentration tends to be high inside the cell, leading to an increased level of activated CAP.

Taken together, the negative control by the Lac repressor and the positive control by CAP/cAMP ensure that cells express the *lac* operon most strongly only when lactose is present and glucose is not. Let's walk through one illustrative example to emphasize the interrelationships among the various players. Imagine cells growing on glucose only. In the presence of glucose, very little cAMP is available to bind to CAP. Therefore, CAP/cAMP binding will be rare and there will be very little stimulation of expression. In the absence of lactose, the Lac repressor will be bound to the operator site most of the time and very little synthesis of the *lac* genes will occur. For these two reasons, expression of the *lac* operon will be at its lowest level. If we then add lactose to the environment, it will be metabolized to the inducer, allolactose, which will bind to and inactivate the Lac repressor. RNA polymerase will then bind to the promoter and transcribe the *lac* operon genes at a low level. Expression will increase further as glucose is metabolized from the surrounding medium, allowing cAMP levels to rise, activated CAP to bind, and the *lac* promoter to become even more available to RNA polymerase.

CONCEPT FIX Inducing *lac* operon expression through negative control and repressing expression through positive control may sound confusing. How can negative control make expression increase? The answer to this apparent paradox lies in focusing your attention on the DNA-binding proteins: the Lac repressor and CAP. In general, if the binding of a protein to DNA results in decreased gene expression, that is negative control. If the binding of a protein results in increased gene expression, that is positive control. Therefore, the binding of the Lac repressor is a clear example of negative control. When this repression is *released*, the *lac* operon is induced and expression increases. *Whether gene expression is under negative or positive control depends on the impact of the respective DNA-binding proteins, not on the impact of the available substrates such as glucose or lactose.* ⬡

The same positive gene regulation system using CAP and cAMP regulates a large number of other operons that control the metabolism of many sugars. In each case, the system functions so that glucose, if it is present in the growth medium, is metabolized first. This type of regulatory system, in which several operons are under the control of a common regulator, is called a regulon.

14.1d Transcription of the *trp* Operon Genes for Tryptophan Biosynthesis Is Repressed When Tryptophan Activates a Repressor

Tryptophan is an essential amino acid used in the synthesis of proteins. If tryptophan is absent from the medium, *E. coli* must manufacture it. If tryptophan is present in the medium, then the cell will use that source rather than make its own.

The genes involved in tryptophan biosynthesis are coordinately controlled in an operon called the *trp* operon **(Figure 14.5, p. 314)**. The five genes in this operon, *trpA* to *trpE*, encode the enzymes for the steps in the tryptophan biosynthesis pathway. Upstream of the *trpE* gene are the operon's promoter and operator sequences. Expression of the *trp* operon is controlled by the Trp repressor, a regulatory protein encoded by the *trpR* gene, which is located elsewhere in the genome (not nearby, as was the case for the repressor gene for the *lac* operon). In contrast to the Lac repressor, the Trp repressor is synthesized in an inactive form in which it cannot bind to the operator.

When tryptophan is absent from the medium and must be made by the cell, the *trp* operon genes are expressed (see Figure 14.5a, p. 314). This is the default state; since the Trp repressor is inactive and cannot bind to the operator, RNA polymerase can bind to the promoter and transcribe the operon. The resulting mRNA is translated to produce the five tryptophan biosynthetic enzymes that catalyze the reactions for tryptophan synthesis.

If tryptophan is present, there is no need for the cell to make it, so the *trp* operon is shut off (see Figure 14.5b, p. 314). This occurs because the tryptophan entering the cell binds to the Trp repressor and activates it. The active Trp repressor then binds to the operator of the *trp* operon and blocks RNA polymerase from binding to the promoter—the operon cannot be transcribed.

For the *trp* operon, then, the presence of tryptophan represses the expression of the tryptophan biosynthesis genes; hence, this operon is an example of a **repressible operon**. Here, tryptophan acts as a **corepressor**, a regulatory molecule that combines with a repressor to activate it and thus shut off the operon.

Let's compare and contrast the two operons we have discussed: (1) In the *lac* operon, the repressor is synthesized in an active form. When the inducer (allolactose) is present, it binds to the repressor and inactivates it. The operon is then transcribed. (2) In the *trp* operon, the repressor is synthesized in an inactive form. When the corepressor (tryptophan) is present, it binds to the repressor and activates it. The active repressor blocks transcription of the operon.

CONCEPT FIX Inducible and repressible operons both illustrate *negative gene regulation* because both are

a. Tryptophan absent from medium: tryptophan must be made by the cell—structural genes transcribed

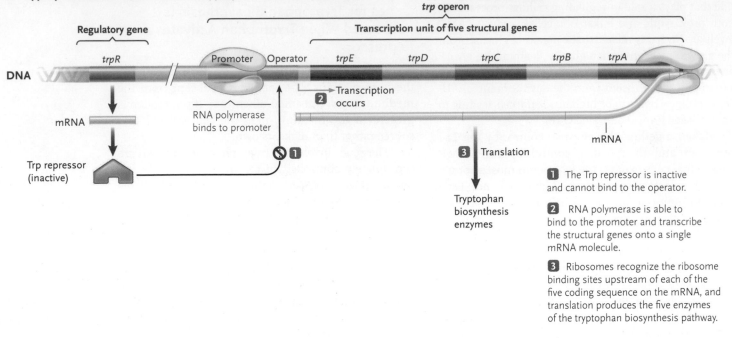

b. Tryptophan present in medium: cell uses tryptophan in medium rather than synthesizing it—structural genes not transcribed

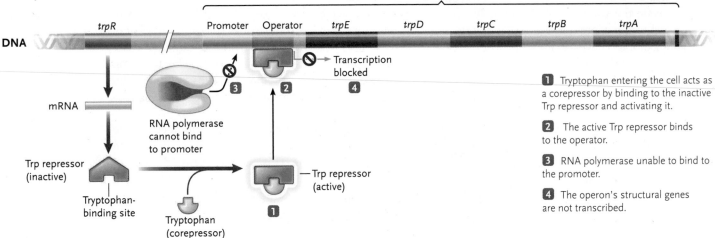

Figure 14.5

Regulation of the repressible *trp* operon by the Trp repressor protein in the absence **(a)** and presence **(b)** of the amino acid tryptophan.

regulated by a repressor that turns off gene expression when it binds DNA. ⬡

In summary, regulation of gene expression in prokaryotic cells occurs primarily at the transcription level. There are also, however, some examples of regulation at the translation level. For example, some proteins can bind to the mRNAs that produce them and modulate their translation. This serves as a feedback mechanism to fine-tune the amounts of the proteins in the cell. In the remainder of the chapter, we discuss the regulation of gene expression in eukaryotes. You will see that regulation occurs at several points in the gene expression pathway and that regulatory mechanisms are more complex than those in prokaryotic cells.

STUDY BREAK

1. Suppose the *lacI* gene is mutated so that the Lac repressor is not made. How does this mutation affect the regulation of the *lac* operon?
2. Answer the equivalent question for the *trp* operon: How would a mutation that prevents the Trp repressor from being made affect the regulation of the *trp* operon?

Bacterial cells can communicate with one another through the production and detection of molecules called autoinducers. When an autoinducer accumulates to high concentration in the local environment, it binds to membrane receptors that initiate a signal cascade, resulting in transcriptional activation of genes. This process, called quorum sensing, provides a mechanism for populations of cells to determine their density and thus coordinate gene expression as a community. For instance, although it is rather futile for an isolated single cell of *Vibrio harveyi* to express genes from its *lux* operon in order to biolumin-esce, hundreds of millions of cells, all expressing *lux* genes, collectively produce biologically significant amounts of light. Such large populations of bio-luminescent bacteria are found in the light organs of squid. In a way, these populations of bacterial cells behave like multicellular organisms. Although various autoinducers are known to mediate communication among members of the same species, a novel compound, called AI-2 **(Figure 1),** has been found to facilitate communication between members of *different* species. AI-2 is unlike any other known autoinducer and is particularly interesting in that it contains an atom of boron, an element whose function in biological systems has been quite mysterious.

FIGURE 1

AI-2, a universal autoinducer containing boron.

14.2 Regulation of Transcription in Eukaryotes

The molecular mechanisms in prokaryotic operon function are a simple means of coordinating synthesis of proteins with related functions. In eukaryotes, the coordinated synthesis of proteins with related functions also occurs, but without the need to organize genes under the control of a single promoter in an operon.

There are two general categories of eukaryotic gene regulation. Short-term regulation involves regulatory events in which gene sets are quickly turned on or off in response to changes in environmental or physiological conditions in the cell's or organism's environment. This type of regulation is most similar to prokaryotic gene regulation. Long-term gene regulation involves regulatory events required for an organism to develop and differentiate. Long-term gene regulation occurs in multicellular eukaryotes and not in simpler, unicellular eukaryotes. The mechanisms we discuss in this and the next section are applicable to both short-term and long-term regulation.

14.2a In Eukaryotes, Regulation of Gene Expression Occurs at Several Levels

The regulation of gene expression is more complicated in eukaryotes than in prokaryotic cells because eukaryotic cells are more complex, because the nuclear DNA is organized with histones into chromatin, and because multicellular eukaryotes produce large numbers and different types of cells. Further, the eukaryotic nuclear envelope separates the processes of transcription and translation, whereas in prokaryotic cells, translation can start on an mRNA that is still being made. Consequently, gene expression in eukaryotes is regulated at more levels. That is, there is transcriptional regulation, post-transcriptional regulation, translational regulation, and posttranslational regulation **(Figure 14.6, p. 316).** The most important of these is transcriptional regulation.

14.2b Regulation of Transcription Initiation Involves the Effects of Proteins Binding to a Gene's Promoter and Regulatory Sites

Transcription initiation is the most common level at which the regulation of gene expression takes place.

Organization of a Eukaryotic Protein-Coding Gene. Figure 14.7, p. 316 shows a eukaryotic gene, emphasizing the regulatory sites involved in its expression. Immediately upstream of the transcription unit is the promoter. The promoter in the figure contains a TATA box, a sequence about 25 bp upstream of the start point for transcription that, as we will shortly see, plays an important role in transcription initiation in many promoters. The TATA box has the 7-bp consensus sequence

5'-TATAAAA-3'

3'-ATATTTT-5'

Promoters without TATA boxes have other sequence elements that play a similar role. In the following discussions, we describe transcription initiation involving a TATA box–containing promoter.

RNA polymerase II itself cannot recognize the promoter sequence. Instead, proteins called **transcription**

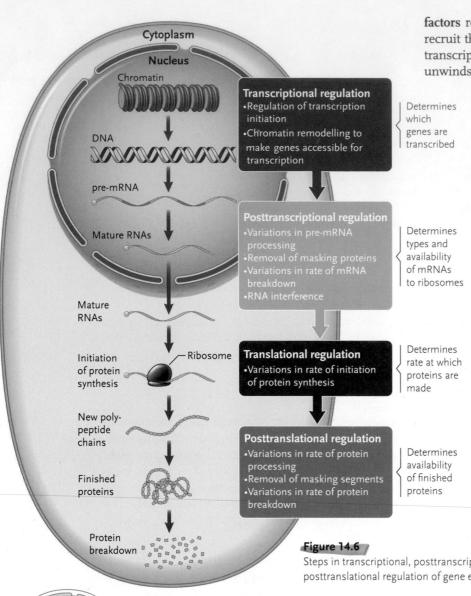

Transcriptional regulation
- Regulation of transcription initiation
- Chromatin remodelling to make genes accessible for transcription

} Determines which genes are transcribed

Posttranscriptional regulation
- Variations in pre-mRNA processing
- Removal of masking proteins
- Variations in rate of mRNA breakdown
- RNA interference

} Determines types and availability of mRNAs to ribosomes

Translational regulation
- Variations in rate of initiation of protein synthesis

} Determines rate at which proteins are made

Posttranslational regulation
- Variations in rate of protein processing
- Removal of masking segments
- Variations in rate of protein breakdown

} Determines availability of finished proteins

Figure 14.6

Steps in transcriptional, posttranscriptional, translational, and posttranslational regulation of gene expression in eukaryotes.

factors recognize and bind to the TATA box and then recruit the polymerase. Once the RNA polymerase II–transcription factor complex forms, the polymerase unwinds the DNA and transcription begins. Adjacent to the promoter, farther upstream, is the **promoter proximal region**, which contains regulatory sequences called **promoter proximal elements**. Regulatory proteins that bind to promoter proximal elements may stimulate or inhibit the rate of transcription initiation. More distant from the beginning of the gene is the **enhancer**. Regulatory proteins binding to regulatory sequences within an enhancer also stimulate or inhibit the rate of transcription initiation. Next we see more specifically how these regulatory sequences are involved in transcription initiation.

Activation of Transcription. To initiate transcription, proteins called **general transcription factors** (also called *basal transcription factors*) bind to the promoter in the area of the TATA box **(Figure 14.8).** These factors recruit the enzyme RNA polymerase II, which alone cannot bind to the promoter, and orient the enzyme to start transcription at the correct place. The combination of general transcription factors with RNA polymerase II is the **transcription initiation complex.** On its own, this complex brings about only a low rate of transcription initiation, which leads to just a few mRNA transcripts.

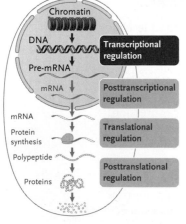

Figure 14.7

Organization of a eukaryotic gene. The transcription unit is the segment that is transcribed into the pre-mRNA; it contains the 5′UTR (untranslated region), exons, introns, and 3′ UTR. Immediately upstream of the transcription unit is the promoter, which often contains the TATA box. Adjacent to the promoter and farther upstream of the transcription unit is the promoter proximal region, which contains regulatory sequences called promoter proximal elements. More distant from the gene is the enhancer, which contains regulatory sequences that control the rate of transcription of the gene. Transcription of the gene produces a pre-mRNA molecule with a 5′ cap and 3′ poly(A) tail; processing of the pre-mRNA to remove introns generates the functional mRNA (see Chapter 13).

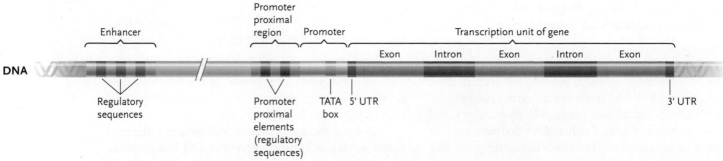

Activators are regulatory proteins that play a role in a positive regulatory system that controls the expression of one or more genes. Activators that bind to the promoter proximal elements interact directly with the general transcription factors at the promoter to stimulate transcription initiation so many more transcripts are synthesized in a given time. Housekeeping genes—genes that are expressed in all cell types for basic cellular functions such as glucose metabolism— have promoter proximal elements that are recognized by activators present in all cell types. By contrast, genes expressed only in particular cell types or at particular times have promoter proximal elements that are recognized by activators found only in those cell types, or at those times when transcription of these genes needs to be activated. To turn this around, the particular set of activators present within a cell at a given time is responsible for determining which genes in that cell are expressed to a significant level.

The DNA-binding and activation functions of activators are properties of two distinct domains in the proteins. (Protein domains are introduced in *The Purple Pages*.) The three-dimensional arrangement of amino acid chains within and between domains also produces highly specialized regions called **motifs**. Several types of motifs, each with a specialized function, are found in proteins, including motifs that insert into the DNA double helix. Motifs found in the DNA-binding domains of regulatory proteins, such as activators, include the helix-turn-helix, zinc finger, and leucine zipper **(Figure 14.9).**

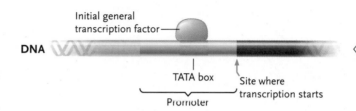

Figure 14.8
Formation of the transcription complex on the promoter of a protein-coding gene by the combination of general transcription factors with RNA polymerase. The general transcription factors are needed for RNA polymerase to bind and initiate transcription at the correct place.

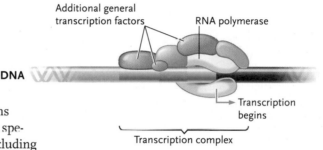

1 The first general transcription factor recognizes and binds to the TATA box of a protein-coding gene's promoter.

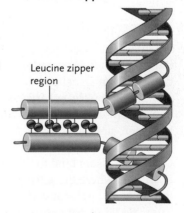

2 Additional general transcription factors and then RNA polymerase add to the complex. A general transcription factor unwinds the promoter DNA, and then transcription begins.

a. Helix-turn-helix

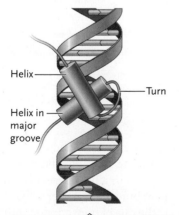

A helix-turn-helix motif is part of a protein bound to DNA. One of the α-helices binds to base pairs in the major groove of the DNA. A looped region of the protein—the turn—connects to a second α-helix that helps hold the first helix in place.

b. Zinc finger

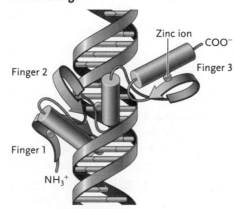

Zinc fingers motifs are parts of proteins named for their resemblance to fingers projecting from a protein, and the presence of a bound zinc atom. Zinc fingers bind to specific base pairs in the grooves of DNA.

c. Leucine zipper

Leucine zipper proteins are dimers, with each monomer consisting of α-helical segments. Hydrophobic interactions between leucine residues within the leucine zipper motif hold the two monomers together. Other α-helices bind to DNA base pairs in the major groove.

Figure 14.9
Three DNA-binding motifs found in activators and other regulatory proteins.

Figure 14.10

Interactions between activators at the enhancer, a coactivator, and general transcription factors at the promoter lead to maximal transcription of the gene.

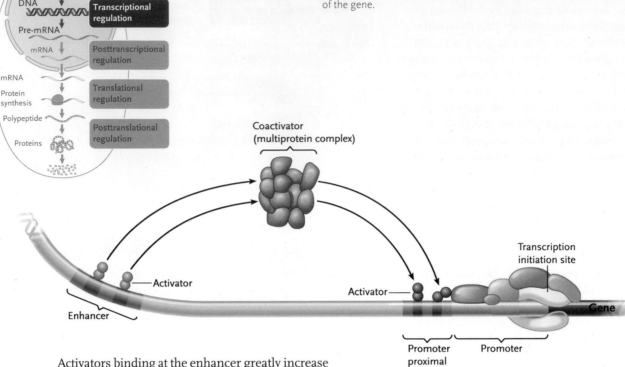

Activators binding at the enhancer greatly increase transcription rates **(Figure 14.10)**. The enhancers of different genes have different sets of regulatory sequences, which bind particular activators. A **coactivator** (also called a *mediator*), a large multiprotein complex, forms a bridge between the activators at the enhancer and the proteins at the promoter and promoter proximal region, causing the DNA to form a loop. The interactions between the activators at the enhancer, the coactivator, the proteins at the promoter, and the RNA polymerase greatly stimulate transcription up to its maximal rate.

Repression of Transcription. In some genes, repressors oppose the effect of activators, thereby blocking or reducing the rate of transcription. The final rate of transcription then depends on the "battle" between the activation signal and the repression signal.

Repressors in eukaryotes work in various ways. Some repressors bind to the same regulatory sequence to which activators bind (often in the enhancer), thereby preventing activators from binding to that site. Other repressors bind to their own specific site in the DNA near where the activator binds and interact with the activator so that it cannot interact with the coactivator. Yet other repressors bind to specific sites in the DNA and recruit **corepressors**, multiprotein complexes analogous to coactivators except that they are negative regulators, inhibiting transcription initiation.

Combinatorial Gene Regulation. Let's review the key elements of transcription regulation for a protein-coding gene. General transcription factors bind to certain promoter sequences such as the TATA box and recruit RNA polymerase II; this results in a basal level of transcription. Specific activators bind to promoter proximal elements and stimulate the rate of transcription initiation. Activators also bind to the enhancer to greatly stimulate transcription of the gene.

How are these events coordinated in regulating gene expression? Any given gene has a specific number and types of promoter proximal elements. In some genes, there may be only one regulatory element, but genes under complex regulatory control have many regulatory elements. Similarly, the number and types of regulatory sequences in the enhancer is specific for each gene.

Both promoter proximal regions and enhancers are important in regulating the transcription of a gene. Each regulatory sequence in those two regions binds a specific regulatory protein. Since some regulatory proteins are activators and others are repressors, the overall effect of regulatory sequences on transcription depends on the particular proteins that bind to them. If activators bind both to the regulatory sequences in the promoter proximal region and to the enhancer, transcription is activated maximally, meaning a high rate of transcription and therefore the production of a high level of the mRNA encoded by the gene. But, if a repressor binds to the enhancer and an activator binds to the promoter proximal element, the amount of gene expression depends upon the relative effects of those two regulatory proteins. For example, if the repressor is strong, gene expression, in terms of the rate of transcription and the consequent level of the mRNA encoded by the gene, will be reduced.

A relatively small number of regulatory proteins (activators and repressors) control transcription of all protein-coding genes. By combining a few regulatory proteins in particular ways, the transcription of a wide array of genes can be controlled. The process is called **combinatorial gene regulation.** Consider a theoretical example of two genes, each with activators already bound to the respective promoter proximal elements **(Figure 14.11).** Maximal transcription of gene *A* requires activators 2, 5, 7, and 8 binding to their regulatory sequences in the enhancer, whereas maximal transcription of gene *B* requires activators 1, 5, 8, and 11 binding to its enhancer. Looked at another way, both genes require activators 5 and 8 combined with other different activators for full activation.

This operating principle solves a basic dilemma in gene regulation—if each gene were regulated by a single, distinct protein, the number of genes encoding regulatory proteins would have to equal the number of genes to be regulated. Regulating the regulators would require another set of genes of equal number, and so on until the coding capacity of any chromosome set, no matter how large, would be exhausted. But because different genes require different combinations of regulatory proteins, the number of genes encoding regulatory proteins can be much lower than the number of genes the regulatory proteins control.

Coordinated Regulation of Transcription of Genes with Related Functions.

In the discussion of prokaryotic operons, you learned that genes with related function are often clustered *and* they are transcribed from one promoter onto a single mRNA. That mRNA is translated to produce the several proteins encoded by the genes. There are no operons in eukaryotes, yet the transcription of genes with related function is coordinately controlled. The preceding discussion of regulatory sequences and binding proteins gives an indication of how coordinated control is accomplished in eukaryotes.

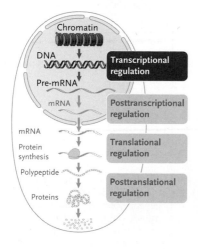

a. A unique combination of activators controls gene A.

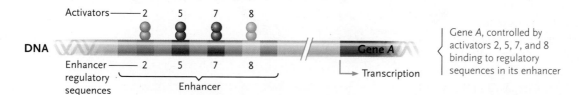

Gene A, controlled by activators 2, 5, 7, and 8 binding to regulatory sequences in its enhancer

b. A different combination of activators controls gene B.

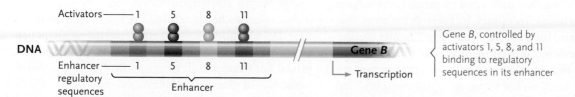

Gene B, controlled by activators 1, 5, 8, and 11 binding to regulatory sequences in its enhancer

Figure 14.11
Combinatorial gene regulation. A relatively small number of regulatory proteins control transcription of all protein-coding genes. Different combinations of activators bind to enhancer regulatory sequences to control the rate of transcription of each gene.

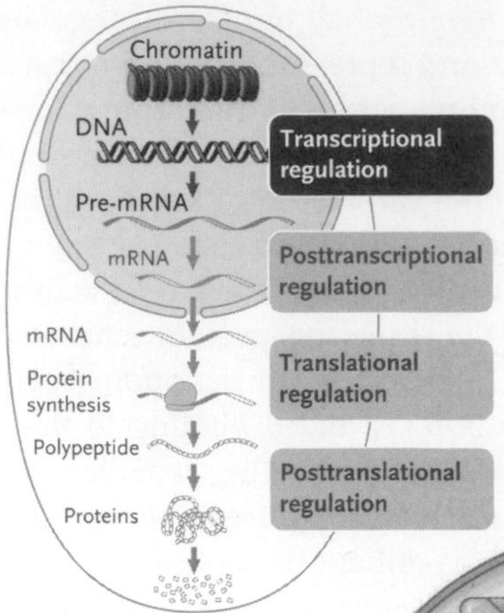

Figure 14.12

Steroid hormone regulation of gene expression. A steroid hormone enters the cell and forms a complex in the cytoplasm with a steroid hormone receptor that is specific to the hormone. Steroid hormone–receptor complexes migrate to the nucleus, bind to the steroid hormone response element next to each gene they control (one such gene is shown in the figure), and affect transcription of those genes.

1 Steroid hormone moves through the plasma membrane into the cell

2 Steroid hormone binds to its specific receptor in the cytoplasm, activating the receptor

3 Hormone–receptor complex enters the nucleus and binds to a specific steroid hormone response element adjacent to genes whose expression is controlled by the hormone. The binding activates transcription of those genes. One gene regulated by the hormone is shown.

4 Transcription produces a pre-mRNA transcript of the gene; processing produces the mRNA, which is translated in the cytoplasm to produce the protein encoded by the gene.

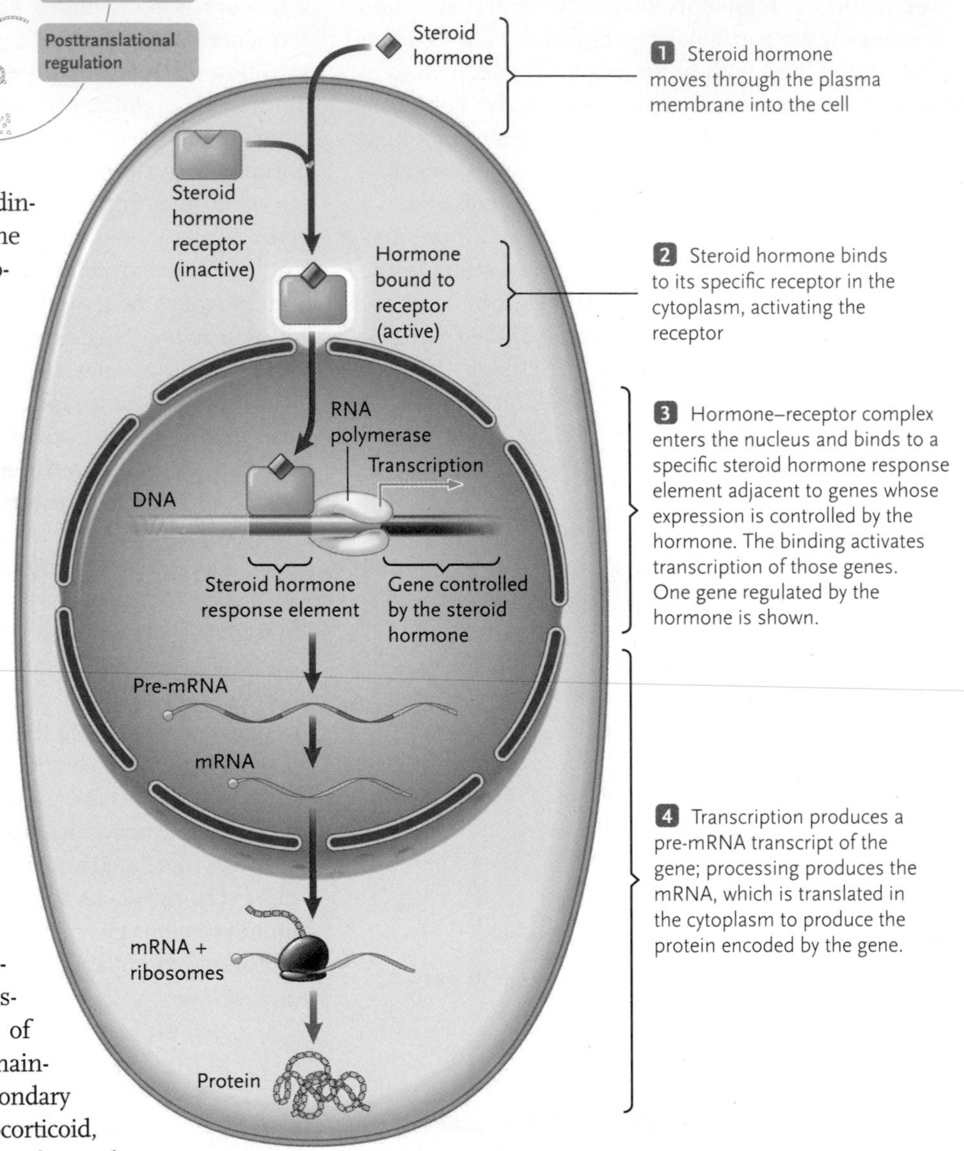

All genes that are coordinately regulated have the same regulatory sequences associated with them. Therefore, with one signal, the transcription of all of the genes can be controlled simultaneously. Consider the control of gene expression by steroid hormones in mammals. A **hormone** is a molecule produced by one tissue and transported via the bloodstream to a target tissue or tissues to alter physiological activity. A **steroid** is a type of lipid derived from cholesterol (see *The Purple Pages*). Examples of steroid hormones are testosterone and glucocorticoid. Testosterone regulates the expression of a large number of genes associated with the maintenance of primary and secondary male characteristics. Glucocorticoid, among other actions, regulates the expression of genes involved in the maintenance of the concentration of glucose and other fuel molecules in the blood. **Figure 14.12** illustrates how a steroid hormone, when it enters a cell, activates gene transcription.

A steroid hormone acts on specific target tissues in the body because only cells in those tissues have **steroid hormone receptors** in their cytoplasm that recognize and bind the hormone (see Chapter 5). The steroid hormone moves through the plasma membrane into the cytoplasm and the receptor binds to it (Figure 14.12). The hormone–receptor complex then enters the nucleus and binds to specific regulatory sequences that are adjacent to the genes whose expression is controlled by the hormone. This binding activates transcription of those genes, and proteins encoded by the genes are synthesized rapidly.

A single steroid hormone can regulate many different genes because all of the genes have an identical DNA sequence—a **steroid hormone response element**—to which the hormone–receptor complex binds. For example, all genes controlled by glucocorticoid have a glucocorticoid response element associated with them. Therefore, the release of glucocorticoid

PEOPLE BEHIND BIOLOGY 14.2

Dr. Shirley Tilghman, Princeton University

Shirley Tilghman was elected the nineteenth president of Princeton University in 2001. She is a distinguished teacher, a strong supporter of women in science, a world-renowned molecular biologist, and a director of Google Inc. Tilghman, who did her undergraduate study at Queen's University in Kingston, Ontario, and her Ph.D. at Temple University in Philadelphia, was involved in the cloning of the first mammalian gene and the subsequent discovery of introns. She is now an international authority on the molecular understanding of gene regulation by genomic imprinting and its implications for cloning in mammals, including humans.

into the bloodstream coordinately activates the transcription of genes with that response element.

14.2c Methylation of DNA Can Control Gene Transcription

Although binding proteins to DNA is a common mechanism for regulating transcription, such regulation can also be achieved through changes to the physical form of the DNA itself. In **DNA methylation**, enzymes add a methyl group (CH_3) to cytosine bases in the DNA. Methylated cytosines in promoter regions can regulate transcription through a process called **silencing**, in which transcription of genes controlled by those promoters is greatly reduced. This is an example of **epigenetics**, a phenomenon in which a change in gene expression is achieved without a change in the DNA sequence of the gene or of the genome.

Silencing by methylation is not universal among eukaryotes, but it is common among vertebrates. For example, genes encoding the blood protein hemoglobin are methylated and inactive in most vertebrate body cells. In the cell lines giving rise to red blood cells, enzymes remove the methyl groups from the promoters of the hemoglobin genes, which can then attract transcription factors and RNA polymerases.

DNA methylation in some cases silences large blocks of genes, or even chromosomes. Recall from Section 11.2e that a dosage compensation mechanism inactivates one of the two X chromosomes in most body cells of female placental mammals, including humans. In X chromosome inactivation—another example of an epigenetic phenomenon—one of the two X chromosomes packs tightly into a mass known as a Barr body, in which most genes of the X chromosome are turned off. The inactivation occurs during embryonic development, and which X chromosome is inactivated in a particular embryonic cell line is a random event. As part of X chromosome inactivation, cytosines in the DNA become methylated.

DNA methylation underlies **genomic imprinting**, an epigenetic phenomenon in which the expression of an allele is determined by the parent that contributed it (see Section 11.5). In genomic imprinting, methylation permanently silences transcription of either the inherited maternal or the inherited paternal allele of a particular gene. The methylation occurs during gametogenesis in a parent. An inherited methylated allele, the *imprinted allele*, is not expressed—it is silenced. The expression of the gene involved therefore depends upon expression of the nonimprinted allele inherited from the other parent. The methylation of the parental allele is maintained as the DNA is replicated, so that the silenced allele remains inactive in progeny cells.

14.2d Chromatin Structure Plays an Important Role in Whether a Gene Is Active or Inactive

Eukaryotic DNA is organized into chromatin by combination with histone proteins (discussed in Section 12.5). Recall that DNA is wrapped around a core of two molecules each of histones H2A, H2B, H3, and H4, forming the nucleosome (see Figure 12.21). The negative charge of DNA and the positive charges of the histone proteins naturally attract each other in nucleosomes and contribute to the structure's stability. Higher levels of chromatin organization occur when histone H1 links adjacent nucleosomes.

Genes in regions of the DNA that are tightly wound around histones in chromatin are less active, because their promoters are less accessible to the proteins that initiate transcription. For a eukaryotic gene to be activated, the chromatin structure must be altered in the vicinity of the promoter to provide access to the general transcription factors for transcription initiation. The process of changing chromatin structure is called **chromatin remodelling**. In one type of chromatin remodelling, an activator binds to a regulatory sequence upstream of the gene's promoter and recruits a **nucleosome remodelling complex.** The multiprotein complex uses the energy of ATP hydrolysis to slide the nucleosome along the DNA to expose the promoter, or to restructure the nucleosome without moving it to allow transcription factors to bind **(Figure 14.13)**. In a second type of chromatin remodelling, an activator binds to a regulatory sequence upstream of the gene's promoter and recruits an enzyme that acetylates (adds acetyl groups: CH_3COO) lysine amino acids in the tails of histones in the nucleosome, where the promoter is located. Acetylation removes the positively charged amino group of the lysine, which makes the histone less attractive to the negatively charged DNA. As a result, the histones loosen their association with DNA, and the promoter becomes accessible. This type of remodelling is reversed by deacetylation enzymes that remove the acetyl groups from the histones.

Many activators use both of these chromatin-remodelling mechanisms to regulate gene activity.

The tails of histones can also be modified by the covalent addition of methyl groups or phosphate groups to affect chromatin structure and gene expression. For example, histone methylation is often associated with gene inactivation. That is, methylation of histones tends to be a property of condensed regions of chromatin, including heterochromatin, where genes are inactive.

Once mRNAs are transcribed from active genes, further regulation occurs at each of the major steps in the pathway from genes to proteins: during pre-mRNA processing and the movement of finished mRNAs to the cytoplasm (posttranscriptional regulation), during protein synthesis (translational regulation), and after translation is complete (posttranslational regulation). The next section takes up the regulatory mechanisms operating at each of these steps.

STUDY BREAK

1. What is the role of histones in gene expression? How does acetylation of the histones affect gene expression?
2. What are the roles of general transcription factors, activators, and coactivators in transcription of a protein-coding gene?

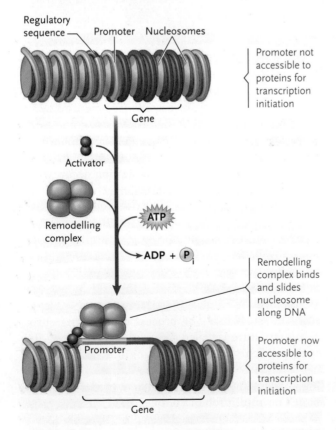

Figure 14.13
Exposing a gene's promoter by chromatin remodelling.

14.3 Posttranscriptional, Translational, and Posttranslational Regulation

The previous sections describe several mechanisms that determine which mRNAs are produced under various conditions. The following sections illustrate that, once a given mRNA is made, there are several opportunities to fine-tune expression through posttranscriptional, translational, and posttranslational controls (refer again to Figure 14.6, p. 316).

14.3a Posttranscriptional Regulation Controls mRNA Availability

Posttranscriptional regulation directs translation by controlling the availability of mRNAs to ribosomes. The controls work by several mechanisms, including changes in pre-mRNA processing and the rate at which mRNAs are degraded.

Variations in Pre-mRNA Processing. In Chapter 13, we noted that mRNAs are transcribed initially as pre-mRNA molecules. These pre-mRNAs are variously processed to produce the finished mRNAs, which then enter protein synthesis. Variations in pre-mRNA processing can regulate *which* proteins are made in cells. As described in Section 13.3, pre-mRNAs can be processed by *alternative splicing*. Alternative splicing produces different mRNAs from the same pre-mRNA by removing different combinations of exons (the amino acid–coding segments) along with the introns (the noncoding spacers). The resulting mRNAs are translated to produce a family of related proteins with various combinations of amino acid sequences derived from the exons. Alternative splicing itself is under regulatory control. Regulatory proteins specific to the type of cell control which exons are removed from pre-mRNA molecules by binding to regulatory sequences within those molecules. The outcome of alternative splicing is that appropriate proteins within a family are synthesized in cell types or tissues in which they function optimally. Perhaps three-quarters of human genes are alternatively spliced at the pre-mRNA level.

Posttranscriptional Control by Masking Proteins. Some posttranscriptional controls operate by means of *masking* proteins that bind to mRNAs and make them unavailable for protein synthesis. These controls are important in many animal eggs, keeping mRNAs in an inactive form until the egg has been fertilized and embryonic development is under way. When an mRNA is to become active, other factors—other proteins, made as part of the developmental pathway—remove the masking proteins and allow the mRNA to enter protein synthesis.

Variations in the Rate of mRNA Breakdown. The rate at which eukaryotic mRNAs break down can also be controlled posttranscriptionally. The mechanism involves a regulatory molecule, such as a steroid hormone, directly or indirectly affecting the mRNA breakdown steps, either slowing or increasing the rate of those steps. For example, in the mammary gland of the rat, the mRNA for casein (a milk protein) has a half-life of about 5 hours (meaning that it takes 5 hours for half of the mRNA present at a given time to break down). The half-life of casein mRNA changes to about 92 hours if the peptide hormone prolactin is present. Prolactin is synthesized in the brain and in other tissues, including the breast. The most important effect of prolactin is to stimulate the mammary glands to produce milk (that is, it stimulates lactation). During milk production, a large amount of casein must be synthesized, and this is accomplished in part by radically decreasing the rate of breakdown of the casein mRNA.

Nucleotide sequences in the 5' UTR (untranslated region; see Section 13.3) also appear to be important in determining mRNA half-life. If the 5' UTR is transferred experimentally from one mRNA to another, the half-life of the receiving mRNA becomes the same as that of the donor mRNA. The controlling sequences in the 5' UTR of an mRNA might be recognized by proteins that regulate its stability.

Regulation of Gene Expression by Small RNAs. Until relatively recently, the commonly accepted view was that regulation of gene expression in prokaryotic and eukaryotic cells involved only protein-based mechanisms. However, in 1998, Andrew Fire of the Stanford University School of Medicine and Craig Mello of the University of Massachusetts Medical School showed that RNA silenced the expression of a particular gene in the nematode worm, *Caenorhabditis elegans*. They called the phenomenon **RNA interference (RNAi)**. Their discovery revolutionized the way scientists thought about and studied gene regulation in eukaryotes. They now understand that posttranscriptional regulation may be carried out, not only by regulatory proteins, but also by noncoding single-stranded RNAs that can bind to mRNAs and affect their translation. We now know that RNAi is widespread among eukaryotes. Fire and Mello received a Nobel Prize in 2006 for their discovery of RNA interference.

Two major groups of small regulatory RNAs are involved in RNAi: **microRNAs (miRNAs)** and **short interfering RNAs (siRNAs)**. The transcription of an miRNA gene and the processing of the transcript to produce the functional miRNA molecule are shown in **Figure 14.14, p. 325**. The miRNA, in a protein complex called the **miRNA-induced silencing complex (miRISC)**, binds to sequences in the 3' UTRs of target mRNAs. If the miRNA and mRNA pair imperfectly, the double-stranded segment formed between the miRNA and the mRNA blocks ribosomes from translating the mRNA (shown in Figure 14.14, p. 325). In this case, the target mRNA is not destroyed, but its expression is silenced. If the miRNA and mRNA pair perfectly, an enzyme in the protein complex cleaves the target mRNA where the miRNA is bound to it, destroying the mRNA and silencing its expression. RNAi by imperfect pairing and translation inhibition is the most common mechanism in animals. RNAi by perfect pairing and RNA degradation is the most common mechanism in plants.

MicroRNA genes have been found in all multicellular eukaryotes that have been examined, and also in some unicellular ones. MicroRNAs play central roles in controlling gene expression in a variety of cellular, physiological, and developmental processes in animals and plants. In animals, for example, miRNAs help regulate specific developmental timing events, gene expression in neurons, brain development, cancer progression, and stem cell division.

The other major type of small regulatory RNAs is the **small interfering RNA (siRNA)**. Whereas miRNA is produced from RNA that is encoded in the cell's genome, siRNA is produced from double-stranded RNA that is *not* encoded by nuclear genes. For example, the replication cycle of many viruses with RNA genomes involves a double-stranded RNA stage. Cells attacked by such a virus can defend themselves using siRNA that they produce from the virus's own RNA. The viral double-stranded RNA enters the cell's RNAi process in a way very similar to that described for miRNAs; double-stranded RNA is cut by Dicer (see Figure 14.14) into short double-stranded RNA molecules, and then a protein complex binds to the molecules and degrades one of the RNA strands to produce single-stranded siRNA. The protein complex is similar to one that acts on the double-stranded RNA precursors of miRNAs. The siRNA with the protein complex in this case is the **siRNA-induced silencing complex (siRISC)**. In the RNAi process, the siRNA in the siRISC acts like the miRNA in the miRISC—single-stranded RNAs complementary to the siRNA are targeted and, in this case, the target RNA is cleaved and the pieces are then degraded. In our viral example, the targeted RNAs would be viral mRNAs for proteins the virus uses to replicate itself, or a single-stranded RNA that is the viral genome itself, or that is produced from the viral genome during replication.

The expression of any gene can be knocked down to low levels or knocked out completely in experiments involving RNAi with siRNA. To silence a gene, researchers introduce into the cell a double-stranded RNA that can be processed by Dicer and the protein complex into an siRNA complementary to the mRNA transcribed from that gene. Knocking down or knocking out the function of a gene is equivalent to creating a mutated version of that gene, but without changing the gene's DNA sequence. Researchers use this experimental approach to identify the functions of genes whose presence has been detected by sequencing complete genomes, but whose function is completely unknown. After an siRNA specific to a gene of interest is introduced into the cell, researchers look for a change in phenotype, such as properties relating to growth or metabolism. If such a change is seen, the researchers now have some insight into the gene's function, and they can investigate the gene with more focus. RNAi using siRNAs may also have some applications in medicine, perhaps to regulate the expression of genes associated with particular human diseases.

14.3b Translational Regulation Controls the Rate of Protein Synthesis

At the next regulatory level, translational regulation controls the rate at which mRNAs are used in protein synthesis. Translational regulation occurs in essentially all cell types and species. For example, translational regulation is involved in cell cycle control in all eukaryotes and in many processes during development in multicellular eukaryotes, such as red blood cell differentiation in animals. Significantly, many viruses exploit translational regulation to control their infection of cells and to shut off the host cell's own genes.

Let's consider the general role of translational regulation in animal development. During early development of most animals, little transcription occurs. The changes in protein synthesis patterns seen in developing cell types and tissues instead derive from the activation, repression, or degradation of maternal mRNAs, the mRNAs that were present in the mother's egg before fertilization. One important mechanism for translational regulation involves adjusting the length of the poly(A) tail of the mRNA. (Recall from Section 13.3 that the poly(A) tail—a string of adenine-containing nucleotides—is added to the 3′ end of the pre-mRNA and is retained on the mRNA produced from the pre-mRNA after introns are removed.) That is, enzymes can change the length of the poly(A) tail on an mRNA in the cytoplasm in either direction: by shortening it or lengthening it. Increases in poly(A) tail length result in increased translation; decreases in length result in decreased translation. For example, during embryogenesis (the formation of the embryo) of the fruit fly, *Drosophila*, key proteins are synthesized when the poly(A) tails on the mRNAs for those proteins are lengthened in a regulated way. Evidence for this came from experiments in which poly(A) tail lengthening was blocked; the result was that embryogenesis was inhibited. But although researchers know that the length of poly(A) tails is regulated in the cytoplasm, how this process occurs is not completely understood.

14.3c Posttranslational Regulation Controls the Availability of Functional Proteins

Posttranslational regulation controls the availability of functional proteins primarily in three ways: chemical modification, processing, and degradation. Chemical modification involves the addition or removal of chemical groups, which reversibly alters the activity of the protein. For example, you saw in Section 8.2 how the addition of phosphate groups to proteins involved in signal transduction pathways either stimulates or inhibits the activity of those proteins. Further, in Section 9.4, you learned how the addition of phosphate groups to target proteins plays a crucial role in regulating how a cell progresses through the cell division cycle. And in Section 14.2, you saw how acetylation of histones altered the properties of the nucleosome, loosening its association with DNA in chromatin.

In processing, proteins are synthesized as inactive precursors, which are converted to an active form under regulatory control. For example, you saw in Section 13.4 that the digestive enzyme pepsin is synthesized as pepsinogen, an inactive precursor that activates by removal of a segment of amino acids. Similarly, the glucose-regulating hormone insulin is synthesized as a precursor called proinsulin; processing of the precursor removes a central segment but leaves the insulin molecule, which consists of two polypeptide chains linked by disulfide bridges.

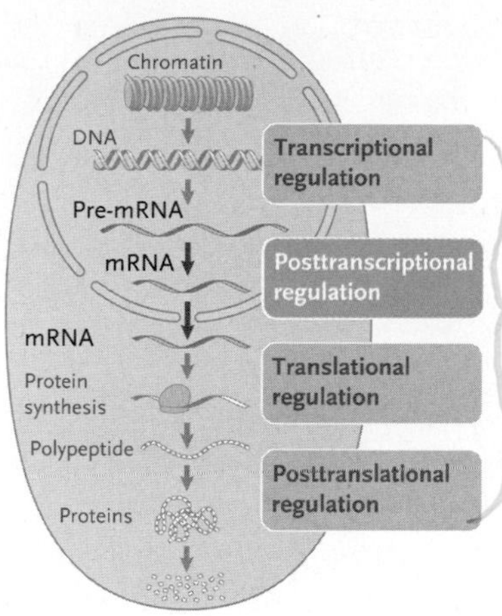

Chromatin
DNA
Transcriptional regulation
Pre-mRNA
mRNA
Posttranscriptional regulation
mRNA
Protein synthesis
Translational regulation
Polypeptide
Proteins
Posttranslational regulation

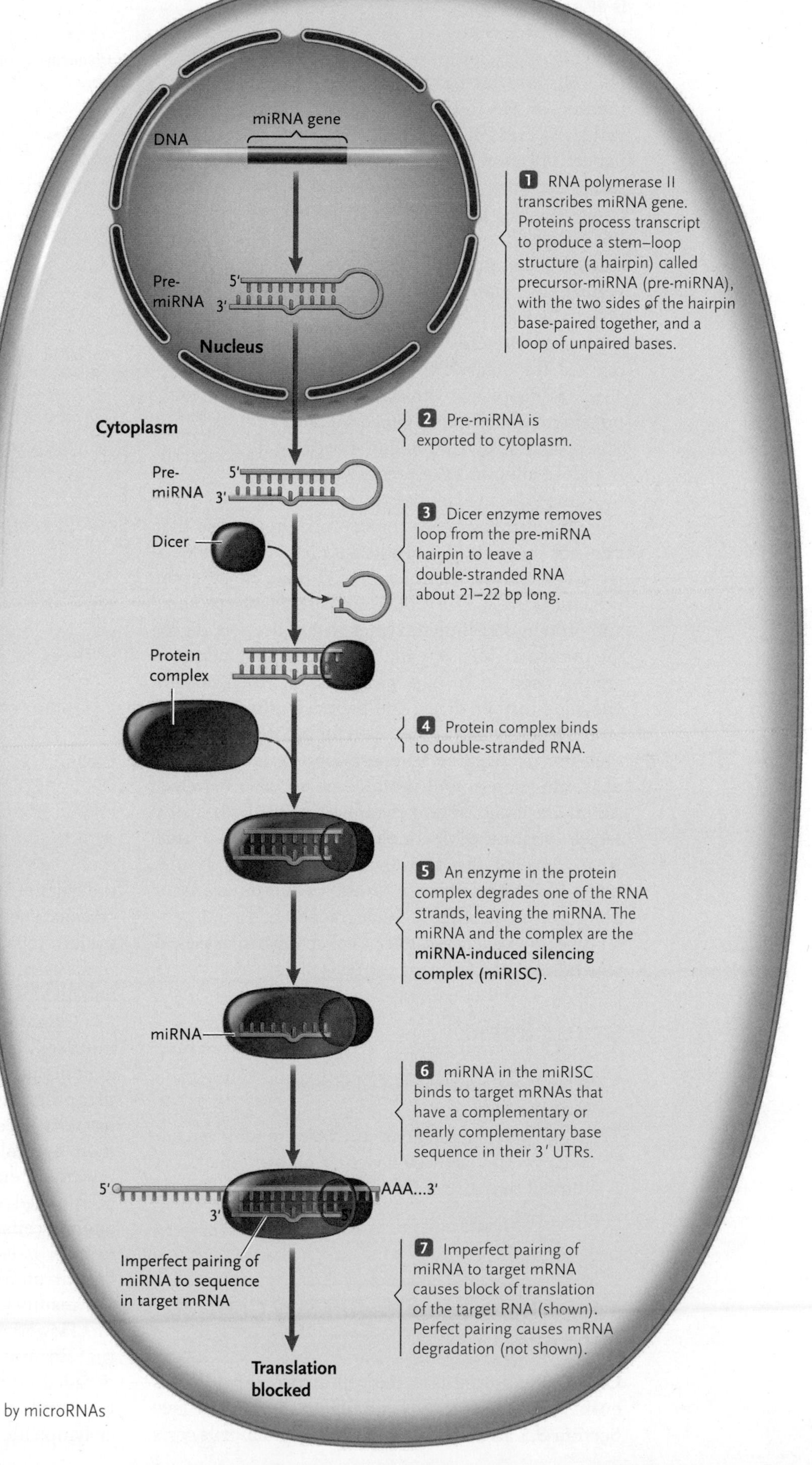

miRNA gene
DNA
1 RNA polymerase II transcribes miRNA gene. Proteins process transcript to produce a stem–loop structure (a hairpin) called precursor-miRNA (pre-miRNA), with the two sides of the hairpin base-paired together, and a loop of unpaired bases.
Pre-miRNA
5′
3′
Nucleus
Cytoplasm
2 Pre-miRNA is exported to cytoplasm.
Pre-miRNA
5′
3′
3 Dicer enzyme removes loop from the pre-miRNA hairpin to leave a double-stranded RNA about 21–22 bp long.
Dicer
Protein complex
4 Protein complex binds to double-stranded RNA.
5 An enzyme in the protein complex degrades one of the RNA strands, leaving the miRNA. The miRNA and the complex are the **miRNA-induced silencing complex (miRISC)**.
miRNA
6 miRNA in the miRISC binds to target mRNAs that have a complementary or nearly complementary base sequence in their 3′ UTRs.
5′
AAA...3′
3′
5′
Imperfect pairing of miRNA to sequence in target mRNA
7 Imperfect pairing of miRNA to target mRNA causes block of translation of the target RNA (shown). Perfect pairing causes mRNA degradation (not shown).
Translation blocked

Figure 14.14
RNA interference—regulation of gene expression by microRNAs (miRNAs).

The rate of degradation of proteins is also under regulatory control. Some proteins in eukaryotic cells last for the lifetime of the individual, whereas others persist only for minutes. Proteins with relatively short cellular lives include many of the proteins regulating transcription. Typically, these short-lived proteins are marked for breakdown by enzymes that attach a "doom tag" consisting of a small protein called *ubiquitin* (**Figure 14.15,** step 1). The protein is given this name because it is indeed ubiquitous—present in almost the same form in essentially all eukaryotes. The ubiquitin tag labels the doomed proteins so that they are recognized and attacked by a *proteasome,* a large cytoplasmic complex of a number of different proteins (step 2). The proteasome unfolds the protein, and protein-digesting enzymes within the core digest the protein into small peptides. The peptides are released from the proteasome, and cytosolic enzymes further digest the peptides into individual amino acids, which are recycled for use in protein synthesis or oxidized as an energy source (step 3). The ubiquitin protein and proteasome are also recycled. Aaron Ciechanover and Avram Hershko, both of the Israel Institute of Technology in Haifa, Israel, and Irwin Rose of the University of California, Irvine, received a Nobel Prize in 2004 for the discovery of ubiquitin-mediated protein degradation.

We now describe cancer, a collection of diseases in which the control of gene expression goes awry.

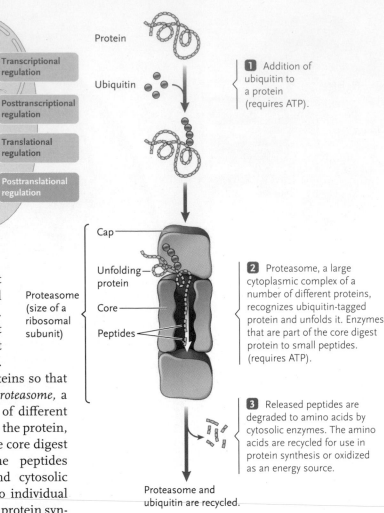

Figure 14.15

Protein degradation by ubiquitin addition and enzymatic digestion within a proteasome.

1 Addition of ubiquitin to a protein (requires ATP).

2 Proteasome, a large cytoplasmic complex of a number of different proteins, recognizes ubiquitin-tagged protein and unfolds it. Enzymes that are part of the core digest protein to small peptides. (requires ATP).

3 Released peptides are degraded to amino acids by cytosolic enzymes. The amino acids are recycled for use in protein synthesis or oxidized as an energy source.

Proteasome and ubiquitin are recycled.

STUDY BREAK

1. How does a microRNA silence gene expression?
2. If the poly(A) tail on an mRNA were removed, what would likely be the effect on the translation of that mRNA?

14.4 The Loss of Regulatory Controls in Cancer

Chapter 8 showed that the cell division cycle in all eukaryotes is carefully regulated by genes (see Section 8.5 and Figure 8.18). For normal cells, it is the balance between internal or external factors that stimulate cell division and corresponding factors that inhibit cell division that governs whether the cell remains in a nondividing state or whether it grows and divides.

Occasionally, differentiated cells of complex multicellular organisms deviate from their normal genetic program and begin to grow and divide inappropriately, giving rise to tissue masses called *tumours* (see Figure 8.19). Such cells have lost their normal regulatory controls and have reverted toward an embryonic developmental state in a process called *dedifferentiation* (**Figure 14.16).** If the altered cells stay together in a single mass, the tumour is *benign.* Benign tumours are usually not life-threatening, and their surgical removal generally results in a complete cure.

However, if the cells of a tumour invade and disrupt surrounding tissues, the tumour is *malignant* and is called a cancer. Sometimes, cells from malignant tumours break off and move through the blood system or lymphatic system, forming new tumours at other

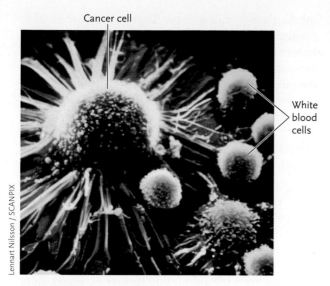

Cancer cell

White blood cells

Lennart Nilsson / SCANPIX

Figure 14.16

A scanning electron micrograph of a cancer cell surrounded by several white blood cells.

locations in the body. The spreading of a malignant tumour is called *metastasis* (meaning "change of state"). Malignant tumours can result in debilitation and death in various ways, including damage to critical organs, metabolic imbalances, hemorrhage, and secondary malignancies. In some cases, malignant tumours can be eliminated from the body by surgery or be destroyed by chemicals *(chemotherapy)* or radiation.

14.4a Cancers Are Genetic Diseases

Experimental evidence of various kinds shows that cancers are genetic diseases:

1. Particular cancers can have a high incidence in some human families. Cancers that run in families are known as **familial (hereditary) cancers**. Cancers that do not appear to be inherited are known as **sporadic (nonhereditary) cancers**. Familial cancers are less frequent than sporadic cancers.
2. Descendants of cancer cells are all cancer cells. In fact, it is the cloned descendants of certain cancer cells that form a tumour.
3. The incidence of cancers increases upon exposure to mutagens, agents that cause mutations in DNA. Particular chemicals and certain kinds of radiation are effective mutagens.
4. Particular chromosomal mutations are associated with specific forms of cancer (see Section 11.3 and Figure 11.12). In these cases, chromosomal breakage affects the expression of genes associated with the regulation of cell division.
5. Some viruses can induce cancer. Some viruses carry "cancer genes" with them while others contain viral genes that disrupt normal cell cycle control of host cells.

All of the characteristics of cancer cells that have been mentioned—dedifferentiation, uncontrolled division, and metastasis—reflect changes in gene expression.

14.4b Three Main Classes of Genes Are Implicated in Cancer

Three major classes of genes are altered frequently in cancers: *proto-oncogenes, tumour suppressor genes,* and microRNA (miRNA) genes.

Proto-oncogenes. **Proto-oncogenes** (*onkos* = bulk or mass) are genes in normal cells that encode various kinds of proteins that stimulate cell division. Examples are growth factors, receptors on target cells that are activated by growth factors (see Chapter 5), components of cellular signal transduction pathways triggered by cell division stimulatory signals (see Chapter 5), and transcription factors that regulate the expression of the structural genes for progression through the cell cycle. In cancer cells, the proto-oncogenes are deregulated and become **oncogenes**, genes that stimulate the cell to progress to the cancerous state of the unregulated cell cycle. Only one of the two proto-oncogene alleles in a cell needs to be altered for the cellular changes to occur. Alterations that can convert a proto-oncogene into an oncogene include the following:

- A mutation in a gene's promoter or other control sequences results in the gene becoming abnormally active.
- A mutation in the coding segment of the gene may produce an altered form of the encoded protein that is abnormally active.
- Translocation, a process in which a segment of a chromosome breaks off and attaches to a different chromosome (discussed in Section 11.3), may move the gene to a new location under the control of an inappropriately powerful promoter or enhancer sequence.
- Infecting viruses may introduce genes whose expression disrupts cell cycle control or alters regulatory proteins to turn genes on in the host.

Tumour Suppressor Genes. **Tumour suppressor genes** are genes in normal cells encoding proteins that inhibit cell division. The best known tumour suppressor gene is *TP53,* so called because its encoded protein, p53, has a molecular weight of 53 000 daltons. Among other activities, normal p53 stops cell division by combining with and inhibiting cyclin-dependent protein kinases that trigger the cell's transition from the G_1 phase to the S phase of the cell cycle (discussed in Section 8.5). This activity is particularly important if the cell has sustained DNA damage. If such a cell undergoes DNA replication and divides, the damage may result in mutation in progeny cells. Mutations can deregulate gene expression and cause a cell to progress toward cancer. However, such cancers may be avoided if p53's action to block the cell from entering S phase gives the cell time to repair the damage or, if the damage cannot be repaired, to trigger the cell to undergo programmed cell death (apoptosis: see Chapter 8). If the *TP53* gene is mutated so that the p53 protein is not produced or is produced in an inactive form, the cyclin-dependent protein kinases are continually active in triggering cell division. As a result, many mutations can result in progeny cells. Inactive *TP53* genes are found in at least 50 percent of all cancers. In general, mutations of tumour suppressor genes contribute to the onset of cancer because the mutations result in a decrease in the inhibitory action of the cell cycle controlling proteins they encode.

Both alleles of a tumour suppressor gene must be inactivated for inhibitory activity to be lost in cancer cells. **Figure 14.17** illustrates inactivation of the tumour-suppressor gene *BRCA1* (*breast cancer 1*) in sporadic and familial forms of breast cancer. *BRCA1* is involved in repair of DNA damage. Inactivating both alleles of *BRCA1* is not by itself sufficient for the development of breast cancer but is one of the gene changes typically involved. Since sporadic breast cancer requires the mutational inactivation of two normal alleles of *BRCA1*, this form of the disease typically occurs later in life than the familial form. For familial breast cancer and other familial cancers, we use the term *predisposition* for the cancer. This term relates to the inactivation mechanism just described. That is, an individual is predisposed to develop a particular cancer if they inherit one mutant allele of an associated tumour suppressor disease, because then a mutation inactivating the other allele is all that is needed to lose the growth inhibitory properties of the tumour suppressor gene's product.

miRNA Genes. Earlier in this chapter, we discussed the role of microRNAs (miRNAs) in regulating expression of target mRNAs. In human cancers, many miRNA genes show altered, cancer-specific expression patterns. Studying these miRNA genes has given scientists insight into the normal activities of their encoded miRNAs in cell cycle control. Some miRNAs regulate the expression of mRNAs that are the transcripts of tumour suppressor genes. If these miRNAs are overexpressed because of alterations of the genes encoding them, expression of the target mRNAs can be completely blocked, thereby removing or decreasing inhibitory signals for cell proliferation. Other miRNAs regulate the translation of mRNAs that are transcripts of particular proto-oncogenes. If these miRNA genes are inactivated, or expression of these genes is markedly reduced, expression of the proto-oncogenes is higher than normal and cell proliferation is stimulated.

CONCEPT FIX This section shows that *cancer genes* are just deregulated versions of the genes that are essential for the normally controlled growth of all cells. ⬡

Figure 14.17

Mutational inactivation of tumour suppressor gene alleles in sporadic **(a)** and familial **(b)** cancers as exemplified by the *BRCA1* gene associated with breast cancer.

a. Sporadic breast cancer. Two independent mutations of the *BRCA1* tumour suppressor.

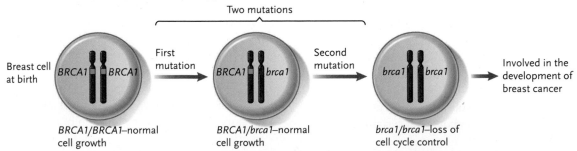

b. Familial breast cancer. An individual has a predisposition for breast cancer because of inheriting one mutated *brca1* allele; mutation of the other normal *BRCA1* allele then occurs.

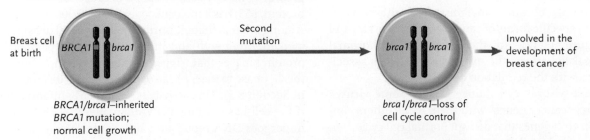

14.4c Cancer Develops Gradually by Multiple Steps

Cancer rarely develops by alteration of a single proto-oncogene to an oncogene, or inactivation of a single tumour suppressor gene. Rather, in almost all cancers, successive alterations in several to many genes gradually accumulate to transform normal cells to cancer cells. This gradual mechanism is called the *multistep progression of cancer.* One example of the steps that can occur, in this case for a form of colorectal cancer, is shown in **Figure 14.18.**

The ravages of cancer, probably more than any other example, bring home the critical extent to which humans and all other multicellular organisms depend on the mechanisms controlling gene expression to develop and live normally. In a sense, the most amazing thing about these control mechanisms is that, in spite of their complexity, they operate without failures throughout most of the lives of all eukaryotes.

STUDY BREAK

1. What is the normal function of a tumour suppressor gene? How do mutations in tumour suppressor genes contribute to the onset of cancer?
2. What is the normal function of a proto-oncogene? How can mutations in proto-oncogenes contribute to the onset of cancer?
3. How can changes in expression of miRNA genes contribute to the onset of cancer?

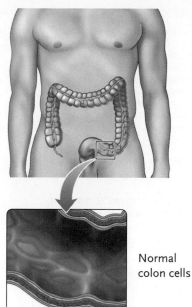

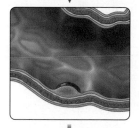

Normal colon cells

Loss of the *APC* tumour suppressor gene activity, and other DNA changes

Small adenoma (benign growth)

ras oncogene activation; loss of *DCC* tumour suppressor gene

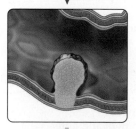

Large adenoma (benign growth)

Loss of *TP53* tumour suppressor gene activity and other mutations

Carcinoma (malignant tumour with metastasis)

Figure 14.18
A multistep model for the development of a type of colorectal cancer.

Review

Access an interactive eBook, chapter-specific interactive learning tools, including flashcards, quizzes, videos, and more in your Biology **CourseMate**, accessed through NelsonBrain.com **Aplia™** is an online interactive learning solution that helps you improve comprehension—and your grade—by integrating a variety of mediums and tools such as videos, tutorials, practice tests, and an interactive eBook.

14.1 Regulation of Gene Expression in Prokaryotic Cells

- Transcriptional control in prokaryotic cells involves short-term changes that turn specific genes on or off in response to changes in environmental conditions. The changes in gene activity are controlled by regulatory proteins that recognize operators of operons (Figure 14.2).

- Regulatory proteins may be repressors, which slow the rate of transcription of operons, or activators, which increase the rate of transcription.

- Some repressors are made in an active form, in which they bind to the operator of an operon and inhibit its transcription. Combination with an inducer blocks the activity of the repressor and allows the operon to be transcribed (Figure 14.3).

- Activators are typically made in inactive form, in which they cannot bind to their binding site next to an operon. Combining with another molecule, often a nucleotide, converts the activator into the form in which it binds with its binding site and recruits RNA polymerase, thereby stimulating transcription of the operon (Figure 14.4).

- Other repressors are made in an inactive form, in which they are unable to inhibit transcription of an operon unless they combine with a corepressor (Figure 14.5).

14.2 Regulation of Transcription in Eukaryotes

- Operons are not found in eukaryotes. Instead, genes that encode proteins with related functions are typically scattered through the genome, while being regulated in a coordinated manner.

- Two general types of gene regulation occur in eukaryotes. Short-term regulation involves relatively rapid changes in gene expression in response to changes in environmental or physiological conditions. Long-term regulation involves changes in gene expression that are associated with the development and differentiation of an organism.

- Gene expression in eukaryotes is regulated at the transcriptional level (where most regulation occurs) and at posttranscriptional, translational, and posttranslational levels (Figures 14.6, 14.7, 14.8).

- Regulation of transcription initiation involves proteins binding to a gene's promoter and regulatory sites. At the promoter, general transcription factors bind and recruit RNA polymerase II, giving a very low level of transcription. Activator proteins bind to promoter proximal elements and increase the rate of transcription. Other activators bind to the enhancer and, through interaction with a coactivator, which also binds to the proteins at the promoter, greatly stimulate the rate of transcription (Figures 14.9–14.11).

- The overall control of transcription of a gene depends on the particular regulatory proteins that bind to promoter proximal elements and enhancers. The regulatory proteins are cell-type specific and may be activators or repressors. This gene regulation is achieved by a relatively low number of regulatory proteins, acting in various combinations (Figure 14.11).

- The coordinate expression of genes with related functions is achieved by each of the related genes having the same regulatory sequences associated with them.

- Transcriptionally active genes have a looser chromatin structure than transcriptionally inactive genes. The change in chromatin structure that accompanies the activation of transcription of a gene involves chromatin remodelling—specific histone modifications—particularly in the region of a gene's promoter (Figure 14.13).

- Sections of chromosomes or whole chromosomes can be inactivated by DNA methylation, a phenomenon called silencing. DNA methylation is also involved in genomic imprinting, in which transcription of either the inherited maternal or the inherited paternal allele of a gene is inhibited permanently.

14.3 Posttranscriptional, Translational, and Posttranslational Regulation

- Posttranscriptional, translational, and posttranslational controls operate primarily to regulate the quantities of proteins synthesized in cells (Figure 14.6).

- Posttranscriptional controls regulate pre-mRNA processing, mRNA availability for translation, and the rate at which mRNAs are degraded. In alternative splicing, different mRNAs are derived from the same pre-mRNA. In another process, small single-stranded RNAs complexed with proteins bind to mRNAs that have complementary sequences, and either the mRNA is cleaved or translation is blocked (Figure 14.14).

- Translational regulation controls the rate at which mRNAs are used by ribosomes in protein synthesis.

- Posttranslational controls regulate the availability of functional proteins. Mechanisms of regulation include the alteration of protein activity by chemical modification, protein activation by processing of inactive precursors, and affecting the rate of degradation of a protein.

14.4 The Loss of Regulatory Controls in Cancer

- In cancer, cells partially or completely dedifferentiate, divide rapidly and uncontrollably, and may break loose to form additional tumours in other parts of the body.

- Proto-oncogenes, tumour suppressor genes, and miRNA genes are typically altered in cancer cells. Proto-oncogenes encode proteins that stimulate cell division. Their altered forms, oncogenes, are abnormally active. Tumour suppressor genes in their normal form encode proteins that inhibit cell division. Mutated forms of these genes lose this inhibitory activity (Figure 14.17). MicroRNA genes control the activity of mRNA transcripts of particular tumour suppressor genes and proto-oncogenes. Alteration of activity of such an miRNA gene can lead to a lower than normal activity of tumour suppressor gene products or a higher than normal activity of proto-oncogene products depending on the target of the miRNA. In either case, cell proliferation can be stimulated.

- Most cancers develop by multistep progression involving the successive alteration of several to many genes (Figure 14.18).

Questions

Self-Test Questions

1. Some genes are under negative regulation. Which of the following is an example of negative regulation in the *lac* operon?
   a. Binding of allolactose makes the Lac repressor unable to bind DNA.
   b. When lactose levels decrease, *lacZ* expression goes down.
   c. When Lac repressor binds the operator, *lacZ* expression goes down.
   d. When glucose levels are high, *lacZ* expression goes down.

2. For the *E. coli lac* operon, which of the following events occurs when glucose is absent and lactose is added?
   a. β-galactosidase decreases in the cell.
   b. The *lacI* gene cannot make Lac repressor protein.
   c. Allolactose binds the Lac repressor protein to remove it from the operator.
   d. The genes *lacZ, lacY,* and *lacA* are turned off.

3. Imagine a mutation in the *E. coli lac* operon that results in constitutive expression (always on). Further analysis confirms that normal amounts of functional Lac repressor protein are present. Where must the mutation be?
   a. in the *lac* promoter
   b. in the operator
   c. in the *lacZ* gene
   d. in the CAP binding site

4. Which of the following statements about the *trp* operon is correct?
   a. Tryptophan is an inducer.
   b. When end-product tryptophan binds to the Trp repressor, it stops transcription of the tryptophan biosynthesis genes.
   c. Trp repressor is synthesized in active form.
   d. Low levels of tryptophan bind to the *trp* operator and block transcription of the tryptophan biosynthesis genes.

5. How does chromatin remodelling activate gene expression?
   a. It allows repressors to disengage from the promoter.
   b. It winds genes tightly around histones.
   c. It inserts nucleosomes into chromatin.
   d. It recruits a protein complex that displaces nucleosomes from the promoter.

6. Which statement about activation of transcription is correct?
   a. RNA polymerase II binds the TATA box.
   b. A coactivator called a mediator forms a bridge between the promoter and the gene to be transcribed.
   c. Transcription factors bind the promoter and RNA polymerase.
   d. Enhancer regions bind to promoter regions.

7. The delivery of mature mRNA to the cytoplasm in eukaryotes is highly controlled. At which level of regulation is this control achieved?
   a. translational regulation
   b. posttranslational regulation
   c. transcriptional regulation
   d. posttranscriptional regulation

8. Perky ears in a certain mammal are coded by a dominant allele; the recessive allele codes for droopy ears. In males of these mammals, the gene encoding ear shape is transcribed only from the chromosome received from the female parent. This is because the gene from the male parent is silenced by methylation. What will be the result of a cross of a droopy female and a homozygous perky male?
   a. Daughters' ears will be perky and sons' ears will be droopy.
   b. All offspring will have perky ears.
   c. Sons will have one perky ear and one droopy ear.
   d. There will be equal numbers of perky-eared and droopy-eared sons and daughters.

9. Which of the following statements describes microRNA accurately?
   a. MicroRNA is encoded by non-protein-coding genes.
   b. MicroRNA has a precursor that is folded and then elongated by a Dicer enzyme.
   c. MicroRNA forms complementary base pairs with tRNA.
   d. MicroRNA is translated in the cytoplasm.

10. Which of the following characteristics is exhibited by typical cancer cells?
    a. They convert oncogenes into proto-oncogenes.
    b. Oncogenes are near repressor genes.
    c. They have a balance of oncogenes and tumour suppressor genes.
    d. *TP53* mutations are one of several likely changes in DNA.

Questions for Discussion

1. In a mutant strain of *E. coli*, the CAP protein is unable to combine with its target region of the *lac* operon. How would you expect the mutation to affect transcription when cells of this strain are subjected to the following conditions?
   a. Lactose and glucose are both available.
   b. Lactose is available, but glucose is not.
   c. Both lactose and glucose are unavailable.

2. Duchenne muscular dystrophy, an inherited genetic disorder, affects boys almost exclusively. Early in childhood, muscle tissue begins to break down in affected individuals, who typically die in their teens or early twenties as a result of respiratory failure. Muscle samples from women who carry the mutation reveal some regions of degenerating muscle tissue adjacent to other regions that are normal. Develop a hypothesis explaining these observations.

3. Eukaryotic transcription is generally controlled by binding of regulatory proteins to DNA sequences rather than by modification of RNA polymerases. Develop a hypothesis explaining why this is so.

Protein microarray, a key tool of proteomics, the study of the complete set of proteins that can be expressed by an organism's genome. Each coloured dot is a protein, with a specific colour for each protein being studied.

Pasteka/SPL/Photo Researchers, Inc.

STUDY PLAN

15.1 DNA Cloning

15.1a Bacterial Enzymes Called Restriction Endonucleases Form the Basis of DNA Cloning

15.1b Bacterial Plasmids Illustrate the Use of Restriction Enzymes in Cloning

15.1c DNA Libraries Contain Collections of Cloned DNA Fragments

15.1d The Polymerase Chain Reaction Amplifies DNA *In Vitro*

15.2 Applications of DNA Technologies

15.2a DNA Technologies Are Used in Molecular Testing for Many Human Genetic Diseases

15.2b DNA Fingerprinting Is Used to Identify Human Individuals and Individuals of Other Species

15.2c Genetic Engineering Uses DNA Technologies to Alter the Genes of a Cell or Organism

15.2d DNA Technologies and Genetic Engineering Are a Subject of Public Concern

15.3 Genome Analysis

15.3a DNA-Sequencing Techniques Are Based on DNA Replication

15.3b Genome Sequence Determination and Annotation Involves Obtaining and Analyzing the Sequences of Complete Genomes

15.3c Functional Genomics Focuses on the Functions of Genes and Other Parts of the Genome

15.3d Differential Gene Activity in Entire Genomes Is Studied with DNA Microarrays

15.3e Studying the Array of Expressed Proteins Is the Next Level of Study of Biological Systems

15.3f Systems Biology Studies the Interactions among All Components of an Organism

15 DNA Technologies and Genomics

WHY IT MATTERS

Imagine yourself as a member of the crew of *Sorcerer II,* a private yacht renovated by maverick biologist J. Craig Venter to serve as an oceanic survey laboratory. Several months out of Halifax, down the Atlantic coast of the United States, and through the Panama Canal into the Pacific, you are now threading among the famed Galapagos Islands. Of course, your mind wanders to the historic voyage of the H.M.S. *Beagle* that brought Charles Darwin to these same waters some 170 years ago. Darwin returned home with specimens of novel species and notebooks filled with the scientific observations, illustrations, and ideas that would revolutionize our understanding of biology; you will return home with frozen seawater samples containing billions of base pairs of DNA sequence that may well, once again, cause us to reconsider cherished beliefs.

Back on land, the DNA is isolated, broken into random fragments, and then sequenced by industrial sequencing robots. Computer programs compare the individual sequences, looking for novel genes and areas of overlap that will help reconstruct the entire genomes of previously unknown organisms and viruses. Analysis of the massive data set reveals a staggering degree of genetic diversity among the unicellular microorganisms in the marine environment; 400 new species are discovered. Scanning for potential protein-coding genes predicts hundreds of thousands of likely proteins, a surprising fraction of them unknown to science.

Venter's survey of genetic diversity in the ocean is an example of the emerging field of metagenomics, in which DNA from an entire community of organisms in a particular niche is harvested collectively, sequenced, and analyzed using some of the DNA technologies described in this chapter. This approach is significant because, until very recently, our understanding of the genetics of the microbial world was based almost exclusively on the very small proportion of species that can be cultivated in the laboratory. With the tools of modern metagenomics, we gain access to the genomes of a whole new world of previously inaccessible organisms.

Metagenomic studies targeted to microbial communities in such diverse environments as the termite gut, deep sea hydrothermal vents, glaciers, geysers, the bovine rumen, and desert soil will certainly identify tens of thousands of novel genes that code for enzymes that may have applications in industrial biofuel production, food processing, pollution control, and drug development. The techniques used to isolate, purify, analyze, and manipulate DNA sequences for such purposes are known as **DNA technologies**. Scientists use DNA technologies both for basic research into the biology of organisms and for applied research. The use of DNA technologies to alter genes for practical purposes is called **genetic engineering.**

Genetic engineering is the latest addition to the broad area known as *biotechnology,* which is any technique applied to biological systems or living organisms to make or modify products or processes for a specific purpose. Thus, biotechnology includes manipulations that do not involve DNA technologies, such as the use of yeast to brew beer and bake bread, and the use of bacteria to make yogurt and cheese.

In this chapter, we focus on how biologists isolate genes and manipulate them for basic and applied research. You will learn about the basic DNA technologies and their applications to research in biology, to genetic engineering, and to the analysis of genomes. You will also learn about some of the risks and controversies surrounding genetic engineering and about some of the scientific, social, and ethical questions related to its application.

We begin our discussion with a description of methods used to obtain genes in large quantities, an essential step for their analysis or manipulation.

15.1 DNA Cloning

Remember from Chapter 8 that a *clone* is a line of genetically identical cells or individuals derived from a single ancestor. By similar reasoning, DNA cloning is a method for producing many copies of a piece of DNA; the piece of DNA is referred to as a *gene of interest,* which is a gene that a researcher wants to study or manipulate. Scientists clone DNA for many reasons. For example, a researcher might be interested in how a particular human gene functions. Each human cell contains only two copies of most genes, amounting to a very small fraction of the total amount of DNA in a diploid cell. In its natural state in the genome, the gene is extremely difficult to study. However, through DNA cloning, a researcher can produce a sample large enough for scientific experimentation.

Cloned genes are used in basic research to find out about their biological functions. For example, researchers can determine the DNA sequence of a cloned gene, giving them the ultimate information about its structure. Also, by manipulating the gene and inducing mutations in it, they can gain information about its function and about how its expression is regulated. Cloned genes can be expressed in bacteria, and the proteins encoded by the cloned genes can be produced in quantity and purified. Those proteins can be used in basic research, or, in the case of genes that encode proteins of pharmaceutical or clinical importance, they can be used in applied research.

An overview of one common method for cloning a gene of interest from a genome is shown in **Figure 15.1, p. 334;** the method uses bacteria (commonly, *Escherichia coli*) and plasmids, the small circular DNA molecules that replicate separately from the bacterial chromosome. The researcher first extracts DNA from cells containing the gene of interest and then cuts this DNA into fragments. One of these fragments will likely carry the desired gene. Each of the fragments is inserted into a plasmid, thus producing a collection of *recombinant DNA molecules*—**recombinant DNA** is DNA from two or more different sources that are joined together. These recombinant plasmids are then introduced into bacteria; each bacterium receives a different plasmid. The bacterium continues growing and dividing, and as it does, the recombinant plasmid DNA is also replicated. The final step is to identify which bacterium contains the plasmid carrying the gene of interest and isolate it for further study.

15.1a Bacterial Enzymes Called Restriction Endonucleases Form the Basis of DNA Cloning

The key to DNA cloning is the specific joining of two DNA molecules from different sources, such as a genomic DNA fragment and a bacterial plasmid (see Figure 15.1, p. 334). This specific joining of DNA is made possible, in part, by bacterial enzymes called **restriction endonucleases** (also called **restriction enzymes**), which were discovered in the late 1960s. Restriction enzymes recognize short, specific DNA sequences called *restriction sites,* typically four to eight

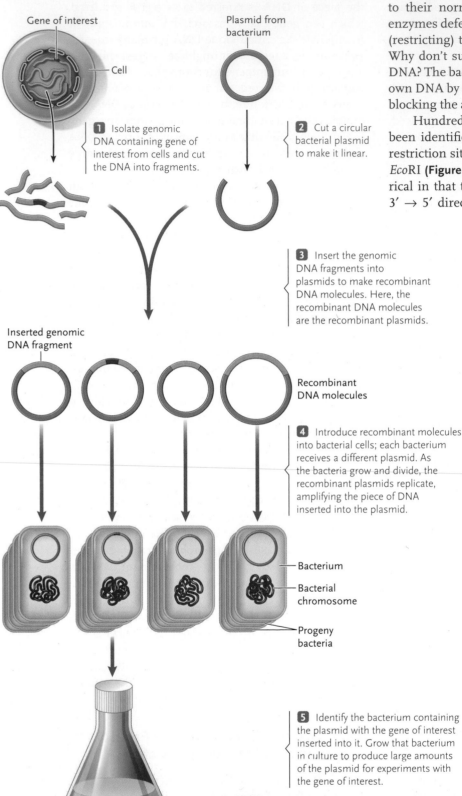

1 Isolate genomic DNA containing gene of interest from cells and cut the DNA into fragments.

2 Cut a circular bacterial plasmid to make it linear.

3 Insert the genomic DNA fragments into plasmids to make recombinant DNA molecules. Here, the recombinant DNA molecules are the recombinant plasmids.

Gene of interest

Cell

Plasmid from bacterium

Inserted genomic DNA fragment

Recombinant DNA molecules

4 Introduce recombinant molecules into bacterial cells; each bacterium receives a different plasmid. As the bacteria grow and divide, the recombinant plasmids replicate, amplifying the piece of DNA inserted into the plasmid.

Bacterium

Bacterial chromosome

Progeny bacteria

5 Identify the bacterium containing the plasmid with the gene of interest inserted into it. Grow that bacterium in culture to produce large amounts of the plasmid for experiments with the gene of interest.

Figure 15.1
Overview of cloning DNA fragments in a bacterial plasmid.

The *restriction* in the name of the enzymes refers to their normal role inside bacteria, in which the enzymes defend against viral attack by breaking down (restricting) the DNA molecules of infecting viruses. Why don't such enzymes break down the cell's own DNA? The bacterium "hides" the restriction sites in its own DNA by methylating bases in those sites, thereby blocking the action of its restriction enzyme.

Hundreds of different restriction enzymes have been identified, each one cutting DNA at a specific restriction site. As illustrated by the restriction site of *Eco*RI **(Figure 15.2),** most restriction sites are symmetrical in that the sequence of nucleotides read in the $3' \rightarrow 5'$ direction on one strand is the same as the sequence read in the $3' \rightarrow 5'$ direction on the complementary strand. A given enzyme always recognizes the same short DNA sequence as its cut site and always cuts at the same place within the sequence. The restriction enzymes most used in cloning—such as *Eco*RI—cleave the sugar–phosphate backbones of DNA to produce DNA fragments with single-stranded ends (Figure 15.2, step 1). The ends are called **sticky ends** because the short, single-stranded regions can form hydrogen bonds with complementary sticky ends on any other DNA molecules cut with the same enzyme. For example, step 2 shows the insertion of a DNA molecule with sticky ends produced by *Eco*RI between two other DNA molecules with the same sticky ends. The pairings leave nicks in the sugar–phosphate backbones of the DNA strands that are sealed by *DNA ligase,* an enzyme that has the same function in DNA replication (step 3). The result is DNA from two different sources joined together—a recombinant DNA molecule.

15.1b Bacterial Plasmids Illustrate the Use of Restriction Enzymes in Cloning

The bacterial plasmids used for cloning are examples of cloning vectors—DNA molecules into which a DNA fragment can be inserted to form a recombinant DNA molecule for cloning. Plasmid cloning vectors are usually natural plasmids that have been modified to have special features. Commonly, plasmid cloning vectors are engineered to contain two genes that are useful in the final steps of a cloning experiment for distinguishing bacteria that have recombinant plasmids from those that do

base pairs long, and cut the DNA at specific locations within those sequences. The DNA fragments produced by cutting a long DNA molecule with a restriction enzyme are known as **restriction fragments.**

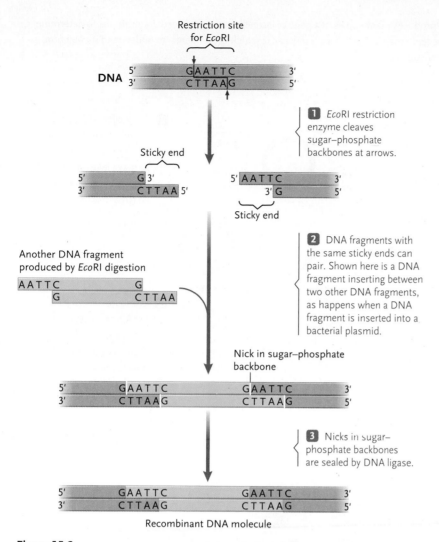

Figure 15.2

The restriction site for the restriction enzyme *Eco*RI, and the generation of a recombinant DNA molecule by complementary base-pairing of DNA fragments produced by digestion with the same restriction enzyme.

Within the figure:

Restriction site for *Eco*RI

DNA 5′ GAATTC 3′
3′ CTTAAG 5′

1 *Eco*RI restriction enzyme cleaves sugar–phosphate backbones at arrows.

Sticky end

5′ G 3′   5′ AATTC 3′
3′ CTTAA 5′   3′ G 5′

Sticky end

2 DNA fragments with the same sticky ends can pair. Shown here is a DNA fragment inserting between two other DNA fragments, as happens when a DNA fragment is inserted into a bacterial plasmid.

Another DNA fragment produced by *Eco*RI digestion

AATTC   G
G   CTTAA

Nick in sugar–phosphate backbone

5′ GAATTC   GAATTC 3′
3′ CTTAAG   CTTAAG 5′

3 Nicks in sugar–phosphate backbones are sealed by DNA ligase.

5′ GAATTC   GAATTC 3′
3′ CTTAAG   CTTAAG 5′

Recombinant DNA molecule

---

not. The *amp*ᴿ gene encodes an enzyme that breaks down the antibiotic ampicillin; when the plasmid is introduced into *E. coli* and the *amp*ᴿ gene is expressed, the bacteria become resistant to ampicillin. The *lacZ*⁺ gene encodes β-galactosidase (part of the *lac* operon from Section 14.1), which hydrolyzes the sugar lactose, as well as a number of synthetic substrates. Restriction sites are located within the *lacZ*⁺ gene but do not alter the gene's function. For a given cloning experiment, one of these restriction sites is chosen.

Cloning a Gene of Interest. Figure 15.3, p. 336, expands on the overview of Figure 15.1, to show the steps used to clone a gene of interest using a plasmid cloning vector and restriction enzymes. Genomic DNA isolated from the organism in which the gene is found is cut with a restriction enzyme, and then, using the same restriction enzyme, a plasmid cloning vector is cut within the *lacZ*⁺ gene (Figure 15.3, steps 1 and 2).

Mixing the DNA fragments and cut plasmid together with DNA ligase produces various joined molecules as the sticky ends pair and the enzyme seals them together. Some of these molecules are recombinant plasmids consisting of, in each case, a DNA fragment inserted into the plasmid cloning vector; others are nonrecombinant plasmids resulting from the cut plasmid being resealed into a circle without an inserted fragment (step 3). In addition, ligase joins pieces of genomic DNA with no plasmid involved. Only the recombinant plasmids are important in the cloning of the gene of interest; we sort out the other two undesired molecules in later steps.

Next, the DNA molecules are transformed—introduced—into ampicillin-sensitive, *lacZ*⁻ *E. coli* (which cannot make β-galactosidase), and the transformed bacteria are spread on a plate of agar growth medium containing ampicillin and the β-galactosidase substrate X-gal (steps 4 and 5). (Recall natural transformation as one of the ways bacteria exchange genes (Chapter 9).) Only bacteria with a plasmid can grow and form colonies because expression of the plasmid's *amp*ᴿ gene is needed to make the bacteria resistant to ampicillin (see Figure 15.3, p. 336, Interpreting the Results). Within each cell of a colony, the plasmids have replicated until a hundred or so are present.

The X-gal in the medium distinguishes between bacteria that have been transformed with recombinant plasmids versus those with nonrecombinant plasmids by *blue-white screening* (see Figure 15.3, p. 336, Interpreting the Results). If a colony produces β-galactosidase, it converts X-gal to a blue product and the colony turns blue, but if a colony does not produce the enzyme, X-gal is unchanged and the colony remains white. Colonies containing nonrecombinant plasmids have an intact *lacZ*⁺ gene, produce the enzyme, and turn blue. Colonies containing recombinant plasmids are white because those plasmids each contain a DNA fragment inserted into the *lacZ*⁺ gene, so they do not produce a functional enzyme. The white colonies are then further examined to find the one containing a recombinant plasmid with the gene of interest.

In 1973, three researchers, Paul Berg, Stanley Cohen, and Herbert Boyer, pioneered the development

Figure 15.3
Cloning a gene of
interest in a plasmid
cloning vector.

PURPOSE: Cloning a gene produces many copies of a gene of interest that can be used, for example, to determine the DNA sequence of the gene, to manipulate the gene in basic research experiments, to understand its function, and to produce the protein encoded by the gene.

PROTOCOL:

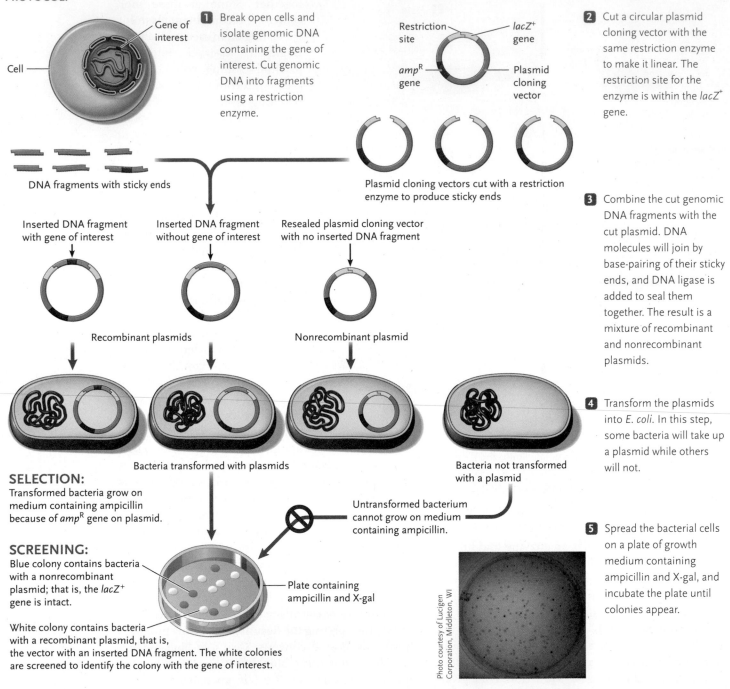

1 Break open cells and isolate genomic DNA containing the gene of interest. Cut genomic DNA into fragments using a restriction enzyme.

2 Cut a circular plasmid cloning vector with the same restriction enzyme to make it linear. The restriction site for the enzyme is within the *lacZ⁺* gene.

3 Combine the cut genomic DNA fragments with the cut plasmid. DNA molecules will join by base-pairing of their sticky ends, and DNA ligase is added to seal them together. The result is a mixture of recombinant and nonrecombinant plasmids.

4 Transform the plasmids into *E. coli*. In this step, some bacteria will take up a plasmid while others will not.

5 Spread the bacterial cells on a plate of growth medium containing ampicillin and X-gal, and incubate the plate until colonies appear.

SELECTION:
Transformed bacteria grow on medium containing ampicillin because of *amp*ᴿ gene on plasmid.

SCREENING:
Blue colony contains bacteria with a nonrecombinant plasmid; that is, the *lacZ⁺* gene is intact.

White colony contains bacteria with a recombinant plasmid, that is, the vector with an inserted DNA fragment. The white colonies are screened to identify the colony with the gene of interest.

Photo courtesy of Lucigen Corporation, Middleton, WI

INTERPRETING THE RESULTS: All of the colonies on the plate contain plasmids because the bacteria that form the colonies are resistant to the ampicillin present in the growth medium. Blue-white screening distinguishes bacterial colonies with nonrecombinant plasmids from those with recombinant plasmids. Blue colonies have nonrecombinant plasmids. These plasmids have intact *lacZ⁺* genes and produce β-galactosidase, which changes X-gal to a blue product. White colonies have recombinant plasmids. These plasmids have DNA fragments inserted into the *lacZ⁺* gene, so they do not produce β-galactosidase. As a result, they cannot convert X-gal to the blue product and the colonies are white. Among the white colonies is a colony containing the plasmid with the gene of interest. Further screening is done to identify that particular white colony (see **Figure 15.4, p. 338**). Once identified, the colony is cultured to produce large quantities of the recombinant plasmid for analysis or manipulation of the gene.

of DNA-cloning techniques using restriction enzymes and bacterial plasmids. Berg received a Nobel Prize in 1980 for his research, which pushed DNA technology to the forefront of biological investigations.

Identifying the Clone Containing the Gene of Interest. How is the clone containing the gene of interest identified among the population of white clones? The gene of interest has a unique DNA sequence, which is the basis for one commonly used identification technique. In this technique, called **DNA hybridization,** the gene of interest is identified in the set of clones when it base-pairs with a short, single-stranded complementary DNA or RNA molecule called a *nucleic acid probe* (Figure 15.4, p. 338). The probe is typically labelled with a radioactive or a nonradioactive tag so investigators can detect it. In our example, if we know the sequence of part of the gene of interest, we can use that information to design and synthesize a nucleic acid probe. Or we can take advantage of DNA sequence similarities of evolutionarily related organisms. For instance, we could make a probe for a human gene based on the sequence of an equivalent mouse gene. Once a colony containing plasmids with the gene of interest has been identified, that colony can be used to produce large quantities of the cloned gene.

15.1c DNA Libraries Contain Collections of Cloned DNA Fragments

As you have seen, the starting point for cloning a gene of interest is a large set of plasmid clones carrying fragments representing the entire DNA of an organism's genome. A collection of clones that contains a copy of every DNA sequence in a genome is called a **genomic library.** A genomic library can be made using plasmid cloning vectors or any other kind of cloning vector. The number of clones in a genomic library increases with the size of the genome. For example, a yeast genomic library of plasmid clones consists of hundreds of plasmids, whereas a human genomic library of plasmid clones consists of thousands of plasmids.

A genomic library is a resource containing the entire DNA of an organism cut into pieces. Just as for a book library, where you can search through the same set of books on various occasions to find different passages of interest, you can search through the same genomic library on various occasions to find and isolate different genes or other DNA sequences.

Researchers also commonly use another kind of DNA library that is made starting with mRNA molecules isolated from a cell. To convert single-stranded mRNA to double-stranded DNA for cloning (RNA cannot be cloned), first the researchers use the enzyme *reverse transcriptase* (made by retroviruses) to make a single-stranded DNA that is complementary to the mRNA. Then they degrade the mRNA strand with an enzyme and use DNA polymerase to make a second

DNA strand that is complementary to the first. The result is **complementary DNA (cDNA).** After adding restriction sites to each end, the researchers insert the cDNA into a cloning vector as described for the genomic library. The entire collection of cloned cDNAs made from the mRNAs isolated from a cell is a **cDNA library.**

Not all genes are active in every cell. Therefore, a cDNA library is limited in that it includes copies of only the genes that were active in the cells used as the starting point for creation of the library. This limitation can be an advantage, however, in identifying genes active in one cell type and not another. cDNA libraries are useful, therefore, for providing clues to the changes in gene activity that are responsible for cell differentiation and specialization. An ingenious method for comparing the cDNA libraries produced by different cell types—the DNA chip—is described later in this chapter.

cDNA libraries provide a critical advantage to genetic engineers who wish to insert eukaryotic genes into bacteria, particularly when the bacteria are to be used as "factories" for making the protein encoded in the gene. The genes in eukaryotic nuclear DNA typically contain many *introns,* spacer sequences that interrupt the amino acid–coding sequence of a gene (see Section 13.3). Because bacterial DNA does not contain introns, bacteria are not equipped to process eukaryotic genes correctly. However, the cDNA copy of a eukaryotic mRNA already has the introns removed, so bacteria can transcribe and translate it accurately to make eukaryotic proteins.

15.1d The Polymerase Chain Reaction Amplifies DNA *In Vitro*

Producing multiple DNA copies by cloning requires a series of techniques and considerable time. A much more rapid process, **polymerase chain reaction (PCR),** produces an extremely large number of copies of a specific DNA sequence from a DNA mixture without having to clone the sequence in a host organism. The process is called *amplification* because it increases the amount of DNA to the point where it can be analyzed or manipulated easily. Developed in 1983 by Kary B. Mullis and F. Faloona at Cetus Corporation (Emeryville, California), PCR has become one of the most important tools in modern molecular biology, finding wide application in all areas of biology. Mullis received a Nobel Prize in 1993 for his role in the development of PCR.

How PCR is performed is shown in **Figure 15.5, p. 339.** PCR is essentially a special case of DNA replication in which a DNA polymerase replicates just a portion of a DNA molecule rather than the whole molecule. PCR takes advantage of a characteristic common to all DNA polymerases: these enzymes add nucleotides only to the 3' end of an existing chain called the *primer* (see Section 12.3). For replication to begin, a primer must be available, base-paired to the template chain. By cycling 20 to 30 times through a series of priming

Figure 15.4

DNA hybridization to identify a DNA sequence of interest.

PURPOSE: Hybridization with a specific DNA probe allows researchers to detect a specific DNA sequence, such as a gene, within a population of DNA molecules. Here, DNA hybridization is used to screen a collection of bacterial colonies to identify those containing a recombinant plasmid with a gene of interest.

PROTOCOL:

1 Prepare master plates of white colonies detected in the blue-white screening step of Figure 15.3, p. 336. These colonies contain bacteria with recombinant plasmids. Hundreds or thousands of colonies can be screened for the gene of interest by using many master plates.

2 Lay a special filter paper on the plate to pick up some cells from each colony. This produces a replica of the colony pattern on the filter.

3 Treat the filter to break open the cells and to denature the released DNA into single strands. The single-stranded DNA sticks to the filter in the same position as the colony from which it was derived.

4 Add a labelled single-stranded DNA probe (DNA or RNA) for the gene of interest and incubate. The label can be radioactive or nonradioactive. If a recombinant plasmid's inserted DNA fragment is complementary to the probe, the two will hybridize, that is, form base pairs. Wash off excess labelled probe.

5 Detect the hybridization event by looking for the labelled tag on the probe. If the probe was radioactively labelled, place the filter against photographic film. The decaying radioactive compound exposes the film, giving a dark spot when the film is developed. Correlate the position of any dark sport on the film to the original colony pattern on the master plate. Isolate the colony and use it to produce large quantities of the gene of interest.

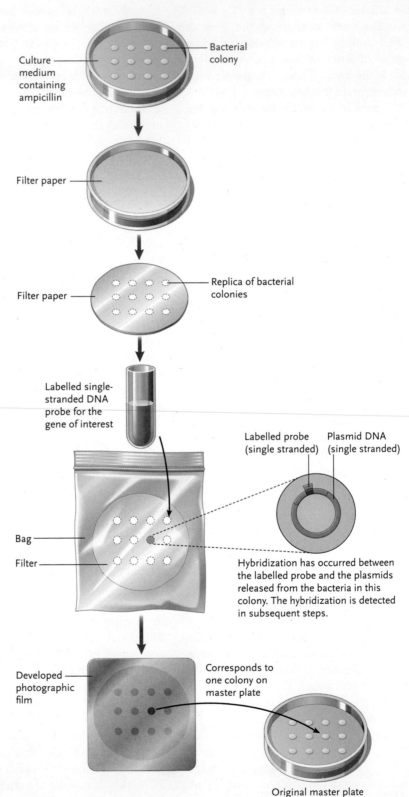

Culture medium containing ampicillin — Bacterial colony

Filter paper

Filter paper — Replica of bacterial colonies

Labelled single-stranded DNA probe for the gene of interest

Labelled probe (single stranded)   Plasmid DNA (single stranded)

Bag

Filter

Hybridization has occurred between the labelled probe and the plasmids released from the bacteria in this colony. The hybridization is detected in subsequent steps.

Developed photographic film — Corresponds to one colony on master plate

Original master plate

INTERPRETING THE RESULTS: DNA hybridization with a labelled probe enables a researcher to identify a sequence of interest. If the probe is for a particular gene, it allows the specific identification of a colony containing bacteria with recombinant plasmids carrying that gene. The specificity of the method depends directly on the probe used. The same collection of bacterial clones can be used again and again to search for recombinant plasmids carrying different genes or different plasmids of interest simply by changing the probe used in the experiment.

Figure 15.5
The polymerase chain reaction (PCR).

PURPOSE: To amplify—produce large numbers of copies of—a target DNA sequence in the test tube without cloning.

PROTOCOL: A polymerase chain reaction mixture has four key elements: (1) the DNA with the target sequence to be amplified; (2) a pair of DNA primers, one complementary to one end of the target sequence and the other complementary to the other end of the target sequence; (3) the four nucleoside triphosphate precursors for DNA synthesis (dATP, dTTP, dGTP, and dCTP); and (4) DNA polymerase. Since PCR uses high temperatures that would break down normal DNA polymerases, a heat-stable DNA polymerase is used. Heat-stable polymerases are isolated from microorganisms that grow in a high-temperature area such as a thermal pool or near a deep-sea vent.

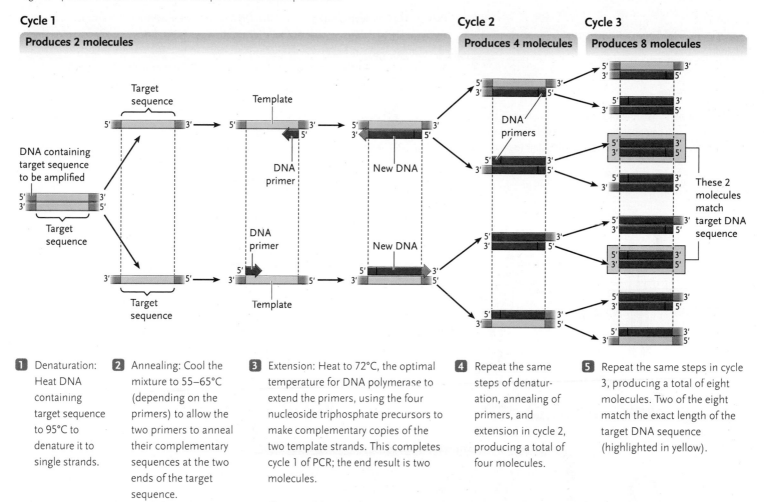

Cycle 1

Produces 2 molecules

Cycle 2

Produces 4 molecules

Cycle 3

Produces 8 molecules

1 Denaturation: Heat DNA containing target sequence to 95°C to denature it to single strands.

2 Annealing: Cool the mixture to 55–65°C (depending on the primers) to allow the two primers to anneal their complementary sequences at the two ends of the target sequence.

3 Extension: Heat to 72°C, the optimal temperature for DNA polymerase to extend the primers, using the four nucleoside triphosphate precursors to make complementary copies of the two template strands. This completes cycle 1 of PCR; the end result is two molecules.

4 Repeat the same steps of denaturation, annealing of primers, and extension in cycle 2, producing a total of four molecules.

5 Repeat the same steps in cycle 3, producing a total of eight molecules. Two of the eight match the exact length of the target DNA sequence (highlighted in yellow).

INTERPRETING THE RESULTS: After three cycles, PCR produces a pair of molecules matching the target sequence. Subsequent cycles amplify these molecules to the point where they outnumber all other molecules in the reaction by many orders of magnitude.

and replication steps, PCR amplifies the target sequence, producing millions of copies.

Since the primers used in PCR are designed to bracket only the sequence of interest, the cycles replicate only this sequence from a mixture of essentially any DNA molecules. Thus, PCR not only finds the "needle in the haystack" among all the sequences in a mixture but also makes millions of copies of the "needle"—the DNA sequence of interest. Usually, no further purification of the amplified sequence is necessary.

CONCEPT FIX Careful attention to Figure 15.5 can help you avoid the common pitfalls in understanding PCR. Notice that

1. the primers are made of DNA, not RNA as in natural DNA replication;

2. the left primer binds to one strand while the right primer binds to the opposite strand of the original DNA;

3. of all the DNA sequences put into the PCR reaction tube, only the *target sequence*, the sequence between the primers, is amplified;

4. although the diagram shows DNA being synthesized left to right on the bottom strand, and right to left on the top strand, the DNA polymerase is reading the template 3′ to 5′ in both cases. ⬡

The characteristics of PCR allow extremely small DNA samples to be amplified to concentrations high enough for analysis. PCR is used, for example, to produce enough DNA for analysis from the root of a single human hair, or from a small amount of blood, semen, or saliva, such as the traces left at the scene of a crime. It is also used to extract and multiply DNA sequences from skeletal remains; ancient sources such as mammoths, Neanderthals, and Egyptian mummies; and, in rare cases, amber-entombed fossils, fossil bones, and fossil plant remains.

A successful outcome of PCR is shown by analyzing a sample of the amplified DNA using **agarose gel electrophoresis** to see if the copies are the same length as the target **(Figure 15.6)**. Gel electrophoresis is a technique by which DNA, RNA, or protein molecules are separated in a gel subjected to an electric

Figure 15.6
Separation of DNA fragments by agarose gel electrophoresis.

PURPOSE: Gel electrophoresis separates DNA molecules, RNA molecules, or proteins according to their sizes, electrical charges, or other properties through a gel in an electric field. Different gel types and conditions are used for different molecules and types of applications. A common gel for separating large DNA fragments is made of agarose.

PROTOCOL:

1 Prepare a gel consisting of a thin slab of agarose and place it in a gel box in between two electrodes. The gel has wells for placing the DNA samples to be analyzed. Add buffer to cover the gels

2 Load DNA sample solutions, such as PCR products, into wells of the gel, alongside a well loaded with marker DNA fragments of known sizes. (The DNA samples, as well as the marker DNA sample, have a dye added to help see the liquid when loading the wells. The dye migrates during electrophoresis, enabling the progress of electrophoresis to be followed.)

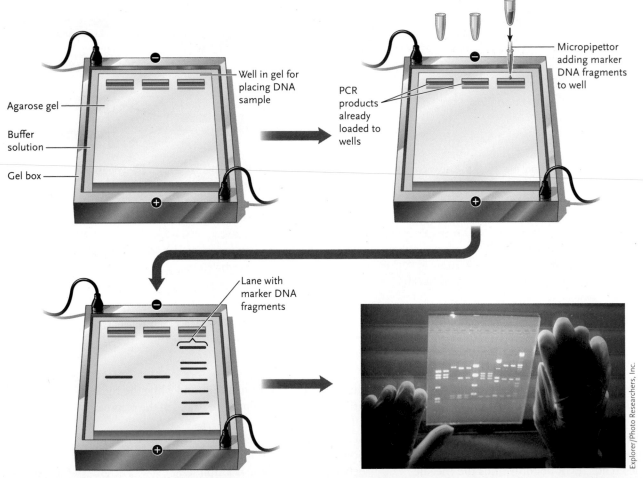

Well in gel for placing DNA sample

Agarose gel

Buffer solution

Gel box

Micropipettor adding marker DNA fragments to well

PCR products already loaded to wells

Lane with marker DNA fragments

Explorer/Photo Researchers, Inc.

3 Apply an electric current to the gel; DNA fragments are negatively charged, so they migrate to the positive pole. Shorter DNA fragments migrate faster than longer DNA fragments. At the completion of separation, DNA fragments of the same length have formed bands in the gel. At this point, the bands are invisible.

4 Stain the gel with a dye that binds to DNA. The dye fluoresces under UV light, enabling the DNA bands to be seen and photographed. An actual gel showing separated DNA bands stained and visualized this way is shown.

INTERPRETING THE RESULTS: Agarose gel electrophoresis separates DNA fragments according to their length. The lengths of the DNA fragments being analyzed are determined by measuring their migration distances and comparing those distances to a calibration curve of the migration distances of the marker bands, which have known lengths. For PCR, agarose gel electrophoresis shows whether DNA of the correct length was amplified. For restriction enzyme digests, this technique shows whether fragments are produced as expected.

field. The type of gel and the conditions used vary with the experiment, but in each case, the gel functions as a molecular sieve to separate the macromolecules based on size, electrical charge, or other properties. To separate large DNA molecules, such as those typically produced by PCR, a gel made of agarose, a natural molecule isolated from seaweed, is used because of its large pore size.

For PCR experiments, the size of the amplified DNA is determined by comparing the position of the DNA band with the positions of DNA fragments of known size separated on the gel at the same time. If that size matches the predicted size for the target DNA, PCR is deemed successful. In some cases, such as DNA from ancient sources, a size prediction may not be possible; in this case, agarose gel electrophoresis analysis simply indicates whether there was DNA in the sample that could be amplified.

The advantages of PCR have made it the technique of choice for researchers, law enforcement agencies, and forensic specialists whose primary interest is in the amplification of specific DNA fragments up to a practical maximum of a few thousand base pairs. Cloning remains the technique of choice for amplification of longer fragments. The major limitation of PCR relates to the primers. To design a primer for PCR, the researcher must first have sequence information about the target DNA. By contrast, cloning can be used to amplify DNA of unknown sequence.

STUDY BREAK

1. What features do restriction enzymes have in common? How do they differ?
2. Plasmid cloning vectors are one type of cloning vector that can be used with *E. coli* as a host organism. What features of a plasmid cloning vector make it useful for constructing and cloning recombinant DNA molecules?
3. What is a cDNA library, and from what cellular material is it derived? How does a cDNA library differ from a genomic library?
4. What information and materials are needed to amplify a region of DNA using PCR?

15.2 Applications of DNA Technologies

The ability to clone pieces of DNA—genes, especially—and to amplify specific segments of DNA by PCR revolutionized biology. These and other DNA technologies are now used for research in all areas of biology, including cloning genes to determine their structure, function, and regulation of expression; manipulating

genes to determine how their products function in cellular or developmental processes; and identifying differences in DNA sequences among individuals in ecological studies. The same DNA technologies also have practical applications, including medical and forensic detection, modification of animals and plants, and the manufacture of commercial products. In this section, case studies provide examples of how the techniques are used to answer questions and solve problems.

15.2a DNA Technologies Are Used in Molecular Testing for Many Human Genetic Diseases

Many human genetic diseases are caused by defects in enzymes or other proteins that result from mutations at the DNA level. Once scientists have identified the specific mutations responsible for human genetic diseases, they can often use DNA technologies to develop molecular tests for those diseases. One example is sickle cell disease (see *Why It Matters* in Chapter 10, Section 10.2f, and Section 11.4a). People with this disease are homozygous for a DNA mutation that affects hemoglobin, the oxygen-carrying molecule of the blood. Hemoglobin consists of two copies each of the α-globin and β-globin polypeptides. The mutation, which is in the β-globin gene, alters one amino acid in the polypeptide. As a consequence, the function of hemoglobin is significantly impaired in individuals homozygous for the mutation (who have sickle cell anemia) and mildly impaired in individuals heterozygous for the mutation (who have sickle cell trait).

The sickle cell mutation changes a restriction site in the DNA **(Figure 15.7)**. Three restriction sites for *Mst*II are associated with the normal β-globin gene, two within the coding sequence of the gene and one

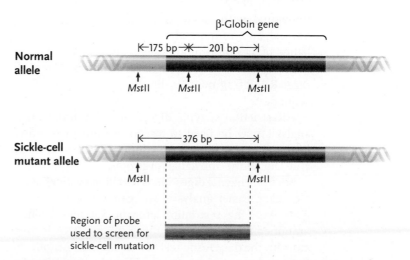

Figure 15.7

Restriction site differences between the normal and sickle cell mutant alleles of the β-globin gene. The figure shows a DNA segment that can be used as a probe to identify these alleles in subsequent analysis **(see Figure 15.8, p. 343).**

Figure 15.6, p. 340, shows an agarose gel containing DNA fragments separated by electrophoresis. The fragments appear orange because a stain has bound to the DNA and is fluorescing under ultraviolet light. The stain is ethidium bromide **(Figure 1)**. This relatively flat molecule slides neatly

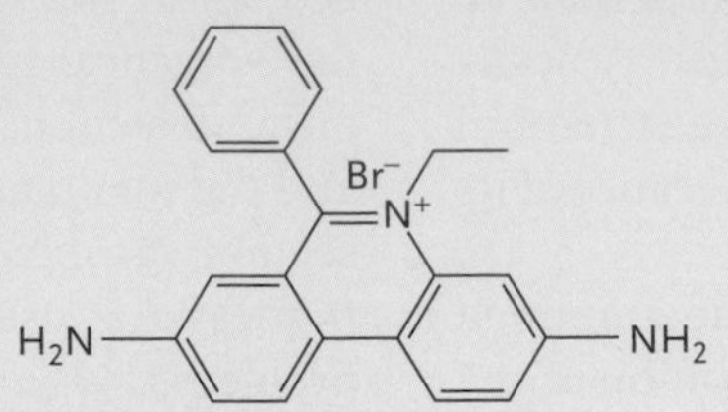

FIGURE 1
Ethidium bromide.

between the bases of DNA by a process called intercalation—hence, its usefulness as a stain. However, intercalation into DNA around replication forks can increase the frequency of addition/deletion mutations in cultured cells.

upstream of the gene. The sickle cell mutation eliminates the middle site of the three. Cutting the β-globin gene with *Mst*II produces two DNA fragments from the normal gene and one fragment from the mutated gene (see Figure 15.7, p. 341). Restriction enzyme–generated DNA fragments of different lengths from the same region of the genome such as in this example are known as **restriction fragment length polymorphisms** (RFLPs, pronounced "riff-lips").

RFLPs are typically analyzed using **Southern blot analysis** (named after its inventor, researcher Edward Southern) **(Figure 15.8)**. In this technique, genomic DNA is digested with a restriction enzyme, and the DNA fragments are separated using agarose gel electrophoresis. The fragments are then transferred—blotted—to a filter paper, and a labelled probe is used to identify a DNA sequence of interest from among the many thousands of fragments on the filter paper.

Analyzing DNA for the sickle cell mutation by *Mst*II digestion and Southern blot analysis is straightforward (see Figure 15.8). An individual with sickle cell disease will have one DNA band of 376 bp detected by the probe (lane A), a healthy individual will have two DNA bands of 175 and 201 bp (lane B), and an individual with sickle cell trait (heterozygous for normal and mutant alleles) will have three DNA bands of 376 bp (mutant allele) and 201 and 175 bp (normal allele) (lane C). The same probe detects all three RFLP fragments by binding to all or part of the sequence.

Restriction enzyme digestion and Southern blot analysis may be used to test for a number of other human genetic diseases, including phenylketonuria and Duchenne muscular dystrophy. In some cases, restriction enzyme digestion is combined with PCR for a quicker, easier analysis. The gene or region of the gene with the restriction enzyme variation is first amplified using PCR, and the amplified DNA is then cut with the diagnostic restriction enzyme. Amplification produces enough DNA so that separation by size on an agarose gel produces clearly visible bands, positioned according to fragment length. Researchers can then determine whether the fragment lengths match

a normal or abnormal RFLP pattern. This method eliminates the need for a probe or for Southern blotting.

15.2b DNA Fingerprinting Is Used to Identify Human Individuals and Individuals of Other Species

Just as each human has a unique set of fingerprints, each also has unique combinations and variations of DNA sequences (with the exception of identical twins) known as *DNA fingerprints*. **DNA fingerprinting** is a technique used to distinguish between individuals of the same species using DNA samples. Invented by Sir Alec Jeffreys in 1985, DNA fingerprinting has become a mainstream technique for distinguishing human individuals, notably in forensics and paternity testing. Although the technique can be applied to all kinds of animals and plants, in this chapter we focus on humans.

DNA Fingerprinting Principles. In DNA fingerprinting, scientists use molecular techniques, most typically PCR, to analyze DNA variations at various loci in the genome. Several loci in noncoding regions of the genome are used for analysis. Each locus is an example of a *short tandem repeat* (STR) sequence, meaning that it has a short sequence of DNA repeated in series, with each repeat about 3 to 5 bp. Each locus has a different repeated sequence, and the number of repeats varies among individuals in a population. For example, one STR locus has the sequence AGAT repeated between 8 and 20 times. As a further source of variation, a given individual is either homozygous or heterozygous for an STR allele; perhaps you are homozygous for the 11-repeat allele or heterozygous for a 9-repeat allele and a 15-repeat allele. Likely your DNA fingerprint for this locus is different from most of the others in your class. Because each individual has an essentially unique combination of alleles (identical twins are the exception), analysis of multiple STR loci can discriminate between DNA of different individuals.

Figure 15.8
Southern blot analysis.

PURPOSE: The Southern blot technique allows researchers to identify DNA fragments of interest after separating DNA fragments on a gel. One application is to compare different samples of genomic DNA cut with a restriction enzyme to detect specific restriction fragment length polymorphisms. Here the technique is used to distinguish between individuals with sickle cell disease, individuals with sickle cell trait, and normal individuals.

PROTOCOL:

1 Isolate genomic DNA and digest with a restriction enzyme. Here, genomic DNA is isolated from three individuals: A, sickle cell disease (homozygous for the sickle cell mutant allele); B, normal (homozygous for the normal allele); and C, sickle cell trait (heterozygous for sickle cell mutant allele). Digest the DNA with *Mst*II.

2 Separate the DNA fragments by agarose gel electrophoresis. The thousands of differently sized DNA fragments produce a smear of DNA down the length of each lane in the gel, which can be seen after staining the DNA. (Gel electrophoresis and gel staining are shown in Figure 15.6, p. 340.)

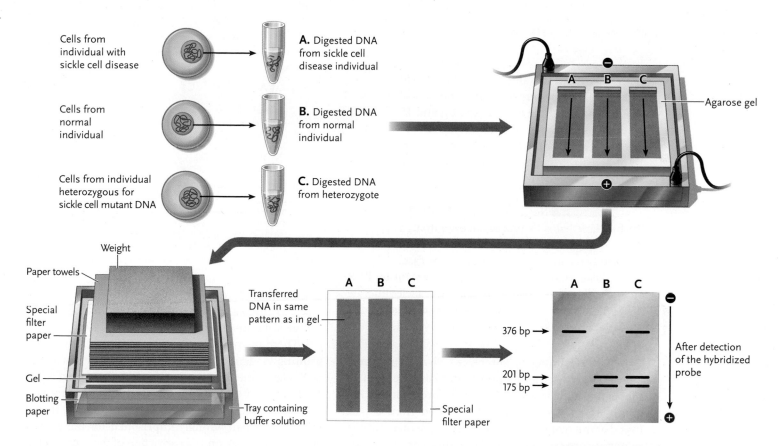

3 Hybridization with a labelled DNA probe to identify DNA fragments of interest cannot be done directly with an agarose gel. Edward Southern devised a method to transfer the DNA fragments from a gel to a special filter paper. First, treat the gel with a solution to denature the DNA into single strands. Next, place the gel on a piece of blotting paper with ends of the paper in the buffer solution and place the special filter paper on top of the gel. Capillary action wicks the buffer solution in the tray up the blotting paper, through the gel and special filter paper, and into the weighted stack of paper towels on top of the gel. The movement of the solution transfers—blots—the single-stranded DNA fragments to the filter paper, where they stick. The pattern of DNA fragments is the same as it was in the gel.

4 To focus on a particular region of the genome, use DNA hybridization with a labelled probe. That is, incubate a labelled, single-stranded probe with the filter and, after washing off excess probe, detect hybridization of the probe with DNA fragments on the filter. For a radioactive probe, place the filter against photographic film, which, after development, will show a band or bands where the probe hybridized. In this experiment, the probe is a cloned piece of DNA from the area shown in Figure 15.7, p. 341 (the β-globin gene) that can bind to all three of the *Mst*II fragments of interest.

INTERPRETING THE RESULTS: The hybridization result indicates that the probe has identified a very specific DNA fragment or fragments in the digested genomic DNA. The RFLPs for the β-globin gene can be seen in Figure 15.7, p. 341. DNA from the sickle cell disease individual cut with *Mst*II results in a single band of 376 bp detected by the probe, while DNA from the normal individual results in two bands, of 201 bp and 175 bp. DNA from a sickle cell trait heterozygote results in three bands, of 376 bp (from the sickle cell mutant allele), and 201 bp and 175 bp (both from the normal allele). This type of analysis in general is useful for distinguishing normal and mutant alleles of genes where the mutation involved alters a restriction site.

a. Alleles at an STR locus

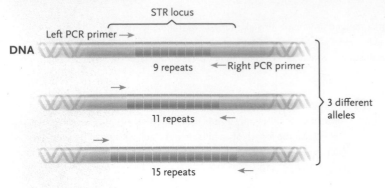

Figure 15.9

Using PCR to obtain a DNA fingerprint for an STR locus.

b. DNA fingerprint analysis of the STR locus by PCR

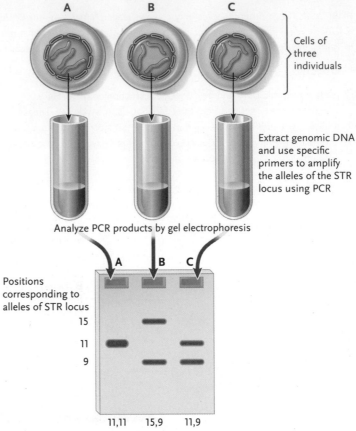

Figure 15.9 illustrates how PCR is used to obtain a DNA fingerprint for a theoretical STR locus with three alleles of 9, 11, and 15 tandem repeats (see Figure 15.9a). Using primers that flank the STR locus, the locus is amplified from genomic DNA using PCR, and the PCR products are analyzed by gel electrophoresis (see Figure 15.9b).

CONCEPT FIX Notice in Figure 15.9b that the first lane has only one band, even though the cell that was the source of DNA was diploid and had two copies of all alleles. In this case, both alleles produce the same size fragment by PCR analysis. Therefore, fragments from both alleles migrate the same distance in the gel. Notice how this band is thicker than the others, indicating more DNA. ⬡

DNA Fingerprinting in Forensics. DNA fingerprints are routinely used to identify criminals or eliminate innocent people as suspects in legal proceedings. For example, a DNA fingerprint prepared from a hair found at the scene of a crime or from a semen sample might be compared with the DNA fingerprint of a suspect to link the suspect with the crime. Or a DNA fingerprint of blood found on a suspect's clothing or possessions might be compared with the DNA fingerprint of a victim. Typically, the evidence is presented in terms of the probability that the particular DNA sample could have come from a random individual. Hence, the media report probability values, such as one in several million, or in several billion, that a person other than the accused could have left his or her DNA at the crime scene.

Although courts initially met with legal challenges to the admissibility of DNA fingerprints, experience has shown that they are highly dependable as a line of evidence if DNA samples are collected and prepared with care and if a sufficient number of polymorphic loci are examined. There is always concern, however, about the possibility of contamination of the sample with DNA from another source during the path from crime scene to forensic lab analysis. Moreover, in some cases, criminals themselves have planted fake DNA samples at crime scenes to confuse the investigation.

There are many examples of the use of DNA fingerprinting to identify a criminal. For example, in a case in England, the DNA fingerprints of more than 4 000 men were made during an investigation of the rape and murder of two teenage girls. The results led to the release of a man wrongly imprisoned for the crimes and to the confession and conviction of the actual killer. And the application of DNA fingerprinting techniques to stored forensic samples has led to the release of a number of people wrongly convicted for rape or murder.

DNA Fingerprinting in Testing Paternity and Establishing Ancestry. DNA fingerprints are also widely used as evidence of paternity because parents and their children share common alleles in their DNA fingerprints. That is, each child receives one allele of each locus from one parent and the other allele from the other parent. A comparison of DNA fingerprints for a number of loci can prove almost infallibly whether a child has been fathered or mothered by a given person. DNA fingerprints have also been used for other investigations, such as confirming that remains discovered in a remote region of Russia were actually those of Czar Nicholas II and members of his family, murdered in 1918 during the Russian revolution.

DNA fingerprinting is also widely used in studies of other organisms, including other animals, plants, and bacteria. Examples include testing for pathogenic *E. coli* in food sources such as hamburger meat, investigating cases of wildlife poaching, detecting genetically modified organisms among living organisms or in food, and comparing the DNA of ancient organisms with that of present-day descendants.

15.2c Genetic Engineering Uses DNA Technologies to Alter the Genes of a Cell or Organism

We have seen the many ways scientists use DNA technologies to ask and answer questions that were once completely inaccessible. Genetic engineering goes beyond gathering information; it is the use of DNA technologies to modify genes of a cell or organism. The goals of genetic engineering include using prokaryotic cells, fungi, animals, and plants as factories for the production of proteins needed in medicine and scientific research; correcting hereditary disorders; and improving animals and crop plants of agricultural importance. In many of these areas, genetic engineering has already been spectacularly successful. The successes and potential benefits of genetic engineering, however, are tempered by ethical and social concerns about its use, along with the fear that the methods may produce toxic or damaging foods or release dangerous and uncontrollable organisms to the environment.

Genetic engineering uses DNA technologies of the kind already discussed in this chapter. DNA—perhaps a modified gene—is introduced into target cells of an organism. Organisms that have undergone a gene transfer are called **transgenic**, meaning that they have been modified to contain genetic information—the *transgene*—from an external source.

The following sections discuss examples of applications of genetic engineering to bacteria, animals, and plants and assess major controversies arising from these projects.

Genetic Engineering of Bacteria to Produce Proteins. Transgenic bacteria have been made, for example, to synthesize proteins for medical applications, break down toxic wastes such as oil spills, produce industrial chemicals such as alcohols, and process minerals. *E. coli* is the organism of choice for many of these applications of DNA technologies.

Using *E. coli* to make a protein from a foreign source is conceptually straightforward **(Figure 15.10)**. First, the gene for the protein is cloned from the appropriate organism. Then the gene is inserted into an **expression vector** that, in addition to the usual features of a cloning vector, contains the regulatory sequences that allow transcription and translation of the gene. For a bacterial expression vector, this means having a promoter and a transcription terminator that are

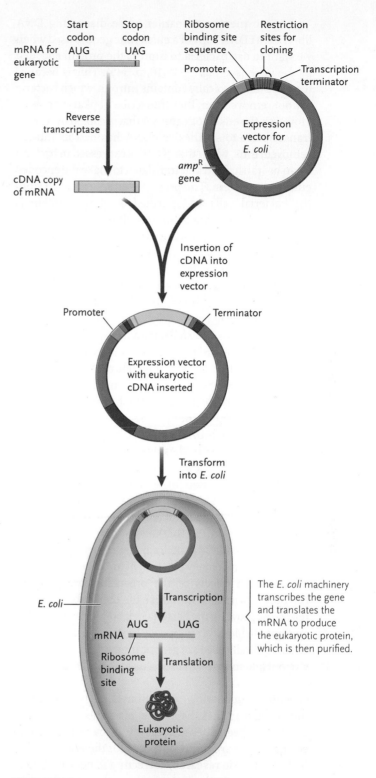

Figure 15.10

Using an expression vector to synthesize a eukaryotic protein.

recognized by the *E. coli* transcriptional machinery and having the ribosome binding site needed for the bacterial ribosome to recognize the start codon of the transgene (see Section 13.1). The regulatory sequences flank the cluster of restriction sites of the expression vector that are used for cloning so that the inserted gene is correctly placed for transcription and translation when the recombinant plasmid is transformed into *E. coli*.

As we mentioned earlier while discussing DNA libraries, a cDNA copy of a eukaryotic gene is used when we want to use bacteria to express the protein encoded by the gene (see Figure 15.10, p. 345). This is because the gene itself typically contains introns, which bacteria cannot remove when they transcribe a eukaryotic gene. However, the eukaryotic mRNA that is copied by reverse transcriptase to synthesize cDNA has had its introns removed; thus, when that cDNA is expressed in bacteria it can be transcribed and translated to make the encoded eukaryotic protein. The protein is either extracted from the bacterial cells and purified or, if the protein is secreted, it is purified from the culture medium.

Expression vectors are available for a number of organisms. They vary in the regulatory sequences they contain and the selectable marker they carry so that the host organism transformed with the vector carrying a gene of interest can be detected and the host can express that gene.

For example, *E. coli* bacteria have been genetically engineered to make the human hormone insulin; the commercial product is called Humulin. Insulin is required by people with some forms of diabetes. Humulin is a perfect copy of the human insulin hormone. Many other proteins, including human growth hormone to treat human growth disorders, tissue plasminogen activator to dissolve blood clots that cause heart attacks, and a vaccine against foot-and-mouth disease of cattle and other cloven-hoofed animals (a highly contagious and sometimes fatal viral disease), have been developed for commercial production in bacteria using similar methods.

A concern is that genetically engineered bacteria may be released accidentally into the environment, where possible adverse effects of the organisms are currently unknown. Scientists minimize the danger of accidental release by growing the bacteria in laboratories that follow appropriate biosafety protocols. In addition, the bacterial strains typically used are genetic mutants that cannot survive outside the growth media used in the laboratory.

Genetic Engineering of Animals. Many animals, including fruit flies, fish, mice, pigs, sheep, goats, and cows, have been altered successfully by genetic engineering. There are many purposes for these alterations, including basic research, correcting genetic disorders in humans and other mammals, and producing pharmaceutically important proteins.

Genetic Engineering Methods for Animals. Several methods are used to introduce a gene of interest into animal cells. The gene may be introduced into *germ-line cells*, which develop into sperm or eggs and thus enable the introduced gene to be passed from generation to generation. Or, the gene may be introduced into *somatic* (body) *cells*, differentiated cells that are not part of lines producing sperm or eggs, in which case the gene is not transmitted from generation to generation.

Germ-line cells of embryos are often used as targets for introducing genes, particularly in mammals **(Figure 15.11).** The treated cells are then cultured in quantity and reintroduced into early embryos. If the technique is successful, some of the introduced cells become founders of cell lines that develop into eggs or sperm with the desired genetic information integrated into their DNA. Individuals produced by crosses using the engineered eggs and sperm then contain the introduced sequences in all of their cells. Several genes have been introduced into the germ lines of mice by this approach, resulting in permanent, heritable changes in the engineered individuals.

A related technique involves introducing desired genes into **stem cells**, which are cells capable of undergoing many divisions in an unspecialized, undifferentiated state, but which can also differentiate into specialized cell types. In mammals, *embryonic stem cells* are found in a mass of cells inside an early-stage embryo (the blastocyst) (see Figure 15.11, step 3) and can differentiate into all of the tissue types of the embryo, whereas *adult stem cells* function to replace specialized cells in various tissues and organs. In mice and other nonhuman mammals, transgenes are introduced into embryonic stem cells, which are then injected into early-stage embryos as in Figure 15.11 (step 3). The stem cells then differentiate into a variety of tissues along with cells of the embryo itself, including sperm and egg cells. Males and females are then bred, leading to offspring that are either homozygotes, containing two copies of the introduced gene, or heterozygotes, containing one introduced gene and one gene that was native to the embryo receiving the engineered stem cells.

Introduction of genes into stem cells has been performed mostly in mice. One of the highly useful results is the production of a *knockout mouse,* a homozygous recessive that receives two copies of a gene altered to a nonfunctional state and thus has no functional copies. The effect of the missing gene on the knockout mouse is a clue to the normal function of the gene. In some cases, knockout mice are used to model human genetic diseases.

For introducing genes into somatic cells, somatic cells are typically removed from the body, cultured, and then transformed with DNA containing the transgene. The modified cells are then reintroduced into the body, where the transgene functions. Because germ cells and their products are not involved, the transgene remains in the individual and is not passed to offspring.

Gene Therapy: Correcting Genetic Disorders. The path to **gene therapy**—correcting genetic disorders—in humans began with experiments using mice. In 1982, Richard Palmiter at the University of Washington, Ralph Brinster of the University of Pennsylvania, and their colleagues injected a growth hormone gene from rats into fertilized mouse eggs and implanted the eggs into a surrogate mother. She gave birth to some normal-sized mouse

Figure 15.11

Introduction of genes into mouse embryos using embryonic germ-line cells.

PURPOSE: To make a transgenic animal that can transmit the transgene to offspring. The embryonic germ-line cells that receive the transgene develop into the reproductive cells of the animal.

PROTOCOL:

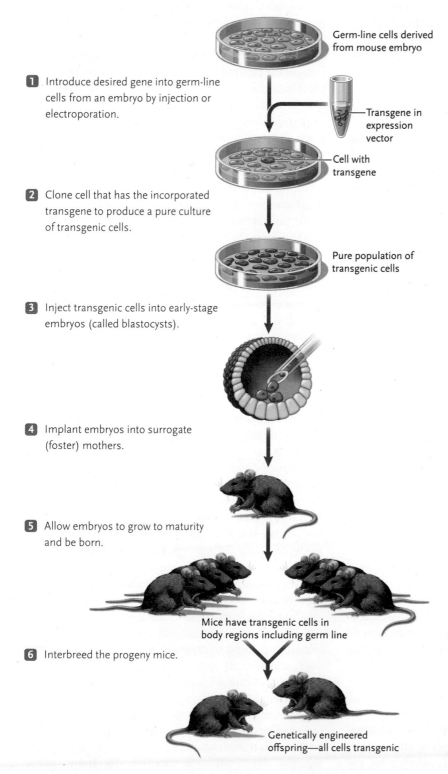

Germ-line cells derived from mouse embryo

1. Introduce desired gene into germ-line cells from an embryo by injection or electroporation.

Transgene in expression vector

Cell with transgene

2. Clone cell that has the incorporated transgene to produce a pure culture of transgenic cells.

Pure population of transgenic cells

3. Inject transgenic cells into early-stage embryos (called blastocysts).

4. Implant embryos into surrogate (foster) mothers.

5. Allow embryos to grow to maturity and be born.

Mice have transgenic cells in body regions including germ line

6. Interbreed the progeny mice.

Genetically engineered offspring—all cells transgenic

INTERPRETING THE RESULTS: The result of the breeding is some offspring in which all cells are transgenic—a genetically engineered animal has been produced.

---

pups that grew more quickly than normal and became about twice the size of their normal litter mates. These *giant mice* (Figure 15.12) attracted extensive media attention from around the world.

Palmiter and Brinster next attempted to cure a genetic disorder by gene therapy. In this experiment, they were able to correct a genetic growth hormone deficiency that produces dwarf mice. They introduced a normal copy of the growth hormone gene into fertilized eggs taken from mutant dwarf mice and implanted the eggs into a surrogate mother. The transgenic mouse pups grew to slightly larger than normal, demonstrating that the genetic defect in those mice had been corrected.

This sort of experiment, in which a gene is introduced into germ-line cells of an animal to correct a genetic disorder, is called **germ-line gene therapy**. For ethical reasons, germ-line gene therapy is not permitted with humans. Instead, humans are treated with **somatic gene therapy**, in which genes are introduced into somatic cells (as described in the previous section).

The first successful use of somatic gene therapy with a human sub-

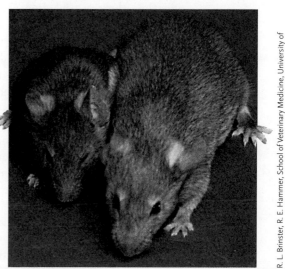

R. L. Brinster, R. E. Hammer, School of Veterinary Medicine, University of Pennsylvania

Figure 15.12

A genetically engineered giant mouse (right) produced by the introduction of a rat growth hormone gene into the animal. A mouse of normal size is on the left.

ject who had a genetic disorder was carried out in the 1990s by W. French Anderson and his colleagues at the National Institutes of Health (NIH) in the United States. The subject was a young girl with *adenosine deaminase deficiency (ADA)*. Without the adenosine deaminase enzyme, white blood cells cannot mature (see Chapter 43); without normally functioning white blood cells, the body's immune response is so deficient that most children with ADA die of infections before reaching puberty. The researchers successfully introduced a functional ADA gene into mature white blood cells isolated from the patient. Those cells were reintroduced into the girl, and expression of the ADA gene provided a temporary cure for her ADA deficiency. The cure was not permanent because mature white blood cells, produced by differentiation of stem cells in the bone marrow, are nondividing cells with a finite lifetime. Therefore, the somatic gene therapy procedure has to be repeated every few months. Indeed, the subject of this example still receives periodic gene therapy to maintain the necessary levels of the ADA enzyme in her blood. In addition, she receives direct doses of the normal enzyme.

Successful somatic gene therapy has also been achieved for sickle cell disease. In December 1998, a 13-year-old boy's bone marrow cells were replaced with stem cells from the umbilical cord of an unrelated infant. The hope was that the stem cells would produce healthy bone marrow cells, the source of blood cells. The procedure worked, and the patient has been declared cured of the disease.

However, despite enormous efforts, human somatic gene therapy has not been the panacea people expected. Relatively little progress has been made since the first gene therapy clinical trial for ADA deficiency was described, and, in fact, there have been major setbacks. In 1999, for example, a teenage patient in a somatic gene therapy trial died as a result of a severe immune response to the viral vector being used to introduce a normal gene to correct his genetic deficiency. Furthermore, some children in gene therapy trials involving the use of retrovirus vectors to introduce genes into blood stem cells have developed a leukemia-like condition. In short, somatic gene therapy is not yet an effective treatment for human genetic disease, even though the approach has been successful in a number of cases to correct models of human genetic disorders in experimental mammals. Although no commercial human gene therapy product has been approved for use, research and clinical trials continue as scientists try to circumvent the difficulties.

Turning Domestic Animals into Protein Factories. Another successful application of genetic engineering turns animals into pharmaceutical factories for the production of proteins required to treat human diseases or other medical conditions. Most of these *pharming* projects, as they are called, engineer the animals to produce the desired proteins in milk, making the production, extraction, and purification of the proteins harmless to the animals.

One of the first successful applications of this approach was carried out with sheep engineered to produce a protein required for normal blood clotting in humans. The protein, called a *clotting factor*, is deficient in people with one form of hemophilia, who require frequent injections of the factor to avoid bleeding to death from even minor injuries. Using DNA-cloning techniques, researchers joined the gene encoding the normal form of the clotting factor to the promoter sequences of the β-lactoglobin gene, which encodes a protein secreted in milk, and introduced it into fertilized eggs. Those cells were implanted into a surrogate mother, and the transgenic sheep born were allowed to mature. The β-lactoglobin promoter controlling the clotting factor gene became activated in mammary gland cells of females, resulting in the production of clotting factor. The clotting factor was then secreted into the milk. Production in the milk is harmless to the sheep and yields the protein in a form that can easily be obtained and purified.

Other similar projects are under development to produce particular proteins in transgenic mammals. These include a protein to treat cystic fibrosis, collagen to correct scars and wrinkles, human milk proteins to be added to infant formulas, and normal hemoglobin for use as an additive to blood transfusions.

Producing Animal Clones. Making transgenic mammals is expensive and inefficient. And because only one copy of the transgene typically becomes incorporated into the treated cell, not all progeny of a transgenic animal inherit that gene. Scientists reasoned that an alternative to breeding a valuable transgenic mammal to produce progeny with the transgene would be to clone the mammal. Each clone would be identical to the original, including the expression of the transgene. That this is possible was shown in 1997 when two scientists, Ian Wilmut and Keith H. S. Campbell of the Roslin Institute, Edinburgh, Scotland, announced that they had successfully cloned a sheep from a single somatic cell derived from an adult sheep **(Figure 15.13)**— the first cloned mammal.

Since the successful cloning experiment producing Dolly, many additional mammals have been cloned, including mice, goats, pigs, monkeys, rabbits, dogs, a male calf appropriately named Gene, and a domestic cat called CC (for *Copy Cat*).

Cloning farm animals has been so successful that several commercial enterprises now provide cloned copies of champion animals. One example is a clone of an American Holstein cow, Zita, who was the U.S. national champion milk producer for many years. Animal breeders estimate that there are now more than 100 cloned animals on U.S. farms, and breeders plan to produce entire herds if government approval is granted.

Figure 15.13

The first cloning of a mammal.

QUESTION: Does the nucleus of an adult mammal contain all the genetic information to specify a new organism? In other words, can mammals be cloned starting with adult cells?

EXPERIMENT: Ian Wilmut, Keith Campbell, and their colleagues fused a mammary gland cell from an adult sheep with an unfertilized egg cell from which the nucleus had been removed, and tested whether that fused cell could produce a lamb.

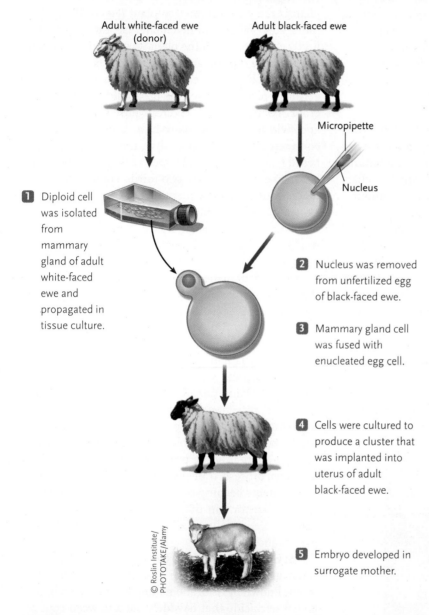

Adult white-faced ewe (donor)

Adult black-faced ewe

Micropipette

Nucleus

1 Diploid cell was isolated from mammary gland of adult white-faced ewe and propagated in tissue culture.

2 Nucleus was removed from unfertilized egg of black-faced ewe.

3 Mammary gland cell was fused with enucleated egg cell.

4 Cells were cultured to produce a cluster that was implanted into uterus of adult black-faced ewe.

5 Embryo developed in surrogate mother.

© Roslin Institute/ PHOTOTAKE/Alamy

RESULT: Dolly was born and grew normally. She was white-faced—a clone of the donor ewe. DNA fingerprinting using STR loci showed her DNA matched that of the donor ewe and not either the ewe who donated the egg, or the ewe who was the surrogate mother.

CONCLUSION: An adult nucleus of a mammal contains all the genetic material necessary to direct the development of a normal new organism, a clone of the original. Dolly was the first cloned mammal. The success rate for Wilmut and Campbell's experiment was very low—Dolly represented less than 0.4% of the fused cells they made—but its significance was huge.

Source: Based on I. Wilmut et al. "Viable offspring derived from fetal and mammalian cells." *Nature.* 1997 Feb 27; 385(6619): 810-3.

The cloning of domestic animals has its drawbacks. Many cloning attempts fail, leading to the death of the transplanted embryos. Cloned animals often suffer from conditions such as birth defects and poor lung development. Genes may be lost during the cloning process or may be expressed abnormally in the cloned animal. For example, molecular studies have shown that the expression of perhaps hundreds of genes in the genomes of clones is regulated abnormally.

CONCEPT FIX In studying Figures 15.11, p. 347, and 15.13, both related to manipulating animal embryos, it may be tempting to see Dolly as an advance in stem cell research. However, Dolly resulted from the transfer of a somatic cell nucleus to an egg cell that was lacking a nucleus. This cloning technique, called somatic cell nuclear transfer (SCNT), doesn't involve stem cells. ◉

Genetic Engineering of Plants. Genetic engineering of plants has led to increased resistance to pests and disease; greater tolerance to heat, drought, and salinity; greater crop yields; faster growth; and resistance to herbicides. Another aim is to produce seeds with higher levels of amino acids. The essential amino acid lysine, for example, is present only in limited quantities in cereal grains such as wheat, rice, oats, barley, and corn; the seeds of legumes such as beans, peas, lentils, soybeans, and peanuts are deficient in the essential amino acid methionine or cysteine. Increasing the amounts of the deficient amino acids in plant seeds by genetic engineering would greatly improve the diet of domestic animals and human populations that rely on seeds as a primary food source. Efforts are also under way to increase the content of vitamins and minerals in crop plants.

Other possibilities for plant genetic engineering include plant pharming to produce pharmaceutical products. Plants are ideal for this purpose because they are primary producers at the bottom rung of the food chain and can be grown in huge numbers with maximum conservation of the Sun's energy captured in photosynthesis.

Some plants, such as *Arabidopsis*, tobacco, potato, cabbage, and carrot, have special advantages for genetic engineering because individual cells can be removed from an adult, altered by the introduction of a desired gene, and then grown in cultures into a multicellular mass of cloned cells called a *callus*. Subsequently, roots, stems, and leaves develop in the callus, forming a young plant that can then be grown in containers or fields by the usual methods. In the plant, each cell contains the introduced gene. The gametes produced by the transgenic plants can then be used in crosses to produce offspring, some of which will have the transgene, as in the similar experiments with animals.

Methods Used to Insert Genes into Plants. Genes are inserted into plant cells by several techniques. One commonly used method takes advantage of a natural process that causes crown gall disease, which is characterized by bulbous, irregular growths—tumours, essentially—that can develop at wound sites on the trunks and limbs of deciduous trees **(Figure 15.14)**. Crown gall disease is caused by the bacterium *Rhizobium radiobacter* (formerly *Agrobacterium tumefaciens*, recently reclassified on the basis of genome analysis). This bacterium contains a large, circular plasmid called the **Ti (tumour-inducing) plasmid.** The interaction between the bacterium and the plant cell it infects stimulates the excision of a segment of the Ti plasmid called *T DNA* (for transforming DNA), which then integrates into the plant cell's genome. Genes on the T DNA are then expressed; the products stimulate the transformed cell to grow and divide and therefore to produce a tumour. The tumours provide essential nutrients for the bacterium. The Ti plasmid is used as a vector for making transgenic plants in much the same way as bacterial plasmids are used as vectors to introduce genes into bacteria **(Figure 15.15)**.

Successful Plant Genetic Engineering Projects. An early visual demonstration of the successful use of genetic engineering techniques to produce a transgenic plant is the glowing tobacco plant **(Figure 15.16)**. The transgenic plant contained luciferase, the gene for the firefly enzyme. When the plant was soaked in the substrate for the enzyme, it became luminescent.

The most widespread application of genetic engineering of plants involves the production of transgenic crops. Thousands of such crops have been developed and field tested, and many have been approved for commercial use. If you analyze the processed plant-based foods at a national supermarket chain, you will likely find that at least two-thirds contain products made from transgenic plants.

In many cases, plants are modified to make them resistant to insect pests, viruses, or herbicides. Crops modified for insect resistance include corn, cotton, and potatoes. The most common approach to making plants resistant to insects is to introduce the gene from the bacterium *Bacillus thuringiensis* that encodes the *Bt* toxin, an organic pesticide. This toxin has been used in powder form to kill insects in agriculture for many years, and now transgenic plants making their own *Bt* toxin are resistant to specific groups of insects that feed on them. Millions of acres of crop plants planted in the United States and Canada are *Bt*-engineered varieties.

Virus infections cause enormous crop losses worldwide. Transgenic crops that are virus resistant would be highly valuable to the agricultural community. There is some promise in this area. By some unknown process, transgenic plants expressing certain viral proteins become resistant to infections by whole viruses that contain those same proteins. Two virus-resistant genetically modified crops made so far are papaya and squash.

Several crops have also been engineered to become resistant to herbicides. For example, *glyphosate* (commonly known by its brand name, Roundup) is a highly potent herbicide that is widely used in weed control. The herbicide works by inhibiting a particular enzyme in the chloroplast. Unfortunately, it also kills crops. But transgenic crops have been made in which a bacterial form of the chloroplast enzyme has been added to the plants. The bacteria-derived enzyme is not affected by Roundup, and farmers who use these herbicide-resistant crops can spray fields of crops to kill weeds without killing the crops. Now most of the corn, soybean, canola, and cotton plants grown in North America are the genetically engineered, glyphosate-resistant ("Roundup-ready") varieties.

Gall

Edward L. Barnard, Florida Department of Agriculture and Consumer Services, Bugwood.org

Figure 15.14
A crown gall tumour on the trunk of a California pepper tree. The tumour, stimulated by genes introduced from the bacterium *Rhizobium radiobacter*, is the bulbous, irregular growth extending from the trunk.

Figure 15.15

Using the Ti plasmid of *Rhizobium radiobacter* to produce transgenic plants.

PURPOSE: To make transgenic plants. This technique is one way to introduce a transgene into a plant for genetic engineering purposes.

PROTOCOL:

1 Isolate the Ti plasmid from *Rhizobium radiobacter*. The plasmid contains a segment called T DNA (T 5 transforming), which induces tumours in plants.

2 Digest the Ti plasmid with a restriction enzyme that cuts within the T DNA. Mix with a gene of interest on a DNA fragment that was produced by digesting with the same enzyme. Use DNA ligase to join the two DNA molecules together to produce a recombinant plasmid.

3 Transform the recombinant Ti plasmid into a disarmed *A. Rhizobium radiobacter* that cannot induce tumours, and use the transformed bacterium to infect cells in plant fragments in a test tube. In infected cells, the T DNA with the inserted gene of interest excises from the Ti plasmid and integrates into the plant cell genome.

4 Culture the transgenic plant fragments to regenerate whole plants.

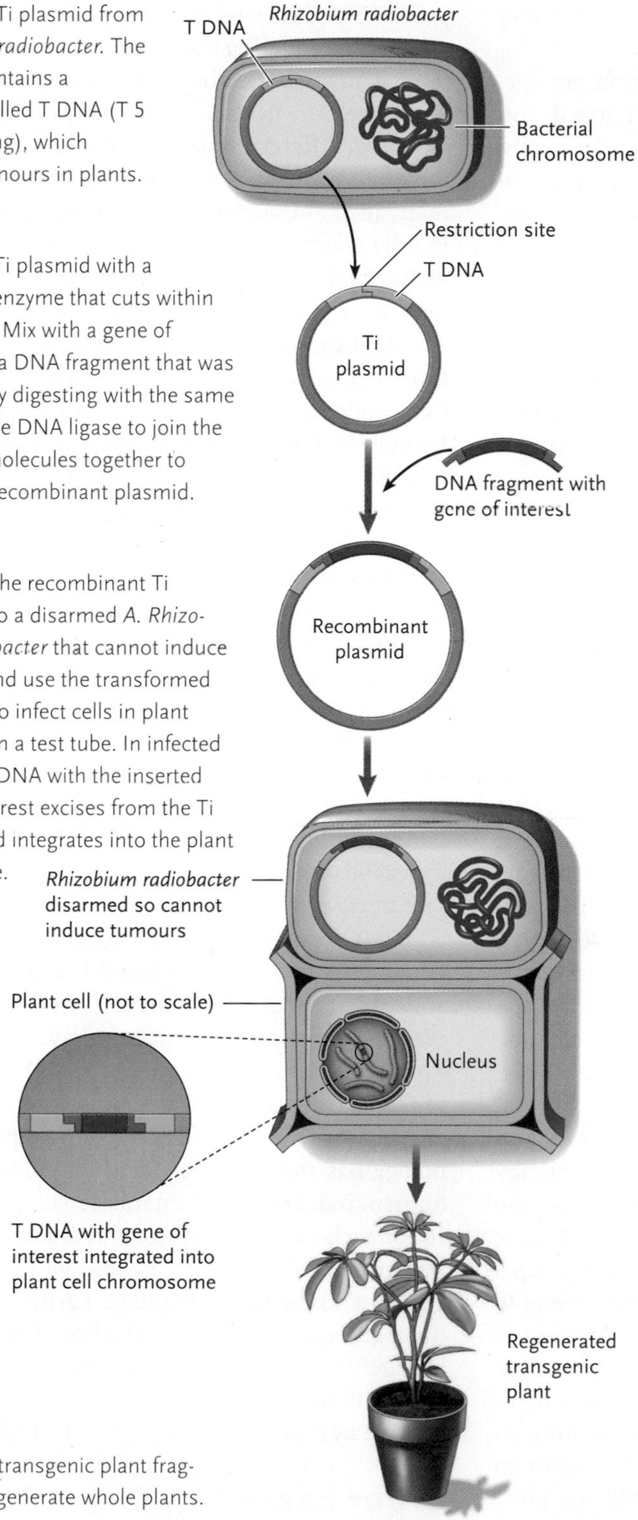

T DNA

Rhizobium radiobacter

Bacterial chromosome

Restriction site

T DNA

Ti plasmid

DNA fragment with gene of interest

Recombinant plasmid

Rhizobium radiobacter disarmed so cannot induce tumours

Plant cell (not to scale)

Nucleus

T DNA with gene of interest integrated into plant cell chromosome

Regenerated transgenic plant

INTERPRETING THE RESULTS: The plant has been genetically engineered to contain a new gene. The transgenic plant will express a new trait based on that gene, perhaps resistance to a herbicide or production of an insect toxin, according to the goal of the experiment.

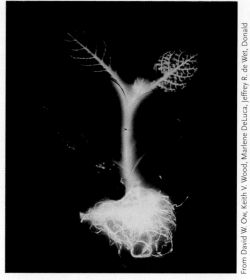

From David W. Ow, Keith V. Wood, Marlene DeLuca, Jeffrey R. de Wet, Donald R. Helinski and Stephen H. Howell, "Transient and stable expression of the firefly luciferase gene in plant cells and transgenic plants." *Science* 14 November 1986, Vol. 234 no. 4778 pp. 856-859. Reprinted with permission from AAAS.

Figure 15.16

A genetically engineered tobacco plant, made capable of luminescence by the introduction of a firefly gene coding for the enzyme luciferase.

Crop plants are also being engineered to alter their nutritional qualities. For example, a strain of rice plants has been produced with seeds rich in β-carotene, a precursor of vitamin A, as well as iron **(Figure 15.17)**. The new rice, which is given a yellow or golden colour by the carotene, may provide improved nutrition for the billions of people who depend on rice as a diet staple. In particular, the rice may help improve the nutrition of children younger than age 5 in southeast Asia, 70% of whom suffer from impaired vision because of vitamin A deficiency.

Plant pharming is also an active area both in university research labs and at biotechnology companies. Plant pharming involves the engineering of transgenic plants to produce medically valuable products. The approach is one described earlier: the gene for the

Regular rice

Genetically engineered golden rice containing β-carotene

Dr. Jorge Mayer, Golden Rice Project

Figure 15.17

Rice genetically engineered to contain β-carotene.

product is cloned into a cloning vector adjacent to a promoter, in this case one active in plants, and the recombinant DNA molecule is introduced into plants. Products under development include vaccines for various bacterial and viral diseases, protease inhibitors to treat or prevent virus infections, collagen to treat scars and wrinkles, and aprotinin to reduce bleeding and clotting during heart surgery.

In contrast to animal genetic engineering, genetically altered plants have been widely developed and appear to be here to stay as mainstays of agriculture. But, as the next section discusses, both animal and plant genetic engineering have not proceeded without concerns.

15.2d DNA Technologies and Genetic Engineering Are a Subject of Public Concern

When recombinant DNA technology was developed in the early 1970s, researchers quickly recognized that in addition to the many anticipated benefits, there might be deleterious outcomes. One key concern at the time was that a bacterium carrying a recombinant DNA molecule might escape into the environment. Perhaps it could transfer that molecule to other bacteria and produce new, potentially harmful, strains. To address these concerns, the U.S. scientists who developed the technology drew up safety guidelines for recombinant DNA research in the United States. Adopted by the NIH, the guidelines listed the precautions to be used in the laboratory when constructing recombinant DNA molecules and included the design and use of host organisms that could survive only in growth media in the laboratory. Since that time, countless experiments involving recombinant DNA molecules have been done in laboratories around the world. These experiments have shown that recombinant DNA manipulations can be done safely. Over time, therefore, the recombinant DNA guidelines have become more relaxed. Nonetheless, stringent regulations still exist for certain areas of recombinant DNA research that pose significant risk, such as cloning genes from highly pathogenic bacteria or viruses, or gene therapy experiments. In essence, as the risk increases, the research facility must increase its security and must obtain more levels of approval by peer scientist groups.

Guidelines for genetic engineering also extend to research in several areas that have been the subject of public concern and debate. Although the public does not seem to be very concerned about genetically engineered microorganisms, for example, those cleaning up oil spills and hazardous chemicals, it is concerned about possible problems with **genetically modified organisms (GMOs)** used as food. A GMO is a transgenic organism; the majority of GMOs are crop plants. Issues are the safety of GMO-containing food and the possible adverse effects of the GMOs to the environment, such as by interbreeding with natural species or by harming beneficial insect species. For example,

could introduced genes providing herbicide or insect resistance move from crop plants into related weed species through cross-pollination, producing "super-weeds" that might be difficult or impossible to control? *Bt*-expressing corn was originally thought to have adverse effects on monarch butterflies who fed on the pollen. The most recent of a series of independent studies investigating this possibility has indicated that the risk to the butterflies is extremely low.

More broadly, different countries have reacted to GMOs in different ways. In Canada, transgenic crops are quite widely planted and harvested. Before commercialization, such GMOs are evaluated for potential risk by appropriate government regulatory agencies, including Health Canada, the Canadian Food Inspection Agency, and Environment Canada.

Political opposition to GMOs has been greater in Europe, dampening the use of transgenic crop plants in the fields and GMOs in food. In 1999, the European Union (EU) imposed a six-year moratorium on all GMOs, leading to a bitter dispute with the United States, Canada, and Argentina, the leading growers of transgenic crops. More recently, the EU has revised the GMO regulations in all member states. Basically, the EU has decided that using genetic engineering in agriculture and food production is permissible provided that the GMO or food containing it is safe for humans, animals, and the environment. All use of GMOs in the field or in food requires authorization following a careful review process.

On a global level, an international agreement, the **Cartagena Protocol on Biosafety**, "promotes biosafety by establishing practical rules and procedures for the safe transfer [between countries], handling and use of GMOs." Separate procedures have been set up for GMOs that are to be introduced into the environment and those that are to be used as food or feed or for processing. Although 161 countries have signed on to the Protocol, several others, mainly GMO exporters such as Canada, the United States, and Argentina, have not.

In sum, the use of DNA technologies in biotechnology has the potential for tremendous benefits to humankind. Such experimentation is not without risk, so for each experiment, researchers must assess that risk and make a judgment about whether to proceed and, if so, how to do so safely. Furthermore, agreed-upon guidelines and protocols should ensure a level of biosafety for researchers, consumers, politicians, and governments.

We now turn to the analysis of whole genomes.

STUDY BREAK

1. What are the principles of DNA fingerprinting?
2. What is a transgenic organism?
3. What is the difference between using germ-line cells and somatic cells for gene therapy?

The discipline of genetics was originally built on the study of rare, naturally occurring mutations. Researchers routinely screened thousands (or sometimes millions) of individuals to collect a handful of useful mutations. Agents that increased the frequency of mutations were often used, but they tended to be nonspecific, and the isolation of particular mutations in specific genes remained a lottery with unfavourable odds.

Michael Smith changed all of that in the late 1970s by demonstrating that *in vitro* DNA synthesis techniques could be used to create mutated sequences. This method of site-directed mutagenesis allowed specific mutations to be introduced into any given DNA sequence. For the first time, geneticists could create the exact changes they were interested in. Smith's work was recognized with the 1993 Nobel Prize in Chemistry.

In addition to his legacy as a scientist, Smith was a generous philanthropist and a strong supporter of public education in science. He died in 2000, three years after retiring from UBC.

15.3 Genome Analysis

The development of DNA technologies for analyzing genes and gene expression revolutionized experimental biology. DNA-sequencing techniques (described in this section) have made it possible to analyze the sequences of cloned genes and genes amplified by PCR. Having the complete sequence of a gene aids researchers tremendously in unravelling how the gene functions. But a gene is only part of a genome. Researchers want to know about the organization of genes in a complete genome, and how genes work together in networks to control life. Of particular interest, of course, is the human genome. The complete sequencing of the approximately 3-billion-base-pair human genome—the Human Genome Project (HGP)—began in 1990. The task was completed in 2003 by an international consortium of researchers and by a private company, Celera Genomics. As part of the official HGP, for purposes of comparison the genomes of several important model organisms commonly used in genetic studies were sequenced: *E. coli* (representing prokaryotic cells), the yeast *Saccharomyces cerevisiae* (representing single-celled eukaryotes), *Drosophila melanogaster* and *Caenorhabditis elegans* (the fruit fly and a nematode worm, respectively, representing multicellular animals of moderate genome complexity), and *Mus musculus* (the mouse, representing a mammal of genome complexity comparable to that of humans). In addition, the sequences of the genomes of many organisms not listed here, including plants, have been completed or are in progress at this time. What researchers are learning from analyzing complete genomes is of enormous importance to our understanding of biology and the evolution of organisms.

15.3a DNA-Sequencing Techniques Are Based on DNA Replication

DNA sequencing is the key technology for genome-sequencing projects. It is also used to determine the sequence of individual genes that have been cloned or amplified by PCR. DNA sequencing was first developed in the late 1970s by Allan M. Maxam, a graduate student, and his mentor, Walter Gilbert, of Harvard University. Within a few years, Frederick Sanger, of Cambridge University, designed the method that is most commonly used today. Gilbert and Sanger were awarded a Nobel Prize in 1980.

The Sanger method is based on the properties of nucleotides known as *dideoxyribonucleotides;* therefore, the method is also called *dideoxy sequencing* **(Figure 15.18, p. 354).** Dideoxyribonucleotides have a single –H bound to the 3′ carbon of the deoxyribose sugar instead of the –OH normally at this position in deoxyribonucleotides. DNA polymerases, the replication enzymes, recognize the dideoxyribonucleotides and place them in the DNA just as they do normal deoxyribonucleotides. However, because a dideoxyribonucleotide has no 3′–OH group available for addition of the next base, replication of a nucleotide chain stops when one of these nucleotides is added to a growing nucleotide chain. (Remember from Section 12.3 that a 3′–OH group must be present at the growing end of a nucleotide chain for the next nucleotide to be added during DNA replication.)

In a dideoxy sequencing reaction, researchers use a mixture of dideoxyribonucleotides and normal nucleotides, so that chain termination will occur randomly at each position where a particular nucleotide appears in the population of DNA molecules being replicated. Each chain-termination event generates a newly synthesized DNA strand that ends with the dideoxyribonucleotide; hence, for this particular strand, the base at the 3′

Figure 15.18

Dideoxy (Sanger) method for sequencing DNA

PURPOSE: Obtain the sequence of a piece of DNA, such as in gene sequencing or genome sequencing. The method is shown here with an automated sequencing system.

PROTOCOL:

1 A dideoxy sequencing reaction has the following components: the fragment of DNA to be sequenced (denatured to single strands); a DNA primer that will bind to the 3′ end of the sequence to be determined; a mixture of the four deoxyribonucleotide precursors for DNA synthesis; and a mixture of the four dideoxyribonucleotide (dd) precursors, each labelled with a different fluorescent molecule, and DNA polymerase to catalyze the DNA synthesis reaction.

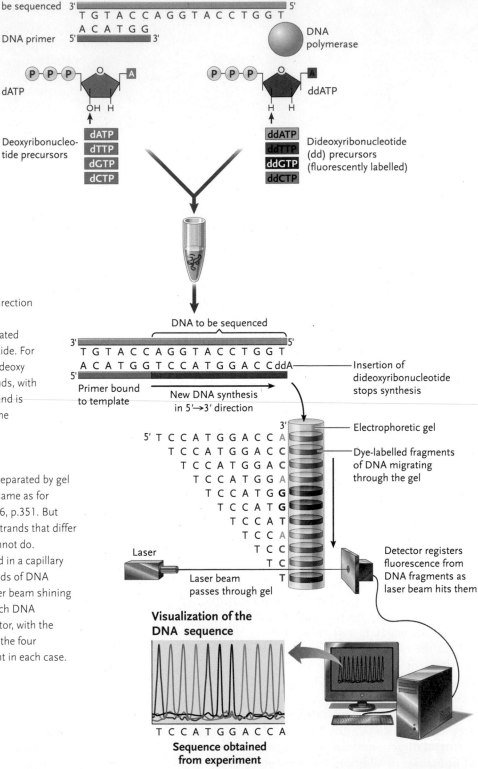

2 The new DNA strand is synthesized in the 5′→3′ direction starting at the 3′ end of the primer. New synthesis continues until a dideoxyribonucleotide is incorporated into the DNA instead of a normal deoxyribonucleotide. For a large population of template DNA strands, the dideoxy sequencing reaction produces a series of new strands, with lengths from one up. At the 3′ end of each new strand is the labelled dideoxyribonucleotide that terminated the synthesis.

3 The labelled strands produced by the reaction are separated by gel electrophoresis. The principle of separation is the same as for agarose gel electrophoresis described in Figure 15.6, p.351. But here it is necessary to discriminate between DNA strands that differ in length by one nucleotide, which agarose gels cannot do. Therefore, a gel made of polyacrylamide is prepared in a capillary tube for separating the DNA fragments. As the bands of DNA fragments move near the bottom of the tube, a laser beam shining through the gel excites the fluorescent labels on each DNA fragment. The fluorescence is registered by a detector, with the wavelength of the fluorescence indicating which of the four dideoxyribonucleotides is at the end of the fragment in each case.

INTERPRETING THE RESULTS: The data from the laser system are sent to a computer that interprets which of the four possible fluorescent labels is at the end of each DNA strand. The results show the colours of the labels as the DNA bands passed the detector. They may be seen on the computer screen or in printouts. The sequence of the newly synthesized DNA, which is complementary to the template strand, is read from left (5′) to right (3′). (The sequence shown here begins after the primer.)

end is known, and, because of base-pairing rules, the base on the template strand being sequenced can be deduced. Once they know the base at the end of each terminated DNA strand, researchers can work out the complete sequence of the template DNA strand.

The dideoxy sequencing method can be used with any pure piece of DNA, such as a cloned DNA fragment, or a fragment amplified by PCR. An unambiguous sequence of about 500 to 750 nucleotides can be obtained from each sequencing experiment.

Genome Analysis Consists of Three Main Areas. The following are the three main areas of genome analysis:

1. **Genome sequence determination and annotation**, which means obtaining the sequences of complete genomes and analyzing the sequences to locate putative genes and other functionally important sequences within the genome.
2. **Functional genomics**, the study of the functions of genes and other parts of the genome. In relation to the genes, this includes developing an understanding of how their expression is regulated, the proteins they encode, and the role of these proteins in the organism's metabolic processes.
3. **Comparative genomics**, the comparison of entire genomes (or extensive portions of them) to understand evolutionary relationships and the basic biological similarities and differences among species.

15.3b Genome Sequence Determination and Annotation Involves Obtaining and Analyzing the Sequences of Complete Genomes

The first genome sequence reported, that of the bacterium *Haemophilus influenzae*, was determined using the whole-genome shotgun method (**Figure 15.19**). In this method, developed by J. Craig Venter and his associates at Celera Genomics, the entire genome is broken into thousands to millions of random, overlapping fragments. Each fragment is cloned and sequenced. The genome sequence is then assembled by computer on the basis of the sequence overlaps between fragments. Originally thought to be inapplicable to the large genomes of eukaryotes, improvements in sequencing technologies and in the computer algorithms have now made it the method of choice for sequencing genomes of all organisms.

By 2009, the genomes of a large number of viruses and hundreds of organisms had been sequenced, and those of more species are continually being added to the list of fully sequenced genomes. Among those already sequenced are cytomegaloviruses; bacteria including *E. coli*; various archaean species; and eukaryotes including the budding yeast *Saccharomyces cerevisiae*, the protist *Plasmodium falciparum* (a malarial parasite), the roundworm *Caenorhabditis elegans*, the plants *Arabidopsis*

Figure 15.19
Whole genome shotgun sequencing.

PURPOSE: Obtain the complete sequence of the genome of an organism.

PROTOCOL:

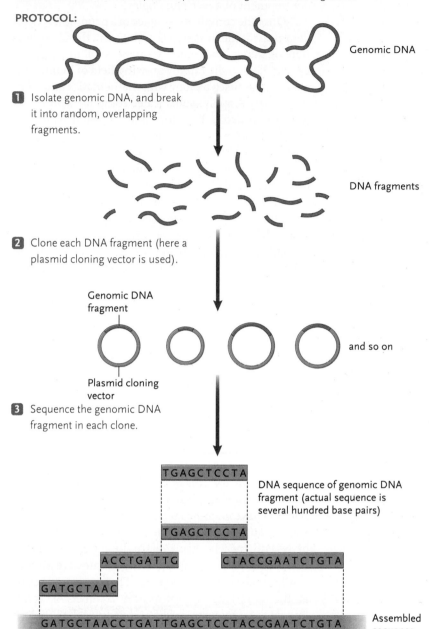

Genomic DNA

1 Isolate genomic DNA, and break it into random, overlapping fragments.

DNA fragments

2 Clone each DNA fragment (here a plasmid cloning vector is used).

Genomic DNA fragment

and so on

Plasmid cloning vector

3 Sequence the genomic DNA fragment in each clone.

TGAGCTCCTA

DNA sequence of genomic DNA fragment (actual sequence is several hundred base pairs)

TGAGCTCCTA

ACCTGATTG   CTACCGAATCTGTA

GATGCTAAC

GATGCTAACCTGATTGAGCTCCTACCGAATCTGTA   Assembled sequence

4 Enter the DNA sequences of the fragments into a computer, and use the computer to assemble overlapping sequences into the continuous sequence of each chromosome of the organism. This technique is analogous to taking 10 copies of a book that has been torn randomly into smaller sets of a few pages each and, by matching overlapping pages of the leaflets, assembling a complete copy of the book with the pages in the correct order.

INTERPRETING THE RESULTS: The method generates the complete sequence of the genome of an organism.

thaliana and rice, the fruit fly *Drosophila melanogaster*, the chicken, the mouse, the rat, the dog, the chimpanzee, and the human. To give you a hint of the breadth of application of the genomic approach to problems in biology, note that Genome Canada, the federally funded agency overseeing genomics research in Canada, supports genomic investigations in infectious disease, cancer medicine, agriculture, aquaculture, industrial enzyme production, forestry, and the development of new technologies.

Once the complete sequence of a genome has been determined, the next step is *annotation*, the identification of genes and other sequences of importance. Researchers in the rapidly growing field of **bioinformatics**, which fuses biology with mathematics and computer science, apply sophisticated computer algorithms in this endeavour. Bioinformatics is also used to predict the structure and function of gene products and to postulate evolutionary relationships of sequences, which are issues for functional and comparative genomicists, respectively.

Protein-coding genes are of particular interest in genome analysis. Using computer analysis, researchers identify possible protein-coding genes by searching for **open reading frames (ORFs)**, that is, a start codon (ATG, at the DNA level) separated by a multiple of three nucleotides from one of the stop codons (TAG, TAA, or TGA at the DNA level). This process is easy for prokaryotic genomes, because the genes have no introns. In eukaryotic protein-coding genes, which typically have introns, more sophisticated algorithms are used to try to identify the junctions between exons and introns in scanning for open reading frames.

With many genomes sequenced, researchers can compare the genomes to learn about genome sizes and the number of protein-coding genes. Table 15.1 gives examples of such data for Bacteria, Archaea, and Eukarya. We can make some general conclusions about the genomes presented. Members of the domain Bacteria have genomes that vary widely in size. *Carsonella ruddii,* a symbiotic bacterium living in the guts of certain insects, has the smallest known cellular genome of any organism (viral genomes are significantly smaller), with 182 genes. That gene number is, at the moment, the minimum number of genes known to be required for life. The largest known bacterial genome is more than 80 times as large as that of *C. ruddii.* Archaean genomes also vary widely in size, the largest known being that of *Methanosarcina acetivorans,* which lives in oxygen-depleted environments such as oil wells and deep sea vents. For members of both domain Bacteria and domain Archaea, genes are densely packed in the genomes, with little space between. Thus, larger genomes of organisms in these two domains tend to reflect increased gene number.

Members of the domain Eukarya vary markedly in form and complexity, and their genomes also show great differences in size. For example, yeast has a very small genome that is about 0.4% the size of the human genome, yet humans have only a little more than three times the number of genes as yeast. There are no rules relating organism complexity and genome size. For

Table 15.1 Genome Sizes and Estimated Number of Genes for Selected Members of Domains Bacteria, Archaea, and Eukarya

Domain and Organism	Genome Size (Mb*)	Number of Genes
Bacteria		
Carsonella ruddii	0.16	182
Mycoplasma genitalium	0.58	523
Escherichia coli	4.6	4 200
Rhizobium radiobacter	5.7	5 482
Archaea		
Thermoplasma acidophilum	1.56	1 509
Methanosarcina acetivorans	5.75	4 662
Eukarya		
Protozoa		
Tetrahymena thermophila (a ciliated protist)	220	> 20 000
Fungi		
Saccharomyces cerevisiae (a budding yeast)	12	~ 6 000
Neurospora crassa (orange bread mould)	40	~ 10 100
Plants		
Arabidopsis thaliana (thale cress)	125	25 900
Oryza sativa (rice)	430	~ 56 000
Invertebrates		
Caenorhabditis elegans (a nematode worm)	100	20 443
Drosophila melanogaster (fruit fly)	180	13 700
Vertebrates		
Takifugu rubripes (pufferfish)	393	> 31 000
Mus musculus (mouse)	2 700	~ 22 000
Homo sapiens (human)	2 900	~ 20 000

*Megabase = one million bases.

instance, the fruit fly and the locust have similar physiological complexity, but the locust genome is 50 times the size of the fruit fly genome and twice the size of the mouse genome. Within a genus, there is not necessarily a consistency. For example, there is a 50-fold variation in the genome size of *Allium* species, which contains the onions and relatives. Even among vertebrates, there is great variation in genome size. The pufferfish, for example, has a 393 Mb genome, while the genomes of the mouse and humans are about seven times as large. And yet, the pufferfish has more genes than either the mouse or the human. But the human genome is not the largest among eukaryotes; the genomes of some amphibians and some ferns are about 200 times as large. In general, though, genes are packed less densely in eukaryotes than they are in prokaryotic cells, although there is no uniformity in the packing, as the pufferfish–mammal comparison shows.

Eukaryotic genomes contain large numbers of noncoding sequences, most of them in the form of repeated sequences of nucleotides of various lengths and numbers. Most of these sequences, which make up from about 25 to 50% of the total genomic DNA in different eukaryotic species, have no determined function at this time.

Let's learn a little more about the human genome in particular. The human genome sequence consists of almost 3 *billion* base pairs. Before genomics, researchers had predicted that human cells had as many as 100 000 different protein-coding genes. The best current estimate is about 20 000 such genes. However, although the number of protein-coding genes is unexpectedly small, the total number of different proteins produced in humans is much greater, and probably approaches the 100 000 figure originally proposed for genes. The additional proteins arise through such processes as alternative splicing during mRNA processing (see Section 13.3) and differences in protein processing.

Many people are shocked to discover that all the protein-coding sequences occupy less than 2% of the human genome. Introns—the noncoding spacers in genes—occupy another 24% of the genome. The rest of the DNA, almost three-quarters of the genome, occupies the spaces between genes. Some of this intergenic DNA is functional and includes regulatory sequences such as promoters and enhancers, but much of it, more than 50% of the total genome, consists of repeated sequences that have no known function.

There are bioethics issues concerning the human genome. To address them, studies of the ethical, legal, economic, and environmental issues surrounding the availability of genomic information have been funded by the U.S. Department of Energy, the NIH, and the GE³LS section of Genome Canada. The following questions are some that are being considered:

- Who should have access to personal genetic information, and how should it be used?
- To what extent should genetic information be private and confidential?
- How will genetic tests be evaluated and regulated?
- How can people be informed sufficiently about the genetic information from genomic analysis so that they can make informed personal medical choices?
- Does a set of genes predispose a person's behaviour, and can the person control that behaviour?

15.3c Functional Genomics Focuses on the Functions of Genes and Other Parts of the Genome

The complete genome sequence for an organism is basically a very long string of A, T, G, and C letters, which means little without further analysis. Discovering the functions of genes and other parts of the genome is one important goal of the analysis. Most of this functional genomics research is focused on the genes because they control the functions of cells and, therefore, of organisms. Functional genomics relies on laboratory experiments by molecular biologists as well as computer analysis by bioinformaticists.

Assigning Gene Function by Sequence Similarity. Computer analysis of a genome sequence will reveal its putative genes. These days there are databases with an enormous amount of sequence information for both DNA and amino acids; information for the latter is typically inferred from gene sequences. For a newly sequenced genome, researchers use those databases to assign functions to the putative genes identified in the initial computer analysis. They look for sequence matches in *sequence similarity searches,* in which an input sequence is compared with all sequences in a database. Such searches can be done using an Internet browser to access the computer programs. For example, to use the BLAST (Basic Local Alignment Search Tool) program at the National Center for Biotechnology Information, a user pastes the putative gene DNA sequence, or the sequence of the protein it encodes, into a browser window and sets the program to work. The BLAST program searches the databases of known sequences and returns the best matches, indicating the degree to which the entered sequence is similar to the sequences found in the databases. The matches are listed in order, from the closest match to the least likely match.

Sequence similarity searching can assign probable functions to genes in a newly obtained genome sequence because homology—descent from a common ancestor—reflects evolutionary relationships. That is, the DNA sequences of two genes from different organisms will be similar if they are homologous genes with a common ancestor. Differences between the genes will have resulted from mutations that occurred over evolutionary time. For example, if a gene from a newly synthesized genome has close sequence similarity to genes that are known to be RNA polymerases in other organisms, then it is highly likely that the gene encodes an RNA polymerase. This information is useful to researchers who wish to study the function of the new gene.

Despite the extensive databases we now have, there are still many putative genes with unknown functions. Indeed, it is a surprising characteristic of each new genome sequence that the functions of many of its genes are previously unknown. Naturally it is a challenging task to determine their functions because there are no clues to begin the investigation.

Assigning Gene Function Experimentally. To prove unequivocally that a gene identified in genome sequencing has a particular function requires experimental analysis. One important approach to assigning gene function experimentally is to knock out or knock down the function of a gene and determine which phenotypic process changes. The altered phenotype informs the researcher about the function of the normal gene. Major projects have been done, or are being done, to systematically knock out or knock down the function of each gene in the genomes of several organisms, including yeast, the fruit fly, and the nematode worm *C. elegans*.

The two main methods used in these experiments are *gene knockouts* and RNA interference (RNAi). A gene knockout uses molecular techniques to disrupt the gene in the chromosome. RNA interference, as discussed in Chapter 14, knocks down the expression of a gene at the translation level. When used experimentally, a small regulatory RNA is transcribed from an expression plasmid introduced into the cell. The sequence of that regulatory RNA can form complementary base pairs with the mRNA of the gene of interest. The base-pairing triggers the RNA interference molecular mechanisms, which knock down the expression of the gene by causing degradation of that gene's mRNA by blocking its translation.

RNA interference has been used to knock down gene expression of each of the approximately 20 000 genes of the nematode worm *C. elegans* one by one. It is not practical to look for any and all changes in phenotype caused by each knockdown, so researchers usually screen for changes in particular phenotypes and correlate those changes to the specific genes affected. For example, screening for changes in fat metabolism reveals the genes involved in that process, and so on. In this general way, RNA interference has been useful in assigning functions for some genes that had not been characterized by sequence similarity searching or other experimental approaches.

15.3d Differential Gene Activity in Entire Genomes Is Studied with DNA Microarrays

As a part of functional genomics research, investigators are interested in comparing which genes are active in different cell types of humans and other organisms, and in tracking the changes in total gene activity in the same cell types as development progresses or as conditions change. In some cases, the researcher wants to know whether or not particular genes are being expressed, and in other cases how the level of expression varies in different circumstances. This research has been revolutionized by a technique

using **DNA microarrays**. The microarrays are also called **DNA chips** because the techniques used to "print" the arrays resemble those used to lay out electronic circuits on a computer chip. The surface of a DNA microarray is divided into a microscopic grid of about 60 000 spaces. On each space of the grid, a computerized system deposits a microscopic spot containing about 10 000 000 copies of a DNA probe that is about 20 nucleotides long.

Studies of gene activity using DNA microarrays involve comparing gene expression under a defined experimental condition with expression under a reference (control) condition. DNA microarrays can be used to answer such basic biological questions as this: How does gene expression change when a cell goes from a resting state (reference condition) to a dividing state (experimental condition); that is, how is gene expression different in different stages of development? DNA microarrays can also be used to address many questions of medical significance, such as the following: How are genes differentially expressed in normal cells and cells of various cancers? In these experiments, investigators might focus on which genes are active and which are inactive under the two conditions, or on how the levels of expression of genes change under the two conditions.

Figure 15.20 shows how a DNA microarray is used to compare gene expression in normal cells and cancer cells in humans. mRNAs are isolated from each cell type, and cDNAs are made from them, incorporating different fluorescent labels: green for one cDNA, red for the other. The two cDNAs are mixed and added to the DNA chip, where they hybridize with any complementary probes. A laser locates and quantifies the green and red fluorescence, enabling a researcher to see which genes are expressed in the cells and, for those that are expressed, to quantify differences in gene expression between the two cell types (see "Interpreting the Results" in Figure 15.20). The results can help researchers understand how the cancer develops and progresses.

DNA microarrays are also used to screen individuals for particular mutations. To detect mutations, the probes spotted onto the chip include probes for the normal sequence of the genes of interest along with probes for sequences of all known mutations. A fluorescent spot at a site on the chip printed with a probe for a given mutation immediately shows the presence of the mutation in the individual. Such a test is currently used to screen patients for whether they carry any one of a number of mutations of the *breast cancer 1 (BRCA1)* gene, known to be associated with the possible development of breast cancer.

In Comparative Genomics, Whole or Large Parts of Genomes Are Compared to Study Basic Biological Differences between Species and Evolutionary Relationships. In comparative genomics studies, genomes or sections of genomes from two or more species, strains,

Figure 15.20

DNA microarray analysis of gene expression levels.

PURPOSE: DNA microarrays can be used in various experiments, including comparing the levels of gene expression in two different tissues, as illustrated here. The power of the technique is that the entire set of genes in a genome can be analyzed simultaneously.

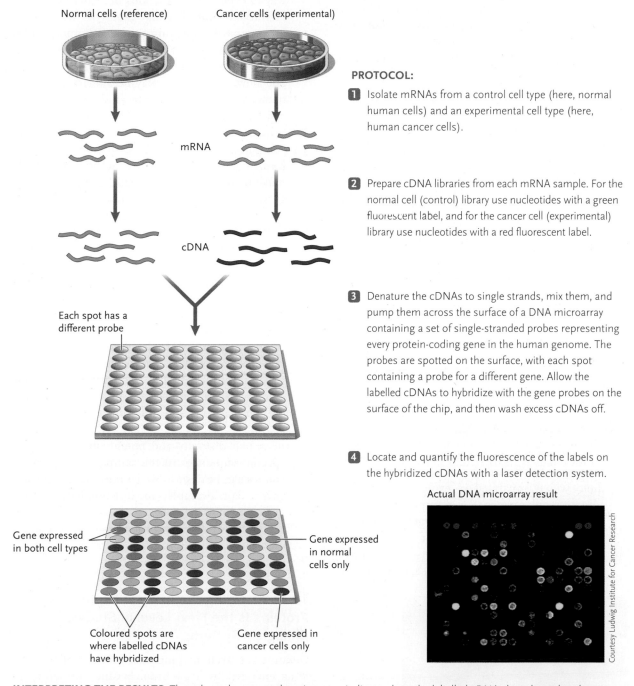

Normal cells (reference)

Cancer cells (experimental)

PROTOCOL:

1 Isolate mRNAs from a control cell type (here, normal human cells) and an experimental cell type (here, human cancer cells).

mRNA

2 Prepare cDNA libraries from each mRNA sample. For the normal cell (control) library use nucleotides with a green fluorescent label, and for the cancer cell (experimental) library use nucleotides with a red fluorescent label.

cDNA

Each spot has a different probe

3 Denature the cDNAs to single strands, mix them, and pump them across the surface of a DNA microarray containing a set of single-stranded probes representing every protein-coding gene in the human genome. The probes are spotted on the surface, with each spot containing a probe for a different gene. Allow the labelled cDNAs to hybridize with the gene probes on the surface of the chip, and then wash excess cDNAs off.

4 Locate and quantify the fluorescence of the labels on the hybridized cDNAs with a laser detection system.

Actual DNA microarray result

Gene expressed in both cell types

Gene expressed in normal cells only

Coloured spots are where labelled cDNAs have hybridized

Gene expressed in cancer cells only

Courtesy Ludwig Institute for Cancer Research

INTERPRETING THE RESULTS: The coloured spots on the microarray indicate where the labelled cDNAs have bound to the gene probes attached to the chip and, therefore, which genes were active in normal and/or cancer cells. Moreover, we can quantify the gene expression in the two cell types by the colour detected. A purely green spot indicates the gene was active in the normal cell, but not in the cancer cell. A purely red spot indicates the gene was active in the cancer cell, but not in the normal cell. A yellow spot indicates the gene was equally active in the two cell types, and other colours tell us the relative levels of gene expression in the two cell types. For this particular experiment, we would be able to see how many genes have altered expression in the cancer cells, and exactly how their expression was changed.

or individuals are analyzed to determine similarities and differences between sequences. Depending on the study, the focus may be on gene sequences, nongene sequences, or both. Various types of research questions can be asked in comparative genomics studies, including the following:

1. What are the evolutionary relationships between two or more genomes? Using DNA or amino acid sequence comparisons to determine evolutionary relationships among organisms is **molecular phylogenetics**, a topic discussed more in Chapter 18. Historically, amino acid sequences were the first to be used in such comparisons, and then DNA sequences. A phylogeny—the evolutionary history of a group of organisms—can potentially be inaccurate if it is based on a small set of sequences, such as those of a gene or genes. However, genome sequences contain much more information. Researchers comparing genome sequences are learning a great deal about how genomes relate to each other, including which sequences are conserved, as well as about how genomes have evolved. For example, in a three-way comparison of genome sequences, investigators have shown that modern humans share approximately 95% of their genes with chimpanzees (our nearest relative), but perhaps as much as 99.5% with Neanderthals **(Figure 15.21)**. Complete genome sequence analysis was also crucial in demonstrating the evolutionary relationships and distinctions between members of the domains Bacteria, Archaea, and Eukarya, in particular confirming the archaeans as being a distinct lineage.

A revelation of genome sequence comparisons is the degree to which different organisms, some of them widely separated in evolutionary origins, contain similar genes. For example, even though the yeast *Saccharomyces cerevisiae* is separated from our species by millions of years of evolutionary history, about 2 300 of its approximately 6 000 genes are related to those of mammals, including many genes that control progress through the cell cycle. The similarities are so close that the yeast and human versions of many genes can be interchanged with little or no effect on cell functions in either organism.

2. What are the functions of human genes? For ethical reasons, direct experimentation with humans is not possible. Comparative genomics provides a way to explore the functions of human genes by identifying homologous genes in nonhuman organisms. By studying the gene homologue in another organism, researchers can gain insight into the normal function of the gene in humans and how its function may be altered. Naturally, there is a lot of interest in studying genes that cause human disease.

3. What genes make us human? Researchers have compared the chimpanzee genome with the human genome to identify genes that potentially make us human. Chimpanzees and humans last shared a common ancestor about 6 million years ago. The investigators found a number of genes unique to the human genome known as *human accelerated regions*. One of these genes encodes an RNA that is not translated into protein. The gene is expressed in a region of the brain that undergoes a developmental change in humans but not in chimpanzees. Exactly what the RNA does is the subject of active research.

4. What organisms or viruses are in a sample? "*Why It Matters*" for this chapter discussed a metagenomics study of marine microbes. Metagenomic studies are comparative genomics studies because the similarities and differences between the genomic sequences obtained indicate the microbial diversity and potentially the array of specific sequences in the sample. Metagenomic studies can be descriptive, or they can be function based. For example, in function-based metagenomic analyses, researchers analyze the DNA sequences in an environmental sample for genes with specific functions. New antibiotics have been discovered using this approach.

15.3e Studying the Array of Expressed Proteins Is the Next Level of Study of Biological Systems

Genome research also includes analysis of the proteins encoded by a genome, because proteins are largely responsible for cell function and, therefore, for all the functions of an organism. The term **proteome** has been coined to refer to the complete set of proteins that can be expressed by an organism's genome. A *cellular proteome* is a subset of those proteins, the collection of proteins found in a particular cell type under a particular set of environmental conditions.

Figure 15.21
Reconstruction of a Neanderthal.

Neanderthal Museum

The study of the proteome is the field of **proteomics.** The number of possible proteins encoded by the genome is larger than the number of protein-coding genes in the genome, at least in eukaryotes. In eukaryotes, alternative splicing of gene transcripts and variation in protein processing mean that expression of a gene may yield more than one protein product. Therefore, proteomics is a more challenging area of research than genomics.

Proteomics has the following two major immediate goals: (1) to determine the number and structure of proteins in the proteome and (2) to determine the functional interactions between the proteins. The interactions between proteins are particularly important because they help us understand how proteins work together to determine the phenotype of the cell. For instance, if a particular set of interacting proteins characterized a lung tumour cell, then drugs could be developed that specifically target the interactions.

What are the tools of proteomics? For many years it has been possible to separate and identify proteins by gel electrophoresis (using polyacrylamide to make the gels, the same material used to separate DNA fragments in DNA sequencing) or mass spectrometry. However, to study an entire cellular proteome, many more proteins must be analyzed simultaneously than is possible with either of these techniques. A big step in this direction is the development of **protein microarrays (protein chips)**, which are similar in concept to DNA microarrays. One type of protein microarray involves binding antibodies prepared against different proteins to different locations on the protein chip. An antibody for a foreign substance such as a protein is generated by the immune system of an animal that has been injected with that substance. The antibody is then isolated from the animal's blood and can be used to bind specifically to the protein in experiments. Proteins are isolated from cells, labelled, and then pumped over the surface of the protein microarray. Each labelled protein binds to the antibody for that protein. After excess proteins are washed off, the protein microarray is analyzed in much the same way as DNA microarrays are, to determine where the proteins bind and to quantify that binding. With this technique, a researcher can quantify proteins in different cell types and in different tissues. Researchers can also compare proteins under different conditions, such as during differentiation, or with and without a particular disease condition, or with and without a particular drug treatment. In the future, we can expect protein arrays to become routine for studying cellular proteomes.

15.3f Systems Biology Studies the Interactions among All Components of an Organism

Traditional biology research focuses on identifying and studying the functions of individual genes, proteins, and cells. Although such research has provided an enormous body of knowledge—this textbook being an example—it provides only a limited insight into how a whole organism functions at the cellular and molecular levels. For instance, studying the individual components of a bicycle separately does not tell you what the whole bicycle is or what it does.

Systems biology seeks to overcome the limitations of the approaches of traditional biology by studying the organism as a whole to unravel the integrated and interacting network of genes, proteins, and biochemical reactions responsible for life. Systems biologists work from the premise that those interactions are responsible for an organism's form and function. Present-day research in systems biology has been stimulated by the development of techniques for genomic and proteomic analysis and by the data from those analyses.

Systems biologists use genomics and proteomics techniques, such as those discussed in this section, along with information from other sources. They typically obtain very complex data and use sophisticated quantitative analysis to generate models for the interactions within an organism.

Systems biologists study organisms of many kinds. Some focus on humans and have the ambitious goal of transforming the practice of medicine. Their vision is to define the interactions between all the components that affect the health of an individual human. It may then be possible to predict more accurately than is currently possible whether a person will develop particular diseases, and to personalize treatments for those diseases.

STUDY BREAK

1. What are the three main areas of genome analysis?
2. What is the principle behind whole-genome shotgun sequencing of genomes?
3. How are possible protein-coding genes identified in a genome sequence of a bacterium? Of a mammal?
4. How can gene function be assigned by a sequence similarity search?
5. How would you determine how a steroid hormone affects gene expression in human tissue culture cells?

Review

  Access an interactive eBook, chapter-specific interactive learning tools, including flashcards, quizzes, videos, and more in your Biology **CourseMate**, accessed through NelsonBrain.com **Aplia™** is an online interactive learning solution that helps you improve comprehension—and your grade—by integrating a variety of mediums and tools such as videos, tutorials, practice tests, and an interactive eBook.

15.1 DNA Cloning

- Producing multiple copies of genes by cloning is a common first step for studying the structure and function of genes or for manipulating genes. Cloning involves cutting genomic DNA and a cloning vector with the same restriction enzyme, joining the fragments to produce recombinant plasmids, and introducing those plasmids into a living cell such as a bacterium, where replication of the plasmid takes place (see Figures 15.1–15.3).

- A clone containing a gene of interest may be identified among a population of clones by using DNA hybridization with a labelled nucleic acid probe (see Figure 15.4).

- A genomic library is a collection of clones that contains a copy of every DNA sequence in the genome. A cDNA (complementary DNA) library is the entire collection of cloned cDNAs made from the mRNAs isolated from a cell. A cDNA library contains only sequences from the genes that are active in the cell when the mRNAs are isolated.

- PCR amplifies a specific target sequence in DNA, such as a gene, defined by a pair of primers. PCR increases DNA quantities by successive cycles of denaturing the template DNA, annealing the primers, and extending the primers in a DNA synthesis reaction catalyzed by DNA polymerase; with each cycle, the amount of DNA doubles (see Figure 15.5).

15.2 Applications of DNA Technologies

- Recombinant DNA and PCR techniques are used in DNA molecular testing for human genetic disease mutations. One approach exploits restriction site differences between normal and mutant alleles of a gene that create restriction fragment length polymorphisms (RFLPs) detectable by DNA hybridization with a labelled nucleic acid probe (see Figures 15.7 and 15.8).

- Human DNA fingerprints are produced from a number of loci in the genome characterized by tandemly repeated sequences that vary in number in all individuals (except identical twins). To produce a fingerprint, the PCR is used to amplify the region of genomic DNA for each locus, and the lengths of the PCR products indicate the alleles an individual has for the repeated sequences at each locus. DNA fingerprints are widely used to establish paternity, ancestry, or criminal guilt (see Figure 15.9).

- Genetic engineering is the introduction of new genes or genetic information to alter the genetic makeup of humans, other animals, plants, and microorganisms such as bacteria and yeast. Genetic engineering primarily aims to correct hereditary defects; improve domestic animals and crop plants; and provide proteins for medicine, research, and other applications (see Figures 15.10, 15.11, and 15.14).

- Genetic engineering has enormous potential for research and applications in medicine, agriculture, and industry. Potential risks include unintended damage to living organisms or the environment.

15.3 Genome Analysis

- Genome analysis consists of two main areas: structural genomics, the sequencing of genomes and the identification of the genes the sequences contain, and functional genomics, the study of the function of genes and other parts of the genome.

- Sequencing a genome involves a replication reaction with a DNA template, a DNA primer, the four normal deoxyribonucleotides, and a mixture of four dideoxyribonucleotides, each labelled with a different fluorescent tag, and DNA polymerase. Replication stops at any place in the sequence in which a dideoxyribonucleotide is substituted for the normal deoxyribonucleotide. The lengths of the terminated DNA chains and the label on them indicate the overall sequence of the DNA chain being sequenced (see Figure 15.18).

- The whole-genome shotgun method of sequencing a genome involves breaking up the entire genome into random, overlapping fragments, cloning each fragment, determining the sequence of the fragment in each clone, and using computer algorithms to assemble overlapping sequences into the sequence of the complete genome (see Figure 15.19).

- Once a gene is sequenced, the sequence of the protein encoded in a prokaryotic gene can be deduced by reading the coding portion of the gene three nucleotides at a time, starting at the AUG codon that indicates the beginning of a coding sequence.

- Complete genome sequences have been obtained for many viruses, a large number of prokaryotic cells, and many eukaryotes, including the human. The sequences have revealed that all eukaryotes share related gene sequences, and they have also revealed a significant proportion of genes whose functions are not currently known.

- Having the complete genome of an organism makes it possible to study the expression of all of the genes in the genome simultaneously, including comparing gene expression in two different cell types. The DNA microarray (or DNA chip) is typically used for the comparison; this technique can provide information about which genes are active in the two cell types, as well as relative levels of expression of those genes (see Figure 15.20).

- Proteomics is the study of the complete set of proteins in an organism or in a particular cell type. Protein numbers, protein structure, and protein interactions are all topics of proteomics.

- Systems biology combines data derived from genomics, proteomics, and other sources of information. Using sophisticated quantitative analysis, it seeks to model the total array of interactions responsible for an organism's form and function.

Questions

Self-Test Questions

1. Restriction enzymes are used in genetic engineering to degrade DNA. How?
   a. They digest DNA, one base at a time, from the 3′ end of the DNA of interest.
   b. They remove mismatched base pairs resulting from errors in ligation.
   c. They break sugar–phosphate bonds in the DNA backbone between particular bases.
   d. They cut PCR primers away from the template DNA.

2. How are genomic libraries and cDNA libraries similar?
   a. They can both be used to express eukaryotic proteins in bacteria.
   b. They both contain the same genes: one in DNA form, one in cDNA form.
   c. They both contain all of the genes in the genome of an organism.
   d. They both depend on bacteria to reproduce the cloned DNA of interest.

3. All of the following enzymes can make nucleic acid polymers. Which one is used in the polymerase chain reaction (PCR)?
   a. DNA polymerase
   b. RNA polymerase
   c. primase
   d. reverse transcriptase

4. Recall that, in gene-cloning experiments of the kind illustrated in Figure 15.3, plasmid vectors are cut open and then the DNA of interest is ligated to the resulting sticky ends. However, ligation is a random process and sometimes vectors simply recircularize without incorporating any fragments of the DNA of interest. All of these vectors in the ligation mix, those carrying the DNA of interest as well as those that are "empty," are then transformed into bacterial hosts for replication. How can colonies of bacteria transformed with empty vectors be identified relative to those colonies of bacteria transformed with "full" vectors carrying passenger DNA?
   a. Full vectors carry DNA that interrupts and inactivates the *lacZ* gene. Colonies are white.
   b. Full vectors make their hosts more antibiotic resistant. Colonies are larger.
   c. Full vectors make their hosts replicate more slowly. Colonies are smaller.
   d. Full vectors have more restriction enzymes to degrade X Gal. Colonies are blue.

5. Which of the following statements about DNA fingerprinting is correct?
   a. It compares one particular stretch of the same DNA between two or more people.
   b. It measures different lengths of DNA produced from digestion of many repeating noncoding regions.
   c. It requires the several DNA fragments to separate on a gel with the longest lengths running the greatest distance.
   d. It can easily differentiate DNA between identical twins.

6. Dolly, a sheep, was an example of reproductive (germ-line) cloning. Which of the following examples of cell fusion was required to perform this process?
   a. The fusion of a somatic cell from one strain with an enucleated egg of another strain
   b. The fusion of an egg from one strain with the egg of a different strain
   c. The fusion of an embryonic diploid cell of one strain with an adult haploid cell (gamete) from another strain

   d. The fusion of two nucleated mammary cells from two different strains

7. Which of the following statements about somatic cell gene therapy is correct?
   a. Red blood cells can be used as a target tissue.
   b. The technique is potentially useful for all types of genetic diseases.
   c. The inserted genes are passed on to the offspring.
   d. The desired DNA can be introduced to somatic cells cultured outside the body.

8. Which of the following observations was revealed by comparative studies of the genome sequence of humans versus other species?
   a. Human genes are, on average, longer than mouse genes.
   b. Humans have significantly more genes than fruit flies, perhaps 100 000 in total.
   c. Many human genes are very similar to those of simple eukaryotes, like yeast.
   d. Humans and chimpanzees have the same DNA sequence, they just express it differently.

9. Which of the following statements about Sanger's DNA sequencing technique is correct?
   a. It uses dideoxyribonucleotides to make new full-length strands of DNA with Taq polymerase.
   b. It requires an RNA primer and the dideoxyribonucleotides ddATP, ddUTP, ddCTP, and ddGTP.
   c. It uses hybridization with a labelled probe to identify the sequence of the DNA in question.
   d. It produces an array of fragments that, once separated, reveal the base sequence of the template DNA.

10. Which of the following research problems could be addressed with a DNA microarray?
    a. Determine the sequence of DNA from several chromosomes in one individual fruit fly.
    b. Synthesize multiple copies of DNA from different tissues in the body of a chimpanzee.
    c. Compare expressed genes in a patient's normal lung cells with those from his cancerous lung cells.
    d. Determine which bacterial proteins are expressed under different environmental conditions.

Questions for Discussion

1. Do you think that genetic engineering is worth the risk? Who do you think should decide whether genetic engineering experiments and projects should be carried out: scientists, judges, politicians?

2. Do you think that human germ-line cells should be modified by genetic engineering to cure birth defects? To increase intelligence or beauty?

3. Write a paragraph supporting genetic engineering and one arguing against it. Which argument carries more weight, in your opinion?

4. A forensic scientist obtained a small DNA sample from a crime scene. To examine the sample, he increased its quantity by PCR. He estimated that there were 50 000 copies of the DNA in his original sample. Derive a simple formula and calculate the number of copies he will have after 15 cycles of PCR.

5. A market puts out a bin of tomatoes that have outstanding colour, flavour, and texture. A sign posted above them identifies them as genetically engineered produce. Most shoppers pick unmodified tomatoes in an adjacent bin, even though they are pale, mealy, and nearly tasteless. Which tomatoes would you pick? Why?

The Chemical, Physical, and Environmental Foundations of Biology

The Scientific Basis of Biology

The information contained in this textbook represents the culmination of hundreds of years of research involving a huge number experiments carried out by countless scientists. The entire content of this book—every observation, experimental result, and generality—is the product of **biological research,** the collective effort of individuals who have worked to understand every aspect of the living world. This section describes how biologists working today pose and find answers to questions.

The Scientific Method

Beginning about 500 years ago in Europe, inquisitive people began to understand that direct observation is the most reliable and productive way to study natural phenomena. By the nineteenth century, researchers were using the **scientific method**—an investigative approach to acquiring knowledge in which scientists make observations about the natural world, develop working explanations about what they observe, and then test those explanations by collecting more information.

Application of the scientific method requires both curiosity and skepticism: successful scientists question the current state of our knowledge and challenge old concepts with new ideas and new observations. Explanations of natural phenomena must be backed up by objective evidence rooted in observation and measurement. Most importantly, scientists share their ideas and results by publishing their work.

Testing a Hypothesis Is Central to the Scientific Method

A **hypothesis** can be defined as a tentative explanation for an observation, phenomenon, or scientific problem that can be tested by further investigation. Scientific hypotheses have two fundamental elements. First a hypothesis must be *testable*. That is, there must be some set of observations or experiments that can be undertaken to support the hypothesis. For example, you may be studying a gene in yeast that you find is activated when cells are placed under conditions of heat stress. You may hypothesize that the protein encoded by this gene is essential for the yeast to survive short-term exposure to high temperature. Using modern molecular techniques, you can test this hypothesis by inactivating the gene in a population of yeast cells and observing if there is a change in heat tolerance. Today, this hypothesis is easily testable. A scientist may have had a similar idea 30 years ago, but given the lack of molecular techniques, the hypothesis would not have been testable at that time.

The second key to a scientific hypothesis is that it must be *falsifiable*. That is, through observation or experimentation you must be able to show that the original hypothesis may not be correct. Getting back to the yeast analogy, it is very possible that through analysis you would find that inactivation of the gene does not change the ability of yeast cells to survive high temperatures.

Scientists test the predictions that come from hypotheses with experimental or observational tests that generate relevant data. And if data from just one study refute a scientific hypothesis (that is, demonstrate that its predictions are incorrect), the scientist must modify the hypothesis and test it again or abandon it altogether. However, no amount of data can prove beyond a doubt that a hypothesis is correct; there may always be a contradictory example somewhere on Earth, and it is impossible to test every imaginable example. That is why scientists say that positive results are consistent with, support, or confirm a hypothesis.

Elements of the Scientific Method

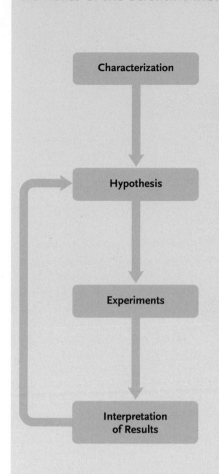

Characterization

1 Before a new hypothesis is formulated, researchers today usually know a fair amount about the subject under study. This characterization comes from years of their own experiments as well as the published research of other scientists working in the same discipline.

Hypothesis

2 Based on earlier findings, create a testable and falsifiable explanation (a hypothesis) of the information gathered. Hypotheses may be expressed in words or in mathematical equations.

Experiments

3 Design and conduct a controlled experiment to test the predictions of the hypothesis, that is, what you would expect to observe if the hypothesis were correct. The experiment must be clearly defined so that it can be repeated by others.

Interpretation of Results

4 Compare the results of the experiment with those predicted by the hypothesis. If the results do not match the predictions, the hypothesis is refuted, and it must be rejected or revised. If the prediction was correct, the hypothesis is confirmed. The data from one set of experiments are subsequently used to develop additional hypotheses to be tested.

An Example of Hypothesis Development and Testing

Consider this simple example of hypothesis development and testing. A friend gives you a plant that she grew on her windowsill. Under her care, the plant always flowered. You place the plant on your windowsill and water it regularly, but the plant never blooms. You know that your friend always gave fertilizer to the plant, and you wonder whether fertilizing the plant will make it flower. In other words, you create a hypothesis with a specific prediction: "This type of plant will flower if it receives fertilizer." This is a good hypothesis because it is not only testable but also falsifiable. To test the hypothesis, you would simply give the plant fertilizer. If it flowers, your hypothesis is confirmed. If it does not bloom, the data force you to reject or revise your hypothesis. With all experiments it is important to include a **control**—a set of individuals that will not be subject to the treatment. To test this specific hypothesis, you need to compare plants that receive fertilizer (the experimental treatment) with plants grown without fertilizer (the control treatment). The presence or absence of fertilizer is the **experimental variable,** and in a controlled experiment, everything except the experimental variable—the flower pots, the soil, the amount of water, and exposure to sunlight—is kept the same between the treated and control individuals. This type of control ensures that any differences in flowering pattern observed between plants that receive the experimental treatment (fertilizer) and those that receive the control treatment (no fertilizer) can be attributed to the experimental variable. Nearly all experiments in biology include **replicates,** multiple subjects that receive either the same experimental treatment or the same control treatment. Scientists use replicates in experiments because individuals typically vary in genetic makeup, size, health, or other characteristics—and because accidents may disrupt a few replicates. By exposing multiple subjects to both treatments, we can use a statistical test to compare the average result of the experimental treatment with the average result of the control treatment, giving us more confidence in the overall findings.

continued on next page

Question: Your friend fertilizes a plant that she grows on her windowsill, and it flowers. After she gives you the plant, you put it on your windowsill, but you do not give it any fertilizer and it does not flower. Will giving the plant fertilizer induce it to flower?

Friend added fertilizer.

You did not add fertilizer.

Experiment: Establish six replicates of an experimental treatment (identical plants grown with fertilizer) and six replicates of a control treatment (identical plants grown without fertilizer).

Experimental Treatment

Add fertilizer

Control Treatment

No fertilizer

Possible Result 1: Neither experimental nor control plants flower.

Possible Result 2: Plants in the experimental group flower, but plants in the control group do not.

Experimentals

Controls

Experimentals

Controls

Conclusion: Fertilizer alone does not cause the plants to flower. Consider alternative hypotheses and conduct additional experiments, each testing a different experimental treatment, such as the amount of water or sunlight the plant receives or the temperature to which it is exposed.

Conclusion: The application of fertilizer induces flowering in this type of plant, confirming your original hypothesis. Pat yourself on the back and apply to graduate school in plant biology.

The Scientific Theory

When a hypothesis stands up to repeated experimental tests, it is gradually accepted as an accurate explanation of natural events. This acceptance may take many years, and it usually involves repeated experimental confirmations. When many different tests have consistently confirmed a hypothesis that addresses many broad questions, it may become regarded as a scientific **theory**—a scientifically acceptable, well-substantiated explanation of some aspect of the natural world. Most scientific theories are supported by exhaustive experimentation; thus, scientists usually regard them as established truths that are unlikely to be contradicted by future research.

In common usage, the word *theory* most often labels an idea as either speculative or downright suspect, as in the expression "It's only a theory." But when scientists talk about theories, they refer to concepts that have withstood the test of many experiments. Because of the difference between the scientific and

continued on next page

common usage of the word *theory*, many people fail to appreciate the extensive evidence that supports scientific theories. For example, virtually every scientist accepts the theory of evolution as a fully supported scientific truth: all species change with time, new species are formed, and older species eventually die off. Although evolutionary biologists debate the details of how evolutionary processes bring about these changes, very few scientists doubt that the theory of evolution is essentially correct. Moreover, *no scientist who has tried to cast doubt on the theory of evolution has ever devised or conducted a study that disproves any part of it*. Unfortunately, the confusion between the scientific and common usage of the word *theory* has led, in part, to endless public debate about supposed faults and inadequacies in the theory of evolution.

Experimental versus Observational Science

In some scientific disciplines, the system under study may be too large or too complex to establish controlled experiments. In astronomy, for example, one cannot manipulate stars and galaxies as if they were potted plants. Astronomy is considered an observational science, as are research themes in ecology and evolutionary biology. Observational science relies on sophisticated statistical techniques to analyze detailed observational data in order to test hypotheses. The statistical tools provide a method for researchers to infer pattern and underlying cause from the collected data.

Many scientific disciplines rely on a combination of observational and experimental science. For example, ecology researchers studying global climate change often set up experiments that take place in the environment. These enable a certain level of control of variables under far more realistic conditions than would be possible in a laboratory. These so-called field experiments complement the analysis of observational data that may reflect changes to our climate that occurred hundreds of years ago.

Measurement and Scale

The SI system of Measurement

The International System of Units is the most widely used system of measurement in the world. Its abbreviation, *SI*, is from the French Système International d'Unités. It was adopted by the eleventh General Conference of Weights and Measures in 1960 and represents the latest modification of the metric system, which was first implemented by the French National Assembly in 1790.

The SI system uses seven base units, each of which measures or describes a different kind of physical quantity. Each unit is strictly defined, although the definitions have been modified (and made more accurate) over time. As an example, the metre was originally defined by the French Academy of Sciences as the length between two marks on a platinum–iridium bar that was designed to represent 1/10 000 000 of the distance from the equator to the North Pole through Paris. This definition was changed in 1983 by the International Bureau of Weights and Measures as the distance travelled by light in absolute vacuum in 1/299 792 458 of a second.

The SI system also uses a series of prefix names and prefix symbols to form the names and symbols of the decimal multiples of the base SI units. Note that the base unit for mass is the kilogram, not the gram. One kilogram equals 1000 g ($1 \text{ kg} = 10^3 \text{ g}$). This list has been extended several times: prefixes now range from yotta, at 10^{24} (one septillion), to yocto, at 10^{-24} (one septillionth).

Factor	Prefix	Symbol	Factor	Prefix	Symbol
10^{24}	yotta	Y	10^{-1}	deci	d
10^{21}	zetta	Z	10^{-2}	centi	c
10^{18}	exa	E	10^{-3}	milli	m
10^{15}	peta	P	10^{-6}	micro	μ
10^{12}	tera	T	10^{-9}	nano	n
10^{9}	giga	G	10^{-12}	pico	p
10^{6}	mega	M	10^{-15}	femto	f
10^{3}	kilo	k	10^{-18}	atto	a
10^{2}	hecto	h	10^{-21}	zepto	z
10^{1}	deca	da	10^{-24}	yocto	y

The Seven Base Units of the SI System

Name	Symbol	Quantity
metre	m	length
kilogram	kg	mass
second	s	time
ampere	A	electric current
kelvin	K	temperature
mole	mol	amount of substance
candela	cd	luminous intensity

Derived SI Units

Several other units have been derived from combinations of the seven base units of measure. Three of the more common concern units of force (newton), pressure (pascal), and energy or heat (joule). The measurement of temperature in degrees Celsius is also considered a derived unit, even though one Celsius degree is the same size as one kelvin. However, $0°C = 273.16 \text{ K}$ (note that no degree symbol is used when expressing temperature in kelvins).

Name	Symbol	Quantity	Expression
newton	N	force	$m \cdot kg \cdot s^{-2}$
pascal	Pa	pressure	$N \cdot m^{-2}$
joule	J	energy and work	$N \cdot m$

Non-SI Units in Common Usage

A number of units not derived from the base SI units are accepted for use with SI units.

Name	Symbol	Value in SI Units
minute	min	60 s
hour	h	3600 s
day	d	86 400 s
litre	L	$1 \, dm^3 = 10^{-3} \, m^3$
angstrom	Å	$10^{-10} \, m$
calorie, a measure of food energy*	cal	4.184 J
unified atomic mass unit or Dalton**	u or Da	$\sim 1.66054 \times 10^{-24} \, kg$

*One food calorie = 1 Cal = 1000 cal
**Value determined experimentally to be 1/12 the mass of an unbound atom of carbon-12.

Scale in Biology

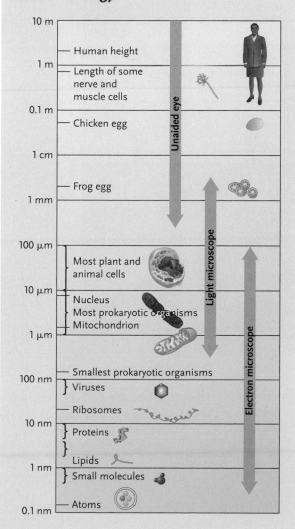

Why Everyone Should Use SI Units

In December 1998, NASA launched the Mars Climate Orbiter on a mission to study the Martian weather and climate. As it approached Mars, the spacecraft received instructions from flight control on Earth to fire thruster engines to enter into a proper orbit about 140 to 150 km above the Martian surface. However, as it approached the planet, a navigation error caused the spacecraft to descend into an orbit of only 57 km above the surface. The spacecraft was soon destroyed by the heat caused by atmospheric friction.

The review of the incident found that the root cause was a mix-up between the use of SI units and an older system of measure, imperial units (e.g., inches, feet, and pounds). More specifically, the software that was used to control the thruster engines of the spacecraft from the ground was written using the imperial unit of force, the pound-force, whereas onboard the spacecraft, information was interpreted in terms of newtons, the metric unit of force. Since 1 pound-force equals about 4.45 N, instructions from the ground were thus multiplied by 4.45.

The total cost of the mission was approximately $327 million.

The Organization of Matter

Any substance in the universe that has mass and occupies space is defined as **matter.** The fundamental scientific concepts that explain how matter is organized in biological systems are no different from those for nonliving forms of matter. Living organisms are built from the same chemical building blocks as nonliving systems and abide by the same fundamental laws of chemistry and physics. Because of this, a basic understanding of how all matter is organized is important for a complete picture of the structure and function of organisms.

Elements and Compounds

All matter is composed of elements. An **element** is a pure substance composed of only one type of atom. Ninety-two different elements occur naturally on Earth. Living organisms are composed of about 25 elements, with only 4 elements—carbon, hydrogen, oxygen, and nitrogen—accounting for more than 96% of the mass of an organism. Seven other elements—calcium, phosphorus, potassium, sulfur, sodium, chlorine, and magnesium—contribute most of the remaining 4%.

The proportions by mass of different elements differ markedly in sea water, the human body, a fruit, and Earth's crust, as shown below.

A **compound** is a substance that contains two or more elements. For example, hydrogen and oxygen are the elements that make up the compound water (H_2O). The chemical and physical properties of compounds are typically distinct from those of their atoms or elements.

Sea water		Human		Pumpkin		Earth's crust	
Oxygen	88.3	Oxygen	65.0	Oxygen	85.0	Oxygen	46.6
Hydrogen	11.0	Carbon	18.5	Hydrogen	10.7	Silicon	27.7
Chlorine	1.9	Hydrogen	9.5	Carbon	3.3	Aluminum	8.1
Sodium	1.1	Nitrogen	3.3	Potassium	0.34	Iron	5.0
Magnesium	0.1	Calcium	2.0	Nitrogen	0.16	Calcium	3.6
Sulfur	0.09	Phosphorus	1.1	Phosphorus	0.05	Sodium	2.8
Potassium	0.04	Potassium	0.35	Calcium	0.02	Potassium	2.6
Calcium	0.04	Sulfur	0.25	Magnesium	0.01	Magnesium	2.1
Carbon	0.003	Sodium	0.15	Iron	0.008	Other elements	1.5
Silicon	0.0029	Chlorine	0.15	Sodium	0.001		
Nitrogen	0.0015	Magnesium	0.05	Zinc	0.0002		
Strontium	0.0008	Iron	0.004	Copper	0.0001		
		Iodine	0.0004				

Andriano/Shutterstock

iStockphoto.com/Hon Lau

The Atom

Elements are composed of **atoms**—the smallest units that retain the chemical and physical properties of an element. Any given element has only one type of atom identified by a standard one- or two-letter symbol. The element carbon is identified by the single letter C, which stands for both the carbon atom and the element.

Atomic Number and Mass Number of the Most Common Elements in Living Organisms

Element	Symbol	Atomic Number	Mass Number of the Most Common Form
Hydrogen	H	1	1
Carbon	C	6	12
Nitrogen	N	7	14
Oxygen	O	8	16
Sodium	Na	11	23
Magnesium	Mg	12	24
Phosphorus	P	15	31
Sulfur	S	16	32
Chlorine	Cl	17	35
Potassium	K	19	39
Calcium	Ca	20	40
Iron	Fe	26	56
Iodine	I	53	127

Each atom consists of an atomic nucleus surrounded by one or more smaller, fast-moving particles called electrons. All atomic nuclei contain one or more positively charged particles called **protons.** The number of protons in the nucleus of each kind of atom is referred to as the **atomic number.** This number does not vary and thus specifically identifies the atom. The smallest atom, hydrogen, has a single proton in its nucleus, so its atomic number is 1. Carbon with six protons, nitrogen with seven protons, and oxygen with eight protons have atomic numbers of 6, 7, and 8, respectively.

With one exception, the nuclei of all atoms also contain uncharged particles called **neutrons,** which occur in variable numbers approximately equal to the number of protons. The single exception is the most common form of hydrogen, which has a nucleus that contains only a single proton. Atoms are assigned a mass number based on the total number of protons and neutrons in the atomic nucleus. Electrons are ignored in determinations of atomic mass because the mass of an electron is very small.

Hydrogen

Nucleus
(1 proton)

1 electron

Carbon

6 protons
6 neutrons

2 electrons

4 electrons

Isotopes

All atoms of a specific element have the same number of protons, but they may differ in the number of neutrons. These distinct forms of an element, where atoms have the same atomic number but different atomic masses, are called **isotopes.** The nuclei of some isotopes are unstable and break down, or *decay*, giving off particles of matter and energy that can be detected as radioactivity. The decay transforms the unstable, radioactive isotope—called a radioisotope—into an atom of another element. For example, the carbon isotope ^{14}C is unstable and undergoes radioactive decay in which one of its neutrons splits into a proton and an electron. The electron is ejected from the nucleus, but the proton is retained, giving a new total of seven protons and seven neutrons, which is characteristic of the most common form of nitrogen. Thus, the decay transforms the carbon atom into an atom of nitrogen.

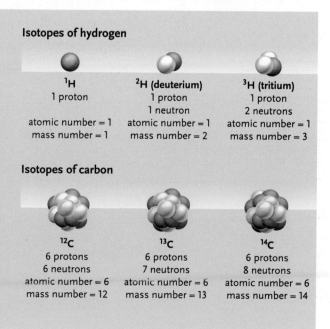

Isotopes of hydrogen

^{1}H
1 proton
atomic number = 1
mass number = 1

^{2}H (deuterium)
1 proton
1 neutron
atomic number = 1
mass number = 2

^{3}H (tritium)
1 proton
2 neutrons
atomic number = 1
mass number = 3

Isotopes of carbon

^{12}C
6 protons
6 neutrons
atomic number = 6
mass number = 12

^{13}C
6 protons
7 neutrons
atomic number = 6
mass number = 13

^{14}C
6 protons
8 neutrons
atomic number = 6
mass number = 14

Use of Radioisotopes

Radioactive decay occurs at a steady, clocklike rate. The length of time it takes for one-half of a sample of a radioisotope to decay is termed its **half-life.** Each type of radioisotope has a characteristic half-life. For example, carbon-14 decays with a fixed half-life of 5730 years, while uranium-238 has a half-life of 4.5 billion years. Because unstable isotopes decay at a fixed rate that is not affected by chemical reactions or environmental conditions such as temperature or pressure, they are used to estimate the age of organic material, rocks, and fossils. These radiometric techniques have been vital in dating animal remains and tracing evolutionary lineages.

A number of radioisotopes that have short half-lives are used in medical imaging and in the treatment of diseases. These isotopes include iodine-123 and thalium-201, which have half-lives of only 13.3 and 3.1 days, respectively.

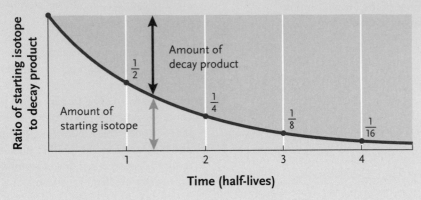

Electrons and Electron Shells

In an atom, the number of electrons is equal to the number of protons in the nucleus. Because electrons carry a negative charge and protons are positively charged, the total structure of an atom is electrically neutral.

Electrons move around the atomic nucleus in **orbitals,** which are grouped into **electron shells.** As shown below, the first shell (I) may be occupied by a maximum of two electrons. The second (II) and third (III) shells can hold a maximum of eight electrons each. The fourth shell can hold 18 electrons (not all shown). Atoms with more than four electron shells are very rare in biological molecules.

The chemical behaviour of an atom depends primarily on the number of electrons in its outermost shell. This is referred to as the **valence shell,** which holds **valence electrons.** Atoms in which the valence shell is not completely filled with electrons tend to be chemically reactive; those with a completely filled valence shell are nonreactive, or inert.

For example, as shown on the left, hydrogen has a single, unpaired electron in its outermost and only electron shell and it is highly reactive; helium has two valence electrons filling its single orbital and is unreactive (stable), or inert. Along with helium, neon and argon are also referred to as inert gases because their outer electron shell is full, which renders them chemically unreactive.

Because an unfilled electron shell is less stable than a filled one, atoms with an incomplete outer shell have a strong tendency to interact with other atoms in a way that causes them to either gain or lose enough electrons to achieve a completed outermost shell. All elements commonly found in living organisms have unfilled outermost shells (purple balls in the accompanying figure table above) and can thus participate chemical reactions with other atoms. Because they are unreactive, helium, neon, and argon are not found in living systems.

Atomic number

Atomic number	Element	I	II	III	IV
			Electron shell		
1	Hydrogen	●			
2	Helium	●●			
6	Carbon	●●	●●●●		
7	Nitrogen	●●	●●●●●		
8	Oxygen	●●	●●●●●●		
10	Neon	●●	●●●●●●●●		
11	Sodium	●●	●●●●●●●●	●	
12	Magnesium	●●	●●●●●●●●	●●	
15	Phosphorus	●●	●●●●●●●●	●●●●●	
16	Sulfur	●●	●●●●●●●●	●●●●●●	
17	Chlorine	●●	●●●●●●●●	●●●●●●●	
18	Argon	●●	●●●●●●●●	●●●●●●●●	
19	Potassium	●●	●●●●●●●●	●●●●●●●●	●
20	Calcium	●●	●●●●●●●●	●●●●●●●●	●●

Chemical Bonds

An atom with an incomplete valence shell has a strong tendency to interact with other atoms so that they have a completely filled valence shell. These interactions, called **chemical bonds,** are caused by closely associated atoms sharing or transferring electrons to complete the valence shell. Four types of chemical bonds are important in biological molecules: ionic bonds, covalent bonds, hydrogen bonds, and van der Waals forces. Because of their importance in hydrogen bonding, polar molecules are also discussed in this section.

Ionic Bonds

Ionic bonds form between atoms that gain or lose valence electrons completely. A sodium atom (Na) readily loses a single electron to achieve a full valence shell (see last section), and chlorine (Cl) readily gains an electron to do the same. After the transfer, the sodium atom, now with 11 protons and 10 electrons, carries a single positive charge. The chlorine atom, now with 17 protons and 18 electrons, carries a single negative charge. In this charged condition, the atoms are called ions: sodium with a positive charge is a cation while chloride with a negative charge is an anion.

Ionic bonds are common among the forces that hold ions, atoms, and molecules together in living organisms because these bonds have three key features:

- They exert an attractive force over greater distances than any other chemical bond.
- Their attractive force extends in all directions.
- They vary in strength depending on the presence of other charged substances.

Ionic bond formation between sodium and chlorine

Crystals of sodium chloride (NaCl)

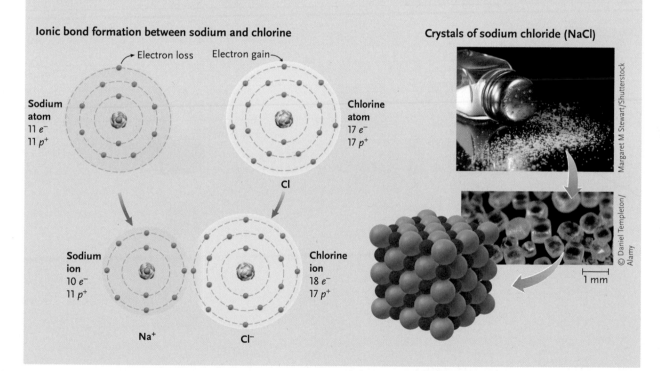

Electron loss
Electron gain

Sodium
atom
11 e^-
11 p^+

Chlorine
atom
17 e^-
17 p^+

Cl

Sodium
ion
10 e^-
11 p^+

Chlorine
ion
18 e^-
17 p^+

Na$^+$

Cl$^-$

Margaret M Stewart/Shutterstock

© Daniel Templeton/Alamy

1 mm

Covalent Bonds

Covalent bonds form between two atoms when they share valence electrons. This is distinct from ionic bonds where electrons are gained or lost from atoms. The term *molecule* refers to two or more atoms held together by covalent bonds. The formation of molecular hydrogen, H_2, by two hydrogen atoms is the simplest example of a covalent bond. If two hydrogen atoms collide, the single electron of each atom may join in a new, combined two-electron orbital that surrounds both nuclei. The two electrons fill the orbital; thus, the hydrogen atoms tend to remain linked stably together. The linkage formed by the shared orbital is a covalent bond.

A **structural formula** represents a covalent bond of a pair of shared electrons as a single line. For example, in H_2, the covalent bond that holds the molecule together is represented as H:H or H—H. Generally speaking, the covalent bonding capacity of an atom is equal to the number of valence shell electrons necessary to fill the shell: hydrogen, 1; oxygen, 2; nitrogen, 3; and carbon, 4.

As shown below, a single oxygen atom has six valence shell electrons, and two oxygen atoms form a single molecule.

Carbon, with four unpaired outer electrons, typically forms four covalent bonds to complete its outermost energy level. An example is methane, CH_4, the main component of natural gas.

Unlike ionic bonds, which extend their attractive force in all directions, the shared orbitals that form covalent bonds extend between atoms at discrete angles and directions, giving covalently bound molecules distinct, three-dimensional forms. For biological molecules such as proteins, which are held together primarily by covalent bonds, the three-dimensional form imparted by these bonds is critical to their functions.

The four covalent bonds formed by the carbon atom are fixed at an angle of 109.5° from each other, forming a tetrahedron. The tetrahedral arrangement of the bonds allows carbon atoms to link extensively to each other in chains and rings in both branched and unbranched form. Such structures form the backbones of an almost unlimited variety of molecules. Carbon can also form double bonds, in which atoms share two pairs of electrons, and triple bonds, in which atoms share three pairs of electrons.

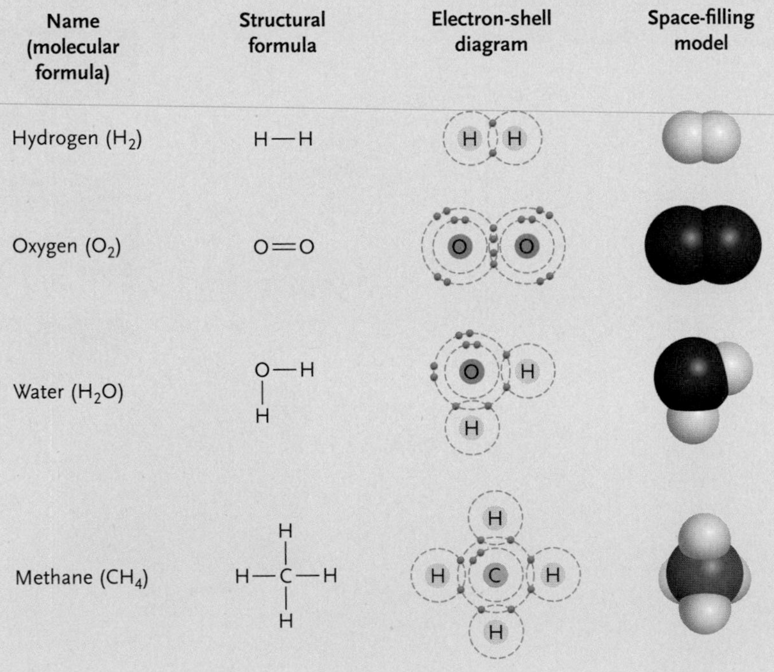

Name (molecular formula)	Structural formula	Electron-shell diagram	Space-filling model
Hydrogen (H_2)	H—H		
Oxygen (O_2)	O=O		
Water (H_2O)	O—H | H		
Methane (CH_4)	H | H—C—H | H		

Polarity and Hydrogen Bonding

Although all covalent bonds involve the sharing of valence electrons, they differ widely in the degree of sharing. **Electronegativity** is the measure of an atom's attraction for the electrons it shares in a chemical bond with another atom. The more electronegative an atom is, the more strongly it attracts shared electrons. Among atoms, electronegativity increases as the number of protons in the nucleus increases and as the distance of electrons from the nucleus increases. The unequal sharing of electrons between two atoms that differ in their electronegativity results in a polar covalent bond.

The atom that attracts the electrons more strongly carries a partial negative charge, and the atom deprived of electrons carries a partial positive charge. The atoms carrying partial charges (denoted by the superscripted $^+$ or $^-$) may give the whole molecule partially positive and negative ends; this is referred to as polarity, and the molecule is termed **polar.**

Polar molecules attract and align themselves with other polar molecules and with charged ions and molecules and tend to exclude nonpolar molecules. Polar molecules that associate readily with water because it is strongly polar are identified as **hydrophilic** (*hydro* = water; *philic* = preferring). Nonpolar substances that are excluded by water and other polar molecules are identified as **hydrophobic** (*phobic* = avoiding).

When hydrogen atoms are made partially positive by sharing electrons unequally with oxygen, nitrogen, or sulfur, they may be attracted to nearby oxygen, nitrogen, or sulfur atoms made partially negative by unequal electron sharing in a different covalent bond. This attractive force is the **hydrogen bond,** illustrated by a dotted line in structural diagrams of molecules. Hydrogen bonds may form between atoms in the same or different molecules.

Individual hydrogen bonds are about 1/20 the strength of a covalent bond. However, large biological molecules may offer many opportunities for hydrogen bonding, both within and between molecules. When numerous, hydrogen bonds are collectively strong and lend stability to the three-dimensional structure of molecules such as proteins. Hydrogen bonds between water molecules are responsible for many of the properties that make water uniquely important to life.

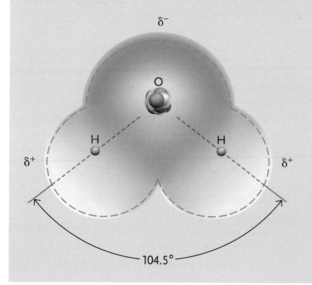

Hydrogen-bond donor		Hydrogen-bond acceptor
δ^- δ^+		δ^-
—N—H	$\cdots\cdots\cdots\cdots\cdots$ Hydrogen bond	N—
—N—H	$\cdots\cdots\cdots\cdots\cdots$	O—
—O—H	$\cdots\cdots\cdots\cdots\cdots$	N—
—O—H	$\cdots\cdots\cdots\cdots\cdots$	O—

Van der Waals Forces

Van der Waals forces are even weaker than hydrogen bonds. These forces develop between nonpolar molecules or regions of molecules when, through their constant motion, electrons accumulate by chance in one part of a molecule or another. This process leads to zones of positive and negative charge, making the molecule polar. If they are oriented in the right way, the polar parts of the molecules are attracted electrically to one another and cause the molecules to stick together briefly. Although an individual bond formed with van der Waals forces is weak and transient, the formation of many bonds of this type can stabilize the shape of a large molecule, such as a protein.

A striking example of the collective power of van der Waals forces concerns the ability of geckos to cling to and walk up vertical smooth surfaces. The toes of the lizard are covered in millions of pads, each one forming a weak interaction using van der Waals forces—with the molecules on the smooth surface.

© Frans Lanting Studio/Alamy

Chemical Reactions

Chemical reactions occur when atoms or molecules interact to form new chemical bonds or break old ones. As a result of bond formation or breakage, atoms are added to or removed from molecules, or the linkages of atoms in molecules are rearranged. When any of these alterations occur, molecules change from one type to another, usually with different chemical and physical properties. In biological systems, chemical reactions are accelerated by *enzymes,* which are discussed in Chapter 4.

The atoms or molecules entering a chemical reaction are called the **reactants,** and those leaving a reaction are the **products.** A chemical reaction is written with an arrow showing the direction of the reaction; reactants are placed to the left of the arrow, and products are placed to the right. Both reactants and products are usually written in chemical shorthand as formulas.

For example, the overall reaction of photosynthesis, in which carbon dioxide and water are combined to produce sugars and oxygen (see Chapter 7), is written as follows:

$$6CO_2 + 6H_2O \rightarrow C_6H_{12}O_6 + 6O_2$$

Carbon   Water   A sugar   Molecular
dioxide   oxygen

The number in front of each formula indicates the number of molecules of that type among the reactants and products (the number 1 is not written). Notice that there are as many atoms of each element to the left of the arrow as there are to the right, even though the products are different from the reactants. This balance reflects the fact that in such reactions, atoms may be rearranged but not created or destroyed. Chemical reactions written in balanced form are known as **chemical equations.**

While some chemical reactions result in all the reactant molecules being converted into products, many reactions are reversible; that is, the products of the forward reaction can become the reactants of the reverse reaction. That a reaction is reversible is illustrated by using opposite-headed arrows. As an example, hydrogen and molecular nitrogen can react to produce ammonia, but ammonia can also break down to produce hydrogen and nitrogen:

$$3H_2 + N_2 \rightleftarrows 2NH_3.$$

Water

All living organisms contain water, and many kinds of organisms live directly in water. Even those that live in dry environments contain water in all their structures—different organisms range from 50% to more than 95% water by mass. The water inside organisms is crucial for life: it is required for many important biochemical reactions and plays major roles in maintaining the shape and organization of cells and tissues.

Hydrogen Bonds and the Properties of Water

The properties of water molecules that make them so important to life depend to a great extent on their polar structure and their ability to link to each other by hydrogen bonds (See "Chemical Bonds").

Hydrogen bonds form readily between water molecules in both liquid water and ice. In liquid water, each water molecule establishes an average of 3.4 hydrogen bonds with its neighbours, forming an arrangement known as the **water lattice.** In liquid water, the hydrogen bonds that hold the lattice together constantly break and reform, allowing the water molecules to break loose from the lattice, slip past one another, and reform the lattice in new positions.

In ice, the water lattice is a rigid, crystalline structure in which each water molecule forms four hydrogen bonds with neighbouring molecules. The rigid ice lattice spaces the water molecules farther apart than the water lattice. Because of this greater spacing, water has the unusual property of being about 10% less dense when solid than when liquid. Imagine what Earth would be like if ice sank to the bottom, as most solids do.

Hydrogen-bond lattice of liquid water

KEY

Hydrogen-bond lattice of ice

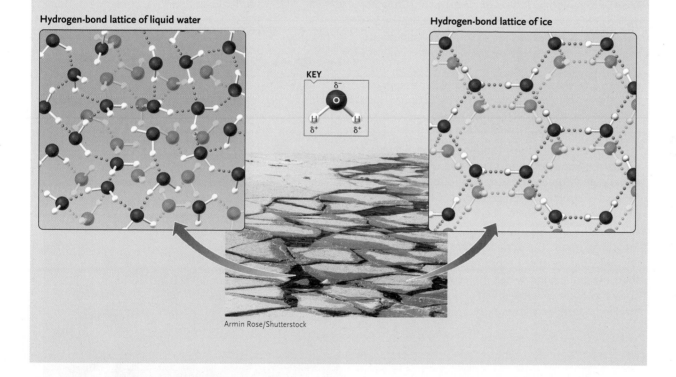

Armin Rose/Shutterstock

Specific Heat and Heat of Vaporization

The hydrogen-bond lattice of liquid water retards the escape of individual water molecules as the water is heated. As heat flows into water, much of it is absorbed in the breakage of hydrogen bonds. As a result, the temperature of water, reflected in the average motion of its molecules, increases relatively slowly as heat is added. This results in water having a high **specific heat,** defined as the amount of heat required to increase the temperature of a given quantity of water. For example, relatively high temperatures and the addition of considerable heat are required to break enough hydrogen bonds to make water boil. The high boiling point maintains water as a liquid over the wide temperature range of 0 to 100°C.

The unique features of H_2O are clear if you compare it to H_2S, which has a similar molecular structure.

H_2S does not form hydrogen bonds and as a result is a gas at room temperature. Without its hydrogen-bond lattice, water would boil at −81°C.

A large amount of heat, 586 cal/g, must be added to give water molecules enough energy of motion to break loose from liquid water and form a gas. This required heat, known as the **heat of vaporization,** allows humans and many other organisms to cool off when hot. In humans, water is released onto the surface of the skin by more than 2.5 million sweat glands; the heat energy absorbed by the water in sweat as the sweat evaporates cools the skin and the underlying blood vessels. The heat loss helps keep body temperature from increasing when environmental temperatures are high. Plants use a similar cooling mechanism as water evaporates from their leaves.

Surface Tension

The hydrogen-bond lattice of water results in water molecules staying together, a phenomenon that is referred to as **cohesion.** For example, in land plants, cohesion holds water molecules in unbroken columns in the microscopic conducting tubes that extend from the roots to the highest leaves. As water evaporates from the leaves, water molecules in the columns, held together by cohesion, move upward through the tubes to replace the lost water.

Related to cohesion is **surface tension,** which is a measure of how difficult it is to stretch or break the surface of a liquid. The water molecules at surfaces facing air can form hydrogen bonds with water molecules beside and below them but not on the sides that face the air. This unbalanced bonding produces a force that places the surface water molecules under tension, making them more resistant to separation than the underlying water molecules. This force is strong enough to allow small insects such as water striders to walk on water.

Creation of surface tension by unbalanced hydrogen bonding

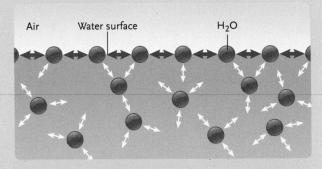

Spider supported by water's surface tension

iStockphoto.com/Alasdair Thomson

Aqueous Solutions

Because water molecules are small and strongly polar, they readily surround other polar and charged molecules and ions. The surface coat, called a **hydration shell,** reduces the attraction between the molecules or ions and promotes their separation and entry into a solution, where they are suspended individually, surrounded by water molecules. Once in solution, the hydration shell prevents the polar molecules or ions from reassociating. In such an aqueous solution, water is called the *solvent,* and the molecules of a substance dissolved in water are called the *solute.*

Sodium chloride (salt) dissolves in water because water molecules quickly form hydration layers around the Na^+ and Cl^- ions in the salt crystals, reducing the attraction between the ions so much that they separate from the crystal and enter the surrounding water lattice as individual ions. In much the same way, hydration shells surround macromolecules such as nucleic acids and proteins, reducing their electrostatic interaction with other molecules.

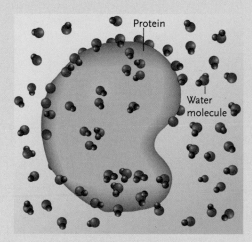

Calculating Solute Concentrations

In the cell, chemical reactions depend on solutes dissolved in aqueous solutions. To understand these reactions, you need to know the number of atoms and molecules involved. **Concentration** is the number of molecules or ions of a substance in a unit volume of space, such as 1 mL or 1 L. The number of molecules or ions in a unit volume cannot be counted directly, but it can be calculated indirectly by using the mass number of atoms as the starting point.

The mass number of an atom is equivalent to the number of protons and neutrons in its nucleus. From the mass number, and the fact that neutrons and protons have approximately the same mass (that is, 1.66×10^{-24} g), you can calculate the mass of an atom of any substance. For an atom of the most common form of carbon, with six protons and six neutrons in its nucleus, the total mass is

$$12 \times (1.66 \times 10^{-24} \text{ g}) = 1.992 \times 10^{-23} \text{ g}.$$

For an oxygen atom, with eight protons and eight neutrons in its nucleus, the total mass is

$$16 \times (1.66 \times 10^{-24} \text{ g}) = 2.656 \times 10^{-23} \text{ g}.$$

Dividing the total mass of a sample of an element by the mass of a single atom gives the number of atoms in the sample. Suppose you have a carbon sample with a mass of 12 g—a mass in grams equal to the atom's mass number. (A mass in grams equal to the mass number is known as the atomic weight of an element.) Dividing 12 g by the mass of one carbon atom gives

$$\frac{12}{(10.992 \times 10^{-23} \text{g})} = 6.02 \times 10^{23} \text{ atoms.}$$

If you divide the atomic weight of oxygen (16 g) by the mass of one oxygen atom, you get the same result:

$$\frac{16}{(2.656 \times 10^{-23} \text{g})} = 6.02 \times 10^{23} \text{ atoms.}$$

In fact, dividing the atomic weight of any element by the mass of an atom of that element always produces the same number: 6.02×10^{23}. This number is called **Avogadro's number** after Amedeo Avogadro, the nineteenth-century Italian chemist who first discovered the relationship.

The same relationship holds for molecules. The **molecular weight** of any molecule is the mass in grams equal to the total mass number of its atoms. For NaCl, the total mass number is $23 + 35 = 58$ (a sodium atom has 11 protons and 12 neutrons, and a chlorine atom has 17 protons and 18 neutrons). The mass of an NaCl molecule is therefore

$$58 \times (1.66 \times 10^{-24} \text{ g}) = 9.628 \times 10^{-23} \text{ g.}$$

Dividing the molecular weight of NaCl (58 g) by the mass of a single NaCl molecule gives

$$\frac{58}{(9.628 \times 10^{-23} \text{g})} = 6.02 \times 10^{23} \text{ atoms.}$$

When concentrations are described, the atomic weight of an element or the molecular weight of a compound—the amount that contains 6.02×10^{23} atoms or molecules—is known as a **mole** (abbreviated **mol**). The number of moles of a substance dissolved in 1 L of solution is known as the **molarity** (abbreviated **M**) of the solution. This relationship is highly useful in chemistry and biology because we know that two solutions with the same volume and molarity but composed of different substances will contain the same number of molecules of the substances.

Dissociation of Water and pH

The most critical property of water that is unrelated to its hydrogen-bond lattice is its ability to separate or dissociate. This occurs when a hydrogen atom that is involved in a hydrogen bond between two water molecules moves from one molecule to the other. What actually leaves is a proton (H^+); the electron is left behind. This proton switch results in the formation of a hydroxide ion (OH^-) and a hydronium ion (H_3O^+).

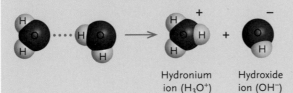

Hydronium ion (H_3O^+)   Hydroxide ion (OH^-)

It is convention to simply use H^+ (the hydrogen ion) to denote the hydronium ion. The proportion of water molecules that dissociate to release hydrogen and hydroxide ions is small. However, because of the dissociation, water always contains some H^+ and OH^- ions.

In pure water, the concentrations of H^+ and OH^- ions are equal. However, adding other substances may alter the relative concentrations of H^+ and OH^-, making them unequal. Some substances, called acids, are proton donors, which release hydrogen ions (and anions) when they are dissolved in water, effectively increasing the H^+ concentration. For example, hydrochloric acid (HCl) dissociates into H^+ and Cl^- when dissolved in water:

$$HCl \rightarrow H^+ + Cl^-.$$

continued on next page

Other substances, called bases, are proton acceptors, which reduce the H^+ concentration of a solution. Most bases dissociate in water into hydroxide ions (OH^-) and cations. The hydroxide ion can act as a base by accepting a proton to produce water. For example, sodium hydroxide (NaOH) separates into Na^+ and OH^- ions when dissolved in water:

$$NaOH \rightarrow Na^+ + OH^-.$$

The excess OH^- combines with H^+ to produce water,

$$OH^- + H^+ \rightarrow H_2O,$$

thereby reducing the H^+ concentration. Basic solutions are also called *alkaline* solutions.

Other bases do not dissociate to produce hydroxide ions directly. For example, ammonia (NH_3), a poisonous gas, acts as a base when dissolved in water, directly accepting a proton from water, producing an ammonium ion, and releasing a hydroxide ion:

$$NH_3 + H_2O \rightarrow NH_4^+ + OH^-.$$

The concentration of H^+ is measured on a numerical scale from 0 to 14, called the pH scale. Because the number of H^+ ions in solution increases exponentially as the acidity increases, the scale is based on logarithms of this number to make the values manageable:

$$pH = -\log_{10} [H^+].$$

In this formula, the brackets indicate concentration in moles per litre. The negative of the logarithm is used to give a positive number for the pH value. For example, in a water solution that is *neutral*—neither acidic nor basic—the concentration of *both* H^+ and OH^- ions is 1×10^{-7} M (0.000 000 1 M). The base 10 logarithm of 1×10^{-7} is -7. The negative of the logarithm -7 is 7. Acidic solutions have pH values less than 7, while basic solutions have pH values greater than 7. Each whole number on the pH scale represents a value 10 times or one-tenth the next number.

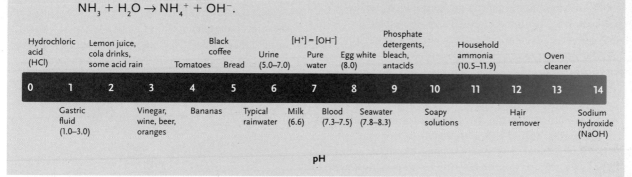

pH

Buffers Keep pH within Limits

Acidity is important to cells because even small changes, on the order of 0.1 or even 0.01 pH unit, can drastically affect biological reactions. In large part, a small change in pH can cause structural changes in proteins that can damage or destroy the proteins' function. Consequently, all living organisms have elaborate systems that control their internal acidity by regulating H^+ concentration near the neutral value of pH 7.

Living organisms control the internal pH of their cells with *buffers*—substances that compensate for pH changes by absorbing or releasing hydrogen ions. When hydrogen ions are released in excess by biological reactions, buffers combine with them and remove them from the solution; if the concentration of hydrogen ions decreases, buffers release H^+ to restore the balance. Most buffers are weak acids, weak bases, or combinations of these substances that dissociate reversibly in water solutions to release or absorb H^+ or OH^-. (Weak acids, such as acetic acid,

or weak bases, such as ammonia, release relatively few H^+ or OH^- ions in an aqueous solution, whereas strong acids or bases dissociate extensively. HCl is a strong acid; NaOH is a strong base.)

The buffering mechanism that maintains blood pH near neutral values is a good example. In humans and many other animals, blood pH is buffered by a chemical system based on carbonic acid (H_2CO_3), a weak acid. In water solutions, carbonic acid dissociates readily into bicarbonate ions (HCO_3^-) and H^+:

$$H_2CO_3 \rightarrow HCO_3^- + H^+.$$

The reaction is reversible. If hydrogen ions are present in excess, the reaction is pushed to the left—the excess H^+ ions combine with bicarbonate ions to form H_2CO_3. If the H^+ concentration declines below normal levels, the reaction is pushed to the right—H_2CO_3 dissociates into HCO_3^- and H^+, restoring the H^+ concentration. The back-and-forth adjustments of the buffer system help keep human blood close to its normal pH of 7.4.

Carbon Compounds

Carbon Bonding

Compounds that contain carbon form the structures of living organisms and take part in all biological reactions as well as serving as energy sources. Collectively, molecules based on carbon are known as organic molecules. All other substances, that is, those without carbon atoms in their structures, are inorganic molecules. A few of the smallest carbon-containing molecules that occur in the environment as minerals or atmospheric gases, such as $CaCO_3$ and CO_2, are also considered inorganic molecules.

Carbon's central role in life's molecules arises from its bonding properties: it can assemble into an astounding variety of chain and ring structures that form the backbones of all biological molecules. The reason for this is that carbon has four unpaired outer electrons that it readily shares to complete its outermost energy level, forming four covalent bonds. With different combinations of single, double, and even triple bonds, an almost limitless array of molecules is possible. Carbon atoms bond covalently to each other and to other atoms, chiefly hydrogen, oxygen, nitrogen, and sulfur, in molecular structures that range in size from a few to thousands or even millions of atoms. Molecules consisting of carbon linked only to hydrogen atoms are called hydrocarbons (*hydro-* refers to hydrogen, not water). The simplest hydrocarbon, CH_4 (methane), consists of a single carbon atom bonded to four hydrogen atoms. Removing one hydrogen atom from methane leaves a methyl group, which occurs in many biological molecules:

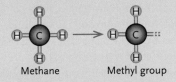

Methane   Methyl group

Now imagine bonding two methyl groups together. Removing a hydrogen atom from the maximum of four bonds, the number of hydrogen atoms in a molecule decreases as the resulting structure, ethane, produces an ethyl group:

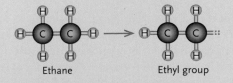

Ethane   Ethyl group

Repeating this process builds a linear hydrocarbon chain:

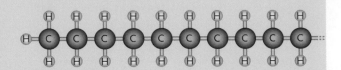

Branches can be added to produce a branched hydrocarbon chain:

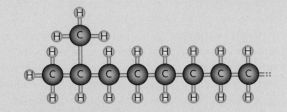

A chain can loop back on itself to form a ring. For example, cyclohexane, C_6H_{12}, has single covalent bonds between each pair of carbon atoms and two hydrogen atoms attached to each carbon atom:

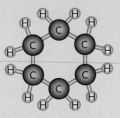

C_6H_{12}, cyclohexane

Hydrocarbons gain added complexity when neighbouring carbon atoms form double or triple bonds. Because each carbon atom can form a maximum of four bonds, the number of hydrogen atoms in a molecule decreases as the number of bonds between any two carbon atoms increases:

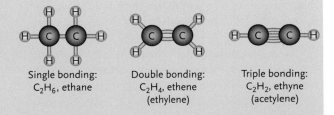

Single bonding: C_2H_6, ethane

Double bonding: C_2H_4, ethene (ethylene)

Triple bonding: C_2H_2, ethyne (acetylene)

continued on next page

Double bonds between carbon atoms are also found in carbon rings:

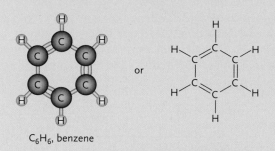

C_6H_6, benzene

We will also use this depiction of a carbon ring in figures:

Many carbon rings can join together to produce larger molecules, as in the string of sugar molecules that makes up a polysaccharide chain:

There is almost no limit to the number of different hydrocarbon structures that carbon and hydrogen can form. However, the molecules of living systems typically contain other elements in addition to carbon and hydrogen. These other elements confer functional properties on organic molecules, producing the four major classes of organic molecules: *carbohydrates, lipids, proteins,* and *nucleic acids*.

Dehydration and Hydrolysis Reactions

In many of the reactions that involve functional groups, the components of a water molecule, —H and —OH, are removed from or added to the groups as they interact. When the components of a water molecule are *removed* during a reaction, usually as part of the assembly of a larger molecule from smaller subunits, the reaction is called a dehydration synthesis reaction or a condensation reaction. For example, this type of reaction occurs when individual sugar molecules combine to form a starch molecule. In hydrolysis, the reverse reaction, the components of a water molecule are *added* to functional groups as molecules are broken into smaller subunits. For example, the breakdown of a protein molecule into individual amino acids occurs by hydrolysis.

Dehydration synthesis reactions

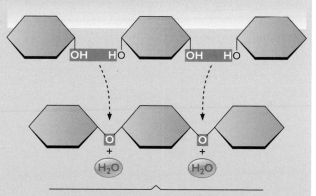

The components of a water molecule are removed as subunits join into a larger molecule.

Hydrolysis

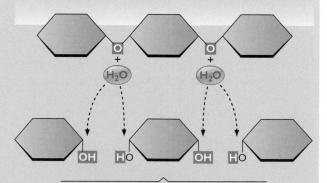

The components of a water molecule are added as molecules are split into smaller subunits.

Functional Groups

Carbohydrates, lipids, proteins, and nucleic acids are synthesized and degraded in living organisms through interactions between small, reactive groups of atoms attached to the organic molecules. The atoms in these reactive groups, called **functional groups,** occur in positions in which their covalent bonds are more readily broken or rearranged than the bonds in other parts of the molecules.

The functional groups that enter most frequently into biological reactions are the *hydroxyl, carbonyl, carboxyl, amino, phosphate,* and *sulfhydryl* groups. The unconnected covalent bonds written to the left of each structure link these functional groups to other atoms in biological molecules, usually carbon atoms. The symbol R is used to represent a chain of carbon atoms.

Common Functional Groups of Organic Molecules

Functional Group	Major Classes of Molecules	Example
Hydroxyl R—OH	Alcohols	Ethyl alcohol (in alcoholic beverages)

A hydroxyl group (—OH) consists of an oxygen atom linked to a hydrogen atom. Hydroxyl groups are polar and confer polarity on the parts of the molecules that contain them. The presence of the hydroxyl group enables an alcohol to form linkages to other organic molecules through dehydration synthesis reactions.

Carbonyl
 	
R—C=O
     |
     H
	Aldehydes	Acetaldehyde

Carbonyl
 	
R—C=O
     |
     C
	Ketones	Acetone (a solvent)

A carbonyl group (C=O) consists of an oxygen atom linked to a carbon atom by a double bond. Carbonyl groups are the reactive parts of aldehydes and ketones, molecules that act as major building blocks of carbohydrates and also take part in the reactions supplying energy for cellular activities. In an aldehyde, the carbonyl group is linked—along with a hydrogen atom—to a carbon atom at the end of a carbon chain, along with a hydrogen atom, as in acetaldehyde. In a ketone, the carbonyl group is linked to a carbon atom in the interior of a carbon chain, as in acetone.

Carboxyl
 	
R—COOH
or
R—C=O
     |
    OH
	Organic acids	Acetic acid (in vinegar)

continued on next page

A carboxyl group (—COOH) is formed by the combination of a carbonyl group and a hydroxyl group. The carboxyl group is the characteristic functional group of organic acids (also called carboxylic acids).

The carboxyl group gives organic molecules acidic properties because its —OH group readily releases the hydrogen as a proton (H^+) in solution.

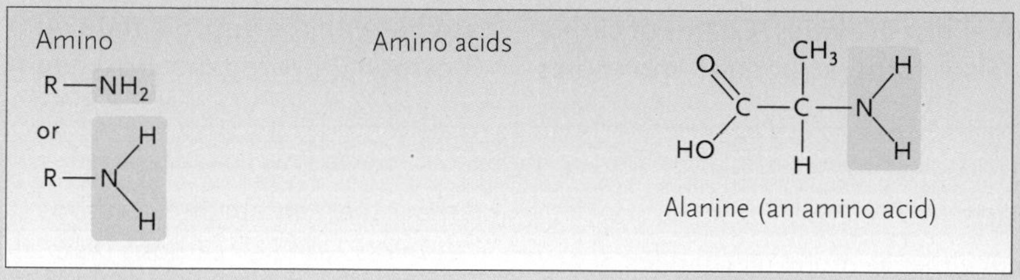

Amino   Amino acids

R —NH$_2$

or

R —N

Alanine (an amino acid)

The amino group (—NH$_2$) consists of a nitrogen atom bonded on one side to two hydrogen atoms; in a

molecule it is linked to an R group on the other side, as in the amino acid alanine and all other amino acids.

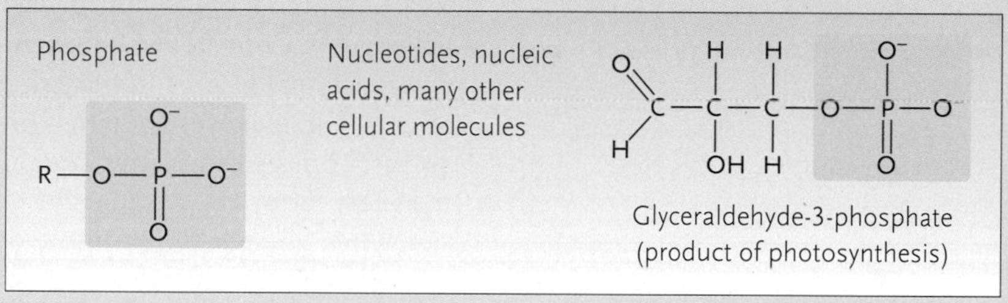

Phosphate   Nucleotides, nucleic acids, many other cellular molecules

R —O—P—O$^-$

Glyceraldehyde-3-phosphate
(product of photosynthesis)

The phosphate group (—OPO_3^{2-}) consists of a central phosphorus atom bonded to four oxygen atoms, as shown at left. Among the large biological molecules linked by phosphate groups is the nucleic acid DNA. Phosphate groups are added to or removed

from biological molecules as part of reactions that conserve or release energy. In addition, they control biological activity—the activity of many proteins is turned on or off by the addition or removal of phosphate groups.

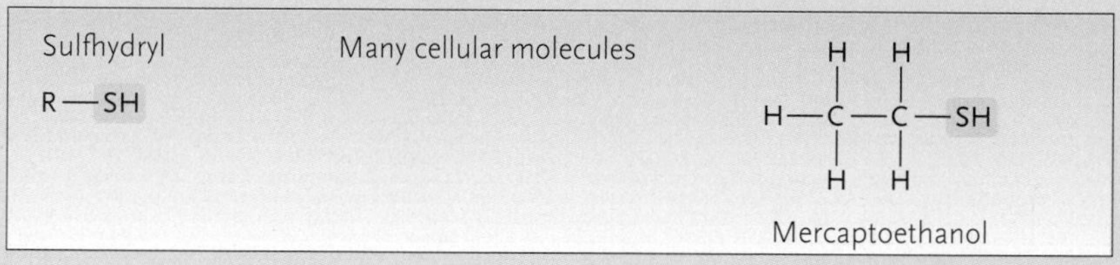

Sulfhydryl   Many cellular molecules

R —SH

Mercaptoethanol

In the sulfhydryl group (—SH), a sulfur atom is linked on one side to a hydrogen atom; in a molecule, the other side is linked to an R group. The sulfhydryl group is easily converted into a covalent linkage in which it

loses its hydrogen atom as it binds. In many of these linking reactions, two sulfhydryl groups interact to form a disulfide linkage (—S—S—). In proteins, the disulfide bond contributes to tertiary structure.

Carbohydrates

Carbohydrates, the most abundant biological molecules, serve many functions. Together with fats, they act as the major fuel substances providing chemical energy for cellular activities. Chains of carbohydrate subunits also form structural molecules such as cellulose, one of the primary constituents of plant cell walls. Carbohydrates get their name because they contain carbon, hydrogen, and oxygen atoms, with the approximate ratio of the atoms being 1 carbon:2 hydrogens:1 oxygen (CH_2O).

Monosaccharides

Carbohydrates occur either as monosaccharides or as chains of monosaccharide units linked together. Monosaccharides are soluble in water, and most have a distinctly sweet taste. Of the monosaccharides, those that contain three carbons (*trioses*), five carbons (*pentoses*), and six carbons (*hexoses*) are most common in living organisms. All monosaccharides can occur in the linear form, where each carbon atom in the chain except one has both an —H and an —OH group attached to it.

Monosaccharides with five or more carbons can fold back on themselves to assume a ring form. Folding into a ring occurs through a reaction between two functional groups in the same monosaccharide, as occurs in glucose. The ring form of most five- and six-carbon sugars is much more common in cells than the linear form.

When glucose forms into a ring, two alternative arrangements are possible (α-glucose and β-glucose) that differ in the arrangements of the —OH group bound to the carbon at position 1. These two different forms of glucose are called isomers, which are discussed below.

Glyceraldehyde
(3 carbons;
a triose)

Ribose
(5 carbons;
a pentose)

Mannose
(6 carbons;
a hexose)

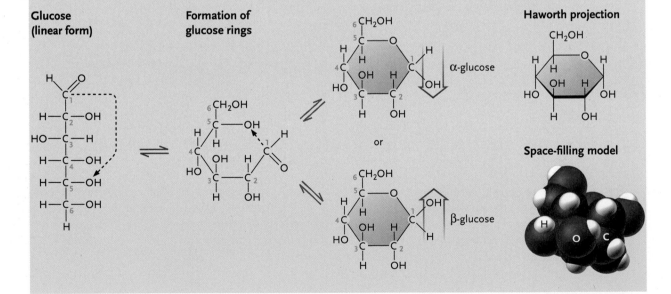

Glucose (linear form)

Formation of glucose rings

α-glucose

or

β-glucose

Haworth projection

Space-filling model

Isomers of the Monosaccharides

Typically, one or more of the carbon atoms in a monosaccharide links to four different atoms or chemical groups. Carbons linked in this way are called *asymmetrical* carbons; they have important effects on the structure of a monosaccharide because they can take either of two fixed positions with respect to other carbons in a carbon chain. For example, the middle carbon of the three-carbon sugar glyceraldehyde is asymmetrical because it shares electrons in covalent bonds with four different atoms or groups: —H, —OH, —CHO, and —CH_2OH. The —H and —OH groups can take either of two positions, with the —OH extending to either the left or the right of the carbon chain relative to the —CHO and —CH_2OH groups:

CHO
|
H — C — OH
|
CH_2OH

D-Glyceraldehyde

CHO
|
HO — C — H
|
CH_2OH

L-Glyceraldehyde

Note that the two forms of glyceraldehyde have the same chemical formula, $C_3H_6O_3$. The difference between the two forms is similar to the difference between your two hands. Although both hands have four fingers and a thumb, they are not identical; rather, they are mirror images of each other. That is, when you hold your right hand in front of a mirror, the reflection looks like your left hand, and vice versa.

Two or more molecules with the same chemical formula but different molecular structures are called isomers. Isomers that are mirror images of each other, like the two forms of glyceraldehyde, are called enantiomers, or optical isomers. One of the enantiomers—the one in which the hydroxyl group extends to the left in the view just shown—is called the l-form (*laevus* = left). The other enantiomer, in which the —OH extends to the right, is called the d-form (*dexter* = right). The difference between l- and d-enantiomers is critical to biological function. Typically, one of the two forms enters much more readily into cellular reactions; just as your left hand does not fit readily into a right-hand glove, enzymes (proteins that accelerate chemical reactions in living organisms) fit best to one of the two forms of an enantiomer. For example, most

of the enzymes that catalyze the biochemical reactions of monosaccharides react more rapidly with the d-form, making this form much more common among cellular carbohydrates than the l-form. Many other kinds of biological molecules besides carbohydrates form enantiomers; an example is the amino acids.

In the ring form of many five- or six-carbon monosaccharides, including glucose, the carbon at the 1 position of the ring is asymmetrical because its four bonds link to different groups of atoms. This asymmetry allows monosaccharides such as glucose to exist as two different enantiomers. The glucose enantiomer with an —OH group pointing below the plane of the ring is known as *alpha-glucose*, or α-*glucose*; the enantiomer with an —OH group pointing above the plane of the ring is known as *beta-glucose*, or β-*glucose*. Other five- and six-carbon monosaccharide rings have similar α- and β-configurations.

The α- and β-rings of monosaccharides can give the polysaccharides assembled from them vastly different chemical properties. For example, starches, which are assembled from α-glucose units, are biologically reactive polysaccharides easily digested by animals; cellulose, which is assembled from β-glucose units, is relatively unreactive and, for most animals, completely indigestible.

Another form of isomerism is found in monosaccharides, as well as in other molecules. Two molecules with the same chemical formula but atoms that are arranged in different ways are called structural isomers. The sugars glucose and fructose are examples of structural isomers.

Glucose
(an aldehyde)

Fructose
(a ketone)

Disaccharides

Disaccharides are typically assembled from two monosaccharides linked by a dehydration synthesis reaction. For example, the disaccharide maltose is formed by the linkage of two α-glucose molecules with oxygen as a bridge between the number 1 carbon of the first glucose unit and the number 4 carbon of the second glucose unit. Bonds of this type, which commonly link monosaccharides into chains, are known as glycosidic bonds. A glycosidic bond between a 1 carbon and a 4 carbon is written in chemical shorthand as a 1→4 linkage. Linkages such as 1→2, 1→3, and 1→6 are also common in carbohydrate chains. The linkages are designated as α or β depending on the orientation of the —OH group at the 1 carbon that forms the bond. In maltose, the —OH group is in the α position. Therefore, the link between the two glucose subunits of maltose is written as an α (1→4) linkage. Maltose, sucrose, and lactose are common disaccharides.

Formation of maltose

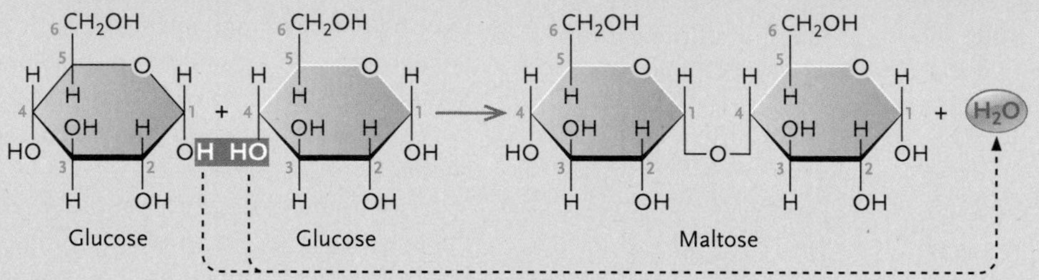

Glucose + Glucose → Maltose + H_2O

Sucrose

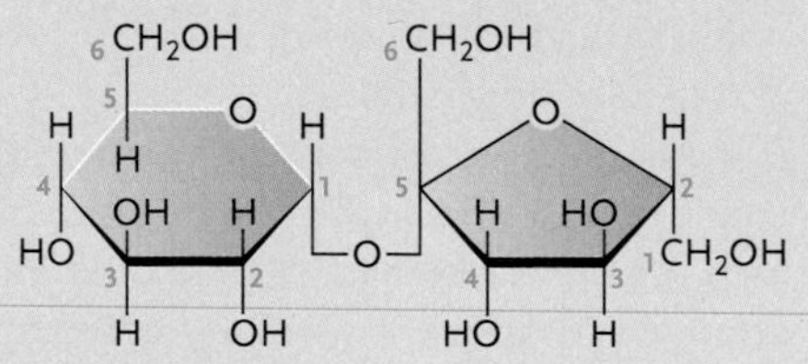

Glucose unit   Fructose unit

Lactose

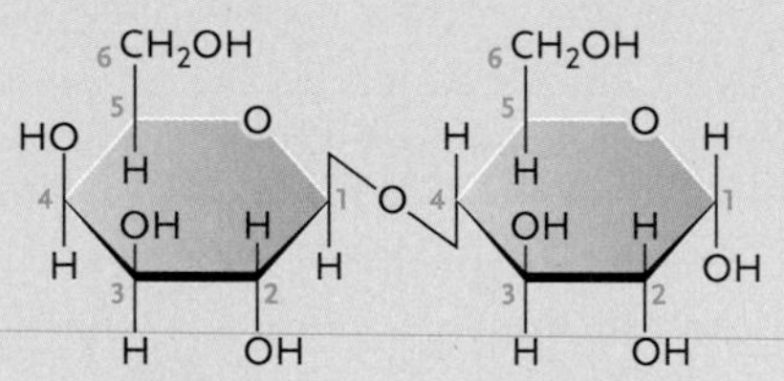

Galactose unit   Glucose unit

Polysaccharides

Polysaccharides are longer chains formed by the end-to-end linking of monosaccharides through dehydration synthesis reactions. A polysaccharide is a type of macromolecule, which is a very large molecule assembled by the covalent linkage of smaller subunit molecules. The subunit for a polysaccharide is the monosaccharide.

The dehydration synthesis reactions that assemble polysaccharides from monosaccharides are examples of polymerization, in which identical or nearly identical subunits, called the monomers of the reaction, join like links in a chain to form a larger molecule called a polymer. Linkage of a relatively small number of nonidentical subunits can create highly diverse and varied biological molecules. Many kinds of polymers are found in cells, not just polysaccharides. DNA is a primary example of a highly diverse polymer assembled from various sequences of only four different types of monomers.

The most common polysaccharides—the plant starches, glycogen and cellulose—are all assembled from hundreds or thousands of glucose units. Other polysaccharides are built up from a variety of different sugar units. Polysaccharides may be linear, unbranched molecules, or they may contain one or more branches in which side chains of sugar units are attached to a main chain.

continued on next page

Amylose, formed from α-glucose units joined end to end in α(1→4) linkages. The coiled structures are induced by the bond angles in the α-linkages.

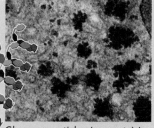

Amylose grains (purple) in plant root tissue (Ed Reschke/Peter Arnold/ Photolibrary)

Glycogen, formed from glucose units joined in chains by α(1→4) linkages; side branches are linked to the chains by α(1→6) linkages (boxed in blue).

Glycogen particles (magenta) in liver cell (Dennis Kunkel Microscopy, Inc./Phototake)

Cellulose, formed from glucose units joined end to end by β(1→4) linkages. Hundreds to thousands of cellulose chains line up side by side, in an arrangement reinforced by hydrogen bonds between the chains, to form cellulose microfibrils in plant cells.

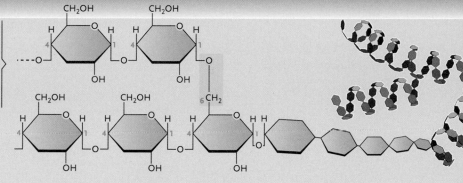

Glucose subunit

Cellulose molecule

Cellulose microfibril

Cellulose microfibrils in plant cell wall (© Biophoto Associates/Photo Researchers, Inc.)

Chitin, formed from β-linkages joining glucose units modified by the addition of nitrogen-containing groups. The external body armor of the tick is reinforced by chitin fibres.

Sergey Toronto/Shutterstock

Proteins

Proteins, which are polymers of amino acids, are the most diverse group of biological macromolecules. Proteins vary hugely in terms of both their chemical composition and their function. Even the simplest prokaryotic cell contains thousands of proteins, each with a defined composition and specific function within the cell. The major protein functions are listed below.

Protein type	Function	Examples
Structural proteins	Support	Microtubule and microfilament proteins form supporting fibres inside cells; collagen and other proteins surround and support animal cells; cell wall proteins support plant cells.
Enzymatic proteins	Increase the rate of biological reactions	Among thousands of examples, DNA polymerase increases the rate of duplication of DNA molecules; RuBP (ribulose 1,5-bisphosphate) carboxylase/oxygenase increases the rates of the first synthetic reactions of photosynthesis; the digestive enzymes lipases and proteases increase the rate breakdown of fats and proteins, respectively.
Membrane transport proteins	Speed up movement of substances across biological membranes	Ion transporters move ions such as Na^+, K^+, and Ca_2^+ across membranes; glucose transporters move glucose into cells; aquaporins allow water molecules to move across membranes.
Motile proteins	Produce cellular movements	Myosin acts on microfilaments (called thin filaments in muscle) to produce muscle movements; dynein acts on microtubules to produce the whipping movements of sperm tails, flagella, and cilia (the last two are whiplike appendages on the surfaces of many eukaryotic cells); kinesin acts on microtubules of the cytoskeleton (the three-dimensional scaffolding of eukaryotic cells responsible for cellular movement, cell division, and the organization of organelles).
Regulatory proteins	Promote or inhibit the activity of other cellular molecules	Nuclear regulatory proteins turn genes on or off to control the activity of DNA; protein kinases add phosphate groups to other proteins to modify their activity.
Receptor proteins	Bind molecules at cell surface or within cell; some trigger internal cellular responses	Hormone receptors bind hormones at the cell surface or within cells and trigger cellular responses; cellular adhesion molecules help hold cells together by binding molecules on other cells; LDL receptors bind cholesterol-containing particles to cell surfaces
Hormones	Carry regulatory signals between cells	Insulin regulates sugar levels in the bloodstream; growth hormone regulates cellular growth and division.
Antibodies	Defend against invading molecules and organisms	Antibodies recognize, bind, and help eliminate essentially any protein of infecting bacteria and viruses, and many other types of molecules, both natural and artificial.
Storage proteins	Hold amino acids and other substances in stored form	Ovalbumin is a storage protein of eggs; apolipoproteins hold cholesterol in stored form for transport through the bloodstream.
Venoms and toxins	Interfere with competing organisms	Ricin is a castor-bean protein that stops protein synthesis; bungarotoxin is a snake venom that causes muscle paralysis.

Amino Acids

All proteins are polymers of amino acids. The generalized structure of an amino acid has a central carbon atom attached to an amino group (—NH₂), a carboxyl group (—COOH), and a hydrogen atom:

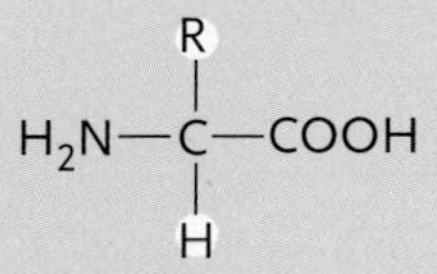

$$H_2N - \underset{\underset{H}{|}}{\overset{\overset{R}{|}}{C}} - COOH$$

The remaining bond of the central carbon is to 1 of 20 different side groups represented by the R. The R group, also called the side chain, ranges from a single hydrogen atom in the amino acid glycine to complex carbon chains or rings in some others. Differences in the side groups give the amino acids their individual properties. When discussing protein structure, amino acids are commonly referred to as amino acid residues or simply residues.

Proteins are synthesized from 20 different amino acids. These 20 are most commonly grouped according to the properties of their side chains. Here, the amino acids are shown in the ionic form common at the pH typical of a cell, 7.2.

Nonpolar amino acids

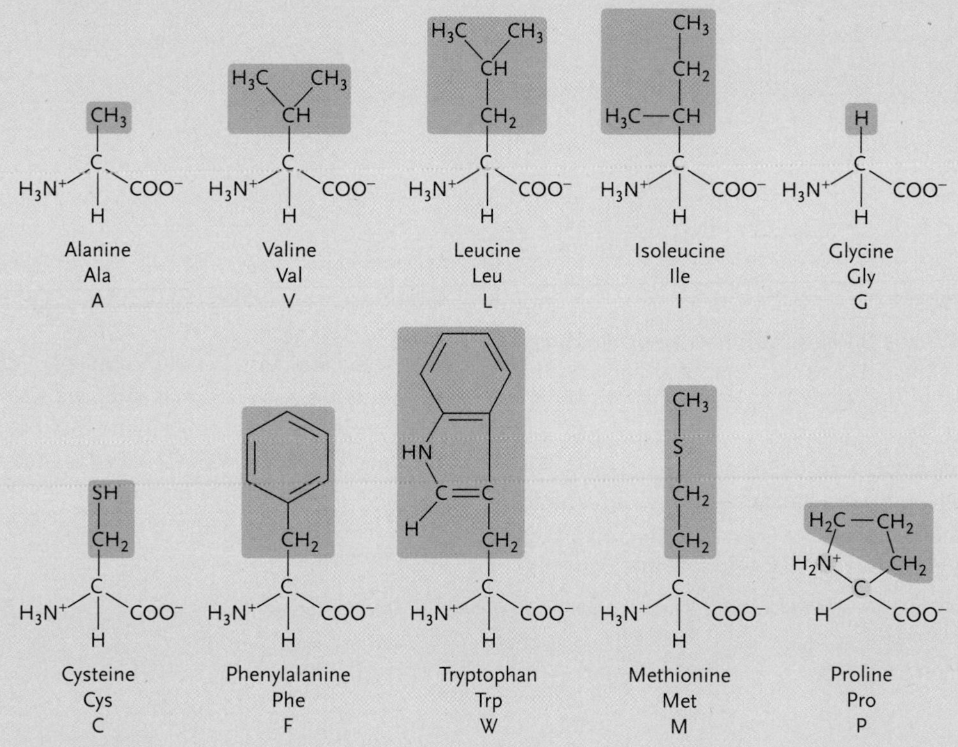

Alanine — Ala — A
Valine — Val — V
Leucine — Leu — L
Isoleucine — Ile — I
Glycine — Gly — G

Cysteine — Cys — C
Phenylalanine — Phe — F
Tryptophan — Trp — W
Methionine — Met — M
Proline — Pro — P

Uncharged polar amino acids

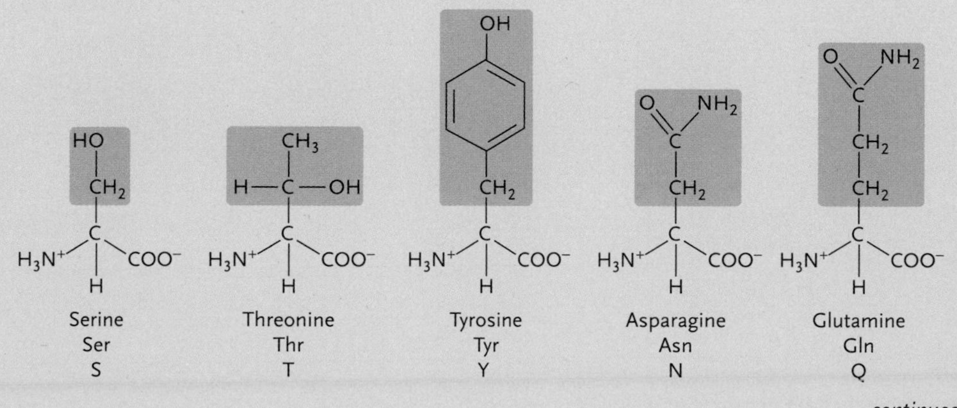

Serine — Ser — S
Threonine — Thr — T
Tyrosine — Tyr — Y
Asparagine — Asn — N
Glutamine — Gln — Q

continued on next page

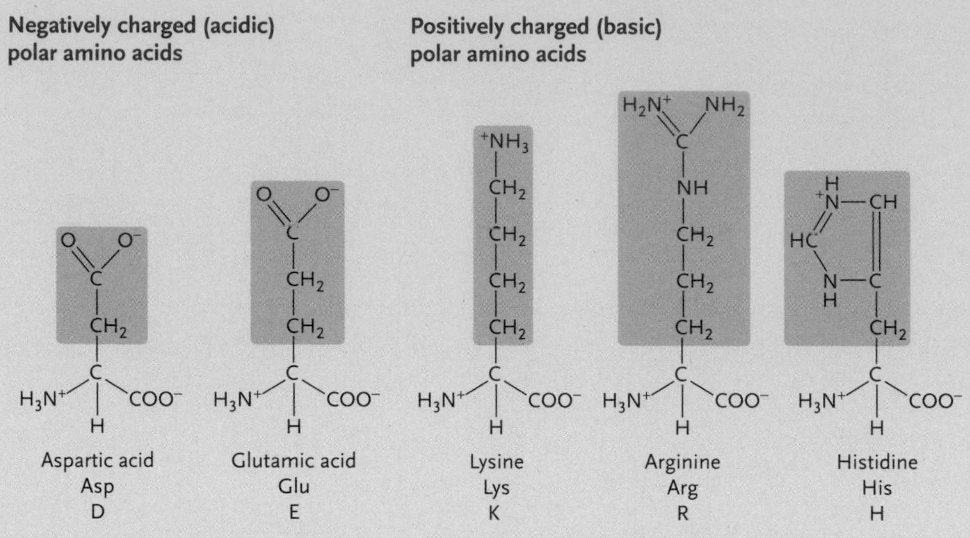

Negatively charged (acidic) polar amino acids

Positively charged (basic) polar amino acids

Aspartic acid
Asp
D

Glutamic acid
Glu
E

Lysine
Lys
K

Arginine
Arg
R

Histidine
His
H

Polypeptides

Covalent bonds link amino acids into chains called **polypeptides.** The link between each pair of amino acids in a polypeptide, a peptide bond, is formed by a dehydration synthesis reaction between the —NH_2 group of one amino acid and the —COOH group of a second. An amino acid chain always has an —NH_2 group at one end, called the N-terminal end, and a —COOH group at the other end, called the C-terminal end. In cells,

amino acids are added only to the —COOH end of the growing peptide strand.

The distinction between a polypeptide and a protein is that a polypeptide is simply a string of amino acids. A protein is a polypeptide that has folded into the specific three-dimensional shape that is required for most proteins to be functional.

The following figure shows the formation of a peptide bond.

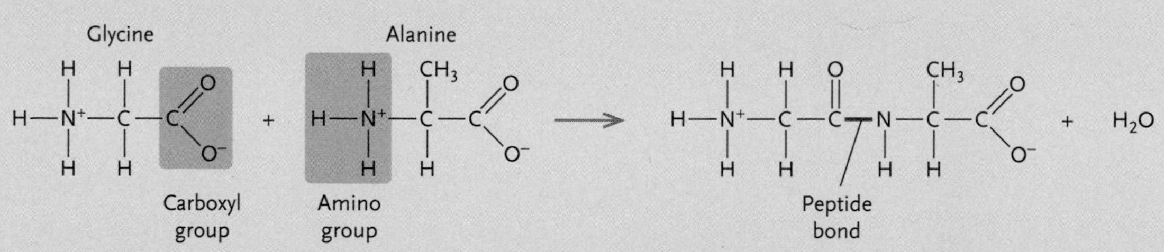

Glycine

Alanine

Carboxyl group

Amino group

Peptide bond

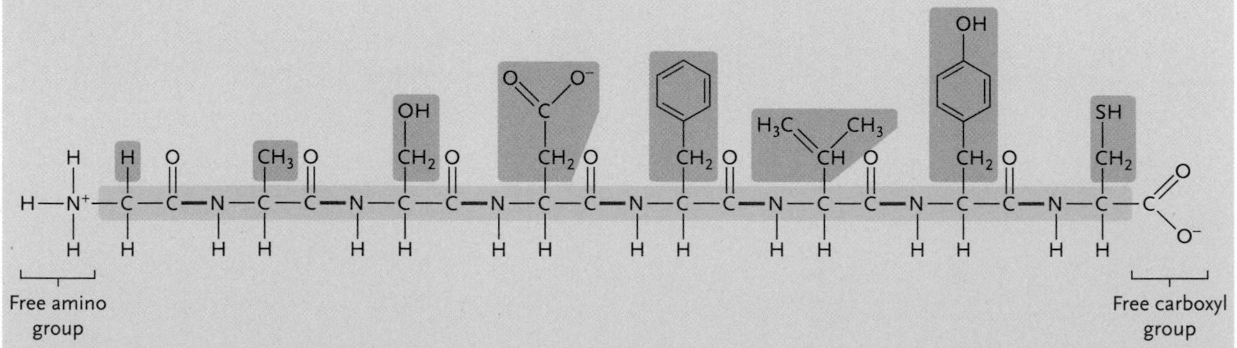

Free amino group

Free carboxyl group

A polypeptide—a linear chain of amino acids.
The backbone of the polypeptide is highlighted in the bottom figure above. The amino end of the polypeptide is called the N-terminus, while the carboxyl end is called the C-terminus.

The Four Levels of Protein Structure

Proteins have potentially four levels of structure, with each level imparting different characteristics and degrees of structural complexity to the molecule. Primary structure is the particular and unique sequence of amino acids forming a polypeptide; secondary structure is produced by the twists and turns of the amino acid chain. Tertiary structure is the folding of the amino acid chain, with its secondary structures, into the overall three-dimensional shape of a protein. All proteins have primary, secondary, and tertiary structures. Quaternary structure, when present, refers to the arrangement of polypeptide chains in a protein that is formed from more than one chain. Each structural level depends upon the level before it.

--- | Ser | Glu | Gly | Asp | Trp | Gln | Leu | His | ---

Primary structure: the sequence of amino acids in a protein.

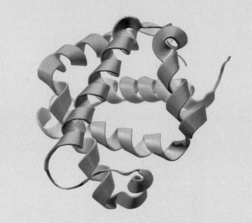

Secondary structure: regions of alpha helix, beta strand, or random coil in a polypeptide chain.

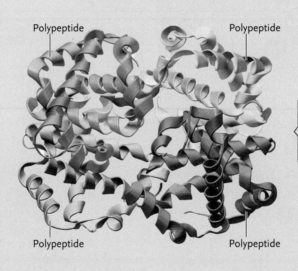

Tertiary structure: overall three-dimensional folding of a polypeptide chain.

Polypeptide   Polypeptide

Polypeptide   Polypeptide

Quaternary structure: the arrangement of polypeptide chains in a protein that contains more than one chain.

Primary Structure

The primary structure of a protein is simply its complete amino acid sequence. The primary sequence is determined by the nucleotide sequence of the coding region of the protein's corresponding gene.

H_3N^+ — | Phe | Val | Asn | Gln | His | Leu | Cys | Gly | Ser | His | Leu | Val | Glu | Ala | Leu | Tyr | Leu | Val | Cys | Gly | Glu | Arg | Gly | Phe | Phe | Tyr | Thr | Pro | Lys | Ala | — COO^-

Secondary Structure

The amino acid chain of a protein, rather than being stretched out in linear form, is folded into arrangements that form the protein's secondary structure. Secondary structure is based on hydrogen bonds between atoms of the backbone. More precisely, the hydrogen bonds form between the hydrogen atom attached to the nitrogen of the backbone and the oxygen attached to one of the carbon atoms of the backbone. Two highly regular secondary structures are the alpha helix and the beta sheet. A third, less regular arrangement, the random coil or loop, imparts flexibility to certain regions of the protein. Most proteins have segments of all three arrangements.

The α helix.

A model of the α helix (left), a coil shape formed when hydrogen bonds form between every N—H group of the backbone and the C═O group of the amino acid four residues earlier. In protein diagrams (right), the α helix is depicted as a cylinder or barrel.

The β sheet.

A β sheet is formed by side-by-side alignment of β strands (picture shows two strands). The sheet is formed by hydrogen bonds between atoms of each strand. In protein diagrams, the β strands are depicted by ribbons with arrowheads pointing toward the C-terminal.

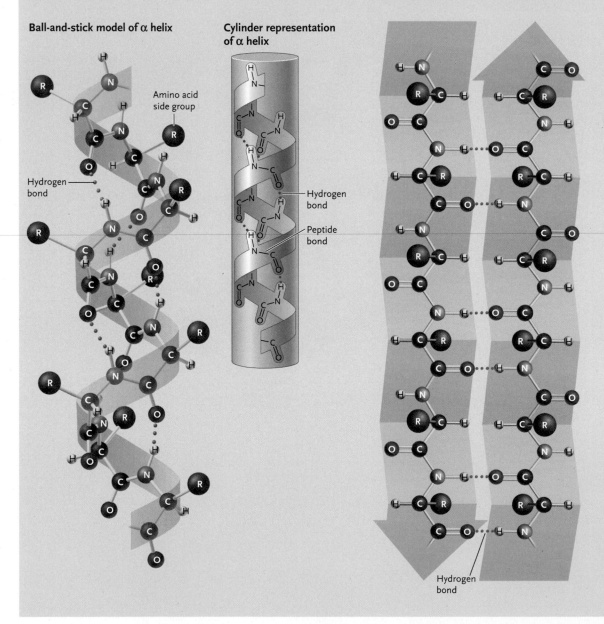

Ball-and-stick model of α helix

Amino acid side group

Hydrogen bond

Cylinder representation of α helix

Hydrogen bond

Peptide bond

Hydrogen bond

Tertiary Structure

The four major interactions between R groups that contribute to tertiary structure are shown below: (1) ionic bonds, (2) hydrogen bonds, (3) hydrophobic interactions, and (4) disulfide bridges. The tertiary structure of most proteins is flexible, allowing them to undergo limited alterations in three-dimensional shape known as conformational changes. These changes contribute to the function of many proteins, particularly enzymes, as well as other proteins involved in cellular movements or in the transport of substances across cell membranes.

Below are two representations of the three-dimensional structure of the enzyme lysozyme. In a ribbon diagram, α helices are shown as a cylinder, β strands are depicted as flat arrows, and random coils are shown as thin ropes. In a space-filling model, spheres represent different atoms. The sizes of the spheres and the intersphere distances are proportional to the actual dimensions. Atoms of different elements are represented by different colours. Disulfide bonds are shown in yellow.

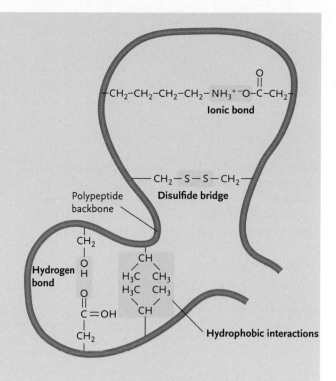

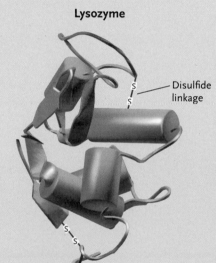

Lysozyme

Disulfide linkage

Space-filling model of lysozyme

Quaternary Structure

Some proteins consist of two or more polypeptides that come together to form a functional protein. An example of a protein that exhibits quaternary structure is collagen. The collagen molecule consists of three helical polypeptides that aggregate to form a triple-helix structure. Collagen is a major component of the connective tissue, is found exclusively in animals, and is the most abundant protein in mammals.

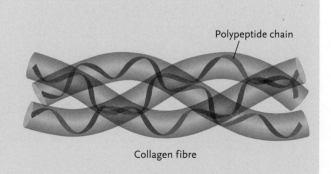

Polypeptide chain

Collagen fibre

Cofactors/Prosthetic Groups

A cofactor (also called a prosthetic group) is a nonprotein chemical compound that is bound to a protein and is required for the protein to function. Many enzymes require cofactors, which can be either organic or inorganic molecules. Many vitamins are essential to life because they act as key cofactors. A good example of a prosthetic group is the molecule heme, which is a key component of the oxygen-carrying protein hemoglobin. Each molecule of hemoglobin contains four heme molecules—one attached to each globin protein. Each heme contains a central iron atom that is responsible for binding molecules of oxygen.

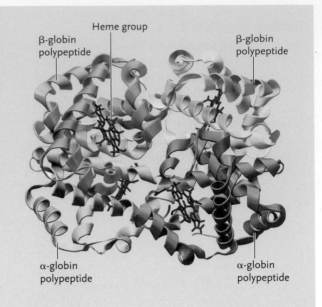

β-globin polypeptide

Heme group

β-globin polypeptide

α-globin polypeptide

α-globin polypeptide

Protein Domains

In many proteins, folding of the polypeptide(s) produces distinct, large structural subdivisions called domains. Often, one domain of a protein is connected to another by a segment of random coil. The hinge formed by the flexible random coil allows domains to move with respect to one another. That different domains of a protein are structurally distinct often reflects that they are functionally distinct as well.

Two domains in an enzyme that assembles DNA molecules

Domain a   Domain b

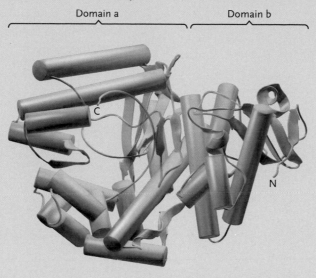

C

N

The same protein, showing the domain surfaces

Domain a   Domain b

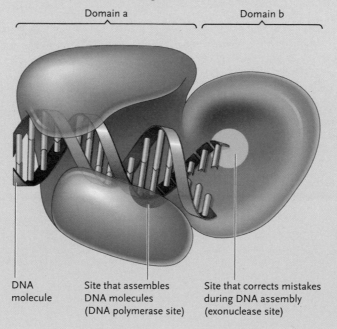

DNA molecule

Site that assembles DNA molecules (DNA polymerase site)

Site that corrects mistakes during DNA assembly (exonuclease site)

Protein Folding and Denaturation

A fundamental biochemical question is, "What determines how a protein will fold into the correct functional conformation?" The first insight came from a classic experiment published by Christian Anfinsen and Edgar Haber in 1962. The researchers studied ribonuclease, an enzyme that hydrolyzes RNA.

When they treated the enzyme chemically to break the disulfide linkages holding the protein in its functional state, the protein unfolded and had no enzyme activity. Unfolding a protein from its active conformation so that it loses its structure and function is called denaturation. This most often involves the use of specific chemicals or heat.

When they removed the denaturing chemicals, the ribonuclease slowly regained full activity because the disulfide linkages reformed, enabling the protein to reassume its functional conformation. The reversal of denaturation is called **renaturation.**

The key conclusion from this experiment was that the amino acid sequence itself specifies the tertiary structure of a protein. Nothing else is required. For this work, Christian Anfinsen received a Nobel Prize in 1972.

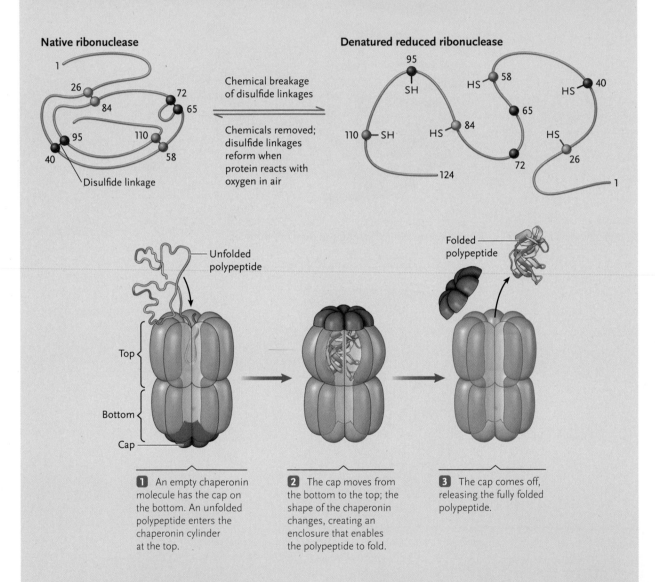

Native ribonuclease

1
26
84
72
65
95 110
40 58

Disulfide linkage

Chemical breakage of disulfide linkages

Chemicals removed; disulfide linkages reform when protein reacts with oxygen in air

Denatured reduced ribonuclease

95
SH
58 HS
40 HS
110 SH
84 HS
65
72
HS
26
124
1

Unfolded polypeptide

Folded polypeptide

Top

Bottom

Cap

1. An empty chaperonin molecule has the cap on the bottom. An unfolded polypeptide enters the chaperonin cylinder at the top.

2. The cap moves from the bottom to the top; the shape of the chaperonin changes, creating an enclosure that enables the polypeptide to fold.

3. The cap comes off, releasing the fully folded polypeptide.

Within the cell, the high density of newly synthesized proteins may impede the proper folding of individual proteins. For many proteins, correct folding is helped by a group of proteins called **chaperone proteins** or **chaperonins** (see figure above).

They function by temporarily binding with newly synthesized proteins, directing their conformation toward the correct tertiary structure, and inhibiting incorrect arrangements as the new proteins fold.

Nucleic Acids

Two types of nucleic acids exist: DNA and RNA. Deoxyribonucleic acid (DNA) stores the hereditary information in all eukaryotes, bacteria, and archaea. In all organisms, ribonucleic acid (RNA) carries out a diversity of functions.

RNA carries the instructions for assembling proteins from DNA to the site of protein synthesis, the ribosome, which is itself composed partially of RNA. Another type of RNA serves to bring amino acids to the ribosome for their assembly into proteins.

Nucleotides

All nucleic acids are polymers of nucleotides. A nucleotide consists of three parts linked by covalent bonds: (1) a nitrogenous base formed from rings of carbon and nitrogen atoms; (2) a five-carbon, ring-shaped sugar; and (3) one to three phosphate groups.

In nucleotides, the nitrogenous bases link covalently to a five-carbon sugar, either **deoxyribose** or **ribose.** The carbons of the two sugars are numbered with a prime symbol—1′, 2′, 3′, 4′, and 5′. The prime symbols are added to distinguish the carbons in the sugars from those in the nitrogenous bases, which are written without primes. The two sugars differ only in the chemical group bound to the 2′ carbon: deoxyribose has an —H at this position, and ribose has an —OH group.

The two types of nitrogenous bases are pyrimidines, with one carbon–nitrogen ring, and purines, with two rings. Three pyrimidine bases—uracil (U), thymine (T), and cytosine (C)—and two purine bases—adenine (A) and guanine (G)—form parts of nucleic acids in cells.

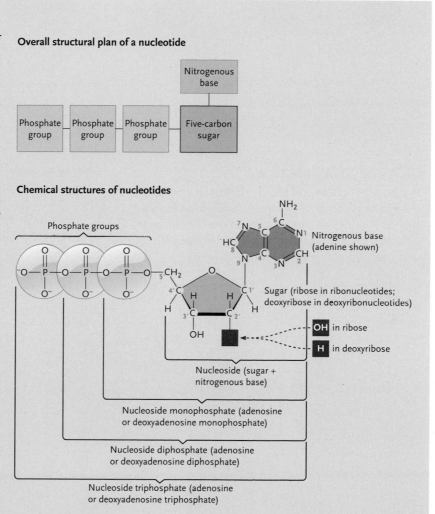

Overall structural plan of a nucleotide

Chemical structures of nucleotides

Phosphate groups

Nitrogenous base (adenine shown)

Sugar (ribose in ribonucleotides; deoxyribose in deoxyribonucleotides)

OH in ribose

H in deoxyribose

Nucleoside (sugar + nitrogenous base)

Nucleoside monophosphate (adenosine or deoxyadenosine monophosphate)

Nucleoside diphosphate (adenosine or deoxyadenosine diphosphate)

Nucleoside triphosphate (adenosine or deoxyadenosine triphosphate)

Pyrimidine and Purine Bases of Nucleic Acids

The three single-ring pyrimidines and two double-ring purines that are the nitrogenous bases of nucleotides.

The red arrows indicate where the bases link to ribose or deoxyribose sugars to form nucleotides.

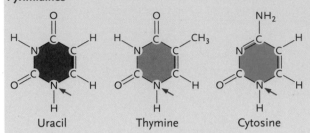

Pyrimidines

Uracil   Thymine   Cytosine

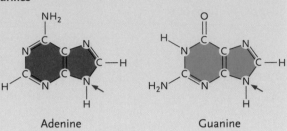

Purines

Adenine   Guanine

DNA and RNA Structure

Nucleotides in DNA and RNA are linked by a bridging phosphate group between the 5′ carbon of one sugar and the 3′ carbon of the next sugar in line. This linkage is called a phosphodiester bond. This arrangement of alternating sugar and phosphate groups forms the backbone of a nucleic acid. The nitrogenous bases of the nucleotides project from this backbone. Note that the nucleotide thymine (T) in DNA is not found in RNA, it is replaced by uracil (U).

DNA

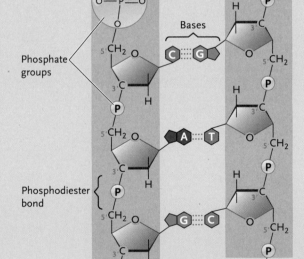

RNA

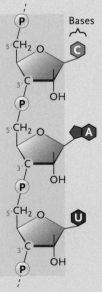

DNA Double Helix

In cells, DNA takes the form of a double helix: two nucleotide chains wrapped around each other in a spiral that resembles a twisted ladder. As shown below, the sides of the ladder are the sugar–phosphate backbones of the two chains, which twist around each other to form the double helix. The rungs of the ladder are the nitrogenous bases, which extend inward from the sugars toward the centre of the helix.

Each rung consists of a pair of nitrogenous bases held in a flat plane roughly perpendicular to the long axis of the helix. The two nucleotide chains of a DNA double helix are held together by hydrogen bonds between the base pairs. A DNA double-helix molecule is also referred to as double-stranded DNA. The space separating the sugar–phosphate backbones of a DNA double helix is just wide enough to accommodate a base pair that consists of one purine and one pyrimidine. Purine–purine base pairs are too wide and pyrimidine–pyrimidine pairs are too narrow to fit this space exactly. More specifically, of the possible purine–pyrimidine pairs, only two combinations, adenine with thymine and guanine with cytosine, can form stable hydrogen bonds so that the base pair fits precisely within the double helix. An adenine–thymine (A–T) pair forms two stabilizing hydrogen bonds; a guanine–cytosine (G–C) pair forms three.

DNA double helix, showing arrangement of sugars, phosphate groups, and bases

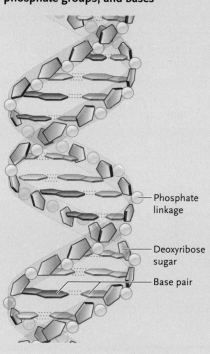

Phosphate linkage

Deoxyribose sugar

Base pair

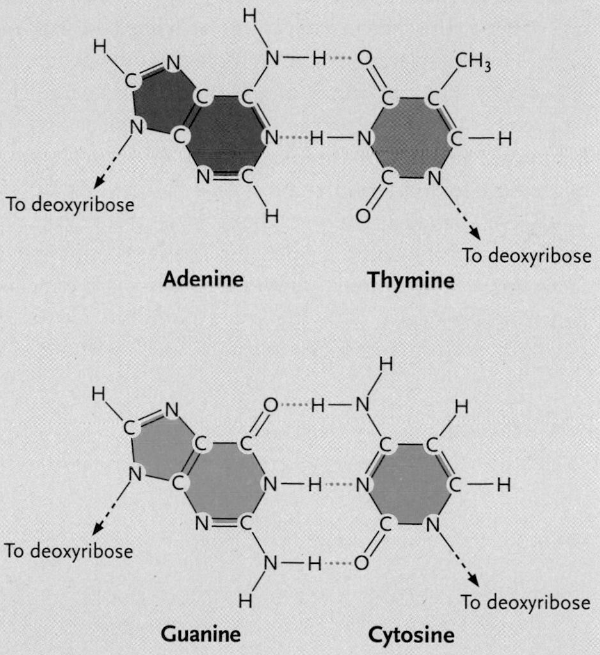

Adenine   Thymine

To deoxyribose

To deoxyribose

Guanine   Cytosine

To deoxyribose

To deoxyribose

Lipids

Lipids are a diverse group of water-insoluble, primarily nonpolar biological molecules composed mostly of hydrogen and carbon (hydrocarbons). The term *lipid* is a catch-all word for a range of nonpolar molecules. They are not large enough to be considered true macromolecules and, unlike nucleic acids and proteins, are not considered polymers of defined monomeric subunits. As a result of their nonpolar character, lipids typically dissolve much more readily in nonpolar solvents, such as acetone and chloroform, than in water. Their insolubility in water underlies their ability to form cell membranes. In addition, some lipids are stored and used in cells as an energy source. Other lipids serve as hormones that regulate cellular activities. Lipids in living organisms can be grouped into one of three categories—fats, phospholipids, and steroids.

Isoprenes and Fatty Acids

The structural backbone of all lipids is derived from one of two hydrocarbon molecules: isoprene and fatty acids. Isoprenes are five-carbon molecules that when linked together can form long hydrocarbon chains. Isoprenes are the structural unit in steroids and a number of phospholipids. A fatty acid consists of a single hydrocarbon chain with a carboxyl group (—COOH) linked at one end. The carboxyl group gives the fatty acid its acidic properties. The fatty acids in living organisms contain four or more carbons in their hydrocarbon chain, with the most common forms having even-numbered chains of 14 to 22 carbons.

As their chain length increases, fatty acids become progressively less water soluble and more solid.

If the hydrocarbon chain of a fatty acid binds the maximum possible number of hydrogen atoms, so that only single bonds link the carbon atoms, the fatty acid is said to be saturated with hydrogen atoms. If one or more double bonds link the carbons, reducing the number of bound hydrogen atoms, the fatty acid is unsaturated. Fatty acids with one double bond are monounsaturated; those with more than one double bond are polyunsaturated. Unlike saturated fatty acids, the presence of double bonds imparts a "kink" in the molecule.

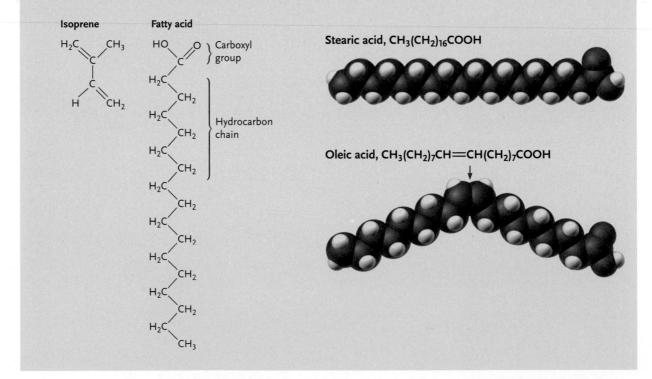

Stearic acid, $CH_3(CH_2)_{16}COOH$

Oleic acid, $CH_3(CH_2)_7CH = CH(CH_2)_7COOH$

Phospholipids

Phosphate-containing lipids, or phospholipids, are the primary lipids of cell membranes. In the most common phospholipids, glycerol forms the backbone for the molecule as in triglycerides, but only two of its binding sites are linked to fatty acids. The third site is linked to a polar phosphate group, which also binds to another polar unit. Thus, a phospholipid contains two hydrophobic fatty acids at one end, attached to a hydrophilic polar group, often called the head group. Molecules that contain both hydrophobic and hydrophilic regions are called amphipathic molecules.

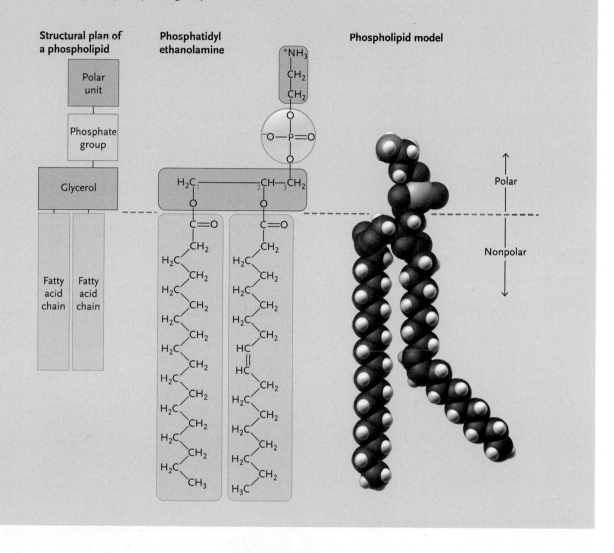

Structural plan of a phospholipid

Phosphatidyl ethanolamine

Phospholipid model

Fats

A fat consists of three fatty acid chains linked to a single molecule of glycerol. Because of this, fats are also often referred to as triacylglycerols or triglycerides. The three fatty acids linked to the glycerol may be different or the same. Different organisms usually have distinctive combinations of fatty acids in their triglycerides. As with individual fatty acids, triglycerides generally become less fluid as the length of their fatty acid chains increases; those with shorter chains remain liquid as oils at biological temperatures, and those with longer chains solidify.

Triglycerides are used widely as stored energy in animals. Gram for gram, they yield more than twice as much energy as carbohydrates. Therefore, fats are an excellent source of energy in the diet. Storing the equivalent amount of energy as carbohydrates rather than fats would add more than 45 kg to the mass of an average man or woman. A layer of fatty tissue just under the skin also serves as an insulating blanket in humans, other mammals, and birds. Triglycerides secreted from special glands in waterfowl and other birds help make feathers water repellent.

Formation of a triglyceride

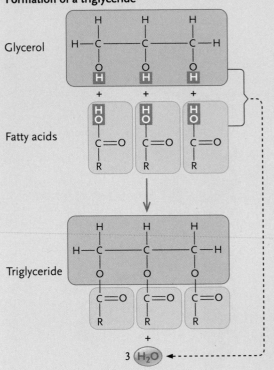

Glycerol

Fatty acids

Triglyceride

3 H_2O

Glyceryl palmitate

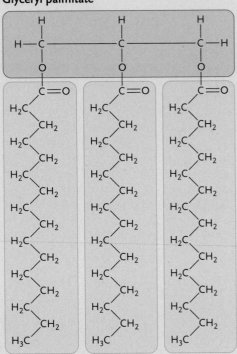

Triglyceride model

Steroids

Steroids are a group of lipids with structures based on a framework of four carbon rings that are derived from isoprene units. Small differences in the side groups attached to the rings distinguish one steroid from another. The most abundant steroids, the sterols, have a single polar —OH group linked to one end of the ring framework and a complex, nonpolar hydrocarbon chain at the other end. Although sterols are almost completely hydrophobic, the single hydroxyl group gives one end of the molecules a slightly polar, hydrophilic character. As a result, sterols also have dual solubility properties and, like phospholipids, tend to assume positions that satisfy these properties.

Cholesterol is an important component of the plasma membrane surrounding animal cells; similar sterols, called phytosterols, occur in plant cell membranes.

Arrangement of carbon rings in a steroid

Cholesterol, a sterol

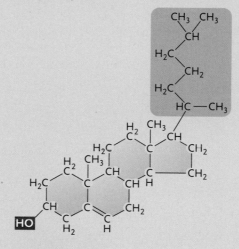

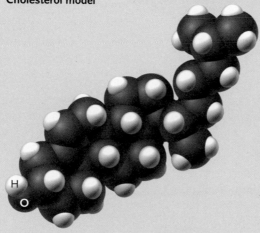

Cholesterol model

The Biosphere

The biosphere is the area occupied by life on Earth, from the depths of the ocean to the sky above. The various physical environments of Earth and their different abiotic factors, such as sunlight, temperature, humidity, wind speed, cloud cover, and rainfall, influence the evolution and diversity of organisms. These abiotic factors contribute to a region's climate, the weather conditions prevailing over an extended period of time. Climates vary on global, regional, and local scales and undergo seasonal changes almost everywhere.

Solar Radiation: Energy from the Sun

The global pattern of environmental diversity results from latitudinal variation in incoming solar radiation, Earth's rotation on its axis, and its orbit around the Sun. Earth's spherical shape causes the intensity of incoming solar radiation to vary from the equator to the poles. Solar radiation is more concentrated near the equator than it is at the poles, causing latitudinal variation in Earth's temperature.

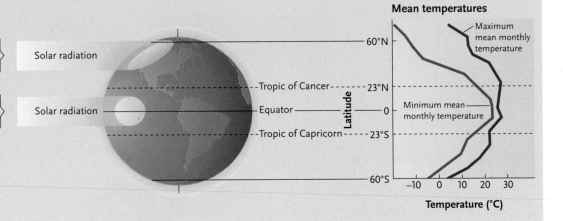

Solar radiation

Near the poles, solar radiation travels a long distance through the atmosphere and strikes a large surface area.

Near the equator, solar radiation travels a short distance through the atmosphere and strikes a small surface area.

Seasonality: Weather throughout the Year

Earth is tilted on its axis by 23.5°. This tilt produces seasonal variation in the intensity of incoming solar radiation. The northern hemisphere receives its maximum illumination, and the southern hemisphere its minimum, on the June solstice (around June 21), when the Sun shines directly over the Tropic of Cancer (23.5° N latitude). The reverse is true on the December solstice (around December 21), when the Sun shines directly over the Tropic of Capricorn (23.5° S latitude). Twice each year, on the vernal and autumnal equinoxes (around March 21 and September 21, respectively), the Sun shines directly over the equator. Only the Tropics, the latitudes between the tropics of Cancer and Capricorn, ever receive intense solar radiation from directly overhead. Moreover, the tropics experience only small seasonal changes in temperature and day length, with high temperatures and day length of approximately 12 hours throughout the year.

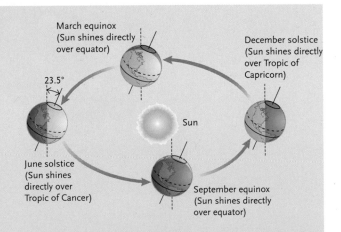

Seasonal variation in temperature and day length increases steadily toward the poles. Polar winters are long and cold, with periods of continuous darkness, and polar summers are short, with periods of continuous light.

Air Circulation: Wind Patterns

Sunlight warms air masses, causing them to expand, lose pressure, and rise in the atmosphere. The unequal heating of air at different latitudes initiates global air movements, producing three circulation cells in each hemisphere. Warm equatorial air masses rise to high altitude before spreading north and south. They eventually sink back to Earth at about 30° N and S latitude. At low altitude, some air masses flow back toward the equator, completing low-latitude circulation cells. Others flow toward the poles, rise at 60° latitude, and divide at high altitude. Some of this air flows toward the equator, completing the pair of middle-latitude circulation cells. The rest moves toward the poles, where it descends and flows toward the equator, forming the polar circulation cells.

The flow of air masses at low altitude creates winds near the planet's surface. But the planet's surface rotates beneath the atmosphere, moving rapidly near the equator, where Earth's diameter is greatest, and more slowly near the poles. Latitudinal variation in the speed of Earth's rotation deflects the movement of the rising and sinking air masses from a strictly north–south path into belts of easterly and westerly winds; this deflection is called the Coriolis effect. Winds near the equator are called the trade winds; those farther from the equator are the temperate westerlies and easterlies, named for their direction of flow.

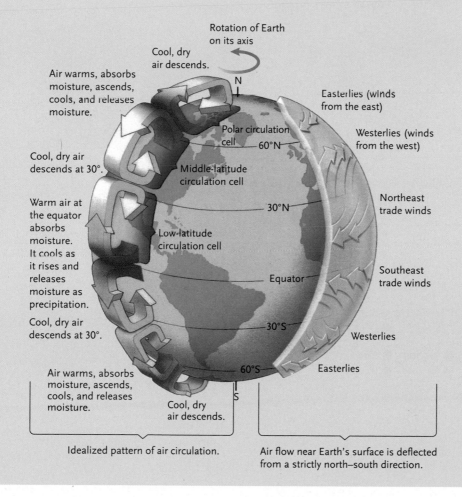

Rotation of Earth on its axis

Cool, dry air descends.

Air warms, absorbs moisture, ascends, cools, and releases moisture.

Cool, dry air descends at 30°.

Warm air at the equator absorbs moisture. It cools as it rises and releases moisture as precipitation.

Cool, dry air descends at 30°.

Air warms, absorbs moisture, ascends, cools, and releases moisture.

Cool, dry air descends.

Polar circulation cell

Middle-latitude circulation cell

Low-latitude circulation cell

N

60°N

30°N

Equator

30°S

60°S

S

Easterlies (winds from the east)

Westerlies (winds from the west)

Northeast trade winds

Southeast trade winds

Westerlies

Easterlies

Idealized pattern of air circulation.

Air flow near Earth's surface is deflected from a strictly north–south direction.

Precipitation

Differences in solar radiation and global air circulation create latitudinal variations in rainfall. Warm air holds more water vapour than cool air does. As air near the equator heats up, it absorbs water, primarily from the oceans. However, the warm air masses expand as they rise, and their heat energy is distributed over a larger volume, causing their temperature to drop. A decrease in temperature without the actual loss of heat energy is called adiabatic cooling. After cooling adiabatically, the rising air masses release moisture as rain. Torrential rainfall is characteristic of warm equatorial regions, where rising, moisture-laden air masses cool as they reach high altitude.

As cool, dry air masses descend at 30° latitude, increased air pressure at low altitude compresses them, concentrating their heat energy, raising their temperature, and increasing their capacity to hold moisture. Descending air masses absorb water at these latitudes, which are typically dry. Some air masses continue moving poleward in the lower atmosphere. When they rise at 60° latitude, they cool adiabatically and release precipitation, creating moist habitats in the northern and southern temperate zones.

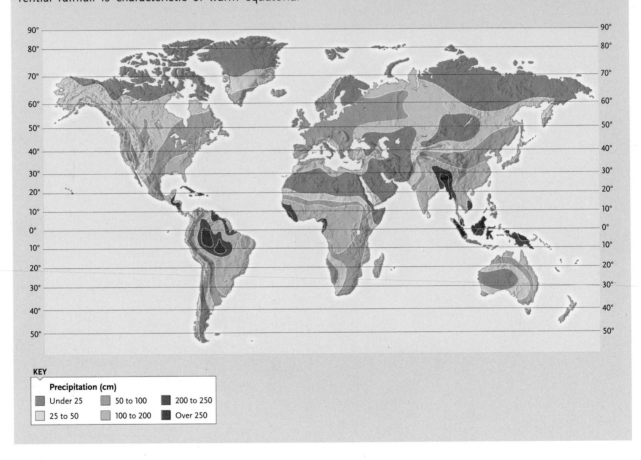

KEY

Precipitation (cm)

- Under 25
- 25 to 50
- 50 to 100
- 100 to 200
- 200 to 250
- Over 250

Ocean Currents

Latitudinal variations in solar radiation also warm the oceans' surface water unevenly. Because the volume of water increases as it warms (= decrease in density), sea level is about 8 cm higher at the equator than at the poles. The volume of water associated with this "slope" is enough to cause surface water to move in response to gravity. The trade winds and temperate westerlies also contribute to the mass flow of water at the ocean surface. Thus, surface water flows in the direction of prevailing winds, forming major currents. Earth's rotation, the positions of landmasses, and the shapes of ocean basins also influence the movements of these currents.

Oceanic circulation is generally clockwise in the northern hemisphere and counterclockwise in the southern hemisphere (see figure below). The trade winds push surface water toward the equator and westward until it contacts the eastern edge of a continent. Swift, narrow, and deep currents of warm, nutrient-poor water run toward the poles, parallel to the east coasts of continents. For example, the Gulf Stream flows northward along the east coast of North America, carrying warm water toward northwestern Europe. Cold water returns from the poles toward the equator in slow, broad, and shallow currents, such as the California Current, that parallel the west coasts of continents.

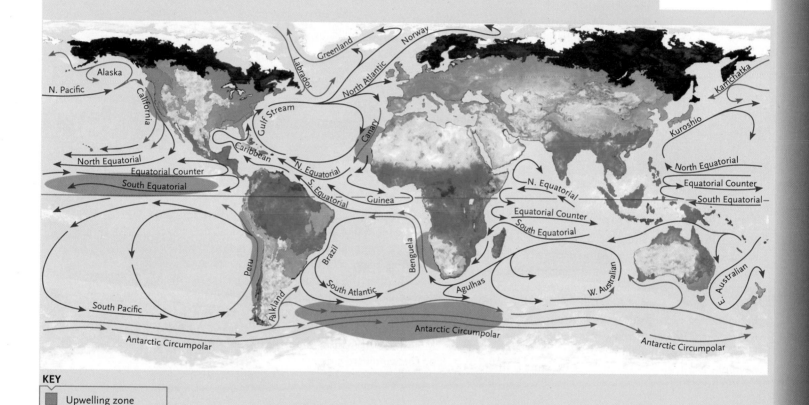

KEY

- ▨ Upwelling zone
- → Warm surface current
- → Cold surface current

Regional and Local Effects

Although global and seasonal patterns determine an area's climate, regional and local effects also influence abiotic conditions. Currents running along sea coasts exchange heat with air masses flowing above them, moderating the temperature over the nearby land. Breezes often blow from the sea toward the land during the day and in the opposite direction at night (see figure below). These local effects sometimes override latitudinal variations in temperature. For example, the climate in London, England, is much milder than that in Winnipeg, even though Winnipeg is slightly farther south. London has a maritime climate, tempered by winds that cross the nearby North Atlantic Current, but Winnipeg's climate is continental, not moderated by the distant ocean.

Ocean currents also affect moisture conditions in coastal habitats. For example, the region off the southeast coast of Newfoundland known as the Grand Banks is one of the foggiest places on Earth. Here, as the warm Gulf Stream current meets the cold Labrador current, the air above the water cools and its water vapour condenses into heavy fog and rain.

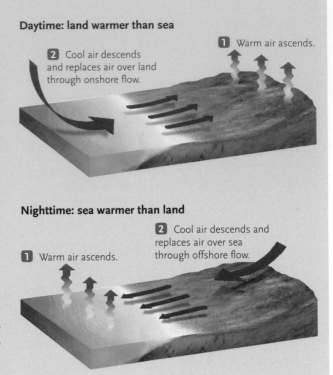

Daytime: land warmer than sea

2 Cool air descends and replaces air over land through onshore flow.

1 Warm air ascends.

Nighttime: sea warmer than land

2 Cool air descends and replaces air over sea through offshore flow.

1 Warm air ascends.

The Effects of Topography

Mountains, valleys, and other topographic features are a major influence on regional climates. In the northern hemisphere, south-facing slopes are warmer and drier than north-facing slopes because they receive more solar radiation. In addition, adiabatic cooling causes air temperature to decline 3 to 6°C for every 1000 m increase in elevation. Mountains also establish regional and local rainfall patterns. For example, warm air masses pick up moisture from the Pacific Ocean and then move inland towards the Rocky Mountains. As air rises to cross the mountains, it cools adiabatically and loses moisture, releasing heavy rainfall on the windward side (see below). After the now-dry air crosses the peaks, it descends and warms, absorbing moisture and forming a rain shadow. Habitats on the leeward side of mountains, such as the eastern slopes of the Rocky Mountains in Alberta, are typically drier than those on the windward side.

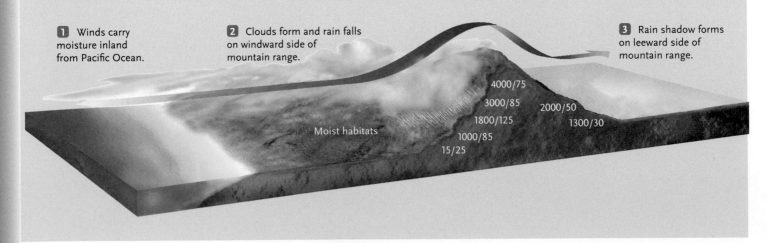

1 Winds carry moisture inland from Pacific Ocean.

2 Clouds form and rain falls on windward side of mountain range.

3 Rain shadow forms on leeward side of mountain range.

4000/75
3000/85   2000/50
1800/125
1300/30
1000/85
Moist habitats
15/25

Microclimate

Although climate influences the overall distributions of organisms, the abiotic conditions that immediately surround them, the microclimate, have the greatest effect on survival and reproduction. For example, a fallen log on the forest floor creates a microclimate in the underlying soil that is shadier, cooler, and moister than the surrounding soil, which is exposed to sun and wind. Many animals, including some insects, worms, salamanders, and snakes, occupy these sheltered sites and avoid the effects of prolonged exposure to the elements.

Aleksander Bolbot/Shutterstock

Biomes

Various climatic factors interact to create and regulate **biomes**—groups of ecosystems that share distinctive combinations of soils, vegetation, and animals. Fourteen different biomes have recently been defined (see below). Why is climate so important in defining biomes? Climatic factors, particularly temperature regimes and water availability, control the rate of photosynthesis by plants, which produce the organic molecules that provide the energy and carbon required by all other organisms in a biome.

In addition, climate influences the type of plants that make up the dominant vegetation of a biome through the selection pressures it creates: certain climatic regions favour certain adaptations and strategies. For example, in arid regions, the dominant plants have adaptations that store water or reduce water loss by evaporation, or that are metabolically active only in the wettest season, have an advantage over other plants. Biomes are often classified climatically (e.g., desert) or on the basis of the dominant vegetation (e.g., grassland, tropical rainforest).

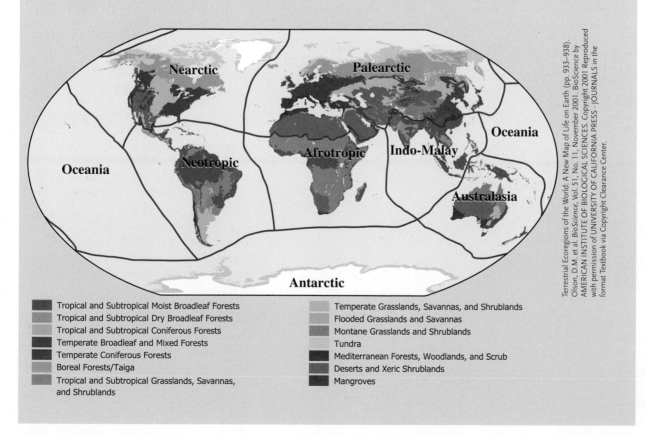

Terrestrial Ecoregions of the World: A New Map of Life on Earth (pp. 933–938). Olson, D.M. et al. *BioScience*, Vol. 51, No. 11, November 2001. BioScience by AMERICAN INSTITUTE OF BIOLOGICAL SCIENCES. Copyright 2001 Reproduced with permission of UNIVERSITY OF CALIFORNIA PRESS - JOURNALS in the format Textbook via Copyright Clearance Center.

- Tropical and Subtropical Moist Broadleaf Forests
- Tropical and Subtropical Dry Broadleaf Forests
- Tropical and Subtropical Coniferous Forests
- Temperate Broadleaf and Mixed Forests
- Temperate Coniferous Forests
- Boreal Forests/Taiga
- Tropical and Subtropical Grasslands, Savannas, and Shrublands
- Temperate Grasslands, Savannas, and Shrublands
- Flooded Grasslands and Savannas
- Montane Grasslands and Shrublands
- Tundra
- Mediterranean Forests, Woodlands, and Scrub
- Deserts and Xeric Shrublands
- Mangroves

History of the Earth

Geological Time Scale and Major Evolutionary Events

The Geological Time Scale and Major Evolutionary Events

Eons (Duration drawn to scale)	Eon	Era	Period	Epoch	Millions of Years Ago	Major Evolutionary Events
Phanerozoic: Cenozoic, Mesozoic, Paleozoic / Proterozoic	Phanerozoic	Cenozoic	Quaternary	Holocene	0.01	
				Pleistocene		Origin of humans; major glaciations
					1.7	
				Pliocene		Origin of apelike human ancestors
					5.2	
				Miocene		Angiosperms and mammals further diversify and dominate terrestrial habitats
					23	
			Tertiary	Oligocene		Divergence of primates; origin of apes
					33.4	
				Eocene		Angiosperms and insects diversify; modern orders of mammals differentiate
					55	
				Paleocene		Grasslands and deciduous woodlands spread; modern birds and mammals diversify; continents approach current positions
					65	
		Mesozoic	Cretaceous			Many lineages diversify: angiosperms, insects, marine invertebrates, fishes, dinosaurs; asteroid impact causes mass extinction at end of period, eliminating dinosaurs and many other groups
					144	
			Jurassic			Gymnosperms abundant in terrestrial habitats; first angiosperms; modern fishes diversify; dinosaurs diversify and dominate terrestrial habitats; frogs, salamanders, lizards, and birds appear; continents continue to separate
					206	
			Triassic			Predatory fishes and reptiles dominate oceans; gymnosperms dominate terrestrial habitats; radiation of dinosaurs; origin of mammals; Pangaea starts to break up; mass extinction at end of period
					251	

(continued)

The Geological Time Scale and Major Evolutionary Events (continued)

Eons (Duration drawn to scale)	Eon	Era	Period	Epoch	Millions of Years Ago	Major Evolutionary Events
Archaean	Phanerozoic (continued)	Paleozoic	Permian			Insects, amphibians, and reptiles abundant and diverse in swamp forests; some reptiles colonize oceans; fishes colonize freshwater habitats; continents coalesce into Pangaea, causing glaciation and decline in sea level; mass extinction at end of period eliminates 85% of species
			Carboniferous		290	Vascular plants form large swamp forests; first seed plants and flying insects; amphibians diversify; first reptiles appear
			Devonian		354	Terrestrial vascular plants diversify; fungi and invertebrates colonize land; first insects appear; first amphibians colonize land; major glaciation at end of period causes mass extinction, mostly of marine life
			Silurian		417	Jawless fishes diversify; first jawed fishes; first vascular plants on land
			Ordovician		443	Major radiations of marine invertebrates and fishes; major glaciation at end of period causes mass extinction of marine life
			Cambrian		490	Diverse radiation of modern animal phyla (Cambrian explosion); simple marine communities
	Proterozoic				543	High concentration of oxygen in atmosphere; origin of aerobic metabolism; origin of eukaryotic cells; evolution and diversification of protists, fungi, soft-bodied animals
	Archaean				2500	Evolution of prokaryotes, including anaerobic bacteria and photosynthetic bacteria; oxygen starts to accumulate in atmosphere
					3800	Formation of Earth at start of era; Earth's crust, atmosphere, and oceans form; origin of life at end of era
					4600	

Model Research Organisms

Certain species or groups of organisms have become favourite subjects for laboratory and field studies because their characteristics make them relatively easy research subjects. In most cases, such **model organisms** became popular because they have rapid development, short life cycles, and small adult size. Thus, researchers can rear and house large numbers of them in the laboratory. Also, as fuller portraits of their genetics and other aspects of their biology emerge, their appeal as research subjects tends to grow because biologists have a better understanding of the biological context within which specific processes occur. Because the fundamental elements of biochemistry, development, and evolution are common to all organisms, research on these small and often simple model organisms provides insight into biological processes that operate in and among larger and more complex organisms.

As a cautionary note, you should also be aware that the very characteristics that make model organisms valuable for research may make them poor representatives of other organisms in that group. Thus, specific findings from *Drosophila* or *Caenorhabditis elegans* may not be generally applicable to other insects or nematodes, respectively. The use of model organisms only, to the exclusion of others, may obscure the richness of biological diversity.

Escherichia coli

We probably know more about *Escherichia coli* than any other organism. For example, microbiologists have deciphered the complete DNA sequence of the genome of a standard laboratory strain of *E. coli*, including the sequence of the approximately 4400 genes in its genome. The functions of about one-third of these genes are still unidentified; however, *E. coli* got its start in laboratory research because of the ease with which it can be grown in cultures. Because *E. coli* cells divide about every 20 minutes under optimal conditions, a clone of 1 billion cells can be grown in a matter of hours in only 10 mL of culture medium. The same amount of medium can accommodate as many as 10 billion cells before the growth rate begins to slow. *E. coli* strains can be grown in the laboratory with minimal equipment, requiring little more than culture vessels in an incubator held at 37°C.

The study of naturally occurring plasmids in *E. coli* and of enzymes that cut DNA at specific sequences eventually resulted in the development of recombinant DNA techniques—procedures to combine DNA from different sources. Today, *E. coli* is used extensively for creating such molecules and for amplifying (cloning) them once they are made. In essence, the biotechnology industry has its foundation in molecular genetics studies of *E. coli*. Large-scale *E. coli* cultures are widely used as "factories" for the production of desired proteins. For example, the human insulin hormone, required for treatment of certain forms of diabetes, can be produced by *E. coli* factories.

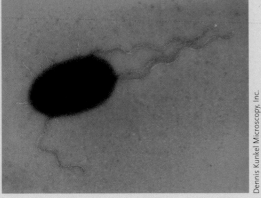

Dennis Kunkel Microscopy, Inc.

Saccharomyces cerevisiae

Commonly known as baker's yeast or brewer's yeast, *Saccharomyces cerevisiae* was probably the first microorganism to have been domesticated by humans—a beer-brewing vessel is basically a *Saccharomyces* culture. Favourite strains of baker's and brewer's yeasts have been kept in continuous cultures for centuries. The yeast has also been widely used in scientific research; its microscopic size and relatively short generation time make it easy and inexpensive to culture in large numbers in the laboratory.

The complete DNA sequence of *S. cerevisiae*, which includes more than 12 million base pairs that encode about 6000 genes, was the first eukaryotic genome to be determined. Plasmids, extrachromosomal segments of DNA, have been produced that are used to introduce genes into yeast cells. Using plasmids, researchers can experimentally alter any of the yeast genes to test their functions and can introduce genes or DNA samples from other organisms for testing or cloning. These genetic engineering studies have demonstrated that many mammalian genes can replace yeast genes when introduced into the fungi, confirming their close relationships, even though mammals and fungi are separated by millions of years of evolution. *S. cerevisiae* has been so important to genetic studies in eukaryotes that it is often called the eukaryotic *E. coli*. Research with another yeast, *Schizosaccharomyces pombe*, has been similarly productive, particularly in studies of genes that control the cell cycle.

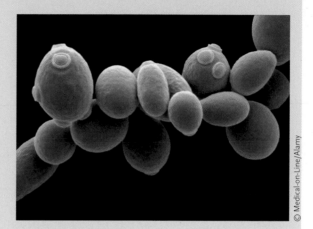

© Medical-on-Line/Alamy

Drosophila melanogaster

The unobtrusive little fruit fly that appears seemingly from nowhere when rotting fruit or a fermented beverage is around is one of the mainstays of genetic research. It was first described in 1830 by C. F. Fallén, who named it *Drosophila,* meaning "dew lover." The species identifier became *melanogaster,* which means "black belly." The great geneticist Thomas Hunt Morgan began to culture *D. melanogaster* in 1909 in the famous "Fly Room" at Columbia University. Many important discoveries in genetics were made in the Fly Room, including sex-linked genes and sex linkage and the first chromosome map. The subsequent development of methods to induce mutations in *Drosophila* led, through studies of the mutants produced, to many other discoveries that collectively established or confirmed essentially all of the major principles and conclusions of eukaryotic genetics.

One reason for the success of *D. melanogaster* as a subject for genetics research is the ease of culturing it. It is usually grown at 25°C in small bottles stopped with a cotton or plastic foam wad and about one-third filled with a fermenting medium that contains water, cornmeal, agar, molasses, and yeast. The several hundred eggs laid by each adult female hatch rapidly and progress through larval and pupal stages to produce adult flies in about 10 days. These are ready to breed within 10 to 12 hours. Males and females can be identified easily with the unaided eye.

Many types of mutations produce morphological differences, such as changes in eye colour, wing shape, or the numbers and shapes of bristles, which can be seen with the unaided eye or under a low-power binocular microscope. The salivary gland cells of the fly larvae have giant chromosomes that are so large that differences can be observed directly with a light microscope. The availability of a wide range of mutants and comprehensive linkage maps of each of its chromosomes, and the ability to manipulate genes readily by molecular techniques, made the fruit fly genome one of the first to be sequenced. The sequencing of *Drosophila*'s genome was completed in 2001; it has approximately 14 000 genes in its 165-million-base-pair genome. (A database of the *Drosophila* genome is available at http://flybase.bio.indiana.edu.) Importantly, the relationship between fruit fly and human genes is close, to the point that many human disease genes have counterparts in the fruit fly genome. This similarity enables the fly genes to be studied as models of human disease genes to better understand the functions of those genes and how alterations in them can lead to disease.

The analysis of fruit fly embryonic development has also contributed significantly to the understanding of development in humans. For example, experiments on mutants that affect fly development have provided insight into the genetic basis of many human birth defects. Before making a career as an environmentalist, David Suzuki studied temperature-sensitive neurological mutants at the University of British Columbia.

Herman Eisenbeiss/ Photo Researchers, Inc.

Caenorhabditis elegans

Researchers studying the tiny, free-living nematode *C. elegans* have made many advances in molecular genetics, animal development, and neurobiology. It is so popular as a model research organism that most workers simply refer to it as "the worm." Several attributes make *C. elegans* a model research organism. The adult is about 1 mm long and thrives on cultures of *E. coli* or other bacteria; thus, thousands can be raised in a culture dish. It completes its life cycle from egg to reproductive adult within three days at room temperature. Furthermore, stock cultures can be kept alive indefinitely by freezing them in liquid nitrogen or in an ultracold freezer (−80°C). Researchers can therefore store new mutants for later research without having to clean, feed, and maintain active cultures. Best of all, the worm is anatomically simple; an adult contains just 959 cells (excluding the gonads). Having a fixed cell number is relatively uncommon among animals, and developmental biologists have made good use of this trait. The eggs, juveniles, and adults of the worm are completely transparent, and researchers can observe cell divisions and cell movements in living animals with straightforward microscopy techniques. There is no need to kill, fix, and stain specimens for study. And virtually every cell in the worm's body is accessible for manipulation by laser microsurgery, microinjection, and similar approaches.

The genome of *C. elegans*, which was sequenced in 1998, is also simple, consisting of 100 million base pairs organized into roughly 17 000 genes on 6 pairs of chromosomes. The genome, which is about the same size as 1 human chromosome, specifies the amino acid sequences of about 10 000 protein molecules—far fewer than are found in more complex animals.

The knowledge gained from research on *C. elegans* is highly relevant to studies of larger and more complex organisms, including vertebrates. Recent research demonstrates some striking similarities among nematodes, fruit flies, and mice in the genetic control of development; in some of the proteins that govern important events such as cell death; and in the molecular signals used for cell-to-cell communication. Using a relatively simple model such as *C. elegans*, researchers can answer research questions more quickly and more efficiently than they could if they studied larger and more complex animals.

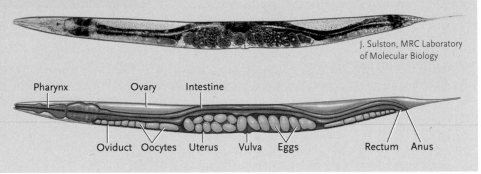

J. Sulston, MRC Laboratory of Molecular Biology

Pharynx   Ovary   Intestine

Oviduct   Oocytes   Uterus   Vulva   Eggs   Rectum   Anus

Arabidopsis thaliana

For plant geneticists, the little white-flowered thale cress, *Arabidopsis thaliana,* has attributes that make it a prime subject for genetic research. A tiny member of the mustard family, *Arabidopsis* is revealing answers to some of the biggest questions in plant development and physiology. Each plant grows only a few centimetres tall, so little laboratory space is required to house a large population. As long as *Arabidopsis* is provided with damp soil containing basic nutrients, it grows easily and rapidly in artificial light. Seeds grow to mature plants in just over a month and then flower and reproduce themselves in another three to four weeks. This permits investigators to perform desired genetic crosses and obtain large numbers of offspring with known, desired genotypes with relative ease.

The *Arabidopsis* genome was the first complete plant genome to be sequenced. Researchers have identified approximately 28 000 genes arranged on 5 pairs of chromosomes. The genome contains relatively little repetitive DNA, so it is fairly easy to isolate *Arabidopsis* genes, which can then be cloned using genetic engineering techniques. Cloned genes are inserted into bacterial plasmids, and the recombinant plasmids are transferred to the bacterial species *Agrobacterium tumefaciens,* which readily infects *Arabidopsis* cells. Amplified by the bacteria, the genes and their protein products can be sequenced or studied in other ways. Typically, researchers use chemical mutagens or recombinant bacteria to introduce changes in the *Arabidopsis* genome.

Courtesy of the Arabidopsis Information Resource, 2005

Danio rerio

The zebrafish (*Danio rerio*) is a small (3 cm) freshwater fish that gets its name from the black and white stripes running along its body. Native to India, it has spread around the world as a favourite aquarium fish. Beginning about 30 years ago, it began to be used in scientific laboratories as a model vertebrate organism for studying the roles of genes in development. Its use is now so widespread that it has been dubbed the "vertebrate fruit fly."

The zebrafish brings many advantages as a model research organism. It can be maintained easily in an ordinary aquarium on a simple diet. Although its generation time is relatively long (3 months for the zebrafish compared with 6 weeks for the mouse), a female zebrafish produces about 200 offspring at a time, compared with an average of 10 for the mouse. Embryonic development of the zebrafish takes place in eggs released to the outside by the female. The embryos develop rapidly, taking only three days from egg laying to hatching. Best of all, the eggs and embryos are transparent, providing an open window that allows researchers to observe developmental stages directly, with little or no disturbance to the embryo. Observational conditions are so favourable that the origin and fate of each cell can be traced from the fertilized egg to the hatchling. Individual nerve cells can be traced, for example, as they grow and make connections in the brain, spinal cord, and peripheral body regions. Removing or transplanting cells and tissues is also relatively easy. Biochemical and molecular studies can be carried out by techniques ranging from the simple addition of reactants to the water surrounding the embryos to injection of chemicals into individual cells.

The advantages of working with the zebrafish have spurred efforts to investigate its genetics, with particular interest in genes that regulate embryonic development. This work has already identified mutants of more than 2000 genes, including more than 400 genes that influence development. Most of the mechanisms controlled by the developmental genes resemble their counterparts in humans and other mammals. Developmental and physiological studies have revealed functions of some zebrafish genes that were previously unknown for their mammalian equivalents.

David Dohnal/Shutterstock

Mus musculus

The "wee, sleekit, cow'rin', tim'rous beastie," as the poet Robert Burns called the mouse (*Mus musculus*), has a much larger stature among scientists. The mouse and its cells have been used to great advantage as models for research on mammalian developmental genetics, immunology, and cancer. The availability of the mouse as a research tool enables scientists to carry out mammalian experiments that would not be practical or ethical with humans. Its small size makes the mouse relatively inexpensive and easy to maintain in the laboratory, and its short generation time, compared with most other mammals, allows genetic crosses to be carried out within a reasonable time span. Mice can be mated when they are 10 weeks old; in 18 to 22 days, the female gives birth to a litter of 5 to 10 offspring. A female may be rebred a little more than a day after giving birth.

Mice have a long and highly productive history as experimental animals. Gregor Mendel, the founder of genetics, is known to have kept mice as part of his studies. Toward the end of the nineteenth century, August Weissmann helped disprove an early evolutionary hypothesis, the inheritance of acquired characters, by cutting off the tails of mice for 22 successive generations and finding that it had no effect on tail length. The first example of a lethal allele was also found in mice, and pioneering experiments on the transplantation of tissues between individuals were conducted with mice. During the 1920s, Fred Griffith laid the groundwork for the research showing that DNA is the hereditary molecule in his work with pneumonia-causing bacteria in mice.

More recently, genetic experiments with mice have revealed more than 500 mutants that cause hereditary diseases, immunological defects, and cancer in mammals, including humans. The mouse has also been the mammal of choice for experiments that introduce and modify genes through genetic engineering. One of the most spectacular results of this research was the production of giant mice by introducing a human growth hormone gene into a line of dwarfed mice that were deficient for this hormone. Genetic engineering has also produced knockout mice (see "Knockouts: Genes and Behaviour," Box 39.1, Chapter 39) in which a gene of interest is completely nonfunctional. The effects of this lack of function often help investigators determine the role of the normal form of the gene. Some knockout mice are defective in genes homologous to human genes that cause

continued on next page

serious diseases, such as cystic fibrosis, so researchers can study the disease in mice with the goal of developing cures or therapies.

The revelations in developmental genetics from studies with the mouse have been of great interest and importance in their own right. In 2002, the sequence of the mouse genome was reported. This sequence is enabling researchers to refine and expand their use of the mouse as a model organism for studies of mammalian biology and mammalian diseases. More and more, as we find that much of what applies to the mouse also applies to humans, the findings in mice have shed new light on human development and

opened pathways to the possible cures of human genetic diseases.

© Peter Skinner/Photo Researchers, Inc.

Anolis Lizards of the Caribbean

The lizard genus *Anolis* has been a model system for studies in ecology and evolutionary biology since the 1960s, when Ernest E. Williams of Harvard University's Museum of Comparative Zoology first began studying it. With more than 400 known species—and new ones being described all the time—*Anolis* is one of the most diverse vertebrate genera known. Most anoles are less than 10 cm long, not including the tail, and many occur at high densities, making it easy to collect a lot of data in a relatively short time. Male anoles defend territories, and their displays make them conspicuous even in dense forests.

Anolis species are widely distributed in South America and Central America, but nearly 40% occupy Caribbean islands. The number of species on an island is generally proportional to the island's size. Cuba, the largest island, has more than 50 species, whereas small islands have just one or two. Studies by Williams and others suggest that the anoles on some large islands are the products of independent adaptive radiations. Eight of the 10 *Anolis* species now found in

Puerto Rico probably evolved on that island from a common ancestor. Similarly, the seven *Anolis* species in Jamaica shared a common ancestor, which was different from the ancestor of the Puerto Rican species. The anole faunas in Cuba and Hispaniola are the products of several independent radiations on each island. Williams discovered that these independent radiations had produced similar-looking species on different islands. He developed the concept of the *ecomorph*, a group of species that have similar morphological, behavioural, and ecological characteristics even though they are not closely related within the genus. Williams named the ecomorphs after the vegetation that they commonly used. For example, grass anoles are small, slender species that usually perch on low, thin vegetation. Trunk-ground anoles have chunky bodies and large heads, and they perch low on tree trunks, frequently jumping to the ground to feed. Although the grass anoles or the trunk-ground anoles on different islands are similar in many ways, they are not closely related to each other. Their resemblances are the products of convergent evolution.

A. cooki

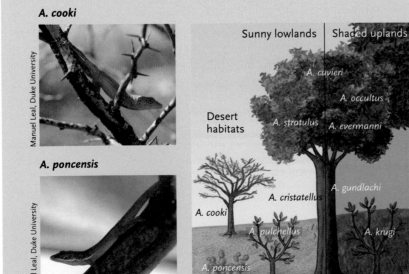

Manuel Leal, Duke University

A. poncensis

Manuel Leal, Duke University

Sunny lowlands | Shaded uplands

Desert habitats

A. cuvieri

A. occultus

A. stratulus   A. evermanni

A. cooki   A. cristatellus   A. gundlachi

A. pulchellus   A. krugi

A. poncensis

A. gundlachi

Manuel Leal, Duke University

A. krugi

Manuel Leal, Duke University

Glossary

3′ end The end of a polynucleotide chain at which a hydroxyl group is bonded to the 3 carbon of a deoxyribose sugar. p. 262

5′ cap In eukaryotes, a guanine-containing nucleotide attached in a reverse orientation to the 5′ end of pre-mRNA and retained in the mRNA produced from it. The 5′ cap on an mRNA is the site where ribosomes attach to initiate translation. p. 291

5′ end The end of a polynucleotide chain at which a phosphate group is bound to the 5 carbon of a deoxyribose sugar. p. 262

10 nm chromatin fibre The most fundamental level of chromatin packing of a eukaryotic chromosome in which DNA winds for almost two turns around an eight-protein nucleosome core particle to form a nucleosome and linker DNA extends between adjacent nucleosomes. The result is a beads-on-a-string type of structure with a 10 nm diameter. p. 278

30 nm chromatin fibre Level of chromatin packing of a eukaryotic chromosome in which histone H1 binds to the 10 nm chromatin fibre, causing it to package into a coiled structure about 30 nm in diameter and with about six nucleosomes per turn. Also referred to as a *solenoid*. p. 278

A site The site where the incoming aminoacyl-tRNA carrying the next amino acid to be added to the polypeptide chain binds to the mRNA. p. 298

abdomen The region of the body that contains much of the digestive tract and sometimes part of the reproductive system; in insects, the region behind the thorax. p. 256

abiotic Nonbiological, often in reference to physical factors in the environment. p. 51

absorption spectrum Curve representing the amount of light absorbed at each wavelength. p. 143

acid Proton donor that releases H (and anions) when dissolved in water. p. 26

acidity The concentration of H in a water solution, compared with the concentration of OH⁻. p. 89

action spectrum Graph produced by plotting the effectiveness of light at each wavelength in driving photosynthesis. p. 144

activation energy The initial input of energy required to start a reaction. p. 81

activator A regulatory protein that controls the expression of one or more genes. pp. 310, 317

active site The region of an enzyme that recognizes and combines with a substrate molecule. p. 84

active transport The mechanism by which ions and molecules move against the concentration gradient across a membrane, from the side with the lower concentration to the side with the higher concentration. p. 104

adenine A purine that base-pairs with either thymine in DNA or uracil in RNA. p. 262

adhesion The adherence of molecules to the walls of conducting tubes, as in plants. p. 45

adult stem cell Mammalian stem cells that can differentiate into a limited number of cell types associated with the tissue in which they occur. p. 346

agarose gel electrophoresis Technique by which DNA, RNA, or molecules are separated in a gel subjected to an electric field. p. 340

alcohol A molecule of the form R—OH in which R is a chain of one or more carbon atoms, each of which is linked to hydrogen atoms. p. 95

alcoholic fermentation Reaction in which pyruvate is converted into ethyl alcohol and CO_2 in a two-step series that also converts NADH into NAD′. p. 133

allele One of two or more versions of a gene. pp. 193, 214

allosteric activator Molecule that converts an enzyme with an allosteric site, a regulatory site outside the active site, from the inactive form to the active form. p. 88

allosteric inhibitor Molecule that converts an enzyme with an allosteric site, a regulatory site outside the active site, from the active form to the inactive form. p. 88

allosteric regulation Specialized control mechanism for enzymes with an allosteric site, a regulatory site outside the active site, that may either slow or accelerate activity depending on the enzyme. p. 86

allosteric site A regulatory site outside the active site. p. 86

alternative hypothesis An explanation of an observed phenomenon that is different from the explanation being tested. p. 56

alternative splicing Mechanism that joins exons in different combinations to produce different mRNAs from a single gene. p. 293

amino acid A molecule that contains both an amino and a carboxyl group. p. 30

amino group Group that acts as an organic base, consisting of a nitrogen atom bonded on one side to two hydrogen atoms and on the other side to a carbon chain. p. 80

aminoacylation The process of adding an amino acid to a tRNA. Also referred to as *charging*. p. 296

aminoacyl–tRNA A tRNA linked to its "correct" amino acid, which is the finished product of charging. p. 296

aminoacyl–tRNA synthetase An enzyme that catalyzes aminoacylation. p. 296

amniocentesis Technique of prenatal diagnosis in which cells are obtained from the amniotic fluid. p. 252

amphipathic Contains a region that is hydrophobic and a region that is hydrophilic. p. 95

amplification An increase in the magnitude of each step as a signal transduction pathway proceeds. p. 111

amyloplast Colourless plastid that stores starch in plants. p. 43

anabolic pathway Type of metabolic pathway in which energy is consumed to build complicated molecules from simpler ones; often called a biosynthetic pathway. p. 77

anabolic reaction Metabolic reaction that requires energy to assemble simple substances into more complex molecules. p. 115

anaerobe An organism that does not require oxygen to live. p. 134

anaphase The phase of mitosis during which the spindle separates sister chromatids and pulls them to opposite spindle poles. p. 168

anchoring junction Cell junction that forms belts that run entirely around cells, "welding" adjacent cells together. p. 45

aneuploid An individual with extra or missing chromosomes. p. 246

antenna A chemosensory appendage attached to the head of some adult arthropods. p. 145

antiparallel Strands of DNA that run in opposite directions. p. 263

antiport A secondary active transport mechanism in which a molecule moves through a membrane channel into a cell and powers the active transport of a second molecule out of the cell. Also referred to as *exchange diffusion*. p. 107

Antenna complex (light-harvesting complex) In photosystems, the sites at which light is absorbed and converted into chemical energy during photosynthesis, an aggregate of many chlorophyll pigments and a number of carotenoid pigments that serve as the primary site of absorbing light energy in the form of photons. p. 145

antibody A highly specific soluble protein molecule that circulates in the blood and lymph, recognizing and binding to antigens and clearing them from the body. p. 227

anticodon The three-nucleotide segment in tRNAs that pairs with a codon in mRNAs. p. 295

apoptosis Programmed cell death. p. 176

arteries In vertebrates, vessels conducting blood away from the heart. p. 235

aster Radiating array produced as microtubules extending from the centrosomes of cells grow in length and extent. p. 172

atmosphere The component of the biosphere that includes the gases and airborne particles enveloping the planet. p. 2

atom The smallest unit that retains the chemical and physical properties of an element. p. F-9

atomic nucleus The nucleus of an atom, containing protons and neutrons. p. 117

atomic number The number of protons in the nucleus of an atom. p. F-9

ATP (adenosine triphosphate) The primary agent that couples exergonic and endergonic reactions. p. 4

ATP cycle Continued breakdown and resynthesis of ATP. p. 81

ATP synthase A membrane-spanning protein complex that couples the energetically favourable transport of protons across a membrane to the synthesis of ATP. p. 127

autosomal dominant inheritance Pattern in which the allele that causes a trait is dominant, and only homozygous recessives are unaffected. p. 250

autosomal recessive inheritance Pattern in which individuals with a trait are homozygous for a recessive allele. p. 250

autosome Chromosome other than a sex chromosome. p. 240

autotroph An organism that produces its own food using CO_2 and other simple inorganic compounds from its environment and energy from the sun or from oxidation of inorganic substances. pp. 61, 140

auxotrophs Mutant strains that are unable to synthesize amino acids. p. 183

Avogadro's number The number 6.022×10^{23}, derived by dividing the atomic weight of any element by the weight of an atom of that element. p. F-18

bacterial chromosome DNA molecule in bacteria in which hereditary information is encoded. p. 279

bacteriophage A virus that infects bacteria. Also referred to as a *phage*. pp. 188, 260

Barr body The inactive, condensed X chromosome seen in the nucleus of female mammals. p. 244

base Proton acceptor that reduces the H concentration of a solution. p. 42

base-pair mismatch An error in the assembly of a new nucleotide chain in which bases other than the correct ones pair together. p. 276

base-pair substitution mutation A particular mutation involving a change from one base pair to another in DNA. p. 304

basic research Research conducted to search for explanations about natural phenomena to satisfy curiosity and advance collective knowledge of living systems. p. 231

bilayer A membrane with two molecular layers. p. 28

binary fission Prokaryotic cell division—splitting or dividing into two parts. p. 163

bioinformatics Field that fuses biology with mathematics and computer science that is used for the analysis of genome sequences. p. 356

biological research The collective effort of individuals who have worked to understand how living systems function. p. F-2

biome A large-scale vegetation type and its associated microorganisms, fungi, and animals. p. F-49

biosphere All regions of Earth's crust, waters, and atmosphere that sustain life. p. 4

biotechnology The manipulation of living organisms to produce useful products. p. 258

biotic Biological, often in reference to living components of the environment. p. 51

blending theory of inheritance Theory suggesting that hereditary traits blend evenly in offspring through mixing of the blood of the two parents. p. 212

blood A fluid connective tissue composed of blood cells suspended in a fluid extracellular matrix, plasma. p. 17

breathing The exchange of gases with the respiratory medium by animals. p. 93

buffer Substance that compensates for pH changes by absorbing or releasing H^+. p. 343

bulk-phase endocytosis Mechanism by which extracellular water is taken into a cell together with any molecules that happen to be in solution in the water. Also referred to as *pinocytosis*. p. 107

Ca^{2+} pump (calcium pump) Pump that pushes Ca^{2+} from the cytoplasm to the cell exterior and from the cytosol into the vesicles of the endoplasmic reticulum. p. 104

Calvin cycle *See* light-independent reaction. p. 4

calyx The outermost whorl of a flower, made up of sepals; early in the development of a flower, it encloses all of the other parts, as in an unopened bud. p. 31

CAM plant A C_4 plant that runs the Calvin and C_4 cycles at different times to circumvent photorespiration. CAM stands for "crassulacean acid metabolism." p. 156

capsule An external layer of sticky or slimy polysaccharides coating the cell wall in many prokaryotes. p. 31

carotenoid Molecule of yellow-orange pigment by which light is absorbed in photosynthesis. p. 8

carrier An individual who carries a mutant allele and could pass it on to offspring but does not display its symptoms. p. 243

carrier protein Transport protein that binds a specific single solute and transports it across the lipid bilayer. p. 101

Cartagena Protocol on Biosafety An international agreement that promotes biosafety as it relates to genetically modified organisms. p. 352

caspase A protease involved in programmed cell death. p. 176

catabolic pathway Type of metabolic pathway in which energy is released by the breakdown of complex molecules to simpler compounds. p. 77

catabolic reaction Cellular reaction that breaks down complex molecules such as sugar to make their energy available for cellular work. p. 81

catalyst Substance with the ability to accelerate a spontaneous reaction without being changed by the reaction. p. 82

cDNA library The entire collection of cloned cDNAs made from the mRNAs isolated from a cell. p. 337

cell Smallest unit with the capacity to live and reproduce. p. 2

cell adhesion molecule A cell surface protein responsible for selectively binding cells together. p. 45

cell adhesion protein Protein that binds cells together by recognizing and binding receptors or chemical groups on other cells or on the extracellular matrix. p. 45

cell culture A living cell grown in a laboratory vessel. p. 166

cell cycle The sequence of events during which a cell experiences a period of growth followed by nuclear division and cytokinesis. p. 67

cell junction Junction that seals the spaces between cells and provides direct communication between cells. p. 45

cell plate In cytokinesis in plants, a new cell wall that forms between the daughter nuclei and grows laterally until it divides the cytoplasm. p. 169

cell theory Three generalizations yielded by microscopic observations: all organisms are composed of one or more cells; the cell is the smallest unit that has the properties of life; and cells arise only from the growth and division of preexisting cells. p. 26

cell wall A rigid external layer of material surrounding the plasma membrane of cells in plants, fungi, bacteria, and some protists, providing cell protection and support. p. 30

cellular respiration The process by which energy-rich molecules are broken down to produce energy in the form of ATP. p. 116

cellular senescence Loss of proliferative ability over time. p. 175

centimorgan *See* map unit. p. 239

central nervous system (CNS) One of the two major divisions of the nervous system containing the brain and spinal cord. p. 37

central vacuole A large, water-filled organelle in plant cells that maintains the turgor of the cell and controls movement of molecules between the cytosol and sap. p. 44

centriole A cylindrical structure consisting of nine triplets of microtubules in the centrosomes of most animal cells. p. 171

centromere A specialized chromosomal region that connects sister chromatids and attaches them to the mitotic spindle. p. 167

centrosome (cell centre) The main microtubule organizing centre of a cell, which organizes the microtubule cytoskeleton during interphase and positions many of the cytoplasmic organelles. pp. 40, 171

channel protein Transport protein that forms a hydrophilic channel in a cell membrane through which water, ions, or other molecules can pass, depending on the protein. p. 101

chaperone protein (chaperonin) "Guide" protein that binds temporarily with newly synthesized proteins, directing their conformation toward the correct tertiary structure and inhibiting incorrect arrangements as the new proteins fold. p. F-36

character A heritable characteristic. p. 212

charging *See* aminoacylation. p. 296

checkpoint Internal control of the cell cycle that prevents a critical phase from beginning until the previous phase is complete. p. 174

chemical bond Link formed when atoms of reactive elements combine into molecules. p. F-11

chemical equation A chemical reaction written in balanced form. p. F-14

chemical reaction A reaction that occurs when atoms or molecules interact to form new chemical bonds or break old ones. p. F-14

chemiosmosis Ability of cells to use the proton-motive force to do work. p. 127

chiasmata *See* crossover. p. 200

chitin A polysaccharide that contains nitrogen and is present in the cell walls of fungi and the exoskeletons of arthropods. p. 45

chlorophyll Molecule of green pigment that absorbs photons of light in photosynthesis. p. 4

chloroplast The site of photosynthesis in plant cells. p. 43

cholesterol The predominant sterol of animal cell membranes. p. 97

chorionic villus sampling Technique of prenatal diagnosis in which cells are obtained from portions of the placenta that develop from tissues of the embryo. p. 252

chromatids One half of a replicated chromosome. Each chromatid is one double helix of DNA. p. 164

chromatin The structural building block of a chromosome, which includes the complex of DNA and its associated proteins. pp. 33, 277

chromatin remodelling Process in which the state of the chromatin is changed so that the proteins that initiate transcription can bind to their promoters. p. 321

chromosomal protein The histone and nonhistone protein associated with DNA structure and regulation in the nucleus. p. 277

chromosome The nuclear unit of genetic information, consisting of a DNA molecule and associated proteins. p. 33

chromosome segregation The equal distribution of daughter chromosomes to each of the two cells that result from cell division. p. 165

chromosome theory of inheritance The principle that genes and their alleles are carried on the chromosomes. p. 223

cilium Motile structure, extending from a cell surface, that moves a cell through fluid or fluid over a cell. p. 41

cisternae (singular, cisterna) Membranous channels and vesicles that make up the endoplasmic reticulum. p. 34

citric acid cycle Series of reactions in which acetyl groups are oxidized completely to carbon dioxide and some ATP molecules are synthesized. Also referred to as *Krebs cycle* and *tricarboxylic acid cycle*. p. 123

clathrin The network of proteins that coat and reinforce the cytoplasmic surface of cell membranes. p. 109

climate The weather conditions prevailing over an extended period of time. p. 153

clone An individual genetically identical to an original cell from which it descended. pp. 166, 183

coactivator (mediator) In eukaryotes, a large multiprotein complex that bridges between activators at an enhancer and proteins at the promoter and promoter proximal region to stimulate transcription. p. 318

coated pit A depression in the plasma membrane that contains receptors for macromolecules to be taken up by endocytosis. p. 109

codominance Condition in which alleles have approximately equal effects in individuals, making the alleles equally detectable in heterozygotes. p. 226

codon Each three-letter word (triplet) of the genetic code. p. 287

coenzymes Organic cofactors that include complex chemical groups of various kinds. p. 84

cofactor An inorganic or organic nonprotein group that is necessary for catalysis to take place. p. 84

cohesion The high resistance of water molecules to separation. p. F-16

colon The main part of the large intestine. p. 178

combinatorial gene regulation The combining of a few regulatory proteins in particular ways so that the transcription of a wide array of genes can be controlled and a large number of cell types can be specified. p. 319

commaless The sequential nature of the words of the nucleic acid code, with no indicators such as commas or spaces to mark the end of one codon and the beginning of the next. p. 288

community Populations of all species that occupy the same area. p. 315

comparative genomics A technique for discovering relatedness among organisms by considering the similarity of their respective genome sequences. p. 355

competitive inhibition Inhibition of an enzyme reaction by an inhibitor molecule that resembles the normal substrate closely enough so that it fits into the active site of the enzyme. p. 85

complementary base-pairing Feature of DNA in which the specific purine–pyrimidine base pairs A–T (adenine–thymine) and G–C (guanine–cytosine) occur to bridge the two sugar–phosphate backbones. p. 263

complementary DNA (cDNA) A DNA molecule that is complementary to an mRNA molecule, synthesized by reverse transcriptase. p. 337

compound A molecule whose component atoms are different. p. F-8

concentration The number of molecules or ions of a substance in a unit volume of space. p. F-18

concentration gradient The concentration difference that drives diffusion. p. 76

conformation The overall three-dimensional shape of a protein. p. 84

conjugation In bacteria, the process by which a copy of part of the DNA of a donor cell moves through the cytoplasmic bridge into the recipient cell where genetic recombination can occur. In ciliate protozoans, a process of sexual reproduction in which individuals of the same species temporarily couple and exchange genetic material. p. 185

contact inhibition The inhibition of movement or -proliferation of normal cells that results from cell–cell contact. p. 175

control Treatment that tells what would be seen in the absence of the experimental manipulation. p. F-3

core The nucleic acid centre of a virus in the free form. p. 279

corepressor In the regulation of gene expression in bacteria, a regulatory molecule that combines with a repressor to activate it and shut off an operon. pp. 313, 318

cotranslational import A mechanism in which proteins end up on the inside (lumen) of the endoplasmic reticulum (ER) as they are translated by ribosome associated with the ER. p. 303

cotransport *See* symport. p. 107

coupled reaction Reaction that occurs when an exergonic reaction is joined to an endergonic reaction, producing an overall reaction that is exergonic. p. 80

covalent bond Bond formed by electron sharing between atoms. p. 13

crista (plural, cristae) Fold that expands the surface area of the inner mitochondrial membrane. p. 38

crossing-over The recombination process in meiosis, in which chromatids exchange segments. p. 200

crossover Site of recombination during meiosis. Also referred to as a *chiasmata*. p. 200

cross-pollination Fertilization of one plant by a different plant. p. 213

C-terminal end The end of an amino acid chain with a —COO group. p. 294

cyclic AMP (cAMP) In particular signal transduction pathways, a second messenger that activates protein kinases, which elicit the cellular response by adding phosphate groups to specific target proteins. cAMP functions in one of two major G protein-coupled receptor-response pathways. p. 313

cyclic electron transport An electron transport pathway associated with photosystem I in photosynthesis that produces ATP without the synthesis of NADPH. p. 149

cyclin In eukaryotes, protein that regulates the activity of CDK (cyclin-dependent kinase) and controls progression through the cell cycle. p. 174

cyclin-dependent kinase (CDK) A protein kinase that controls the cell cycle in eukaryotes. p. 174

cytochrome Protein with a heme prosthetic group that contains an iron atom. p. 125

cytokinesis Division of the cytoplasm into two daughter cells following the nuclear division stage of mitosis. p. 169

cytoplasmic inheritance Pattern in which inheritance follows that of genes in the cytoplasmic organelles, mitochondria, or chloroplasts. p. 253

cytoplasmic streaming Intracellular movement of cytoplasm. p. 41

cytosine A pyrimidine that base-pairs with guanine in nucleic acids. p. 262

cytoskeleton The interconnected system of protein fibres and tubes that extends throughout the cytoplasm of a eukaryotic cell. p. 29

cytosol Aqueous solution in the cytoplasm containing ions and various organic molecules. p. 29

dalton A standard unit of mass, about 1.66×10^{24} grams. p. 327

decomposer A small organism, such as a bacterium or fungus, that feeds on the remains of dead organisms, breaking down complex biological molecules or structures into simpler raw materials. p. 140

degeneracy (redundancy) The feature of the genetic code in which, with two exceptions, more than one codon represents each amino acid. p. 288

deletion Chromosomal alteration that occurs if a broken segment is lost from a chromosome. p. 245

denaturation A loss of both the structure and function of a protein due to extreme conditions that unfold it from its conformation. p. F-36

deoxyribonucleic acid (DNA) The large, double-stranded, helical molecule that contains the genetic material of all living organisms. p. 258

deoxyribose A five-carbon sugar to which the nitrogenous bases in nucleotides of DNA link covlently. p. F-37

descent with modification Biological evolution. p. 17

development A series of programmed changes encoded in DNA, through which a fertilized egg divides into many cells that ultimately are transformed into an adult, which is itself capable of reproduction. p. 8

diffusion The net movement of ions or molecules from a region of higher concentration to a region of lower concentration. p. 100

digestion The splitting of carbohydrates, proteins, lipids, and nucleic acids in foods into chemical subunits small enough to be absorbed into the body fluids and cells of an animal. p. 37

dihybrid A zygote produced from a cross that involves two characters. p. 219

dihybrid cross A cross between two individuals that are heterozygous for two pairs of alleles. p. 220

diploid An organism or cell with two copies of each type of chromosome in its nucleus. p. 164

discontinuous replication Replication in which a DNA strand is formed in short lengths that are synthesized in the direction opposite of DNA unwinding. p. 270

DNA *See* deoxyribonucleic acid. p. 258

DNA chip *See* DNA microarray. p. 358

DNA fingerprinting Technique in which DNA samples are used to distinguish between individuals of the same species. p. 342

DNA helicase An enzyme that catalyzes the unwinding of DNA template strands. p. 269

DNA hybridization Technique in which a gene or sequence of interest is identified in a set of clones when it base-pairs with a single-stranded DNA or RNA molecule called a nucleic acid probe. p. 337

DNA ligase In DNA replication, an enzyme that seals the nicks left after RNA primers are replaced with DNA. p. 270

DNA methylation Process in which a methyl group is added enzymatically to cytosine bases in the DNA. p. 321

DNA microarray A solid surface divided into a microscopic grid of thousands of spaces each containing thousands of copies of a DNA probe. DNA chips are used commonly for analysis of gene activity and for detecting differences between cell types. Also referred to as a *DNA chip*. p. 358

DNA polymerase An enzyme that assembles complementary nucleotide chains during DNA replication. p. 275

DNA polymerase I A specialized polymerase responsible for removing RNA primers and replacing them with DNA. p. 270

DNA polymerase III The main, "general purpose" polymerase for replicating DNA. p. 270

DNA repair mechanism Mechanism to correct base-pair mismatches that escape proofreading. p. 276

DNA technologies Techniques to isolate, purify, analyze, and manipulate DNA sequences. p. 333

dominance The masking effect of one allele over another. p. 215

dominant The allele expressed when more than one allele is present. p. 10

double helix Two nucleotide chains wrapped around each other in a spiral. p. 13

double-helix model Model of DNA consisting of two complementary sugar–phosphate backbones. p. 263

duplication Chromosomal alteration that occurs if a segment is broken from one chromosome and inserted into its homologue. p. 245

E site The site where an exiting tRNA binds prior to its release from the ribosome. p. 298

ecology The study of the interactions between organisms and their environments. p. 1

ecosystem A group of biological communities interacting with their shared physical environment. p. 23

electrochemical gradient A difference in chemical concentration and electric potential across a membrane. p. 105

electromagnetic spectrum The range of wavelengths or frequencies of electromagnetic radiation extending from gamma rays to the longest radio waves and including visible light. p. 2

electron Negatively charged particle outside the nucleus of an atom. p. 4

electron microscope Microscope that uses electrons to illuminate the specimen. p. 27

electron transfer system Stage of cellular respiration in which high-energy electrons produced from glycolysis, pyruvate oxidation, and the citric acid cycle are delivered to oxygen by a sequence of electron carriers. p. 119

electronegativity The measure of an atom's attraction for the electrons it shares in a chemical bond with another atom. p. F-13

element A pure substance that cannot be broken down into simpler substances by ordinary chemical or physical techniques. p. F-8

elongation factor Proteins that promote various steps in the elongation of peptides during translation. p. 300

embryo An organism in its early stage of reproductive development, beginning in the first moments after fertilization. p. 45

embryonic stem cell Stem cells in the mammalian embryo that can differentiate into any cell type. p. 346

endergonic reaction Reaction that can proceed only if free energy is supplied. p. 77

endocytic vesicle Vesicle that carries proteins and other molecules from the plasma membrane to destinations within the cell. p. 36

endocytosis In eukaryotes, the process by which molecules are brought into the cell from the exterior involving a bulging in of the plasma membrane that pinches off to form an endocytic vesicle. p. 36

endomembrane system In eukaryotes, a collection of interrelated internal membranous sacs that divide a cell into functional and structural compartments. p. 34

endoplasmic reticulum (ER) In eukaryotes, an extensive interconnected network of cisternae that is responsible for the synthesis, transport, and initial modification of proteins and lipids. p. 34

endosymbiont hypothesis The proposal that the membranous organelles of eukaryotic cells (mitochondria and chloroplasts) may have originated from symbiotic relationships between two prokaryotic cells. p. 65

endosymbiosis A symbiotic association in which one symbiont or partner lives inside the other. p. 64

endothermic Reactions that absorb energy. p. 76

end-product inhibition *See* feedback inhibition. p. 88

energy The capacity to do work. p. 67

energy coupling The process by which ATP is brought in close contact with a reactant molecule involved in an endergonic reaction, and when the ATP is hydrolyzed, the terminal phosphate group is transferred to the reactant molecule. p. 79

energy levels Regions of space within an atom where electrons are found. Also referred to as *energy shells*. p. 116

enhancer In eukaryotes, a region at a significant distance from the beginning of a gene containing regulatory sequences that determine whether the gene is transcribed at its maximum possible rate. p. 316

enthalpy Potential energy in a system. p. 76

entropy Disorder, in thermodynamics. p. 74

envelope Outer glycoprotein layer surrounding the capsid of some viruses, derived in part from host cell plasma membrane. p. 33

enzyme Protein that accelerates the rate of a cellular reaction. p. 82

epigenetics The study of changes to gene expression that do not arise from changes in the DNA sequence (ie. mutations). Epigenetic changes may arise from chemical modification of bases (e.g. methylation), chromatin remodelling, protein or RNA binding etc. p. 321

epistasis Interaction of genes, with one or more alleles of a gene at one locus inhibiting or masking the effects of one or more alleles of a gene at a different locus. p. 228

equilibrium point A state of balance between opposing factors that push a reaction in either direction. p. 77

ER (endoplasmic reticulum) lumen The enclosed space surrounded by a cisterna. p. 34

essential nutrient Any of the essential amino acids, fatty acids, vitamins, and minerals required in the diet of an animal. p. 14

euchromatin In eukaryotes, regions of loosely packed chromatin fibres in interphase nuclei. p. 278

eukaryote Organism in which the DNA is enclosed in a nucleus. p. 30

eukaryotic chromosome A DNA molecule, with its associated proteins, in the nucleus of a eukaryotic cell. p. 33

euploid An individual with a normal set of chromosomes. p. 246

exchange diffusion *See* antiport. p. 107

exergonic reaction Reaction that has a negative ΔG because it releases free energy. p. 77

exocytosis In eukaryotes, the process by which a secretory vesicle fuses with the plasma membrane and releases the vesicle contents to the exterior. p. 36

exon An amino acid–coding sequence present in pre-mRNA that is retained in a spliced mRNA that is translated to produce a polypeptide. p. 292

exothermic Processes that release energy. p. 76

experimental variable The variable to which any difference in observations of experimental treatment subjects and control treatment subjects is attributed. p. F-3

expression vector A plasmid that can not only carry cloned genes, but can also drive their expression. p. 345

eye The organ animals use to sense light. p. 9

F^- cell Recipient cell in conjugation between bacteria. p. 187

F^+ cell Donor cell in conjugation between bacteria. p. 187

F_1 generation The first generation of offspring from a genetic cross. p. 214

F_2 generation The second generation of offspring from a genetic cross. p. 214

F pilus Structure on the cell surface that allows an F^+ donor bacterial cell to attach to an F^- recipient bacterial cell. Also referred to as a *sex pilus*. p. 187

facilitated diffusion Mechanism by which polar and charged molecules diffuse across membranes with the help of transport proteins. p. 100

fat Neutral lipid that is semisolid at biological temperatures. p. 98

fatty acid One of two components of a neutral lipid, containing a single hydrocarbon chain with a carboxyl group linked at one end. p. 37

feather A sturdy, lightweight structure of birds, derived from scales in the skin of their ancestors. p. 13

feedback inhibition In enzyme reactions, regulation in which the product of a reaction acts as a regulator of the reaction. Also referred to as *end-product inhibition*. p. 88

fermentation Process in which electrons carried by NADH are transferred to an organic acceptor molecule rather than to the electron transfer system. p. 132

fertilization The fusion of the nuclei of an egg and sperm cell, which initiates development of a new individual. p. 191

first law of thermodynamics The principle that energy can be transferred and transformed but cannot be created or destroyed. p. 73

flagellum (plural, flagella) A long, threadlike, cellular appendage responsible for movement; found in both prokaryotes and eukaryotes, but with different structures and modes of locomotion. p. 31

fluid mosaic model Model proposing that the membrane consists of a fluid phospholipid bilayer in which proteins are embedded and float freely. p. 93

follicle The ovum and follicle cells. p. 39

food chain A depiction of the trophic structure of a community, a portrait of who eats whom. p. 349

fossil The remains or traces of an organism of a past geologic age embedded and preserved in Earth's crust. p. 10

frameshift mutation Mutation in a protein-coding gene that causes the reading frame of an mRNA transcribed from the gene to be altered, resulting in the production of a different, and nonfunctional, amino acid sequence in the polypeptide. p. 304

free energy The energy in a system that is available to do work. p. 76

freeze-fracture technique Technique in which experimenters freeze a block of cells rapidly and then fracture the block to split the lipid bilayer and expose the hydrophobic membrane interior. p. 95

functional genomics The study of the functions of genes and of other parts of the genome. p. 355

functional groups The atoms in reactive groups. p. F-22

furrow In cytokinesis, a groove that girdles the cell and gradually deepens until it cuts the cytoplasm into two parts. p. 169

G_0 phase The phase of the cell cycle in eukaryotes in which many cell types stop dividing. p. 166

G_1 phase The initial growth stage of the cell cycle in eukaryotes, during which the cell makes proteins and other types of cellular molecules but not nuclear DNA. p. 165

G_2 phase The phase of the cell cycle in eukaryotes during which the cell continues to synthesize proteins and grow, completing interphase. p. 165

gamete A haploid cell, an egg or sperm. Haploid cells fuse during sexual reproduction to form a diploid zygote. p. 191

gametophyte An individual of the haploid generation produced when a spore germinates and grows directly by mitotic divisions in organisms that undergo alternation of generations. p. 192

gap junction Junction that opens direct channels allowing ions and small molecules to pass directly from one cell to another. p. 46

gated channel Ion transporter in a membrane that switches between open, closed, or intermediate states. p. 101

gene A unit containing the code for a protein molecule or one of its parts, or for functioning RNA molecules such as tRNA and rRNA. p. 43

gene therapy Correction of genetic disorders using genetic engineering techniques. p. 346

general transcription factor (basal transcription factor) In eukaryotes, a protein that binds to the promoter of a gene in the area of the TATA box and recruits and orients RNA polymerase II to initiate transcription at the correct place. p. 316

generalized transduction Transfer of bacterial genes between bacteria using virulent phages that have incorporated random DNA fragments of the bacterial genome. p. 188

genetic code The nucleotide information that specifies the amino acid sequence of a polypeptide. p. 286

genetic counselling Counselling that allows prospective parents to assess the possibility that they might have a child affected by a genetic disorder. p. 251

genetic engineering The use of DNA technologies to alter genes for practical purposes. p. 333

genetic recombination The process by which the combinations of alleles for different genes in two parental individuals become shuffled into new combinations in offspring individuals. p. 181

genetic screening Biochemical or molecular tests for identifying inherited disorders after a child is born. p. 252

genetically modified organism (GMO) A transgenic organism. p. 352

genomic library A collection of clones that contains a copy of every DNA sequence in a genome. p. 337

genome The entire collection of DNA sequence for a given organism. p. 65

genomic imprinting Pattern of inheritance in which the expression of a nuclear gene is based on whether an individual organism inherits the gene from the male or the female parent. pp. 253, 321

genotype The genetic constitution of an organism. p. 215

genus A Linnaean taxonomic category ranking below a family and above a species. p. 4

germ-line gene therapy Therapy in which a gene is introduced into germ-line cells of an animal to correct a genetic disorder. p. 347

glycocalyx A carbohydrate coat covering the cell surface. p. 31

glycogen Energy-providing carbohydrates stored in animal cells. p. 130

glycolysis Stage of cellular respiration in which sugars such as glucose are partially oxidized and broken down into smaller molecules. p. 120

Golgi complex In eukaryotes, the organelle responsible for the final modification, sorting, and distribution of proteins and lipids. p. 36

guanine A purine that base-pairs with cytosine in nucleic acids. p. 262

half-life The time it takes for half of a given amount of a radioisotope to decay. p. F-10

haploid An organism or cell with only one copy of each type of chromosome in its nuclei. p. 164

heat of vaporization The heat required to give water molecules enough energy of motion to break loose from liquid water and form a gas. p. F-16

hemolymph The circulatory fluid of invertebrates with open circulatory systems, including molluscs and arthropods. p. 116

heterochromatin In eukaryotes, regions of densely packed chromatin fibres in interphase nuclei. p. 278

heterotroph An organism that acquires energy and nutrients by eating other organisms or their remains. p. 140

heterozygote An individual with two different alleles of a gene. p. 215

heterozygous The state of possessing two different alleles of a gene. p. 215

Hfr cell A special donor cell that can transfer genes on a bacterial chromosome to a recipient bacterium. p. 187

histone A small, positively charged (basic) protein that is complexed with DNA in the chromosomes of eukaryotes. p. 278

homologous Similar. p. 182

homozygote An individual with two copies of the same allele. p. 215

homozygous State of possessing two copies of the same allele. p. 215

host A species that is fed upon by a parasite. p. 64

human immunodeficiency virus (HIV) A retrovirus that causes acquired immune deficiency syndrome (AIDS). p. 206

hydrocarbon Molecule consisting of carbon linked only to hydrogen atoms. p. 95

hydrogen bond Noncovalent bond formed by unequal electron sharing between hydrogen atoms and oxygen, nitrogen, or sulfur atoms. p. F-13

hydrolysis Reaction in which the components of a water molecule are added to functional groups as molecules are broken into smaller subunits. p. 37

hydrophilic Polar molecules that associate readily with water. p. F-13

hydrophobic Nonpolar substances that are excluded by water and other polar molecules. p. F-13

hydrosphere The component of the biosphere that encompasses all of the waters on Earth, including oceans, rivers, and polar ice caps. p. 4

hydroxyl group Group consisting of an oxygen atom linked to a hydrogen atom on one side and to a carbon chain on the other side. p. 262

hypertonic Solution containing dissolved substances at higher concentrations than the cells it surrounds. p. 103

hypothesis A "working explanation" of observed facts. p. F-2

hypotonic Solution containing dissolved substances at lower concentrations than the cells it surrounds. p. 103

imprinting The process of learning the identity of a caretaker and potential future mate during a critical period. p. 253

incomplete dominance Condition in which the effects of recessive alleles can be detected to some extent in heterozygotes. p. 224

independent assortment Mendel's principle that the alleles of the genes that govern two characters segregate independently during formation of gametes. p. 220

inducer Concerning regulation of gene expression in bacteria, a molecule that turns on the transcription of the genes in an operon. p. 311

inducible operon Operon whose expression is increased by an inducer molecule. p. 311

ingestion The feeding methods used to take food into the digestive cavity. p. 88

inheritance The transmission of DNA (i.e., genetic information) from one generation to the next. p. 187

initiator codon *See* start codon. p. 288

inner boundary membrane Membrane lying just inside the outer boundary membrane of a chloroplast, enclosing the stroma. p. 44

inner mitochondrial membrane Membrane surrounding the mitochondrial matrix. p. 38

inorganic molecule Molecule without carbon atoms in its structure. p. 140

insertion sequence (IS) A transposable element that contains only genes for its transposition. p. 202

integral membrane protein Protein embedded in a phospholipid bilayer. p. 98

interkinesis A brief interphase separating the two meiotic divisions. p. 194

intermediate filament A cytoskeletal filament about 10 nm in diameter that provides mechanical strength to cells in tissues. p. 41

interphase The first stage of the mitotic cell cycle, during which the cell grows and replicates its DNA before undergoing mitosis and cytokinesis. p. 165

intestine The portion of digestive system where organic matter is hydrolyzed by enzymes secreted into the digestive tube. As muscular contractions of the intestinal wall move the mixture along, cells lining the intestine absorb the molecular subunits produced by digestion. pp. 30, 46, 89

intron A non–protein-coding sequence that interrupts the protein-coding sequence in a eukaryotic gene. Introns are removed by splicing in the processing of pre-mRNA to mRNA. p. 292

invagination The process in which cells changing shape and pushing inward from the surface produce an indentation, such as the dorsal lip of the blastopore. p. 31

inversion Chromosomal alteration that occurs if a broken segment reattaches to the same chromosome from which it was lost, but in reversed orientation, so that the order of genes in the segment is reversed with respect to the other genes of the chromosome. p. 245

invertebrate An animal without a vertebral column. p. 9

inverted repeat Enables the transposase enzyme to identify the ends of the transposable element when it catalyzes transposition. p. 202

ion A positively or negatively charged atom. p. 7

ionic bond Bond that results from electrical attractions between atoms that have lost or gained electrons. p. 100

isotonic Equal concentration of water inside and outside cells. p. 103

isotope A distinct form of the atoms of an element, with the same number of protons but a different number of neutrons. p. F-9

karyotype A characteristic of a species consisting of the shapes and sizes of all of the chromosomes at metaphase. p. 168

kinetic energy The energy of motion. p. 72

kinetochore A specialized structure consisting of -proteins attached to a centromere that mediates the attachment and movement of chromosomes along the mitotic spindle. p. 167

Krebs cycle *See* citric acid cycle. p. 122

lactate fermentation Reaction in which pyruvate is converted into lactate. p. 132

lagging strand A DNA strand assembled discontinuously in the direction opposite to DNA unwinding. p. 270

leading strand A DNA strand assembled in the direction of DNA unwinding. p. 270

leading strand template The "old" DNA used as a template for synthesis of "new" DNA in the direction of DNA unwinding. p. 270

light The portion of the electromagnetic spectrum that humans can detect with their eyes. p. 2

light microscope Microscope that uses light to illuminate the specimen. p. 27

light-dependent reaction The first stage of photosynthesis, in which the energy of sunlight is absorbed and converted into chemical energy in the form of ATP and NADPH. p. 159

light-independent reaction The second stage of photosynthesis, in which electrons are used as a source of energy to convert inorganic CO_2 to an organic form. Also referred to as the *Calvin cycle*. p. 150

linkage The phenomenon of genes being located on the same chromosome. p. 235

linkage map Map of a chromosome showing the relative locations of genes based on recombination frequencies. p 237

linked genes Genes on the same chromosome. p. 235

linker A short segment of DNA extending between one nucleosome and the next in a eukaryotic chromosome. p. 278

liver A large organ whose many functions include aiding in digestion, removing toxins from the body, and regulating the chemicals in the blood. p. 35

locus The particular site on a chromosome at which a gene is located. p. 223

loss of imprinting A phenomenon in which the imprinting mechanism for a gene does not work, resulting in both alleles of the gene being active. p. 254

lumen The inside of the digestive tube. p. 34

lung One of a pair of invaginated respiratory surfaces, buried in the body interior where they are less susceptible to drying out; the organs of respiration in mammals, birds, reptiles, and most amphibians. p. 31

lysogenic cycle Cycle in which the D **macromolecule** A very large molecule assembled by the covalent linkage of smaller subunit molecules. p. 50

lysogenic cycle Cycle in which the DNA of the bacteriophage is integrated into the DNA of the host bacterial cell and may remain for many generations. p. 189

lysosome Membrane-bound vesicle containing hydrolytic enzymes for the digestion of many complex molecules. p. 37

lytic cycle The series of events from infection of one bacterial cell by a phage through the release of progeny phages from lysed cells. p. 188

magnification The ratio of an object as viewed to its real size. p. 27

mammary glands Specialized organs of female mammals that produce energy-rich milk, a watery mixture of fats, sugars, proteins, vitamins, and minerals. p. 323

map unit The unit of a linkage map, equivalent to a recombination frequency of 1%. Also referred to as a *centimorgan*. p. 239

maternal chromosome The chromosome derived from the female parent of an organism. p. 193

mating The pairing of a male and a female for the purpose of sexual reproduction. p. 14

matter Anything that occupies space and has mass. p. F-8

meiocytes Cells that are destined to divide by meiosis. p. 193

meiosis The division of diploid cells to haploid progeny, consisting of two sequential rounds of nuclear and cellular division. p. 191

meiosis I The first division of the meiotic cell cycle in which homologous chromosomes pair and undergo an exchange of chromosome segments, and then the homologous chromosomes separate, resulting in two cells, each with the haploid number of chromosomes and with each chromosome still consisting of two chromatids. p. 193

meiosis II The second division of the meiotic cell cycle in which the sister chromatids in each of the two cells produced by meiosis I separate and segregate into different cells, resulting in four cells each with the haploid number of chromosomes. p. 193

membrane potential An electrical voltage that measures the potential inside a cell membrane relative to the fluid just outside; it is negative under resting conditions and becomes positive during an action potential. p. 105

messenger RNA (mRNA) An RNA molecule that serves as a template for protein synthesis. p. 286

metabolism The biochemical reactions that allow a cell or organism to extract energy from its surroundings and use that energy to maintain itself, grow, and reproduce. p. 77

metaphase The phase of mitosis during which the spindle reaches its final form and the spindle microtubules move the chromosomes into alignment at the spindle midpoint. p. 167

micelle A sphere composed of a single layer of lipid molecules. p. 96

microbody A small, membrane-bound organelle that carries out vital reactions linking metabolic pathways. p. 32

microfilament A cytoskeletal filament composed of actin. p. 41

microRNAs (miRNAs) Small RNAs that regulate gene expression by binding to specific mRNAs and decreasing their translation. p. 323

microscope Instrument of microscopy with different magnifications and resolutions of specimens. p. 27

microscopy Technique for producing visible images of objects that are too small to be seen by the human eye. p. 27

microtubule A cytoskeletal component formed by the polymerization of tubulin into rigid, hollow rods about 25 nm in diameter. p. 39

microtubule organizing centre (MTOC) An anchoring point near the centre of a eukaryotic cell from which most microtubules extend outward. p. 171

middle lamella Layer of gel-like polysaccharides that holds together walls of adjacent plant cells. p. 45

minimal medium A growth medium containing the minimal ingredients that enable a nonmutant organism, such as *E. coli*, to grow. p. 183

mismatch repair Repair system that removes mismatched bases from newly synthesized DNA strands. p. 276

missense mutation A base-pair substitution mutation in a protein-coding gene that results in a different amino acid in the encoded polypeptide than the normal one. p. 305

mitochondrial matrix The innermost compartment of the mitochondrion. p. 39

mitochondrion Membrane-bound organelle responsible for synthesis of most of the ATP in eukaryotic cells. p. 38

mitosis Nuclear division that produces daughter nuclei that are exact genetic copies of the parental nucleus. p. 161

mitotic spindle The complex of microtubules that orchestrate the separation of chromosomes during mitosis. p. 167

mobile elements Particular segments of DNA that can move from one place to another; they cut and paste DNA backbones using a type of recombination that does not require homology. p. 201

model organism An organism with characteristics that make it a particularly useful subject of research because it is likely to produce results widely applicable to other organisms. p. F-52

molarity (M) The number of moles of a substance dissolved in 1 L of solution. p. F-18

mole (mol) The atomic weight of an element or the molecular weight of a compound. p. F-18

molecular weight The weight of a molecule in grams, equal to the total mass number of its atoms. p. F-18

molecule A unit composed of atoms combined chemically in fixed numbers and ratios. p. 1

monohybrid An F_1 heterozygote produced from a genetic cross that involves a single character. p. 215

monohybrid cross A genetic cross between two individuals that are each heterozygous for the same pair of alleles. p. 215

monomers Identical or nearly identical subunits that link together to form polymers during polymerization. p. 56

monosaccharides The smallest carbohydrates, containing three to seven carbon atoms. p. 81

morphogenesis Orderly, genetically programmed changes in the size, shape, and proportion of body parts of an organism; the process by which specialized tissues and organs form. p. 8

morphology The form or shape of an organism or of part of an organism. p. 64

motif A highly specialized region in a protein produced by the three-dimensional arrangement of amino acid chains within and between domains. p. 317

mould Asexual, spore-producing stage of many multicellular fungi. p. 27

mRNA splicing Process that removes introns from pre-mRNAs and joins exons together. p. 292

multicellular organism Individual consisting of interdependent cells. p. 26

multiple alleles More than two different alleles of a gene. p. 226

mutation A spontaneous and heritable change in DNA. pp. 277, 304

Na⁺/K⁺ pump Pump that pushes 3 Na⁺ out of the cell and 2 K⁺ into the cell in the same pumping cycle. Also referred to as the *sodium–potassium pump*. p. 105

natural history The branch of biology that examines the form and variety of organisms in their natural environments. p. 221

nucleoid The central region of a prokaryotic cell with no boundary membrane separating it from the cytoplasm, where DNA replication and RNA transcription occur. pp. 29, 54, 163, 279

neutron Uncharged particle in the nucleus of an atom. p. F-9

nitrogenous base A nitrogen-containing molecule with the properties of a base. p. 79

noncompetitive inhibition Inhibition of an enzyme reaction by an inhibitor molecule that binds to the enzyme at a site other than the active site and, therefore, does not compete directly with the substrate for binding to the active site. p. 86

nondisjunction The failure of homologous pairs to separate during the first meiotic division or of chromatids to separate during the second meiotic division. p. 246

nonhistone protein All of the proteins associated with DNA in a eukaryotic chromosome that are not histones. p. 279

nonsense codon *See* stop codon. p. 288

nonsense mutation A base-pair substitution mutation in a gene in which the base-pair change results in a change from a sense codon to a nonsense codon in the mRNA. The polypeptide translated from the mRNA is shorter than the normal polypeptide because of the mutation. p. 305

N-terminal end The end of a polypeptide chain with an —NH₃ group. p. 294

nuclear envelope In eukaryotes, membranes separating the nucleus from the cytoplasm. p. 33

nuclear localization signal *See* nucellus. p. 304

nuclear pore Opening in the membrane of the nuclear envelope through which large molecules, such as RNA and proteins, move between the nucleus and the cytoplasm. p. 33

nucleolus The nuclear site of rRNA transcription, processing, and ribosome assembly in eukaryotes. p. 34

nucleoplasm The liquid or semiliquid substance within the nucleus. p. 33

nucleosome The basic structural unit of chromatin in eukaryotes, consisting of DNA wrapped around a histone core. p. 278

nucleosome core particle An eight-protein particle formed by the combination of two molecules each of H2A, H2B, H3, and H4, around which DNA winds for almost two turns. p. 278

nucleosome remodelling complex A multi-protein structure that moves, or modifies, nucleosomes in such a way that exposes promoters to the transcription machinery. p. 321

nucleotide The monomer of nucleic acids consisting of a five-carbon sugar, a nitrogenous base, and a phosphate. p. F-37

nucleus The central region of eukaryotic cells, separated by membranes from the surrounding cytoplasm, where DNA replication and messenger RNA transcription occur. p. 30

nutrition The processes by which an organism takes in, digests, absorbs, and converts food into organic compounds. p. 183

oil Neutral lipid that is liquid at biological temperatures. p. 93

Okazaki fragments Relatively short segments of DNA synthesized on the "lagging" strand at a replication fork. p. 270

ommatidium (plural, ommatidia) A faceted visual unit of a compound eye. p. 9

oncogene A gene that, when deregulated, capable of inducing one or more characteristics of cancer cells. pp. 176, 327

one gene–one enzyme hypothesis Hypothesis showing the direct relationship between genes and enzymes. p. 286

one gene–one polypeptide hypothesis Restatement of the one gene–one enzyme hypothesis, taking into account that some proteins consist of more than one polypeptide and not all proteins are enzymes. p. 286

open reading frames (ORFs) Segments of DNA sequence that contain start and stop codons. Such sequences are candidate genes. p. 356

operator A DNA regulatory sequence that controls transcription of an operon. p. 310

operon A cluster of prokaryotic genes and the DNA sequences involved in their regulation. p. 310

orbital The region of space where the electron "lives" most of the time. p. F-10

organelles The nucleus and other specialized internal structures and compartments of eukaryotic cells. p. 29

organic molecule Molecule based on carbon. p. 29

origin of replication (ori) A specific region at which replication of a bacterial chromosome commences. pp. 163, 269

outer boundary membrane A smooth membrane that surrounds a chloroplast, enclosing the stroma. p. 44

outer mitochondrial membrane The smooth membrane covering the outside of a mitochondrion. p. 38

oval window An opening in the bony wall that separates the middle ear from the inner ear. p. 9

oxidation The removal of electrons from a substance. p. 60

oxidative phosphorylation Synthesis of ATP in which ATP synthase uses an H⁺ gradient built by the electron transfer system as the energy source to make the ATP. p. 127

oxidized Substance from which the electrons are removed during oxidation. p. 117

P generation The parental individuals used in an initial cross. p. 214

P site The site in the ribosome where the tRNA carrying the growing polypeptide chain is bound. p. 298

pairing Process in meiosis in which homologous chromosomes come together and pair. Also referred to as *synapsis*. p. 194

parental Phenotypes identical to the original parental individuals. p. 164

partial diploid A condition in which part of the genome of a haploid organism is diploid. Recipients in bacterial conjugation between an Hfr and an F cell become partial diploids for part of the Hfr bacterial chromosome. p. 187

passive transport The transport of substances across cell membranes without expenditure of energy, as in diffusion. p. 100

paternal chromosome The chromosome derived from the male parent of an organism. p. 193

pedigree Chart that shows all parents and offspring for as many generations as possible, the sex of individuals in the different generations, and the presence or absence of a trait of interest. p. 243

pepsin An enzyme made in the stomach that breaks down proteins. p. 89

pepsinogen The inactive precursor molecule for pepsin. p. 302

peptidyl transferase An enzyme that catalyzes the reaction in which an amino acid is cleaved from the tRNA in the P site of the ribosome and forms a peptide bond with the amino acid on the tRNA in the A site of the ribosome. p. 300

peptidyl–tRNA A tRNA linked to a growing polypeptide chain containing two or more amino acids. p. 299

peripheral membrane protein Protein held to membrane surfaces by noncovalent bonds formed with the polar parts of integral membrane proteins or membrane lipids. p. 99

permafrost Perpetually frozen ground below the topsoil. p. 258

peroxisome Microbody that produces hydrogen peroxide as a by-product. p. 302

pilus (plural, pili) A hair or hairlike appendage on the surface of a prokaryote. p. 31

phage *See* bacteriophage. p. 188

phagocytosis Process in which some types of cells engulf bacteria or other cellular debris to break them down. pp. 37, 109

phenotype The outward appearance of an organism. p. 215

phosphate group Group consisting of a central phosphorus atom held in four linkages: two that bind—OH groups to the central phosphorus atom, a third that binds an oxygen atom to the central phosphorus atom, and a fourth that links the phosphate group to an oxygen atom. p. 71

phosphodiester bond The linkage of nucleotides in polynucleotide chains by a bridging phosphate group between the 5 carbon of one sugar and the 3 carbon of the next sugar in line. p. 262

phospholipid A phosphate-containing lipid. p. 95

phosphorylation The addition of a phosphate group to a molecule. p. 71

photoautotroph A photosynthetic organism that uses light as its energy source and carbon dioxide as its carbon source. p. 140

photons Discrete particles or packets of energy. p. 3

photophosphorylation The synthesis of ATP coupled to the transfer of electrons energized by photons of light. p. 148

photorespiration A process that metabolizes a by-product of photosynthesis. p. 152

photosynthesis The conversion of light energy to chemical energy in the form of sugar and other organic molecules. p. 140

photosystem A large complex into which the light-absorbing pigments for photosynthesis are organized with proteins and other molecules. p. 145

photosystem I In photosynthesis, a protein complex in the thylakoid membrane that uses energy absorbed from sunlight to synthesize NADPH. p. 145

photosystem II In photosynthesis, a protein complex in the thylakoid membrane that uses energy absorbed from sunlight to synthesize ATP. p. 145

phototrophy A nutritional strategy in which light is used as source of energy. p. 140

phytosterol A sterol that occurs in plant cell membranes. p. 97

pigment A molecule that can absorb photons of light. p. 4

pinocytosis *See* bulk-phase endocytosis. p. 107

plasma membrane The outer limit of the cytoplasm responsible for the regulation of substances moving into and out of cells. pp. 28, 93

plasmid A DNA molecule in the cytoplasm of certain prokaryotes, which often contains genes with functions that supplement those in the nucleoid and which can replicate independently of the nucleoid DNA and be passed along during cell division. p. 279

plastids A family of plant organelles. p. 43

pleiotropy Condition in which single genes affect more than one character of an organism. p. 230

ploidy The number of chromosome sets of a cell or species. p. 165

pollutant Materials or energy in a form or quantity that organisms do not usually encounter. p. 19

poly(A) tail The string of A nucleotides added posttranscriptionally to the 3′ end of a pre-mRNA molecule and retained in the mRNA produced from it that enables the mRNA to be translated efficiently and protects it from attack by RNA-digesting enzymes in the cytoplasm. p. 292

polygenic inheritance Inheritance in which several to many different genes contribute to the same character. p. 229

polymerase chain reaction (pCR) Process that amplifies a specific DNA sequence from a DNA mixture to an extremely large number of copies. p. 337

polypeptide The chain of amino acids formed by sequential peptide bonds. p. F-30

polyploid An individual with one or more extra copies of the entire haploid complement of chromosomes. p. 247

polysaccharide Chain with more than 10 linked monosaccharide subunits. p. 30

polysome The entire structure of an mRNA molecule and the multiple associated ribosomes that are translating it simultaneously. p. 300

posttranslational import A process for sorting proteins that are translated on cytosolic ribosomes and then moved into organelles. p. 303

potential energy Stored energy. p. 72

precursor mRNA (pre-mRNA) The primary transcript of a eukaryotic protein-coding gene, which is processed to form messenger RNA. p. 291

prediction A statement about what the researcher expects to happen to one variable if another variable changes. p. 7

pregnancy The period of mammalian development in which the embryo develops in the uterus of the mother. p. 252

prenatal diagnosis Techniques in which cells derived from a developing embryo or its surrounding tissues or fluids are tested for the presence of mutant alleles or chromosomal alterations. p. 252

primary active transport Transport in which the same protein that transports a substance also hydrolyzes ATP to power the transport directly. p. 104

primary structure The sequence of amino acids in a protein. p. 99

primase An enzyme that assembles the primer for a new DNA strand during DNA replication. p. 269

primer A short nucleotide chain made of RNA that is laid down as the first series of nucleotides in a new DNA strand or made of DNA for use in the polymerase chain reaction pCR). p. 269

Principle of Independent Assortment Mendel's principle that the alleles of the genes that govern two characters segregate independently during formation of gametes. p. 221

Principle of Segregation Mendel's principle that the pairs of alleles that control a character segregate as gametes are formed and that half the gametes carry one allele and the other half carry the other allele. p. 215

probability The possibility that an outcome will occur if it is a matter of chance. p. 217

product An atom or molecule leaving a chemical reaction. p. F-14

product rule Mathematical rule in which the final probability is found by multiplying individual probabilities. p. 217

prokaryote Organism in which the DNA is suspended in the cell interior without separation from other cellular components by a discrete membrane. p. 29

prokaryotic chromosome A single, typically circular DNA molecule. p. 30

prokaryotic flagellum A long, threadlike protein fibre that rotates in a socket in the plasma membrane and cell wall to push a prokaryotic cell through a liquid medium. p. 31

prometaphase A transition period between prophase and metaphase during which the microtubules of the mitotic spindle attach to the kinetochores and the chromosomes shuffle until they align in the centre of the cell. p. 167

promoter The site to which RNA polymerase binds for initiating transcription of a gene. p. 289

promoter proximal region Upstream of a eukaryotic gene, a region containing regulatory sequences for transcription called promoter proximal elements. p. 316

proofreading mechanism Mechanism of DNA polymerase to back up and remove mispaired nucleotides from a newly synthesized DNA strand. p. 276

prophage A viral genome inserted in the host cell DNA. p. 189

prophase The beginning phase of mitosis during which the duplicated chromosomes within the nucleus condense from a greatly extended state into compact, rodlike structures. p. 166

protein Molecules that carry out most of the activities of life, including the synthesis of all other biological molecules. A protein consists of one or more polypeptides depending on the protein. p. 4

protein chip *See* protein microarray. p. 361

protein kinase Enzyme that transfers a phosphate group from ATP to one or more sites on particular proteins. p. 111

protein microarray Similar in concept to a DNA microarray, a solid surface with a microscopic grid with thousands of spaces containing probes for analyzing the proteome, the complete set of proteins encoded by the genome of an organism. Also referred to as a *protein chip*. p. 361

protein phosphatase Enzyme that removes phosphate groups from target proteins. p. 111

proteome The complete set of proteins that can be expressed by the genome of an organism. p. 360

proteomics The study of the proteome. p. 361

protobiont The term given to a group of abiotically produced organic molecules that are surrounded by a membrane or membranelike structure. p. 57

proton Positively charged particle in the nucleus of an atom. p. F-9

proton-motive force Stored energy that contributes to ATP synthesis and to the cotransport of substances to and from mitochondria. p. 127

proto-oncogene A gene that encodes various kinds of proteins that stimulate cell division. Mutated proto-oncogenes contribute to the development of cancer. p. 327

proton pump Pump that moves hydrogen ions across membranes and pushes hydrogen ions across the plasma membrane from the cytoplasm to the cell exterior. Also referred to as H^+ *pump*. p. 4

prototrophs Strains that are able to synthesize the necessary amino acids. p. 183

provirus The inserted viral DNA. p. 206

Punnett square Method for determining the genotypes and phenotypes of offspring and their expected proportions. p. 218

purine A type of nitrogenous base with two carbon–nitrogen rings. p. 56

pyrimidine A type of nitrogenous base with one carbon–nitrogen ring. p. 56

radioactivity The giving off of particles of matter and energy by decaying nuclei. p. 260

radioisotope An unstable, radioactive isotope. p. 261

radiometric dating A dating method that uses measurements of certain radioactive isotopes to calculate the absolute ages in years of rocks and minerals. p. 53

reactants The atoms or molecules entering a chemical reaction. p. F-14

reaction centre Part of photosystems I and II in chloroplasts of plants. In the light-dependent reactions of photosynthesis, the reaction centre receives light energy absorbed by the antenna complex in the same photosystem. p. 145

reading frame A particular grouping of triplet bases read by transfer RNA during translation. pp. 288, 299

receptor protein Protein that recognizes and binds molecules from other cells that act as chemical signals. p. 47

receptor-mediated endocytosis The selective uptake of macromolecules that bind to cell surface receptors concentrated in clathrin-coated pits. p. 109

recessive An allele that is masked by a dominant allele. p. 211

recombinant Phenotype with a different combination of traits from those of the original parents. p. 186

recombinant DNA DNA from two or more different sources joined together. p. 333

recombination The physical exchange of segments between the chromatids of homologous chromosomes or between the chromosomes of prokaryotic cells or viruses. p. 181

recombination frequency In the construction of linkage maps of diploid eukaryotic organisms, the percentage of testcross progeny that are recombinants. p. 195

redox reaction Coupled oxidation–reduction reaction in which electrons are removed from a donor molecule and simultaneously added to an acceptor molecule. p. 117

reduced Substance that receives electrons during reduction. p. 117

reduction The addition of electrons to a substance. p. 60

release The process in which urine is released into the environment from the distal end of the excretory tubule. p. 4

release (termination) factor A protein that recognizes stop codons in the A site of a ribosome translating an mRNA and terminates translation. Also referred to as the *termination factor*. p. 300

replica plating Technique for identifying and counting genetic recombinants in conjugation, transformation, or transduction experiments in which the colony pattern on a plate containing solid growth medium is pressed onto sterile velveteen and transferred to other plates containing different combinations of nutrients. p. 183

replicates Multiple subjects that receive either the same experimental treatment or the same control treatment. p. F-3

replication bubble A structure resulting from bi-directional DNA replication from a given origin. Two forks, travelling in opposite directions, create a bubble. p. 273

replication fork The region of DNA synthesis where the parental strands separate and two new daughter strands elongate. p. 269

replication origin The site at which DNA replication begins. p. 163

repressible operon Operon whose expression is prevented by a repressor molecule. p. 313

repressor A regulatory protein that prevents the operon genes from being expressed. p. 310

reproduction The process in which parents produce offspring. p. 17

resolution The minimum distance two points in a specimen can be separated and still be seen as two points. p. 27

restriction endonuclease (restriction enzyme) An enzyme that cuts DNA at a specific sequence. p. 333

restriction fragment A DNA fragment produced by cutting a long DNA molecule with a restriction enzyme. p. 334

restriction fragment length polymorphisms (RFLPs) When comparing different individuals, restriction enzyme–generated DNA fragments of different lengths from the same region of the genome. p. 342

retrotransposon A transposable element that transposes via an intermediate RNA copy of the transposable element. p. 205

retrovirus A virus with an RNA genome that replicates via a DNA intermediate. p. 206

reverse transcriptase An enzyme that uses RNA as a template to make a DNA copy of the retrotransposon. Reverse transcriptase is used to make DNA copies of RNA in test tube reactions. p. 206

reversible The term indicating that a reaction may go from left to right or from right to left, depending on conditions. p. 71

ribonucleic acid (RNA) A polymer assembled from repeating nucleotide monomers in which the five-carbon sugar is ribose. Cellular RNAs are mRNA (which is translated to produce a polypeptide), tRNA (which brings an amino acid to the ribosome for assembly into a polypeptide during translation), and rRNA (which is a structural component of ribosomes). The genetic material of some viruses is RNA. p. 26

ribose A five-carbon sugar to which the nitrogenous bases in nucleotides link covalently. p. F-37

ribosomal RNA (rRNA) The RNA component of ribosomes. p. 30

ribosome A ribonucleoprotein particle that carries out protein synthesis by translating mRNA into chains of amino acids. pp. 30, 286, 296

ribosome binding site In translation initiation in prokaryotes, a sequence just upstream of the start codon that directs the small ribosomal subunit to bind and orient correctly for the complete ribosome to assemble and start translating in the correct spot. p. 298

ribozyme An RNA-based catalyst that is part of the biochemical machinery of all cells. p. 58

RNA *See* ribonucleic acid. p. 26

RNA interference (RNAi) The phenomenon of silencing a gene posttranscriptionally by a small, single-stranded RNA that is complementary to part of an mRNA. p. 323

RNA polymerase An enzyme that catalyzes the assembly of nucleotides into an RNA strand. p. 286

rough ER Endoplasmic reticulum with many ribosomes studding its outer surface. p. 34

RuBP carboxylase/oxygenase (rubisco) An enzyme that catalyzes the key reaction of the Calvin cycle, carbon fixation, in which CO_2 combines with RuBP (ribulose 1,5-bisphosphate) to form 3-phosphoglycerate. p. 131

ruminant An animal that has a complex, four-chambered stomach. p. 98

S phase The phase of the cell cycle during which DNA replication occurs. p. 165

saturated fatty acid Fatty acid with only single bonds linking the carbon atoms. p. 96

scientific method An investigative approach in which scientists make observations about the natural world, develop working explanations about what they observe, and then test those explanations by collecting more information. p. F-2

scientific theory A broadly applicable idea or hypothesis that has been confirmed by every conceivable test. p. F-4

second law of thermodynamics Principle that for any process in which a system changes from an initial to a final state, the total disorder of the system and its surroundings always increases. p. 74

secondary active transport Transport indirectly driven by ATP hydrolysis. p. 104

secondary structure Regions of alpha helix, beta strand, or random coil in a polypeptide chain. p. 98

secretion A selective process in which specific small molecules and ions are transported from the body fluids (in animals with open circulatory systems) or blood (in animals with closed circulatory systems) into the excretory tubules. p. 49

secretory vesicle Vesicle that transports proteins to the plasma membrane. p. 36

semen The secretions of several accessory glands in which sperm are mixed prior to ejaculation. p. 339

semiconservative replication The process of DNA replication in which the two parental strands separate and each serves as a template for the synthesis of new progeny double-stranded DNA molecules. p. 264

sense codon A codon that specifies an amino acid. p. 295

sex chromosomes Chromosomes that are different in male and female individuals of the same species. p. 195

sex pilus *See* F pilus. p. 187

sex-linked gene Gene located on a sex chromosome. p. 240

sexual reproduction The mode of reproduction in which male and female parents produce offspring through the union of egg and sperm generated by meiosis. p. 191

short interfering RNAs (siRNAs) Small RNA molecules that regulate expression of certain genes by binding to their mRNA and reducing translation. p. 323

signal peptide A short segment of amino acids to which the signal recognition particle binds, temporarily blocking further translation. A signal peptide is found on polypeptides that are sorted to the endoplasmic reticulum. Also referred to as *signal sequence*. p. 303

signal recognition particle (SRP) Protein–RNA complex that binds to signal sequences and targets polypeptide chains to the endoplasmic reticulum. p. 303

signal sequence *See* signal peptide. p. 303

signal transduction The series of events by which a signal molecule released from a controlling cell causes a response (affects the function) of target cells with receptors for the signal. Target cells process the signal in the three sequential steps of reception, transduction, and response. p. 8

silencing Phenomenon in which methylation of cytosines in eukaryotic promoters inhibits transcription and turns the genes off. p. 321

silent mutation A base-pair substitution mutation in a protein-coding gene that does not alter the amino acid specified by the gene. p. 305

simple diffusion Mechanism by which certain small substances diffuse through the lipid part of a biological membrane. p. 100

single-stranded binding protein (SSB) Protein that coats single-stranded segments of DNA, stabilizing the DNA for the replication process. p. 269

siRNA-induced silencing complex (siRISC) A group of proteins, recruited when siRNA binds to mRNA, that degrade the target mRNA. p. 324

sister chromatid One of two exact copies of a chromosome duplicated during replication. p. 165

slime layer A coat typically composed of polysaccharides that is loosely associated with bacterial cells. p. 31

small interfering RNA (siRNA) A class of single-stranded RNAs that cause RNA interference. p. 323

small ribonucleoprotein particle A complex of RNA and proteins. p. 292

smooth ER Endoplasmic reticulum with no ribosomes attached to its membrane surfaces. Smooth ER has various functions, including synthesis of lipids that become part of cell membranes. p. 35

sodium–potassium pump *See* Na^+/K^+ pump. p. 105

solenoid *See* 30 nm chromatin fibre. p. 278

solute The molecules of a substance dissolved in water. p. 100

solution Substance formed when molecules and ions separate and are suspended individually, surrounded by water molecules. p. 13

solvent The water in a solution in which the hydration layer prevents polar molecules or ions from reassociating. p. 114

somatic cell Any of the cells of an organism's body other than reproductive cells. p. 191

somatic gene therapy Gene therapy in which genes are introduced into somatic cells. p. 347

Southern blot analysis Technique in which labelled probes are used to detect specific DNA fragments that have been separated by gel electrophoresis. p. 342

species A group of populations in which the individuals are so closely related in structure, biochemistry, and behaviour that they can successfully interbreed. p. 4

specialized transduction Transfer of bacterial genes between bacteria using temperate phages that have incorporated fragments of the bacterial genome as they make the transition from the lysogenic cycle to the lytic cycle. p. 189

specific heat The amount of heat required to increase the temperature of a given quantity of water. p. F-16

spindle The structure that separates sister chromatids and moves them to opposite spindle poles. p. 164

spindle pole One of the pair of centrosomes in a cell undergoing mitosis from which bundles of microtubules radiate to form the part of the spindle from that pole. p. 167

spliceosome A complex formed between the pre-mRNA and small ribonucleoprotein particles, in which mRNA splicing takes place. p. 292

spontaneous reaction Chemical or physical reaction that occurs without outside help. p. 75

sporadic (nonhereditary) cancers p. 327

spore A haploid reproductive structure, usually a single cell, that can develop into a new individual without fusing with another cell; found in plants, fungi, and certain protists. p. 192

sporophyte An individual of the diploid generation produced through fertilization in organisms that undergo alternation of generations; it produces haploid spores. p. 192

stability The ability of a community to maintain its species composition and relative abundances when environmental disturbances eliminate some species from the community. p. 60

starch Energy-providing carbohydrates stored in plant cells. p. 43

start codon The first codon read in an mRNA in translation—AUG. Also referred to as the *initiator codon*. p. 288

stem cell Undifferentiated cells in most multicellular organisms that can divide without differentiating and also can divide and differentiate into specialized cell types. p. 346

steroid A type of lipid derived from cholesterol. p. 320

steroid hormone receptor Internal receptor that turns on specific genes when it is activated by binding a signal molecule. p. 320

steroid hormone response element The DNA sequence to which the hormone receptor complex binds. p. 320

sterol Steroid with a single polar —OH group linked to one end of the ring framework and a complex, nonpolar hydrocarbon chain at the other end. p. 97

sticky end End of a DNA fragment, with a single-stranded structure that can form hydrogen bonds with a complementary sticky end on any other DNA molecule cut with the same enzyme. p. 334

stomach The portion of the digestive system in which food is stored and digestion begins. p. 46

stop codon A codon that does not specify amino acids. The three nonsense codons are UAG, UAA, and UGA. Also referred to as the *nonsense codon* and *termination codon*. p. 288

strict aerobe Cell with an absolute requirement for oxygen to survive, unable to live solely by fermentations. p. 134

strict anaerobe Organism in which fermentation is the only source of ATP. p. 134

stroma An inner compartment of a chloroplast, enclosed by two boundary membranes and containing a third membrane system. p. 44

stromatolite Fossilized remains of ancient cyanobacterial mats that carried out photosynthesis by the water-splitting reaction. p. 61

structural genomics The sequencing of genomes and the analysis of the nucleotide sequences to locate genes and other functionally important sequences within the genome. p. 362

substrate The particular reacting molecule or molecular group that an enzyme catalyzes. p. 21

substrate-level phosphorylation An enzyme-catalyzed reaction that transfers a phosphate group from a substrate to ADP. p. 122

sugar–phosphate backbone Structure in a polynucleotide chain that is formed when deoxyribose sugars are linked by phosphate groups in an alternating sugar–phosphate–sugar–phosphate pattern. p. 262

sum rule Mathematical rule in which final probability is found by summing individual probabilities. p. 217

surface tension The force that places surface water molecules under tension, making them more resistant to separation than the underlying water molecules. p. F-16

symbiosis An interspecific interaction in which the ecological relations of two or more species are intimately tied together. p. 64

symport The transport of two molecules in the same direction across a membrane. Also referred to as *cotransport*. p. 107

synapsis *See* pairing. p. 194

systems biology An area of biology that studies the organism as a whole to unravel the integrated and interacting network of genes, proteins, and biochemical reactions responsible for life. p. 361

TATA box A regulatory DNA sequence found in the promoters of many eukaryotic genes transcribed by RNA polymerase II. p. 290

telomerase An enzyme that adds telomere repeats to chromosome ends. p. 274

telomeres Repeats of simple-sequence DNA that maintain the ends of linear chromosomes. p. 274

telophase The final phase of mitosis, during which the spindle disassembles, the chromosomes decondense, and the nuclei re-form. p. 169

temperate bacteriophage Bacteriophage that may enter an inactive phase (lysogenic cycle) in which the host cell replicates and passes on the bacteriophage DNA for generations before the phage becomes active and kills the host (lytic cycle). p. 189

template A nucleotide chain used in DNA replication for the assembly of a complementary chain. p. 206

template strand The DNA strand that is copied into an RNA molecule during gene transcription. p. 286

termination codon *See* stop codon. p. 288

termination factor *See* release factor. p. 300

terminator Specific DNA sequence for a gene that signals the end of transcription of a gene. Terminators are common for prokaryotic genes. p. 289

testcross A genetic cross between an individual with the dominant phenotype and a homozygous recessive individual. p. 218

tetrad Homologous pair consisting of four chromatids. p. 194

thermodynamics The study of the energy flow during chemical and physical reactions. p. 72

thylakoids Flattened, closed sacs that make up a membrane system within the stroma of a chloroplast. p. 44

thymine A pyrimidine that base-pairs with adenine. p. 262

Ti (tumour-inducing) plasmid A plasmid used to make transgenic plants. p. 350

tight junction Region of tight connection between membranes of adjacent cells. p. 46

tonoplast The membrane that surrounds the central vacuole in a plant cell. p. 44

topoisomerase An enzyme that relieves the overtwisting and strain of DNA ahead of the replication fork. p. 269

trait A particular variation in a genetic or phenotypic character. p. 212

transcription The mechanism by which the information encoded in DNA is made into a complementary RNA copy. p. 286

transcription factor Proteins that recognize and bind to the TATA box and then recruit the polymerase. pp. 289, 315

transcription initiation complex Combination of general transcription factors with RNA polymerase II. p. 316

transcription unit A region of DNA that transcribes a single primary transcript. pp. 289, 310

transduction In cell signalling, the process of changing a signal into the form necessary to cause the cellular response. In prokaryotes, the process in which DNA is transferred from donor to recipient bacterial cells by an infecting bacteriophage. p. 188

transfer RNA (tRNA) The RNA that brings amino acids to the ribosome for addition to the polypeptide chain. p. 64

transformation The conversion of the hereditary type of a cell by the uptake of DNA released by the breakdown of another cell. pp. 188, 260

transgenic An organism that has been modified to contain genetic information from an external source. p. 345

translocation In genetics, a chromosomal alteration that occurs if a broken segment is attached to a different, non-homologous chromosome. In vascular plants, the long-distance transport of substances by xylem and phloem. p. 245

transit sequence A part of a gene sequence that targets the protein product to an organelle or endoplasmic lumen etc. p. 303

transition state An intermediate arrangement of atoms and bonds that both the reactants and the products of a reaction can assume. p. 81

translation The use of the information encoded in the RNA to assemble amino acids into a polypeptide. p. 286

transport The controlled movement of ions and molecules from one side of a membrane to the other. p. 4

transport protein A protein embedded in the cell membrane that forms a channel allowing selected polar molecules and ions to pass across the membrane. p. 28

transposable element (TE) A sequence of DNA that can move from one place to another within the genome of a cell. p. 201

transposase An enzyme that catalyzes some of the reactions inserting or removing the transposable element from the DNA. p. 202

transposition Mechanism of movement of transposable elements involving nonhomologous recombination. p. 201

transposon A bacterial transposable element with an inverted repeat sequence at each end enclosing a central region with one or more genes. p. 202

tricarboxylic acid cycle *See* citric acid cycle. p. 122

triglyceride A nonpolar compound produced when a fatty acid binds by a dehydration synthesis reaction at each of glycerol's three —OH-bearing sites. p. 130

true-breeding Individual that passes traits without change from one generation to the next. p. 213

tumour-suppressor gene A gene that encodes proteins that inhibit cell division. p. 327

umbilical cord A long tissue with blood vessels linking the embryo and the placenta. p. 346

universal A feature of the nucleic acid code, with the same codons specifying the same amino acids in all living organisms. p. 288

unsaturated Fatty acid with one or more double bonds linking the carbons. p. 95

vagina The muscular canal that leads from the cervix to the exterior. p. 241

valence electron An electron in the outermost energy level of an atom. p. F-10

vertebrate A member of the monophyletic group of tetrapod animals that possess a vertebral column. p. 10

vesicle A small, membrane-bound compartment that transfers substances between parts of the endomembrane system. p. 34

vibrio Any of various short, motile, S-shaped or comma-shaped bacteria of the genus *Vibrio*. p. 114

virulent bacteriophage Bacteriophage that kills its host bacterial cells during each cycle of infection. p. 188

virus An infectious agent that contains either DNA or RNA surrounded by a protein coat. p. 260

water lattice An arrangement formed when a water molecule in liquid water establishes an average of 3.4 hydrogen bonds with its neighbours. p. F-15

wavelength The distance between two successive peaks of electromagnetic radiation. p. 2

wax A substance insoluble in water that is formed when fatty acids combine with long-chain alcohols or hydrocarbon structures. p. 17

wobble hypothesis Hypothesis stating that the complete set of 61 sense codons can be read by fewer than 61 distinct tRNAs because of particular pairing properties of the bases in the anticodons. p. 295

X chromosome Sex chromosome that occurs paired in female cells and single in male cells. p. 240

X-linked recessive inheritance Pattern in which displayed traits are due to inheritance of recessive alleles carried on the X chromosome. p. 251

X-ray diffraction Method for deducing the position of atoms in a molecule. p. 262

Y chromosome Sex chromosome that is paired with an X chromosome in male cells. p. 195

yeast A single-celled fungus that reproduces by budding or fission. p. 26

zygote A fertilized egg. p. 191

Chapter 1

1. c 2. a 3. a 4. a 5. c 6. b 7. d 8. d 9. d 10. a

Chapter 2

1. b 2. e 3. d 4. d 5. c 6. b 7. d 8. a 9. b 10. a

Chapter 3

1. c 2. b 3. e 4. d 5. c 6. a 7. d 8. e 9. b 10. a

Chapter 4

1. c 2. d 3. d 4. b 5. d 6. c 7. b 8. a 9. b 10. b

Chapter 5

1. a 2. d 3. c 4. c 5. b 6. b 7. b 8. c 9. e 10. e

Chapter 6

1. a 2. c 3. d 4. d 5. c 6. a 7. b 8. c 9. e 10. d

Chapter 7

1. d 2. c 3. d 4. c 5. c 6. d 7. a 8. c 9. c 10. c

Chapter 8

1. c 2. d 3. c 4. a 5. b 6. b 7. b 8. d 9. b 10. b

Chapter 9

1. d 2. d 3. c 4. d 5. b 6. a 7. a 8. b 9. d 10. c

Chapter 10

1. c

2. (a) The *CC* parent produces all *C* gametes, and the *Cc* parent produces 1/2 *C* and 1/2 *c* gametes. All offspring would have coloured seeds—half homozygous *CC* and half heterozygous *Cc*. (b) Both parents produce 1/2 *C* and 1/2 *c* gametes. Of the offspring, three-fourths would have coloured seeds (1/4 *CC* + 1/2 *Cc*) and one-fourth would have colourless seeds (1/4 *cc*). (c) The *Cc* parent produces 1/2 *C* gametes and 1/2 *c* gametes, and the *cc* parent produces all *c* gametes. Half of the offspring are coloured (1/2 *Cc*), and half are colourless (1/2 *cc*).

3. The genotypes of the parents are *Tt* and *tt*.

4. The taster parents could have a nontaster child, but nontaster parents are not expected to have a child who can taste PTC. The chance that they might have a taster child is 3/4. The chance

of a nontaster child being born to the taster couple is 1/4. Because each combination of gametes is an independent event, the chance of the couple having a second child, or any child, who cannot taste PTC is expected to be 1/4.

5. (a) All *A B*. (b) 1/2 *A B* + 1/2 *a B*. (c) 1/2 *A b* + 1/2 *a b*. (d) 1/4 *A B* + 1/4 *A b* + 1/4 *a B* + 1/4 *a b*.

6. (a) All *Aa BB*. (b) 1/4 *AA BB* + 1/4 *AA Bb* + 1/4 *Aa BB* + 1/4 *Aa Bb*. (c) 1/4 *Aa Bb* + 1/4 *Aa bb* + 1/4 *aa Bb* + 1/4 *aa bb*. (d) 1/4 *Aa Bb* + 1/8 *AA Bb* + 1/8 *Aa BB* + 1/8 *Aa bb* + 1/8 *aa Bb* + 1/16 *AA BB* + 1/16 *AA bb* + 1/16 *aa BB* + 1/16 *aa bb*.

7. (a) All *A B C*. (b) 1/2 *A B c* + 1/2 *a B c*. (c) 1/4 *A B C* + 1/4 *A B c* + 1/4 *a B C* + 1/4 *a B c*. (d) 1/8 *A B C* + 1/8 *A B c* + 1/8 *A b C* + 1/8 *A b c* + 1/8 *a B C* + 1/8 *a B c* + 1/8 *a b C* + 1/8 *a b c*.

8. This diagram is incorrect because it does not show that each gamete will contain one allele from each of the two genes involved in this cross. The gametes should be *Mh*, *MH*, *mH*, and *mh*.

9. Because the man can produce only 1 type of allele for each of the 10 genes, he can produce only 1 type of sperm cell with respect to these genes. The woman can produce 2 types of alleles for each of her 2 heterozygous genes, so she can produce $2 \times 2 = 4$ different types of eggs with respect to the 10 genes. In general, as the number of heterozygous genes increases, the number of possible types of gametes increases as 2^n, where $n =$ the number of heterozygous genes.

10. Use a standard testcross; that is, cross the guinea pig with rough, black fur with a double-recessive individual, *rr bb* (smooth, white fur). If your animal is homozygous *RR BB*, you would expect all the offspring to have rough, black fur.

11. One gene probably controls pod colour. One allele, for green pods, is dominant; the other allele, for yellow pods, is recessive.

12. The cross *RR* × *Rr* will produce 1/2 *RR* and 1/2 *Rr* offspring. The cross *Rr* × *Rr* will produce 1/4 *RR*, 1/2 *Rr*, and 1/4 *rr* as combinations of alleles. However, the 1/4 *rr* combination is lethal, so it does not appear among the offspring. Therefore, the offspring will be born with only two types, *RR* and *Rr*, with twice as many *Rr* as *rr* in a 1:2 ratio (or 1/3 *RR* + 2/3 *Rr*).

13. The parental cross is *GG TT RR* × *gg tt rr*. All offspring of this cross are expected to be tall plants with green pods and round seeds, or *Gg Tt Rr*. When crossed, this heterozygous F_1 generation is expected to produce eight different phenotypes among the offspring: green-tall-round, green-dwarf-round,

yellow-tall-round, green-tall-wrinkled, yellow-dwarf-round, green-dwarf-wrinkled, yellow-tall-wrinkled, and yellow-dwarf-wrinkled, in a 27:9:9:9:3:3:3:1 ratio.

14. The genotypes are bird 1, *Ff Pp*; bird 2, *FF PP*; bird 3, *Ff PP*; and bird 4, *Ff Pp*.

15. Yes, it can be determined that the child is not hers, because the father must be AB to have both an A and B child with a type O wife; none of the woman's children could have type O blood with an AB father.

16. The cross is expected to produce white, tabby, and black kittens in a 12:3:1 ratio.

17. The mother is homozygous recessive for both genes, and the father must be heterozygous for both genes. The child is homozygous recessive for both genes. The chance of having a child with normal hands is 1/2, and that of having a child with woolly hair is 1/2. Using the product rule of probability, the probability of having a child with normal hands and woolly hair is $1/2 \times 1/2 = 1/4$.

Chapter 11

1. All sons will be colour-blind, but none of the daughters will be. However, all daughters will be heterozygous carriers of the trait.

2. The chance that her son will be colour-blind is 1/2, regardless of whether she marries a normal or colour-blind male.

3. All these questions can be answered from the pedigree. Polydactyly is caused by a dominant allele, and the trait is not sex linked. The genotypes of each person are as shown below:

4. The sequence of the genes is ADBC.

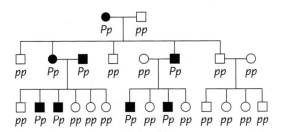

5. Let the allele for wild-type grey body colour be b^+, and the allele for black body be b. Let the allele for wild-type red eye colour be p^+, and the allele for purple eyes be p. Then the parents are as follows:

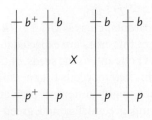

The F$_1$ flies with black bodies and red eyes are as follows:

The flies with grey bodies and purple eyes are as shown:

6. The genes are linked by their presence on the same chromosome (an autosome), but they are not sex linked. Because the F$_1$ females must have produced 600 gametes to give these 600 progeny, and because $42 + 30$ of these were recombinant, the percentage of recombinant gametes is 72/600, or 12%, which implies that 12 map units separate the two genes.

7. Because this trait is probably carried on the Y chromosome, which a man transmits to all his sons, all will have hairy ears. None of the daughters will have hairy ears because they do not have a Y chromosome.

8. You might suspect that a recessive allele is sex linked and is carried on one of the two X chromosomes of the female parent in the cross. When present on the single X of the male (or if present on both Xs of a female), the gene is lethal.

Chapter 12

1. c 2. b 3. a 4. a 5. d 6. c 7. b 8. a 9. d 10. d

Chapter 13

1. c 2. a 3. d 4. b 5. d 6. b 7. b 8. c 9. a 10. b

Chapter 14

1. c 2. c 3. b 4. b 5. d 6. c 7. d 8. a 9. a 10. d

Chapter 15

1. c 2. d 3. a 4. a 5. b 6. a 7. d 8. c 9. d 10. c

Index

The letter i designates illustration; t designates table; **bold** *designates defined or introduced term.*

ABO blood group, 227
Acetyl coenzyme A (acetyl-CoA), 118, 119i, 122, 123, 123i, 124i, 129, 130i, 131, 131i, 132i
Acetyl groups, oxidization of, 123–124, 123i, 124i
Achondroplasia, 251
Action spectrum, **144**–145, 144i
Activation energy, 81–83, 81i, 84–85
   as kinetic barrier, 81–82
   reduction of, by enzymes, 82–85
Activators, **310**, **317**
Active membrane transport, 104–106
   antiport, 107
   ATP, 104
   characteristics of transport mechanisms, 104, 105t
   exchange diffusion, **107**
   main functions, 104
   primary active transport, **104**–106
   pumps, 104–105, 105i
   secondary active transport, 107
   symport, 107
Active site, **84**
Acyclic nucleoside phosphonates, 271
Adenine, 260, **262**
Adenine–thymine (A-T) base pair, 251, 263
Adenosine deaminase deficiency (ADA), 348
Adenosine diphosphate (ADP), 60, 79
Agarose gel electrophoresis, **340**, 340i
Agre, Peter, 101
Agrobacterium tumefaciens. See Rhizobium radiobacter
AI-2 inducer, 315
Alcohol fermentation, **133**
Alexandra, Czarina, 243
Algae
   photorespiration, 153
   volvocine, 68i
ALH84001 (meteorite), 50–51, 50i
Alkaptonuria, 284
Alleles, 193, **214**
   dominant, **215**
   multiple, 226–227
Allolactose, 311
Allosteric activator, **88**
Allosteric inhibitor, **88**
Allosteric regulation, 86, 87i, 88
Allosteric site, **86**
α helix, F-32, F-32i
Alternative splicing, **293**–294, 323
Alzheimer's disease, 116, 135
Amino acid, 59, F-29–F-30, F-29i, F-30i
Aminoacylation, 296, 297t
Aminoacyl–tRNA, **296**
Aminoacyl– tRNA synthetases, **296**
Amino group, F-23, F-23i
Amniocentesis, 252, 252i

Amplification, 111, 111i
Amplification of DNA. *See* Polymerase chain reaction (PCR)
Amylopectin, 215
Amyloplasts, 43
Amyotrophic lateral sclerosis (ALS), 116
Anabolic pathway, **77**, 78i
Anaerobes, 134
Anaerobic respiration, 133–136
Anaphase, **168**–169
Anaphase II, 195
Anchoring junctions, 45–46
Anderson, W. French, 348
Aneugens, 198
Aneuploids, 198, 246–247
Anfinsen, Christian, F-36
Angelman syndrome (AS), 253–254
Angiosperms. *See* Flowering plants
Animal cells, 32i, 45–47
   anchoring junctions, 45–46
   cell adhesion molecules, 45
   cell junctions, 45–47
   extracellular matrix (ECM), 45, 47, 47i
   gap junctions, 46
   tight junction, 46–47
Animals
   camouflage, 19
   clones, 348–349, 349i
   and colour, 17–18
   ecological light pollution, effects of, 19–20
   life cycle pattern, 192
   life cycles, 191i
   life in darkness, 20–23
   pharming, 348
   pollinators, 18i
Annotation, 356. *See also* Genome sequence determination and annotation
Anolis lizard, F-56
Anoxygenic photosynthesis, 61
Antibiotics, 202
Antibodies, 361
Anticodon, **295**
Antioxidants, 136
Antiparallel polynucleotide chains, 263, 264i
Antiport, 107
Apical complex, 508
Apoptosis, 176–177
Aquaporins, 101, 102i
Aquatic photoautotrophs, 153, 154i
Aqueous solutions, F-17
Arabidopsis, 350
Archaea
   cell architecture, 62
   domain, 26
   evolutionary origin, 62–63
   phototrophy, 140
Arginine auxotrophs (*arg* mutants), 284–286, 285i

A site (aminoacyl site), **298**
Aspartame, 250
Aspergillus, 27i
Astrobiology, 63
Atomic number, **F-9**, F-10t
Atoms, **F-9**, F-9i
ATP (adenosine triphosphate), 79–81
  active transport, 104
  ATP synthesis, 4–5, 128
  cellular respiration, 4, 116–136
  chemical structure of, 79, 79i
  chemiosmosis, 125–127, 148
  chemiosmotic theory, 128
  energy coupling, **79–80**, 80i
  energy-harnessing reactions, 60
  formation, 6i
  hydrolysis reaction, 79–80, 79i
  light reactions, 140
  Luft syndrome, 115–116
  photosynthesis, 4
  regeneration, 80–81
  yield from oxidation of glucose, 129–130
ATP/ADP cycle, 81i
ATP cycle, **81**, 81i
ATP synthase, 127–128
Autoinducer, 315
Autophagy, 37
Autosomal dominant inheritance, 249t
Autosomal recessive inheritance, 249t, 250
Autosomes, **240**
Autotrophs, **61**, **140**
Auxotrophs, **183**
Avery, Oswald, 188, 259–260
Avogadro's number, **F-18**

Bacillus thuringiensis, 350
Bacon, Francis, 7
  anaerobic respiration, 133–136
  cell architecture, 62
  Cyanobacteria, 61, 62, 62i
  domain, 26
  electron transport system, 134
  evolutionary origin, 62–63
  genetically engineered, 345–346
  genetic recombination in, 183–190
  Pseudomonas fluorescens, 27i
Bacterial chromosome, **279**
Bacterial conjugation, 184–188
  F factor and, 185, 185i, 187
  genetic mapping by, 187–188
  transfer of genetic information, 184–185, 185i, 186i
Bacteriophages, 52i, **188**, **260**
  replication cycle, 260
Bacteriorhodopsin, **4**, 6i, 7
Banded iron, 61, 62i
Barr body, 248, 321
Basal transcription factors. *See* General transcription
    factors
Base analogues, 271
Base-pair mismatches, 276
Bateson, William, 284
Beadle, George, 284–286

Berg, Paul, 335, 337
Beta-carotene, 5i
β-Galactosidase, 310, 311
β-globin gene, 341
β-lactoglobin gene, 348
β sheet, F-32, F-32i
Binary fission, **163**
Bioethics, 357
Bioinformatics, **356**
Biological clocks, 14–16
  and changing seasons, 15
  circadian rhythms, 14–15
  jet lag, 16
  timekeeping in human brain, 16i
Biological research, **F-2**
Bioluminescence, 21–23, 22i
Biomes, F-49
Biosphere
  air circulation, F-45, F-45i
  ocean currents, F-47–F-48, F-47i, F-48i
  precipitation, F-46, F-46i
  seasonality, F-44, F-44i
  solar radiation, F-44, F-44i
  topography, F-48
Biotechnology, 333
Bisphenol A, 198
Blackburn, Elizabeth, 274
BLAST (Basic Local Alignment Search Tool)
    program, 357
Blending theory of inheritance, 212–213
Blind mole rat (*Spalax* sp.), 21i
Blood type, 227
Blue-white screening, 335, 336i
Bone marrow, 178
Boyer, Herbert, 335
Brain, timekeeping in, 16i
Brenner, Sydney, 177
Bright field microscopy, 28i
Brinster, Ralph, 347–348
Brown, Robert, 25
Brutlag, Douglas L., 276
Bt toxin, 350
Buffers, F-19
Bulkphase endocytosis, **107**, 108i
Burkitt lymphoma, 246

Caenorhabditis elegans, F-54
Calcium pump, 104–105
Callus, 350
Calvin cycle, 4, 140–141, 140i, 147i, 149–152, 151i
CAM (crassulacean acid metabolism) plants,
    156, 156i
Camouflage, 19
Campbell, Keith H.S., 348
cAMP (cyclic AMP), 314
Cancer
  of the breast, 328, 328i
  breast cancer 1 (BRCA1) gene, 358
  Burkitt lymphoma, 246
  cells, 176
  colorectal, 329i
  development of, 329, 329i

familial (hereditary) cancers, **327**
loss of cell cycle controls, 176
loss of imprinting and, 254
loss of regulatory controls, 326–329
microRNA in, 323
miRNA genes, 328
proto-oncogenes, **327**
rapid cell division, 274
sporadic (nonhereditary) cancers, **327**
stem cells, 178
translocation of chromosome 8, 246
tumour suppressor genes, **327**
Carbohydrates, F-24–F-27
carbon dioxide conversion to, 150–151
cellular respiration, 130, 131i
disaccharides, F-26
isomers of monosaccharides, F-25, F-25i
monosaccharides, F-24, F-24i
polysaccharides, F-26–F-27, F-27i
units, 141
Carbonaceous chondrites, 56
Carbon bonding, F-20–F-21, F-20i, F-21i
Carbon compounds, F-20–F-23
Carbon dioxide (CO_2), 150
Carbon dioxide concentrating mechanism, 153, 154i
Carbon fixation, 141, 156
Carbonyl group, F-22–F-23, F-22i
Carmine, structure of, 5i
Carotenoids, 143, 144i
Carrier proteins, 101, 102i
Carsonella ruddii, 356
Caspases, 178
Catabolic pathway, **77**, 78i
Catalase, 135
Catalyst, **82**
C_4 cycle, 154, 155i
Cech, Thomas, 58
Celera Genomics, 353, 355
Cell cultures, **166**
Cell cycles, 161–180
bacterial, 163i
cell growth and division, 162–163
eukaryotic cell cycle, 164–171
in prokaryotic organisms, 163–164
Cell-death genes, 176–177
Cell membranes, 92–114
active membrane transport, 104–106
cell signalling, 109–111
endocytosis, 107–109
exocytosis, 107
fluidity, 96
fluid mosaic model, **93**–94, 93i
lipid fabric of, 94–97
membrane asymmetry, 94
membrane proteins, 97–100
membrane receptors, 110–111
myelin, 94
passive membrane transport, 100–104
phospholipids, **95**–96
sodium–potassium pump, **105**
structure, 93–94
temperature and membrane fluidity, 96–97

Cell plate formation, 170
Cells, 25–49
animal, 45–47
cell theory, tenets of, 26
coupling reaction, 79–81
cytoplasm, 29
development of, 57–60
NA in, 28–29, 30, 33–34
early studies, 25–26
eukaryotic, 29, 31–43
examples of, 27i
internal structure, 25i
membrane-defined compartment, 57–59
nucleic acids, 26
order, 51, 52i, 74
oxidation–reduction reactions, 60
plant, 43–45
plasma membrane, 28, 29i
prokaryotic, 29, 30–31
respiration, 38–39
and second law of thermodynamics, 74–75, 75i
structure and function, 26–30
three domains of life, 26–27, 62, 63i
units of measure, 27i
Cellular respiration, 4, 115–136
anaerobic respiration, 133–136
chemical basis of, 116–118
defined, **116**
efficiency of, 129–132
electron transport chain, 123, 125, 126i
fermentation, 132–133
glucose, 116, 117i
glycolysis, 118, 119i, **120**–122, 120i, 121i
organic molecules, oxidation of, 130
oxidative phosphorylation, 118, 123–129
oxygen and, 116, 132–136
photosynthesis *vs.*, 157, 158i
pyruvate oxidation and the citric acid cycle, 118, 122–123, 122i
rate of glucose oxidation, 131
regulation of, 131–132
respiratory intermediates, 130–131
Cellular senescence, 175–176
Central dogma, 58, 58i, 286
Central vacuoles, 43, 44
Centrioles, 42–43, 43i, **171**
Centrosome, **171**, 172i
Cephalopod mollusc, 10i. *See also* Octopus
Cézanne, Paul, 1
Channel proteins, **101**, 102i
Chaperone proteins
chaperonins, **F-36**
Characters, **212**
Chargaff, Erwin, 262
Chargaff's rules, 262
Chase, Martha, 260, 261i
C–H bond, 116, 117i
Chemical bonds, **F-11**– F-14
Chemical equilibrium, 77, **77**
Chemiosmosis, 125–127, 148
Chemiosmotic theory, 127, 128
Chiasmata, **200**

Chlamydomonas reinhardtii, 2i, 4, 8, 8i, 68i
Chlorophylls, 4, 5i, 44
   chlorophyll *a*, 5i, 143, 144i
   chlorophyll *b*, 143, 144i
   light absorption, 143–144, 147
Chloroplasts, 43–44, 44i, 64–65, 141–142, 141i
Cholesterol, 97, 97i
Chorionic villus sampling, 252
Chromatids, **164**
Chromatin, **277**
Chromatin fibres, 278
Chromatin remodelling, **321**, 322, 322i
Chromosomal proteins, of eukaryotes, **277**
Chromosomes
   alterations, 245– 249, 249t
   aneuploidy of sex chromosomes, 247–248
   autosomal aneuploidy, 247
   chromosome 21, 195, 247, 248i
   complement of, 164
   diploid, **164**, 165, 192
   eukaryotic cells, 163–165
   haploid, **164**, 192
   kinetochore-based movement, 172–173
   linkage map, **237**–239, 239i
   locus, **223**, 223i
   maternal, 193
   meiosis, 192–193
   paternal, 193
   ploidy, **165**, 194
   segregation, 163, 164–165, **165**, 200–201, 213, 214–219, 216i, 222i
   sex, 195, 247–248
   XX in females, 240–241
   XY in males, 240–241
Chromosome theory of inheritance, 222–223
Cidofovir, 271
Ciechanover, Aaron, 326
Cilia, 41–43, 42i
Circadian rhythms, 14–15, 14i
Circadian timekeeping, 15i
Cisterna, 34
Citric acid cycle, **123**–124, 123i, 124i
Classification, **17**–18
Clathrin, **109**
Clone, 165, **166**, **183**. *See also* DNA cloning
Closed system, 72, 73i
Clotting factor, 348
Coactivator, **318**
Coated pit, **109**
Codominance, **226**
Codon, **287**–288
Co-evolution, 18
Cofactor, 84, F-33
Cohen, Stanley, 335
Collagens, 47
Colour
   and animal behaviour, 17, 18
   Newton's experiments, 7
   photon absorption, 4
Colour-blindness, red–green, 243
Combinatorial gene regulation, 318–**319**
Commaless, 288

Comparative genomics, 355, 358
Competitive inhibition, **85**, 86i, 87
Complementary base-pairing, 263
Complementary DNA (cDNA), **337**, 346
Compound eyes, 9–10
Compound microscope, 25, 26i
Concentration, **F-18**
Confocal laser scanning microscopy, 28i
Conjugated system, 4
Conservative replication model, 264–265, 267i
Contact inhibition, **175**
Control, **F-3**
Copernicus, Nicolaus, 7
Corepressor, **313**, **318**
Cork cells, 25, 25i
Correns, Carl, 221
Covalent modification, 88
C_4 plants, 154–156
Crassulacean acid metabolism (CAM), **156**
Crick, Francis H.C., 258, 262, 263–264, 295
Crossing-over, 200
Crossovers, **200**
Cross-pollination, 213
Crown gall disease, 350
Cyanide, 135
Cyanobacteria, 61, 62, 62i
Cyclic electron transport, **149**
Cyclin, **174**
Cyclin:CDK, 174, 174i, 175
Cyclin-dependent kinases (CDKs), **174**
Cystic fibrosis, 92–93, 112, 250, 348
Cystic fibrosis transmembrane conductance regulator (CFTR), 92, 92i, 112
Cytochrome complex. *See* Protein complex III (cytochrome complex)
Cytochrome oxidase, 136
Cytokeratins, 39
Cytokinesis, **169**–170, 171i
Cytokinetic ring, **163**
Cytoplasm, 29
Cytoplasmic inheritance, 253
Cytoplasmic streaming, 41
Cytosine, 260, **262**
Cytoskeletons, 29, 31, 39–40, 40i
Cytosol, 29, 31, 119

Dark field microscopy, 28i
Darkness
   bioluminescence, 21–23, 22i
   life in, 20–23
Darwin, Charles, 10, 18, 332
Decomposers, 140
Dedifferentiation, 326
Degas, Edgar, 1
Dehydrogenases, 118
Deletion, chromosomal alteration, 245, 246, 246i
de Mairan, Jean-Jacques d'Ortous, 14
Denaturation, **F-36**, F-36i
Deoxyribonucleoside triphosphates, 265–266
Deoxyribose, 266, **F-37**
Dephosphorylation, 88

Dephosphorylation reaction, 72
Desaturase enzymes, 96–97
Descartes, René, 7
de Vries, Hugo, 221
Dick, John, 178
Dideoxyribonucleotides, 353
Dideoxy sequencing, 353, 354i, 355
Diffusion, **100**, 100i
Dihybrid, **219**
Dihybrid cross, **220**
Diploid, 55i, **164**, 333
Disaccharides, F-26
Discontinuous replication, **270**, 271i
Dispersive replication model, 265, 267i
Disorder (randomness). *See* Entropy
DNA (deoxyribonucleic acid). *See also* Chromosomes;
    Genetic recombination
  ancient DNA (aDNA), 257–258
  complementary base-pairing, 263
  complementary DNA (cDNA), **337**, 346
  cDNA library, 337
  correction of replication errors, 276–277
  damage by light, 13i
  defined, **258**
  DNA organization, 277–281
  double-helix model, **263**, 264i, F-39i
  eukaryotic cells, 33–34, 277–279
  evolution of, 59–60
  heredity molecule, 257–261, 261i
  methylation, **321**
  mobile elements, 201–207
  nucleotide bases, 260, 286
  polynucleotide chain, 262–264
  prokaryotic organisms, 163, 279–280
  recombinant, **333**
  short tandem repeat (STR) sequence, 342
  structure, 261–264, F-38, F-38i
  system of information transfer, 58–59, 63
  T DNA, 350
  template strand, **286**
DNA chips. *See* DNA microarrays
DNA cloning, 333–341, 334i, 348–349
  animals, 348–349
  applications, 333
  plasmid cloning vectors, 334–335, 337
  restriction endonucleases, **333**–334
  somatic cell nuclear transfer (SCNT), 349
DNA fingerprinting
  in forensics, 344
  paternity tests, 344–345
  principles, 342, 344
DNA helicase, **269**, 273i
DNA hybridization, **337**
DNA ligase, 273i
DNA microarrays, 358–360, 359i
DNA polymerase I, **270**, 273i
DNA polymerase III, **270**, 273i
DNA repair mechanisms, **276**
DNA replication, 264–276
  conservative replication model, 264–265, 267i
  continuous and discontinuous synthesis, 270, 271, 271i
  dispersive replication model, 265, 267i

DNA polymerases, 265–269
  enzymes of, 265, 268–269, 270–271, 273i
  molecular model, 272i
  multiple replication origins, 273
  new DNA synthesis, 269
  origin of replication (*ori*), 269
  replication bubble, **273**
  replication fork, **269**
  RNA primers, 269–270, 337, 339, 341
  semiconservative replication, 264–265, 266i
  telomerases, 273–274
DNA sequencing, 353–355
DNA technologies
  applications, 341–352
  defined, **333**
  DNA fingerprinting, 342–345
  and genetic engineering, 345–352
  human genetic diseases, testing, 341–342
  risks of, 352
Domains of life, 26–27, 63i
Dominant allele, **215**
Double-helix model, **263**, 264i, F-39i
Down syndrome, 195, 247, 248i
D1 protein, 146
Drosophila melanogaster (fruit fly), 235–237,
    241–243, F-53
Drosopterin, 241
Duchenne muscular dystrophy, 251
Duck (*Anas* spp.), 19i
Duplication, chromosomal alteration, 245, 246, 246i
Dwarfing, 225
Dynein motor proteins, 43
Dyneins, 40

E. coli (*Escherichia coli*), 183–184, 185i, 188, 189, 260,
    265, 271, 308, 310i, 311i, 312i, 333, 334i, 345,
    346, F-52
Earth
  early history, 53–54
  primordial atmosphere, 55
Earthworms (*Lumbricus*), 310
Eclectus parrot (*Eclectus rotatus*), 17i
Edidin, Michael A., 94
Electrochemical gradients, **106**
Electromagnetic radiation, 2
Electromagnetic spectrum, 2–3, 3i, 142i
Electrons
  linear electron transport, **147**, 148–149
  orbitals, **F-10**
  in pigment molecules, 142–143, 143i
  valence electrons, **F-10**
Electron shells, **F-10**, F-10t
Electron transport chains (ETCs), 65, 125, 126i
  bacteria, 134
  cellular respiration, 123, 125, 126i
  photosynthetic chain, 146, 147i
  uncoupling chemiosmosis and, 128–129
11-*Cis*-retinal, structure of, 5i
Elongation stage, of translation, 299–300
Emergence, concept of, 51–52
Endergonic reaction, **78**, 78i
Endocytosis, 37i, 107–109

Endomembrane system
 defined, **66**
 endoplasmic reticulum, 67i
 eukaryotic cells, 34–38
 nuclear envelope, 67i
 origin of, 66
Endoplasmic reticulum (ER), 34–35, 35i, 39i, 67i
Endosymbiosis, theory of, **64**–65, 65i
Endothermic reaction, **76**
Energy
 activation, 81–83, 81i, 84–85
 defined, **72**
 forms and states, 72
 free, **76**–80
 kinetic, **72**, 73, 73i
 potential, **72**, 73, 73i
 thermodynamics, 72–75
Energy coupling, **79**–80, 80i
Engelmann, Theodor, 144
Enhancer, 316
Enthalpy (H), **75**
Entropy, **74**, 75
Enzyme activity
 allosteric activator, **88**
 allosteric inhibitor, **88**
 allosteric regulation and, 86, 87i, 88
 conditions and factors affecting, 85–88
 covalent modification, 88
 enzyme and substrate concentration and, 85
 enzyme inhibitors and, 85–86, 87i
 feedback inhibition, **88**, 88i
 irreversible inhibition, 86, 135
 pH changes and, 89, 89i
 temperature changes and, 89–90, 89i
Enzyme concentration, 85, 86i
Enzyme reverse transcriptase, 337
Enzymes, 56, 58, 59, 60, 81–90
 acceleration of biological reactions, 82–85
 in biological reactions, 81–85
 catalytic cycle of, 84i
 defined, **82**
 dehydrogenases, 118
 desaturase, 96–97
 of DNA replication, 273
 enzymatic reactions, 83–84
 PEP carboxylase, 155
 phosphatases, 71
 restriction, **333**–337
 restriction sites, 333, 334, 335i
 substrate–enzyme interaction, 84, 84i
Epigenetics, **321**
Epistasis, 228
Escherich, Theodor, 183
E site (exit site), **298**
Ethidium bromide, 342
Euchromatin, **278**
Eudorina elegans, 68i
Eukarya, domain of life, 26, 31
Eukaryotes
 cell respiration, 119, 132–133
 chromosomal proteins of, **277**
 and energy barrier, 67

 gene organization in, 316i
 photosynthesis, 141–142
 protein-coding gene, 289, 290i, 291, 315–316
 synthesis of mRNA, 291–294
 transcription in, 315–322
 translation in, 294
 transposable elements in, 203, 205–206
Eukaryotic cell cycle, 164–174
 chromosome replication and segregation, 164–165
 coordination of mitotic cell cycle, 174–175
 cytokinesis, **169**–170, 171i
 internal checkpoints, **174**
 internal regulation of cell division, 174
 interphase, 165–166
 mitosis, 166–169
 mitotic spindle, 171–174
 regulation, 174–178
Eukaryotic cells, 31–43, 64–68
 animal cell, 33i
 apoptosis, 176–177
 cellular respiration, 38–39
 centrioles, 42–43, 43i, **171**
 chromosomes, 163–164
 cilia, 41–43, 42i
 cytoskeletons, 39–41, 40i
 cytosol, 29, 31, 119
 distinguishing characteristics, 64
 DNA organization, 277–279
 DNA packing, 278
 endocytosis, 37i, 107–109
 endomembrane system, 34–38
 endoplasmic reticulum, 34–35, 35i, 39i
 exocytosis, 37i
 flagella, 41–43, 42i
 fossil evidence of, 53
 Golgi complex, 35–36, 36i, 38i, 39i
 histones, 277, **278**–279
 intermediate filament, 39, 40i, 41
 loss of proliferative ability, 175
 lysosomes, 37
 microfilament, 39, 40i, 41
 microtubule, 39–40, 40i
 mitochondria, 38–39, 39i, 64–65, 67
 mitosis, 164–169
 motor protein, 40, 41i
 nonhistone proteins, 277, **279**
 nucleolus, 34
 nucleus, 31, 33–34, 33i
 plant cell, 33i
 plasma membrane, 31
 ribosomes, 34, 34i
 specialized, 67
Eukaryotic transposons, 205
Euploids, **246**
European barn swallow (*Hirundo rustica rustica*), 17i
Evolution
 of DNA, 59–60
 evolutionary timeline of life, 53i
 major events in, F-50t–F-51t
 modern cell, 57–60
Exchange diffusion, **107**
Exergonic reaction, **77**–78, 78i

Exocytosis, 37i, 107, 108i
Exons, **292**
Exon shuffling, 293, 294
Exothermic reaction, **76**
Experimental science, F-5
Experimental variable, **F-3**
Expression vector, **345**, 346
Extracellular matrix (ECM), 45, 47, 47i
Extraterrestrial life, 56, 68–69
Extraterrestrial origins hypothesis
    of macromolecules, 56
Extremophile, 62
Eye, **9**–10, 11i
  ocellus, **8**
Eyespot, 8. *See also* Ocellus

Facilitated diffusion, **100**–101, 103
Facultative anaerobes, 134
Faloona, F., 337
Familial (hereditary) cancers, **327**
Familial hypercholesterolemia, 225
Fats, cellular respiration, 130
Fatty acids, 95, 96, F-40
  hydrogenation, 98
  and membrane fluidity, 96, 96i
  saturated, 96, 96i
  unsaturated, 96, 96i, 97, 98
F^+ cells, 187
F- cells, 187
Feedback inhibition, **88**, 88i
Fermentation, **132**–133
Ferredoxin, 146
Fertilization, **191**
F factor (fertility plasmid), 185, 186i, 187, 280i
F_1 generation, **214**
F_2 generation, **214**
Fibroblast growth factor (FGF), 251
Fibronectins, 47
Fire, Andrew, 323
Fish
  zebrafish (*Danio rerio*), 161–162, F-55
5' carbon, of deoxyribose sugar, **262**
Fixation phase, **150**
Flagella, 41–43, 42i
Fleming, Alexander, 87
Flowering plants, 18i
Fluid mosaic model, of membrane structure,
    93–94, 93i
Fluorescence, 143
Fluorescence microscopy, 28i
Fossil prokaryote cells, 61i
F pilus, 185i, 186i, 187
Franklin, Rosalind, 258, 262–263, 263i, 264
Free energy, **76**–80
Free-running phenomenon, 14
Freeze-fracture technique, 94, 95i
Frye, David, 94
Frye-Edidin experiment, 94i
Functional genomics, 355, 357–358
Functional groups, F-22–F-23
Fungi, life cycle pattern, 192
Furrowing, 169–170, 171i

Gametes, **191**, 213
Gametophytes, **192**
Gangliosides, 226
Gap junctions, 45–46
Garrod, Archibald, 284
Gated channel proteins, **101**, **102i**
Gene imprinting, 253–254
Gene knockouts, 358
Generalized transduction, 188, 189i
General transcription factors, **316**
Gene regulation
  combinatorial, 318, 319, 319i
  in eukaryotes, 315–322, 316i
  negative, 313–314
  positive, 311–313
  posttranscriptional, 322–324
  posttranslational, 324, 326
  in prokaryotes, 309–314
  translational, 324
Genes
  breast cancer 1 (BRCA1) gene, 358
  cell-death, 176–177
  eukaryotic protein-coding, 289, 290i, 291, 315–316
  functions, 357–358
  homologous, 357
  of interest, 333, 335–337
  linked, **235**
  non-protein coding, 289
  resistance, 202
  sex-linked, 240–245
  synthesis of mRNA in eukaryotes, 291–294
Gene silencing, 321
Gene therapy, **346**–348
Genetically modified organisms (GMOs), 352
Genetic code, **286**–288
Genetic counselling, **251**–252
Genetic engineering
  of animals, 346, 348–349
  biosafety, 352
  defined, **333**
  DNA technologies, 345–352
  gene therapy, **346**–348
  guidelines for, 352
  pharming, 348, 351–352
  of plants, 349–353
  protein production, 345–346, 348
Genetic mapping, 188–189
Genetic recombination, 181–210, 198, 199–200
  in bacteria, 183–190
  in eukaryotes, 191–201
  in fruit flies, 235–240
  Hfr cells and, 187
  mechanism of, 182–183
  mobile elements, 201–207
Genetics
  blending theory of inheritance, 212–213
  and cancer, 327
  chromosome theory of inheritance, 222–223
  codominance, **226**
  epistasis, 228
  genotype, **215**
  heterozygote, **215**

Genetics (*continued*)
  incomplete dominance, **224–226**
  Mandel's experiments, 212–223
  monohybrid, **215**
  phenotype, **215**
  pleiotropy, 230
  polygenic inheritance, 229–330
  principle of independent assortment,
      219–221, 220i
Genetic screening, 252
Genetic variability, 198–201
  alternative combinations at meiosis II, 201
  mechanisms, 198–199, 199i
  random fertilization, 201
  random segregation of chromosomes,
      200–201
Genome, **66–67**
  bioethics, 357
  human, 357, 360
  introns, 357
  sequence analysis, 355–357, 360
  sizes, 356–357, 356t
Genome analysis
  comparative genomics, 355, 358–360
  functional genomics, 355, 357–358
  genome sequence determination and annotation,
      355–357
Genome Canada, 355, 357
Genome sequence determination and annotation,
    355–357
Genomic imprinting, 321
Genomic library, **337**
Genotype, **215**
Geological time scale, F-50t–F-51t
Germ-line gene therapy, **347**
Gey, George, 166
Gey, Margaret, 166
Gibberellin, 225
Gibbs, Josiah Willard, 76
Gilbert, Walter, 353
Glucocorticoids, 320
Glucose, 116, 117i
  ATP yield from, 129–130
  glycolysis, 119i, 120–122, 120i, 121i
  rate of oxidation, 131
Glutamine, synthesis of, 80i
Glycolysis, 119i, **120–122**, 120i, 121i
Glycoproteins, 47
Glyphosate, 350
G_0, of interphase, **166**, 168i
G_1, of interphase, **165**, 166, 168i
G_2, of interphase, **165**, 166, 168i
Golgi, Camillo, 35–36
Golgi complex, 35–36, 36i, 38i, 39i
Gonium pectorale, 68i
G3P molecule, 151
G3P (three-carbon sugar glyceraldehyde-3-phosphate)
    molecules, 150–151
Greider, Carol, 274
Griffith, Frederick, 188, 259
Guanine, 260, **262**
Guanine–cytosine (G–C) base pair, 251, 263

Haber, Edgar, F-36
Habitable zone, 54, 55i
Haemophilus influenzae, 355
Haldane, John, 55
Half-life, **F-10**
Halobacterium salinarum, 6i
Halobacterium, 4–5, 7
Haploid, **164**
Harvey, William, 7
Hayflick, Leonard, 175
Haynes, Robert, 278
Heat of evaporation, **F-16**
HeLa cells, 166
Helianthus annuus, 27i
Helicase. *See* DNA helicase
Hemophilia, 243–244, 348
Herpes viruses, 271
Herrick, James, 211
Hershey, Alfred D., 260, 261i
Hershko, Avram, 326
Heterochromatin, **278**
Heterotrophs, **61**, **140**
Heterozygote, **215**
Heterozygous, **215**
Histones, 277, **278**–279
  acetylation/deacetylation, 322
  methylation, 322
Homology, 357
Hooke, Robert, 25
Horizontal gene transfer (HGT), 66, 66i
Hormones, **320**
  melatonin, 15
  prolactin, 323
Horvitz, Robert, 177
Human blood type, 227
Human genetic diseases, 253–254, 341–342
Human genome, 357
Human Genome Project (HGP), 353
Human sex-linked genes, 243–244
Humulin, 346
Hüner, Norm, 150
Hunt, Timothy R., 174
Huntington disease, 116
Hutt Lagoon, 6i
Hydration shell, **F-17**
Hydrogenation, 98
Hydrolysis, 79–80, 79i
Hydrolysis reaction, F-21
Hydrothermal vents hypothesis, 56, 56i
Hydroxyl group, F-22, F-22i
Hypertonic solution, 103–104, 103i
Hypothesis, F-2–F-4
Hypotonic solution, 103

Immune system
  phagocytes, 37
Incomplete dominance, **224–226**
Independent assortment, **220**. *See also* Principle
    of independent assortment
Indigo, structure of, 5i
Induced-fit hypothesis, 84

Inducer, **311**
Inducible operon, **311**
Inductive resonance, 143
Inheritance. *See also* Mendel, Gregor
  autosomal dominant, 249t
  autosomal recessive, 249t, 250
  blending theory, 212–213
  changes in number of chromosomes
    and, 246–249
  chromosomal alterations and, 245– 249, 249t
  chromosome theory of, 222–223
  cytoplasmic, 253
  maternal, 253
  nontraditional patterns of, 253–254
  sex-linked genes, 243–244, 252i
  uniparental, 253
Initiation stage, of translation, 298–299
Initiator codon, **288**, 290i
Insertion sequences (IS), **202**
Insulin, 346
Integral membrane proteins, 98–99
Integrins, 47
Interkinesis, **194**, 195
Intermediate filament, 39, 40i, 41
International System of Units. *See* SI system of
    measurement
Interphase, 165–166
Introns, 292–294, 357
Inversion, 246
Inversion, chromosomal alteration, 245,
    246, 246i
Inverted repeat sequence, 202
Irons, Ernest, 211–212
Irreversible inhibition, 86, 135
Isolated system, 72, 73i
Isomerism, F-5, F-25i
Isoprenes, F-40
Isotonic conditions, 103i, 104
Isotopes, **F-9**, F-9i

Jacob, François, 163, 187, 188
Jeffreys, Sir Alec, 342
Jet lag, 16, 16i

Karyotype, **168**
Kearns–Sayre syndrome, 253
Kepler, Johannes, 7
Kepler Mission, 69
Kepler spacecraft, 68i
Khorana, H. Ghobind, 288
Kinesin molecule, 41i
Kinesins, 40
Kinetic energy, **72**, 73, 73i
Kinetic instability, 81
King penguin (*Aptenodytes patagonicus*), 17i
Klinefelter syndrome, 248t
Kornberg, Arthur, 271, 276, 289
Kreb's cycle, 310

Lacks, Henrietta, 166
Lac operon, in *E. coli*, 310i, 311i, 312i
Lactate fermentation, **132**, 133i

Lagging strand, **270**, 271i
Landsteiner, Karl, 227
Large ribosomal subunits, 296
Lateral inhibition, **191**
Leading strand, of DNA replication, **270**
Leading strand template, **270**, 271i
Leber hereditary optic neuropathy, 253
Leder, Philip, 287–288
Lederberg, Joshua, 183, 184, 187, 188
Leopold, Duke of Albany, 243
Lester, Diane, 225
Life
  chemical origins of, 52–57
  common ancestry, 62–63
  earliest forms of, 60–64
  emergent, 51, 52i
  evolutionary timeline, 53i
  extraterrestrial, 56, 68–69
  major macromolecules of, 54
  modern cell, evolution of, 57–60
  multicellularity, rise of, 64–68
  and second law of thermodynamics, **74**–75, 74i, 75i
  seven characteristics of, 51, 52i, 63–64
  in solar system, 54
Light
  absorption of, 3–4, 142–144
  and behaviour, 17–20
  damage to biological molecules, 12–14
  defined, **2–3**
  ecological pollution, 19–20
  as energy source, 4–5
  as information source, 6–10
  Newton's experiments, 7
  particle-wave duality, 3
  physical nature of, 2–4
  and plants, 17–19
  and time, 14–16
  uniqueness of, 10–12
  wavelengths, 2–3, 3i
Light pollution, 20i
Light reactions
  ATP generation, 148
  photosynthesis, 140–141, 148, 148i
  stoichiometry, 148–149
Light sensory
  eye and, 9–10
  sightless organisms, 7–9
Linear electron transport, **147**, 148–149
Linkage, **235**
Linkage map, of chromosome, **237**–239, 239i
Linked genes, **235**
Linker, **278**
Lipid bilayer, 93–94, 95
Lipids, F-40–F-43
  cell membrane, 94–97
  defined, 94–95
  fats, F-42, F-42t
  fatty acids, F-40
  isoprenes, F-40
  phospholipids, F-41, F-41t
  steroids, F-43, F-43t
Lipid vesicles, 57– 58, 58i

Lipoprotein (LDL) receptor, 225
Liposomes, 57–58, 58i
L1 ligase ribozyme, 60
Lock-and-key hypothesis, 84
Locus, **223**, 223i
Loss of imprinting and, 254
Lou Gehrig's disease. *See* Amyotrophic lateral
    sclerosis (ALS)
LUCA (last universal common ancestor), **64**
Luft, Rolf, 115
Luft syndrome, 115–116
Lyosomal storage diseases, 37
Lysogenic cycle, **188**, 190i
Lysosomes, 37
Lysozymes, F-33i
Lytic cycle, **188**, 190i

MacLeod, Colin, 260
Macromolecules
  composition of life, 54
  deep-sea (hydrothermal) vents
    hypothesis, 56
    extraterrestrial origins hypothesis, 56
    polymerization hypothesis, 56–57
    reducing atmosphere hypothesis, 54–56
    synthesized outside of living cells, 54–57
Malaria, 251
Mapping. *See* Genetic mapping
Map unit, **239**
Mars, 258
Martin, David, 225
Masking proteins, 323
Maternal chromosome, 193
Maternal inheritance, 253
Matter
  atoms, **F-9**, F-9i
  compounds, **F-8**
  elements, **F-8**, F-8t
  isotopes, **F-9**, F-9i
  organization of, **F-8**–F-11
  radioisotopes, F-10
Maxam, Allan M., 353
McCarty, Maclyn, 260
McClintock, Barbara, 203, 205
Meiocytes, 193
Meiosis, 191–201
  and chromosome, 192–193, 222–223, 222i
  daughter cells, 193–198
  defined, **191**
  generation of genetic variability, 198–201
  misdivision, 247i
  in organismal life cycles, 191–192
  prophase I, 194–195, 197i
  prophase II, 195, 197i
  vs. mitosis, 202i, 203i
Melanin, 13–14, 13i, 228
Melanocytes, 13
Melatonin, 15
Mello, Craig, 323
Membrane asymmetry, 94
Membrane potential, **106–107**
Membrane proteins, 97–100

attachment/recognition, 98, 99i
enzymatic activity, 98, 99i
functions, 98, 99i
integral, 98
peripheral, **99**–100
signal transduction, 98, 99i
transmembrane proteins, 99, 99i
transport function, 98, 99i
Mendel, Gregor, 212–223, F-55
  contribution to genetics, 221
  garden peas experiments, 212–223
  hypotheses, 216
  independent assortment, 219–221, 220i
  principle of segregation, 214–216, 216i, 222i
  probability in crosses, 216–218
  single-character crosses, 213–214
  testcross, 218–221
  true-breeding, **213**
Menten, Maud, 83
Meselson, Matthew, 265, 267i
Messenger RNA (mRNA), 30, 34, 65, **286**–288, 291–294
  intron removal, 292–293
  polypeptide synthesis, 294–305
  precursor mRNA, 291–292
  pre-mRNA processing, 322–323
  rates in breakdown of, 323
Metabolism
  anabolic pathways, **77**, 78i
  catabolic pathway, **77**, 78i
  defined, **77**
  lactose, in prokaryotic cells, 310–311
  metabolic pathways, 77–78
Metagenomics, 333, 339
Metaphase, **167**
Metaphase I, 195
Metaphase II, 195
Metastasis, 176, 327
Meteorite, 50–51, 50i, 56, 57i
Methane, redox reaction, 117–118, 117i
Methanosarcina acetivorans, 356
Methylation, **321**, 322
Met–tRNA, 298, 298i
Mexican cave fish (*Astyanax mexicanus*), 20i
Michaelis, Leonor, 83
Michaelis–Menten equation, 83
Micrasterias, 27i
Microfilament, 39, 40i, 41
MicroRNAs (miRNAs), **323**, 328
Microscopy, 25–26, 27, 28i
  electron, 28i
  light, 28i
Microtubule, 39–40, 40i
Microtubule motor proteins, 172–173, 173i
Microtubule organizing centre (MTOC), 171
Microtubules, 39–40, 40i
Miescher, Johann Friedrich, 258
Miller, Stanley, 55
Miller–Urey experiment, 55–56, 56i
Minimal medium, 183
miRNA-induced silencing complex (miRISC), 323
Mitchell, Peter, 127, 128
Mitochondria, 38–39, 39i, 64–65, 67, 115–116, 119

Mitochondrial myopathy, 253
Mitochondrial encephalomyopathy, 253
Mitosis
    anaphase, **168**–169
    eukaryotic cell cycle, 164–169, 167i
    interphase, 165, 167
    metaphase, **167**
    prokaryotic cells, 163–164
    prometaphase, **167**
    prophase, **166**–167, 168i
    stages, **166**–167, 168i, 170i
    telophase, **169**
    vs. meiosis, 202i, 203i
Mitotic spindle, **167**, 171–174, 173i
    animal and plant spindles, 171–172
    movement of chromosomes, 172–173
Mobile elements, 201–207
    defined, **201**
    in eukaryotes, 203, 205–206
    prokaryotic, 201–202
    retrotransposons, 205–206
Model research organisms
    Anolis lizard, F-56
    baker's yeast (*Saccharomyces cerevisiae*), F-53
    Caenorhabditis elegans, F-54
    Drosophila melanogaster (fruitfly), F-53
    Escherichia coli, F-52
    house mouse (*Mus musculus*), F-55–F-56
    white-flowered thale cress (*Arabidopsis
        thaliana*), F-54
    zebrafish (*Danio rerio*), F-55
Molarity, **F-18**
Mole, **F-18**
Molecular weight, **F-18**
Monohybrid, **215**
Monohybrid cross, **215**
Monomers, 56
Monosaccharides, F-24, F-24i
Moorhead, Paul, 175
Morgan, Thomas H., 235–237, 241, 243, F-53
Motifs, proteins, **317**, 317i
Mouse, house, (*Mus musculus*), F-55–F-56
mRNA splicing, **292**
Mullis, Kary B., 337
Multicellularity, 64–68
Multiple alleles, **226**–227
Munnich, Arnold, 251
Murchison meteorite, 56, 57i
Mus musculus (mouse)
    as model organism, F-55–F-56
Mutation, 215, 241
    and alteration of enzymes, 284–286
    defined, **277**
    human genetic diseases, 253–254,
        341–342
Myelin, 94
Myoclonic epilepsy, 253

NADPH (nicotinamide adenine dinucleotide
    phosphate), 4, 140
Nedelcu, Aurora, 199
Neurospora crassa, 284

Neutrons, **F-9**
Newton, Sir Isaac, 7
Nicholas II, Czar, 243, 344
Nicotinamide adenine dinucleotide (NADH), **118**, 119i,
        120, 120i, 121i, 122, 122i, 123, 123i, 124i, 125, 126i,
        127, 129, 130i, 131i, 132, 133, 133i, 146
Nirenberg, Marshall, 287–288
Nitrogen isotope, 265
Nomansky (differential interference contrast)
        microscopy, 28i
Noncompetitive inhibition, **86**, 86i
Nondisjunction, 246, 247i
Nonhistone proteins, 277, **279**
Nonkinetochore microtubules, 172
Nonsense codons. *See* Stop codons
Non-SI units, common, F-7t
Nuclear envelope, endomembrane system, 67i
Nucleic acid probe, 337, 338i
Nucleic acids, F-37–F-39
Nuclein, 258
Nucleoid, 30i, **163**
Nucleosome core particle, **278**
Nucleosome remodelling complex, **321**
Nucleotides, F-7, F-37i

Observational science, F-5
Ocean currents, F-47–F-48, F-47i, F-48i
Ocellus, 8, 10
Octopus, 10i, 181, 182
Oenothera biennis, 18i
Okazaki, Reiji, 270
Okazaki fragment, **270**
Ommatidia, 9–10
Ommatidium, 9i
Ommochrome, 241
Oncogene, **327**
Oncogenes, **176**
One gene–one enzyme hypothesis, 286
One gene–one polypeptide hypothesis, 286
Oparin, Aleksander, 55
Oparin–Haldane hypothesis, 55
Open system, 72, 73i, 74–75
Open reading frame. *See* Reading frame
Operator, **310**
Operon, 309–**310**
    inducible, 311
    repressible, **313**
Orbitals, **F-10**
Order, as characteristic of life, 51, 52i, 74
Organelles, 29
Organisms
    sightless, 7–9
    transgenic, 345
Origin of replication (*ori*), **163**, 269
Osmosis, 103–104
Oxidation–reduction (redox) reactions, 60, 117–118
Oxidative phosphorylation, 118, 123–129, 126i
    chemiosmosis, 125–127
    defined, **127**
    electron transfer system, 126i
    electron transport chain, 125, 126i
    uncoupling electron transport and chemiosmosis, 128–129

Oxidizing atmosphere, 55
Oxygen (O_2)
  and anaerobes, 134–135
  cellular respiration, 116, 132–136
Oxygenic photosynthesis, 61–62, 145

p53, 327–328
Pairing, **194**
Palmiter, Richard, 347–348
Paramecium, 28i
Parkinson's disease, 116, 135
Partial diploid, 187
Particle-wave duality, 3
Passive transport, **100**–104
  diffusion, **100**, 100i
  facilitated diffusion, **100**–101
  osmosis, 103–104
  simple diffusion, **100**, 101i, 103i
Paternal chromosome, 193
Pax-6, 10
Pedigree, **243**, 244i
Penicillin, 87, 202
PEP carboxylase, 155
Peppered moth (*Biston betularia*), 20i
Peptidoglycan, 87
Peptidyl–tRNA, **299**
Peripheral membrane proteins, **99**–100
P generation, **214**
pH, F-18–F-19
Phage lambda (l), 189
Phagocytes, 37
Phagocytosis, **109**, 109i
Pharming, 348, 351–352
Phase-contrast microscopy, 28i
Phenotype, **215**
Phenylalanine (F), 112
Phenylketonuria (PKU), 250, 252
Phenylthiocarbamide (PTC), 226
Philippine tarsier (*Tarsius syrichta*), 20i
Phosphate group, F-23, F-23i
Phosphodiester bond, 262
Phosphoenolpyruvate (PEP), 154, 155, 156
Phosphofructokinase, 131
Phospholipids, **95**–96, F-41, F-41t
Phosphorylation, 88
  cascade, 111
Photomorphogenesis, 8i
Photon, **3**
  absorption of light, 4i, 143i
  and light, 3–4
Photooxidative damage, 12
Photoperiod-dependent phenomena, 15i
Photoreceptor, 6–7
Photorespiration, **152**–157
  aquatic photoautotrophs, 153, 154i
  CAM plants, 156–157
  CO_2-concentrating mechanisms,
    152–157
  C_4 plants, 154–156
  high temperature and, 153–154, 154t
  Rubisco, 151–153, 152i

Photosynthesis, 4, 6i, 44, 116, 139–159
  anoxygenic, 61
  apparatus, 142–146
  Calvin cycle of, 4, 140–141, 140i, 147i, 149–152, 151i
  chlorophylls, 143–144
  chloroplast, 141
  defined, 140
  energy flow linking respiration with, 116i
  equation, 141
  and life, 139–140
  light absorption, 142–144
  light reaction, 140–141, 148, 148i
  oxygenic, 61–62
  photorespiration, 152–157
  photosystems, 144–145
  pigment molecules, 142–143
  vs. cellular respiration, 157, 158i
Photosystem I, 145, 146
Photosystem II, 12i, 145–146, 145i, 147i
Photosystems, 144–145
Phototaxis, 8
Phototrophy, 140
Phycoerythrobilin, structure of, 5i
Phytochrome, 8
Phytoplankton, 139–140
Pigments, **4**
  common, structure of, 5
  photosynthetic, 145
Pili, 31
Pinocytosis. *See* Bulkphase endocytosis
Planaria, 9i
Plant cells, 32i, 43–45
  central vacuoles, 43, 44
  chloroplast, 43–44, 44i, 64–65, 141
  plasmodesmata, 44–45
  stroma, 44, 147i
  thylakoids, 44, 147i
  wall of, 44–45, 45i
Plants
  colour, role of, 17–18
  genetic engineering of, 349–353
  life cycle pattern, 192
  light sensory, 8–9
Plasma membrane, **93**. *See also* Cell membranes
Plasmid cloning vectors, 334–335, 337
Plasmids, 185, **279**–280
Plasmodesmata, 44–45
Plastids, 42
Pleiotropy, 230
Ploidy, **165**, 194
Pneumonia, 188, 259–260, 259i
Pollination, 17–18
  flower–pollinator interactions, 18
Poly(A) tail, **292**, 324
Polygenic inheritance, 229–330
Polymerase chain reaction (PCR), **337**, 339–340, 339i, 342, 344, 344i
Polymerization, 57, 57i
Polymers, **56**–57
Polynucleotide chain, 262–264
Polypeptide, 286, F-30, F-30i
  chains, 296, 298, 299–300

Polypeptide synthesis. *See* Translation
Polyploids, **247**
Polyploidy, 248–249
Polysaccharides, F-26–F-27, F-27i
Potential energy, **72**, 73, 73i
Prader–Willi syndrome (PWS), 253–254
Precipitation, F-46, F-46i
Precursor mRNA (pre-mRNA), **291–292**
Prenatal diagnosis, **252**
Primary active transport, **104–106**
Primary producers, 140
Primase, 273i
Primer, **269–270**, 270i, 337, 339, 341
Principle of independent assortment, 219–221, 220i
Principle of Segregation (Mendel), 214–216, 216i, 222i
Probability, 216–217
    in Mandel's crosses, 217–218
    product rule, 217
    sum rule, 217
Progeria, 234–235
Prokaryotes, 62
    translation in, 294
    transposable elements in, 201–202
Prokaryotic cells, 30–31
    binary fission, **163**
    cycles, 163–164
    cytokinetic ring, **163**
    cytoskeletons, 31
    division, 163
    DNA organization, 279–280
    fossil, 53, 61i
    gene expression in, 309–314
    mitosis, 163–164
    nucleoid, 30i, **163**
    origin of replication, **163**
    plasma membrane, 30–31
    plasmids, **279–280**
    replicated chromosomes, distribution of, 163
    rolling circle replication, 280
    structure and function, 30i
    wall of, 30–31
Prolactin, 323
Prometaphase, **167**
Prometaphase I, 195
Prometaphase II, 195
Promoter, **289**, 290i, 315
Promoter proximal elements, **316**
Promoter proximal region, **316**
Proofreading mechanism, **276**, 276i
Prophage, **189**
Prophase, **166–167**, 168i
Prophase I, 194–195, 197i
Prophase II, 195, 197i
Prosthetic group, F-33
Proteasome, 326, 326i
Protein chips. *See* Protein microarrays
Protein complex I (NADH dehydrogenase), 125
Protein complex II (succinate dehydrogenase), 125
Protein complex III (cytochrome complex), 125, 146
Protein complex IV (cytochrome oxidase), 125
Protein kinases, 111
Protein microarrays, **361**

Protein phosphatases, 111
Proteins, F-28–F-36, F-28i
    amino acid, F-29–F-30, F-29i, F-30i
    aquaporins, 101, 102i
    carrier, 101, 102i
    cellular respiration, 130
    channel, **101**, 102i
    chaperonins, **F-36**
    cofactor/prosthetic group, F-33
    domains, 317, F-35, F-35i
    D1 protein, 146
    evolution of, 59
    ferredoxin, 146
    folding, F-36
    gated channel, 101, 102i
    genetic engineering, 345–346, **348**
    in genome research, 360–361
    membrane, 93–94, 97–100
    motifs, 317, 317i
    polypeptides, F-30, F-30i
    primary structure, F-31
    quaternary structure, F-33
    secondary structure, F-32
    structure, 293, F-31–F-33
    tertiary structure, F-33
Proteoglycans, 47
Proteome, **360–361**
Proteomics, **361**
Protobiont, **57–58**
Proton-motive force, **127**
Proton pumps, 104
Protons, **F-9**
Proto-oncogenes, **327**
Prototrophs, **183**
Provirus, **206**
P site (peptidyl site), **298**
Punnett square, 218, 218i, 252i
Purine bases of nucleic acid, F-37, F-38i
Purines, 262, 263
Pyrimidine bases of nucleic acid, F-37, F-38i
Pyrimidines, 262, 263
Pyruvate oxidation and citric acid cycle, **118**, 122–123, 122i

Quantitative traits, 229
Quorum sensing, 315

Radioisotopes, F-10
Ranunculus ficaria, 18i
Rasputin, Grigori Efimovich, 243
Reactive oxygen species (ROS), 134–135, 199
Reading frame, 288, **299**, 356
Receptor-mediated endocytosis, 108i, 109
Recessive inheritance
    X-linked recessive traits, 243–244, 251, 252i
Red–green colour-blindness, 243
Redox reactions. *See* Oxidation–reduction (redox) reactions
Reducing atmosphere, 55
Reducing atmosphere hypothesis, 54–56
Reduction phase, **150**

Red-winged blackbird (*Agelaius phoeniceus*), 17i
Regeneration phase, **150**
Regulatory protein, **310**
Release factor (RF), 303
Renaturation, **F-36**
Replicates, **F-3**
Replication bubble, **273**
Replication fork, **269**
Repressible operon, **313**
Repressor, 310, 318
Resistance genes, 202
Restriction endonucleases, **333–334**
Restriction fragment length polymorphisms (RFLPs), **342**
Restriction fragments, **334**
Restriction sites, 333, 334, 335i
Retrotransposons, **205–206**
Retrovirus, **206**, 206i
Reverse transcriptase, **206**
Rhizobium radiobacter, 350
Rhodopsin, 6, 8i
Ribose, **F-37**
Ribosome binding site, **298**
Ribosomes, **296**
   prokaryotic *vs.* eukaryotic, 298
   role in translation, 296, 298
Ribozymes, **58–59**, 59i
RNA (ribonucleic acid)
   central dogma, 58, 58i, 286
   genetic code, **286–288**
   messenger RNA (mRNA), 30, 34, 65, **286**–288, 291–294
   microRNAs (miRNAs), 323
   miRNA-induced silencing complex (miRISC), 323
   precursor mRNA (pre-mRNA), **291–292**
   ribosomal RNA (rRNA), 30, 34, 296–298
   ribozymes, **58–59**, 59i
   small interfering RNA (siRNA), **323**–324
   structure, F-38, F-38i
   transcription, **286**, 287i, 289, 290i
   transfer RNA (tRNA), 65, 294–296
RNA interference (RNAi), 323, 358
RNA polymerase, 286
RNA polymerase II, 315–316
Roberts, Richard, 292
Rolling circle replication, 280
Roscovitine, 177
Rose, Irwin, 326
Roundup, 350
Rubisco (ribulose-1,5-bisphosphate carboxylase oxygenase), 151–153

Saccharomyces cerevisiae, 133, 355, F-53
Sanger, Frederick, 353
Sanger method, 353. *See also* Dideoxy sequencing
Scale, in biology, F-7i
Scanning electron microscopy (SEM), 28i
Scenedesmus, 28i
Schleiden, Matthias, 25
Schrödinger, Erwin, 278
Schwann, Theodor, 26
Scientific method, F-2–F-5
Scientific theory, F-4
Scops owl (*Otus scops*), 19i

Scriver, Charles, 231
Seasonality, F-44, F-44i
Segregate (separate), **215**
Self-fertilization, **213**
Self-pollination, **213**
Semiconservative DNA replication, 264–265, 266i
Sex-linked genes, 240–245
   defined, **240**
   in fruit flies, 241–243
   human sex determination, 240–241
   in humans, 243–244
   inactivation of one X chromosome, 244–245, 321
Sexual reproduction, 181–182, 191
Sharp, Phillip, 292
Short interfering RNAs (siRNAs), 323
Short tandem repeat (STR) sequence, 342
Sickle cell disease, 211–212, 225, 230, 250, 251, 341–342, 348
Signal transduction, 71, 109–112, 110i
Signal peptide. *See* Signal sequence
Signal sequence, 303
Simple diffusion, **100**, 101i
Simultaneous hermaphrodites, 310
Single-lens eye, 10
Single-stranded binding proteins (SSBs), **269**, 273i
Sister chromatids, **165**
SI system of measurement, F-6–F-7
   base units, F-6t
   derived SI units, F-6t
   prefix names and symbols, F-6t
Sliding clamp, **268**, 273i
Slipper limpet, 181–182
siRNA-induced silencing complex (siRISC), **324**
Small interfering RNA (siRNA), **323–324**
Small nuclear RNA (snRNA), 292
Small ribonucleoprotein particles, **292**
Small ribosomal subunits, 296
Smith, Michael, 353
Sodium–potassium pump, **105**, 106i
Solar radiation, F-44, F-44i
Solar radiation spectrum, 12i
Solenoid, **278**. *See also* 30 nm chromatin fibre
Somatic cell nuclear transfer (SCNT), 349
Somatic cells, **191**, 346
Somatic gene therapy, **347–348**
Southern blot analysis, 342, 343i
Specialized transduction, **189**, 190
Specific heat, **F-16**
Spectrophotometer, 144
Sphagnum moss, 192
S phase, **165**
Spindle, of microtubules, 164
Spindle poles, **167**
Spliceosome, **292**
Spontaneous reaction, **75**–78, 76i, 82i
Sporadic (nonhereditary) cancers, **327**
Spores, **192**
Sporophytes, **192**
SRY gene, 240–241
Stahl, Franklin, 265, 267i
Start, **288**
Stem cells, 178, **346**

Steroid, **320**, F-43, F-43t
Steroid hormone receptor, **320**, 320i
Steroid hormone response element, **320**, 320i
Sterols, 97
Sticky ends, **334**, 335i
Stoichiometry, 148–149
Stop codons, **288**
Streptococcus pneumoniae, 188, 259–260, 259i
Strict aerobes, 134
Strict anaerobes, 134, 135
Stroma, 44, 147i
Stromatolites, **61**, 61i
Sturtevant, Alfred, 235, 237
Substrate concentration, 86i
Substrate-level phosphorylation, 122
Substrate(s), binding of, 84i
Sugar–phosphate backbone, **262**, 262i
Sulfhydryl group, F-23, F-23i
Sulfolobus acidocaldarius, 27i
Sulston, John, 177
Sun, the, 3i, 139–140
Superoxide dismutase, 135
Suprachiasmatic nucleus (SCN), 16i
Surface area, and volume, 29i
Surroundings, 72
Sutton, Walter, 222
Symport, 107
Synapsis, **194**
Synaptonemal complex, 199, 200i
System
    closed, 72, 73i
    isolated, 72, 73i
    open, 72, 73i, 74–75
    in thermodynamics, 72
Systematic biology, **361**
Systematics, classification, 17–18
Szostak, Jack, 58, 274

Target protein, 111
Tata box, 315–316
Tatum, Edward L., 183, 184, 187, 284–286
Tay–Sachs disease, 37, 226
T DNA, 350
Teleomerase, 273–**274**
Telomere, 176, **274**, 275i
Telophase, **169**
Telophase I, 195
Telophase II, 195
Temperate bacteriophage, **189**
Template strand, **286**
10 nm chromatin fibre, 278
Termination codons. *See* Stop codons
Termination factor. *See* Release factor (RF)
Terminators, **289**
Testcross, **218–219**
Testosterone, 320
Tetraploids, 247
Tetraploid zygote, 249
Theory, **F-4**
Thermodynamics
    chemical equilibrium, **77**
    defined, **72**

endothermic reaction, **76**
entropy, **74**, 75
exergonic reaction, 76–**78**, 78i
exothermic reaction, **76**
first law of, 72–**73**, 73i
free energy, **76**–80
laws of, 72–75
second law of, **74**–75, 74i, 75i
spontaneous reaction, **75**–78, 76i, 82i
surroundings, 72
system, 72
thermodynamically unstable reaction, 81
universe, 72
30 nm chromatin fibre, 278
3' carbon, of deoxyribose sugar, **262**
Thylakoids, 44, 147i
Thymine, 260, **262**
Tight junction, 46–47
Tilghman, Shirley, 321
Ti (tumour-inducing) plasmid, 350, 351i
Topography, F-48
Topoisomerase, **269**, 273i
TP53, 327–328
T2 phage, 260
Transcription
    combinatorial gene regulation, 318–319
    coordinated regulation of, 319–321
    gene expression, in prokaryotic cells, 309–315
    of *lac* operon, 311–313
    regulation of, in eukaryotes, 315–322
    repression of, 318
    RNA, **286**, 287i, 289, 290i
    of *trp* operon, 313, 314
Transcription factors, **289**, **315–316**
Transcription unit, **289**, **310**
Transduction, **188**, 188–190
Trans fats, 98
Transfer RNA (tRNA), 65, 294–296
    structure, 294–295, 296i
Transformation, 188, 259–**260**
Transforming principle, 259–260
Transgenic organisms, **345**
Transition state, **81**, 82
Transit method, 68i
Translation, **286**, 287i, 294–305
    elongation stage, 299–300, 299i
    initiation stage, 298–299
    rRNA, 296, 298
    simultaneous, 300–302
    termination stage, 300
    tRNAs, 294–296
Translocation, 246
    chromosomal alteration, 245, 246, 246i
Transmembrane proteins, 99, 99i
Transmission-electron microscopy (TEM), 28i
Transpeptidase, 87
Transport. *See* Active membrane transport
Transposable elements (TEs), **201**. *See also* Mobile
    elements
Transposase, **202**
Transposition, **201**, 204i
Transposons, **202**

Trematon, Viscount Rupert, 243
Trichonympha, 27i
Triple-X syndrome, 248, 248t
Triploids, 247
Triploid zygote, 249
Trisomy 21. *See* Down syndrome
trp operon, 313, 314i
True-breeding, **213**
Tryptophan synthesis, 313–314
Tschermak, Erich von, 221
Tsui, Lap-Chee, 112
Tumours, 176
   benign, 326
   malignant, 326–327
Tumour suppressor genes, **327**
Turgor pressure, 103, 103i
Turner syndrome, 248t
Twenty Thousand Leagues under the Sea
      (Verne), 23

Ubiquitin, 326, 326i
Uchida, Ayako, 294
Ultraviolet light, 12–14, 13i, 18
Uncoupling, electron transport and chemiosmosis,
      128–129
Uniparental inheritance, 253
Universe, in thermodynamics, 72
Urey, Harold, 55

Valence electrons, **F-10**
Valence shell, **F-10**
van Leeuwenhoek, Anton, 7, 25, 26i
Venter, J. Craig, 332–333, 355
Verne, Jules, 23, 355
Victoria, Queen, 243
Virchow, Rudolf, 26
Virulent bacteriophages, 188
Viruses, 51, 52i, **260**
   herpes viruses, 271
Vision
   lateral inhibition, **191**
   photoreceptors, 6–7
Volvocine algae, 68i
Volvox aureu, 68i

Wald, George, 10, 68
Warning signals
Water, F-15–F-19
   and carbon fixation, 141
   dissociation of, F-18–F-19, F-19i
   heat of evaporation, **F-16**
   hydrogen bonds, F-15
   hydration shell, **F-17**
   oxygenic photosynthesis, 145
   properties of, F-15
   solute concentrations, F-18
   specific heat, **F-16**
Water lattice, **F-15**
Watson, James D., 258, 262, 263–264
Wavelengths, 2–3, 3i
Weissmann, August, F-55
White-flowered thale cress (*Arabidopsis
      thaliana*), F-54
Whole-genome shotgun method, 355, 355i
Whyte, Lyle, 63
Wilkins, Maurice H.F., 262–263
Williams, Ernest E., F-56
Wilmut, Ian, 348
Wobble hypothesis, **295**
Wolfenden, Richard, 71
Wollman, Elie L., 188

X chromosome
   defined, **240**
   in females, 240
   inactivation, 244–245, 321
X-linked recessive inheritance, 251, 252i
X-ray diffraction, **262**
XYY syndrome, 248t

Y chromosome, 240

Zebrafish (*Danio rerio*), 161–162, F-55
Zimmerly, Steve, 295
Zinder, Norton, 188
Z scheme, 148
Zygote, **191**
   tetraploid, 249
   triploid, 249